S0-BBX-953

Modern College Physics

Large spark chambers at the bevatron in the University of California Lawrence Berkeley Laboratory, Berkeley, blaze with light as nuclear particles pass through them. With the help of a computer, scientists will later identify the particles by kinematic analysis of the spark trails in photographs like this one.

Modern College Physics

SIXTH EDITION

Harvey E. White, Ph.D., Sc.D.
University of California, Berkeley

Van Nostrand Reinhold Company
New York · Cincinnati · Toronto · London · Melbourne

Van Nostrand Reinhold Company Regional Offices:
New York Cincinnati Chicago Millbrae Dallas

Van Nostrand Reinhold Company International Offices:
London Toronto Melbourne

Library of Congress Catalog Card Number: 72-76834

Manufactured in the United States of America

Published by Van Nostrand Reinhold Company
450 West 33rd Street, New York, N. Y. 10001

Published simultaneously in Canada by Van Nostrand Reinhold Ltd.

Cover and text design by Morris Karol

15 14 13 12 11 10 9 8 7 6 5 4 3 2 1

Preface

In recent years, there has been a growing awareness of the tremendous impact that science and technology have had on modern society. This, plus the results of the latest research in the field of physics, has necessitated a particularly thorough revision of MODERN COLLEGE PHYSICS.

My objective has been to write a book for the physics student of the 1970s, while preserving the fundamental organization, level, and manner of presentation in previous editions. The text is still designed for a one-year college general physics course that does not require any calculus.

In order to increase the pedagogical utility of the text, only one system of units, the *MKSA* system, has been introduced and used throughout this edition. By confining the student's attention to one system, the concepts of mass and weight are greatly simplified, and the basic principles of physics are better illuminated. The English system of units and its conversion to the *MKSA* system are given in Appendix I.

Among the sections new to this edition are: a discussion of the largest particle accelerator in the world at Batavia, Illinois; some important details of the two-mile long electron linear accelerator at Stanford University; the structure of neutrons and protons; and the theories of white dwarfs, neutron stars (pulsars), and black holes. These, and other new topics, represent the latest research in the frontiers of physics; they are also some of the very topics likely to be encountered by the student in the newspapers and many different magazines long after he has finished his physics course.

When MODERN COLLEGE PHYSICS was first written, my purpose was to provide my colleagues with an effective teaching tool. Through the many revisions I have strived to improve the usefulness of the text. In this edition fifty new biographical sketches of famous scientists and Nobel Laureates have been added. Nearly two hundred worked problems with step-by-step solutions have been introduced, and over one thousand new problems can be found at the ends of the chapters. The total number of illustrations now exceeds 1100.

As was the case in past editions, the keynote of the 6th edition is flexibility. The sixty-six chapters in this edition are so arranged that good stopping points occur at the ends of Chapters 20, 30, and 40, thereby permitting effective use of the text in schools on either the semester or the quarter system. It is suggested that the three introductory chapters of the book be assigned as independent readings, first, to develop an interest in the subject of physics, and second, to serve as a review of the metric system.

The author wishes to thank the many teachers and students whose comments and constructive criticisms have been most helpful. I would also like to thank the editor of the manuscript, George Lobell, who has made a number of valuable suggestions.

Berkeley, California HARVEY E. WHITE

Acknowledgments

I sincerely thank the following for their comments and suggestions:

Professor Reverdy E. Baldwin
Jamestown Community College

Professor W. R. Butler
David Lipscomb College

Professor J. D'Amario
Harford Junior College

Professor Martin L. Goodson
Indiana State University

Professor Alexander R. Grone
Hudson Valley Community College

Professor William Everett Hunt
David Lipscomb College

Professor Abe Korn
New York City Community College

Professor Paul Nail
Central Technical Institute

Professor Salvatore J. Radano
Harford Junior College

Professor Robert Schermer
Springfield Technical Community College

Professor James F. Sullivan
Ohio College of Applied Science

Professor E. W. Winter
San Antonio College

Contents

APPENDICES

Introduction A historical

Physics may be defined as that branch of knowledge dealing with the inanimate world and its natural phenomena. The incentive and motivation that drive men on to learn more and more about the world around them stem from the pioneering instinct to explore the unknown. This curiosity of the human mind extends to all things—from the stars and galaxies to the tiniest bits of matter known, the molecules, the atoms, and the elementary particles.

In order to introduce physics in its proper perspective, a brief history of the natural sciences from the time of the early Greeks is given here. It is beyond the scope of this Introduction to give more than a brief insight into the lives of a few of the great men of science, along with a brief statement of some of their discoveries.

THE EARLY GREEKS

The outstanding contributions made by the early Greeks to art, literature, biology, medicine, and mathematics far outweigh their meager contributions to the physical sciences. In all their observations and reasoning about the physical world, they failed to test any of their theories by performing experiments, and hence misinterpreted many of the physical laws of nature.

Pythagoras (580–500 B.C.) was one of the wise men of ancient Greece. The son of a rich father, he was tutored in mathematics and philosophy, and before the age of 20, had traveled widely, to discover the Hindu and Buddhist religions. While in Egypt he solved the famous right-triangle relation that now bears his name. He believed the world was round and, along with the sun and planets, moved around an invisible sun called *Hestia.*

Pythagoras had a great belief in numbers, which, interestingly enough, led him to a study of music. He constructed an instrument with strings to test the relation between pitch and the lengths of the cords. Out of this grew his idea that harmonic intervals in music are related to numbers.

Fig. A1. Hippocrates (460–377 B.C.), Greek Physician.

Fig. A2. Aristotle (384–322 B.C.), Greek Philosopher.

Empedocles (490–430 B.C.), Greek philosopher, poet, statesman, and scientific thinker, held that there are four ultimate unchangeable elements—four primal divinities, of which all structures in the world are made—*fire, air, water,* and *earth.* These four roots of all things are eternally brought into union, and eternally parted by two active forces, love and strife. These forces, he said, can be seen working among men and pervading the whole world. Nothing new can come into being; the only change that can occur is a change in the juxtaposition of elements.

Hippocrates (460–377 B.C.) was a famous Greek physician who is often called the Father of Medicine. Although he had little to do with physics, his writings were the foundation of medical and biological knowledge. Several famous aphorisms of his include: "One man's meat is another man's poison," and "Desperate diseases need desperate remedies." His scrupulous attention to professional ethics survives to this day in the name of the oath to serve, taken by most medical doctors, "The Hippocratic Oath" (some take the more general and less stringent Oath of Menomiades).

Democritus (460–370 B.C.), probably the greatest of the early Greek physical philosophers, and contemporary of Socrates, was a native of Thrace. Democritus postulated that the universe is made up of free space with an almost infinite number of invisible particles arranged in different forms we call matter. He also believed in the indestructibility of these particles, and argued that the creation of new matter is impossible. To Democritus, the earth being the center of the universe was quite unnecessary.

Aristotle (384–322 B.C.), the great philosopher, logician, moralist, political thinker, biologist, and founder of literary criticism, spent his early years as a student and fellow worker of Plato. Observing that leaves from a tree flutter slowly to the ground, while stones dropped from the same height fall quickly, led him to an erroneous conclusion regarding falling bodies. His statement that heavy bodies fall proportionately faster than light ones was taught in universities for nearly 2000 years before it was challenged and corrected.

Aristotle was a prolific writer and although much of his work was lost, enough remains to stagger the imagination. With no experimentation to guide him, he attacked all the established landmarks concerning the physical world. He denied the evolution of life put forward by Empedocles, and disbelieved the atomic theory of Democritus. He refused to accept the idea that the earth moves, and strongly endorsed the idea of a geocentric universe.

Euclid (330–275 B.C.) was the most famous of all Greek mathematicians, his text books of geometry having been in use for

2000 years. Chief among these is the *Elements,* comprised of thirteen books and first translated from Arabic to Latin in 1482. Not until the present century, with the theory of relativity, did non-Euclidian geometry come into prominence. His most famous works include: *Data* (geometry), *Phaenomena* (astronomy), *Optics and Divisions of Superfacies.*

Fig. A3. Euclid (330–275 B.C.), Greek Mathematician.

Aristarchus (310–230 B.C.), Greek astronomer, wrote a book on *The Sizes and Distances of the Sun and Moon.* In a book entitled *The Sand Reckoner,* Archimedes tells us that Aristarchus of Samos published a book in which it was stated that the fixed stars and the sun are at rest in space, and the earth revolves around the sun in the circumference of a circle. The sun, he says, lies in the center of the orbit, and the sphere of the fixed stars is very great compared with the circle in which the earth revolves. In spite of this remarkable publication, the fame of Aristotle was so great that his own geocentric model of the universe was accepted and taught in the universities of Europe for 2000 years.

Archimedes (287–212 B.C.), Greek mathematician and inventor, was born at Syracuse in Sicily. He was the son of Pheidias, an astronomer, and was on intimate terms with—if not a relative of —Hiero, King of Syracuse. Of the many stories of legends told of him and King Hiero, the one of the lever is perhaps the most famous. Having made the claim "Give me a place to stand on and I will move the earth," King Hiero summoned him for an explanation. He is said to have set one end of a lever to a ship that was just ready to be launched, and King Hiero himself, by pushing lightly upon the other end, moved the ship into the water.

Fig. A4. Archimedes (287–212 B.C.), Greek Mathematician.

Another time, King Hiero, suspecting that the goldsmith had not made his crown of pure gold, as instructed, gave Archimedes the task of learning the truth without harming the crown. Just when he felt he would have to tell the King it could not be done, Archimedes stepped into the bath and noticed how the water ran over the edge. Springing from the bath he ran naked through the streets shouting "Eureka." To find the volume of the metal had stumped him, but now he knew that by submerging the crown in a vessel filled with water, the volume of the overflow water would equal the volume of the metal. Knowing the actual weight of the crown and its volume, he calculated its density and found it to be less than the density of pure gold. A confession from the goldsmith confirmed the King's suspicions and Archmedes' experimental observations.

2000 YEARS LATER

From the time of the ancient Greeks until the 15th and 16th centuries, little or no significant progress was made in science, and

Fig. A5. Nicolaus Copernicus (1473–1543), German Physicist.

little information was added to man's knowledge of the world around him. For nearly 2000 years the teachings of Aristotle were propounded in all the great universities throughout the civilized world. Although everything Aristotle had said about the physical world was wrong, his great powers of observation led him to interpret correctly much in the field of the life sciences.

From the late 1500s to the beginning of the 20th century, all natural laws were discovered through planned experiments. The relations we call natural laws are simply quantitative mathematical descriptions and representations of the way nature behaves. Each law is accepted as valid when it can be experimentally verified by repeated quantitative measurements.

All physical laws discovered before the turn of the 20th century go to make up that vast field of knowledge we call Classical Physics. It is appropriate that we present here, in chronological order, the names of a few of the outstanding scientists of this era and include a brief comment regarding some of the contributions they made to scientific knowledge.

Since many of the students studying physics today are planning a career in medicine or one of the other life sciences, some of the great men of science in these areas will be included in the remainder of this chapter.

Nicolaus Copernicus (1473–1543) was born on February 19, 1473 at Thorn in Poland. He studied mathematics at the University of Cracow and, after graduation, traveled first to Bologna, then to Rome, and finally to Ferrara, where he obtained a Doctor's degree in Canon Law. Later at Padua he studied medicine and practiced his skills on the poor as well as the rich. Yet he found time during all his work to study his great love, astronomy.

Copernicus assumed that the earth is a planet, like Venus, Mars, and Jupiter, and that all the planets move in circles around the sun. He visualized the earth rotating on an axis to account for the apparent daily motion of the sun, moon, and stars, and said that the latter are too far away for any motion of the earth to show an observable change in their relative positions. He listed the order of the known planets from the sun outward, and in his honor the solar system is frequently called the *Copernican System.*

This man cared little for fame, but he wanted to know the truth, and when he found it he wanted to pass it on to others. His great powers of observation, and his remarkable insight into complex problems, are set forth in his new theory of the universe in a book entitled *De Revolutionibus Orbium Coelestium* published near the end of his life.

Galileo Galilei (1564–1642) was born at Pisa, February 15, 1564, the son of an Italian nobleman and accomplished musician. In addition to becoming a student of science, he was recognized as an outstanding poet, musician, and art critic. As a student in a monastery near Florence, he excelled in the classics.

At the age of 17, Galileo returned to Pisa to study medicine, and there in the great cathedral he observed the isochronism of a pendulum. The story goes that while attending church one morning he was bored with the sermon, and became interested in the period of oscillation of the long chandelier, set swinging when its candles were lighted. Using the pulse of his heartbeat to time it, he found the time it took to make each swing. Later, when it was swinging through a smaller arc, he found the time of each oscillation to be the same. Startled by this result, he repeated the timing even when the swing of the pendulum was barely discernible and found the period unchanged.

Fig. A6. Galileo Galilei (1564–1642), Italian Physicist.

In 1608, a Dutch spectacle-lens maker, Hans Lippershey, discovered that by using two lenses he could observe distant objects greatly magnified. Rumors of this discovery reached Galileo nine months later and overnight he worked out the required lenses. After building a telescope of his own, he was soon observing the heavens. To his astonishment the moon had mountain ranges, while the sun contained large black spots that changed overnight. He also observed that the lacy draperies of the Milky Way were composed of individual stars, and that the planet Jupiter has moons of its own.

At the age of 24, Galileo wrote a treatise on the center of gravity of solids, and the following year was appointed professor of mathematics at the University of Pisa. In the year 1590, Galileo was pondering over the question of falling bodies and found apparent inconsistencies in Aristotle's teachings. As tests, he is said to have dropped various objects from different levels of the leaning tower of Pisa and to have timed their fall and measured their velocities.

On one occasion, Galileo is alleged to have attracted a large crowd to the leaning tower, where he climbed the spiral staircase to the bell chamber at the top, and there through an open archway dropped two stones, one large and one small. These two bodies fell side-by-side and struck the ground together, thus sounding the death knell of an old hypothesis and the birth of a new era in science.

Whether this particular incident is true or not, the importance of Galileo's many authentic experiments lies not in the fact that they demonstrated the fallacy of Aristotle's reasoning, but that they presented to the world a new and more reliable scientific method, the method of experimentation.

While at Pisa, Galileo carried out many experiments and public demonstrations of principles which laid the foundations of mechanics and the laws of projectiles. Because he was the first to demonstrate the power of experimentation, he is justly referred to as the Father of Experimental Physics.

Tycho Brahe (1546–1601), noted Danish astronomer, born of a noble family, entered the University of Copenhagen at the age of 13. A year later he was deeply impressed by an eclipse of the sun, which was visible from Copenhagen. What struck him most was the fact that it had been predicted with extreme accuracy. Tycho resolved then and there to study astronomy, and accepting a position as Director of the Observatory of Uraniborg, Denmark, spent some 20 years observing the planets, the moon, and the stars. Without a telescope, he made remarkably accurate observations of the planets and catalogued thousands of star positions and their time of observation.

Fig. A7. Johannes Kepler (1571–1630), German Astronomer.

Fortunately, there came into his life, not long before his death, a brilliant young mathematician named Johannes Kepler. Upon his deathbed Tycho left all his tables of observations to Kepler, and made the young man promise to publish them as the *Rudolphine Tables.* Although Tycho vehemently rejected the Copernican system, Kepler kept his word and, using the massive tables, proved beyond a shadow of a doubt that the planets move in orbits around a stationary and massive sun.

Johannes Kepler (1571–1630) was born December 27, 1571, of a poor but noble family and became one of the greatest of all German astronomers. Kepler was educated at the University of Maulbronn. It was in his position as professor of astronomy at Gratz that he first became interested in the planets. When he heard that Tycho Brahe had recorded great quantities of data on the motions of stellar objects, Kepler went to see this grand old man. There he became a close and devoted friend of Tycho Brahe and promised to tabulate and publish his recorded observations.

Fig. A8. Sir William Harvey (1578–1657), English Physician.

Using Tycho's data, Kepler made a careful study of the motions of Mars. He tried to fit the different recorded positions of the planet to concentric circular orbits for Mars and the earth around the sun. Although the observations did not fit a circular orbit, he noted that Mars seemed to move faster when its distance from the sun was less than the average, and to move more slowly when it was a little farther away. At last he tried an ellipse, with the sun at one focus, and all observations fit within the limits of observational error. Thus he discovered that the planets move in elliptical orbits, not circles.

In 1609 Kepler published his *Comentaries on Mars,* in which his first two Laws of Planetary Motion are to be found. Kepler's Third Law of Planetary Motion came a little later. Kepler was a sickly, but religious, man for most of his 59 years. He was twice married, and sired 12 children. He died penniless.

Sir William Harvey (1578–1657) was an English physician who introduced the experimental method and quantitative deductions into physiology. He described accurately the circulation of the blood through the heart and body, and calculated the amount of blood pumped through the heart in one hour, and in one day. He proved that the blood circulates and is not generated in the liver from food for a single passage in the blood vessels, as was previously believed. He described the embryology of the chick and other lower life forms, and postulated that almost all animals, even man himself, are produced from eggs.

Fig. A9. René Descartes (1596–1650), French Mathematician.

René Descartes (1596–1650), French mathematician, gained fame for his invention of coordinate geometry: "Cartesian Coordinates." He laid the foundations of analytical geometry in his treatise *Geometry,* published in 1637. He attempted to show that the science of all natural phenomena may be reduced to geometry and applied mathematics, and provided a systematic classification of all curves. He not only dissected various animals, explaining some of the principal functions of the human body, but also wrote the first text book on physiology, entitled *L'Homme.*

Fig. A10. Isaac Newton (1642–1727), English Physicist.

Sir Isaac Newton (1642–1727), English physicist and mathematician, was born in England on Christmas day, 1642. He obtained his education at Trinity College, Cambridge, where in 1665 he was awarded the Master of Arts degree. At just this time, the prevalence of the black plague forced him into retirement at his old home in Woolsthorpe, where, in two years, 1665 and 1666, his genius developed. In this period he invented the calculus, discovered the composition of white light, and conceived the idea of universal gravitation. In the years that followed, he published much of his work on mechanics and optics and developed his ideas on gravitation which were published in 1687 in his *Principia.* At the age of fifty he suffered a nervous breakdown, and never again did any extensive scientific work, but devoted his time to theology. He became very absent-minded and slovenly in his personal appearance. He never married. His *Principia* is considered to be one of the greatest monuments of the human intellect. In it, Newton lays the foundations of mechanics which are broad enough to include all future developments, and these he applies to the motions of heavenly bodies under the law of gravitation. He was elected to Parliament, was president of the Royal Society for twenty years, and was knighted by Queen Anne

Fig. A11. Antoine Lavoisier (1743–1794), French Chemist.

Fig. A12. Michael Faraday (1791–1867), English Physicist.

in 1705. The greatness of this modest man is illustrated by a remark of his made on his deathbed, "If I have seen farther than others, it is by standing on the shoulders of giants."

Antoine Lavoisier (1743–1794), French chemist, became famous for his remarkable interpretations of chemical experiments, performed by his colleagues and other contemporaries. This work earned for him the title of "Founder of Modern Chemistry." He also studied astronomy and botany, and in 1790 served as a member of the commission which established the metric system. He realized the function of oxygen in combustion, and named the light gas in his experiments "hydrogen." His publication *Traite Elementaire de Chimie* revolutionized the language of chemistry, by advancing the notion that any chemical action can be expressed as an equation.

Augustin Fresnel (1788–1827), French physicist, was born at Broglie, Normandy, on May 10, 1788. Educated at École Centrale in Caen, the École Polytechnique, and the École des Ponls et Chaussees, he started his career as a civil engineer. He became interested in optics at the age of 26, and soon performed experiments on the interference of light. Later he developed ingenious methods for producing polarized light and then studied the interference of polarized light. He obtained circularly polarized light by means of a special glass prism now known as a *Fresnel rhomb.*

Although Fresnel received scant recognition in his lifetime, he did more than anyone else to put the wave theory of light on a firm mathematical basis. His true scientific attitude is illustrated by a statement from one of his memoirs, "All the compliments that I have received from Arago, Laplace, and Biot never gave so much pleasure as the discovery of a theoretic truth, or the confirmation of a calculation by experiment."

Michael Faraday (1791–1867), English experimental physicist, was born the son of a blacksmith. Faraday's early life was spent earning his living as a bookbinder's apprentice. Taking time from his work to read some of the books passing through his hands, Faraday became intensely interested in science and developed a passionate desire to make science his life work. His chance finally came when he was made a valet and assistant to the great English scientist Sir Humphrey Davy of the Royal Institute. As a young man he openly proclaimed that women were nothing in his life, and even wrote and published a poem in criticism of falling in love. At the age of 29, he saw, fell desperately in love with, and married Sarah Barnhard, who became a devoted and inspiring companion for the nearly 50 remaining years of his life. Four months after his marriage, he made the famous discovery of the motion of a wire carrying a current in the field of a magnet. Since a current-carrying wire would move in a magnetic field, should not the reverse be true and a magnet be made to produce current in a wire? For days he experimented with magnets and coils of wire until, in desperation, he plunged a magnet down into a coil and observed that a current was generated in the coil. Why had he not discovered this before? The motion was the connecting link he had failed to realize. For this discovery the whole scientific world sought to honor him. So many universities gave him honorary degrees that he soon had to turn down such honors. He refused the presidency of both the Royal Institute and the Royal Society of London, and also refused to be knighted. Like all great scientists, he loved his work more than these honors.

Fig. A13. Karl Gauss (1777–1855), German Physicist.

Karl Gauss (1777–1855), mathematician and physicist, was born of a poor German family April 30, 1777. Educated by the reigning duke, he began his mathematical researches at a very early age. After the publication of a number of mathematical papers, he was appointed first director of the new observatory at Gottingen in 1807. There he carried out researches in optics, particularly with systems of several lenses.

Gauss became interested in magnetism at the late age of 53, and before long he was formulating a theory of the earth's magnetism. In studying magnetism, he developed a system of magnetic units based on the fundamental units of *length, mass,* and *time.* The unit of magnetic field strength called the *Gauss* is named in his honor.

Fig. A14. Charles Darwin (1809–1882), English Naturalist.

Joseph Henry (1797–1878), American physicist and scientific administrator, was born in Albany, New York, in 1797. He attended a country school, but quit at the age of 13. Later he attended the Albany Academy. Becoming interested in electricity and magnetism, he invented the magnetic telegraph and the electric relay, and discovered the phenomenon of self-induction. In 1832 he became professor of natural philosophy at Princeton, and in 1842 was elected by Congress as first secretary of the Smithsonian Institution in Washington, D.C. In this capacity, he founded the U.S. Weather Bureau and inaugurated the idea of distributing scientific publications to libraries and scientific bodies all over the world. He was the principal figure in the organization of the National Academy of Sciences, of which he was the second president. By general consent, Henry was the foremost American physicist of his time.

Charles Darwin (1809–1882), English naturalist, gained fame from a voyage around the world in 1831 on His Majesties Ship "Beagle." During this cruise he carried on research which culminated in 1859 in *The Origin of the Species by Means of Natural*

Selection. He published his theory of natural selection in 1871, in *The Descent of Man,* stating that man had come into being a longer time ago than had previously been suspected and was a contemporary of animal forms which no longer exist.

Fig. A15. Claude Bernard (1813–1878), French Physiologist.

Claude Bernard (1813–1878), French physiologist, proved that the body can build complex chemicals as we'l as break them down. He demonstrated the production of glycogen in the liver, and showed that the liver secretes bile and prepares sugar at the expense of elements of the blood passing through it. Bernard established the existence of vasomotor nerves—both vasodilator and vasoconstrictor. He analyzed the functions of the pancreas gland, the secretion of which he proved to be of great importance in the process of digestion.

Johann G. Mendel (1822–1884), Austrian biologist, was born the son of a peasant and rose to the position of Abbott at the Augustinian Monastery in Brunn. His researches in hybridization of plants resulted in "Versuche an Pflanzen-hybriden" in 1866, in which two laws of heredity were conclusively established. His work, lost in an obscure journal for thirty-four years, was rediscovered in 1900 by three independent investigators. Mendel's mathematical analyses of his research on peas gave great impetus to the study of heredity and introduced the concepts and rules based on dominant and recessive characteristics.

Fig. A16. Johann G. Mendel (1822–1884), Austrian Biologist.

Louis Pasteur (1822–1895), French biologist and founder of microbiology, became Director of the École Normale at Paris in 1857 and professor at the Sorbonne in 1867. He gained well-deserved fame from having discovered the role of bacteria in fermentation, advanced the germ theory of infection, and discovered immunology. He also carried on great research in anthrax, hydrophobia (rabies), vaccination against diphtheria, cholera, yellow fever, plague, and tuberculosis. The process of killing harmful bacteria in milk by heat is known as pasteurization. Pasteur's last great work was the discovery of the rabies vaccine, for which the Pasteur Institute was founded.

James Clerk Maxwell (1831–1879), Scottish physicist, was born November 13, 1831 in Edinburgh, Scotland. He became professor of natural philosophy in Marischal College at the age of 25, and held the chair of physics and astronomy at King's College, London, from 1860 to 1868. His contributions to knowledge began at the age of 15, when a short paper he wrote on his mechanical method of tracing Cartesian ovals was read to the Royal Society of Edinburgh. At 18 he wrote a paper on "The Equilibrium of Elastic Solids," which laid the foundations for one of the most unique discoveries of his life, the double refraction produced in liquids when under a heavy shearing stress.

Maxwell's interests extended to the publication of papers on "The Stability of Saturn's Rings," "Perception of Color," and "Color Blindness."

While the kinetic theory of gases was put on a firm foundation by Clausius in 1857, Maxwell derived the equation for the distribution of velocities for the molecules in a gas, which is known as Maxwell's Law. His greatest book was published under the title *The Kinetic Theory of Gases.*

At the age of 40 he wrote an outstanding textbook on the *Theory of Heat,* and 5 years later a treatise on "Matter and Motion." Maxwell's research and development in electricity led to an outstanding treatise called "Electricity and Magnetism." He showed how to reduce all electric and magnetic phenomena to motions of a medium. As a test of his theory, he said that the velocity of light should be equal to the ratio of the electromagnetic and electrostatic units, and that light itself is propagated as an electromagnetic wave. That this is correct is borne out by hundreds of precision experiments that have been made since his time.

Fig. A17. Louis Pasteur (1822–1895), French Biologist.

Wilhelm Konrad von Röntgen (1845–1923), born at Lennep on March 27, 1845, received his education in Holland and Switzerland. His scientific career began at the age of 25 when he became an assistant in the physics laboratory at Würzburg, Germany. After a teaching career extending over a period of 25 years, which carried him to the University of Strasburg, then to Hohenheim, back to Strasburg, then to Giessen, and finally to Würzburg again, he discovered X rays in his laboratory at Würzburg in 1895. For this discovery, he received the Rumford Medal of the Royal Society in 1896 and the first Nobel Prize in physics in 1901. Röntgen also conducted researches in light, heat, and elasticity, but none of these works compares in importance with his discovery of X rays.

Fig. A18. James Clerk Maxwell (1831–1879), English Physicist.

Antoine Henri Becquerel (1852–1908), French physicist, was born in Paris on December 15, 1852. Antoine succeeded to his father's chair at the Museum of Natural History in 1892. In 1896 he discovered radioactivity, the phenomenon for which he is most famous. The invisible but penetrating rays emitted by uranium and other radioactive elements are now called Becquerel rays. For these researches he was granted the Nobel Prize in physics in 1903.

Pierre Curie (1859–1906) and **Marie Curie** (1867–1934) were French physicists. Pierre Curie was educated at the Sorbonne where he later became professor of physics. Although he experimented on piezoelectricity and other subjects, he is chiefly noted for his work on radioactivity performed jointly with his

Fig. A19. William Konrad von Röntgen (1845–1923), German Physicist.

Fig. A20. Marie Curie (1867–1934) and Pierre Curie (1859–1906), French Physicists.

wife, Marie Sklodowska, whom he married in 1895. Marie was born in Poland on November 7, 1867, where she received her early scientific training from her father. Becoming involved in a student's revolutionary organization, she left Poland for Paris where she took a degree at the university. Two years after the discovery of radioactivity by Becquerel, Pierre and Madame Curie isolated polonium and radium from pitchblende by a long and laborious physical-chemical process. In 1903 they were awarded the Davy Medal of the Royal Society, and (jointly with Becquerel) the Nobel Prize in physics. Professor Curie, who was elected to the Academy of Sciences in 1905, was run over and killed by a carriage in 1906. Succeeding him as professor at the university, Madame Curie in 1911 was awarded the Nobel Prize in chemistry. She has the rare distinction of having had a share in the awards of two Nobel Prizes.

All the basic laws of nature that come under the heading of Classical Physics were well-established and in widespread use by the turn of the 20th century. Newton's Laws of Motion and Law of Gravitation became the basic laws of Mechanics, and Coulomb's Law, Ohm's Law, Ampere's Theorem, Faraday's Law, Kirchhoff's Laws, and Maxwell's Equations became the basic principles of Electricity and Magnetism. The foundations of Physical and Geometrical Optics were well-established by Snell, Newton, Young, and Fresnel, while Heat had come into its own through Rumford, Davy, Carnot, Joule, Clausius and Kelvin.

Although the atomic theory of matter was proposed over 2000 years ago by the early Greek philosopher Democritus, Maxwell was able to put the Kinetic Theory of Gases on a firm foundation by 1871, and J. J. Thomson had discovered the electron and measured its charge by 1899.

The Quantum Theory began with Max Planck when, in 1901, he gave an explanation of the often-measured radiation from a hot body. Light and heat, he said, are emitted as small chunks of energy called *quanta.*

In 1905 Albert Einstein introduced his Special Theory of Relativity, and in 1911 Ernest Rutherford put forward the experimental evidence for a nuclear atom. Two years later, in 1913, Niels Bohr developed his theory of the hydrogen atom, and because of its great success, established the Quantum Theory as a new concept in the nature of all matter.

It was not an easy matter at that time for physicists, well-versed in classical mechanics and electrodynamics, to accept the Quantum Theory, and it is not surprising to find that it took nearly 10 years after Bohr's theory for it to be generally accepted.

In the 20 years that followed the Bohr Theory, the detailed

electronic structure of many atoms was worked out by such people as E. C. Stoner, F. Hund, H. N. Russel, F. A. Saunders, and I. S. Bowen, and the subject was well on its way to satisfactory conclusion.

At this same time, the Quantum Theory was extended to a number of natural phenomena, and under the guidance of W. Heisenberg, E. Schrödinger, and P. A. M. Dirac, it took on a new mathematical formulation called Quantum Mechanics, or Wave Mechanics.

In 1916 R. A. Millikan experimentally determined with high precision the value of Planck's universal constant of action h, and Hess in Austria rose high into the stratosphere in a balloon and discovered cosmic rays.

In 1919 Ernest Rutherford carried out the first disintegration of atomic nuclei, using alpha particles from polonium. Bombarding nitrogen atoms with helium, he produced two different atoms, oxygen and hydrogen. This achieved for the first time in history the dream of the alchemist, who for centuries had tried to change base metals into gold.

Fig. A21. Sir Joseph John Thomson (1856–1940), English Physicist.

By the year 1924, the French physicist De Broglie proposed that all moving particles, such as electrons and protons, have a wavelength associated with their motion, as well as a momentum and energy. His basic law was soon proven experimentally by the crystal diffraction and interference of electron and proton beams. Later it was beautifully demonstrated by neutron beams.

In 1926 G. E. Uhlenbeck and S. Goudsmit proposed that all electrons spin like a top around an axis through their center. The Quantum Theory applied to this spinning electron accounts for the doubling of energy levels in the atoms of all the alkali metals, and the multiplicity of levels in all atoms of the Periodic Table of the Elements.

Fig. A22. Max Planck (1858–1947), German Theoretical Physicist.

In 1927 W. Heisenberg introduced his so-called "Uncertainty Principle," showing how the quantum nature of matter imposes limitations on all measurements that might be made of atomic collisions and events. Also, this same year W. Pauli put forward a hard and fast rule known today as the Pauli Exclusion Principle. According to Pauli, the maximum number of electrons that can exist in any electron shell in any atom is determined by a simple mathematical formula involving a quantum number.

During the 1930s the quantum theory was expanded in its application to atomic behavior, and through the development of a mathematical process called wave mechanics became the basic method for describing all atomic events.

The cyclotron, a device for accelerating atomic particles to high speeds, was invented by E. O. Lawrence in 1931. The first

Fig. A23. Albert Einstein (1879–1955), German–Swiss Physicist.

Fig. A24. Lord Ernest Rutherford (1871–1937), English Physicist.

cyclotron, which was only 3 inches in diameter, is still in existence, and is to be contrasted with today's accelerators, such as the giant one at Batavia, Illinois which is slightly over 1 mile in diameter.

In 1932 James Chadwick discovered the neutron, one of the main constituents of all atomic nuclei in the universe, and C. D. Anderson discovered the positively charged electron called a positron. The reason the neutron was so long in being discovered is that it is electrically neutral and, once freed from a nucleus, disintegrates spontaneously with a mean life of 1000 seconds. The elusiveness of the positron, an antiparticle, is attributed to its very short life, for when it meets an ordinary electron the two are annihilated.

The laboratory production of radioactive atoms was discovered by Irene Curie Joliot, and her husband F. Joliot, in 1934. It is not surprising that, growing up in the environment of a laboratory devoted to radioactivity, the daughter of Madame Curie should fall in love with a young student in the same laboratory, as well as with the excitement of experimental research. Since that time hundreds of radioactive isotopes have been produced and used in laboratories all over the world.

In 1938 C. D. Anderson and S. H. Nedermeyer discovered π mesons among the cosmic rays coming down through the earth's atmosphere. Today we know that these short-lived particles are created high in the earth's atmosphere by fast-moving hydrogen nuclei coming from outer space.

One year later in 1939, the great discovery of the fission of uranium was made by O. Hahn and F. Strassmann. With the entry of the United States into World War II, the research and development of an atomic explosive device became a classified project. The first successful nuclear explosion in the history of man took place on July 16, 1945 on the desert sands of Alamogordo, New Mexico. Many peaceful uses of nuclear explosives are being researched today.

The first self-sustaining nuclear pile reactor was developed under the guidance of E. Fermi in 1942. Using the principle of the fission of uranium, nuclear reactors of many kinds have been developed, and today such devices are used to develop electrical power in a number of cities throughout the world and to propel surface ships and submarines.

With the invention of the bubble chamber in 1952 by D. H. Glaser and its application to the operation of a huge liquid-hydrogen bubble chamber by L. Alvarez in 1954, many new and strange elementary particles have been discovered. Although a great deal is already known about these particles, no one knows where many of them fit into the structure of atoms.

Since the termination of World War II in 1945, many discoveries have been made in the field of physics. The subject is becoming more complicated and at the same time more compartmentalized, so that today we have such fields as high-energy nuclear physics, low-energy nuclear physics, microwaves, low-temperature physics, plasma physics, the physics of the upper atmosphere, solid-state physics, etc.

In this Introduction, only a few of the highlights of the development of physics over the centuries have been presented. In the 68 chapters that follow, nearly all of the subjects mentioned above will be treated in detail.

All line-drawn portraits of famous scientists reproduced in this Introduction were rendered by Edward Diffenderfer of San Francisco, and are published here with his kind approval.

Fig. A25. Niels Bohr (1885–1962), Danish Physicist.

Fig. A26. Ernest O. Lawrence (1901–1958), American Physicist.

Introduction B
optical illusions

On July 20, 1969, Neil A. Armstrong, a 38-year old American citizen, became the first human to set foot on the moon. Within minutes his co-astronaut Edwin E. Aldrin also stepped out of the lunar module and the two of them walked for over two hours on lunar soil. High overhead, their companion Michael Collins circled only 69 miles above the lunar surface, awaiting Armstrong and Aldrin's return to the command ship, and their historical return to mother earth.

This, the greatest achievement of mankind since the beginning of time, required 10 years in the planning, and hundreds of thousands of people in the construction and testing of the rockets, computers, electronic equipment, spacecraft, and ships. In spite of the high monetary costs of both the above projects, man's curiosity of the world around him, his compelling drive to explore the unknown, and the fact that positive results seemed a certainty were the principal forces that made them a reality.

In all of these developments in the physical sciences, as well as many others in the field of medicine and the life sciences in general, the subject we call physics has played a most important role. So important is this role that many authorities in other fields of knowledge and endeavor consider physics to be the most basic of all the sciences. A knowledge of the fundamental principles of physics is today an essential part of the education of all who desire to become proficient in the physical and medical professions.

One of the reasons physics is called an exact science is that reproducible experiments are performed and observations are made with high-precision measuring instruments. Laws and theories are formulated from the measured results of these experiments and then used to predict the results of new experiments. If these new experimental results do not agree with theory, the theory is either modified and brought into agreement or it is discarded for a new and better theory. Physics may be defined as that branch of knowledge treating the inanimate world and its phenomena and includes the subjects of:

Mechanics	**Atomic Structure**
Properties of Matter	**Quantum Mechanics**
Heat	**Wave Mechanics**
Sound	**Relativity**
Light	**Solid State Physics**
Electricity	**Nuclear Structure**
Magnetism	**Elementary Particles**

B.1. Physics as an Objective Method

It has long been known to scientists that when experiments are to be performed, one cannot rely too much upon the human senses of touch, sight, hearing, etc., to make accurate observations. Methods of measurement that rely upon the senses entirely are called *subjective methods.* Methods that make use of scientific instruments are generally called *objective methods.*

In the early history of science, laws were frequently discovered by the use of subjective methods. Progress was slow, however, until such methods were replaced by objective methods using measuring instruments devised to give greater and greater precision.

It is true that many scientific discoveries have been made in the past with what we now would call the crudest of apparatus and equipment. It is the development of precision instruments and apparatus, however, that has led, particularly within the last several decades, to discoveries that are far-reaching in their theoretical implications and are of extreme practical importance to the advancement of civilization.

As an introduction to the subject of physics, we will first consider a number of experiments illustrating the false impressions so easily arrived at from the use of subjective methods of observation. Although these experiments are of the nature of an entertainment, they do have more serious aspects, for they demonstrate the necessity for using objective methods in advancing science.

B.2. Subjective Methods

If someone asks you to determine the temperature of a pan of water, your first impulse, if the water is not too hot, is to use your

Fig. B1. Experiment illustrating the uncertainty of subjective methods of measurement.

hand or your finger-tips and not to bother looking for a thermometer. To illustrate the gross inaccuracy of the touch in determining temperature, consider the three pans of water as shown in Fig. B1. If the hand is first held for some little time in the pan containing *cold* water and then plunged into the *warm* water, the senses tell you it is hot. If, however, the hand is first held in the *hot* water and then plunged into the *warm* water, your senses tell you it is cold. Your conclusion in either case is thus influenced by your experiences immediately preceding your determination of the temperature of the middle pan. When a thermometer is used in this experiment the same temperature will be indicated in either case. Although this latter would be called an objective method of measurement, one still relies upon the senses to obtain a reading of the thermometer scale.

If the length and breadth of a table top are to be measured, a *foot rule*, a *yardstick*, or a *meter stick* should be used and not the *span of a hand*. In a similar way the time that it takes a sprinter to run the *"one-hundred yard dash"* is measured by a *clock*, a *watch*, or a *chronometer* and not by the *heart beat* or *pulse*.

B.3. The Eye

In making many scientific measurements the eye is considered as the most useful of all recording instruments. In some instances, however, the eye is not and should not be used directly in making observations, since it cannot be relied upon to observe what is really there. To illustrate how unreliable the sense of vision can be in some cases, we will consider in the next section a number of examples commonly referred to as "optical illusions."

Despite its many and sometimes serious imperfections and limitations, the human eye is a marvelous optical instrument. It is nature's priceless gift to man, enabling him to enjoy the beauties of form, color, and motion made possible by light. Optically the eye is like an exceptionally fine camera with an elaborate lens system on the one side and a sensitive screen or photographic film, called the *retina*, on the other (see Fig. B2). The refracting media of the eye consist of the *cornea*, the *aqueous humor*, the *crystalline lens*, and *vitreous humor*, and its function is to focus an image of the objects to be seen on the retina. Like a camera, the eye contains an *iris diaphragm* which opens wider for faint light and closes down to a bare pinhole opening for very bright sunlight. It is this iris that contains the pigment determining the color of the eye.

In the retina of the eye the light pulses are received by tiny *cones* and *rods* whose function it seems to be is to change the light

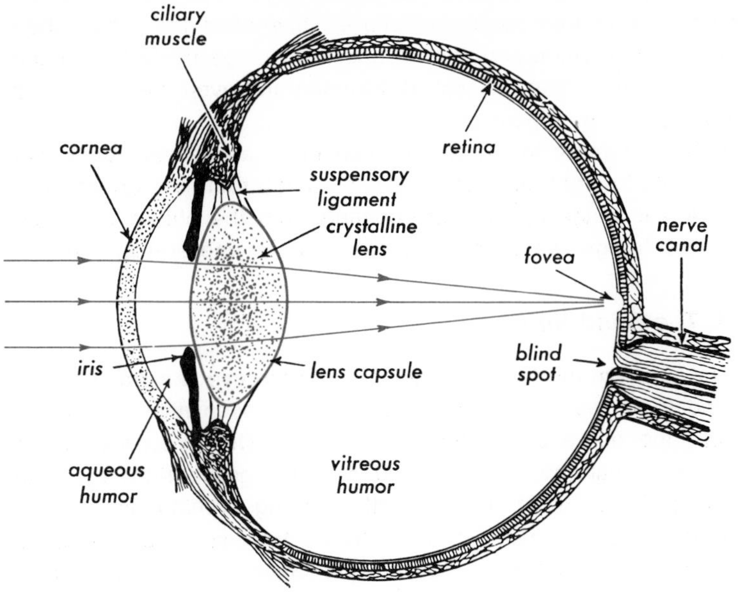

Fig. B2. Cross-sectional diagram of the human eye.

Fig. B3. Experiment illustrating the blind spot of the eye.

into electricity. Each cone and rod is connected with an individual nerve which conducts the electricity through the nerve canal to the brain. Just how these electrical impulses are produced by the cell-like structures, the cones and rods, and how they are interpreted by the brain as vision, is still only vaguely understood by scientists. Experiments show that the cones respond only to bright light and are particularly responsible for the detection and distinction of color, whereas the rods are sensitive to very feeble light, to motion, and to slight variations in intensity.

At the very center of the retina is a small yellowish-looking spot called the *fovea.* This small region contains a large number of

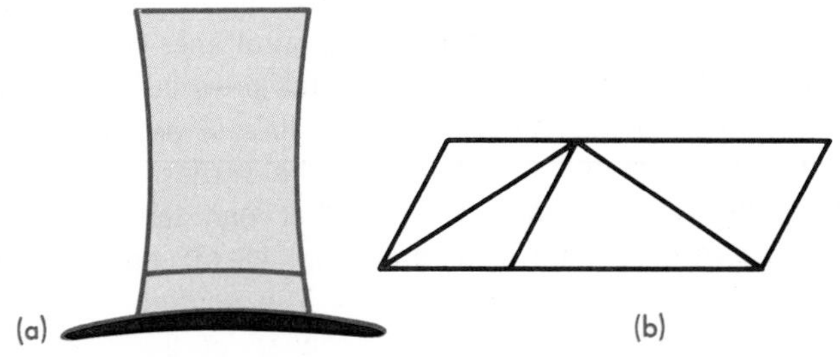

Fig. B4. Optical illusions with lines and angles.

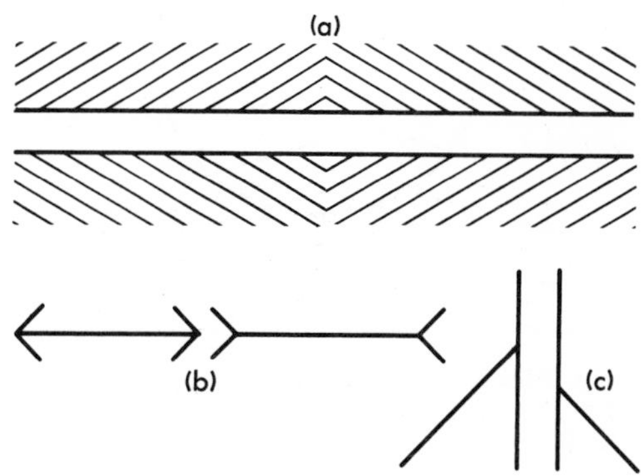

Fig. B5. Optical illusions with lines and angles.

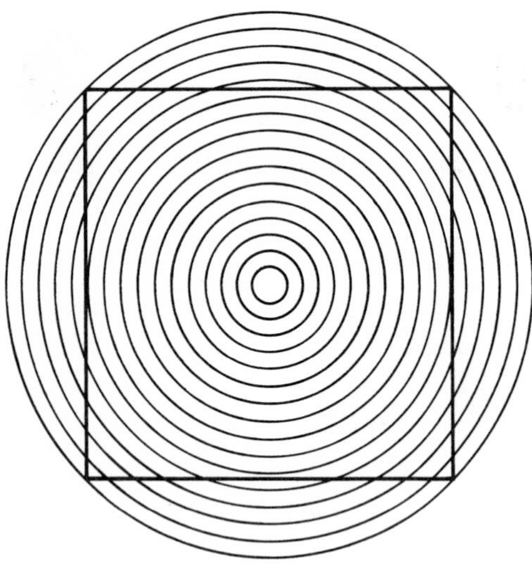

Fig. B6(a). The perfect square appears to be distorted by the concentric circles.

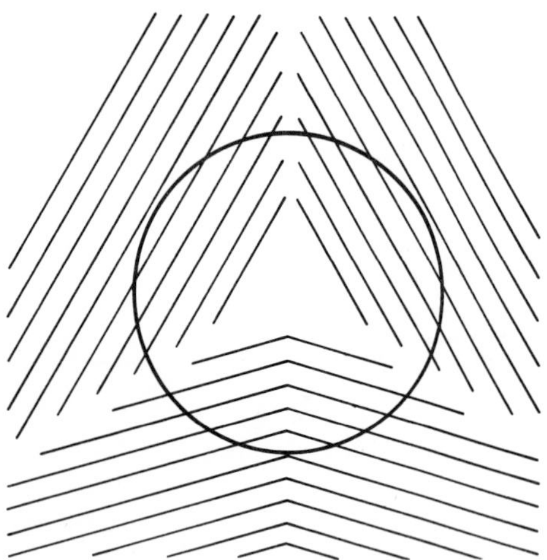

Fig. B6(b). The perfect circle appears to be distorted by the straight lines and angles.

cones, but no rods. It is on this spot in each eye that the words and letters of this page are focused one after the other when reading. Note when scrutinizing one word or particularly a single letter in a word that the rest of the page and even the words and letters close by appear indistinct.

It is customary to divide into two parts all sensory data that contribute to sight perception of any object: first, the formation of the retinal image by the light coming from the object, and second, the integrative property of the brain to interpret this image.

B.4. The Blind Spot

Not far from the fovea on the retina of the eye is a small region called the *blind spot.* This spot, which is insensitive to light, is where the nerve canal joins the eyeball. The existence of the blind spot can be demonstrated by closing the right eye and holding the book at arm's length, looking continuously at the center of the circle of Fig. B3 with the left eye. Both the circle and square will be seen from this distance. If the book is now moved slowly toward the eye, still fixing the eye upon the circle, a position (about 8 to 10 inches from the eye) will be reached where the square disappears. When both eyes are open, no position will be found where either the cross or the square disappears. One eye always sees that part of an object to which the other eye is blind. A similar experiment with the right eye focused on the square will cause the circle to disappear. A further discussion of the human eye and how it functions as an optical instrument is given in Chap. 33.

B.5. Optical Illusions

Of the hundreds of well-known optical illusions, only a few of the most interesting ones will be presented here. In Fig. B4 there are two figures classified as illusions in lines and angles. In the first figure the brim of the hat is as long as the hat is high. In the second figure the diagonal lines of the two parallelograms are equal in length. In Fig. B5 (a) the two horizontal lines are parallel and straight and in (b) the two horizontal lines are of equal length. In (c) the lower right-hand slanted line, if extended, will intersect the left-hand line where it joins the vertical.

Straight lines and circles mixed together can lead to many illusions. The perfect square in diagram Fig. B6 (a), and the perfect circle in (b) illustrate typical effects. The square in Fig. B7 appears distorted at the lower right because of the lines and angles forming the background. The square in Fig. B8 contains seven diagonal parallel lines. The short line segments of equal length make the diagonals appear to be inclined one to the other. Measurement with a ruler, or detailed scrutiny of the diagram, however, will confirm that they are parallel.

The final illusion in lines and angles is the word "OPTICS" in Fig. B9. Although the letters appear to be tipping alternately to the right and left, look at the diagram from a distance of 2 to 4 meters and the letters will appear to be straight.

B.6. Perspective

Figure B10 is an example of perspective, an illusion suggesting depth. In reality the drawing is on the flat surface of the paper and, therefore, two dimensional. By the use of converging lines for the sidewalk, curb, and windows the picture seems to be three dimensional. Actually the three people in the picture have exactly equal heights, as can be verified by measuring them. The optical images of these three figures formed on the retina have the same height. The illusion that the young girl is much taller than the other two must be attributed to the brain.

A second example called the "stairway to heaven," shown in Fig. B11, is of interest to psychologists. The figure is actually a two dimensional drawing, yet is interpreted by the brain as a three dimensional object. Walking up the steps in a counter-clockwise direction seems to lead perpetually to the same starting point. While this object can be constructed, there is a fallacy in its operations in the real world. The third perspective illusion is shown in Fig. B12. Unlike the previous figure this object cannot be constructed. (However, if the figure is cut through the center, both ends can be constructed.)

B.7. Equivocal Figures

The next set of illusions, shown in Fig. B13, are classified as equivocal figures. These illustrate the phenomenon of fluctuation in the process of vision. In (a) six cubes may be seen stacked 3, 2, 1, or seven cubes may be seen stacked 2, 3, 2. In (b) a folded sheet of paper is seen opening either toward or away from the reader. In (c) is a flight of steps seen from above looking down, or from below looking up.

Figure B14 (d) is one of the most interesting of all illusions. To appreciate the effect fully, one must himself perform the experiment with a small wire cube about 3 to 5 cm in size. The cube is held by a small handle at one corner and viewed with one eye at a distance of from 50 to 75 cm. By the principle of fluctuation,

Fig. B7. A perfect square appears distorted by straight lines and angles forming the background.

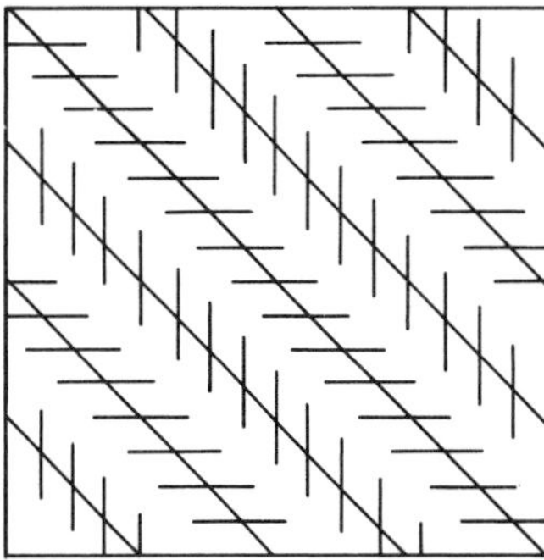

Fig. B8. The long slanted lines are parallel to each other, yet they appear to be otherwise.

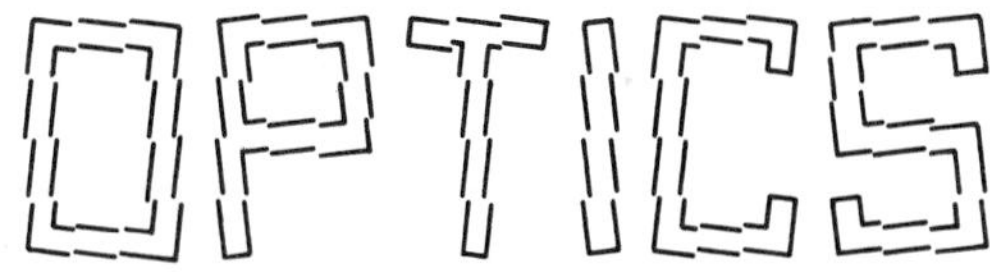

Fig. B9. The short line segments forming consecutive letters of the word "optics" make the letters appear to tip to the right and left.

Fig. B10. Which figure is tallest? Measure them.

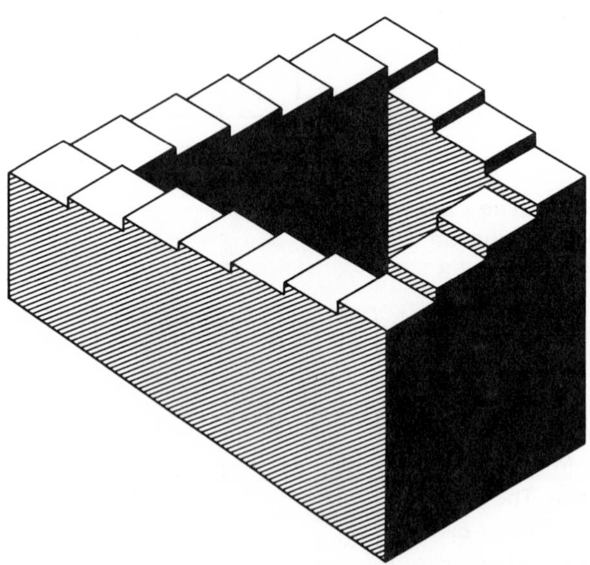

Fig. B11. "Stairway to heaven."

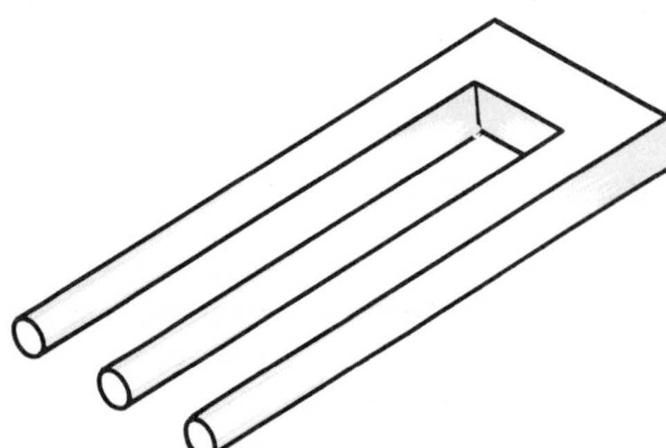

Fig. B12. An illusion in perspective and dimensions.

the observer next tries to make the farthest corner of the cube appear as the nearest corner. When this condition is attained, the cube upon being turned about a horizontal or vertical axis will appear to turn in the opposite direction. A little practice in the fluctuation of the visual senses is required in this experiment, and it is well worth performing.

B.8. Relative Areas

In Fig. B14 are two pairs of similar figures of equal area. The slanting lines at the ends make the lower figure in each case appear to be larger than the one immediately above. Such figures should be cut from white cardboard and held one above the other. When the upper figure is interchanged with the corresponding lower figure, one figure seems to grow and the other to shrink before your eyes.

B.9. Irradiation

In Fig. B15 are two small squares of equal size, a white square on a black background, and a black square on a white background. When an image of this is formed on the retina of the eye, the cones and rods just beyond the white edges are stimulated by those nearby, thus causing the white square to be larger than the black one. This phenomenon is called *irradiation* or *brightness contrast.*

A similar phenomenon is illustrated in Fig. B16 where gray spots are seen at the intersections of the white lines. The white lines look brighter because they are viewed against a dark background. Consequently, the small areas at the intersections, where white is bordered with white, appear less bright, or gray. If you direct your attention to one of the gray spots, it will appear white, and all other intersections will be gray. The one white spot is now seen by the cones in the fovea of the eye, whereas the gray spots are seen by the many rods farther out from the retinal center.

B.10. Color Illusions

There exist a larger number of illusions that are classified as *color illusions.* One of these is diagrammed in Fig. B17. A disk painted black and white as shown will appear to be colored when set rotating at a relatively low speed. The colors to be seen are rather faint pastel shades of violet, blue, green, yellow, and pink. The speed of the wheel should be from about 4 to 15 revolutions per second (rps). The explanation usually given for the phenom-

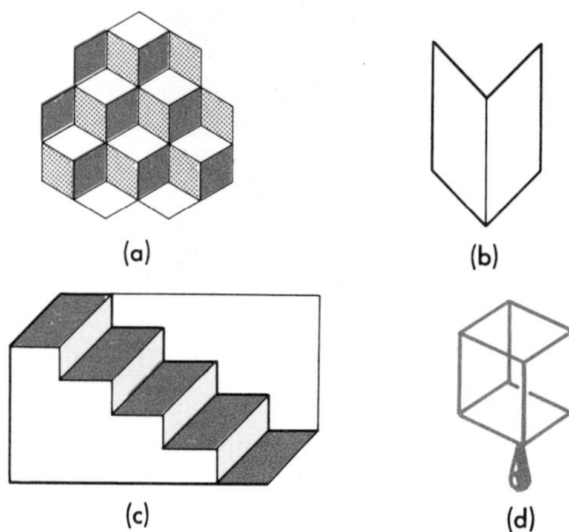

Fig. B13. Optical illusions illustrating fluctuation of the attention.

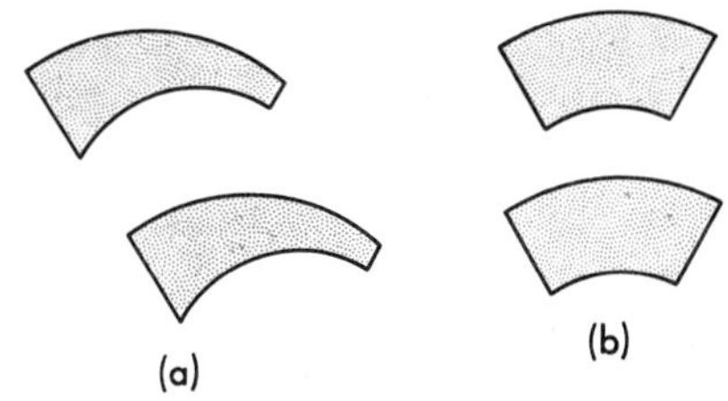

Fig. B14. Optical illusions of area.

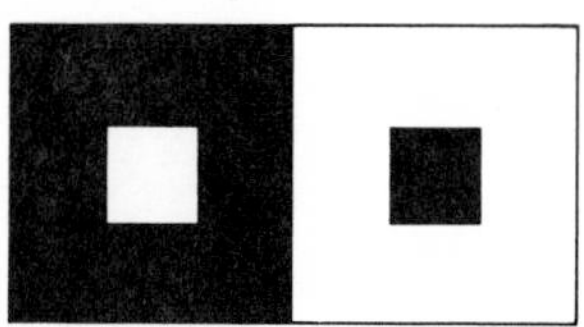

Fig. B15. The small squares are of the same size.

Fig. B16. Illustrations of irradiation.

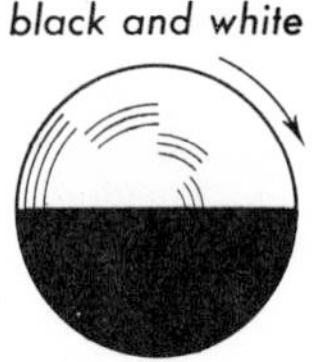

Fig. B17. Diagram of an experiment demonstrating color illusions.

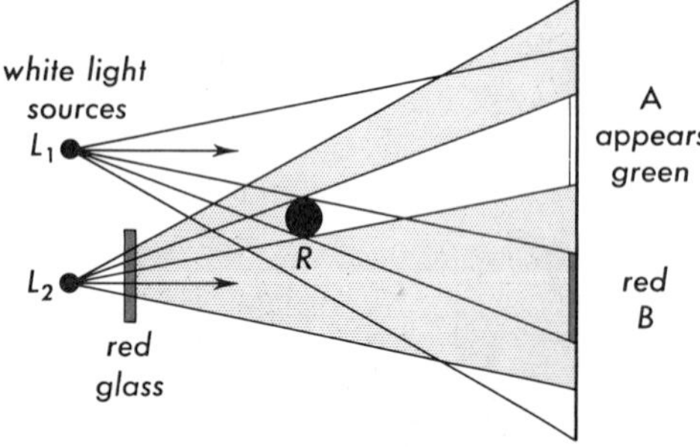

Fig. B18. Experimental demonstrations of complementary colors attributed to background.

enon is that the retina of the eye responds more quickly to some colors than to others. Since the white image of the disk moves around on the retina and since white light contains all the colors of the rainbow, some colors are perceived at each given spot on the retina sooner than others, and the effect of color is produced.

The second demonstration, as shown in Fig. B18, illustrates the appearance of color by virtue of contrast. If a white patch of light, for example, is seen on a background of red, it will appear to be pale green. If, on the other hand, a white patch is seen on a background of green, it will appear to be pink. The experiment may be performed with two similar arc lights producing white light. Each of these is made to cast a shadow of the same rod R on a white screen. If a piece of red glass is placed in front of light L_2 as shown in the figure, the white patch of light at A will appear to be pale green. If a green glass is inserted in its place, the region A will appear pink. In each case, A receives light from L_1 only and must therefore be really white. Red and green of the proper shades are complementary colors and when they are added together produce white light. The subject of mixing of colors will be taken up in detail in Chap. 34.

B.11. Circles and Spirals

If this page of the book is held about 1 ft in front of the observer's eyes and the book moved rapidly in a circle about 2 to 3 in. in diameter, the spiral in Fig. B19 will appear to rotate in the direction of motion. A set of alternately dark and light concentric circles will show the same effect, the apparent rotation being due to the persistence of vision.

We have seen in the previous illustrations how some optical illusions break down or diminish under critical inspection. There are others, however, that persist. No amount of staring or thought will teach you to see the circles of Fig. B20 as anything other than spirals.

B.12. The Trapezoidal Window

One of the most striking optical illusions in perspective is that of a slowly rotating window having the design shown in Fig. B21. This device is cut from a single sheet of $\frac{1}{4}$-in. plywood, painted white, grey, and black on both sides,* and mounted on a slowly rotating motor-driven shaft.

Viewed in a darkened room, with front and side illumination of

* In constructing such a window make all dimensions proportional to the reproduction in Fig. B21.

the window by two lights shielded from the audience, the window appears to rotate first in one direction, then the other.

An added effect is obtained by hanging a brightly colored ball at the upper corner of the small end. The ball appears to continue around in the same direction while the window appears to oscillate back and forth.

Another striking effect is to place a colored rod through the upper center window pane, as shown dotted in the figure. The rod's apparent behavior must be observed to be appreciated.

Fig. B19. Illusion of rotation.

Fig. B20. Circles appear to be spirals.

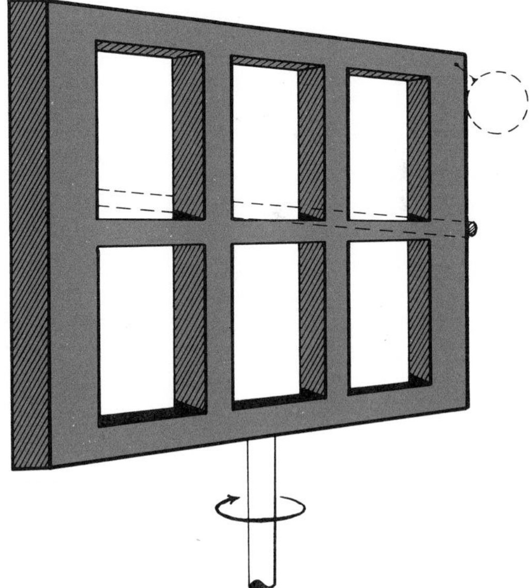

Fig. B21. Rotating slowly and continuously in one direction, this trapezoidal-shaped window appears to oscillate back and forth.

B.13. The Stroboscopic Effect

In moving pictures, when a wagon with spoked wheels is coming to a stop, the wheels are often noticed to stand still, then turn backward, stop, turn forward, and then stop again. This phenomenon, known as the "stroboscopic effect," is due to interrupted illumination of the moving-picture screen and can be illustrated in many ways. An interesting experiment illustrating the phenomenon is shown in Fig. B22. Two disks are mounted on the shafts of two separate motors. The smaller disk A with a narrow slot is used to interrupt the light beam illuminating the larger disk. The disk B is green with black circles and dots arranged exactly as shown. Suppose now that disk A makes 16 rps, thus illuminating disk B with 16 short flashes of light per second. Suppose also that B makes only 1 rps, and that one flash of light comes when the disk has the position shown in the figure. If the attention is confined to the circle at position (1), the two enclosed dots are one above the other. When the second flash of light appears, the circle (2) will be in position (1) and the two dots will appear to have shifted slightly clockwise. When the next flash of light comes, the circle (3) will be in position (1) and the two dots will have shifted still farther. This process continued shows that the circles will appear to stand still and the dots to rotate within them.

If the light flashes in any such experiment as the one described above are slower than 16 per second, the illuminated object will appear to flicker badly. If, however, the flashes come at an increasingly higher rate, the flicker will soon disappear entirely and the illumination will seem to be steady. The reason for this is that each retinal image is somehow retained by the vision mechanism for about $\frac{1}{16}$ of a second. This is called the *persistence of vision.*

B.14. Fatigue and Complementary Images

When the eyes are subjected to bright light for some little time, the retina seems to show tiring or *fatigue.* Furthermore, continued

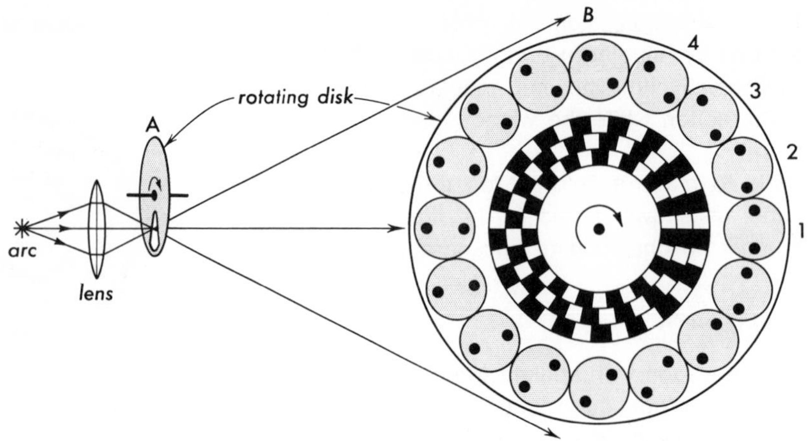

Fig. B22. Experimental arrangement for demonstrating the stroboscopic effect.

subjection of any part of the retina to one particular color causes only those cone sensitive to that color to tire. When the same retinal area is subsequently subjected to white light, the previously inactive cones respond more strongly than those originally stimulated and a complementary color is seen. The following pairs of colors are complementary to each other:

red — blue-green
blue — yellow
green — magenta
black — white

To observe such colored images, fix the attention on the black star in the lower right-hand corner of the field of the flag in Fig. B23 and keep it there for about 15 to 20 seconds. Then turn the eyes toward a white wall of the room, or toward the open sky, and in one or two seconds the American flag will appear in all of its true colors. Similar effects can be observed with other color photographs.

After-images of this kind are always complementary in color to the original pictures; black becomes white, yellow becomes blue, green becomes magenta, magenta becomes green, etc.

For supplementary reading on optical illusions, see *Am. J. Phys.,* **14,** 104 (1946), and *Experiments in Optical Illusions* by Nelson F. Beeler and Franklin M. Branley, Thomas Y. Crowell Co., New York, 1951.

*Figure B23 is a color photograph inserted after p. 532.

questions

1. Briefly explain the difference between a subjective method and an objective method of measuring temperature.

2. How would you measure the length of a table using a subjective method of measurement? Assume you want to determine its length as accurately as possible and you had no ruler.

3. If you had no measuring stick or tape measure, how could you make use of a subjective capability to measure the length of a certain city block?

4. Briefly explain how the subjective method of measurement would enter into any measurement of the length of an automobile. Assume a yard stick or tape measurement is used.

5. In motion pictures the propeller of an airplane coming down the runway seems to stand still, stop, then turn backward. Explain this phenomenon.

6. Explain why the flag shown in Fig. B23 appears to be red, white, and blue when viewed as an after-image.

7. One end of a board of unknown length is raised higher than the other to form an inclined plane. A ball started from the top is allowed to roll to the bottom. Using subjective methods alone, how would you find (a) the length of the incline, and (b) the number of seconds it takes to get to the bottom?

8. Using match sticks and some quick-drying glue, make a small cube of the kind shown in Fig. B13(d). When the glue is dry, perform the experiment described in Sec. B.7 and write a brief description of your observations.

9. Using the pattern of Fig. B14(a), cut two equivalent figures from a piece of cardboard. Place one above the other, and then interchange their positions. Briefly explain why the top one always seems to be the smaller.

Introduction C units of measurements

Physics is a science based upon measured observations of physical phenomena. It extends from the macroscopic world of natural phenomena on the one hand, to the submicroscopic world of atoms, nuclei, and elementary particles on the other. It is essential, therefore, that as we begin the study of physics we first become familiar with the units in which measurements are made.

Every measurement, whether it be a *distance,* a *weight,* an interval of *time,* a *velocity,* or an *electric current,* requires two components: first, a *number;* and second, a *unit.* One might, for example, obtain as the result of the measurements of three distances, 18.75 kilometers, 76.4 meters, and 6.50 centimeters, or as the result of the measurements of three masses, 2.648 kilograms, 65.9 grams, and 29.6 milligrams, or as the result of the measurement of three time intervals, 4.95 hours, 27.0 minutes, and 85.7 seconds. As the result of a planned laboratory experiment, and the recording of appropriate data, one might, for example, obtain such results as, 465 kilocalories, 29.60 amperes, 72.8 kilometers per hour, 1250 watts, or 96.2 joules, etc. In all the above listed data the unit is just as essential as the number preceding it.

Although there are numerous different units in which measured or calculated data may be recorded, it is found that each one can be expressed in terms of not more than four particular units. These four, called *fundamental units,* are the units of *length, mass, time,* and *electric current.* All other units are called *derived units* since, as we shall see, they can always be expressed as some combination of the four fundamental units. In the United States two widely different systems of units are commonly used: (a) the *English system,* and (b) the *metric system.* In nearly all American industries the cumbersome English system of *inches, feet, yard,* and *mile* are used as units of length, and the *ounce, pound,* and *ton* are used as units of *weight.*

In all science laboratories the world over the metric system is used in the making of all measurements and the recording of data. For this reason the metric system will be used throughout this text, and any reference to the English units will be given for comparison purposes only. See Appendix I.

C.1. The Standard Meter, a Unit of Length

The standard meter is a platinum–iridium bar about 40 in. long which is kept in the vaults of the International Bureau of Weights and Measures near Paris, France. Three facsimiles of this bar are to be found at the United States Bureau of Standards in Washington, D.C. Each of these duplicate copies may be called *International Prototype Meter* and is now the standard of length in the United States. From these prototypes, all other measuring rods and tapes are standardized.

When the standard meter was first devised, it was intended that it have a length equal to one ten-millionth part of the distance from one of the earth's poles to the equator. Although more recent measurements of the earth's dimensions have shown that the distance from pole to equator is about 10,000,880 *standard meters,* the two groove marks, one on either end of the original platinum–iridium bar, are now taken to be exactly one meter apart.

Since it is always possible that the original French standard meter might be somehow destroyed, scientists have long looked for an indestructable standard. After many years of work, and many different proposals, a legal standard has been adopted by all the major powers of the world. The standard meter is now specified in terms of the wavelength of a particular kind of light.

By means of a high precision optical instrument, known as the *Michelson interferometer,* the standard meter* is now officially and legally defined in terms of the wavelength of light from a source containing *krypton gas* (chemical element 36):

1 meter = 1,650,763.73 wavelengths

(for orange light of krypton)

The basic principles of the Michelson interferometer are presented in Chap. 47.

The standard meter is divided into 100 equal parts. Each of these parts is called a *centimeter:*

* Adopted as the International legal standard of length, October 14, 1960, by the General Conference on Weights and Measures in Paris, France.

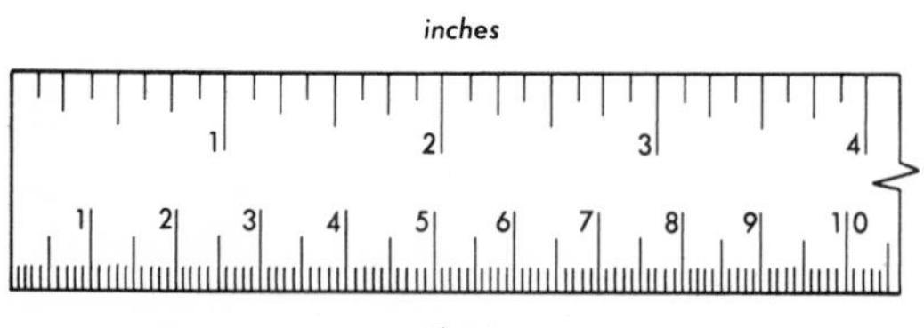

Fig. C1. Diagram comparing the centimeter scale with the inch scale.

1 meter = 100 centimeters
1 m = 100 cm

The centimeter is further divided into ten equal parts. Each of these parts is called a *millimeter* (see Fig. C1):

1 centimeter = 10 millimeters
1 cm = 10 mm
1 m = 1000 mm

The millimeter is further divided into 1000 equal parts. Each of these parts is called a *micron:*

1 millimeter = 1000 microns
1 mm = 1000 μ

When large distances are to be measured, a larger unit called the *kilometer* is used. One kilometer is equivalent to 1000 meters:

1 kilometer = 1000 meters
1 Km = 1000 m

In civil life in the United States the yard is used as the standard of length. By an act of Congress in 1866 the yard was legally defined as exactly 3600/3937 part of a standard meter. Since the yard contains exactly 36 inches, this gives the relation

1 meter = 39.370 inches

The standard unit of length used in this book is the *meter.*

C.2. The Standard Kilogram, a Unit of Mass

The standard unit of mass is the *kilogram,* a block of platinum also preserved at the International Bureau of Weights and Measures near Paris. Two copies of this kilogram (which may be called International Prototype Kilograms) are kept in the vaults of the U.S. Bureau of Standards. The kilogram is divided into 1000 equal parts called *grams:*

1000 grams = 1 kilogram
1000 g = 1 Kg

The original intent was to base the standard kilogram upon the gram, which is the mass of one cubic centimeter of pure water taken at a temperature of four degrees centigrade.

For comparison purposes the standard pound is legally defined in terms of the standard kilogram by the relation that its mass shall equal 0.4536 kilogram:

453.6 g weighs 1 lb

Following this we have the relations

28.35 g weighs 1 oz
1 lb = 16 oz

The standard unit of mass used in this text is the *kilogram.*

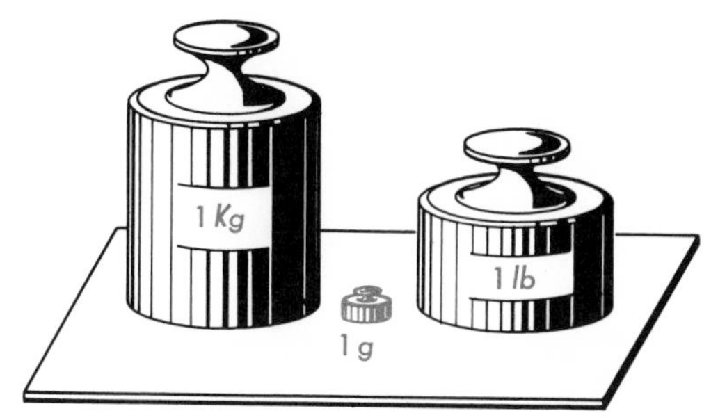

Fig. C2. The mass of a standard kilogram is 2.205 times the mass of a standard pound weight.

C.3. The Standard Second, a Unit of Time

Three kinds of time are always recognized by astronomers: first, *sidereal time;* second *apparent solar time;* and third, *mean solar time.* The last is the time used in civil life and in most science laboratories. If at any given point on the earth's surface we adjust the gnomon of a sundial to lie in the North and South vertical plane, the time interval between two successive transits of the sun's shadow over the 12 o'clock mark is called the *apparent solar day.* For several reasons, one being that the earth's orbit around the sun is elliptical, this interval of time varies slightly from day to day. An apparent solar day in December is about one minute longer than an apparent solar day in September. It is clear, therefore, why in this day of accurate timepieces we do not regulate our clocks to apparent solar time.

The *average* length of all apparent solar days throughout a solar year is called the *mean solar day.* Since there are 3600 seconds in one hour, 24 hours in one day, and 365.241 days in one tropical year, there are approximately 3600 × 24 × 365.241, or 31,556,822 seconds in one year. The *tropical year* is defined as the time between two successive passages of the vernal equinox by the sun. Since tropical years vary slightly, the *second* is defined as*

$$\frac{1}{31{,}556{,}825.9747} \text{ part of tropical year 1900}$$

The second is abbreviated s.

For astronomical purposes, a different time scale known as sidereal time is used. There is one more sidereal day in one solar year than there are mean solar days. One solar year equals 366.241 sidereal days. The reason for the additional day is that in making one complete turn around the sun in its orbit the earth has actually made 366.241 rotations with respect to the fixed stars. The sidereal second as ticked off by an astronomical clock is therefore slightly shorter than the second given by an ordinary clock keeping mean solar time. The standard unit of time used in this text is the *second.*

Although the following relations are well known to everyone, they are written here to show the abbreviations that will be used in this text:

1 day = 24 h
1 h = 60 min
1 min = 60 s

C.4. The Standard Ampere, a Unit of Electric Current

The ampere is a unit of electric current and is defined in terms of the standard *meter, kilogram,* and *second.* Although it is a special subject treated in Chap. 26, the ampere is defined as that current which, when flowing in two very long straight and parallel wires, 1 meter apart in free space, will produce a force of 2.0×10^{-7} Kg m/s^2 per meter length on each wire. Since we will not use this fourth unit until we get to electricity and magnetism later on in the text, the meaning of this definition will be left until then.

By including the ampere with the other three fundamental units, we can bring together all the subjects of *mechanics, sound, light, electricity and magnetism,* and *atomic and nuclear physics.* Together, this system of units will be described as the *MKSA*

* International standard adopted on October 14, 1960, by the General Conference on Weights and Measures, at Paris, France.

system. These four symbols stand for *meter, kilogram, second,* and *ampere.*

The chief advantage of metric units over the English system of feet, pounds, and seconds is that all units are divided into 10, 100, or 1000 equal parts. This enables fractional parts to be expressed as decimals. Decimals, it is well known, are easier to manipulate than fractions in the addition, subtraction, multiplication, and division of two or more quantities. This system has recently been named after the "Standards Institute" as the SI-system of units.*

C.5. Powers of Ten Notation

In speaking of the size and shape of an object or the time interval between the occurrence of two events, it is convenient to express very large numbers and very small decimals in an abbreviated form. This is done principally to conserve time and space. It is convenient for the astronomer in the study of stars, on the one hand, and the physicist and chemist in the study of atoms, on the other. The abbreviations in common use are based upon powers of ten as follows:

$$
\begin{array}{rlrl}
10 = 10^{1} & & 1 = 10^{0} \\
100 = 10^{2} & & 0.1 = 10^{-1} \\
1000 = 10^{3} & & 0.01 = 10^{-2} \\
10{,}000 = 10^{4} & & 0.001 = 10^{-3} \\
100{,}000 = 10^{5} & & 0.0001 = 10^{-4} \\
1{,}000{,}000 = 10^{6} & & 0.00001 = 10^{-5}
\end{array}
$$

The abbreviated form on the right side of each equation is mathematically correct. For example,

$$10^{3} = 10 \times 10 \times 10 = 1000$$

and

$$10^{-3} = \frac{1}{10^{3}} = \frac{1}{1000} = 0.001$$

*The International Organization for Standardization (ISO) is a non-treaty organization comprised of national standards bodies of some 56 nations. The Standards Institute (SI) is one of the founding members and is this nation's representative member. Copies of all ISO recommendations and other informational documents published by ISO may be obtained in the U.S. through the Standards Institute, at the following address: American National Standards Institute, 1430 Broadway, New York, N.Y. 10018.

In every case, *the exponent is seen to give directly the number of digits the decimal point is moved from unity,* positive integers specifying the number of places the decimal point is moved to the right to make large numbers, and negative integers specifying the number of places it is moved to the left to make small fractions. To illustrate the use of this system, suppose we say that a large passenger plane has a mass of seven hundred thousand kilograms. This can be written

$$700{,}000 \text{ Kg} = 7 \times 100{,}000 \text{ Kg}$$

$$m = 7 \times 10^5 \text{ Kg}$$

In the abbreviated notation the mass is therefore written 7×10^5 Kg. If more than one numeral occurs, any one of several abbreviations might be written. For example, in the case of large numbers,

$$840{,}000{,}000 = 84 \times 10{,}000{,}000 = 84 \times 10^7$$

or

$$840{,}000{,}000 = 8.4 \times 100{,}000{,}000 = 8.4 \times 10^8$$

In the case of small numbers, on the other hand,

$$0.0024 = 2.4 \times 10^{-3}, \text{ or } 24 \times 10^{-4}$$

To illustrate the advantages of this abbreviated notation, the mass of the *earth* and the mass of an *electron* are found by experiment to be as follows:

$$\text{mass of the earth, } m = 5.97 \times 10^{24} \text{ Kg}$$

$$\text{mass of an electron, } m = 9.11 \times 10^{-31} \text{ Kg}$$

If these are written down in complete decimal form they would appear as follows:

mass of the earth =
5,970,000,000,000,000,000,000,000 Kg

mass of the electron =
0.000,000,000,000,000,000,000,000,000,000,911 Kg

At a meeting held by the International Union for Pure and Applied Physics a few years ago, the following symbolism was adopted for general use:*

*International standard adopted on October 14, 1960, by the General Conference on Weights and Measures, at Paris, France.

10^3	Kilo	K	10^{-3}	milli	m
10^6	Mega	M	10^{-6}	micro	μ
10^9	Giga	G	10^{-9}	nano	n
10^{12}	Terra	T	10^{-12}	pico	p

One of the reasons for adopting these notations was that B, for billion, stands for 10^9 in the United States, and for 10^{12} in Great Britain. Because the term "billion" is so thoroughly entrenched in the minds of scientists in the United States, only a few have adopted G and T, while the change from k to K for *one thousand* is becoming more common.

The multiplication and division of large and small numbers in the abbreviated notation involves the addition and subtraction of exponents.

Rule 1. When a power number is changed from numerator to denominator, or vice versa, the sign of the exponent is changed. For example,

$$\frac{5}{2 \times 10^{-6}} \text{ equals } \frac{5 \times 10^{6}}{2}$$

Rule 2. When two power numbers are multiplied, their exponents are added. For example,

$$3 \times 10^5 \times 2 \times 10^4 = 3 \times 2 \times 10^{5+4} = 6 \times 10^9$$

Again,

$$3 \times 10^{17} \times 2 \times 10^{-12} = 3 \times 2 \times 10^{17-12} = 6 \times 10^5$$

Rule 3. When one power number is divided by another, their exponents are subtracted. For example,

$$\frac{8 \times 10^9}{2 \times 10^4} = \frac{8 \times 10^{9-4}}{2} = 4 \times 10^5$$

Again,

$$\frac{6 \times 10^{-7}}{3 \times 10^{-2}} = \frac{6 \times 10^{-7+2}}{3} = 2 \times 10^{-5}$$

C.6. Significant Figures

A slide rule is a simple mechanical device used for carrying out the arithmetic processes of *multiplication* and *division.* Since slide rules are easy to use, and inexpensive ones are adequate for most purposes, every physics student should acquire a slide rule and learn how to use it.

The beginner should select a straight or circular inexpensive rule about ten inches in length or 5 inches in diameter, and one that contains at least four, but not more than six scales. The scales most commonly used are the *A*, *B*, *C*, and *D* scales. Before learning to use a slide rule you should clearly understand the meaning of the term *significant figures.* The three lists of numbers given below will help to illustrate its meaning.

1. *All digits other than terminal zeros to the left of the decimal point are significant.* The measurement 42.65 Kg contains four significant figures; 42,650 also contains four significant figures.

2. *The first significant figure of a number is the first digit that is not zero.* The measurement 0.0132 grams contains three significant figures.

3. *Zeros to the right of a decimal point, and to the right of a non-zero digit are significant.* The reading 46.270 kilometers contains five significant figures.

In powers of ten notation a simple rule may be applied to specify significant figures. This assumes that at least one nonzero digit appears in front of the decimal point.

4. *All zeros that appear in the base number are significant.* The reading 2.40×10^5 meters contains three significant figures. If this figure is desired to four or more significant figures it may be assumed that zeros follow the last zero shown.

A	B	C
Three significant figures	Four significant figures	Five significant figures
374	5279	24794
21.5	63.08	6.9428
6.05	0.1062	0.37625
0.00328	0.04503	0.053177
546000	692700	46009

If numbers like those in column C are to be used in any slide rule calculation, they should be reduced to four significant figures if the first figure begins with 1, 2, or 3, and three significant figures if the first figure begins with 4, 5, 6, 7, 8, or 9. These particular numbers would, therefore, be assumed to be 2479, 694, 3763, 532, and 460, respectively. Since many of the measurements made in the science laboratory are accurate to only three or four significant figures, the use of a slide rule is usually, but not always, sufficient and justified.

Most slide rules are capable of handling the multiplication and division of numbers to three or four significant figures only. Furthermore, the answers are correct to three or four significant figures only.

When illustrating basic scientific principles by experiment, or by mathematical problems, some measurements may be specified by small whole numbers and others to several significant figures. Suppose for example that a small car is said to travel a distance of 9 meters in 2.15 seconds, and we wish to calculate the average speed. If the answer is to be expressed to *three significant figures* it is common practice to assume both quantities are known to at least three figures:

$$v = \frac{9 \text{ m}}{2.150 \text{ s}} = 4.19 \frac{\text{m}}{\text{s}}$$

What has been done to obtain this answer is to assume that the numerator has the value 9.00 m, and upon dividing by 2.150 s, obtain 4.186 m/s, which to three significant figures is 4.19 m/s.

If a calculator or computer is used in working problems, it is quite proper to carry each figure out as far as it is specified. When the final answer is obtained it is customary to express it to one more figure than the significant figures found in the number containing the least number of significant figures. Usually the rules given above for slide rule accuracy are adequate.

problems

1. Solve each of the following problems and give your answers in powers of ten notation: (a) 5000×600, (b) 200×0.0058, (c) $3500 \times 0.000480 \div 0.00120$, and (d) $0.30 \times 550{,}000 \div 0.0015$.

2. Solve each of the following problems and express your answers in powers of ten notation: (a) $4.0 \times 10^4 \times 6.0 \times 10^7$, (b) $4.20 \times 10^6 \times 5.0 \times 10^{-2}$, (c) $8.20 \times 10^4 \times 5.0 \times 10^6 \div 2.0 \times 10^{-3}$, and (d) $2.60 \times 10^{-5} \times 4.0 \times 10^{-5} \div 6.50 \times 10^{-16}$.

3. Solve each of the following problems and express your answers in powers of ten notation: (a) $3.50 \times 10^6 \times 4.20 \times 10^3$, (b) $6.0 \times 10^{14} \times 5.50 \times 10^{-12}$, (c) $7.50 \times 10^4 \times 3.20 \times 10^7 \div 4.0 \times 10^4$, and (d) $2.80 \times 10^{-4} \times 5.0 \times 10^{-8} \div 3.50 \times 10^{-8}$. [Ans. (a) 1.470×10^{10}, (b) 3.30×10^3, (c) 6.0×10^7, (d) 4.0×10^{-4}.]

4. Solve each of the following problems and express your answers in powers of ten notation: (a) 2400×3650, (b) $38{,}000 \times 0.150$, (c) $2800 \times 0.00520 \div 0.0070$, (d) $0.0640 \times 5000 \div 2400$.

5. A rectangular plot of ground has the dimensions 2.80 m by 4.40 m. Find its area.

6. A square sheet of metal is 45.0 cm on a side. Find its area in square meters. [Ans. 0.2025 m^2.]

7. A room is 2.80 m high, 4.60 m long, and 3.50 m wide. Find its volume.

8. A refrigerator in a large restaurant is 2.40 m by 3.50 m by 3.50 m in size. Find its volume.

9. An asteroid is 2.0 m in diameter, and has an average density of 6.50 grams per cubic centimeter. Find (a) its volume in cubic meters, (b) its volume in cubic centimeters, and (c) its total mass in kilograms. The volume of a sphere is $(4/3)\pi r^3$. [Ans. (a) 4.19 m^3, (b) 4.19×10^6 cm^3, (c) 2.724×10^4 g.]

10. A truck load of bricks has the dimensions 1.50 m by 0.80 m by 2.40 m. If brick material has an average density of 5.50 g per cubic centimeter, find the volume of the bricks in (a) cubic meters, (b) cubic centimeters; (c) find the total mass in kilograms.

11. If the average man today has a life expectancy of 70.0 years, how many seconds will he live?

12. If a dog lives 12.50 years, to how many seconds is this equivalent? [Ans. 3.945×10^8s.]

1 Speed and velocity

Nearly all introductory courses in basic physics, whether they employ the simplest algebra or the more advanced calculus, begin with the subject of mechanics. Mechanics is important because the treatment of all other subjects relies, of necessity, upon an understanding of this subject.

We may define mechanics as that branch of physics dealing with the motions and states of material bodies. The subject is usually divided into two parts, *kinematics* and *dynamics.* Dynamics may be further divided into two parts, *statics* and *kinetics.*

The subject of statics deals with material bodies in a state of equilibrium, a condition brought about by the action of balanced forces. Kinetics deals with changes in motion brought about by one or more unbalanced forces. Kinematics, which deals with analytical and mathematical descriptions of all kinds of motion, will serve as the starting point for mechanics.

1.1 The Kinematics of Speed

Speed is defined as the time rate of change of *position.* Change of position means the *distance traveled,* and time rate refers to the *elapsed time.* As an equation

$$\text{speed} = \frac{\text{change of position}}{\text{elapsed time}} \qquad (1a)$$

Change of position is illustrated in Fig. 1A. A car traveling with uniform speed along a straight line passes the point A at one instant of time t_1 and the point B at some later instant of time t_2. If the positions of points A and B are measured from some point of origin O, the distances can be expressed as x_1 and x_2, respectively.

With these symbols, the change in position Δx is equal to x_2 −

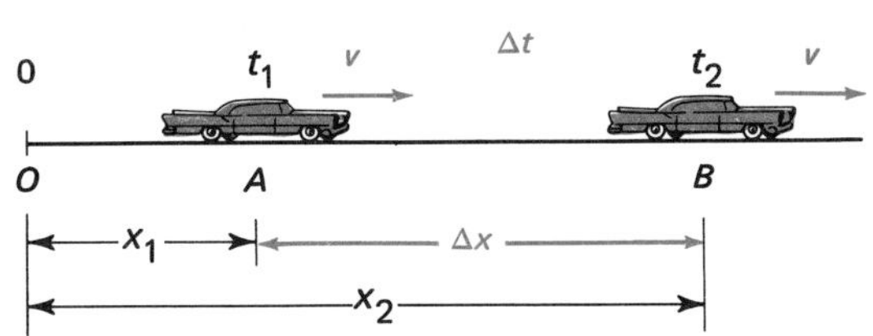

Fig. 1A. Diagram of a body moving with constant speed and constant velocity.

x_1, and the elapsed time to travel Δt is equal to $t_2 - t_1$:

$$\Delta x = x_2 - x_1$$

$$\Delta t = t_2 - t_1$$

In symbols we may therefore write Eq.(1a) as

$$v = \frac{\Delta x}{\Delta t} \tag{1b}$$

increment notation

where v is the speed, Δx is the *change in position,* and Δt is the *elapsed time* or *time of travel.*

As a general rule, measured or calculated quantities are given as increments and are taken as small differences between a succession of quantities. When a single distance and time are given, however, it is customary to write

$$v = \frac{x_2 - x_1}{t_2 - t_1} \tag{1c}$$

Example 1. A man takes 2.0 h to drive to a distant city 180.0 Km away. What is his average speed?
Solution. To find the answer we use Eq.(1c), and substitute the given quantities, $x_2 - x_1 = 180.0$ Km and $t_2 - t_1 = 2.0$ h:

$$v = \frac{x_2 - x_1}{t_2 - t_1} = \frac{180 \text{ Km}}{2 \text{ h}} = 90.0 \frac{\text{Km}}{\text{h}}$$

The answer is 90.0 Km/h. The units are just as important as the numbers and must be included in the answer.

If in the answer to this example, the unit 1 Km in the numerator is replaced by its equivalent of 1000 m, and the unit 1 h in the denominator is replaced by its equivalent of 3600 s, the answer can be written

$$v = 90 \frac{\text{Km}}{\text{h}} = 90 \frac{1000 \text{ m}}{3600 \text{ s}} = 2.50 \frac{\text{m}}{\text{s}}$$

The answer is read *two point five zero meters per second.* Both answers are exactly equal; they are just expressed in different units.

It should be noted at this stage that all units are indicated by roman letters, while all symbols for measurable quantities are printed in italics.

In the above example the car could have traveled with varying speeds. Certainly, the driver of the car must have changed his speed in order to pass another car, go around a corner, or avoid hitting someone. Equation (1c), therefore, represents an average speed over the distance traveled. In these specific and typical examples where $x_1 = 0$ and $t_1 = 0$, Eq.(1c) can be written in the simpler form

$$\bar{v} = \frac{x}{t} \tag{1d}$$

where $\bar{v}$ stands for an *average speed.*

1.2. Constant (or Uniform) Speed

A body traveling equal distances in equal intervals of time is said to be moving with constant speed. Suppose, as a demonstration of the scientific method, we perform an experiment of the kind shown in Fig. 1B. A toy automobile is pulled across the table top by means of a cord wrapped around a drum, and a stopclock is used to measure the time. A small synchronous motor M, with a geared-down shaft making 1 rps, and a drum about 2.5 cm in diameter, makes a suitable power unit.

Markers A and B are located a short distance apart, and the distance x between them is measured with a meter stick. The car is started, and, as it passes marker A, the clock is started; as it passes marker B, the clock is stopped. The time t in seconds, as read on the clock, is then recorded. This procedure is then repeated with the markers father and farther apart, and the data recorded in a table. Suppose this experiment has been performed at five different distances and the data recorded are those shown in the first three columns of Table 1A.

To find how x and t are related to each other, it is most informative to plot a graph of the two measured quantities. If we plot x vertically and t horizontally, as shown in Fig. 1C, we obtain the points shown as ×'s. When a smooth line is drawn through these points, it is observed to be a straight line. Furthermore, this straight line passes through the origin $x = 0$ and $t = 0$. From the fact that the graph is a straight line, one concludes that the two quantities x and t are directly proportional to each other:

$$x \propto t$$

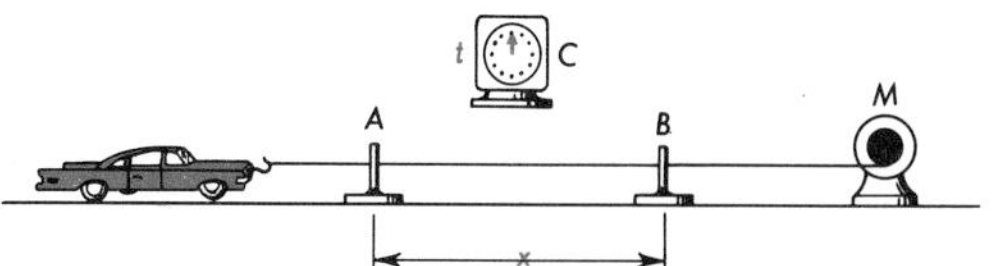

Fig. 1B. Experimental arrangement for measuring the speed of a car.

TABLE 1A
Recorded data for car experiment

Trial	*Distance* x (m)	*Time* t (s)	*Calculated* v (m/s)
0	0	0	—
1	0.398	5.3	0.0751
2	0.864	11.5	0.0751
3	1.089	14.5	0.0751
4	1.420	18.9	0.0751
5	1.743	23.2	0.0751

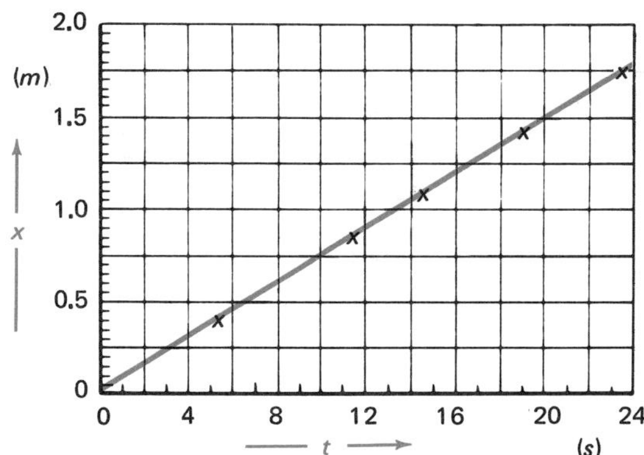

Fig. 1C. Graph of the data recorded in the car experiment.

This means that the ratio of these two measured quantities is constant. Calling this constant v, and dividing each distance x by its corresponding time t, we obtain the last column in Table 1A. We write, therefore,

$$v = \frac{x}{t} \tag{1e}$$

TABLE 1B
Increment calculations for car experiment

Trial interval	Δx (m)	Δt (s)	$\frac{\Delta x}{\Delta t}$ (m/s)
0–1	0.398	5.3	0.0751
1–2	0.466	6.2	0.0752
2–3	0.225	3.0	0.0750
3–4	0.331	4.4	0.0752
4–5	0.323	4.3	0.0751

This then represents the kind of motion we call *constant speed.* In the more general relation for speed, Eq.(1b), distance increments Δx, divided by their corresponding time increments Δt, should be constant in this special experiment. Taking differences between successive x's and t's we obtain the values shown in Table 1B.

Although this is a simple experiment illustrating a simple principle in mechanics, its purpose is that of illustrating the scientific method, namely, of making measurements of a given phenomenon and, from the recorded observations, of finding the simplest relations between them.

1.3. Distance Traveled

If the speed of a body is known, the distance traveled can be calculated for any given interval of time. From Eq.(1e), we obtain

$$x = vt \tag{1f}$$

Example 2. If a body moves with a speed of 4.50 m/s, how far will it travel in 2.0 min?
Solution. To find the distance traveled we use Eq.(1f), and substitute the given quantities, $v = 4.50$ m/s and $t = 2.0$ min:

$$x = v\,t = 4.5\ \frac{\text{m}}{\text{s}} \times 2.0\ \text{min}$$

$$x = 9.0\ \frac{\text{m min}}{\text{s}}$$

In order to eliminate *time* units in this answer, they must both be expressed in the same units. To do this, the minutes may be changed to seconds as follows:

$$x = 4.50\ \frac{\text{m}}{\text{s}} \times 120\ \text{s} = 540\ \text{m}$$

Note that *seconds* in the numerator and *seconds* in the denominator are eliminated by cancellation, leaving m in the answer as the unit of length. This illustrates a common practice that should be followed in the solving of all problems. Always express like quantities in the same units.

Dividing both sides of Eq.(1f) by v, we obtain

$$t = \frac{x}{v} \tag{1g}$$

This is an equation for the time of travel in terms of x and v.

Example 3. If a plane cruises with a constant speed of 450 Km/h, how long will it take to fly 2400 Km?
Solution. By direct substitution of the given quantities into Eq.(1g), $v = 450$ Km/h and $x = 2400$ Km, we obtain

$$t = \frac{x}{v} = \frac{2400 \text{ Km}}{450 \text{ Km/h}} = 5.33 \text{ h}$$

1.4. Vectors and Scalars

Nearly all physical measurements, whether they are made with the simplest of instruments or with the most complex of apparatus, may be classified as *vector* or *scalar* quantities. *Measurable quantities that have magnitude and direction are called vectors.* Examples of vector quantities are *displacement, velocity, acceleration,* and *force. Measurable quantities that have magnitude only are called scalars.* Examples of scalar quantities are *speed, volume, area,* and *mass.*

The importance of this seemingly trivial distinction between quantities that have direction and those that do not is realized when in solving certain problems the simple process of the addition of two or more like quantities becomes necessary.

No difficulty is generally encountered with scalars since such quantities are added algebraically. For example, in the addition of volumes, the sum of 2 gal and 3 gal is 5 gal. The addition of two vectors, on the other hand, is more complicated and requires a special process called *vector addition.* (This process will be treated in detail in Chap. 5.)

1.5. Speed and Velocity

The terms *speed* and *velocity* are often used synonymously. Strictly speaking, however, *speed is a scalar quantity* while *velocity is a vector quantity.*

Speed is a term applied only to the magnitude of velocity and does not specify the direction of motion. In moving along a straight line, *speed* and *velocity* are numerically equal to each other. If, however, the speed along a curved path is constant, the velocity is not considered to be constant because of its changing direction.

When a body moves with constant speed along a straight line whose direction is specified, it is customary to speak of its *velocity.* Movement along a straight or curved path, with no reference being made to direction, is properly referred to as *speed.*

A body moving along the same straight line, traveling equal distances in equal intervals of time, is moving with constant velocity.

Speed and velocity always have the *dimensions* of *length divided by time,* i.e., ℓ/t, and both are given by the Eqs.(1a) through (1g).

1.6. Constant and Variable Velocity

In mechanics, it is often convenient to neglect the size and shape of a body and to consider its motion as that of a small *body,* or *particle,* of negligible size. For example, in describing the motion of an airplane flying between two cities, it is not necessary to give a detailed description of the plane in order to give its position and progress. Hence, it is customary to think of the motion of a body as the motion of a geometrical point, or particle.

If the statement is made that a body travels 30 Km in 1 h, it does not necessarily mean that its speed or velocity is constant. Moving due East in a straight line, the body either moved with a *constant velocity* or with a *variable velocity.* A constant velocity is defined as one in which equal displacements are traversed in equal intervals of time and the direction is at all times that of the same straight line. In other words, the distance traveled in any 1 second is equal to that traveled in any other second. See Fig. 1C.

A particle has a *variable velocity* when, in equal intervals of time, its displacements are unequal. In such cases it is customary to speak of the *average velocity.* Average velocity, $\bar{v}$, is defined by Eq.(1c), where $t_2 - t_1$ is the total time required to travel the distance $x_2 - x_1$.

1.7. Curvilinear Motion

Motion along a curved path is called curvilinear motion. When a particle moves along a curved path as shown in Fig. 1D, it may have a constant or variable speed. The term *speed* is used here in place of velocity since the path is not straight. A *constant speed* is defined as one in which the distances traveled in equal intervals of time are equal, the distances being measured along the curved path.

A body has a variable velocity when, in equal intervals of time, its displacements are not equal. In such cases it is customary to speak of the *average velocity,* or of the *instantaneous velocity.* Instantaneous velocity is a concept used in describing the velocity of a body at any given *instant* of time. An instant in time has no duration and consequently a body cannot move any distance in an instant. The meaning of the term instantaneous velocity, therefore, involves distance and time in a very special way.

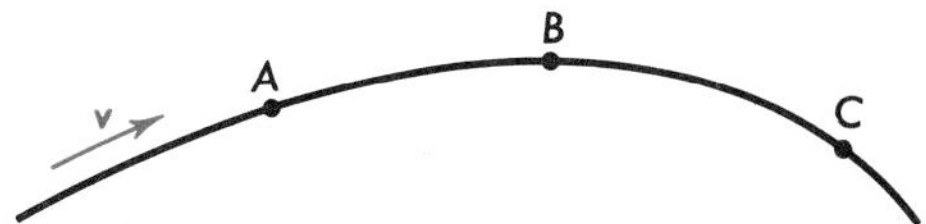

Fig. 1D. Motion along a curved path.

1.8. Instantaneous Velocity

Suppose we perform an experiment with a moving car as shown in Fig. 1B, and from the *time* and *distance* measurements plot the graph shown in Fig. 1E. The dots along the vertical *x* axis represent the car's distance from the starting point 0 at the end of each second of time. Since these are not equally spaced, the velocity is changing in magnitude. The entire diagram is called a distance-time graph.

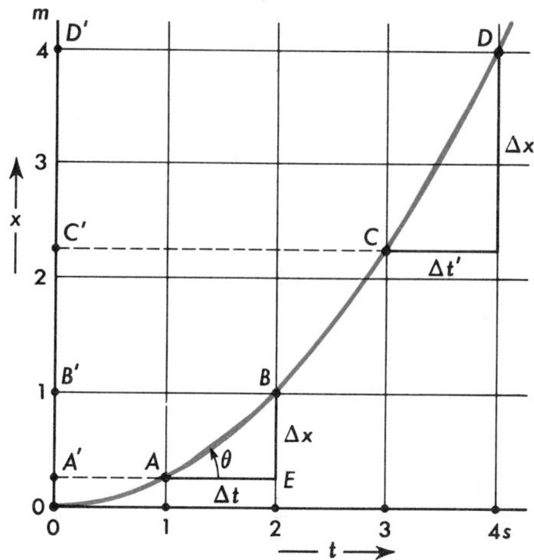

Fig. 1E. Distance–time graph for a car moving with a variable velocity.

Consider the average velocity of the car over the distance AB. In the notation of increments the distance A′B′ is Δx and the corresponding time interval 1–2 is Δt. These are shown as the sides of a right triangle AEB. The average velocity is, therefore,

$$\bar{v} = \frac{\Delta x}{\Delta t} \tag{1h}$$

and is represented on the graph as tan θ. The value tan θ is called the *slope* of the line AB.

If we now move the point B toward A, making the increments Δx and Δt smaller and smaller, the average velocity v will change in the following way. As Δt approaches zero, the quotient $\Delta x/\Delta t$ approaches the average velocity at A, and in the limit this average value is called the *instantaneous velocity:*

$$v_{\text{inst}} = \lim_{\Delta t \to 0} \frac{\Delta x}{\Delta t} = \frac{dx}{dt}$$

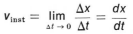

$$v_i = \frac{dt}{dx} \tag{1i}$$

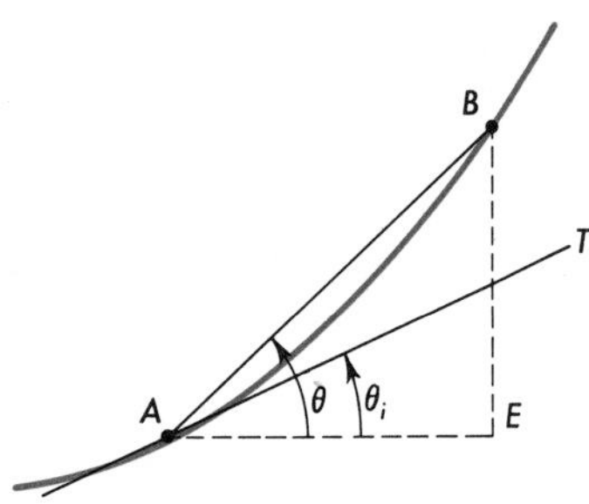

Fig. 1F. Distance–time graph showing the instantaneous velocity at A as tan θ_i.

It is shown by the detail in Fig. 1F that as the point B approaches A, the angle θ changes and in the limit when $\Delta t = 0$, the line AB becomes the tangent to the curve at A, and we can write

$$\frac{dx}{dt} = \tan \theta_i = v_i \tag{1j}$$

In words, the instantaneous velocity at any time t is given by the trigonometric tangent of the angle the tangent line makes at that point on the distance–time curve.

problems

1. In the Olympic Games of 1968 the 1600 m relay was won by the United States in 2 min 56.1 s. Find the average speed of the four runners in m/s.

2. In the 1968 Olympic Games the men's 400 m free style swimming race was won by Mike Burton of the United States in 4 min 9.0 s. Find his average speed.

3. In the 1968 Olympic Games the 50 Km walk was won by Abdon Pamich of Italy, in 4 h, 11 min, and 11.2 s. Find his average speed in m/s. [Ans. 3.318 m/s.]

4. In the 1968 Olympic Games all but two of the following races set a new world record. The distances and times for these races were: (a) 100 m in 9.9 s, (b) 200 m in 19.8 s, (c) 400 m in 43.8 s, (d) 800 m in 1 min 44.3 s, (e) 1500 m in 3 min 34.9 s, (f) 5000 m in 14 min 5 s, and (g) 10,000 m in 29 min 27.4 s. Calculate the average speed of each runner in m/s. (h) Make a graph of these results by plotting speed vertically, and distance to 5000 m horizontally.

5. An astronaut in a space ship circles the earth 650 Km above the surface in 1 h 32 min and 10 s. If the average radius of the earth is 6370 Km, find the speed of the astronaut.

6. An astronaut circles the planet Mars 100 Km above the surface in 1 h 42 min and 6 s. If the average radius of Mars is 3332 Km, what is the astronaut's speed in m/s? [Ans. 3.521 Km/s.]

7. If a car averages 90.0 Km/h, how long will it take to drive from Los Angeles to San Francisco, a distance of 640 Km?

8. A small plane cruises at a speed of 320 Km/h. How long will it take the pilot to fly from Denver to Chicago, a distance of 1500 Km?

9. A jet passenger plane travels across the United States, from New York to San Francisco, a distance of 4500 Km in 5 h and 20 min. Calculate the average speed in (a) Km/h, and (b) m/s. [Ans. (a) 844 Km/h, (b) 234.4 m/s.]

10. A superjet flies from San Francisco to Hawaii, a distance of 3500 Km, in 3 h 42 min. Find the average cruising speed in (a) Km/h, and (b) m/s.

11. A propeller-driven plane leaving a New York airport for London, England, maintains a cruising speed of 600 Km/h. A jet plane leaving the same airport 1 h and 40 min later cruises at a speed of 920 Km/h. (a) How long will it take the second plane to overtake the first, and (b) how far will they both have traveled?

12.* Two airplanes leave the same airport at the same time to fly to the same distant city. One has a cruising speed of 450 Km/h, and the other a speed of 670 Km/h. If the faster plane arrives at the distant city 40 min ahead of the other, (a) how far is the distant city, and (b) what are the two flight times? [Ans. (a) 914 Km, (b) 2 h 1.82 min, and 1 h 21.82 min.]

13. In the 1972 Winter Olympic Games Ard Schenk of the Netherlands won the following men's speed skating races: (a) 1500 m in a time of 2 min 2.96 sec; (b) 5000 m in a time of 7 min 23.61 sec; and (c) 10,000 m in a time of 15 min 1.35 sec. Calculate his average speed for each of these events.

*All starred problems involve greater difficulty in their solution.

2 Accelerated motion

Acceleration is that part of kinematics dealing with changes in speed and velocity. A thorough understanding of accelerated motion is important to all fields of physics, from the ultra-microscopic structure of nucleii of atoms on the one hand, to the planetary motion of satellites and the distant stars on the other. There are numerous examples in nature where the accelerated motion of a body is essentially constant over long periods of time, as well as examples of where it is continually changing.

2.1. Accelerated Motion

Acceleration is defined as the time rate of change of velocity. A car "picking up speed" has a *positive acceleration,* while another car slowing down has a *negative acceleration.* If a car is standing still or moving with constant velocity, it has no acceleration.

By the above definition of acceleration we may write as an equation

$$\text{acceleration} = \frac{\text{change in velocity}}{\text{elapsed time}} \tag{2a}$$

Consider as an illustration of accelerated motion the car shown in Fig. 2A. Due to a constantly acting force, exerted by the motor through the drive wheels, this car is continually accelerated as it moves along the straight line AB. As it passes A it has a relatively low velocity v_1, while farther along its path at the point B it is moving faster and has a velocity v_2. With this symbolism, v_1 is called the *initial velocity,* and v_2 is called the *final velocity.*

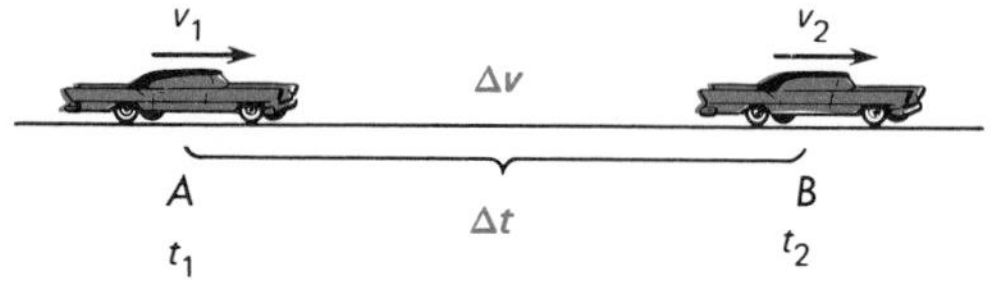

Fig. 2A. A car is accelerated for a period of time Δt.

If we let Δv represent the change in velocity, we can write

$$\Delta v = v_2 - v_1$$

If the instant the car passes the point A is called the *initial time* t_1, and the instant the car passes point B is called the *final time* t_2, the elapsed time Δt is given by

$$\Delta t = t_2 - t_1$$

By letting a represent the acceleration we can now write Eq. (2a) in the form

$$a = \frac{v_2 - v_1}{t_2 - t_1} \tag{2b}$$

or

$$a = \frac{\Delta v}{\Delta t} \tag{2c}$$

increment notation

Example 1. Suppose that at A, in Fig. 2A, the velocity of the car is 6.0 m/s, that at B it has increased to 30.0 m/s, and that it takes 4.0 s to go from A to B. What is the acceleration?
Solution. By direct substitution in Eq.(2b), of the known quantities, $v_1 = 6.0$ m/s, $v_2 = 30.0$ m/s, $t_2 - t_1 = 4.0$ s, we obtain

$$a = \frac{v_2 - v_1}{t_2 - t_1} = \frac{30 \text{ m/s} - 6 \text{ m/s}}{4 \text{ s} - 0 \text{ s}}$$

$$a = \frac{24 \text{ m/s}}{4 \text{ s}} = 6.0 \frac{\text{m}}{\text{s}^2}$$

The answer is read *six point zero meters per second per second.*

2.2. Negative Acceleration

When a body is slowing down, the initial velocity is greater than the final velocity, and the acceleration as given by Eq.(2b) is negative.

Example 2. In going up a long, steep hill a car slows down from 86.0 Km/h to 38.0 Km/h in 4.0 min. Find the acceleration.

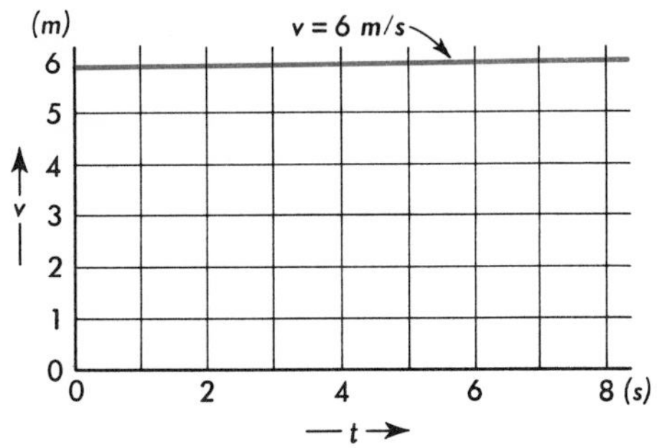

Fig. 2B. Velocity–time graph of a body moving with constant velocity.

Solution. Here we can use Eq.(2b) and make direct substitutions of the known quantities, $v_1 = 86.0$ Km/h, $v_2 = 38.0$ Km/h, and $t_2 - t_1 = 4.0$ min, and obtain

$$a = \frac{v_2 - v_1}{t_2 - t_1} = \frac{38\ \text{Km/h} - 86\ \text{Km/h}}{4\ \text{min}}$$

$$a = \frac{-48\ \text{Km/h}}{4\ \text{min}} = -12.0\ \frac{\text{Km}}{\text{h min}}$$

This answer can be read as *minus twelve point zero kilometers per hour per minute.* The answer can be left this way with two different units of time in the denominator, or changed to the same units by replacing 1 h by its equivalent of 60 min:

$$a = -12.0\ \frac{\text{Km}}{60\ \text{min min}} = -0.20\ \frac{\text{Km}}{\text{min}^2}$$

This answer can be read as *minus zero point two zero kilometers per minute per minute,* or *minus zero point two zero kilometers per minute squared.*

To express the answer in meters and seconds, we can write

$$a = -2.0\ \frac{1000\ \text{m}}{(60\ \text{s})^2} = -0.556\ \frac{\text{m}}{\text{s}^2}$$

This answer may be read *minus zero point five five six meters per second squared.*

2.3. Average Acceleration

In describing accelerated motion in the preceding section, nothing is said about the velocity of a body all along its path. It has only been said that at a time t_1 the body has one specific velocity v_1, and at a later time t_2 it has a different velocity v_2.

There are many different ways in which a body may accelerate or decelerate as it moves along from one point to another. To develop some of the basic principles for treating such motions, we first consider a **velocity–time** *graph* for a body moving with **constant velocity** (see Fig. 2B). In this simplest of cases the curve is a straight horizontal line. It shows that the velocity has the same value at all times, and that the distance traveled is given by Eq.(1b):

$$v = \frac{\Delta x}{\Delta t}$$

Next, let us consider three cars (a), (b), and (c), moving along a straight and level road at 5 m/s (approximately 11 mi/h). Simultaneously, at a time t_1, each car begins to accelerate and increases its velocity according to the curves in Fig. 2C. Starting at time $t_1 = 1$ s, car (a) accelerates rapidly at first, then more slowly to reach a velocity of 20 m/s at a time $t_2 = 6$ s. The second car (b) accelerates uniformly, acquiring the same final velocity at the same time t_2. Car (c), on the other hand, accelerates slowly at first and then more rapidly to acquire the same velocity as shown.

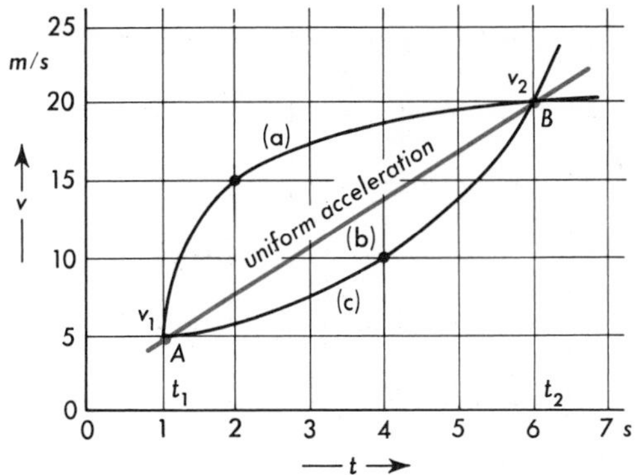

Fig. 2C. Velocity–time graph for three bodies moving with variable velocities but having the same average accelerations.

For all three of these cars, the average acceleration between $t_1 = 1$ s and $t_2 = 6$ s is the same, and is given by Eqs.(2b) and (2c):

$$\bar{a} = \frac{v_2 - v_1}{t_2 - t_1} = \frac{\Delta v}{\Delta t} \tag{2d}$$

$$\bar{a} = \frac{20\ \text{m/s} - 5\ \text{m/s}}{6\ \text{s} - 1\ \text{s}} = \frac{15\ \text{m/s}}{5\ \text{s}} = 3\ \frac{\text{m}}{\text{s}}$$

The bar over the a signifies *average acceleration.*

The distance each car has traveled during the same 5 s, however, is quite different. For car (a), the velocity increases from 5 m/s to 15 m/s during the short time of 1 s, and then from 15 m/s to 20 m/s in the longer time of 4 s. These two velocity changes correspond to average accelerations of 10 m/s^2 during the first second, and 1.25 m/s^2 during the next 4 s.

For car (c), the velocity increases from 5 m/s to 10 m/s in 3 s, and from 10 m/s to 20 m/s in the next 2 s. These correspond to average accelerations of 1.67 m/s^2 and 5 m/s^2, respectively.

The motion of car (b) is a special case, and is called **constant** or **uniform acceleration.** During each time increment Δt, large or small, and all along the path, the velocity increases by 3 m/s every second of time. Any chosen velocity increment Δv, divided by the corresponding time increment Δt, will give the same value of a.

Initially, at time $t_1 = 1$ s, the velocity for car (b) is 5 m/s. Constant acceleration of 3 m/s^2 means that 1 s later, the velocity has

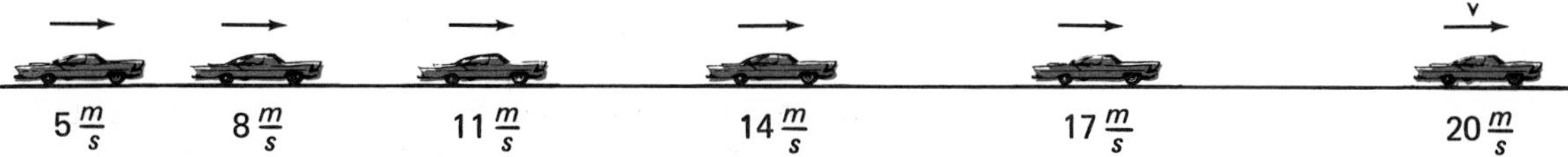

Fig. 2D. Diagram showing instantaneous velocity at the end of each second for a uniformly accelerated car.

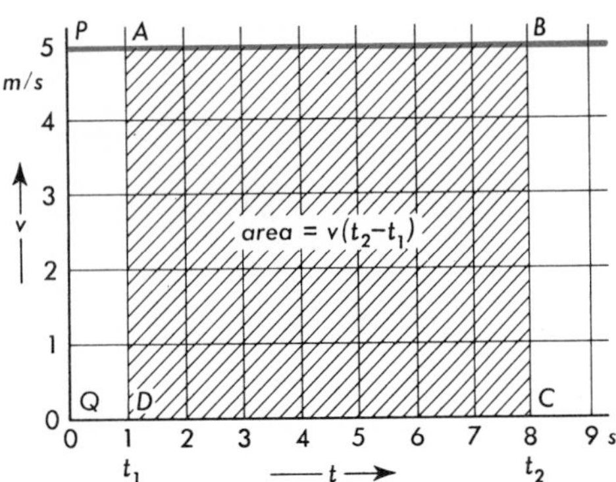

Fig. 2E. Velocity–time graph for constant velocity, showing that distance traveled is given by the area under the curve.

increased to 8 m/s. At the end of 2 s it is 11 m/s, at the end of 3 s it is 14 m/s, at the end of 4 s it is 17 m/s, and at the end of 5 s it is 20 m/s (see Fig. 2D). Constant acceleration is, therefore, one in which the velocity changes by equal amounts in equal intervals of time.

2.4. Distance Traveled

A convenient analytical expression for calculating the distance traveled by a body moving with constant velocity is derived in Chap. 1, and is expressed by Eq.(1b):

$$\Delta x = v\,\Delta t$$

This relation may be rewritten as

$$\Delta x = v(t_2 - t_1)$$

or

$$\Delta x = vt_2 - vt_1 \tag{2e}$$

Since the product of any two quantities can be represented graphically as an area, we can represent Eq.(2e) by drawing a velocity–time graph as shown in Fig. 2E. Although this diagram is constructed using the specific values, $v = 5$ m/s, $t_1 = 1$ s, and $t_2 = 8$ s, the following treatment holds for all bodies moving with constant velocity.

The product vt_1 in Eq.(2e) is represented by the area PADQ, and vt_2 is represented by the area PBCQ. The distance traveled Δx is given by the difference between these two areas, i.e., by $vt_2 - vt_1$, which on the graph is area ABCD. We can therefore write

$$\Delta x = \text{area ABCD}$$

If we apply the specific values $v = 5$ m/s, $t_1 = 1$ s, and $t_2 = 8$ s to Eq.(2e), we obtain for the distance traveled

$$\Delta x = 5\,\frac{\text{m}}{\text{s}}\,8\text{ s} - 5\,\frac{\text{m}}{\text{s}}\,1\text{ s}$$

$$\Delta x = 40\text{ m} - 5\text{ m} = 35\text{ m}$$

Observe that the product 5 m/s $\times$ 8 s is represented by the area PBCQ, the product 5 m/s $\times$ 1 s by the area PADQ, and their difference $\Delta x = 35$ m, by area ABCD.

The principles illustrated here for constant velocity are applicable to accelerated motion in general, and may be stated as follows: *The area under any curve on a velocity-time graph represents the distance traveled.*

We now consider the special case of uniformly accelerated motion and from the area under a curve find an equation for distance traveled (see Fig. 2F). Although the diagram is constructed for the specific values for car (b) in Fig. 2C, the following treatment holds for all bodies moving with uniform acceleration.

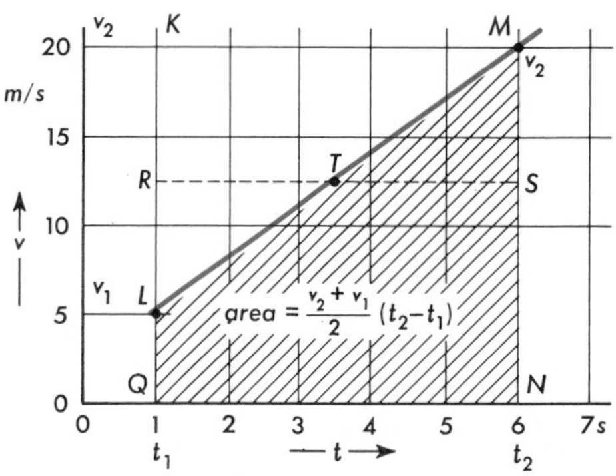

Fig. 2F. Velocity–time graph for uniform acceleration, showing that distance traveled is given by the area under the curve.

From the diagram we now write for the distance traveled

$$\Delta x = \text{area LMNQ} \tag{2f}$$

To find this area we draw the horizontal line RS intersecting the line LM at the midpoint T. This bisects the line KL at the point R, such that the line

$$\text{RQ} = \frac{\text{KQ} + \text{LQ}}{2} = \frac{v_2 + v_1}{2} \tag{2g}$$

and the area RTL is equal to area MST. This makes

$$\text{area RSNQ} = \text{area LMNQ}$$

and we can write, from Eq.(2g)

$$\Delta x = \text{area RSNQ} \tag{2h}$$

In terms of the sides of the rectangle, this can be written

$$\Delta x = \text{RQ} \times \text{QN}$$

and since

$$\text{QN} = t_2 - t_1$$

we can use Eq.(2h) and obtain

$$\Delta x = \frac{v_2 + v_1}{2}(t_2 - t_1) \tag{2i}$$

This important equation can also be written

$$\Delta x = \frac{v_2 + v_1}{2}\Delta t \tag{2j}$$

Since a body moving with uniform acceleration always produces a straight line when plotted on a velocity–time graph, Eq. (2j) may be applied to *constant acceleration* in general.

For the specific example shown in Fig. 2E, direct substitution gives

$$\Delta x = \frac{20\ \text{m/s} + 5\ \text{m/s}}{2}\ 5\ \text{s} = 62.5\ \text{m}$$

The distance traveled is read *sixty two point five meters.*

Note that Eq.(2j) applies to constant acceleration only, and that the average velocity is given by

$$v = \frac{v_2 + v_1}{2}$$

2.5. Derived Equations

It is common practice in mechanics to measure distance intervals and time intervals from a zero point. When this is done the increment notation may be simplified by writing x for Δx, and t for Δt. For constant velocity, $\Delta x = v\ \Delta t$ is written in the form

$$x = vt$$

Similarly, if we solve Eq.(2d) for v_2,

$$v_2 = v_1 + a(t_2 - t_1)$$

and write Δt for $t_2 - t_1$,

$$v_2 = v_1 + a\ \Delta t$$

and then t for Δt, we obtain

$$v_2 = v_1 + at \qquad (2k)$$

basic equation

The same simplification applied to Eq.(2j) gives the second important equation:

$$x = \frac{v_2 + v_1}{2}\ t \qquad (2\ell)$$

basic equation

These two basic equations should be memorized since all problems concerned with uniform acceleration can be solved by their use.

By combining Eq.(2k) with Eq.(2ℓ), a new and useful equation can be derived. To do this, Eq.(2ℓ) is solved for v_2 as the unknown:

$$v_2 = \frac{2x}{t} - v_1$$

Replacing v_2 in Eq.(2k) by its equivalent, $(2x/t) - v_1$, we obtain

$$\frac{2x}{t} - v_1 = v_1 + at$$

which, upon solving for x, gives for the distance traveled

$$x = v_1 t + \tfrac{1}{2}at^2 \qquad (2m)$$

derived equation

Another useful *derived equation* can be obtained by eliminating t from the same two equations. Solving each of Eqs.(2k) and (2ℓ) for t, we obtain

$$t = \frac{v_2 - v_1}{a} \quad \text{and} \quad t = \frac{2x}{v_2 + v_1}$$

Setting the right-hand sides of these equations equal to each other and solving for v_2^2, we obtain

$$v_2^2 = v_1^2 + 2ax \qquad (2n)$$

derived equation

These two derived equations give no additional information to that given by Eqs.(2k) and (2ℓ); they are simply rearrangements of the same quantities. In the derived form, however, they are more readily applied to certain types of problems.

Example 3. A train is traveling at 8.0 m/s when the throttle is suddenly opened full, and kept open for a distance of 1.50 Km. If the acceleration is constant at 0.20 m/s², what is the final velocity?

Solution. The given quantities are $v_1 = 8.0$ m/s, $x = 1500$ m, and $a = 0.20$ m/s². Since the unknown is v_2, we can use Eq.(2n), and make direct substitutions as follows:

$$v_2^2 = \left(8\,\frac{\text{m}}{\text{s}}\right)^2 + 2 \times 0.2\,\frac{\text{m}}{\text{s}^2} \times 1500\text{ m}$$

$$v_2^2 = 64\,\frac{\text{m}^2}{\text{s}^2} + 600\,\frac{\text{m}^2}{\text{s}^2} = 664\,\frac{\text{m}^2}{\text{s}^2}$$

$$v_2 = 25.77\,\frac{\text{m}}{\text{s}}$$

The answer is read *twenty-five point seven seven meters per second.*

2.6. Starting from Rest

When a body starts from rest and undergoes constant acceleration, the initial velocity $v_1 = 0$. Under these conditions the factor v_1 in the above Eqs.(2k), (2ℓ), (2m), and (2n) is replaced by zero, and the subscript is dropped from v_2, to give

$$v = at \tag{2o}$$

$$x = \tfrac{1}{2}vt \tag{2p}$$

$$x = \tfrac{1}{2}at^2 \tag{2q}$$

$$v^2 = 2ax \tag{2r}$$

These are frequently called *special equations* of motion. Because of the importance of the equations developed in this chapter, the student would do well to memorize the four general equations for uniformly accelerated motion, Eqs.(2k), (2ℓ), (2m), and (2n). The special equations need not be memorized, since they are readily obtained by placing $v_1 = 0$.

Example 4. A jet airplane starting from rest at one end of a runway acquires its takeoff speed of 150.0 m/s in 40.0 s. What is its acceleration?

Solution. The acceleration is obtained from the special Eq.(2o). Solving for a, and substituting the known quantities, $v = 150.0$ m/s and $t = 40.0$ s, we obtain

$$a = \frac{v}{t} = \frac{150 \text{ m/s}}{40 \text{ s}} = 3.75 \frac{\text{m}}{\text{s}^2}$$

The answer is read *three point seven five meters per second squared.*

---

problems

1. A jet airliner starts from rest at the end of a runway and acquires its take-off speed of 80.0 m/s in 45 s. Find (a) its acceleration, (b) the distance traveled, and (c) the speed at the end of 25 s.

2. Starting from rest on a launching pad, a rocket acquires a vertical velocity of 145.0 m/s in 12 s. Find (a) the acceleration, and (b) the distance traveled.

3. Starting from rest at the end of a runway, a jet passenger plane acquires its take-off speed of 85.0 m/s in 48.0 s. Find (a) the acceleration, and (b) the distance traveled. Find the distance traveled the first 10.0 s. [Ans. (a) 1.771 m/s^2, (b) 2040 m, (c) 88.6 m.]

4. A man on a motorcycle starts from rest and acquires a speed of 30.0 m/s in a distance of 120 m. Find (a) the acceleration, and (b) the time of travel.

5. A passenger car starting from rest has an acceleration of 1.80 m/s^2 for 12.0 s. After 5.0 s at the speed acquired, the brakes are applied bringing the car to rest in an additional time of 10.0 s. Find (a) the constant speed acquired, (b) the acceleration during the time the brakes are applied, and (c) the total distance traveled.

6. A freight train with a speed of 12.0 m/s at the top of a long grade acquires a speed of 88.0 m/s when it reaches the bottom 4 min 36 s later. Assuming constant acceleration, find (a) the acceleration, and (b) the distance traveled. [Ans. (a) 0.2754 m/s^2, (b) 10,490 m.]

7. A car starts from rest and maintains a uniform acceleration of 0.15 m/s for a distance of 2.0 Km. Find (a) its final speed, and (b) its time of travel.

8. A man driving a truck at a constant speed of 25.0 m/s suddenly applies the brakes, bringing the truck to a stop in 5.0 s. Find (a) the acceleration, (b) the distance traveled, (c) the speed at the end of 3.0 s, and (d) the distance traveled during these 3.0 s.

9. A plane initially at rest is catapulted into the air at a speed of 55.0 m/s, in 2.20 s. Calculate (a) the acceleration, and (b) the length of the catapult. [Ans. (a) 25.0 m/s^2, (b) 60.5 m.]

10. A jet plane is catapulted into the air with a speed of 62.0 m/s in 2.80 s. Calculate (a) the acceleration, and (b) the length of the catapult.

11. A heavy box falls from a truck that is traveling along a highway at 90.0 Km/h. If it slides along the pavement for a distance of 45 m before coming to rest, find (a) its initial speed in m/s, (b) its acceleration, and (c) the time taken to come to rest.

12.* A car starts from rest and undergoes a constant acceleration of 3.0 m/s^2. A motorcycle starts from the same point 4.0 s later, and maintains a constant acceleration of 5.0 m/s^2. Find (a) the time taken for the motorcycle to overtake the car, (b) the distance both have traveled, (c) the speed of the motorcycle the instant it passes, and (d) the speed of the car at the instant of passing. [Ans. (a) 13.75 s, (b) 473 m, (c) 68.8 m/s, (d) 53.2 m/s.]

13.* A locomotive starting from rest maintains a constant acceleration of 1.0 m/s^2. A car starting from rest at the same position 10.0 s later travels a parallel road with a constant acceleration of 2.0 m/s^2. Find (a) the time required for the car to overtake the locomotive, (b) the distance both have traveled, (c) the speed of the car, and (d) the speed of the locomotive as they pass.

14. Starting from rest a car undergoes a constant acceleration of 2.0 m/s² for 10.0 s, then a constant acceleration of 1.0 m/s² for 10 s. Find (a) the velocity acquired, and (b) the distance traveled.

15. A motorcycle starts from rest and maintains a constant acceleration of 3.0 m/s² for 6.0 s, then a constant acceleration of 2.0 m/s² for another 6.0 s. Find (a) the acquired velocity, and (b) the total distance traveled. [Ans. (a) 30.0 m/s, (b) 216.0 m.]

16. A motorcycle starts from rest and maintains constant accelerations of 3.0 m/s² for 4.0 s, 2.0 m/s² for 4.0 s, and 1.0 m/s² for 4.0 s. Find (a) the final velocity, and (b) the total distance traveled.

17. Starting from rest, a car undergoes a constant acceleration of 2.50 m/s² for 12.0 s, next maintains the acquired speed for 20.0 s, and then applies the brakes bringing it to rest in 10.0 s. Find (a) the total distance traveled, and (b) draw a velocity-time graph as a check for your answer.

18. A car starts from rest and maintains constant accelerations of 3.60 m/s² for 5.0 s, 2.50 m/s² for 4.0 s, and 1.60 m/s² for 5.0 s. Find (a) the maximum speed reached, (b) the total distance traveled, and (c) plot a velocity-time graph for this problem. [Ans. (a) 36.0 m/s, (b) 297.0 m.]

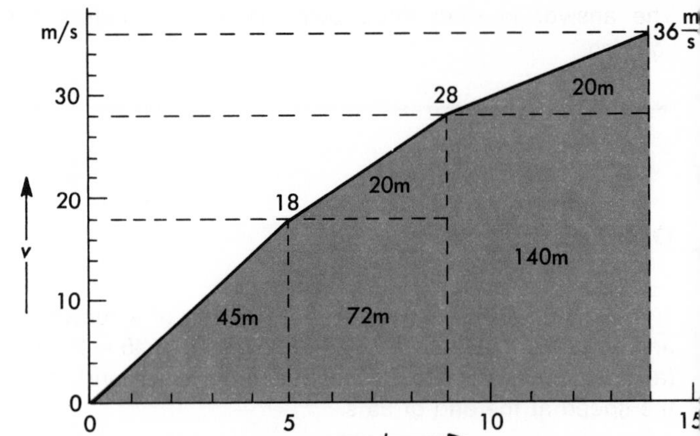

Prob. 18. Velocity–time graph.

Gravity and falling bodies

Centuries ago the great philosopher Aristotle* (384–322 B.C.) taught that heavy bodies fall proportionately faster than lighter ones. It took the world nearly 2000 years to produce a challenger of Aristotle's scientific teachings. In the year 1590, Galileo* was pondering over the question of falling bodies and found apparent inconsistencies in Aristotle's teachings.

Neglecting friction, said Galileo, all bodies, large and small, fall with the same acceleration. This, the law of falling bodies, is a physical paradox for it contradicts the conclusion the average person might reach from general observations.

One useful and informative method of studying the law of falling bodies is to follow Galileo's early experiments and roll a steel ball down an inclined plane. Starting from rest at the top, the ball increases in velocity, reaching a maximum at the very bottom. By setting up markers at measured distances x from the top, and using a stopwatch to measure the time t of descent to each marker, observed values x and t can be substituted in Eq.(2q) to calculate the acceleration a.

If this experiment is repeated with the inclined plane at different angles of inclination, the acceleration, as one would expect, is found to increase with the steepness of the incline. If the angle θ the incline makes with the horizontal is 90°, the ball will fall free of the incline, and the acceleration, which is the maximum value measured in the experiment, is called the acceleration due to gravity.

On one occasion, Galileo is alleged to have attracted a large crowd to the Leaning Tower of Pisa, where he climbed the spiral staircase to the bell chamber at the top and there through an open archway dropped two stones, one large and one small. These two bodies fell side by side and struck the ground together,

*See Introduction Chap. A for biographies of Aristotle and Galileo.

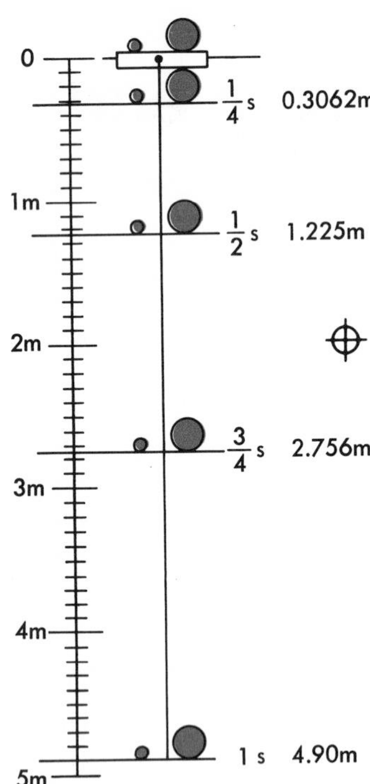

Fig. 3A. All bodies falling freely under the constant pull of gravity fall a distance of 4.90 m in the first second.

thus sounding the death knell of an old hypothesis and the birth of a new era in science.

Whether this particular incident is actually true or not, the importance of Galileo's many authentic experiments lies not in the fact that they demonstrated the fallacy of Aristotle's reasoning, but that they presented to the world a new and more reliable scientific method, the method of experimentation.

3.1. Gravitation

The principle that all objects fall with the same acceleration can be demonstrated in various ways. One of these is illustrated in Fig. 3A, where two steel balls, one large and one small, are supported in the groove of a wooden block about 5 m above the ground. When the block is tipped by pulling a cord, both balls fall off together and strike the ground together. Dropped from a height of 4.90 m, the time of fall is exactly 1 s. The ball images in the figure show the positions at the end of each quarter of the first second.

If the balls in the experiment are replaced by two marbles of the same size, one steel and the other wood, they too will fall side by side and strike the ground together. In this case, the steel marble weighs fifteen times that of the wood. (Density of steel is 7900 Kg/m^3; density of wood is 530 Kg/m^3.)

The question of air friction usually arises in this latter experiment, for careful observation will show that the wooden ball lags ever so slightly behind the steel ball. This lagging due to air friction increases the farther they fall, and is even more pronounced when a still lighter object, like a feather or leaf, is allowed to fall at the same time. Due to its large surface area, a feather or leaf flutters to the ground, being held back by the large amount of air that must be pushed aside to let it by.

In the absence of air, even a feather will fall with the acce'eration of a solid steel ball. An experiment illustrating just this is shown in Fig. 3B. A long glass cylinder containing a feather and silver coin is connected by a flexible tube to a vacuum pump. If after evacuation the tube is turned upside down, the feather and the coin will be observed to fall together. When the air is once more admitted to the cylinder, the feather will again flutter slowly to the bottom. *In the absence of air friction, all bodies fall with the same acceleration.*

During the fourth U.S.A. lunar landing mission of Apollo 15, in July, 1971, one of the astronauts on the moon, David R. Scott, performed the experiment of dropping a feather and a hammer simultaneously from the same height. Millions of viewers here on the earth observed this experiment on television, and saw the feather and hammer fall side by side and hit the ground together. Since the moon has no atmosphere this experiment was performed in essentially a perfect vacuum.

In the treatment of falling bodies given in the remainder of this chapter, air friction is entirely neglected. The formulas presented and used in working problems are known to hold only approximately. In most practical cases, however, the calculated results are so nearly realized experimentally that corrections for air friction need only be made where the distances and velocities involved are large. A detailed discussion of the effects of air friction on falling bodies is given in Chap. 7.

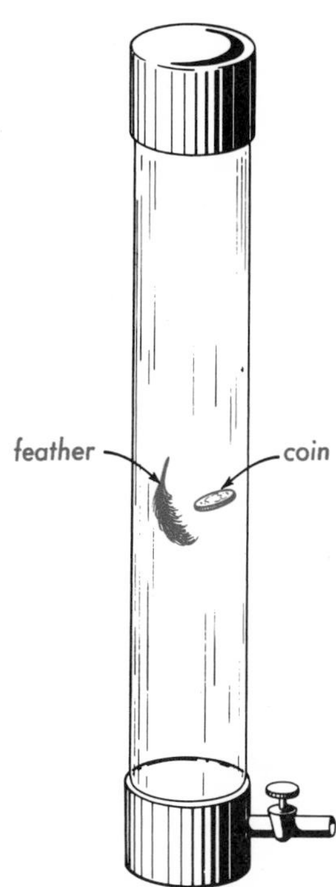

Fig. 3B. In a vacuum, a feather and coin fall with the same acceleration and strike the bottom together.

3.2. Free-Fall Experiment

Let us perform an experiment on free fall and, by making quantitative measurements, apply the graphical method of analysis to determine a relation between *distance* and *time of fall.* The experimental arrangement to be used is shown in Fig. 3C. A small steel ball is dropped from different fixed positions, and its time of fall is determined for each distance. Because the time of fall is less than a second, for the heights to be used, an electrically operated stop-clock with one-hundredth of a second divisions around its dial is used. To reduce the subjective errors introduced by the observer starting and stopping the clock, electric switching is employed. Repeated falls from the same height will then show that interpolations between marks on the clock dial are significant, and the time averages can be given to thousandths of a second.

When the switch K is in position A, an electric current supplied by the battery C energizes the electromagnet E and holds the steel ball suspended ready for dropping. When switch K is snapped to position B, the electromagnet circuit is opened, releasing the ball, and the clock circuit is closed, starting the clock. When the ball strikes the lower switch L, contacts D are instantly opened, stopping the clock. The time t is then recorded, along with the distance of fall h. By dropping the ball a number of times, the slight differences will not only demonstrate the reliability of the timing mechanism, but enable good average values to be obtained.

This procedure should be repeated with the electromagnet higher and higher, and the measurements of distance and time recorded in a table. Suppose this experiment has been performed at five different heights and the data recorded as shown by the first three columns in Table 3A.

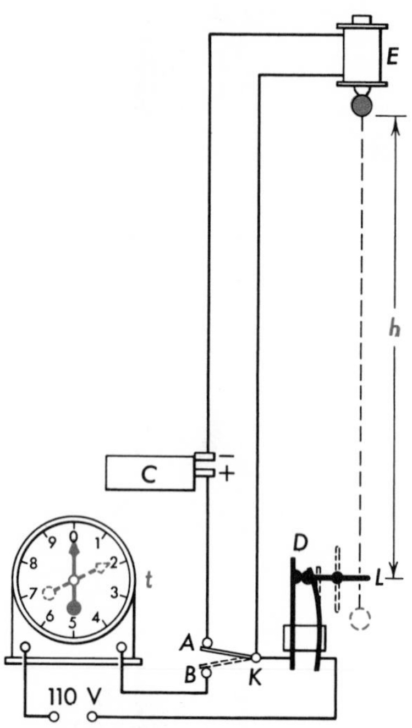

Fig. 3C. Falling-body experiment.

To see how h and t are related to each other, we shall follow the analytical method described in the preceding chapter. First we plot h vertically and t horizontally, as shown in Fig. 3D. When a smooth line is drawn through these points (dots with circles), the curve obtained has the general appearance of a parabola. Taking the same steps described in detail in Sec. 2.3, we next try plotting h against t^2, as shown in Fig. 3E. The fact that this graph yields a straight line shows that h is proportional to t^2:

$$h \propto t^2$$

Replacing the proportionality sign by an equal sign, and putting in a proportionality constant, we obtain

$$h = kt^2 \tag{3a}$$

The values of h/t^2 calculated from the experimental data give 4.90 m/s^2 as an average value of the constant k.

This result shows clearly that, with little or no air friction, a falling body has a uniform downward acceleration, and that this acceleration is given by an equation of the form Eq.(2q):

$$h = \tfrac{1}{2}at^2$$

analytical notation

For free fall it is convenient to represent the acceleration due to gravity by the letter g. Starting from rest,

$$h = \tfrac{1}{2}gt^2 \tag{3b}$$

for free fall only

To determine the value of g from the above experiment, we first solve Eq.(3b) for g:

$$g = \frac{2h}{t^2} \tag{3c}$$

The result of substituting values of h and t from Table 3A into Eq.(3c) is shown in the right-hand column.

The average value of these five determinations of the acceleration due to gravity is

$$g = 9.80 \ \frac{\text{m}}{\text{s}^2}$$

TABLE 3A
Recorded data for the freely falling steel ball

Trial	*Distance* h (m)	*Time* t (s)	h/t^2 (m/s^2)	$2h/t^2$ (m/s^2)
1	0.356	0.270	4.88	9.76
2	0.824	0.410	4.90	9.80
3	1.262	0.508	4.89	9.78
4	1.867	0.616	4.92	9.84
5	2.362	0.694	4.90	9.80

When different-sized masses are used in an experiment of this kind, the final result, within the limits of experimental error, is the same. It is for this reason that the special letter g is often used in formulas to represent free-fall acceleration.

If, for example, an object falls from rest and we wish to calculate the velocity acquired by falling a distance h, Eq.(2r) may be used. Replacing a by g, and x by h, we obtain

$$v^2 = 2gh$$

which, upon taking the square roots of both sides, becomes

$$v = \sqrt{2gh} \tag{3d}$$

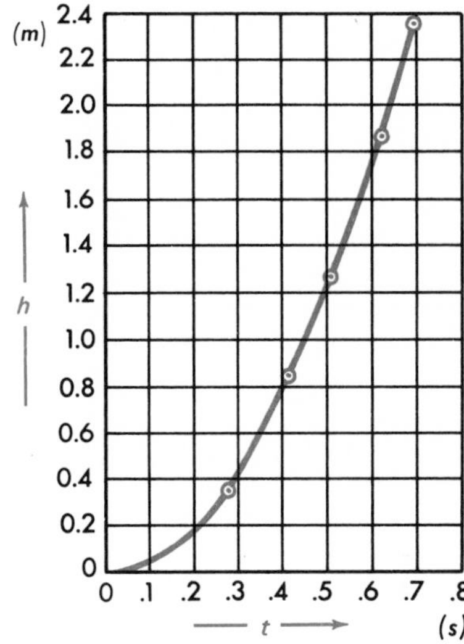

Fig. 3D. Graph for the freely falling body experiment.

3.3. The Acceleration Due to Gravity

Experiments carried on at many points over the earth show that the acceleration due to gravity is not everywhere the same; there are slight variations. Although these variations are small and are not of any consequence in most practical problems, they do exist and should be mentioned.

In general, the values of g lie between a minimum of 9.7804 m/s^2 at the equator and a maximum of 9.8321 m/s^2 at the North and South poles. Referring here to the equator and the poles is only a generalization, for not all points on the equator have the same values as quoted above, nor do all points on any one latitude have the same value. Irregularities of the earth's structure give rise to minute random differences.

The International Committee on Weights and Measures has adopted as a standard or accepted value, 9.80665 m/s^2. For practical purposes, however, it is customary to use the even-numbered value 9.80 m/s^2. For freely falling bodies, then, we shall assume that

$$g = 9.80 \frac{\text{m}}{\text{s}^2} \qquad g = 980 \frac{\text{cm}}{\text{s}^2} \tag{3e}$$

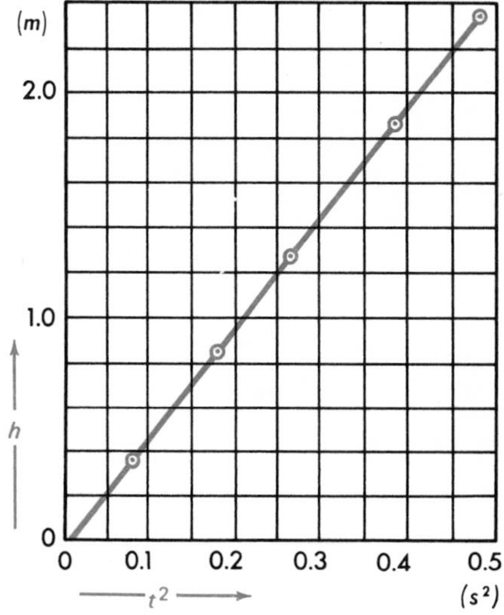

Fig. 3E. Straight-line graph for free-fall experiment.

The formulas developed for accelerated motion, given at the end of Chap. 2, with the distance x replaced by the letter h, and a replaced by g, are

$$v_2 = v_1 + gt \tag{3f}$$

$$h = \frac{v_2 + v_1}{2} t \tag{3g}$$

$$v_2^2 = v_1^2 + 2gh \tag{3h}$$

$$h = v_1 t + \tfrac{1}{2} g t^2 \tag{3i}$$

All four of these equations apply to freely falling bodies.

Example 1. A boy drops several stones into a well. Upon measuring the time it takes each stone to hit the water, he finds an average of 2.50 s. (a) How deep is the well, and (b) with what speed does each stone hit the water?

Solution. To find the answer to (a) we first write the known quantities, $v_1 = 0$, $t = 2.50$ s, and $g = 9.80$ m/s^2. The unknown quantity is h. Examining equations we find Eq.(3i) is the best relation between these quantities:

$$h = v_1 t + \tfrac{1}{2} g t^2$$

Upon direct substitution of known quantities, we obtain

$$h = 0 \times 2.5 \text{ s} + \tfrac{1}{2} 9.80 \text{ m/s}^2 \times (2.50 \text{ s})^2$$

$$h = 0 + 4.90 \text{ m/s}^2 \times 6.25 \text{ s}^2$$

$$h = 30.63 \text{ m}$$

To find the answer to part (b) we list the known quantities: $h = 30.63$ m, $v_1 = 0$, $t = 2.50$ s, and $g = 9.80$ m/s^2. The unknown quantity is v_2. Examining given equations we find Eq.(3h) to be a relation involving appropriate quantities:

$$v_2^2 = v_1^2 + 2gh$$

Upon direct substitution of known quanties, we obtain

$$v_2^2 = (0)^2 + 2 \times 9.80 \text{ m/s}^2 \times 30.63 \text{ m}$$

$$v_2^2 = 600 \text{ m}^2/\text{s}^2$$

Taking the square root, we obtain

$$v_2 = 24.50 \text{ m/s}$$

Example 2. A boy standing near the edge of a cliff 125.0 m above a river throws a stone downward with a speed of 10.0 m/s. (a) With what speed will the stone hit the water, and (b) how long will it take to descend?

Solution. To find the answer to (a) we first give the known quantities, $v_1 = 10.0$ m/s, $h = 125.0$ m, and $g = 9.80$ m/s^2. With v_2 as the unknown quantity, Eq.(3h) is selected:

$$v_2^2 = v_1^2 + 2gh$$

By direct substitution of all the known quantities, we obtain

$$v_2^2 = \left(10\,\frac{\text{m}}{\text{s}}\right)^2 + 2 \times 9.8\,\frac{\text{m}}{\text{s}^2} \times 125\text{ m}$$

$$v_2^2 = 100\,\frac{\text{m}^2}{\text{s}^2} + 2450\,\frac{\text{m}^2}{\text{s}^2} = 2550\,\frac{\text{m}^2}{\text{s}^2}$$

By taking the square root of both sides of the equation, we obtain

$$v_2 = 50.5\,\frac{\text{m}}{\text{s}}$$

For the answer to part (b), we again list all of the known quantities, $v_2 = 50.5$ m/s, $v_1 = 10$ m/s, and $g = 9.80$ m/s^2. The unknown is t. The relation containing these four quantities is Eq.(3f):

$$v_2 = v_1 + gt$$

Solving for the unknown, we find

$$t = \frac{v_2 - v_1}{g}$$

and upon substituting,

$$t = \frac{50.5\text{ m/s} - 10\text{ m/s}}{9.80\text{ m/s}^2}$$

$$t = \frac{40.5\text{ m/s}}{9.80\text{ m/s}^2} = 4.13\text{ s}$$

The stone, therefore, hits the water in a time of 4.13 s, and with a speed of 50.5 m/s.

In special cases where the body is dropped from rest, the initial velocity is zero, and we can set $v_1 = 0$ to Eqs.(3f), (3g),

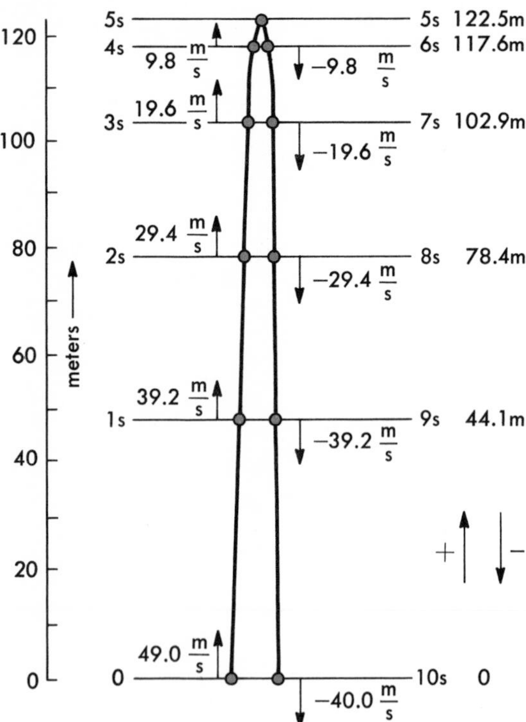

Fig. 3F. The upward motion of a body is just the same as the downward motion, but in reverse. A stone thrown upward returns to the ground with the same speed.

(3h), and (3i), and obtain four special equations:

$$v_2 = gt \tag{3j}$$

$$h = \frac{v_2}{2}\,t \tag{3k}$$

$$v_2{}^2 = 2gh \tag{3ℓ}$$

$$h = \frac{1}{2}\,gt^2 \tag{3m}$$

falling from rest

3.4. Projection Straight Upward

When a body is projected straight upward, its speed will rapidly diminish until at some point it comes momentarily to rest and then falls back toward the earth, acquiring again at the ground the same speed it had upon projection. Experiment shows that the time taken to rise to the highest point of its trajectory is equal to the time taken to fall from there to the ground. This implies that the upward motions are just the same as the downward motions, but in reverse, and that the time and speed for any point along the path are given by the same equations for free fall, Eqs.(3f), (3g), (3h), and (3i).

In Fig. 3F, a particle is shown projected upward with a velocity of 49.0 m/s. After each second's time, its speed on the way up is shown to be the same as its speed at the same level on the way down.

To treat the motion mathematically, it is convenient to use Eqs.(3f), (3g), (3h), and (3i), taking the point of projection as the *origin,* and adopting the following convention of signs, for projection upward:

(1) Distances above the origin are positive.
(2) Distances below the origin are negative.
(3) Velocities upward are positive.
(4) Velocities downward are negative.
(5) Acceleration downward (gravity) is negative.

Whether a body is moving up or down, the acceleration g is always downward. Using the above sign conventions, with Eqs.(3f) to (3i), the value of g should always be substituted with a minus sign.

It is good practice in solving problems in general to carry out the following steps:

1. *Make a list of all the known quantities.*
2. *Add the unknown quantity to the list.*
3. *Select an equation involving these quantities.*
4. *Solve this equation for the unknown quantity.*
5. *Substitute the known quantities.*
6. *Carry out the necessary calculations to find the value of the unknown.*

Example 3. A ball is thrown straight upward with a speed of 39.20 m/s. Calculate the time it takes to reach the highest point.
Solution. Taking the upward direction as positive, the known quantities are $v_1 = 39.20$ m/s and $g = -9.80$ m/s². At the highest point where the ball comes momentarily to rest, $v_2 = 0$. Since t is the unknown, Eq.(3f) is selected as the appropriate equation:

$$v_2 = v_1 + gt$$

Solving this relation for the unknown t, we get

$$t = \frac{v_2 - v_1}{g}$$

and substituting known values, we find

$$t = \frac{0 - 39.2 \text{ m/s}}{-9.80 \text{ m/s}^2} = 4.0 \text{ s}$$

In 4.0 s, therefore, the ball will reach its highest point. In another 4.0 s it will fall to the ground, as shown in Fig. 3F.

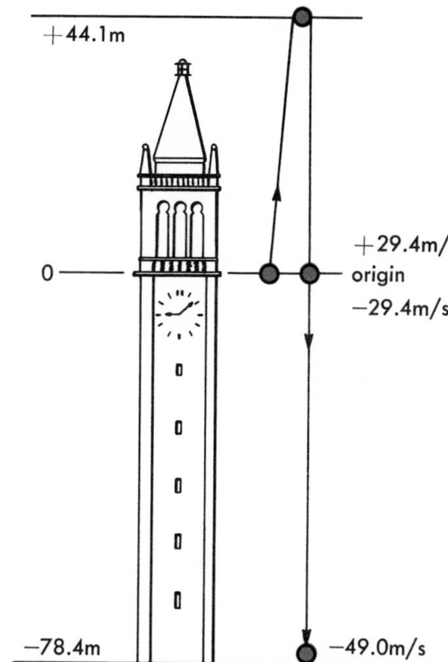

Fig. 3G. A body projected upward rises to a predetermined height, then falls with increasing speed. See Example 4 for numerical values.

Example 4. An arrow is shot straight upward with a velocity of 29.40 m/s, from a point 78.4 m above the ground. See Fig. 3G. Find (a) the maximum height to which the arrow rises, (b) the time to reach its highest point, (c) the total time to reach the origin, (d) the velocity upon arrival at the ground, and (e) the total time of flight.
Solution. The given quantities for part (a) are $v_1 = 29.40$ m/s and $g = -9.80$ m/s². It is clear that at the highest point in its path $v_2 = 0$. The unknown quantity is h. The equation involving all of these quantities, and only these, is Eq.(3h):

$$v_2^2 = v_1^2 + 2\,g\,h$$

(a) Solving for h,

$$h = \frac{v_2^2 - v_1^2}{2\,g}$$

and substituting the known quantities,

$$h = \frac{0 - (29.4 \text{ m/s})^2}{2 \times (-9.80 \text{ m/s}^2)}$$

we obtain

$$h = \frac{-864.4 \text{ m}^2/\text{s}^2}{-19.60 \text{ m/s}^2} = 44.1 \text{ m}$$

(b) Upon reaching the highest point where the arrow comes momentarily to rest, $v_2 = 0$. The other given quantities are $h = 44.1$ m and $v_1 = 29.40$ m/s. With time as the unknown quantity, we may use either Eq.(3g) or Eq.(3i). Using the simpler of the two relations, Eq.(3g),

$$h = \frac{v_2 + v_1}{2} t$$

and solving for t, we obtain

$$t = \frac{2h}{v_2 + v_1}$$

and, upon substituting known quantities, find

$$t = \frac{2 \times 44.1 \text{ m}}{0 + 29.4 \text{ m/s}} = 3.0 \text{ s}$$

(c) Upon returning to the starting point, the origin, the arrow height $h = 0$. The other quantities are $v_1 = 29.40$ m/s and $g = -9.80$ m/s^2. With t as the unknown quantity, we select Eq.(3i):

$$h = v_1 t + \frac{1}{2} gt^2$$

Upon substituting $h = 0$,

$$0 = v_1 t + \frac{1}{2} gt^2$$

and dividing by t, we obtain

$$0 = v_1 + \frac{1}{2} gt$$

Upon solving for t, we find

$$t = \frac{2v_1}{g}$$

and by substituting the known quantities, obtain

$$t = \frac{-2 \times 29.4 \text{ m/s}}{-9.80 \text{ m/s}^2} = 6.0 \text{ s}$$

(d) Upon reaching the ground at the foot of the tower the arrow is below the origin, and at a point where $h = -78.4$ m. Since v_2 is the unknown, Eq.(3h) is selected:

$$v_2{}^2 = v_1{}^2 + 2\,gh$$

Substituting known quantities,

$$v_2{}^2 = (29.4 \text{ m/s})^2 + 2 \times (-9.80 \text{ m/s}^2)(-78.4 \text{ m})$$

$$v_2{}^2 = 864.4 \text{ m}^2/\text{s}^2 + 1536.6 \text{ m}^2/\text{s}^2$$

$$v_2{}^2 = 2401 \text{ m}^2/\text{s}^2$$

Taking the square root of both sides of the equation, we obtain

$$v_2 = +49.0 \text{ m/s}$$

$$v_2 = -49.0 \text{ m/s}$$

Of these two answers only the one with a minus sign is real. The answer $v_2 = +49.0$ m/s is imaginary and would correspond to that upward projection of the arrow from the ground that would cause the arrow to retrace its path in reverse.

(e) To find the total time of flight we start with the known quantities, $v_1 = 29.4$ m/s, $g = -9.80$ m/s, and $v_2 = 49.0$ m/s. Selecting Eq.(3f),

$$v_2 = v_1 + gt$$

and solving for the unknown quantity t, we obtain

$$t = \frac{v_2 - v_1}{g}$$

$$t = \frac{-49.0 \text{ m/s} - 29.4 \text{ m/s}}{-9.80 \text{ m/s}^2}$$

$$t = \frac{-78.4 \text{ m/s}}{-9.80 \text{ m/s}^2} = 8.0 \text{ s}$$

problems

1. A boy drops a stone in a well and finds it takes 2.60 s to hit the water. (a) How deep is the well, and (b) with what speed does the stone hit the water?

2. A sandbag, dropped as ballast from a balloon, hits the ground with a speed of 147.0 m/s. (a) How high is the balloon, and (b) how long is the sandbag in the air?

3. Working on a tall building a workman accidentally drops a hammer. If it takes 7.60 s to reach the ground, (a) how high was the man working, and (b) with what speed does it hit the ground? [Ans. (a) 283.0 m, (b) 74.5 m/s.]

4. A stone is dropped from a bridge 60.0 m above the water. (a) How long is the stone in the air, and (b) with what speed does it hit the water?

5. An arrow, shot straight upward, reaches a height of 99.2 m. (a) With what velocity does it leave the bow, and (b) how long is it in the air?

6. A ball thrown straight upward reaches a height of 80.0 m. Calculate (a) the time to reach the highest point, and (b) the speed of the ball upon arrival at the point of origin. [Ans. (a) 4.04 s, (b) −39.59 m/s.]

7. A stone is projected straight upward with an initial velocity of 45.0 m/s. Find (a) how long the ball is in the air, and (b) how high it rises.

8. A boy standing on a bridge 150 m above the canyon floor throws a stone downward with a speed of 20.0 m/s. (a) With what velocity will it hit the ground, and (b) how long will it take to descend?

9. While standing on a bridge 80.0 m above the water, a boy throws a stone straight downward with a velocity of 15.0 m/s. (a) With what speed will the stone hit the water, and (b) how long will it take to descend? [Ans. (a) 42.3 m/s, (b) 2.790 s.]

10. A ball is thrown straight upward with a speed of 19.60 m/s. Find (a) the height to which it rises, (b) the total time it is in the air, (c) its height above the ground at the end of 1.50 s, and (d) its velocity at the end of 1.50 s.

11.* Arrows are shot vertically upward at 2.0 s intervals, with an initial velocity of 39.20 m/s. After several arrows have been shot, (a) how long will each arrow be in the air when another passes it, and (b) at what distances above the origin will arrows be passing each other?

12.* Darts are shot vertically upward at 2.0 s intervals, with an initial velocity of 34.30 m/s. After several darts have been shot, (a) how long will each dart be in the air when another dart passes it, and (b) at what distances above the origin will darts be passing each other? (c) Draw a graph of height vs time in seconds. [Ans. (a) 0.50 s, 1.50 s, 2.50 s, 4.50 s, 5.50 s, 6.50 s, (b) 15.92 m, 40.4 m and 55.1 m.]

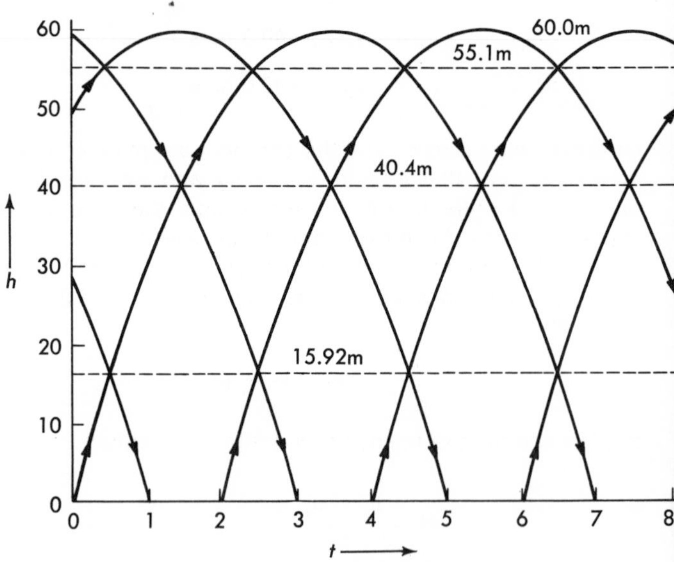

Prob. 12. Height–time graph.

13.* An arrow is shot vertically upward with a velocity of 49.0 m/s. After 3.0 s another arrow is shot vertically upward, from the same spot, with a velocity of 39.20

m/s. (a) How long after the second arrow is shot will the two arrows pass each other, and (b) how far above the origin will they be?

14.* A dart is shot vertically upward with a velocity of 60.0 m/s. After 3.0 s an arrow is shot vertically upward, from the same spot, with a velocity of 50.0 m/s. (a) How long after the arrow is shot will the two pass each other? (b) How far above the origin do they pass?

15. A boy standing on a bridge throws a stone vertically upward with a velocity of 29.4 m/s. Find (a) the velocity, and (b) the position of the stone at the end of 7 s. [Ans. (a) −39.2 m/s, (b) −34.3 m.]

16. A stone is thrown vertically upward with a velocity of 45.0 m/s. At the end of 10 s (a) where is the stone located, and (b) with what speed is it moving?

4 Newton's first and second laws of motion

The analytical treatment of the motions of bodies given in the preceding chapters may be described as that part of mechanics called *kinematics.* The definitions and laws are expressed there in terms of distance, time, speed, velocity, and acceleration. In this and succeeding chapters, we will study the causes for motion and in so doing introduce the concepts of *mass* and *force* into the equations.

When force and mass are added to the kinematic equations of motion, the analytical equations derived are referred to as *dynamics.*

To Isaac Newton* goes the credit of having been the first to systematically introduce these concepts into mechanics and to formulate the fundamental laws governing all motion. These laws resolve themselves into three sets of relations commonly referred to as "Newton's Laws of Motion."

4.1. Newton's First Law of Motion

Newton's First Law of Motion is given in Latin in his famous book *Principia.* Lex. I. *"Corpus omne perseverare in statu suo quiesendi vel movendi uniformiter in directum, nisi quatenus illud a viribus impressis cogitur statum suum mutare."*

Translated: "Every body perseveres in its state of rest or of uniform motion in a straight line, except in so far as it is compelled to change that state by impressed forces."

More appropriately, it may be stated: *A body at rest or in uniform motion will remain at rest or in uniform motion unless some external force is applied to it.*

This law can be demonstrated by many simple experiments. In

* See Introduction Chap. A for biography of Isaac Newton.

Fig. 4A. A tablecloth can be pulled from a table without dislodging the dishes.

Fig. 4B. The smooth track can quickly be moved so as not to set the car in motion.

Fig. 4A a tablecloth is shown in the process of being removed from under the dishes and silverware on a table without disturbing their original setting. In Fig. 4B a small car is shown free to·move on a smooth, hard track. If the track is jerked quickly to right or left, the wheels of the car will turn, but the car itself will tend to remain at rest.

In both of these experiments the dishes and the car are at rest. They tend to remain at rest because the sudden motion of the objects on which they are resting exerts no large force for any appreciable length of time. Actually, the dishes and the car do move slightly because of frictional forces between the moving parts in contact. The tendency for each body to remain at rest is due to that property, common to all material bodies, called *inertia.*

The inertia of a body may be defined as that property of a body which tends to resist a change in its state of rest or motion. Mass is defined as a quantitative measure of inertia.

Inertia and mass are both measured in the same units, in grams, or kilograms.

A third experiment illustrating inertia, and Newton's First Law, is illustrated in Fig. 4C. A mass *M* of 1000 g is suspended by a piece of thread A, then pulled downward by another piece of the same thread B. If the force *F* is a slow steady pull, the thread will always break at A; whereas if it is a sudden jerk, it will always break at B. In the first case, the tension in the upper thread is greater and is equivalent to the force *F* plus the weight of the mass *M.* In the second case, the force *F* is momentarily very large, causing the thread to break before the mass *M*

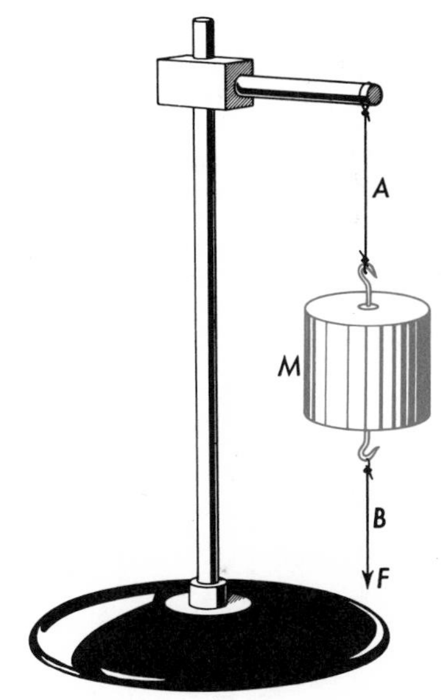

Fig. 4C. A slow, steady pull at *F* breaks the thread at A, while a quick pull at *F* breaks the thread at B.

has had time to move down far enough to stretch and break the upper thread. It is the inertia of M that permits the very large force F to be momentarily applied only to the lower thread.

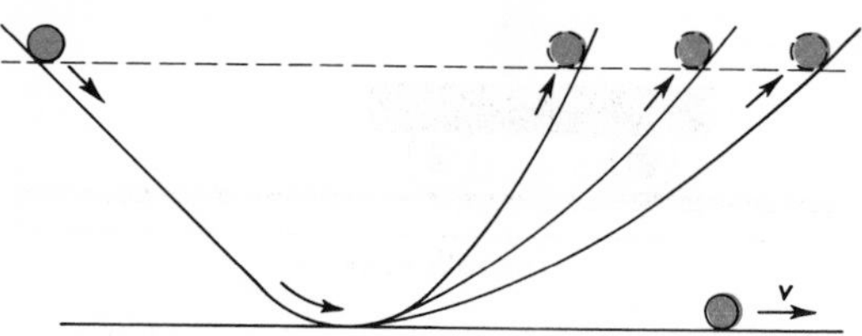

Fig. 4D. Demonstration of inertia experiment performed first by Galileo.

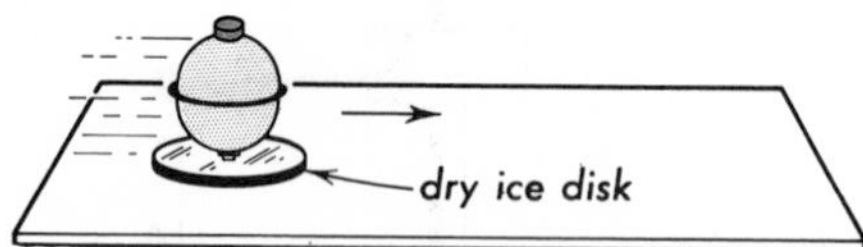

Fig. 4E. Demonstration of the inertia of a body moving with uniform velocity.

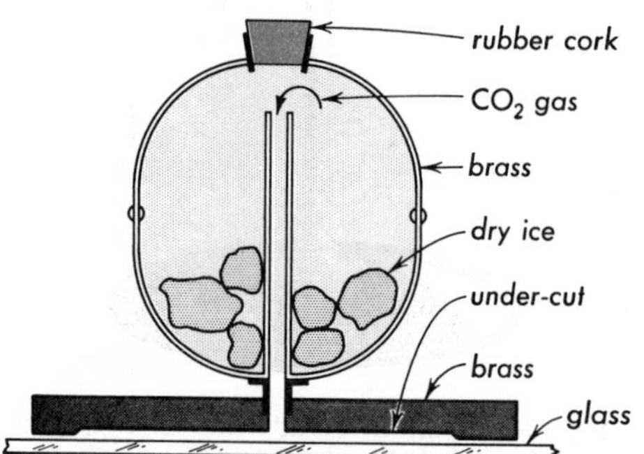

Fig. 4F. Cross-sectional diagram of "dry ice disk."

4.2. Inertia and Motion

The three preceding demonstrations are concerned with bodies at rest. The second part of Newton's First Law of Motion is concerned with moving bodies, and a restatement of the law confined to this aspect would change the law to read:

A body in uniform motion will remain in uniform motion unless some external force is applied to it.

This aspect of Newton's First Law was first recognized by Galileo. In order to study the acceleration due to gravity, he used an inclined plane to reduce the acceleration due to gravity, thereby permitting better measurements. He observed that a ball rolling down one incline would roll up another to approximately the same height regardless of the inclination of the second plane (see Fig. 4D). Furthermore, if the ball were allowed to roll out on a level plane when it reached the bottom of the incline, it could never achieve its original height but tended to roll on and on. Due to friction it would eventually stop.

A most striking demonstration of this property of inertia is provided by a "dry ice disk" as shown in Fig. 4E. Here, friction is reduced to practically zero by a metal disk that rides over a glass plate and literally floats on a thin layer of carbon dioxide gas.* When this body is given a very slight push, it rides across the plate and seems to keep going on and on, with constant velocity, as if by magic. What keeps the body moving in the same straight line is its inertia. The above law, of course, neglects friction, for we know that, left to itself, friction will eventually bring the body to rest. The greater the friction, the sooner it will stop. The lesser the friction, the longer it will move.

4.3. Inertia and Mass

Mass is a measure of inertia. In the metric system, inertia and mass are measured in *grams* and *kilograms.* In the English system

* A cross-section diagram of this dry ice disk is shown in Fig. 4F. A thin-walled, brass or copper ball about 10 cm in diameter is soldered to a flat, circular brass disk about 2 cm thick and 15 cm in diameter. Thin-walled vessels of this kind are used as floats in certain plumbing utilities and may be purchased in most hardware stores. Dry ice is available in almost every drugstore soda fountain, and one loading will last a couple of hours. The bottom surface of the disk is undercut several thousandths of a centimeter, and a hole about 0.5 cm in diameter is

they are both measured in *slugs.* Figure 4G is a diagram illustrating the relative sizes of these three units. They are shown in a hooked weight form convenient for use in experiments. If one were to weigh these three fundamental units of mass, 1 slug would weigh 32 lb, 1 Kg would weigh 9.8 newtons, and 1 g would weigh 980 dynes. The difference between mass and weight will be taken up in detail Sec. 4.5.

Fig. 4G. Units of mass are also units of inertia.

4.4. Newton's Second Law of Motion

Newton's Second Law of Motion is stated in Latin in his *Principia:* Lex II. *"Mutationem motus, Proportionalem esse vi motrici impressae, et fiere secundum lineam rectam qua vis illa imprimitur."* Translated, this says: *"When a body is acted upon by a constant force, its resulting acceleration is proportional to the force and inversely proportional to the mass."* Symbolically,

$$a \propto \frac{F}{m}$$

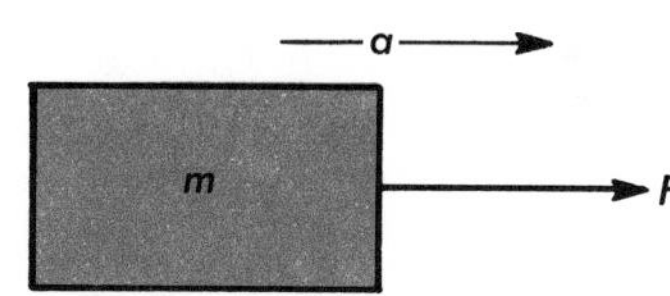

Fig. 4H. Acted upon by a constant force *F,* a mass *m* moves with an acceleration *a* [see Eq.(5b)].

This law is stated as a proportionality because it holds regardless of the units in which each of the three quantities are measured. If the units are properly chosen, an equal-sign may be inserted and the law written as an equation,

$$a = \frac{F}{m}$$

Multiplying both sides of the equation by *m* we obtain the so-called "force equation," which forms the basis of so many principles in mechanics:

$$F = ma \qquad (4a)$$

force = mass × acceleration

To the above statement of Newton's Second Law should be added the statement that *the acceleration takes place in the direction of the acting force.* See Fig. 4H.

---

drilled through the center. A short section of metal tubing is mounted directly above this center and prevents the dry ice from clogging the hole. A larger hole in the top is provided for the insertion of dry ice, and a tight-fitting cork closes the opening.

Example 1. Neglecting friction, what constant force will give a mass of 50.0 Kg an acceleration of 5.0 m/s^2?
Solution. The known quantities are $m = 50.0$ Kg and $a = 5.0$ m/s^2. Upon direct substitution in Eq.(4a) we obtain

$$F = 50 \text{ Kg} \times 5 \frac{\text{m}}{\text{s}^2} = 250.0 \frac{\text{Kg m}}{\text{s}^2}$$

The answer is a force of 250.0 Km m/s^2. Thus force is not so simple a concept as it might seem at first hand; it involves all three of the fundamental units, *length, mass,* and *time.*

According to the *MKSA* system (meter-kilogram-second-ampere system), unit force is called the newton in honor of Sir Isaac Newton. *The newton is defined as that force which, applied to a mass of 1 Kg, will give it an acceleration of 1 m/s^2:*

$$1 \text{ newton} = 1 \text{ Kg} \times 1 \frac{\text{m}}{\text{s}^2} \tag{4b}$$

As a unit of force, the newton is represented by the capital letter N.

In the cgs system of units (centimeter, gram, second system), Eq.(4b) becomes

$$1 \text{ dyne} = 1 \text{ g} \times 1 \frac{\text{cm}}{\text{s}^2}$$

Example 2. Neglecting friction, what constant force will give a mass of 50.0 g an acceleration of 5.0 cm/s^2?
Solution. By substituting the given values into the force equation, Eq.(4a), we obtain

$$F = 50 \text{ g} \times 5 \frac{\text{cm}}{\text{s}^2} = 250.0 \frac{\text{g cm}}{\text{s}^2}$$

The answer is a force of 250.0 g cm/s^2. By definition

$$1 \text{ dyne} = 1 \frac{\text{g cm}}{\text{s}^2}$$

According to this definition, the answer to the above problem is written

$$F = 250.0 \text{ dynes}$$

Newtons and dynes are absolute units of force. They arise from the force equation when the absolute units of *mass* and *time* are used.

Since 1 Kg = 1000 g, and 1 m = 100 cm,

$$1 \text{ newton} = 10^5 \text{ dynes}$$

4.5. Weight and Mass

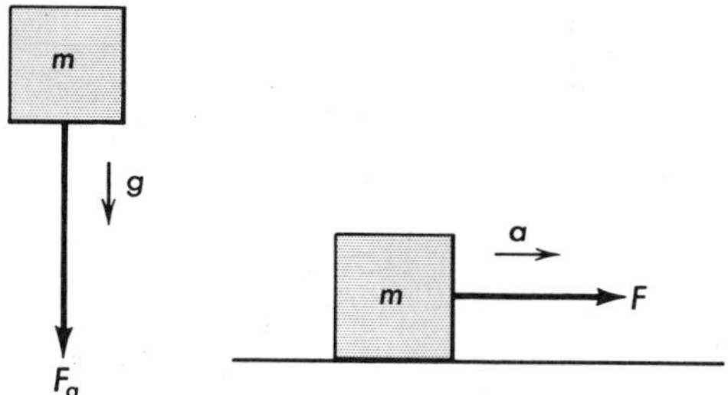

Fig. 4I. A mass *m* falling freely has an acceleration *g*; pulled by a force *F* it has an acceleration *a*.

When a mass *m* is allowed to fall freely, it is the constant downward force of gravity on the mass that gives rise to its constant downward acceleration. If Newton's Second Law is applied to this motion, the force *F* is none other than the weight F_g of the body, and the acceleration *a* is the acceleration due to gravity *g*. For falling bodies, the force equation, $F = ma$, is written in different symbols. See Fig. 4I.

$$F_g = mg \qquad (4c)$$

weight = mass × gravitational acceleration

In absolute units, the weight of a body is expressed in newtons or dynes.

It is important to note that the weight of a body is given by *mg* whether it is falling freely or whether it is resting on a table where $a = 0$.

Weight and *force* have both magnitude and direction and are therefore vector quantities. Mass, on the other hand, is a scalar quantity since it has only magnitude. The distinction between *weight* and *mass* is illustrated by imagining a given body being carried out into free space far removed from other bodies and their gravitational attraction. There, a body at rest will still have its mass but it will have no weight. That such a body has its mass would be demonstrated if another mass were to bump into it. The smaller the mass of the incoming body, the less would be the recoil of the first mass from the impact.

Weight here on the earth is due to the gravitational attraction of the earth upon a mass at its surface and will be treated in

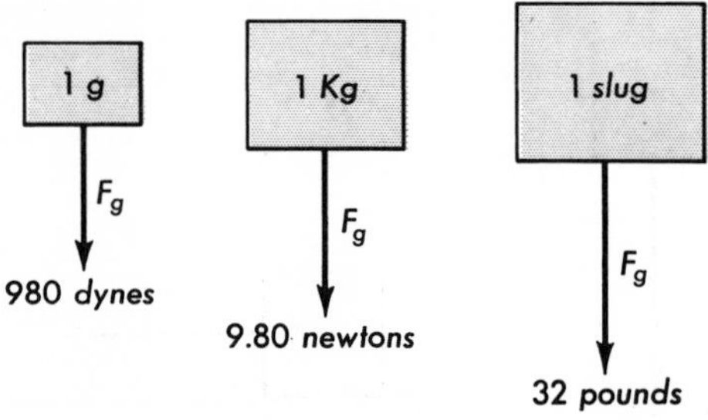

Fig. 4J. Weight is a force equal in magnitude to the mass multiplied by the acceleration due to gravity: $F_g = mg$.

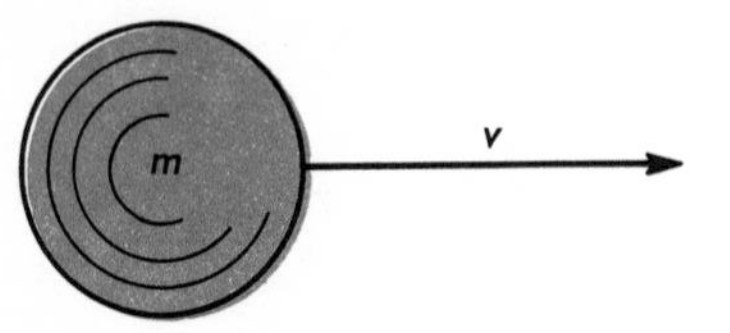

Fig. 4K. Any mass *m* moving with a velocity *v* has momentum *mv*.

detail in Chap. 6. In the equation $F_g = mg$, we may define g as the *weight per unit mass.* F_g is equal to the *mass* times the *weight per unit mass.*

Example 3. Calculate the weight of a body having a mass of 1.0 Kg.
Solution. By Eq.(4c)

$$F_g = 1 \text{ Kg} \times 9.80 \frac{\text{m}}{\text{s}^2} = 9.80 \frac{\text{Kg m}}{\text{s}^2} = 9.80 \text{ N} \tag{4d}$$

This answer shows that to lift a mass of 1 Kg requires an upward force of 9.80 N and that the weight and mass differ from each other numerically by a ratio equal to the acceleration due to gravity. By similar calculations to the above, the weight of a 1-g mass is found to be 980 dynes (see Fig. 4J).

4.6. Momentum

The concept of momentum involves both *mass* and *velocity* and is defined as the product of these two quantities:

$$\textbf{momentum} = \textbf{mass} \times \textbf{velocity}$$

$$p = mv \tag{4e}$$

According to this definition, all moving bodies have momentum (see Fig. 4K). A small mass m moving with a high velocity V may well have the same momentum as a large mass M moving with a low velocity v. The concept is particularly important in describing the impacts between colliding bodies, and applies to all masses large and small. Such applications will be treated in detail in a number of the following chapters.

Example 4. A mass of 50.0 Kg moves along a straight and level path with a velocity of 2.40 m/s. Find its momentum.
Solution. Since momentum, as given by Eq.(4e), has the product of *mass times velocity,* we obtain

$$p = 50.0 \text{ Kg} \times 2.40 \text{ m/s}$$

$$p = 120.0 \text{ Kg m/s}$$

This answer is read *one-hundred twenty point zero kilogram meters per second.*

Newton's second law of motion is best stated in terms of momentum: *The rate at which the momentum of a body changes is proportional to the impressed force and takes place in the direction of the straight line in which the force acts.*

As an equation in words,

$$\text{force} = \frac{\text{change in momentum}}{\text{change in time}}$$

or in increment symbols

$$F = \frac{\Delta(mv)}{\Delta t} \tag{4f}$$

Assuming the mass to remain unchanged, this can be written

$$F = m\,\frac{\Delta v}{\Delta t} \tag{4g}$$

In Chap. 2, acceleration is defined as the rate of change of velocity and written as

$$a = \frac{\Delta v}{\Delta t}$$

or

$$a = \frac{v_2 - v_1}{t} \tag{4h}$$

where t represents the elapsed time.

If the acceleration a, in the force equation $F = ma$, is replaced by the second of these expressions, Newton's second law of motion takes on a new and useful form:

$$F = m\,\frac{v_2 - v_1}{t} \tag{4i}$$

This equation is used in solving problems where the initial and final velocities are involved.

Example 5. A 2000-Kg automobile is moving with a velocity of 12.0 m/s. What constant force, applied for a period of 8.0 s, will increase its velocity to 40.0 m/s?
Solution. The given quantities are $m = 2000$ Kg, $v_2 = 40.0$ m/s, $v_1 = 12.0$ m/s, and $t = 8.0$ s. By direct substitution in Eq.(4i), we obtain

$$F = 2000 \text{ Kg} \frac{40 \text{ m/s} - 12 \text{ m/s}}{8 \text{ s}} = 7000 \frac{\text{Kg m}}{\text{s}}$$

The answer is 7000 N.

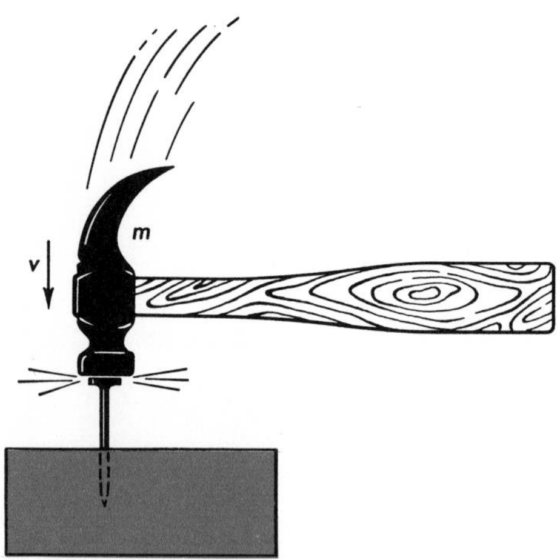

Fig. 4L. The impulse of a hammer drives a nail into a block of wood.

4.7. Impulse

If we multiply both sides of Eq.(4i) by the time t, we obtain another concept, and a new relation between measurable quantities:

$$Ft = mv_2 - mv_1 \tag{4j}$$

This is called the *impulse equation* in which $F \times t$ is the impulse and $mv_2 - mv_1$ is the change in momentum. Its meaning is illustrated in Fig. 4L, where a hammer is shown driving a nail into a block of wood. Moving with a velocity v, the hammer head of mass m strikes the nail a blow of force F. Lasting for only a fraction of a second, this force has by an impulse driven the nail a short distance into the wood. If F represents the average force, and t the time interval during which the force acts,

$$\text{impulse} = F \times t \tag{4k}$$

When a body starts from rest, the initial velocity v_1 of Eq.(4j) is zero, and

$$Ft = mv \tag{4\ell}$$

As the result of an impulse Ft, a body initially at rest acquires a momentum mv. Conversely, a body moving with a momentum mv can be brought to rest by an impulse $-Ft$. The minus sign indicates that the force is opposite in direction to the velocity.

Example 6. A hammer head with a mass of 1.50 Kg, moving with a velocity of 6.0 m/s, strikes the head of a large nail and drives it into a block of hard wood. If the hammer comes to rest in 0.0010 s, find (a) the impulse, (b) the average force, and (c) the distance the nail is driven into the wood.
Solution. The given quantities are $m = 1.50$ Kg, $v = 6.0$ m/s, and $t = 0.0010$ s. By direct substitution of the first two quantities into Eq.(4ℓ), we obtain

$$Ft = mv = 1.5 \text{ Kg} \times 6.0 \text{ m/s} = 9.0 \text{ Kg m/s}$$

Solving Eq.(4ℓ) for F, and substituting the time t, we obtain

$$F = \frac{mv}{t} = \frac{-9.0 \text{ Kg m/s}}{0.001 \text{ s}} = 9000 \text{ N}$$

To find the distance the nail is driven into the wood, the equations for accelerated motion may be used. Using Eq.(2ℓ), and substituting given quantities, we obtain

$$x = \frac{v_2 - v_1}{2} t = \frac{6.0 \text{ m/s} - 0}{2} 0.0010 \text{ s}$$

$$x = 0.0030 \text{ m}$$

which is equivalent to 3.0 mm.

That such a large force as 9000 N is really exerted is due in part to the very short time in which the force acts, and can be demonstrated by trying to push a nail into a block of wood by piling weights on top of it. The force stopping the hammer is oppositely directed to the motion. The hammer velocity is down, and the stopping force is up.

4.8. Demonstration of Newton's Second Law of Motion

An experiment demonstrating the relation between a constant force acting on a body, and the change in momentum it acquires as a result of that force, is shown in Fig. 4M. A small mass m_1 is accelerated along a straight horizontal track MN by means of a thread passing over two pulleys P, to a small mass m_2. Compressed air inside the hollow track, escaping from tiny holes along the top of the track, causes the car to ride on a cushion of air with virtually no friction. Such air tracks are commonly used in physics laboratories for experiments in mechanics.

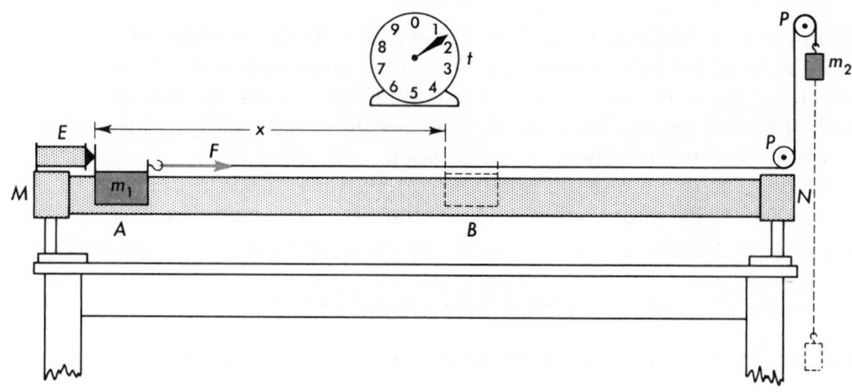

Fig. 4M. Air track for studying the dynamics of motion.

TABLE 4A
Recorded data for momentum experiment

Trial	Mass m_1 (Kg)	Mass m_2 (Kg)	Distance x (m)	Time t (s)
0	1.0	0.020	0	0
1	1.0	0.020	0.75	2.79
2	1.0	0.020	1.00	3.23
3	1.0	0.020	1.25	3.61
4	1.0	0.020	1.50	3.95
5	1.0	0.020	1.75	4.27
6	1.0	0.020	2.00	4.56

A switching circuit to release the mass m_1 from the electromagnet E, and simultaneously start the stopclock, may be used to time the moving car from its starting position A, to a distant marker B.

By recording values of m_1, m_2, x, and t for a number of trial runs, it is possible to establish a relation between the *time* and the *change in momentum* of the moving mass. Typical data recorded in this experiment are given in Table 4A. It should be noted from the diagram that, neglecting the thread and pulleys, the total moving mass is $m_1 + m_2$, or 1.02 Kg, while the accelerating force is m_2g, or 0.196 N. Using this or similar recorded data, the velocities v, the momentum mv, and the ratios $\Delta mv/\Delta t$ can be calculated. This will be left as a student exercise.

problems

1. A horizontal force applied to a 24.0-Kg mass will give it an acceleration of 5.80 m/s^2. Find the magnitude of the force.

2. A horizontal force of 35.0 N is applied to a mass of 15.0 Kg. Find the acceleration.

3. What force is required to accelerate a 2000-Kg car from 5.0 m/s to 25.0 m/s, in a time of 5.0 s. [Ans. 8.0×10^3 N.]

4. A 25-g golf ball, moving with a speed of 40.0 m/s, lands in soft dirt and becomes embedded a distance of 8.0 cm. Assuming constant acceleration during impact, find (a) the time of stopping, (b) the average force, and (c) the change in momentum.

5. A car with a mass of 2400 Kg starts from rest and acquires a speed of 32.0 m/s in 12.0 s. Assuming constant acceleration, find (a) the weight of the car, (b) the average acceleration, and (c) the average force.

6. A jet plane, loaded with passengers, has a mass of 1.250×10^5 Kg. If, with this load, the plane requires a speed of 60.0 m/s for take-off on a 2000 m runway, find (a) the acceleration required, (b) the time the wheels leave the ground, (c) the thrust of the propellers, and (d) the momentum of the plane. [Ans. (a) 0.90 m/s^2, (b) 66.7 s, (c) 1.225 $\times$ 10^6 N, (d) 7.50 $\times$ 10^6 Kg m/s.]

7. Starting from rest a 10,000-Kg truck maintains a constant acceleration until it acquires a speed of 30.0 m/s. If the time required to attain this speed is 15.0 s, find (a) the acceleration, (b) the forward thrust of the wheels on the pavement, and (c) the momentum acquired.

8. A 2000-Kg car starting from rest maintains a constant acceleration of 2.20 m/s^2 for 16 s. Find (a) the velocity acquired, (b) the forward thrust of the wheels on the pavement, and (c) the momentum of the car.

9. A 3.0-Kg sledge hammer is used to drive spikes into railroad ties. If a hammer speed of 5.0 m/s drives a nail 1.0 cm into a tie, find (a) the acceleration, (b) the time of impact, and (c) the change in momentum. [Ans. (a) 1.250 $\times$ 10^3 m/s^2, (b) 4.0 $\times$ 10^{-3} s, (c) 15.0 Kg m/s.]

10. A jet passenger plane has a mass of 5.0 $\times$ 10^4 Kg when fully loaded. Its take-off speed is 180.0 Km/h. Starting from rest it requires 1.80 Km for take-off. Find (a) the plane's weight, (b) the plane's take-off speed in m/s, (c) the acceleration, (d) the thrust of its motors, (e) the time needed for take-off, and (f) its momentum.

11. Starting from rest, a train locomotive, with a mass of 3.50 $\times$ 10^4 Kg, maintains a constant acceleration of 0.80 m/s^2 for 12.0 s. Find (a) the locomotive's weight, (b) its acquired velocity, and (c) its momentum.

12. Find the force required to give a mass of 70.0 Kg an acceleration of 4.50 m/s^2, (a) horizontally, and (b) vertically upward. [Ans. (a) 315.0 N, (b) 1001 N.]

13. A hammer with a mass of 0.80 Kg, moving with a velocity of 7.0 m/s, strikes the head of a nail, driving it 2.0 cm into a block of wood. Find (a) the acceleration, (b) the force exerted, (c) the time, and (d) the momentum.

14. A truck traveling along the highway at 108.0 Km/h drops a 50.0-Kg box. If the box slides a distance of 45.0 m, find (a) the initial speed of the box when it strikes the roadway, (b) the weight of the box, (c) the acceleration, (d) the time to stop, and (e) the momentum.

15. A 1500-Kg car starting from rest undergoes an acceleration of 2.50 m/s^2 for 8.0 s, then an acceleration of 1.50 m/s^2 for 10.0 s. Find (a) the weight of the car, (b) the force applied during the first 8.0 s, (c) the force applied during the second acceleration, and (d) the total distance traveled. [Ans. (a) 14,700 N, (b) 3,750 N, (c) 2,250 N, (d) 315.0 m.]

5 Vector addition and composition of forces

All of us are familiar with the mathematical operations of addition, subtraction, multiplication, and division. These are the processes used when two or more scalar quantities such as mass, area, time, or volume are combined. Scalars present no special treatment so long as the quantities to be combined are of the same kind and have the same units.

The addition of vector quantities requires specialized treatment since all magnitudes and directions of the quantities to be added must simultaneously be taken into account. Vector quantities commonly used in mechanics are *displacement, force, velocity, acceleration, momentum, torque, angular velocity,* and *angular momentum;* displacement and force are taken up in this chapter.

5.1. Vector Addition

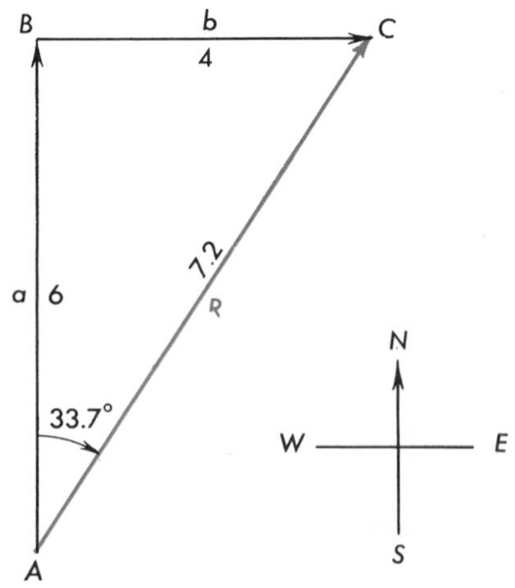

Fig. 5A. Diagram illustrating vector addition as applied to displacement.

The process of vector addition will first be illustrated by an example involving two displacements. Suppose that a ship starts from a point A as diagrammed in Fig. 5A, and sails due north for a distance of 6 Km to a point B, where it changes course and sails due east for a distance of 4 Km to a point C. Although the ship has sailed a total distance of 6 + 4 or 10 Km, it is obvious that its distance from the starting point is not given by this arithmetic sum.

To find the actual displacement, that is, the distance from the starting point, a diagram like that shown may be drawn to some selected scale. With a pencil and a ruler (a centimeter scale) a vertical line AB, 6 cm long, is drawn to represent the displacement *6 Km north.* The line BC is next drawn to the right from B and 4 cm long to represent *4 Km east.* The right triangle is finally completed by joining A and C. With an arrowhead at C, the hypotenuse R, measuring 7.2 cm, represents the resultant displacement of 7.2 Km.

Vectorially, we write

$$\overrightarrow{AB} + \overrightarrow{BC} = \overrightarrow{AC}$$

$$\vec{R} = \vec{a} + \vec{b}$$

Using a protractor, the angle A is measured to be 33.7°. The direction of the resultant vector R is therefore 33.7° east of north.

It is customary in any vector diagram to represent all vector quantities by arrows, each arrow being drawn in the proper direction and to the proper length. A little practice in drawing will show that, regardless of what scale is used to make the diagram, the resultant must be the same in magnitude and direction, and that the more carefully the diagram is drawn, the more accurate will be the measured result.

To calculate the magnitude of the resultant R in Fig. 5A, use is made of the Pythagorean theorem in geometry that, for any right triangle, *the square of the hypotenuse is equal to the sum of the squares of the other two sides:*

$$R^2 = a^2 + b^2$$

Substitute the two values of a and b:

$$R^2 = (6)^2 + (4)^2 = 52$$

By taking the square root* of 52, we obtain

$$R = 7.21 \text{ Km}$$

Example 1. A man walks east for a distance of 10.0 Km, then turns and walks north-east for a distance of 5.0 Km. Find the resultant displacement.

Solution. Following the procedure outlined above, a horizontal line AB is first drawn 10.0 cm long and labeled as shown in Fig. 5B. The second vector, BC, is next drawn north-east in direction,

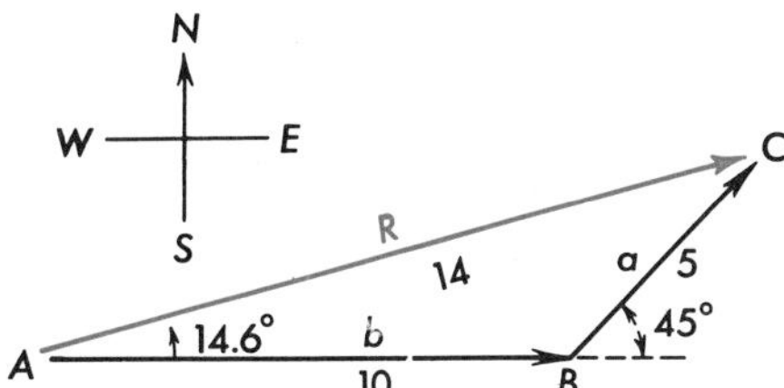

Fig. 5B. Vector diagram for Example 1.

* A simplified method for finding the square root of a number to an accuracy of three figures is the following. By inspection, a guess of the square root is made to two figures. For example, if the number is 685, inspection shows that it lies between $(20)^2 = 400$ and $(30)^2 = 900$, and that a reasonable guess might be 25. The original number is then divided by 25 and gives 27.4 The average of these two numbers, 26.2, is then the square root to three figures. If greater accuracy is desired, the averaged number may be assumed to be an original guess and the process repeated.

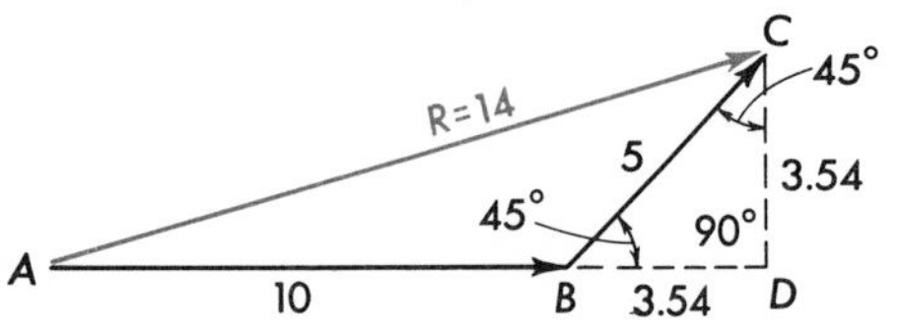

Fig. 5C. Vector diagram for Example 1.

i.e., at 45°, and 5.0 cm long. The resultant R is then drawn and measured; its length is found to be 14.0 cm, which represents a displacement of 14.0 Km. The angle at A measured with a protractor is found to be 14.6°. The answer, therefore, is 14.0 Km in a direction 14.6° north of east.

To calculate the magnitude of R, it is seen that a right triangle can be formed as shown in Fig. 5C. The right triangle theorem is then applied to the triangle BCD:

$$(BC)^2 = (BD)^2 + (CD)^2$$

Since two angles of BCD are equal to each other, the triangle is isosceles and the sides BD and CD are equal: BD = CD. Therefore,

$$(BC)^2 = 2(BD)^2 = 25.0$$

from which $$(BD)^2 = 25/2$$

and $$BD = \sqrt{12.5} = 3.540$$

Applying the same theorem to the right triangle ADC, we get

$$R^2 = (3.54)^2 + (13.54)^2 = 195.8$$

from which $$R = 14.0 \text{ Km}$$

5.2. The Parallelogram Method of Vector Addition

There are two generally accepted methods of vector addition; namely, the triangle method described in the preceding section and shown in Figs. 5A and 5B, and the parallelogram method described below. Consider, as an illustration of the latter, the addition of the same two vectors given in Fig. 5B, $b = 10$ Km and $a = 5$ Km, the two making an angle of 45° with each other.

As shown at the left in Fig. 5D, the vectors are first drawn outward from the same origin A. From D a dotted line is next drawn parallel to vector b, and from B a dotted line is drawn parallel to vector a, as in diagram (b). From the point C, where these two lines cross, the diagonal line AC is drawn in and labeled with an arrowhead as the resultant R.

A comparison of the parallelogram with the triangle in Fig. 5B shows that if the same scale is used the triangle ABC in both diagrams is identical. Both methods, regardless of the scale used, lead to the same numerical result. In solving certain problems, the triangle method will be found more convenient, while in solving others, the parallelogram is more readily applicable.

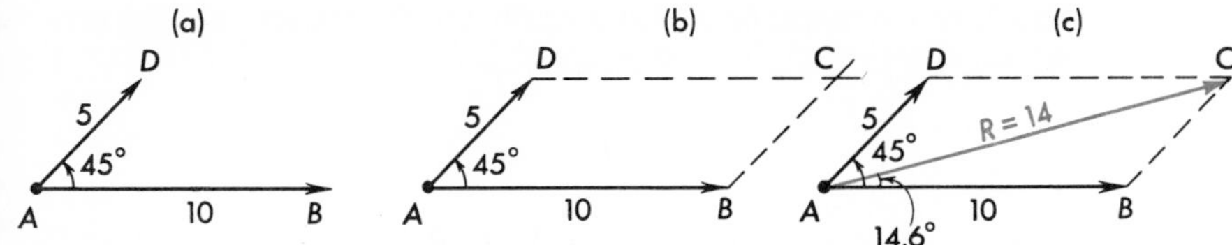

Fig. 5D. Diagram illustrating the parallelogram method of vector addition.

There are two common systems by which the directions of vector quantities are designated: one is to refer all angles to the points of the compass as in Figs. 5A and 5B; and the other is to specify all angles with reference to the *x axis,* as in Figs. 5D and 5E. In navigation, for example, the *true bearing* of a ship is measured from the *north* clockwise around the compass. To sail east is to have a true bearing of 90°, and to sail southwest is to have a true bearing of 225°.

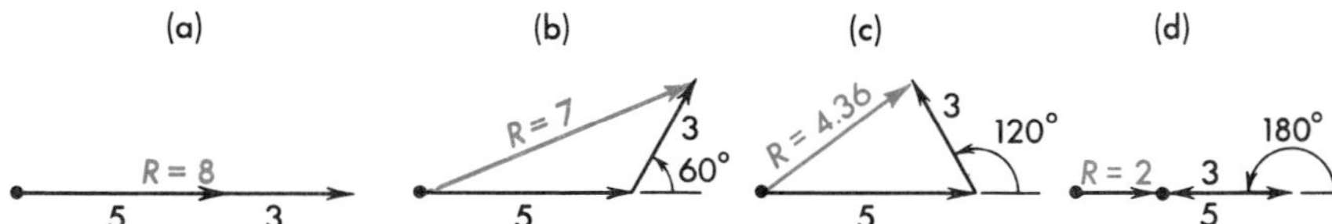

Fig. 5E. Diagram illustrating the triangle method of vector addition.

When directions are referred to the *x axis,* angles measured in a counterclockwise direction from the $+x$ axis are called $+$; those measured clockwise from the same line are called $-$. For example, the direction-angle for the second vector in Fig. 5E(b) is $+60°$, or $-300°$.

5.3. Weight is a Vector

Everyone knows that when he weighs himself as illustrated in Fig. 5F he is measuring the downward force he exerts on the footboard of the scales, and that this force causes some mechanism within the scales to indicate his weight. The greater the downward force, the greater is the indicated weight. We are not interested here in the system of levers, weights, or springs within the scales, but rather with the downward force we call our *weight.*

Fig. 5F. Weight is a downward force. The earth attracts all bodies toward its center.

Weight, as explained in detail in the last chapter, is due to the gravitational attraction of the earth for all bodies, and is given by Eq.(4c) in the previous chapter as

$$F_g = mg$$

As illustrated in Fig. 5G, gravitational forces always act in the direction of a line joining the body and the center of the earth and they are, therefore, perpendicular to the earth's surface at the body.

The term "force" is not confined to weight alone but to the action of any one body upon another. For example, in towing an automobile as shown in Fig. 5H, there are two forces acting: (1) a downward force F_g due to gravity, and (2) a horizontal force F due to a pull on the towline. The latter force is supplied by some external object or machine. In pushing a lawnmower there are also two forces: (1) the downward force F_g due to gravity and (2) a diagonal force F due to some person pushing on the lawnmower handle.

Regardless of the direction in which a force may act, its magnitude may be expressed in *newtons.* The justification for this is illustrated in Fig. 5I, where spring scales are used to measure forces. In diagram (a), the 3.0-Kg mass exerts a downward force of 29.4 N. A horizontal force of the same magnitude is produced by running the cord over a pulley as in diagram (b).

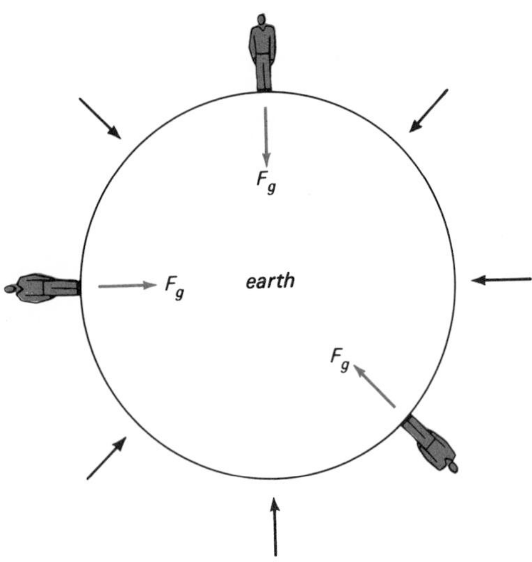

Fig. 5G. Weight is a force due to gravitational attraction, and gravitational force acts in the direction of a line joining the body and the center of the earth.

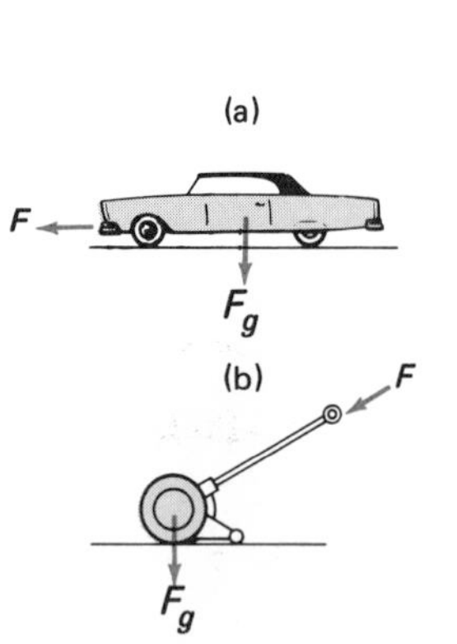

Fig. 5H. Illustration of two independent forces acting on the same body.

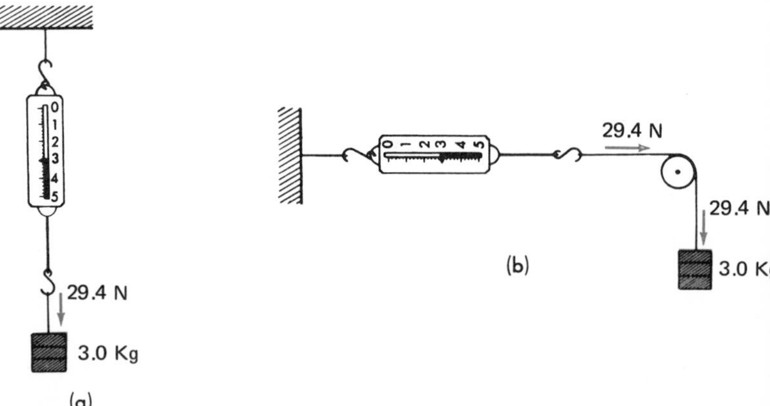

Fig. 5I. The magnitudes of all forces, whether they are vertical, horizontal, or at any angle, may be expressed in terms of newtons.

This is not to imply that gravitational attraction is responsible for all forces, for it is not; it is only to indicate that all forces, whatever their origin or direction, may be expressed in terms of weight.

5.4. Forces Are Added Vectorially

Since forces have both magnitude and direction, they are vector quantities and, therefore, subject to the rules of *vector addition.* Consider the diagram in Fig. 5J, illustrating a heavy trunk being pulled along the floor by two ropes. With steady pulls of 25 N and 40 N exerted in directions at 90° from each other, the trunk moves in a direction indicated by the dotted arrow. By vector addition, a *resultant* force R can now be found which, upon taking the place of the two forces shown, will produce the same motion.

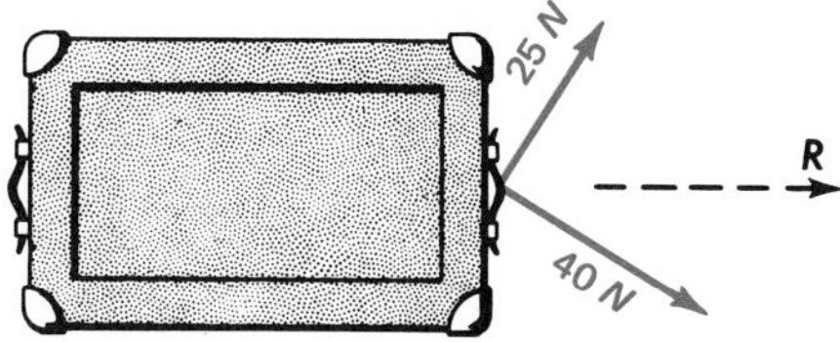

Fig. 5J. Two forces acting at an angle to each other are equivalent to a single force acting in a direction between them.

The addition of the two force vectors of Fig. 5J is illustrated in Fig. 5K. Starting at O, the two vectors a and b are first drawn to scale and in their proper directions. The dotted lines QS and PS are next drawn in to complete the parallelogram, and then followed by the diagonal R. With an arrowhead at S, the diagonal represents the resultant whose magnitude R and direction θ are to be calculated by trigonometry.

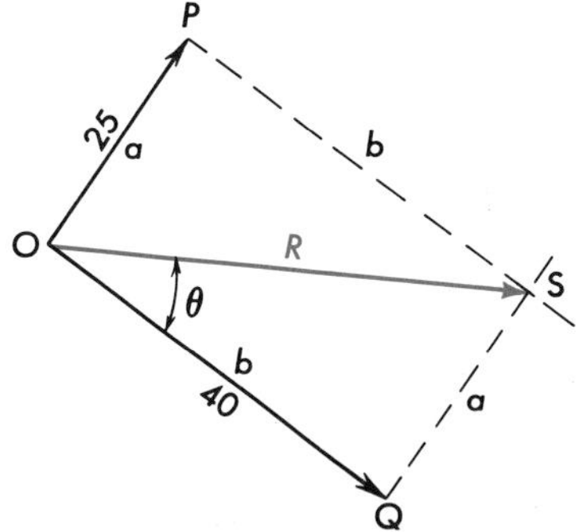

Fig. 5K. Diagram illustrating the addition of two forces acting at an angle of 90° with each other.

Since a and b make an angle of 90° with each other, OQS is a right triangle with the sides a, b, and R. By definition from trigonometry,

$$\frac{a}{b} = \tan \theta$$

In this equation, substitute known values, as follows:

$$\frac{25}{40} = 0.6250 = \tan \theta$$

Look up 0.6250 in the tangent column of the table of trigonometric functions (appearing on the inside back cover). We find that $\theta = 32°$. Again, by definition,

$$\frac{b}{R} = \cos \theta$$

Since R is the unknown to be calculated, multiply both sides by $R/\cos \theta$ and obtain

$$\frac{b}{\cos \theta} = R$$

Look up the natural cosine of 32°; then, by substitution,

$$R = \frac{40}{0.8480} = 47.2 \text{ N}$$

The resultant force is, therefore, equal to 47.2 N at an angle of 32° with OQ.

Example 2. A boat is being towed through a canal by two ropes, one on either side of the canal, as shown at the left in Fig. 5L. If the applied forces are 400 and 600 N, respectively, and the angle between the ropes is 60°, find the magnitude of the resultant force on the boat and the angles the ropes make with the canal. Assume the resultant forec to be parallel to the canal.

Solution. The triangle method is applied to the solution of this problem at the right in Fig. 5L. First a vector b, 6 cm long, is drawn down and to the right to represent the one force of 600 N.

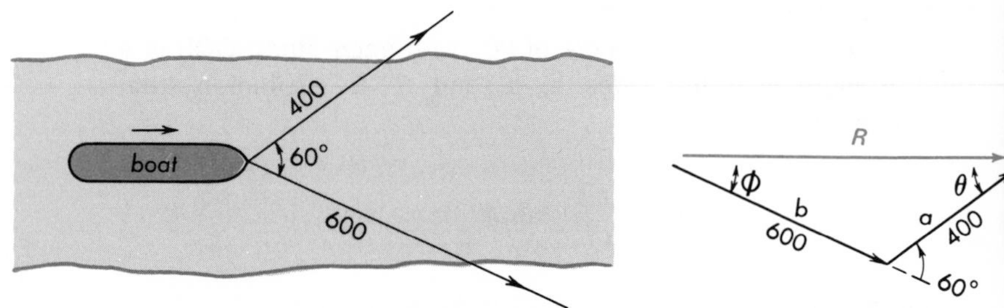

Fig. 5L. The pull of two ropes at an angle on a canal boat is equivalent to a single force straight along the canal.

From the end of this vector, and at an angle of 60°, the second vector a, 4 cm long, is drawn to represent the other force of 400 N. The line R is then drawn in with an arrowhead to represent the resultant force on the boat. By trigonometry the unknown quantities, (1) the magnitude of R, (2) the angle θ, and (3) the angle ϕ, can be calculated as follows.

Use the law of cosines for an oblique triangle:

$$R^2 = a^2 + b^2 + 2ab \cos 60° \tag{5a}$$

Look up the cosine of 60° in tables and substitute the value in this equation:

$$R^2 = (400)^2 + (600)^2 + 2(400)(600) \times 0.500$$

from which

$$R^2 = 160{,}000 + 360{,}000 + 240{,}000$$

so that

$$R^2 = 760{,}000 \quad \text{and} \quad R = 872$$

The resultant force $R = 872$ N.

To find angles ϕ and θ, either the law of sines or the law of cosines may be used. Using the law of cosines to find angle ϕ,

$$\cos \phi = \frac{b^2 + R^2 - a^2}{2bR} = \frac{(600)^2 + (872)^2 - (400)^2}{2 \times 600 \times 872}$$

Thus

$$\cos \phi = 0.9178$$

which from the table of cosines gives

$$\phi = 23.4^\circ$$

Use the law of sines to find the angle θ:

$$\frac{a}{\sin \phi} = \frac{b}{\sin \theta} \tag{5b}$$

Solving for $\sin \theta$, and substituting, we find

$$\sin \theta = \frac{b \sin \phi}{a} = \frac{600 \times 0.3979}{400} = 0.5969$$

From the tables of natural sines, we obtain

$$\theta = 36.65^\circ$$

5.5. Force Polygon

When three or more forces act simultaneously upon a body, a single force, called their resultant, can be found which acting alone upon that body will produce the same result. To find such a resultant force, the *polygon method* of vector addition is often employed. In principle, this is an extension of the triangle method and consists of placing the tail of one vector at the head of the one preceding it, and continuing this process until all vectors have been added.

An illustration of the polygon method applied to five forces is given in Fig. 5M. The space diagram [Fig. 5M(a)] shows the forces acting on a body of P, while the *vector diagram* (b) shows the vector addition and the resultant force *R*. Starting at A as the origin, vector AB is drawn 8 cm long, parallel to the 8-N vector in diagram (a). Vector BC is next drawn 7 cm long and parallel to the 7-N vector. These are followed in succession by vectors CD, DE, and EF, respectively. With all five vectors added, the resultant *R* is found by joining the last arrowhead F with the origin A, and adding an arrowhead pointing toward F.

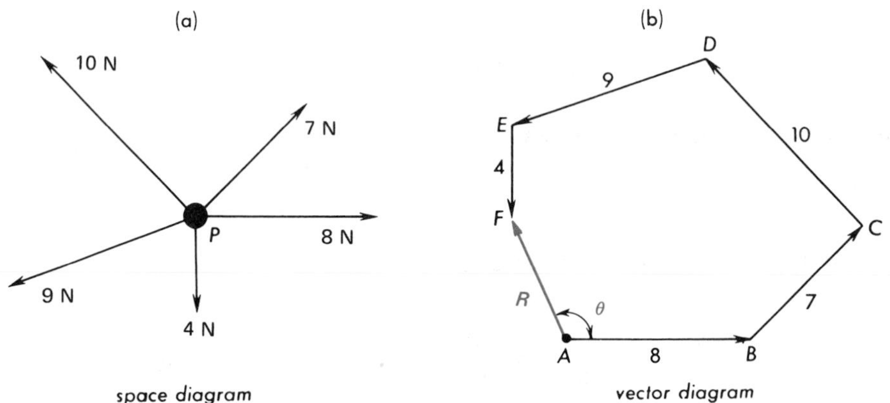

Fig. 5M. Diagrams illustrating the graphical addition of five forces to find their resultant. (The polygon method.)

Drawn to scale, the measured length of *R* will give the magnitude of the resultant force, and the measured angle θ will give the direction in which it acts. To calculate the resultant force *R* in such a problem, the polygon may be divided up into triangles and all sides and angles of the triangles calculated in their turn.

It is important to know that regardless of the order in which the vectors are drawn to form the force polygon the resultant must, of necessity, be the same. For example, if the vectors were added in the order 4 N, 7 N, 9 N, 8 N, and 10 N, each to scale and in its proper direction, the resultant would have the direction and magnitude of *R* in Fig. 5M. It would be well for the student to construct such other diagrams and find to his own satisfaction that the resultant always comes out the same.

5.6. Resolution of a Force into Components

Many of the problems in mechanics are most easily solved by the so-called *"method of components."* To apply this method to typical problems, it is necessary that we first see how a single vector may be resolved into two components. Consider as an illustration the known force F, making an angle of θ degrees with the x axis as shown in Fig. 5N.

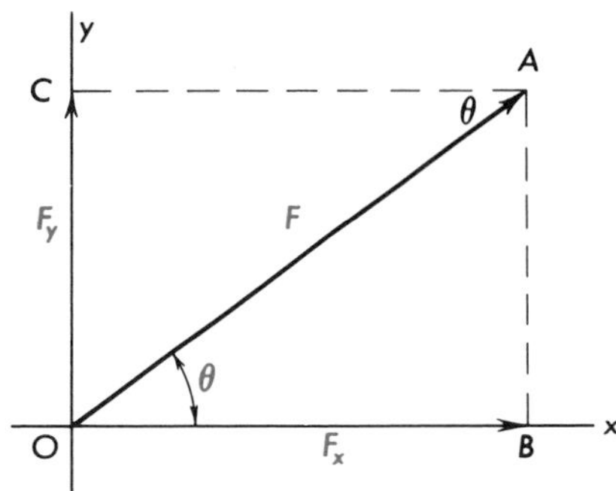

Fig. 5N. The resolution of a vector into two rectangular components.

By drawing lines from A, perpendicular to the x and y axes, the component forces F_x and F_y are equivalent to the original force F, since by adding them vectorially they give F as a resultant. With F_x and F_y perpendicular to each other, triangles OAB and OAC are equivalent right triangles with corresponding sides equal. F_y = AB and F_x = AC. By trigonometry, then,

$$\frac{F_x}{F} = \cos\theta,$$

$$\frac{F_y}{F} = \sin\theta, \qquad (5c)$$

$$\frac{F_y}{F_x} = \tan\theta$$

Since F and θ are usually the known quantities, the first two equations are the most useful in finding the magnitudes of force components. These may be rewritten

$$F_x = F\cos\theta$$

$$F_y = F\sin\theta \qquad (5d)$$

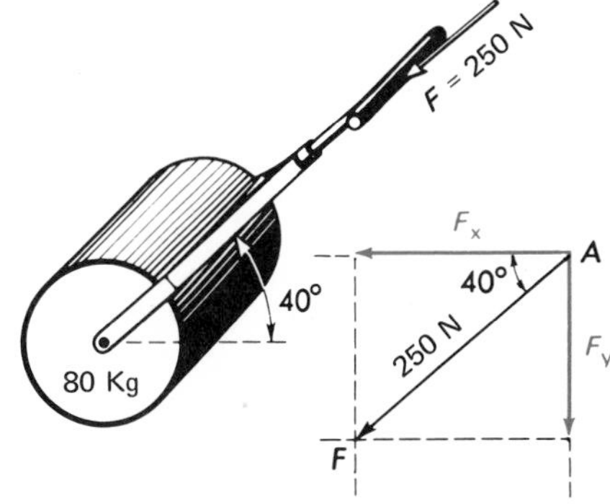

Fig. 5O. The force on the handle of a lawn roller is resolved into two components.

Example 3. A force of 250 N is applied to the handle of an 80-Kg lawn roller (see Fig. 5O). Calculate (a) the horizontal and vertical components of this force if the handle makes an angle of 40° with the horizontal, and (b) the force exerted by the roller on the ground.

Solution. The graphical solution to (a) is shown at the right in Fig. 5O. The magnitudes of the two components F_x and F_y are calculated by direct substitutions in Eq.(5d):

$$F_x = 250\text{ N} \times \cos 40°$$

$$F_y = 250\text{ N} \times \sin 40°$$

From the tables of natural sines and cosines, substitution gives

$$F_x = 250 \times 0.7660 = 191.5 \text{ N}$$

$$F_y = 250 \times 0.6428 = 160.7 \text{ N}$$

The horizontal component, $F_x = 191.5$ N, is the force causing the roller to move, while the vertical component, $F_y = 160.7$ N, acting straight downward must be added to the weight of the roller to find the total downward force F exerted by the roller on the ground:

$$F = 80 \times 9.80 + 160.7 = 945 \text{ N}$$

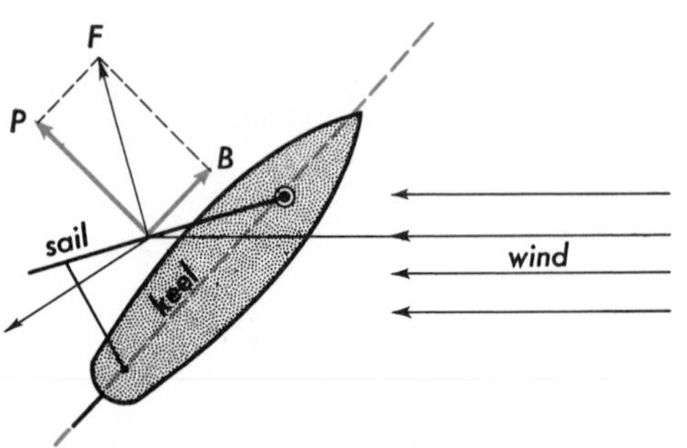

Fig. 5P. A boat sailing into the wind. An example of the resolution of a force F into two rectangular components, P and B.

5.7. The Sailboat

A problem that puzzles many people, particularly those more or less familiar with sailboats, is that of sailing across the water into the wind. This phenomenon, commonly known as *tacking,* is another illustration of the resolution of a force into rectangular components.

As shown in Fig. 5P, the wind is from the east and the boat is headed north-east. When the sail is properly set, the wind, in blowing across the canvas, is deflected away in such a way that it exerts a force F normal to the surface as shown. By resolving this force into two rectangular components, one parallel and the other perpendicular to the keel, the force B, responsible for the boat's motion, is found.

The other component, P, has little effect upon the boat since it is perpendicular to the motion. It is a useless force which tends to tip the boat and move it to leeward. To reduce tipping or being pushed sideways, sailboats are equipped with a deep heavy keel. By increasing the angle between the sail and the wind, the force F will increase but the forward component will decrease. If the boat is headed more directly into the wind, without changing the relative position of the sail and the keel, the useful component B will again decrease. Most rapid progress upwind is attained when the wind and keel make an angle of 45° and the sails are so rigged that the rudder is parallel to the keel.

5.8. The Inclined Plane

When a car, motorcycle, bicycle, or other vehicle stands at the top of a hill, and the brakes are suddenly released, it rolls down the hill with ever increasing speed. Neglecting all forces of friction, a subject which will be taken into account in Chap. 7, such a body will maintain *constant acceleration* down the incline.

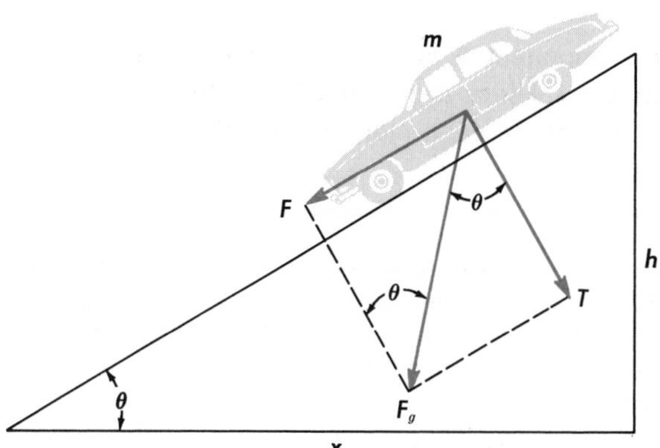

Fig. 5Q. With the brakes released a car on a hill moves downward with uniform acceleration.

Consider Fig. 5Q in which a car of mass m is shown on a hill with a 50% grade. Such a grade is one in which for every horizontal distance $x = 100$ m, there is a vertical rise of $h = 50$ m. The angle θ of the incline is, therefore, given by

$$\tan\theta = \frac{h}{x} \tag{5e}$$

which for a 50% grade gives

$$\tan\theta = \frac{50\text{ m}}{100\text{ m}} = 0.500$$

From a table of tangents, we find

$$\theta = 26.56°$$

To find the accelerating force we resolve the car's weight,

$$F_g = mg \tag{5f}$$

into two components, F and T, one parallel and the other perpendicular to the incline. Observe that the two right triangles formed repeat the angle θ, and that the force components are given by

$$F = F_g \sin \theta \tag{5g}$$

$$T = F_g \cos \theta \tag{5h}$$

The component F is the force accelerating the car, and the component T keeps it in contact with the incline, neither helping nor hindering the car's motion down the hill.

Example 4. A car with a mass of 1500 Kg stands at rest at the top of a 20% grade. If the brakes are suddenly released, find (a) the weight of the car, (b) the accelerating force, (c) the acceleration, (d) the velocity acquired after traveling 120.0 m, and (e) the time of travel.

Solution. The given quantities are $m = 1500$ Kg, $g = 9.80$ m/s^2, and slope = 20%. We first find the angle θ by direct substitution in Eq.(5e):

$$\tan \theta = \frac{h}{x} = \frac{20}{100} = 0.200$$

$$\theta = 11.31°$$

Direct substitution in Eq.(5f) gives for the car's weight:

$$F_g = mg = 1500 \text{ Kg} \times 9.80 \frac{\text{m}}{\text{s}^2}$$

$$F_g = 14{,}700 \text{ N}$$

By direct substitution in Eq.(5g) we obtain for the accelerating force,

$$F = F_g \sin \theta = 14{,}700 \text{ N} \times 0.1961$$

$$F = 2883 \text{ N}$$

We now use Newton's force equation, Eq.(4a), to find the acceleration:

$$a = \frac{F}{m} = \frac{2883 \text{ N}}{1500 \text{ Kg}}$$

$$a = 1.922 \frac{\text{m}}{\text{s}^2}$$

To find the velocity we employ Eq.(2r), solve for v, and substitute known quantities to obtain

$$v = \sqrt{2ax} = \sqrt{2 \times 1.922 \times 120.0}$$

$$v = 21.48\ \frac{\text{m}}{\text{s}}$$

For the time of travel we use Eq.(2o), solve for t, and substitute known quantities, and obtain

$$t = \frac{v}{a} = \frac{21.48\ \text{m/s}}{1.922\ \text{m/s}^2}$$

$$t = 11.18\ \text{s}$$

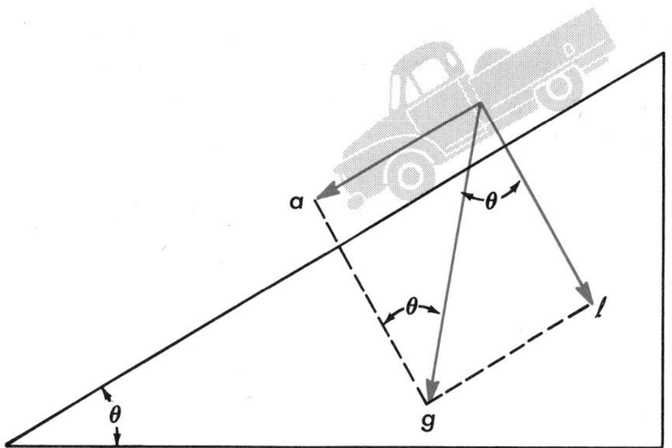

Fig. 5R. The acceleration due to gravity, g, is a vector quantity, and is shown here resolved into two components, a and ℓ.

It is not necessary to know the mass or weight of a body to find its acceleration down an inclined plane. Since acceleration is a vector quantity, g is straight downward, and can be resolved into two components as shown in Fig. 5R. From geometry we can write

$$a = g \sin \theta \qquad (5i)$$

By direct substitution of known quantities in this equation we find for the car in the preceding example,

$$a = g \sin \theta = 9.80\ \frac{\text{m}}{\text{s}^2} \times 0.1961$$

$$a = 1.922\ \frac{\text{m}}{\text{s}^2}$$

The velocity acquired by a body freely moving down an incline is given by Eq.(2r) as

$$v^2 = 2ax$$

Substituting Eq.(5i) for the acceleration, we find

$$v^2 = 2gx \sin \theta$$

Since $x \sin \theta$ is equal to h, the height of the incline, the equation can be simplified to

$$v^2 = 2gh$$

or (5j)

$$v = \sqrt{2gh}$$

This equation means that the velocity acquired by a body accelerated freely down an incline is given by the velocity of a body falling freely from rest from a height h equal to that of the incline.

Although the velocity acquired on different slopes of the same height is the same, it should be noted that the *acceleration, distance traveled, time of travel,* and *angle* θ are different.

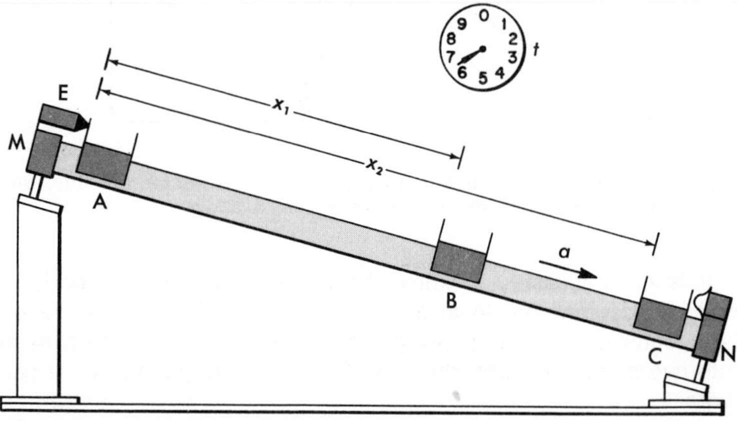

Fig. 5S. Lecture demonstration or laboratory experiment of acceleration down an inclined plane, made with an air track.

In the laboratory an air-track may be used to study the acceleration of a known mass down an inclined plane. An air-track of the kind shown in Fig. 5S is practically frictionless, and by raising one end and timing the rate of descent through a measured distance, the acceleration can be calculated.

5.9. Conditions for Equilibrium

When one or more forces act upon a body at rest, and their resultant sum is not zero, the body will be set into motion. Under such conditions there is an *unbalanced force* acting, and this force alone accounts for the acceleration. If, however, the vector sum of all the forces acting is zero, the body is in equilibrium and the body will either remain at rest or, if moving, maintain constant velocity. Stated in another way. *"Any object remaining at rest, or moving with uniform motion, is in equilibrium and the resultant of all forces acting upon it is zero."*

If two and only two forces act upon a body in equilibrium, a little study will show that they must be equal in magnitude and opposite in direction. A book lying on the table and a lamp hanging from the ceiling are good examples of dual forces in equilibrium (see Figs. 5T and 5U).

The two forces acting on the book are F_g, the downward pull of the earth, called the *weight,* and F, the upward thrust of the table. Since the book is in equilibrium, the force F is equal in magnitude to the weight F_g. For the lamp in Fig. 5U, the downward force or weight F_g is counterbalanced by the upward force T exerted by the cord. Here again, the forces are equal in magnitude and opposite in direction.

It is important to note that a body moving with constant velocity is in equilibrium: since there is no acceleration, there is no unbalanced force.

In the game of tug-of-war, when two opposing teams are pulling with equal but opposite forces at the ends of a rope, a condition of equilibrium exists. As illustrated in Fig. 5V, the force F of 5000 N acting to pull the knot K to the right is counterbalanced by an equal but opposite force $-F$ of 5000 N pulling it to the left. If the two forces become unequal, equilibrium will no longer exist and the knot K will move in the direction of the greater force. It should be noted in the equilibrium case that the tension in the rope is 5000 N and not 10,000 N. This apparent paradox can be explained away by supposing that one team ties its end of the rope to a post. The other team, still pulling with its 5000 N, maintains the same equilibrium conditions as before and in so doing maintains the tension of 5000 N. One team can be looked upon as holding the rope so the other team can pull.

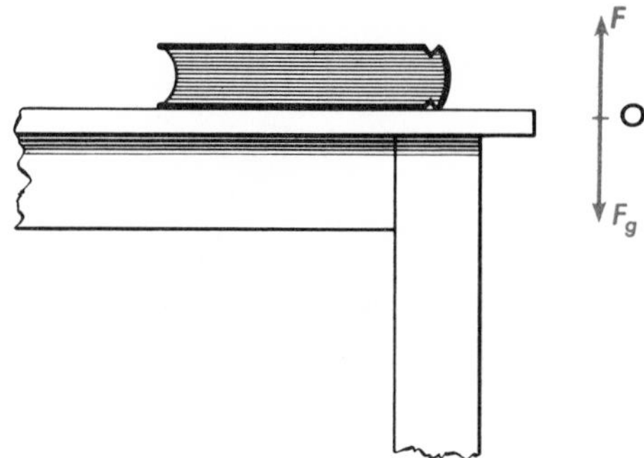

Fig. 5T. A book lying on a table is in equilibrium.

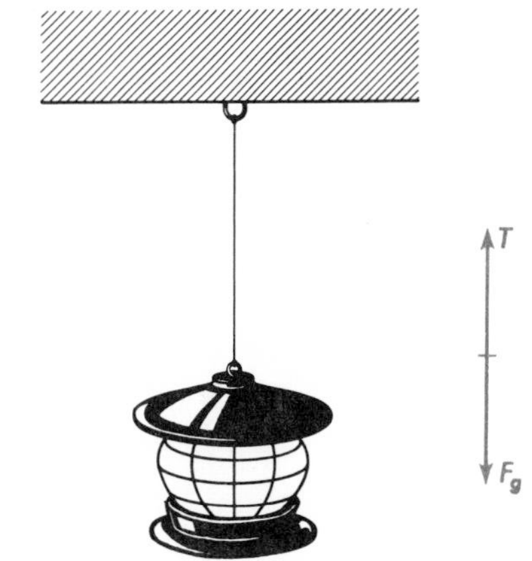

Fig. 5U. A lamp hanging from the ceiling is in equilibrium.

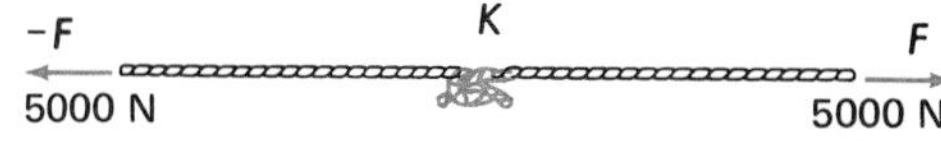

Fig. 5V. The tension in the rope is 5000 N.

5.10. Three Forces in Equilibrium

When, as the result of the action of three forces, a body is in equilibrium, the *resultant* of all three forces must be zero. In other

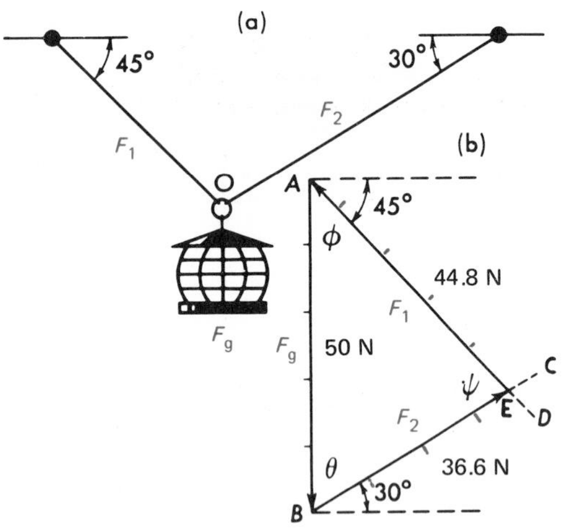

Fig. 5W. Three forces produce equilibrium if their vector sum is zero.

words, *to be in equilibrium, the vector sum of the three forces must be zero.*

$$\Sigma \vec{F} = 0$$

This means that if we draw vectors to scale and add them in their respective directions we will obtain a closed polygon. In this case of three forces the polygon is a triangle. As an illustration, consider the street light suspended from two poles as shown in Fig. 5W.

The three forces acting through the common point O are F_g, the weight of the lamp (50 N) acting straight downward; F_1, the pull of one rope at 45° up and to the left; and F_2, the pull of the other rope at 30° up and to the right. The force triangle is shown in diagram (b), where vectorially

$$\overrightarrow{F_g} + \overrightarrow{F_1} + \overrightarrow{F_2} = 0 \tag{5k}$$

In constructing this diagram, the conditions of equilibrium are imposed as a means of determining the magnitude of the forces F_1 and F_2. The graphical procedure is as follows: A vector of length 5 units is first drawn straight downward to represent F_g, the weight of the light. To the head of this vector at B, a dotted line BC is drawn parallel to the rope exerting the force F_2. From A, another dotted line AD is drawn parallel to the rope exerting the force F_1. At E, where these two lines intersect, the vectors F_1 and F_2 are terminated and arrowheads inserted in the directions shown. The solid lines AE and BE, when measured, are found to have lengths of 4.48 and 3.66 units and represent the forces $F_1 =$ 44.8 N and $F_2 =$ 36.6 N, respectively.

To solve the same problem analytically, the internal angles of the triangle ABE are first determined and then the law of sines is applied to find the lengths of the sides AE and BE. Using the angles given in diagram (b), subtraction gives angle $\phi = 45°$, angle $\theta = 60°$, and angle $\psi = 75°$. By the law of sines,

$$\frac{\text{AE}}{\sin\theta} = \frac{F_g}{\sin\psi}$$

or

$$\text{AE} = \frac{F_g \sin 60°}{\sin 75°} = \frac{50 \times 0.866}{0.966} = 44.8 \text{ N}$$

and

$$\frac{BE}{\sin \phi} = \frac{F_g}{\sin \psi}$$

or

$$BE = \frac{F_g \sin 45^\circ}{\sin 75^\circ} = \frac{50 \times 0.707}{0.966} = 36.6 \text{ N}$$

The magnitudes of the forces are therefore $F_1 = 44.8$ N and $F_2 = 36.6$ N.

An experiment illustrating the equilibrium for a car on an inclined plane is shown in Fig. 5X. A car with a mass of 1000 g is held in equilibrium on a 26.5° inclined plane by two cords passing over pulleys to masses of 446 g and 895 g. One cord runs parallel and the other perpendicular to the incline. If P is increased or decreased slightly the car will move up or down the plane, whereas if M is increased slightly the car will be lifted from the plane. The removal of the inclined plane entirely does not alter the equilibrium of the suspended mass. The three forces acting to maintain equilibrium are P, M, and F_g.

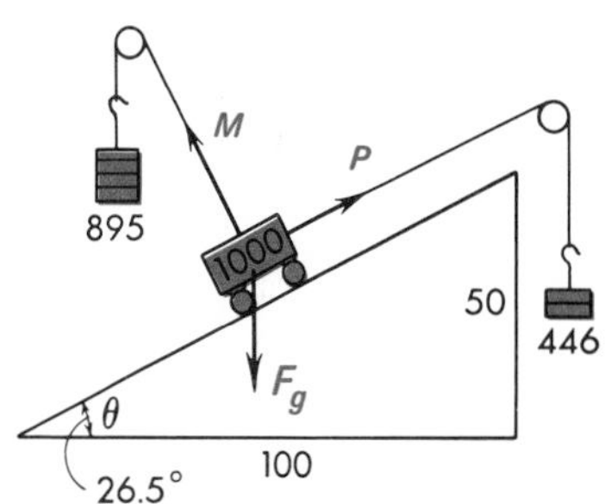

Fig. 5X. Experiment illustrating equilibrium conditions for a car on an inclined plane.

Gram masses may be used as weights in this experimental demonstration since the respective forces they exert are obtained by multiplying each mass by the same factor g ($g = 980 \text{ cm/s}^2$). The resultant three forces of 437,000 dynes, 877,000 dynes, and 980,000 dynes, respectively, when added vectorially, will form a closed triangle. Although mass is a scalar and not a vector, the masses are directly proportional to their weights, and their numbers 446, 895, and 1000 can be used just as well in drawing the vectors to scale to form a closed triangle. This is left as an exercise for the student.

problems

1. Two forces, 28.0 N and 34.0 N, respectively, are applied to pull a boat through the water. If the angle between the forces is 35°, find (a) the magnitude of the resultant, and (b) the direction it makes with the stronger of the two forces.

2. Two forces, 650 N and 870 N, respectively, are used to pull a car out of the ditch. If the angle between the forces is 52°, find (a) the magnitude of the resultant, and (b) the direction it makes with the larger force.

3. Find the resultant of two forces, 125.0 N at 30° and 165.0 N at 140°. Directions are specified with respect to the $+x$ axis. Make a vector diagram. [Ans. 169.5 N at 96.2°.]

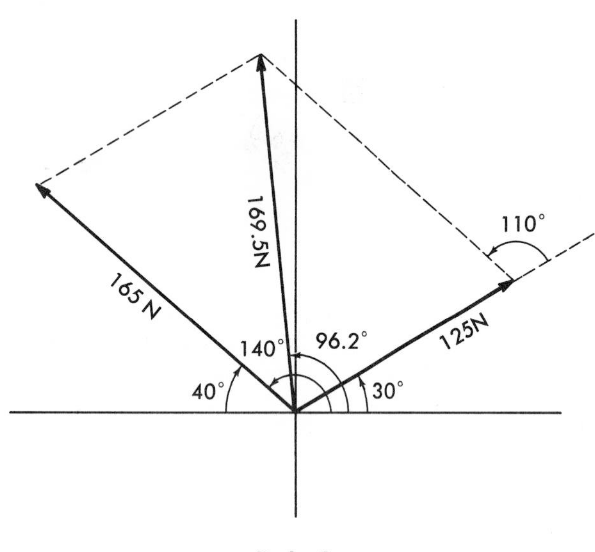

Prob. 3.

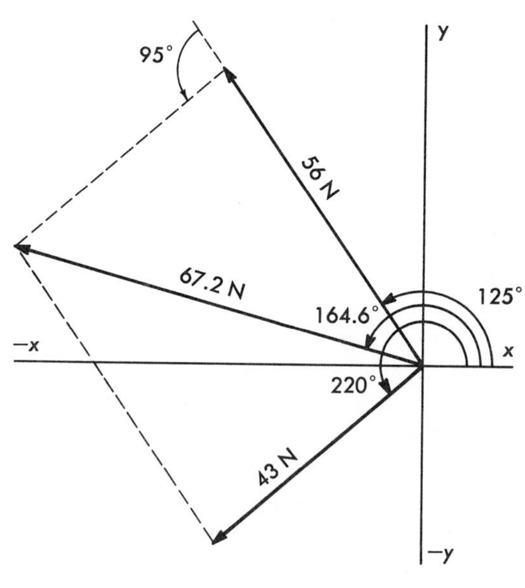

Prob. 6.

4. A truck is being pulled by two ropes making an angle of 30° with each other. If the forces are 3650 N and 4820 N, respectively, what are the magnitude and direction of the force? Make a diagram to scale, and check your answer.

5. Find the magnitude and direction of the resultant of two forces, 95.0 N at 42° and 75.0 N at 148°. Directions are specified with respect to the $+x$ axis. Make a vector diagram to scale.

6. Find the magnitude and direction of the resultant of two forces, 56.0 N at 125° and 43.0 N at 220°. Directions are specified with respect to the $+x$ axis. Make a vector diagram. [Ans. 67.2 N at 164.6°.]

7. Find the x and y components of a force of 250 N, inclined at an angle of 34° with the $+x$ axis. Make a diagram.

8. A force of 1000 N is to be resolved into two components at right angles to each other. What are the magnitudes of the two forces if one is exactly three times the other? (b) What is the angle between the larger component and the force?

9. A car on a steep incline leading up a mountain has a mass of 5000 Kg when fully loaded. (a) What is the tension in the cable if the incline makes an angle of 26° with the horizontal? (b) What are the magnitudes of the three forces that keep the car in equilibrium? Make a diagram. [Ans. (a) 2.148×10^4 N, (b) 2.148×10^4 N, 4.40×10^4 N, and 4.90×10^4 N.]

10.* When a sailboat is tacking correctly its keel makes an angle of 45° with respect to the wind. If the wind is from the west, and the boom makes an angle of 25° with the keel, find the forward thrust on the boat. Assume the wind exerts a force of 1200 N normal to the boom and sail. Make a diagram showing all important forces.

11. A street lamp with a mass of 15.0 Kg hangs in the middle of the street. It is supported by two cables of equal length, from poles of equal height. The ropes make equal angles of 36° with the horizontal. Find the tension in each rope. Make a force diagram.

12. A lawn roller has a mass of 50.0 Kg. If the force on the handle for pushing it along the level at constant

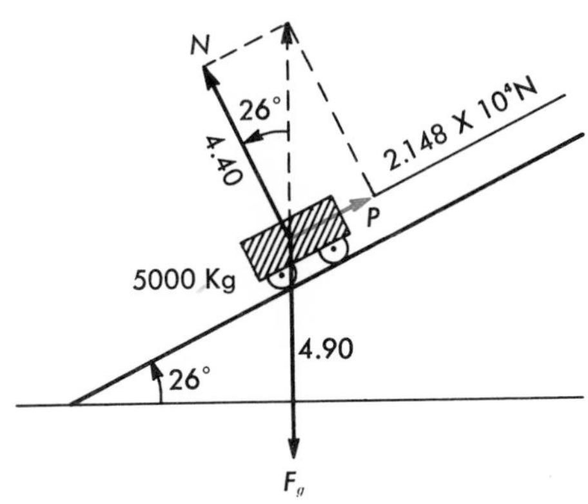

Prob. 9.

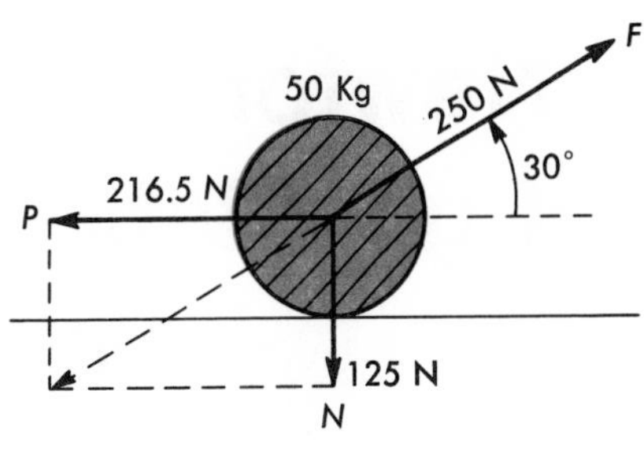

Prob. 12.

speed is 250.0 N, at angle of 30° with the horizontal, find (a) the horizontal component of the force, and (b) the vertical component. (c) What is the roller's total downward force on the ground? Make a force diagram for parts (a) and (b). [Ans. (a) 216.5 N, (b) 125 N, (c) 615 N.]

13. The following three forces act upon a mass M: 40.0 N at 15°, 25.0 N at 80°, and 30.0 N at 150°. Find the resultant force. Make a scale diagram of the *x* and *y* components of all forces.

14.* The following four forces act upon a mass of 50.0 Kg: 60.0 N at 20°, 55.0 N at 110°, 35.0 N at 225°, and 30.0 N at 330°. All forces are measured from the + *x* axis. Solve by the method of components. Make a diagram to scale, and show components of all forces.

15. A block of steel with a mass of 6.70 Kg is placed on a wooden slide inclined at an angle of 35.5° with the horizontal. Calculate (a) the accelerating force, and (b) the acceleration of the block. Neglect the frictional resistance to sliding. [Ans. (a) 38.13 N, (b) 5.69 m/s^2.]

16. A boy on a sled starts from rest and slides down a hill making an angle of 23.5° with the horizontal. If the total mass of the boy and his sled is 72.0 Kg, and the distance he slides is 125.0 m, find (a) the accelerating force, (b) the acceleration, (c) the velocity at the bottom of the hill, and (d) the time taken to reach the bottom. Neglect friction.

17. A man on skis starts from rest at the top of a slope and slides straight forward a distance of 60.0 m. If the slope makes an angle of 18.5° with the horizontal, find (a) his acceleration, (b) the velocity obtained, and (c) the time of travel.

6 Newton's law of gravitation and third law of motion

Nearly everyone has heard the story of how young Isaac Newton, while sitting under an apple tree one day, was struck on the head by a falling apple. This incident set Newton to thinking about falling bodies and led him at the early age of twenty-three to the discovery of the law of gravity.

6.1. Newton's Law of Gravitation

It has often been said incorrectly that Newton discovered gravity. What Newton discovered was the *universal law of gravitation. Any two bodies attract each other with a force proportional to the product of their masses and inversely proportional to the square of the distance between them.* Written in algebraic symbols,

$$F \propto \frac{m_1 m_2}{d^2}$$

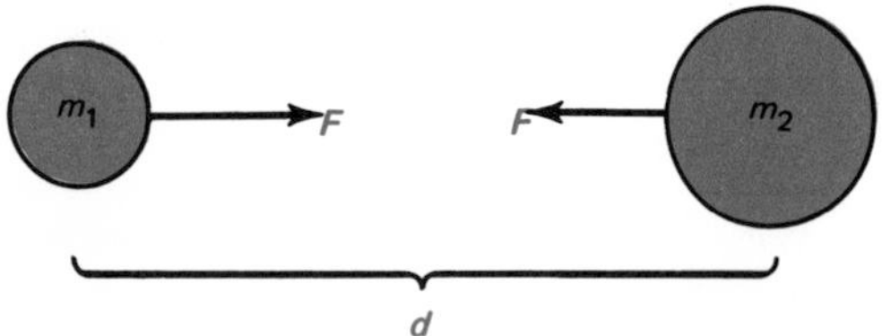

Fig. 6A. The gravitational attraction of one body of mass m_1 for another of mass m_2.

As illustrated in Fig. 6A, F is the force of attraction, m_1 and m_2 are the two masses, and d is the distance between them. Mass m_1 pulls on m_2 with a force F to the left and m_2 pulls on m_1 with an equal force F to the right. These two forces are equal in magnitude but opposite in direction.*

To make an equation of this symbolism it is only necessary to replace the proportionality constant above by an equal sign and insert a constant on either side of the equality:

* Newton's law of gravitation is presented before his third law of motion since gravitational forces always exist in pairs, and are needed to explain action and reaction forces as they apply to bodies at rest and in motion.

$$F = -G \frac{m_1 m_2}{d^2} \tag{6a}$$

The minus sign signifies the force is one of attraction.

Experiment shows that, if F is measured in newtons, m_1 and m_2 in kilograms, and d in meters, the "Newtonian constant of gravitation" G has the value

$$G = 6.673231 \times 10^{-11} \frac{\text{m}^3}{\text{Kg s}^2} \tag{6b}$$

If F is in dynes, m_1 and m_2 in grams, and d in centimeters,

$$G = 6.673231 \times 10^{-8} \frac{\text{cm}^3}{\text{g s}^2}$$

To obtain some idea of the magnitude of gravitational forces, consider the following example.

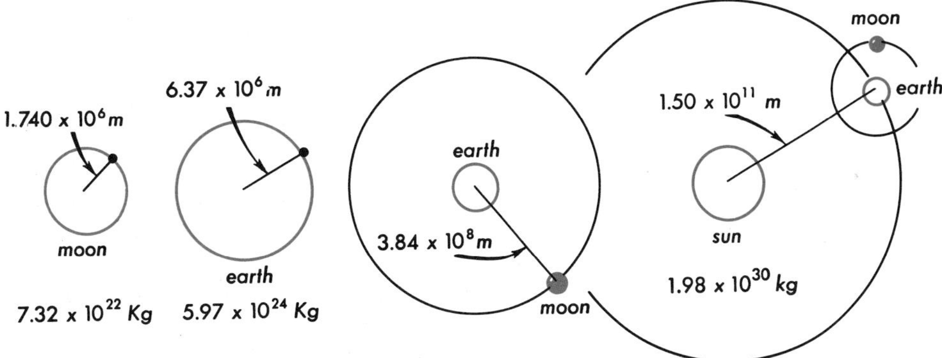

Fig. 6B. Gravitational attraction keeps the moon in its orbit around the earth, and the earth in its orbit around the sun.

Example 1. Calculate the force of attraction between two masses of 1.0 Kg each, held in the hands 10.0 cm apart.

Solution. The given quantities to be substituted in Eq.(6a) are $m_1 = m_2 = 1.0$ Kg and $d = 0.10$ m. Upon substitution, we obtain

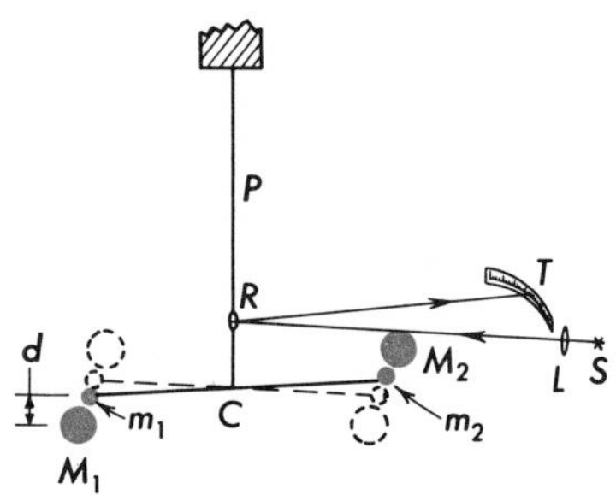

Fig. 6C. The Cavendish experiment: weighing the earth.

*Henry Cavendish (1731–1810), English chemist and physicist, elder son of Lord Charles Cavendish, brother of the Duke of Devonshire, and Lady Anne Grey, daughter of the Duke of Kent, was born at Nice on October 10, 1731. Although one of the richest men of his time through inheritance, he devoted his life to scientific work. He had little interest in society, always avoided the attention of his fellows, and never married. He was a member of the Royal Society and is best known for his experiments on gravitational attraction. He is also noted for his contribution to the chemistry of gases, and for his work on electrical capacitors and the inverse square law of force between electrical charges.

$$F = -G\frac{m_1 m_2}{d^2}$$

$$F = -6.67 \times 10^{-11} \frac{\text{m}^3}{\text{Kg s}^2} \cdot \frac{1 \text{ Kg} \times 1 \text{ Kg}}{(0.1 \text{ m})^2}$$

$$F = -6.67 \times 10^{-9} \frac{\text{Kg m}}{\text{s}^2}$$

$$F = -6.67 \times 10^{-9} \text{ N}$$

This force is far too small to be detected by the muscle senses of the hands or arms.

6.2. The Cavendish Experiment

This famous experiment was performed by Henry Cavendish* in the years 1797 to 1798, and is frequently referred to as "weighing the earth." The principal features of the experiment consisted of determining the attracting forces between two pairs of lead spheres by means of a torsion balance and from these measurements determining the value of G. A diagram of the apparatus is shown in Fig. 6C. A rod 1.8 m long was supported at its center by a long wire P. At the ends of the rod were two lead balls, m_1 and m_2, each 5 cm in diameter. Two lead spheres, M_1 and M_2, each 31 cm in diameter, were then placed on either side as shown. Gravitational attraction between m_1 and M_1 and between m_2 and M_2 caused the rod C to turn through a small angle and come to rest in some position like that shown by the solid line.

The shifting of M_1 and M_2 to the opposite sides of m_1 and m_2 caused the rod C to turn to a new position indicated by the dotted line. The angle through which the rod turned was measured by a small telescope or by reflection of a beam of light from a small mirror R onto a distant scale. From previous measurements of the stiffness of the supporting wire P, and a measure of the angle turned through, the force of attraction between the masses could be calculated.

If we neglect cross attractions of the right sphere on the left ball and the left sphere on the right ball, this angle between the two positions is assumed to be four times as great as that caused by the deflection of the rod, due to the attraction force of only one sphere on one ball.

It will now be shown how this measured force F in such an experiment makes it possible to calculate the earth's mass. If we know the masses of m_1 and M_1 by weighing, and the distance between them, d, from measurement, these known values can be substituted in Eq.(6a) and the only unknown quantity, G, calculated. The value which will be found is that given in Eqs.(6b) and (6c).

Consider now the attraction between the earth, of unknown mass M, and a 1-Kg mass on its surface, as shown in Fig. 6D. In this instance, the force on the 1-Kg mass is known. The force is just 9.80 N, for it can be calculated from Newton's second law, Eq.(4c), using the measured acceleration due to gravity $g = 9.80$ m/s² (see Fig. 4J).

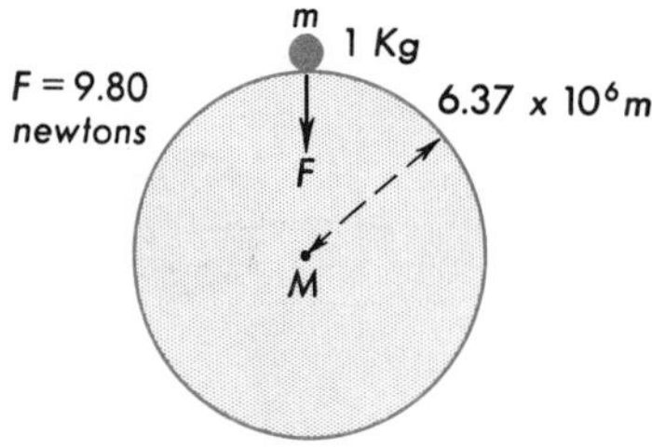

Fig. 6D. The earth exerts a downward force of 9.80 newtons on each kilogram of mass on its surface.

From experimental measurements and calculations, the following quantities are therefore known:

$$m = 1.0 \text{ Kg}$$

$$F = -9.80 \text{ N}$$

$$G = 6.67 \times 10^{-11} \text{ m}^3/\text{Kg s}^2$$

$$d = 6.37 \times 10^6 \text{ m}$$

Substituting these values in Eq.(6a), the only unknown quantity, the mass of the earth M, can be calculated. Letting $m_1 = m$ and $m_2 = M$,

$$F = -G\,\frac{m \times M}{d^2} \tag{6c}$$

Solving for M, and substituting the known quantities, we obtain

$$M = \frac{F \times d^2}{m \times G} = \frac{9.80 \times (6.37 \times 10^6)^2}{1 \times 6.67 \times 10^{-11}} = 5.97 \times 10^{24} \text{ Kg}$$

This is a reasonable value for the earth's mass, for if it is divided by the earth's volume, $\frac{4}{3}\pi r^3$, the average density of 5400 Kg/m³ or 5.4 g/cm³ is obtained. The average density of the rocks found at and near the earth's surface is 2700 Kg/m³ or 2.7 g/cm³. This means, therefore, that deep within the earth's body the average density must rise to 8000 to 10,000 Kg/m³. Such values are entirely reasonable since most metals have just such densities

The above experiment is assumed, therefore, to be correct in principle and to be a means for determining the mass of the earth:

$$\text{Earth's mass } M = 5.97 \times 10^{24} \text{ Kg}$$

6.3. Newton's Third Law of Motion

Of Newtons' three laws of motion the third is the least understood. This is probably due to the fact that it is seldom used in solving problems, and often when it is used it is incorrectly applied.

Newton's Third Law, as published in Latin in his *Principia,* is: Lex. III. *Actioni contrariam semper et aequalem esse reactionem; sive corporum duorum actiones in se mutuo semper esse aequales et in partes contrarias dirigi.* Translated this says: "Reaction is always equal and opposite to action; that is to say, the actions of two bodies upon each other are always equal and directly opposite."

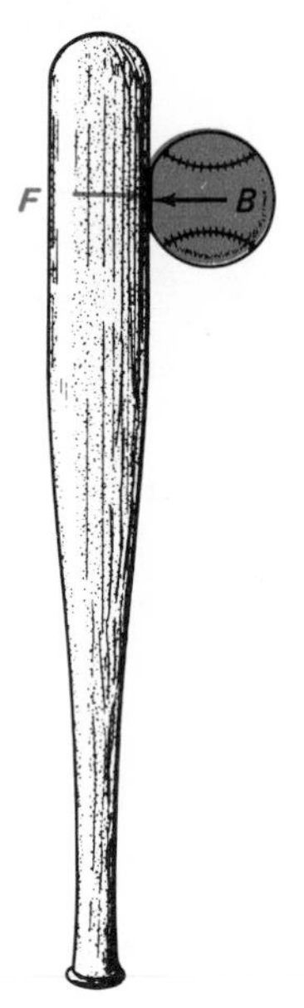

Fig. 6E. A bat at all times exerts a force on the ball equal in magnitude to the force that the ball exerts on the bat.

The principle of action and reaction may be illustrated by a bat striking a ball (Fig. 6E). During impact the bat exerts a force F on the ball, and the ball exerts an equal but opposite force B on the bat. The force F being exerted on the ball gives it an acceleration to the right, while the force B being exerted on the bat gives it an acceleration to the left. The ball speeds up during the impact and acquires a high velocity, while the bat in the same time interval slows down to a lower velocity. The impulse Ft from the bat gives the ball a momentum mv [see Eq.(4ℓ)]. The impulse Bt from the ball decreases the momentum of the bat from a higher value to one of lower value.

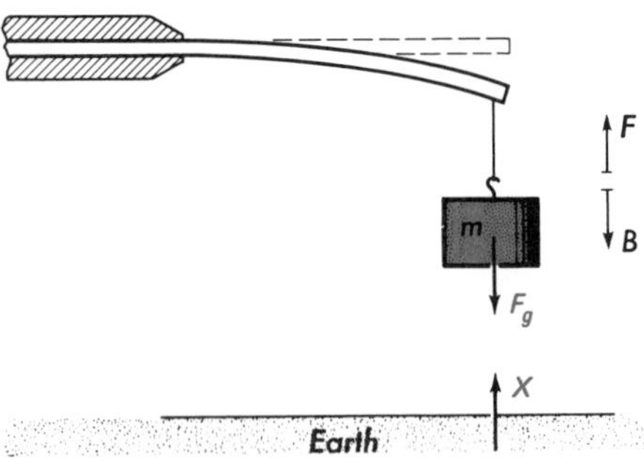

Fig. 6F. Diagram illustrating Newton's third law of motion. Forces always exist in pairs.

Consider the second example of a block hanging by a cord as illustrated in Fig. 6F. The weight of the block F_g is the force with which the earth pulls downward on the block, while the equal and opposite force X is the upward force exerted by the block on the earth.

In addition to this pair of forces, the block exerts a downward force B on the cord, while the cord pulls upward with the reaction force F. Although to many people these forces may seem confusing, it should be pointed out that Newton himself had some difficulty in applying his third law to certain problems. The difficulty arises from trying to apply action and reaction forces to the same body when in reality they apply to different ones.

It is important to note that the action force and the reaction force in Newton's third law of motion act on different bodies. Whether a body is at rest or in motion, the state of that body depends upon the forces acting on it and not upon the forces it exerts on something else. So far as the body is concerned, the latter do not determine its motion.

6.4. Isolating a Body

Forces are vector quantities and must be added by the principles of vector addition. To illustrate, the block in Fig. 6F remains at rest because two equal and opposite forces are acting upon it. To see what these forces are, the body is isolated by drawing a dotted line around it as shown in Fig. 6G. Only those forces acting on the body from outside this boundary determine its state or motion. The earth is pulling down on the block with a force F_g while the cord is pulling up on the block with an equal but opposite force F. By vector addition shown at the right, the resultant force must be zero. (It should be noted that F and F_g are not an action and reaction pair, even though they happen here to be equal.)

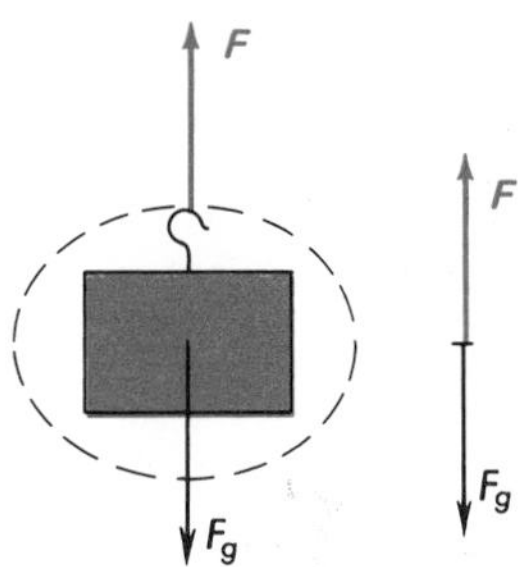

Fig. 6G. Balanced forces produce equilibrium.

Suppose in Fig. 6F that the force F is increased to a value greater than F_g. The block will then have an unbalanced force acting and it will be accelerated upward. By vector addition, as shown in Fig. 6H, the resultant upward force is equal to $F - F_g$. The acceleration can be calculated by applying Newton's second law, $F = ma$, the force here being $F - F_g$:

$$F - F_g = ma \tag{6d}$$

resultant force = mass × acceleration

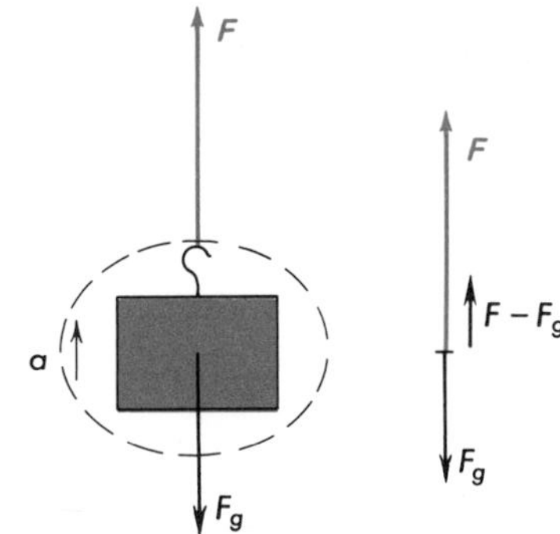

Fig. 6H. Because of a resultant force, $F - F_g$, the body is accelerated upward.

If, on the other hand, the force F is smaller than the weight F_g, the body will be accelerated downward and $F_g - F$ is the resultant force acting. Again applying Newton's second law,

$$F_g - F = ma \tag{6e}$$

resultant force = mass × acceleration

In each case, the smaller force is subtracted from the larger to make the acceleration come out with a positive sign in the direction of motion.

Example 2. A 1000-Kg elevator car is raised and lowered by a cable fastened at the top. Calculate the upward force exerted by the cable when the elevator (a) starts up with an acceleration of 1.50 m/s^2; (b) is rising with constant velocity; (c) starts down with an acceleration of 1.50 m/s^2; and (d) goes down with constant velocity.

Solution. (a) For acceleration upward, the known quantities are $m = 1000$ Kg, $F_g = 1000 \text{ Kg} \times 9.80 \text{ m/s}^2$, and $a = 1.50 \text{ m/s}^2$. The unknown is the force F. Selecting Eq.(6d), and solving for F, we

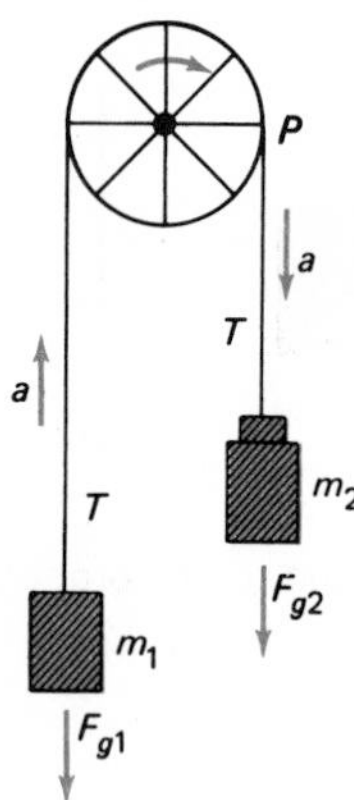

Fig. 6l. Schematic diagram of the Atwood machine.

obtain

$$F = F_g + ma$$

Substituting known quantities, we find

$$F = 1000 \text{ Kg} \times 9.80 \text{ m/s}^2 + 1000 \text{ Kg} \times 1.50 \text{ m/s}^2$$

$$F = 9800 \text{ N} + 1500 \text{ N} = 11{,}300 \text{ N}$$

(b) Moving upward with constant velocity, the elevator has no acceleration. With $a = 0$, Eq.(6d) becomes

$$F - F_g = 0 \qquad \text{or} \qquad F = F_g$$

The upward force, or tension in the cable, equals the weight of the elevator, 9800 N.

(c) For acceleration downward, Eq.(6e) is used. Solving for F, we obtain

$$F = F_g - ma$$

and substituting known quantities, we find

$$F = 1000 \text{ Kg} \times 9.80 \text{ m/s}^2 - 1000 \text{ Kg} \times 1.50 \text{ m/s}^2$$

$$F = 9800 \text{ N} - 1500 \text{ N} = 8{,}300 \text{ N}$$

(d) Moving downward with constant velocity, the elevator has no acceleration, and the tension in the cable is just the weight of the car, 9800 N.

6.5. The Atwood Machine

The Atwood Machine is a contrivance often used in the physics laboratory for determining the acceleration of gravity. The experiment involves the application of Newton's second law to the acceleration of a set of masses, as shown in Fig. 6l. Two equal masses are fastened to the ends of a long cord which passes over a light-weight ball-bearing pulley, P. At a given instant, a small mass, called a rider, is added to one side, thus setting the system moving with an acceleration a.

By measuring the distances moved in 1, 2, 3, 4, and 5 s, and knowing the values of the masses m_1 and m_2, the acceleration a can be calculated.

The first step in deriving the appropriate equation to be used for this experiment is to use the *force equation,* $F = ma$. On the left side of Fig. 6l there is the downward force due to gravity, acting on mass m_1:

$$F_{g1} = m_1 g \tag{6f}$$

Similarly, on the right side, there is the downward pull on m_2:

$$F_{g2} = m_2 g \tag{6g}$$

Since these two forces oppose each other, the resultant force F, causing the acceleration of the system, is their difference $F_{g2} - F_{g1}$:

$$F = F_{g2} - F_{g1} \tag{6h}$$

From Eqs.(6f) and (6g), and subtracting equals from equals, we obtain

$$F_{g2} - F_{g1} = m_2 g - m_1 g$$

By the distributive law, this gives

$$F_{g2} - F_{g1} = (m_2 - m_1)g \tag{6i}$$

Neglecting the mass of the cord and pulley, the total moving mass is $m_2 + m_1$. Therefore, by substituting in the force equation,

$$(m_2 - m_1)g = (m_2 + m_1)a$$

$$\textbf{force} = \textbf{mass} \times \textbf{acceleration}$$

which upon solving for g becomes

$$g = \frac{m_2 + m_1}{m_2 - m_1}\, a \tag{6j}$$

To calculate the tension in the cord passing over the pulley, the force equation can be applied to either one of the masses separately. For example, the forces acting on m_1 are F_{g1} acting downward, and T acting upward. Since m_1 is moving upward with the acceleration a, the tension T is greater than F_{g1}. The resultant of these two forces is therefore upward and equal to $T - F_{g1}$. By the force equation, we can write

$$T - F_{g1} = m_1 a \tag{6k}$$

Knowing F_{g1}, m_1, and a from Eq.(6j), the tension T can be calculated.

Example 3. A 6.0-Kg mass and a 9.0-Kg mass are fastened to opposite ends of a cord, and the cord hung over a pulley. Neglecting the mass of the cord and pulley, find (a) the resultant force accelerating the system, (b) the acceleration of the system, and (c) the tension in the cord.

Solution. The known quantities are $m_1 = 6.0$ Kg, $m_2 = 9.0$ Kg, and $g = 9.80$ m/s^2. (a) To find the resultant force accelerating the system, Eq.(6h) can be used with Eq.(6i):

$$F = (m_2 - m_1)g$$

which upon substitution gives

$$F = (9 \text{ Kg} - 6 \text{ Kg})\ 9.80 \text{ m/s}^2$$

$$F = 29.40 \text{ N}$$

(b) The acceleration of the system is found using Eq.(6j). Solving for a,

$$a = \frac{m_2 - m_1}{m_2 + m_1} g$$

and substituting, we find

$$a = \frac{3 \text{ Kg}}{15 \text{ Kg}}\ 9.80 \text{ m/s}^2 = 1.960 \text{ m/s}^2$$

(c) The tension in the cord is found using Eq.(6k). Solving for T,

$$T = F_{g1} + m_1\, a$$

and substituting known quantities, gives

$$T = 6 \text{ Kg} \times 9.80 \text{ m/s}^2 + 6 \text{ Kg} \times 1.96 \text{ m/s}^2$$

$$T = 70.6 \text{ N}$$

6.6. The Train-and-Track Experiment

Another illustration of Newton's third law is that of a train on a track, both of which, the track as well as the train, are free to move. The drive wheels push back on the track with a force B, and the track pushes forward on the wheels with an equal and opposite force F. These two form an action and reaction pair.

In Fig. 6J, the track is mounted on a large wheel with its axis of rotation vertical. With the track free to move, both forces of the pair are seen to be real; the track moves backward and the train moves forward. The track moves backward because the wheels exert a force *B* upon it in that direction, and the train goes forward because the track exerts a force *F* upon it in that direcftion. If, when the train acquires a certain velocity, the power is shut off, the force *F vanishes*—so also does *B*—and by Newton's first law of motion the train and track would be expected to continue to move with constant speed.

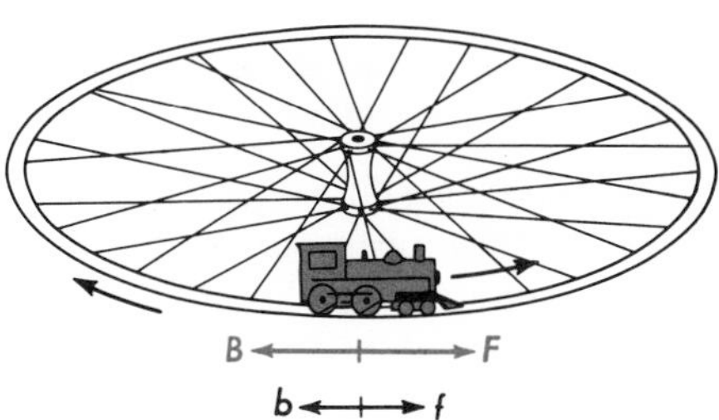

Fig. 6J. Demonstration of Newton's third law of motion. The train moves forward, and the track, if free to move, moves backward.

In a practical case, however, the track is not only fastened down, but there is some frictional resistance to motion. Because of this friction the track pushes backward on the wheels with a force *b*, and the wheels push forward on the track with an equal but opposite force *f*.

In order to keep a train moving with constant speed, a minimum force *B* great enough to overcome friction must continually be supplied to the locomotive drive wheels. The two forces acting on the train, then, are *F* and *b*, and if these are equal and opposite they have a zero resultant. There being no resultant force, there is no acceleration, and the train continues to move with constant velocity.

To start the train moving, and to maintain an acceleration, *F* must be greater than *b*. Under these conditions the acceleration, by Newton's second law, is

$$F - b = ma \qquad (6\ell)$$

resultant force = mass × acceleration

problems

1. Two automobiles of 2500 Kg each are standing with their centers of mass 3.0 m apart. Calculate the gravitational force of attraction between them.

2. A space platform with a mass of 15,000 Kg circles the earth at a distance of 400 Km above the earth's surface. (a) Calculate the gravitational pull of the earth on the platform, and (b) the weight of the platform when it is at rest on the earth's surface.

3. Two large steel spheres, each with a mass of 2.0×10^5 Kg, are located 2.0 m apart. Find the gravitational force of attraction between them. [Ans. 0.667 N.]

4. Two 4.0-Kg bowling balls used in a tournament lie on a shelf with their centers 30.0 cm apart. Calculate the force of attraction between them.

5. Three solid steel spheres, each with a mass of 50.0 Kg, are located at the corners of an equilateral triangle. Find the gravitational force on each sphere if each side of the triangle is 30.0 cm.

6. An elevator car with 10 persons aboard has a total mass of 1500 Kg. Find the tension in the cables supporting this load if the car is (a) standing still, (b) moving upward with an acceleration of 0.60 m/s^2, and (c) moving downward with the same acceleration. [Ans. (a) 1.470×10^4 N, (b) 1.560×10^4 N, (c) 1.380×10^4 N.]

7. Two masses of 4.60 Kg and 5.40 Kg, respectively, are fastened to opposite ends of a strong cord, and the cord hung over a pulley. Neglecting the mass of the cord and pulley, calculate (a) the resultant force acting to accelerate the system, (b) the acceleration of the system, and (c) the tension in the cord.

8. A 6.80-Kg mass and a 9.20-Kg mass are fastened to opposite ends of a cord, and the cord hung over a pulley. Neglecting the mass of the cord and pulley, find (a) the resultant force accelerating the system, (b) the acceleration of the system, and (c) the tension in the cord.

9. A man stands on some scales in an elevator car at rest on the first floor of a building. He notes that the scales show his mass to be 75.0 Kg. When the car starts up he observes that the scale pointer moves up to 80.0 Kg, then drops down to 70.0 Kg, then comes to rest at 75.0 Kg when the door opens. He is now at rest on the fourth floor. Find (a) the acceleration of the car starting up, and (b) the acceleration while slowing down at the fourth floor. [Ans. (a) 0.653 m/s^2, (b) -0.653 m/s^2.]

10. A boy stands on some scales in an elevator car at rest on the fifth floor. He sees that the scales show his mass to be 50.0 Kg. When the car starts down he observes the scale pointer moves down to 45.0 Kg, then rises to 55.0 Kg, then back to 50.0 Kg as the door opens. He is now at rest at the first floor. Find (a) the acceleration of the car starting down from the fifth floor, and (b) the acceleration slowing down at the first floor.

11. A girl stands on some scales in an elevator car at rest on the eighth floor of a building. The pointer shows her mass to be 60.0 Kg. The car starts down with an acceleration of 2.0 m/s^2, then decelerates at 2.0 m/s^2, and comes to rest at the 1st floor. Find (a) her apparent mass when the car starts down, and (b) when it slows down to a stop.

12. A man stands on some scales in an elevator car at rest on the first floor of a building. He notes that the scales show his mass to be 75.0 Kg. The car starts up with an acceleration of 2.0 m/s^2, then decelerates to 2.0 m/s^2, and then comes to rest on the fifth floor. Find his apparent mass when (a) the car starts up, and (b) when it slows down. [Ans. (a) 90.3 Kg, (b) 59.7 Kg.]

13.* A small car with ball-bearing wheels and a mass of 250.0 Kg rests on a level table top. A cord fastened to the car passes over a pulley at the end of the table, and a mass of 80.0 Kg hangs from the end of the cord. Assume the cord between the car and the pulley is horizontal. Upon release of the car, find (a) the resultant force accelerating the system, (b) the acceleration of the car, and (c) the tension in the string. Neglect the mass of the cord and pulley. Make a diagram.

14.* A 60.0-Kg car rests on ball-bearing wheels on a table top. A string fastened to the car passes over a pulley at the end of the table, and to another similar car on a 30° inclined plane. Calculate (a) the force accelerating the system, (b) the acceleration, and (c) the tension in the cord. Make a diagram.

7 Friction and streamlining

The formulas presented, the experiments described, and the problems solved in the preceding chapters on mechanics were idealized to the extent that all friction, including air friction, was neglected. Since friction does exist, and in some cases is not negligibly small, a quantitative treatment of friction becomes a necessity in the solution of many problems.

When a force is applied to pull a heavy box across the floor, or a stalled car is towed along a straight and level road, because of friction, acceleration may not be involved as one might expect from the simple *force equation* $F = ma$.

7.1. Friction

Whenever one body slides over another, frictional forces opposing the motion are developed between them. Such forces are due largely to the atomic and molecular attractive forces at the small *contact areas* (see Fig. 7A). Within limits, the smoothness of the surfaces does not greatly affect f, the force of sliding friction. If the surfaces are smooth there will be many small areas in contact, while if they are rough there may be fewer but larger ones. It is well known that surfaces of the same material show greater friction than do surfaces of different materials. This is one of the reasons why machine bearings are often made of one metal like bronze while their rotating shafts are made of another like steel.

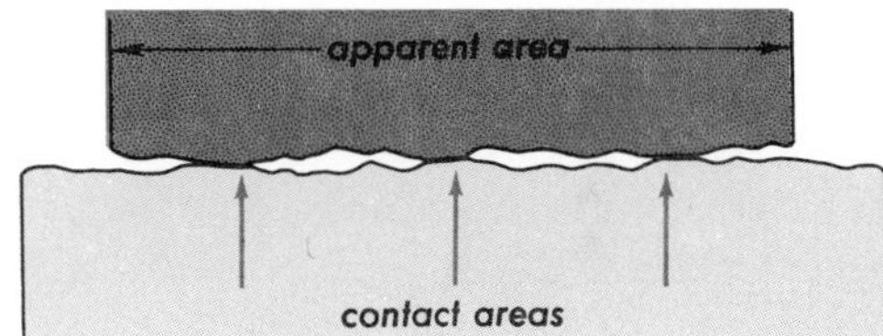

Fig. 7A. The relatively small contact areas between two bodies have a much larger apparent contact area.

Experiments show that to start a body sliding requires a greater force than that needed to keep it moving. In other words *static friction*, or *starting friction*, is greater than *kinetic friction*. Once a body is moving, however, the force of sliding friction increases only slightly with increasing speed and then remains nearly constant over a moderate range of speeds.

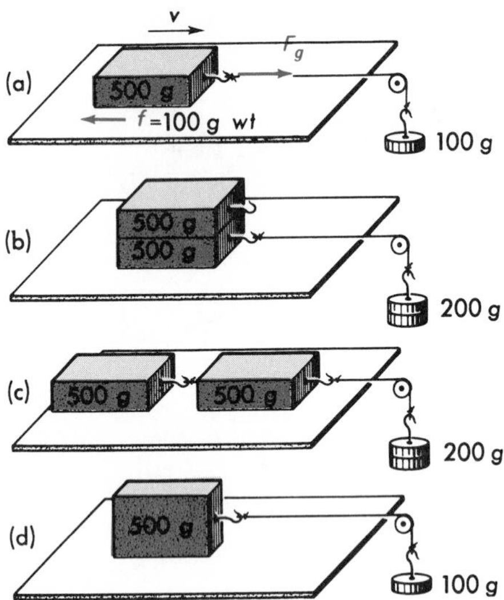

Fig. 7B. Sliding friction is proportional to the normal force pushing the surface together and is independent of the apparent area of contact.

Experiments,* particularly with metals in contact, show that, when one surface is pressed against another and sliding is brought about, the enormous pressures existing at the tiny contact areas cause a kind of welding of the two materials. With all materials in general, the atoms and molecules are so close together at the contact areas that strong mutual attractive forces often pull microscopic bits of material from one body to the other as they move along. In order to start a body moving, these bonds must be simultaneously broken; once it is moving, however, these bonds are broken smoothly and continuously.†

The general statement can be made that wherever there is motion there is friction. All forms of friction may be classified as one of three kinds—

sliding friction
rolling friction
fluid friction

Sliding and rolling friction are usually confined to solids, while fluid friction applies to liquids and gases. Generally speaking, sliding friction is greater than fluid friction at low speeds, while the reverse is true at high speeds.

7.2. Sliding Friction

A quantitative treatment of sliding friction will be given here as the result of a simple laboratory experiment illustrated in Fig. 7B. In diagram (a), a block of wood of mass 500 g is shown being pulled with uniform speed across a table top by the weight F_g of a 100-g mass. The latter force has been arrived at by trying different loads on the hook at the right. A load greater than 100 g will accelerate the block, while a load smaller than 100 g will allow it to stop. Moving with constant speed, the applied force F_g is just counterbalanced by *f*, the force of sliding friction.

In diagram (b), a second block of mass 500 g is added to make the sliding mass 1000 g. By experiment, the force required to pull the two with constant speed is given by the weight of a 200-g mass. Should a third and then a fourth block be added successively, the weights of 300- and 400-g masses, respectively, will be found necessary to pull them. From these results we can draw the following conclusions:

* Review by Frederic Palmer, *Am J. Phys.,* **17,** 327 (1949).

† For details on all kinds of friction origins see *Am. J. Phys.,* **31,** No. 12, 1963.

The force of sliding friction f is directly proportional to the total downward or normal force N:

$$f \propto N \tag{7a}$$

When the two blocks in diagram (b) are connected in tandem, one behind the other as in diagram (c), the force of friction is still the weight of a 200-g mass.

Again, if the single block in diagram (a) is turned on edge as in diagram (d), the weight of a 100-g mass is just enough to slide it with constant speed. These observations, along with the results of other similar experiments, may be explained largely in terms of molecular attractive forces. In general, the total contact area where molecular attraction is effective (see Fig. 7A) is small compared with the total apparent area. When a greater force is applied normal to the surfaces, the contact areas increase in size and number, and the following relations are found to hold reasonably true:

(1) The total contact area is proportional to the total normal force.
(2) The total contact area is independent of the total apparent area.
(3) The force of sliding friction is proportional to the total contact area.
*(4) The force of sliding friction is proportional to the total normal force.**

Introducing the Greek letter μ as a constant of proportionality, Eq.(7a) becomes

$$f = \mu N \tag{7b}$$

μ is called the *coefficient of sliding friction,* and is defined as the ratio

$$\mu = \frac{f}{N} \tag{7c}$$

By knowing the value of μ for a given pair of surfaces, one is able to calculate the force of friction f in terms of the normal force N. Average values of μ for a number of surfaces are given in Table 7A.

* Curiously enough, an increased normal force increases the pressure over the apparent area but not over the contact area. The proportionate increase in total contact area with increased force means that the force of friction on unit contact area is independent of apparent pressure.

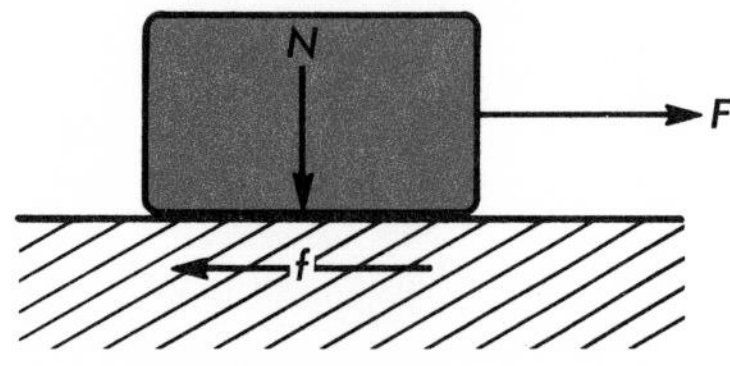

Fig. 7C. Sliding friction f is proportional to the normal force N pushing the surfaces together.

TABLE 7A
Coefficients of sliding friction for a few common materials (Average values for dry surfaces)

Material	μ
Oak on oak	0.25
Rubber on concrete	0.70
Metals on oak	0.55
Metals on elm	0.20
Hemp on oak	0.53
Pine on pine	0.35
Steel on steel	0.18
Greased surfaces	0.05
Iron on concrete	0.30
Leather on metals	0.56
Steel on babbit	0.14
Rubber on oak	0.46

TABLE 7B
Coefficient of sliding friction of pine on walnut wood

Speed (cm/s)	μ
0	0.210
1.00	0.142
2.30	0.154
3.87	0.163
6.21	0.172
8.54	0.177
10.00	0.179
11.50	0.181
12.81	0.183
17.50	0.184

As an illustration of the general use of the coefficient of sliding friction, consider the following problem, diagrammed in Fig. 7C.

Example 1. What force is required to pull a 60.0-Kg box across a smooth oak floor?
Solution. From Table 7A, μ for metals on oak is 0.55. The normal force N is the weight of the box, or

$$N = 60 \text{ Kg} \times 9.80 \text{ m/s}^2 = 588 \text{ N}$$

Substituting in Eq.(7b), the force of friction is found to be

$$f = 588 \text{ N} \times 0.55 = 323.4 \text{ N}$$

The general observation that sliding friction increases only slightly at low speeds and levels off to become practically constant at higher speeds is illustrated by the experimental values given in Table 7B.

If the force F applied to a body is greater than that required to overcome friction f, the resultant force $F - f$ is effective in producing acceleration. As an equation of motion, Newton's force equation takes the form

$$F - f = ma \qquad (7d)$$

resultant force = mass × acceleration

Solving for F, we get

$$F = f + ma$$

or,

$$F = \mu N + ma$$

7.3. Angle of Uniform Slip

One method of measuring the coefficient of sliding friction is to place a block on an inclined plane and then tilt the plane until the block slides down with constant speed (see Fig. 7D). When this condition exists, Eq.(7b) can be imposed directly upon the components of the weight F_g. The component F is equal in magnitude to f, the sliding friction, and the component T is the normal force pushing the two surfaces together, and is equal to N. If θ is the angle of the incline, then

$$\mu = \frac{f}{N} = \frac{F}{N} = \frac{F_g \sin \theta}{F_g \cos \theta} = \tan \theta$$

which gives

$$\mu = \tan \theta \qquad (7e)$$

The coefficient of friction μ equals the tangent of the angle of uniform slip. The angle of uniform slip is defined as that angle of an incline that will keep a body sliding down it with constant speed. At a steeper angle the force component F down the plane is greater than that required to overcome friction f, and the difference between them produces an acceleration as given by Eq.(7d).

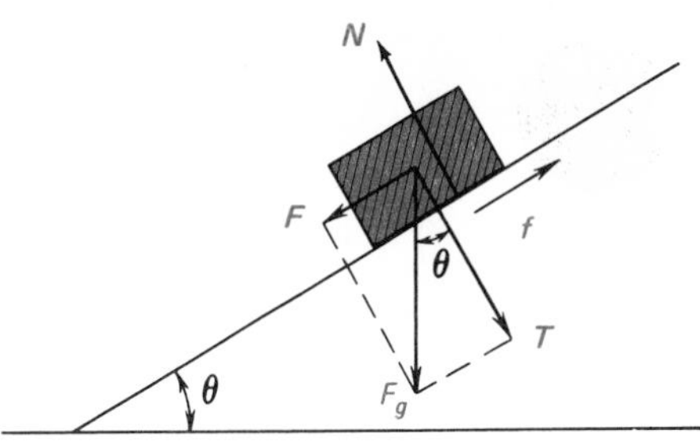

Fig. 7D. Illustration of the angle of uniform slip for a block on an inclined plane.

Example 2. The angle of uniform slip for a 40.0-Kg metal box sliding down a wooden plank is 23°. (a) Find the coefficient of sliding friction. If the plank is tilted up to 35° with the horizontal, find (b) the normal component of the weight of the box, (c) the parallel component of the force, (d) the retarding force of friction, (e) the resultant accelerating force down the plank, and (f) the acceleration of the box. See Fig. 7E.

Solution. The coefficient of sliding friction is obtained using Eq.(7e), and by the direct substitution of 23° as the angle of uniform slip:

$$\mu = \tan 23° = 0.424$$

(b) When the plank is tilted to 35°, the normal component of the weight of the metal box is given by

$$N = F_g \cos 35°$$

which, upon substitution of the mass, gives

$$N = 40 \text{ Kg} \times 9.80 \text{ m/s}^2 \times 0.819$$

$$N = 321.0 \text{ N}$$

(c) The corresponding parallel component is given by

$$F = F_g \sin 35°$$

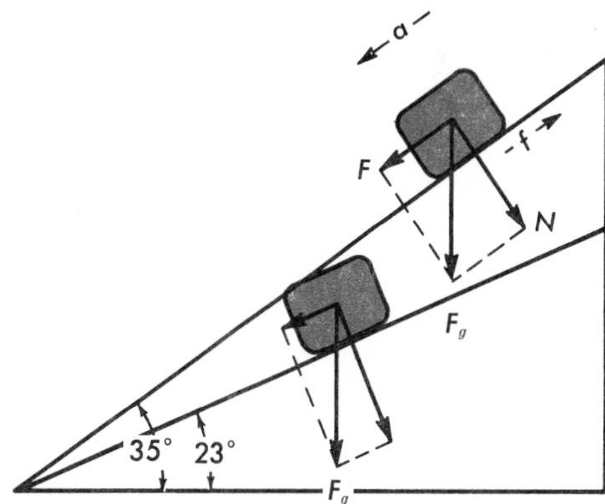

Fig. 7E. Force component diagram for Example 2: acceleration with sliding friction.

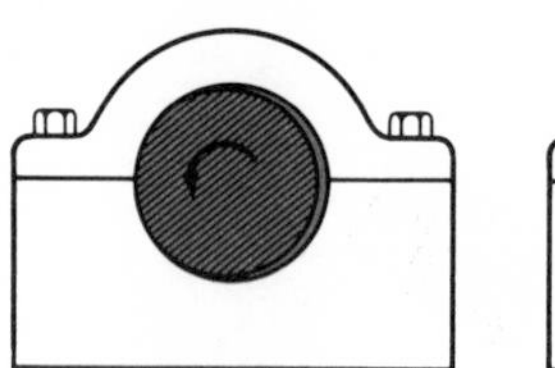
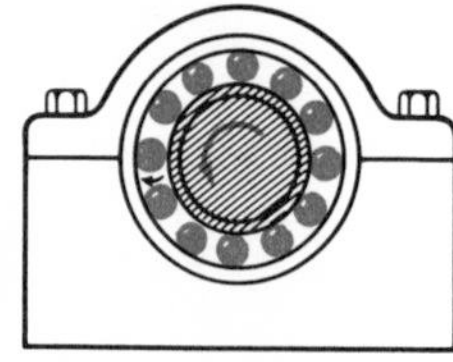

Fig. 7F. Sleeve bearings and ball bearings illustrate the two kinds of friction: (a) sliding friction and (b) rolling friction. (Note: the clearance in the sleeve bearing is exaggerated.)

which, upon substitution, gives

$$F = 40 \text{ Kg} \times 9.80 \text{ m/s}^2 \times 0.574$$

$$F = 225.0 \text{ N}$$

(d) The retarding force of friction is given by Eq.(7b). By direct substitution of known quantities,

$$f = \mu N = 0.424 \times 321 \text{ N} = 136.1 \text{ N}$$

(e) The resultant force down the plank is just $F - f$:

$$F - f = 225.0 \text{ N} - 136.1 \text{ N} = 88.9 \text{ N}$$

(f) The acceleration down the plank is given by Eq.(7d). Solving first for the unknown a, we obtain

$$a = \frac{F - f}{m}$$

which, upon direct substitution, gives

$$a = \frac{88.9 \text{ N}}{40 \text{ Kg}} = 2.222 \frac{\text{m}}{\text{s}^2}$$

7.4. Rolling Friction

A comparison of the force required to slide a heavy box along the ground with the force required to move it on rollers shows that sliding friction is many times greater than rolling friction. It is for this reason that wheels are used on vehicles instead of runners, and that ball-bearings are employed in some machines in place of sleeve-bearings.

A comparison of the sleeve type of bearing with a ball-bearing is made in Fig. 7F. The rotating axle, as shown at the left, slides on the bottom of the sleeve at low speeds and climbs part way up the side as the speed increases. The purpose of lubricating such bearings with oils and greases is to keep the two metal surfaces from coming into direct contact. Properly lubricated, the axle rides on a thin film of oil. In diagram (b) it may be seen how the axle rolls around on the balls with little or no possibility for sliding. The balls themselves roll in a groove called a "race."

The harder a rolling wheel or ball, and the harder the surface over which it rolls, the less is the force of rolling friction. A better understanding of the origin of rolling friction is to be gained by a comparison of the different kinds of wheels shown in Fig. 7G. For a hard wheel on a soft dirt road, as shown in (a), the applied force is continually pulling the wheel over a mound developed in the ground. For a soft wheel on a hard paved road, as in (b), the road is continually pushing the wheel out of shape. For a hard wheel on a hard road, both wheel and road are distorted ever so little, so that the force of friction is exceedingly small.

The same equations that hold for sliding friction also hold for rolling friction, the only difference being that the coefficients for rolling friction are exceedingly small:

$$f = \mu N \tag{7f}$$

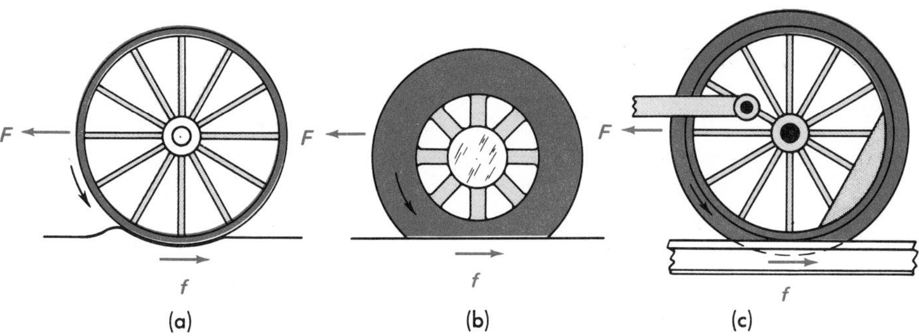

Fig. 7G. Rolling friction between soft and hard surfaces: (a) wagon wheel, (b) soft automobile tire, and (c) locomotive drive wheel.

7.5. Fluid Friction

Friction in a gas or liquid manifests itself when the fluid is made to flow around a stationary obstacle or an object is made to move through a previously stationary fluid. Such friction is involved in the propulsion of ships through the water, and automobiles, trains, and airplanes through the air. In any discussion or treatment of fluid friction, it makes no difference whether the fluid is considered as moving and the object as standing still, or vice versa. It is only necessary to specify that there is a relative motion between the two.

Experiments show that, at relatively low speeds, the flow of fluid around an object is smooth and regular and that fluid friction is proportional to the speed [see Fig. 7H(a)]:

$$f \propto v \quad \text{or} \quad f = Kv \tag{7g}$$

where K is a constant of proportionality.

TABLE 7C
Coefficients of rolling friction

Cast iron on rails	$\mu = 0.004$
Rubber tires on concrete	$\mu = 0.030$
Ball-bearing on steel	$\mu = 0.002$

If, initially, $v = 0$, frictional resistance to motion is zero and an applied force is entriely effective in producing acceleration. As the speed increases, however, friction increases proportionally so that less and less force is available for acceleration. Newton's second law, applied to motion through a fluid, therefore takes the same form as Eq.(7d), where f is given by Eq.(7g):

$$F = Kv + ma \tag{7h}$$

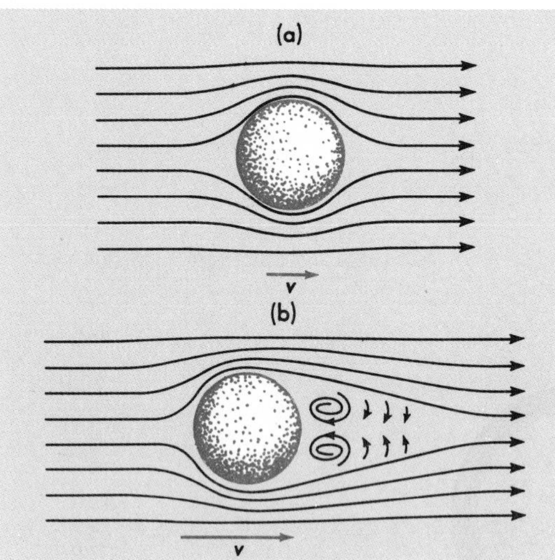

Fig. 7H. (a) Low-velocity fluid showing laminar flow. (b) High-velocity fluid showing turbulent flow.

The above equations hold only for "laminar flow," that is, for relatively low velocities. As the speed increases, a point is reached where "turbulence" sets in and the force of friction increases rapidly and becomes proportional to the square of the velocity:

$$f \propto v^2 \qquad \text{or} \qquad f = Tv^2 \tag{7i}$$

Turbulent flow is characterized by small eddy currents that form behind the object as shown in Fig. 7H(b). Not only does the fluid have to move out and around the obstacle quickly, but considerable energy is taken up by the eddies. This, of course, results in greater loss of energy and therefore greater friction. When the velocity is increased still further, the eddies, instead of forming symmetrical pairs, form alternately on one side and then on the other, leaving a long trail of vortex motions like those shown in Fig. 7I. These strings of whirlwinds or whirlpools are commonly referred to as *Kármán trails.* The existence of such trails is illustrated by the flapping of the rope on a flagpole. The waving of the flag at the top of the pole is direct evidence of the whirlwinds that follow each other alternately along the sides. As the speed of a streamlined body approaches the speed of sound, friction again increases rapidly, becoming proportional to the cube of the speed: $f \propto v^3$.

7.6. Terminal Velocity

It is well known that raindrops fall with a speed that depends upon their size and not upon the height from which they fall. Starting from rest, a particle falling in a gas or a liquid increases in velocity until the retarding force of friction becomes as great as the downward force of gravity. When this condition is reached, the body is in equilibrium and falls with a constant velocity called its *terminal velocity.*

The terminal velocity for small particles like fog drops is so low that the air stream around them is one of *laminar flow.* It was Stokes who first discovered that the terminal velocity of small particles is proportional to their weight. This relation is known, not surprisingly, as *Stokes' law.**

*Sir George G. Stokes (1819–1903), British mathematician and physicist, is well known for his fundamental contribution to hydrodynamics, diffraction, double refraction, and the polarization of light. He received the Rumford Medal in 1852 and the Copley Medal in 1893, and was at one time president of the Royal Society.

For increasingly larger bodies, terminal velocity increases and turbulent flow sets in, to be eventually the predominating part of frictional resistance. Under these conditions, both the resistance to laminar flow and the resistance to turbulent flow exist, so that, equating downward forces to upward forces of friction,

$$F = Kv + Tv^2 \qquad (7j)$$

This equation applies not only to falling bodies but to airplanes in the air and ships in the water. Their speed remains constant where the resistance is just equalized by the forward thrust of the propellers.

If a parachutist delays the opening of his chute long enough, he will attain a terminal velocity of from 130 to 150 mi/h. At such speeds wind resistance pushes upward with a total force equal to his weight, with the result that he is no longer accelerated.

7.7. Streamlining

By shaping a body to the streamlines of the fluid through which it is moving, the retarding force of friction may be greatly reduced. This is particularly effective at high speeds where the conditions of turbulent flow would otherwise predominate.

Referring to Fig. 7H(b) it may be seen that by adding a tail to an object, so that its cross-section has the form shown in Fig. 7J, the tendency to form eddy currents can be reduced and the body made to slip through the fluid with a minimum disturbance.

The experiment diagrammed in Fig. 7K shows that a long pointed tail and a rounded or pointed nose are both effective in cutting down resistance. The diagrams picture a small wind tunnel through which a stream of air is drawn by a fan F. Objects for which wind resistance is to be measured are suspended from a support connected at the center to a spring balance. Parts of a streamlined body are tested in the order shown in Fig. 7L. Their wind resistance changes in the order indicated. Note that it is greatest for the top figure and smallest for the bottom one.

The bodies of airplanes, torpedoes, and ships are streamlined to cut down resistance and hence permit higher speed with the same forward thrust of the propellers. Bombs are streamlined to enable them to acquire higher terminal velocities. Automobiles, if they are to travel at high speeds, should be streamlined to make more efficient use of gasoline.

Experiments with airplane and automobile models in wind tunnels show the importance of streamlining for speeds as low as 30 mi/h. The findings from such tests are confirmed by full-sized planes in the air and by cars on the speedway or open road.

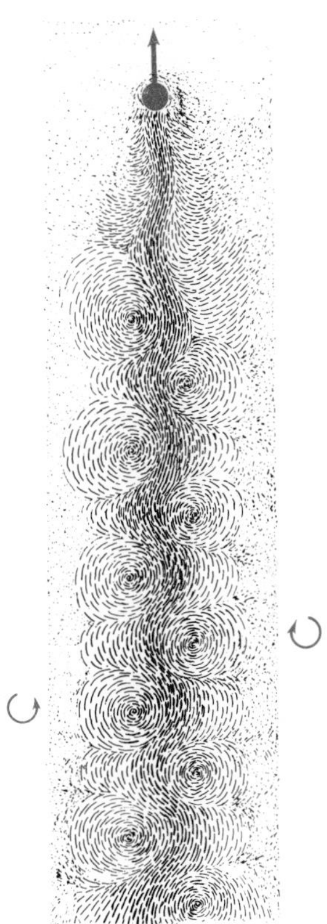

Fig. 7I. Eddies set up by pulling an obstacle through still water form a Kármán trail.

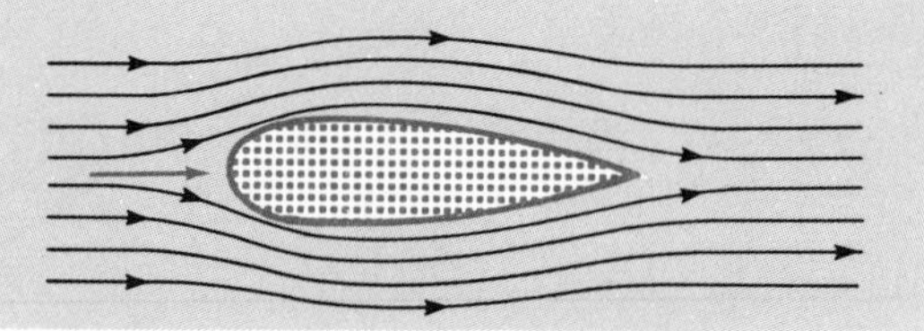

Fig. 7J. The flow of air or water around a properly shaped body may be smooth and steady.

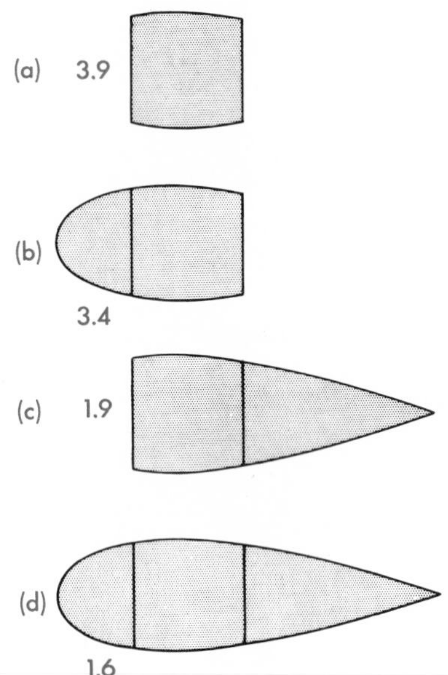

Fig. 7L. Test bodies for the wind tunnel shown in Fig. 7K.

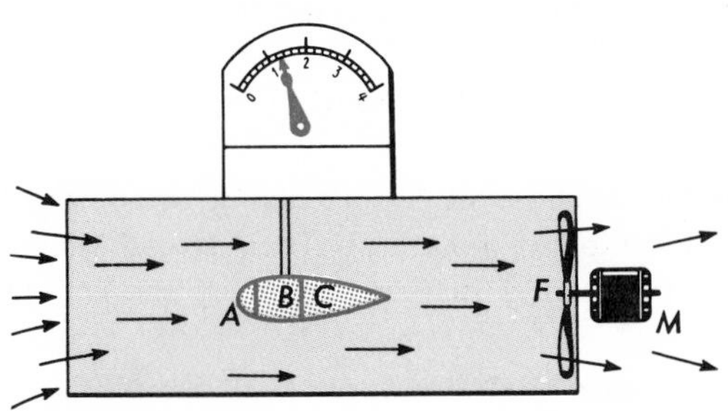

Fig. 7K. Diagram of a wind tunnel for testing the air friction of an airfoil or streamlined body.

7.8. *Airplanes*

The necessity for streamlining all outside structures of an airplane where high speeds must be maintained is quite clear. For land planes, *solid friction* is of importance only during takeoff. Once a plane is in the air, friction is almost entirely due to turbulent flow and is approximately proportional to the square of the velocity.

In Fig. 7M a streamlined plane is shown in a climb. If the plane rises with constant velocity, the conditions of equilibrium exist and all forces acting form a closed polygon. The external forces acting on an airplane may be reduced to three: *weight, thrust,* and *friction* (see Fig. 7N).

The weight F_g may be assumed to act vertically downward

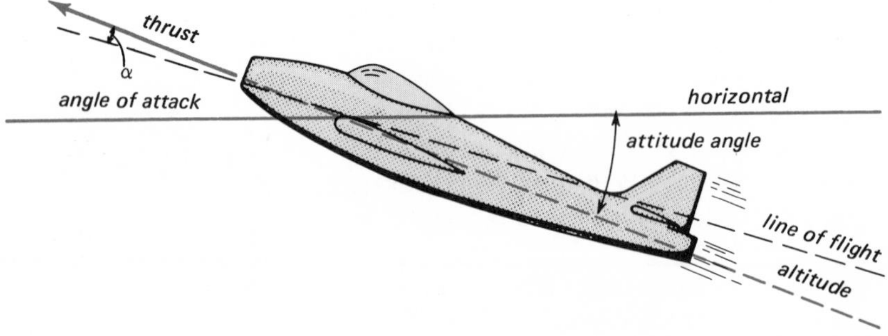

Fig. 7M. Diagram of a plane in a climb. Angle α represents the angle of attack.

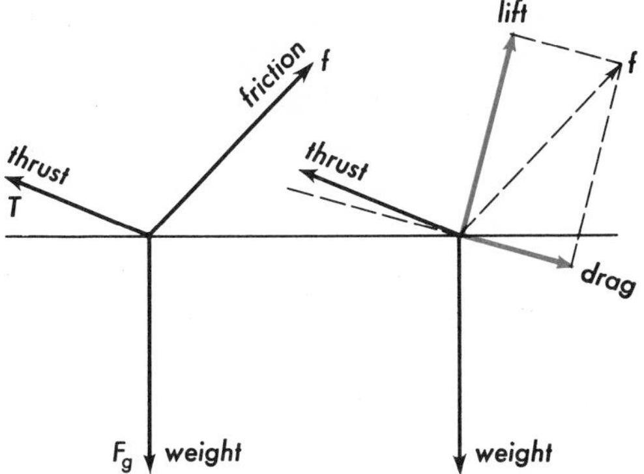

Fig. 7N. Force diagrams for an airplane, showing the origin of lift and drag.

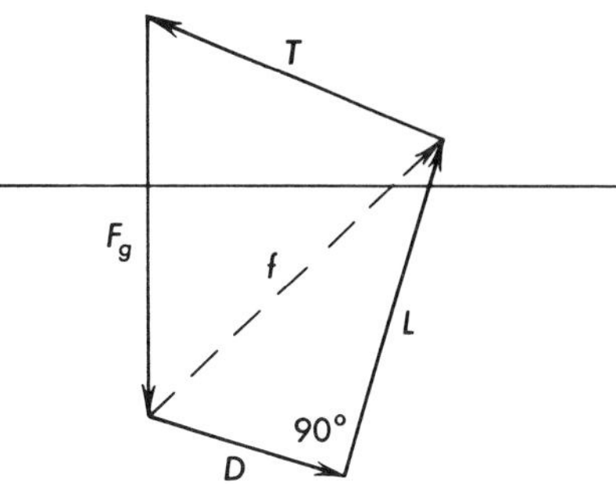

Fig. 7O. Force polygon for plane flying at constant velocity, in a climb, as shown in Fig. 7M.

through the center of gravity of the plane. The thrust T is the result of the push of the exhaust gases leaving the jet engine and acts in the direction of the plane axis. The frictional f is the resultant force of air friction on the plane and acts in a direction upward and back as shown in Fig. 7N. The angle between the plane's *attitude* and the horizontal is called the *angle of attack.* Note that the line of flight, the path along which the plane is flying, is not quite the same as the plane's attitude.

It is customary to resolve the frictional force into two components: one, a useful component perpendicular to the line of flight and called *lift,* and the other a detrimental component parallel to the line of flight called the *drag.* The conditions of equilibrium require that these combined forces form a closed polygon as shown in Fig. 7O. The latter polygon is often used to determine certain factors in the performance of a plane. For example, if the forward thrust and weight are known, and the line of flight determined, the force polygon may be used to find the lift L and the drag D.

When a plane is in level flight and has constant velocity, T and D are practically horizontal, equal in magnitude, and opposite in direction, while F_g and L are vertical, equal in magnitude, and opposite in direction. With the motor throttled down and the plane in a dive at constant velocity, equilibrium conditions exist again and the forces form a closed polygon.

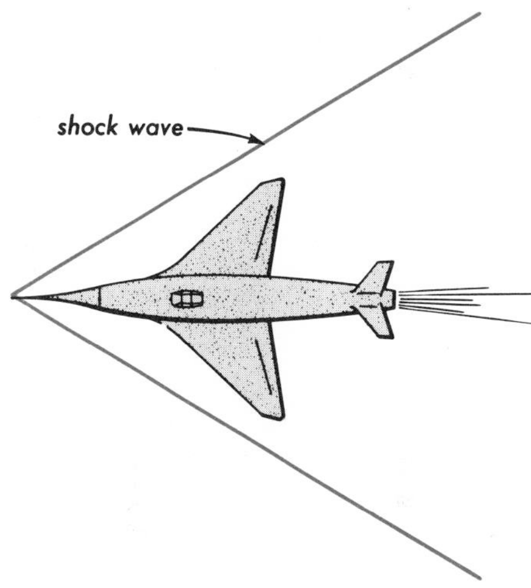

Fig. 7P. Shock wave produced by jet or rocket plane at supersonic velocity.

7.9. Supersonic Speeds

The rapid development of rockets and jet-propelled planes, all capable of acquiring and maintaining speeds greater than the speed of sound, has increased the importance of studying high-speed air flow around bodies of different size and shape. The flow of air around missiles moving with *supersonic speed,* that is, a speed greater than the speed of sound, is characterized by the existence in the air of discontinuities known as *shock waves.*

These sudden discontinuities, shown in Fig. 7P, are the result of sudden encounters of the air with an impenetrable body. At subsonic speeds the fluid seems to be forewarned and begins its outward flow in advance of the arrival of the leading edge. With supersonic speed, however, the fluid in front of the missile is undisturbed, while immediately behind the missile it is moving sideways. The sudden impulse at the nose creates a high-pressure region which, traveling outward with the speed of sound, creates the conical-shaped shock wave that changes the direction of air flow.

It is customary in supersonic studies to specify the speed of a body relative to the speed of sound. The ratio between these two speeds is called the *Mach number:*

$$\text{Mach number} = \frac{\text{speed of body}}{\text{speed of sound}} \tag{7k}$$

problems

1. An oak box is pulled across the oak floor of a mountain cabin. Find the magnitude of the horizontal force if the box weighs 135.0 Kg.

2. A boy removes his shoe and places it on a smooth board. If the angle of uniform slip is found to be 34°, find the coefficient of sliding friction.

3. The angle of uniform slip for a sheet metal box on a wooden chute is 28.6°. What is the value of the coefficient of sliding friction? [Ans. 0.545.]

4. A large metal box is placed on an oak plank, and one end of the metal plank raised until the box slides freely down. If the plank makes an angle of 26° with the horizontal, what is the value of the coefficient of sliding friction?

5. A metal chest with a mass of 75.0 Kg is pulled along the floor of a warehouse by a force of 350.0 N applied at an angle of 40° with the horizontal. Find (a) the horizontal, and (b) the vertical components of the force, (c) the resultant force exerted on the floor, and (d) the coefficient of sliding friction. Make a diagram.

6. A metal box with a mass of 50.0 Kg is placed on a wooden chute making an angle of 30° with the horizontal. If the coefficient of sliding friction is 0.250, find (a) the parallel component, and (b) the perpendicular component of the box's weight, and (c) its acceleration down the chute. Make a diagram. [Ans. (a) 245.0 N, (b) 424 N, (c) 2.780 m/s^2.]

7. A 70-Kg box falls from a truck going 90.0 Km/h along a straight and level highway. If the box slides for a distance of 80.0 m before coming to rest, find (a) the initial velociy in m/s, (b) the acceleration, (c) the force of friction, and (d) the coefficient of sliding friction.

8.* The angle of uniform slip for a 50.0-Kg box sliding down a wooden plank is 23°. (a) Find the coefficient of sliding friction. If the plank is tilted up to 35°, find

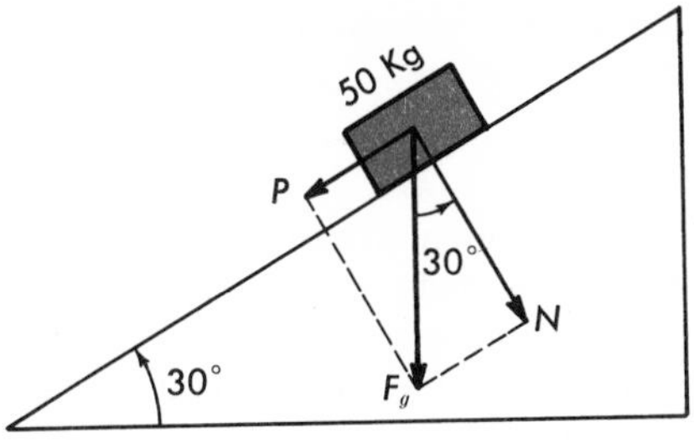

Prob. 6.

(b) the parallel component of the weight, (c) the normal component of the weight, (d) the retarding force of friction, (e) the resultant force down the chute, and (f) the acceleration of the box. Make a diagram.

9. A 65.0-Kg trunk is placed on an oak chute, inclined at an angle of 35° with the horizontal. Find (a) the weight of the trunk, (b) the parallel component of the force, (c) the normal component of the force, (d) the resultant force down the chute, and (e) the acceleration down the chute if the coefficient of sliding friction is 0.550. Make a diagram. [Ans. (a) 637 N, (b) 365.4 N, (c) 522 N, (d) 78.3 N, (e) 1.205 m/s².]

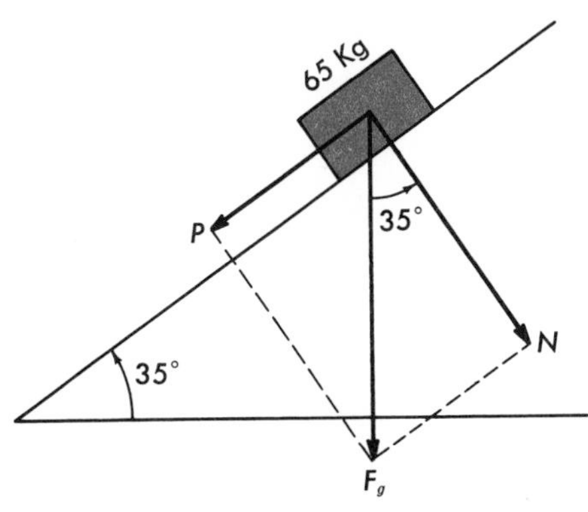

Prob. 9.

10. A constant horizontal force of 250.0 N is applied to slide a 50.0-Kg box along a warehouse floor. If the coefficient of sliding friction is 0.332, find (a) the force required to overcome friction, (b) the excess force, and (c) the accelerating force.

11.* A jet passenger plane with a net mass of 1.50×10^5 Kg maintains a constant velocity in a power climb from an airport. The attitude angle is 20°, the line of flight is 14°, and the combined thrust of the engines is 0.850×10^6 N. Find (a) the magnitude, (b) the direction of the frictional force, (c) the magnitude of the lift, and (d) the drag. Make a diagram.

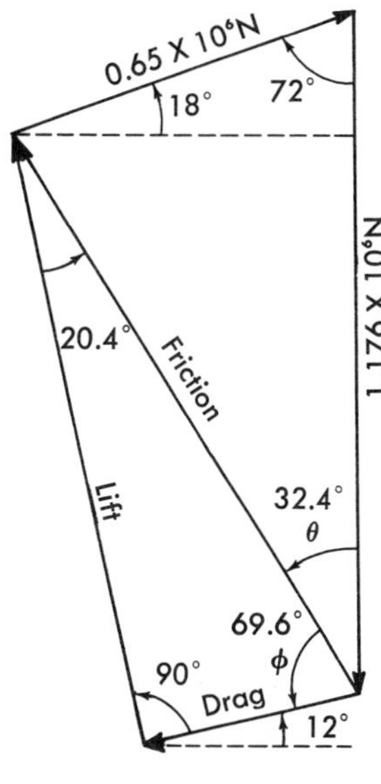

Prob. 12.

12.* A jet passenger plane with a mass of 1.20×10^5 Kg maintains a constant take-off velocity in a power climb as it leaves the airport. The attitude angle is 18°, the line of flight is 12°, and the combined forward thrust of the engines is 6.50×10^5 N. Find (a) the force of friction, and (b) its direction. Calculate (c) the lift, and (d) the drag. Make a diagram to scale. [Ans. (a) 1.155×10^6 N, (b) 32.4° with the vertical, (c) 1.082×10^6 N, (d) 0.404×10^6 N.]

13. A motor car with a mass of 1800 Kg is traveling along a straight and level highway with a speed of 25.0 m/s, when the clutch is depressed, permitting the car to coast to a stop. If the car comes to rest after traveling a distance of 340.0 m, find (a) the acceleration, (b) the force of friction, and (c) the coefficient of rolling friction.

14. A boy on a bicycle is pedaling along a straight and level road at 25.20 Km/h. When he stops pedaling he finds he can travel a distance of 210.0 m before stopping. Find (a) his velocity in m/s when he stops pedaling, (b) his acceleration while coasting, and (c) the coefficient of rolling friction.

Projectiles

When a shotput or javelin is hurled into the air at a track-and-field meet of a school, university, or the Olympic Games, the maximum distance it travels is of greatest importance to the performer. Neglecting air friction, which is relatively unimportant in these two track events, the objects follow a parabolic path. The horizontal distance reached is determined by the *magnitude* and the *direction* of the initial velocity. In this chapter we are concerned with the paths of projectiles.

8.1. Horizontal Projection

If one body falls freely from rest at the same time that another is projected horizontally from the same height, the two will strike the ground simultaneously. An experimental proof of this fundamental observation may be obtained by an experiment of the type diagrammed in Fig. 8A.

Two identical marbles, M and N, are supported by a rod and trough, respectively, in such a way that when the compressed spring S is released the rod R springs to the right, dropping M and projecting N horizontally. Marble M, falling with the acceleration g due to gravity, and marble N, traversing the longer path ABCDE, strike the ground at the same time. Repetition of the experiment with higher or lower projection velocities and from different heights always ends with the same result: both marbles hit the ground simultaneously.

The first conclusion that may be drawn from this experiment is that the downward acceleration of any projectile is the same as that of a freely falling body and takes place independently of its horizontal motion. Furthermore, an experimental measurement of *times* and *distances* shows that the horizontal velocity of projection continues unchanged and takes place independently of the vertical motion.

In other words, a projectile carries out two motions independently: (1) a constant horizontal velocity v; and (2) a vertically downward acceleration g. With an initial horizontal velocity v,

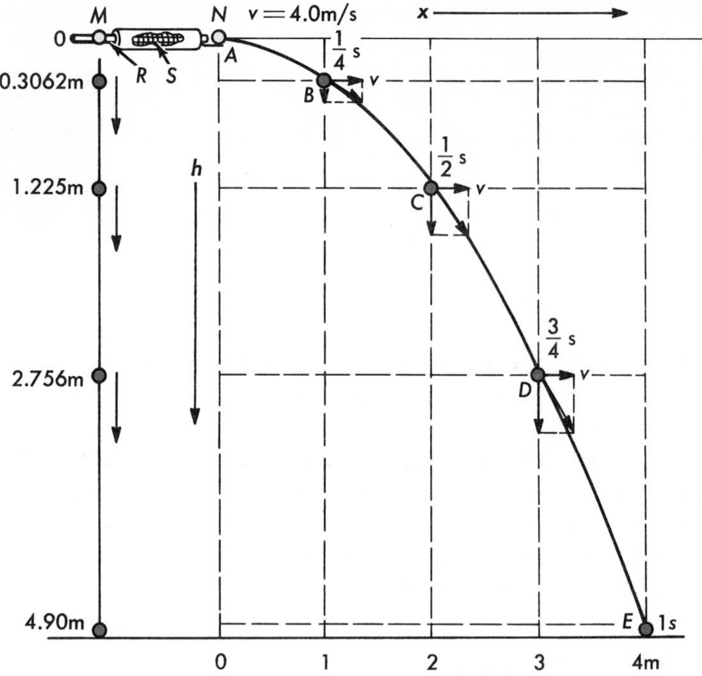

Fig. 8A. A body dropped from rest and another projected horizontally strike the ground at the same time.

the horizontal distance x traveled is proportional to the time t and is given by the equation

$$x = vt \tag{8a}$$

As the marble falls at the same time with an acceleration g, the vertical distance h is proportional to the square of the time and is given by

$$h = \tfrac{1}{2}gt^2 \tag{8b}$$

where g is given by Eq.(3e).

An experimental verification of these two equations is illustrated by the numerical values given in the diagram. With an initial velocity of 4.0 m/s, marble N falls a distance of 0.3062 m in $\frac{1}{4}$ s and at the same time travels a horizontal distance of 1.0 m. In $\frac{1}{2}$ s it falls 1.225 m, which is four times as far, and travels horizontally

2.0 m; in $\frac{3}{4}$ s it falls 2.756 m, or nine times as far, and travels horizontally 3.0 m, etc. Since the motion obeys both formulas at the same time, the path traversed is a *parabola.*

As a proof the path is parabolic, Eq.(8a) is first solved for t, then both sides of the equation squared to obtain

$$t^2 = \frac{x^2}{v^2}$$

If we substitute x^2/v^2 for t^2 in Eq.(8b), we obtain

$$h = \frac{1}{2} g \frac{x^2}{v^2}$$

which can be written

$$h = \left(\frac{g}{2v^2}\right) x^2 \tag{8c}$$

For any specified value of the initial velocity v, the terms in parentheses are all constants, and we may write

$$h = kx^2$$

which is the equation of a parabola.

Figure 8A is a graph of this equation, in which $g = 9.80$ m/s^2, and $v = 4.0$ m/s. For example, for $x = 4.0$ m, substitution in Eq.(8c) gives $h = 4.90$ m.

For the purposes of solving problems, the motions of projectiles are usually determined by calculating the horizontal and vertical motions separately and combining the results by vector addition. In all cases considered in this section, where the initial projection is horizontal and the *initial vertical velocity* is zero, we can apply the special Eqs.(3j), (3k), (3ℓ), and (3m).

Example 1. An arrow is shot horizontally with a velocity of 20.0 m/s from the top of a tower 60.0 m high. (a) How long will it take to reach the ground, and (b) with what velocity will it strike?

Solution. The time required to reach the ground is the time of free fall given by Eq.(3m) or Eq.(8b). By solving for t, and substituting the known quantities $h = 60.0$ m, $v = 20.0$ m/s, and $g = 9.80$ m/s^2, we obtain

$$t = \sqrt{\frac{2h}{g}} = \sqrt{\frac{2 \times 60 \text{ m}}{9.80 \text{ m/s}^2}}$$

$$t = \sqrt{12.24 \text{ s}^2} = 3.499 \text{ s}$$

Arriving at the ground the stone will have a horizontal velocity $v_x = 20.0$ m/s, and a vertical velocity given by Eq.(3j):

$$v_y = gt \tag{8d}$$

By direct substitution, we obtain

$$v_y = 9.80 \text{ m/s}^2 \times 3.499 \text{ s} = 34.29 \text{ m/s}$$

Combining these two velocities vectorially as shown in Fig. 8B, we find

$$v = \sqrt{v_x^2 + v_y^2} = \sqrt{(20)^2 + (34.29)^2}$$

$$v = \sqrt{1576 \text{ m}^2/\text{s}^2} = 39.70 \text{ m/s}$$

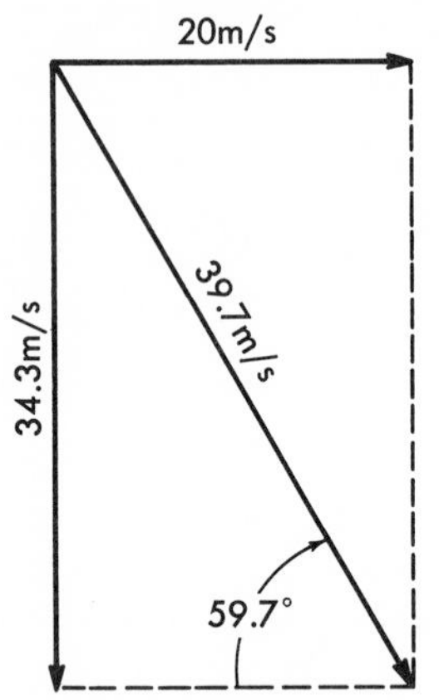

Fig. 8B. Combined velocity components of a projectile, Example 1.

The angle θ is seen from the right triangle to be given by

$$\tan \theta = \frac{34.29}{20.0} = 1.715$$

$$\theta = 59.8°$$

Another illustration of horizontal projection is to be found in the dropping of mailbags, or other loads by a low-flying plane in level flight (see Fig. 8C). Sweeping down in a dive from a greater height, a plane may level off at a low elevation and, sighting on a

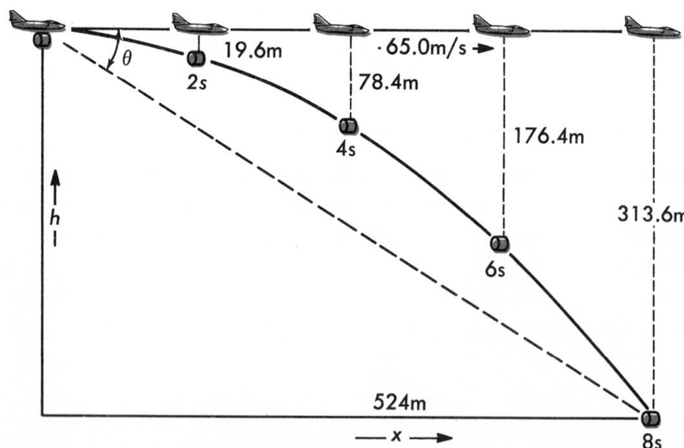

Fig. 8C. For the first few seconds after release, a falling body remains directly beneath the plane. Later, wind resistance causes it to lag behind.

target, release a mailbag when the proper angle θ is reached. As the bag falls with increasing speed, its horizontal velocity remains constant and equal to the velocity of the plane.

If air friction is neglected, the mailbag should stay directly beneath the plane at all points along its path. To find the angle θ at which the bag should be released, two factors must be taken into account: (1) the speed of the plane, and (2) the height above the target. From the height h, the time of fall can be calculated, and from the time of fall the horizontal distance can be computed.

If x represents the horizontal distance traveled and h the vertical height, the right triangle in Fig. 8C gives

$$\tan \theta = h/x \tag{8e}$$

where x and h are given in Eqs.(8a) and (8b).

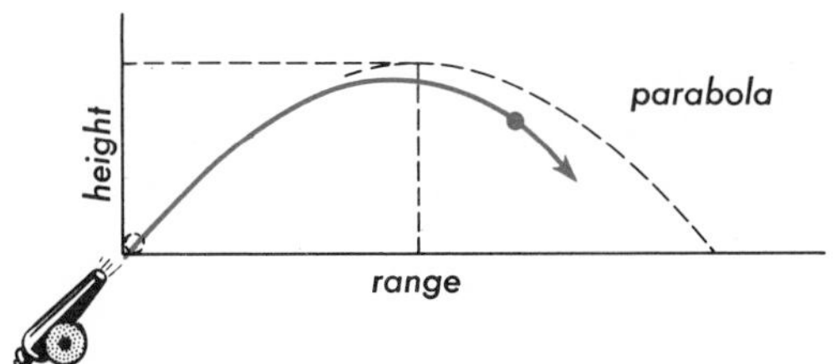

Fig. 8D. Projectiles tend to follow a parabolic path. Because of air friction, they fall short.

8.2. Projectiles

Many missiles when projected into the air follow a parabolic path. Such is the case only for low speeds where the retarding force of air friction is negligible. For high-speed projectiles the air continually slows the motion down and the path departs from a parabola as indicated in Fig. 8D. The higher the velocity, the greater is the force of air friction and the greater is the departure from a parabolic path.

In general, it is convenient to neglect air friction, calculate the theoretical path of a projectile, and then if necessary make corrections for air friction. As a rule, the known factors concerning a given projectile are v, the initial velocity of projection, and θ, the angle of departure. The latter is always measured from the horizontal, and in the case of bullets and shells is the *elevation angle* of the gun. The factors to be calculated are (1) the *time of flight,* (2) the *maximum height* reached, and (3) the *range* attained.

The time of flight of a projectile will here be defined as the time required for it to return to the same level from which it was fired. The maximum height, called the summit, is defined as the greatest vertical distance reached, as measured from the horizontal projection plane, while the range is the horizontal distance from the point of projection to the point where the projectile returns again to the projection plane.

8.3. Calculation of Trajectories

To calculate the height and range of a projectile, the initial velocity of projection is resolved into two components, one vertical and the other horizontal. This is illustrated in Fig. 8E. Calling v the velocity of projection and θ the elevation angle, the x and v components of velocity are given by the following trigonometric functions:

$$\sin\theta = \frac{v_y}{v} \qquad \text{and} \qquad \cos\theta = \frac{v_x}{v}$$

Solving for v_y and v_x, we obtain

$$v_y = v\sin\theta \tag{8f}$$

$$v_x = v\cos\theta \tag{8g}$$

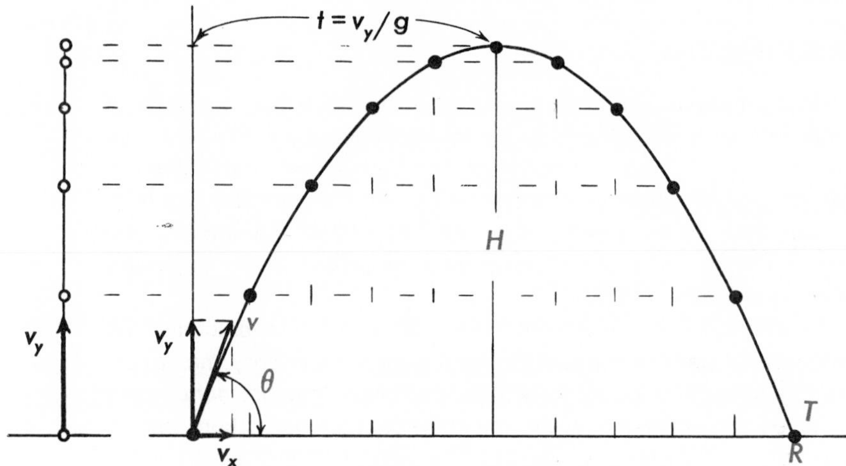

Fig. 8E. The path of a projectile showing H, the maximum height reached; T, the time of flight; and R, the range.

The traversal of the actual trajectory is a combination of two motions, one the motion of a particle projected vertically upward with an initial velocity v_y, the other a horizontal velocity v_x that remains constant. In other words, a particle projected vertically upward with a velocity of v_y will rise to the same height and in the same time as another projected at an angle θ with a velocity v.

Since the time required to reach the highest point is equal to the time required to fall the same distance, the formula for free fall may be employed. The formula for an object falling from rest is Eq.(8d):

$$v_y = gt$$

By solving for t, and substituting from Eq.(8f), we find

$$t = \frac{v_y}{g} = \frac{v \sin \theta}{g}$$

Because t is the time to rise, or the time to fall, the total time of flight will be $2t$. Therefore, the time of flight T is

$$T = \frac{2v \sin \theta}{g} \tag{8h}$$

time of flight

To find the height H, Eq.(3ℓ) is used. The letter h is replaced by H, and the letter v_2 by v_y:

$$(v_y)^2 = 2gH$$

Solving this equation for H, we obtain

$$H = \frac{(v_y)^2}{2g}$$

Using Eq.(8f) substitute $v \sin \theta$ for v_y, and we have

$$H = \frac{(v \sin \theta)^2}{2g} \tag{8i}$$

maximum height

To find the range R, the equation for constant velocity, $x = vt$, is used. Replacing the letter x by R, v by $v \cos \theta$, and t by the total time of flight, $T = 2v \sin \theta/g$, we obtain

$$R = v \cos \theta \times \frac{2v \sin \theta}{g}$$

or

$$R = \frac{2v^2 \sin \theta \cos \theta}{g}$$

To put this formula into another form, use is made of the trigonometric relation that $2 \sin \theta \cos \theta = \sin 2\theta$. Substitution gives

$$R = \frac{v^2}{g} \sin 2\theta \tag{8j}$$

range

In this form it is seen at once that, for a given velocity v, the range is a maximum when the sin 2θ is a maximum. Since the sine has its maximum value of unity for an angle of 90°, the angle θ above will be 45°. Furthermore, the range for any angle any number of degrees greater than 45° will be equal to the range for an equal number of degrees less than 45°. This is illustrated in Fig. 8F, for example, by the equal ranges of 31.89 m for the 15° and 75° projections, and the equal ranges of 55.2 m for the 30° and 60° projections.

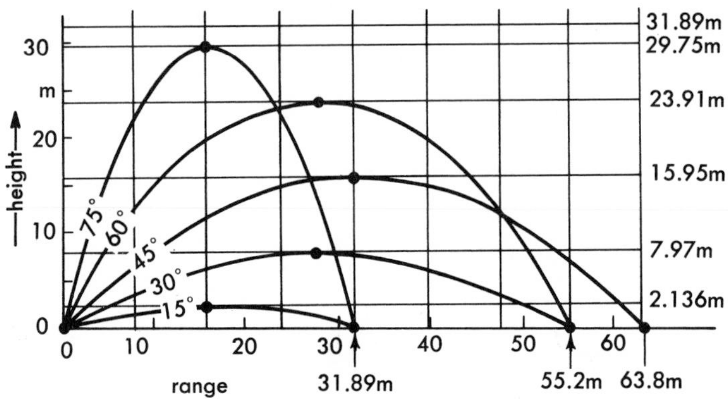

Fig. 8F. Diagram illustrating the shape of the trajectories of objects projected at different elevation angles. The vertical and horizontal scales are for the special case where the velocity of projection is 25.0 m/s.

Example 2. A baseball is thrown with a velocity of 25.0 m/s at an elevation angle of 65°. Calculate (a) the time of flight, (b) the maximum height reached, and (c) the range.

Solution. The given quantities are $v = 25.0$ m/s, $\theta = 65°$, and $g = 9.80$ m/s^2. To find the time of flight, direct substitution of these quantities in Eq.(8h) gives

$$T = \frac{2v \sin \theta}{g} = \frac{2 \times 25 \times 0.9063}{9.80} = 4.62 \text{ s}$$

(b) To find the maximum height substitute known quantities in

Eq.(8i):

$$H = \frac{(v \sin \theta)^2}{2g} = \frac{(25 \times 0.9063)^2}{2 \times 9.80} = 26.17 \text{ m}$$

(c) To find the range, direct substitution in Eq.(8j) gives

$$R = \frac{v^2}{g} \sin 2\theta = \frac{(25)^2}{9.80} 0.7660 = 48.9 \text{ m}$$

Observe where this trajectory would be on Fig. 8F.

8.4. Monkey and Hunter Experiment

A hunter aims and shoots an arrow at a monkey in a tree. At the instant the arrow leaves the bow, the monkey drops from the branch upon which he has been sitting. The two should meet in mid-air regardless of the speed of the arrow.

If gravity could be eliminated, the arrow, as shown in Fig. 8G, would travel the straight-line path AM, and the monkey would stay at M and be hit there. With gravity acting, however, the arrow travels the path ABC and the monkey drops from M to C. During each fraction of a second, indicated by $t = 1$, 2, 3, and 4, both

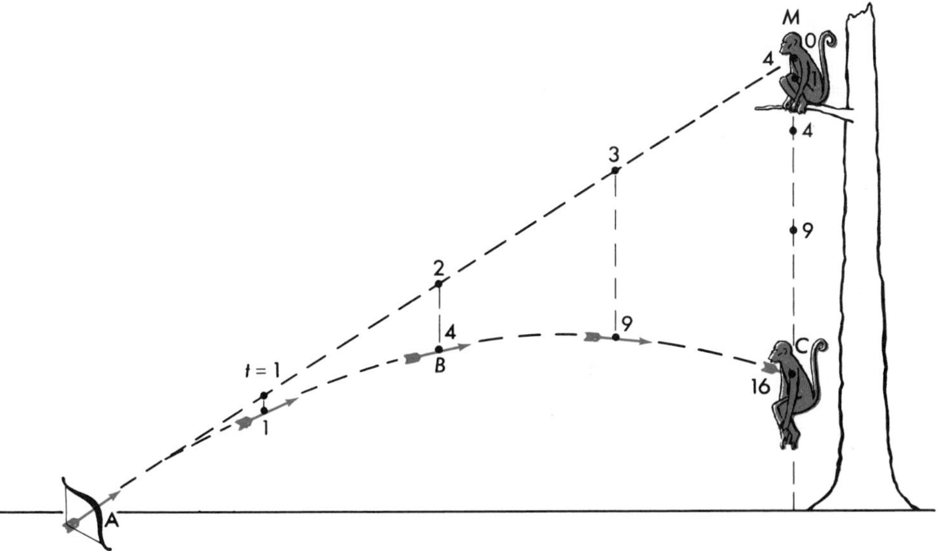

Fig. 8G. Diagram illustrating the monkey and hunter experiment.

fall the same distance from their gravity-free positions and collide at C. The greater the speed of the missile, the shorter will be the distance MC.*

8.5. Rocket Flight into Space

The first American man to be launched into space by a rocket was carried aloft in a Mercury capsule boosted by a Redstone rocket from Cape Canaveral, Florida, on May 5, 1961. The astronaut, Alan Shepard, who piloted the pressurized space capsule in which he was jettisoned, followed a path similar to that shown in Fig. 8H.

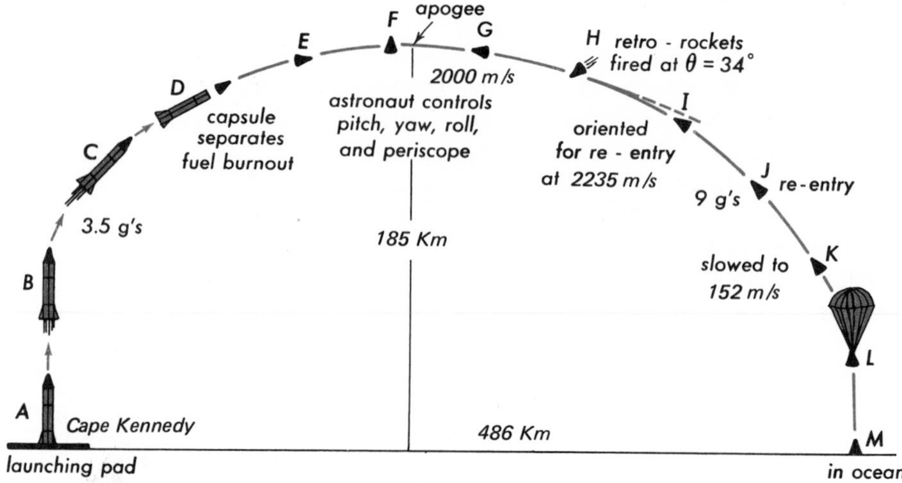

Fig. 8H. Diagram of the flight path taken by the first American astronaut to be launched into space, May 5, 1961.

Although the details of this history-making event will not be given here,† an analysis of some of the forces, velocities, and accelerations to which the rocket and astronaut were subjected at several points of the flight will be presented. The following cases are typical of space flight in general, and the equations

* This experiment may be performed by blowing a small wooden marble through a tube (about a foot long). A toy monkey is released at M by a small electromagnet. Two fine copper wires completing the electric circuit are crossed just in front of the tube at A. When the projectile passes this point the circuit is broken, releasing M. The mass M should have a small piece of iron at the top for the magnetic attraction.

† For details of Alan Shepard's space flight, see *Life Magazine,* May 12 and 19, 1961.

can be applied equally well to orbiting satellites and to flights to the moon and planets.

Since the value of g in Shepard's flight diminished by less than 5% at an altitude of 185 Km, and its direction changed by less than 5° over the 486 Km range, it will be assumed that g remains constant over the entire flight path.

Case A. Before Vertical Launch. When the entire rocket assembly is at rest on the launching pad, just prior to takeoff, all velocities and accelerations are zero, and all forces are in equilibrium (see Fig. 8I). At this time there are two equal forces acting on the rocket, F_g, the downward pull of the earth, and P, the upward push of the launching pad. The downward force is given by

$$F_g = Mg \tag{8k}$$

where M is the total mass of the rocket and its payload.

Assuming the upward direction as positive, g the acceleration due to gravity is negative, and so is F_g. Since the upward force P on the total mass M must be equal to F_g in magnitude,

$$P = -Mg \tag{8ℓ}$$

Note that if a specific value of M is inserted, and the value of g with its negative value, P will be positive.

In a similar way the two equal but opposite forces acting on the astronaut are f_g, the downward pull of the earth, and p, the upward thrust of his supporting cradle. These forces are given by

$$f_g = mg \tag{8m}$$

$$p = -mg \tag{8n}$$

showing that for each kilogram mass of the rocket structure, or its contents, the force p is equal to 9.8 N. Under these conditions the force is said to be "1 g."

Case B. Vertical Climb. When the rocket is accelerating vertically upward after launching (see Fig. 8J), the two forces acting on the total mass M are P, the upward thrust of the rocket engines, and F_g, the downward pull of the earth. The force F giving rise to the upward acceleration a is the vector resultant of these two forces

$$\vec{P} + \vec{F_g} = \vec{F}$$

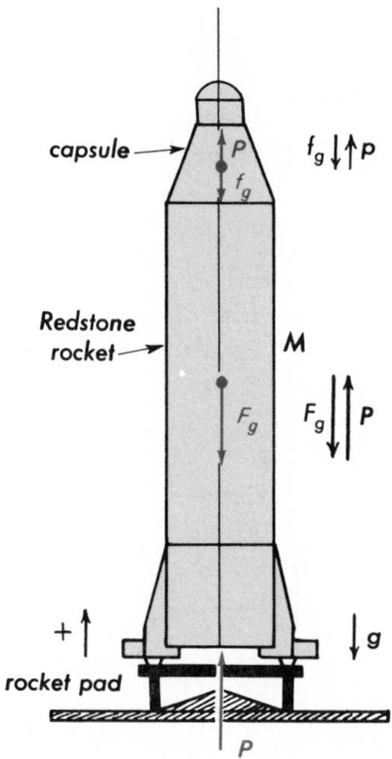

Fig. 8I. Diagram of a rocket and its manned space capsule at rest on its launching pad and ready for vertical takeoff.

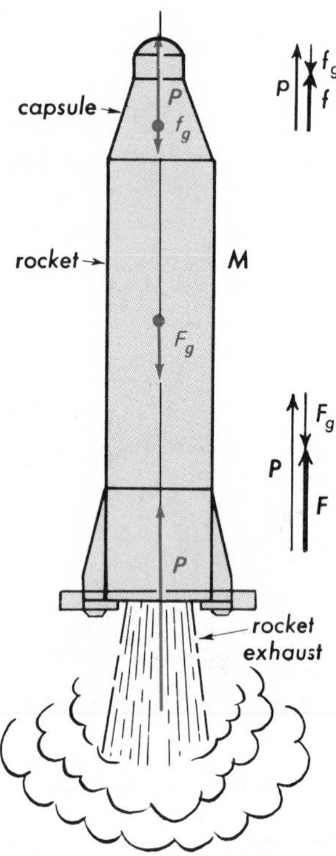

Fig. 8J. Force diagram for a rocket and its astronaut pilot during vertical flight under rocket thrust.

where

$$F_g = Mg$$

To lift the rocket from the ground, P must be greater than F_g, and their vector resultant F will be the force that produces the upward acceleration:

$$F = Ma$$

Applying these same principles to the astronaut in the capsule shown at the top in Fig. 8J, we observe that

$$\overrightarrow{p} + \overrightarrow{f_g} = \overrightarrow{f} \tag{8o}$$

where p is the thrust of the cradle on the astronaut's body and f_g is the downward pull of the earth on the same mass. The resultant f is the force that gives the astronaut the same upward acceleration as the rocket:

$$f = ma \tag{8p}$$

Example 3. A huge rocket with an 80.0-Kg astronaut aboard is climbing vertically upward with an acceleration of 45.0 m/s². Find the total force of the cradle on the man's body, (a) in g's and (b) in newtons.

Solution. (a) With an upward acceleration of 45 m/s², we divide by $g = -9.80$ m/s², and obtain

$$\frac{+45 \text{ m/s}^2}{-9.80 \text{ m/s}^2} = -4.59$$

This means that the upward acceleration of the rocket and astronaut can be written

$$a = -4.59\ g$$

where g is -9.80 m/s².

To find the upward force on the astronaut, we use Eq.(8o). Solving for p, we obtain

$$\overrightarrow{p} = \overrightarrow{f} - \overrightarrow{f_g}$$

and substituting Eq.(8p) and Eq.(8m), we get

$$p = ma - mg$$

$$p = m(a - g)$$

$$p = m(-4.59\ g - g) = -m(5.59\ g) \qquad (8q)$$

The astronaut is said to be taking 5.59 g's, or 5.59 times his normal weight.

(b) To find the upward force on his body, we insert his mass in Eq.(8q), and obtain

$$p = -80\ \text{Kg} \times 5.59\ (-9.80\ \text{m/s}^2)$$

$$p = 4383\ \text{N}$$

This is 5.59 times the astronaut's weight.

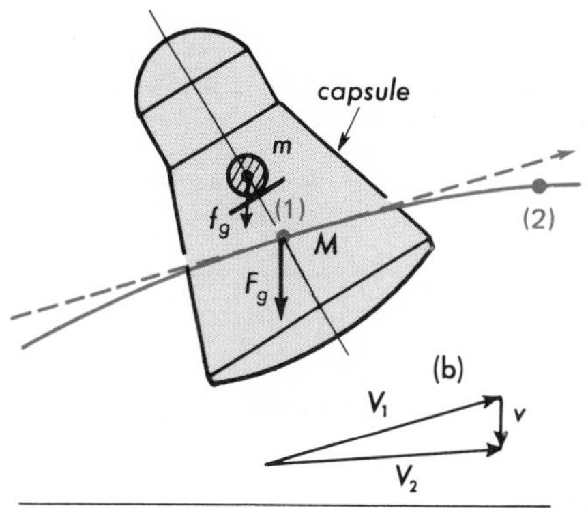

Fig. 8K. Diagram of a free jettisoned space capsule as it travels without rocket thrust along its flight path.

Case C. Free Jettisoned Space Capsule. After the space capsule carrying the astronaut has been jettisoned from the rocket, as shown at D in Fig. 8H, the vehicle becomes a free projectile. From point D to point H, where the retrorockets are fired, the downward pull of the earth F_g is the only force acting on the body. This force gives rise to a downward acceleration g and is responsible for the continually changing direction of the capsule as it travels along its flight path.

In the velocity diagram, Fig. 8K(b), V_1 represents the instantaneous velocity of the capsule as it passes point (1); v is the change in velocity imparted by F_g during the time it takes to reach point (2); and V_2 is the instantaneous velocity as it passes point (2):

$$v = gt$$

Since there is no thrust P from rocket motors for this part of the flight, the cradle exerts no force on the astronaut, and he exerts no force on the cradle. While the capsule, the astronaut, and the cradle fall with the same acceleration g, the concept of weightlessness prevails throughout the moving system.

When the velocity of the capsule is great enough (about 7,791.4 m/s), it will orbit the earth as a satellite. In orbital flight the retrorockets are necessary to deflect and slow the capsule to begin its return to earth. In this particular flight of Shepard's, however, the retrorockets were used only as a test of this manned capability.

TABLE 8A
Flight Data for a U.S. 3-Stage Rocket Leaving Cape Kennedy to Circle the Earth, Prior to Take-Off for the Moon (1971)

	Stage Propellants	*Fuel Mass* (Kg)	*Average Thrust* (N)	*Time* (s)	*Altitude*[1] (m)	*Attitude*[2] (Deg.)	*Velocity*[3] (m/s)	*Total Mass*[4] (Kg)
1st	LOX	1.500×10^6	3.4223×10^7	Ign. (0)	60	0	408.64	2,913,814
	RP-1	0.653×10^6		Cutoff (165)	66,846	−68.07	2,724.4	836,233
2nd	LOX	3.793×10^5	4.7557×10^6	Ign. (166)	68,130	−68.05	2,732.6	666,311
	LH_2	0.725×10^6		Cutoff (557)	187,450	−96.95	6,968.1	211,517
3rd	LOX	8.688×10^5	8.8686×10^5	Ign. (558)	187,544	−96.95	6,971.7	166,433
	LH_2	1.973×10^5		Cutoff (703)	191,350	−113.25	7,791.4	136,343

Notes: [1]Altitude of the c.g. (center of gravity) of the mass.
[2]Attitude with respect to the launch point, not local vertical.
[3]Velocity referenced to a fixed spacial point, not a point on the earth.
[4]Cutoff masses include spent booster.

problems

1. A small plane flying food to a snow-bound herd of cattle comes down to a 100.0 m elevation where, traveling at 110.0 Km/h in straight and level flight, the pilot releases a bail of hay. Find (a) the time to hit the ground, (b) the horizontal distance traveled, (c) the vertical velocity acquired, and (d) the velocity of impact.

2. A girl standing on a bridge 100.0 m above the water throws a stone horizontally outward with a velocity of 12.0 m/s. Find (a) the time it takes to hit the water, (b) the distance away from the bridge when it hits the water, (c) the vertical velocity acquired, and (d) the velocity of impact. Make a scale diagram.

3. A fire hose 18.0 m above the ground shoots a horizontal stream of water with a speed of 18.0 m/s. Find (a) the time for the water to hit the ground, (b) the horizontal distance traveled, (c) the vertical velocity, and (d) the velocity of impact. [Ans. (a) 1.917 s, (b) 34.51 m, (c) 18.79 m/s, (d) 26.01 m/s at 43.8° with vertical.]

4. A dart is shot into the air with a velocity of 60.0 m/s at an elevation angle of 35°. Find (a) the time of flight, (b) the height reached, and (c) the range.

5. A stone is thrown by a sling with a velocity of 55.0 m/s at an elevation angle of 50°. Neglecting air friction, what is (a) its time of flight, (b) its range, and (c) its maximum height?

6. An arrow is shot into the air with a velocity of 46.0 m/s at an elevation angle of 70°. Find (a) its time of flight, (b) its maximum height reached, and (c) its range. Make a diagram. [Ans. (a) 8.63 s, (b) 91.2 m, (c) 132.8 m.]

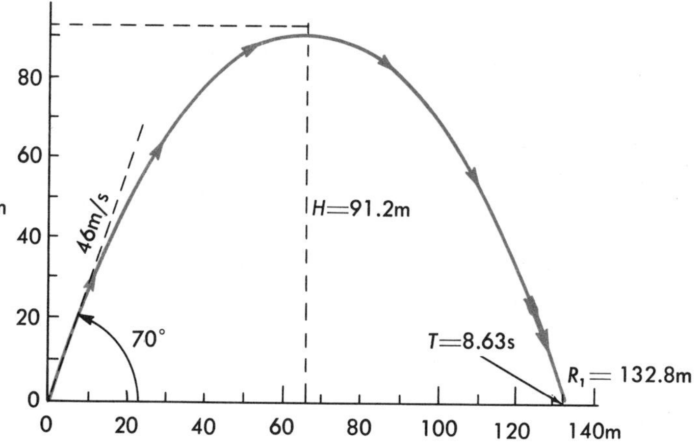

Prob. 6.

7. The Olympic record with the 16-lb shot put was set by Randy Matson of the United States in the 1968 Olympic Games, with a toss of 20.54 m. Photographs show the initial angle of projection was 45°. Assuming the start and finish of the shot put were at the same level, find (a) the velocity of projection, (b) the maximum height reached, and (c) the time of flight.

8. The Olympic record for the javelin throw was made by Janis Lusis of the USSR in 1968, with a toss of 90.10 m. Photographs show the projection angle to be 45°. Assuming the end points of the trajectory are at the same level, find (a) the projection velocity, (b) the maximum height reached, and (c) the time of flight.

9. An arrow is shot into the air with a speed of 50.0 m/s. If it reaches a maximum height of 120.0 m, (a) at what angle was it projected? (b) What is its time of flight, and (c) what is its range? (d) Make a diagram. [Ans. (a) 75.9°, (b) 9.90 s, (c) 120.4 m, (d) See diagram.]

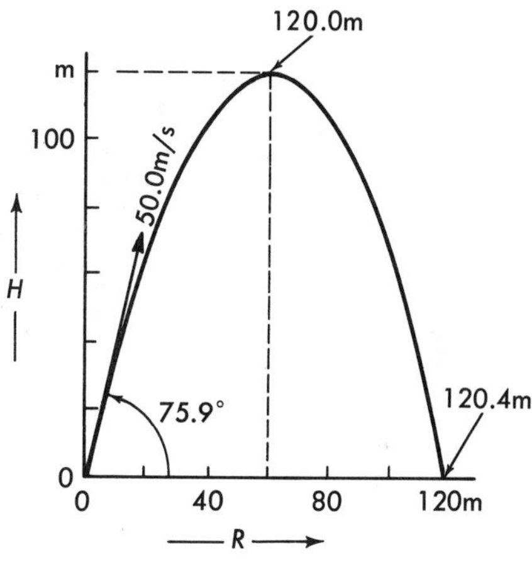

Prob. 9.

10. A boy shoots a stone from a sling-shot with a speed of 50.0 m/s. If the maximum height reached is 56.0 m, (a) what is the elevation angle? Find (b) the time of flight, and (c) the range.

11. An arrow is shot into the air at an elevation angle of 30°. If its projection velocity is 45.0 m/s, find (a) the vertical component of its initial velocity, and (b) its horizontal component. After 2.0 s have elapsed, find (c) the height of the arrow, (d) the horizontal distance traveled, (e) its vertical component of velocity, and (f) its horizontal component. Find (g) the maximum height reached, and (h) its range.

12. An arrow is shot into the air with a velocity of 50.0 m/s at an elevation angle of 75°. Find (a) its time of flight, (b) its maximum height, and (c) its range. At the end of 2.0 s find (d) its horizontal distance from the starting point, and (e) its vertical distance. At the end of 7.0 s find (f) its vertical velocity, (g) its horizontal velocity, and (h) its direction. Make a diagram. [Ans. (a) 9.86 s, (b) 119.0 m, (c) 127.6 m, (d) 25.88 m, (e)

77.0 m, (f) −20.3 m/s, (g) 12.94 m/s, (h) 57.5° down from the horizontal.]

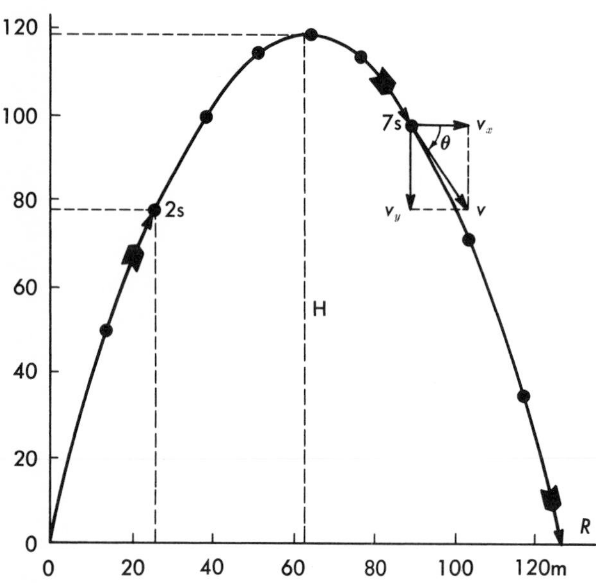

13.* A 3.0 × 10⁶-Kg Saturn rocket takes off from the ground with 3 astronauts aboard. Under full thrust of its rocket motors of 3.0 × 10^7 N, the fuel is burned rapidly and the rocket loses considerable weight as it rises. At an altitude of 16 Km the rocket's mass has dropped to 1.50 × 10^6 Kg. Find (a) the rocket's weight, (b) its acceleration in m/s, and (c) the force on the astronauts' bodies in *g*'s.

14.* When a Saturn rocket starts up from its launching pad, its thrust of 3.30 × 10^7 N is slightly greater than the rocket's weight of 3.0 × 10^7 N. Burning fuel at a high, constant rate the weight drops rapidly and reaches half value at a given height. At this point what will be (a) the rocket's acceleration, and (b) the force on the astronauts in *g*'s?

15. A 3.300 × 10^6-Kg Saturn rocket lifts off its launching pad with a thrust of 3.40 × 10^7 N. Find (a) that part of the upward force that accelerates the rocket, and (b) the acceleration. [Ans. (a) 1.660 × 10^6 N, (b) 0.503 m/s^2.]

16. A 3-stage rocket with a liftoff mass of 2.914 × 10^6 Kg takes off from Cape Kennedy. If the total thrust of the first stage Saturn rocket, with its five engines, is 3.430 × 10^7 N, find (a) the initial lift-off acceleration in m/s, and (b) the acceleration in *g*'s near burnout when the total mass has decreased to 8.362 × 10^5 Kg. Assume vertical rise and $g = 9.80$ m/s^2 throughout the first stage flight.

17. A 3-stage rocket with a lift-off mass of 2.920 × 10^6 Kg takes off from Cape Kennedy. The total thrust of the first stage with its five engines is 3.430 × 10^7 N. Find the initial vertical lift-off acceleration (a) in m/s^2, and (b) in *g*'s. Also find (c) the resultant force, and (d) the acceleration in m/s^2 just prior to burnout when the total mass has decreased to 8.38 × 10^5 Kg. Assume at burnout the attitude is 67.25° with respect to the local vertical, and the acceleration due to the earth's gravitational field is 9.70 m/s^2.

18. The third stage of a rocket going into orbit around the earth has an average thrust of 8.868 × 10^5 N. The mass of the rocket is 1.664 × 10^5 Kg at ignition, and 1.363 × 10^5 Kg at burnout. Assuming the rocket's attitude is parallel to the earth's surface throughout the flight, find (a) the acceleration just after ignition, and (b) just prior to burnout. [Ans. (a) 5.33 m/s^2, (b) 6.51 m/s^2.]

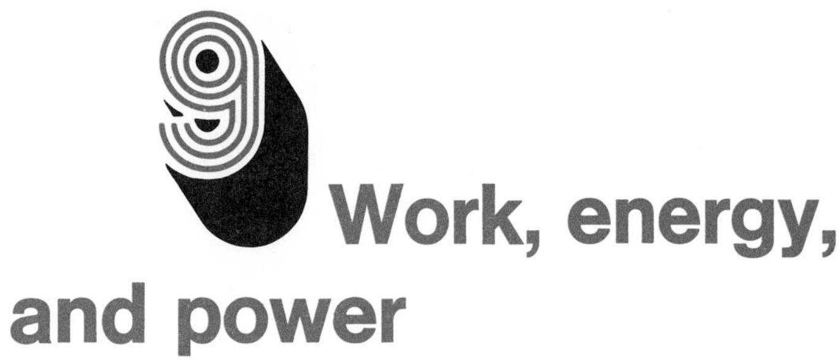

9 Work, energy, and power

It is well known that there are many forms of energy: heat, sound, light, mechanical, nuclear, chemical, electrical, etc. Each form plays an important role in our every day life. In this chapter we are concerned with mechanical energy, work, and power, and in particular with kinetic energy and potential energy.

There is little doubt that the most important concept in all nature is energy. It is important because it represents a fundamental entity common to all forms of matter in all parts of the known physical world. Closely associated with energy is another concept, *work,* a term used in civil life to describe the expenditure of one's stored-up bodily energy. Because energy is most easily described in terms of work, this latter concept will first be treated in detail.

9.1. Work

In its simplest mechanical form, *work* is defined as *the force times the distance* through which the force acts:

$$\text{work} = \text{force} \times \text{distance}$$

If the direction of the force and the distance moved are both vertically upward, we write

$$W = F \times h \tag{9a}$$

and if the directions are both horizontal, it is customary to write

$$W = F \times x \tag{9b}$$

Consider the general problem of calculating the work done in

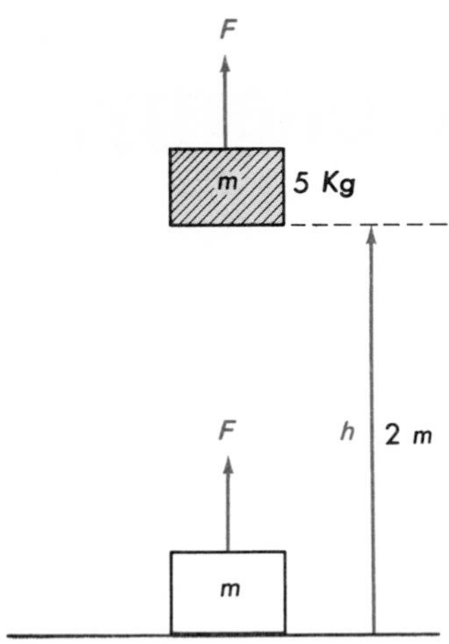

Fig. 9A. Work is defined as force × distance.

lifting a mass m to a height h above the ground (see Fig. 9A). By Newton's second law of motion ($F = ma$), the force required to lift any mass m is equal to its own weight:

$$F_g = mg$$

If we substitute the weight mg for F in Eq.(9a), we obtain

$$W = mg \times h \qquad (9c)$$

Example 1. Find the work done in lifting a 5.0-Kg mass to a height of 3.0 m.

Solution. The known quantities are $m = 5.0$ Kg, $h = 3.0$ m, and $g = 9.80$ m/s^2. By direct substitution of these quantities in Eq.(9c), we obtain

$$W = mgh = 5 \text{ Kg} \times 9.80 \text{ m/s}_2 \times 3 \text{ m}$$

$$W = 147.0 \text{ Kg m}^2/\text{s}^2$$

Since force in newtons has the units of Kg m^2/s^2, the answer can also be written

$$W = 147.0 \text{ newton meters}$$

$$W = 147.0 \text{ N m}$$

Work in the *MKSA* system of units is seen to have the absolete units Kg m^2/s^2, which are equal to the derived units, *newton meters.* In the *cgs* system of units, the corresponding absolute units are g cm^2/s^2, which are equal to the derived units *dyne centimeters.*

9.2. *Joules* and Ergs*

In the *MKSA* system of units, a force of 1 *newton* acting through a distance of 1 m performs an amount of work equivalent to *1 joule:*

$$1 \text{ newton meter} = 1 \text{ joule} \qquad (9d)$$

In the *cgs* system, the *dyne cm* as a unit of work is called the *erg:*

***James Prescott Joule (1818–1889), English physicist, was born December 24, 1818, near Manchester. He owned a large brewery but devoted his life to scientific research. In 1840, he stated the law of the electrical equivalent of heat, and later the first law of thermodynamics. He determined the mechanical equivalent of heat in four different ways. In addition, with Lord Kelvin he performed work on the compression of gases and the heat changes that take place when they escape through small holes. His numerous scientific papers were published by the Royal Society of London in 1884.**

$$1 \text{ dyne cm} = 1 \text{ erg} \quad (9e)$$

A force of 1 dyne acting through a distance of 1 cm does 1 erg of work.

Example 2. Calculate the work done in lifting a mass of 8.0 Kg to a height of 2.50 m.
Solution. The known quantities are m = 8.0 Kg, h = 2.5 m, and g = 9.80 m/s². Substitution in Eq.(9a) gives

$$W = 8 \text{ Kg} \times 9.8 \frac{\text{m}}{\text{s}^2} \times 2.5 \text{ m}$$

$$W = 196.0 \frac{\text{Kg m}^2}{\text{s}^2}$$

$$W = 196.0 \text{ Nm}$$

$$W = 196.0 \text{ joules}$$

The joule as a unit of work is abbreviated J. Hence the work done in this example is

$$W = 196.0 \text{ J}$$

9.3. Work Done Against Friction

In sliding a mass of 5 Kg along a horizontal plane a distance of 2 m (see Fig. 9B) the work done *will not* in general be as great as that required to lift the same mass 2 m vertically.

Suppose, for example, that the coefficient of sliding friction for the block in the diagram is $\mu = 0.25$. By calculation then, the force of friction is [see Eq.(7b)]

$$f = \mu N = 0.25 \times 5 \text{ Kg} \times 9.8 \text{ m/s}^2$$

$$f = 12.25 \text{ N}$$

Since a force of 12.25 newtons will slide the block, the work done, by Eq.(9b), will be

$$W = 12.25 \text{ N} \times 2 \text{ m}$$
$$= 24.5 \text{ Nm}$$
$$= 24.5 \text{ J}$$

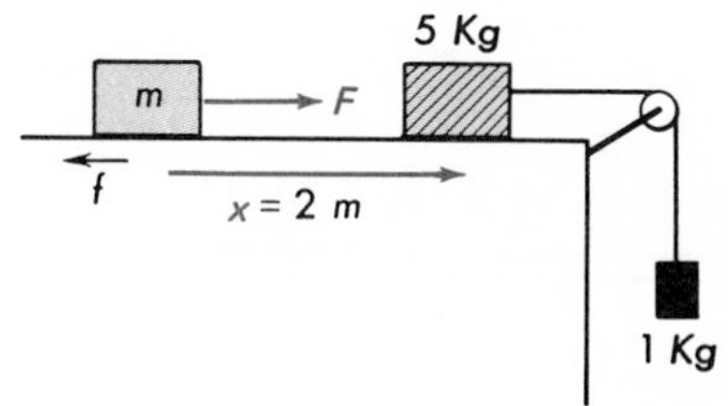

Fig. 9B. To slide a body horizontally, work must be done against friction.

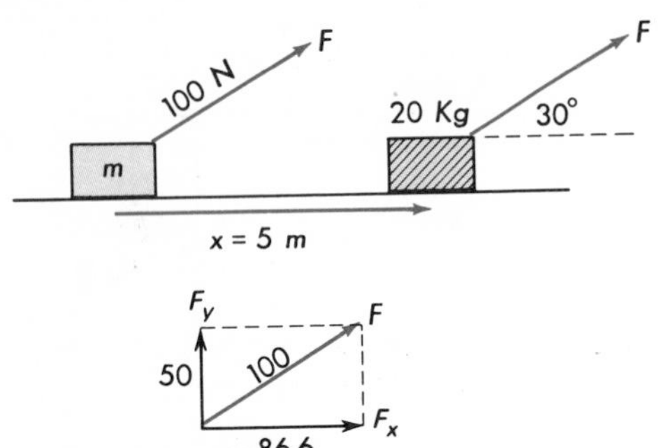

Fig. 9C. Force and distance are measured in the same direction in calculating work.

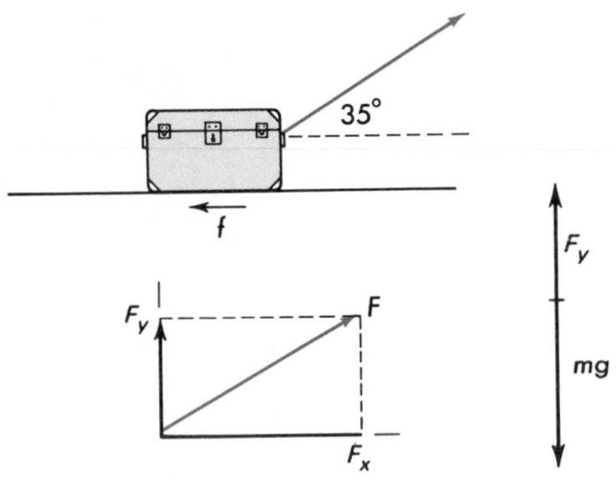

Fig. 9D. Work is done in sliding a trunk along the floor.

This is only one-quarter as much work as that required to lift the same 5-Kg mass an equal vertical distance of 2 m (see Fig. 9A). By reducing the friction between the block and the plane, the force F can be reduced still further. Such a reduction can be accomplished by smoothing and lubricating the sliding surfaces, or better by mounting the block on wheels. If the friction were eliminated entirely, the work done in moving any object in a horizontal direction would be practically zero, for once started it would by Newton's first law of motion continue moving with constant velocity. A vertical lift, however, requires at least an amount of work equal to the weight mg times the height h.

When a force acting on an object is applied at angle with the direction of motion, only the component of the force in the direction of motion is effective in doing work. This is illustrated in Fig. 9C, where a force of 100 N applied at an angle of 30° moves a 20-Kg mass a distance of 5 m. In the bottom diagram, F is resolved into two components, F_x horizontally and F_y vertically.

By calculation or by graphical construction,

$$F_x = F \cos 30^\circ = 100 \times 0.866 = 86.6 \text{ N}$$

$$F_y = F \sin 30^\circ = 100 \times 0.500 = 50.0 \text{ N}$$

The vertical force of 50 N, being perpendicular to the direction of motion, does no work since the distance moved upward is zero. Work is done only by the horizontal force F_x:

$$W = 86.6 \text{ N} \times 5 \text{ m} = 433 \text{ J}$$

While the vertical force does not enter directly into the calculation of work, it does help to lift the body and thereby reduce the friction between the sliding surfaces. As an illustration, consider the following problem.

Example 3. A trunk with a mass of 100.0 Kg is pulled 20.0 m across the floor by a rope making an angle of 35° with the horizontal (see Fig. 9D). If the coefficient of sliding friction is 0.25, find (a) the tension in the rope, and (b) the work done.

Solution. The force F is resolved into two components,

$$F_x = F \cos 35^\circ = 0.819\, F$$

$$F_y = F \sin 35^\circ = 0.574\, F$$

To find the horizontal force of friction ($f = \mu N$), the normal force N is calculated as the resultant of two forces acting on the block: mg downward due to gravity and F_y upward due to the pull of the rope.

Therefore,

$$N = mg - F_y$$

and the force of friction is

$$f = \mu N = 0.25\ (mg - F_y)$$

To overcome friction and slide the body, the component F_x must be at least equal to f. Set $f = F_x$,

$$F_x = 0.25\ (mg - F_y)$$

Substitute for F_x and F_y from the above relations, and multiply out,

$$0.819\ F = 0.25\ mg - 0.25 \times 0.574\ F$$

Collect factors containing F, on the left, and substitute for m and g,

$$0.963\ F = 0.25 \times 100\ \text{Kg} \times 9.8\ \frac{\text{m}}{\text{s}^2}$$

Therefore

(a) $$F = 254.4\ \text{N}$$

By Eq.(9b) the work done is $F_x \times x$,

$$W = 0.819 \times 254.4\ \text{N} \times 20\ \text{m}$$

(b) $$W = 4167\ \text{J}$$

9.4. Potential Energy

Mechanical energy is divided into two categories, *potential energy* (E_p) and *kinetic energy* (E_k). *A body is said to have potential energy if by virtue of its position or state it is able to do work.* A car at the top of a hill or a wound clock spring is an example of an object with potential energy. The clock spring may keep a clock running for a certain length of time, and a car may, by coasting

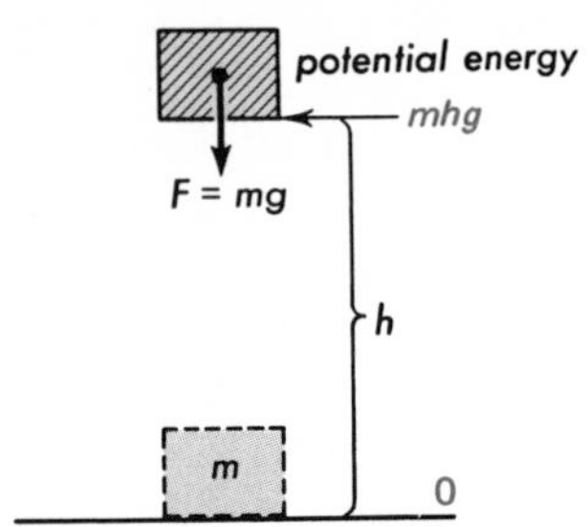

Fig. 9E. A body has potential energy by virtue of its position or state.

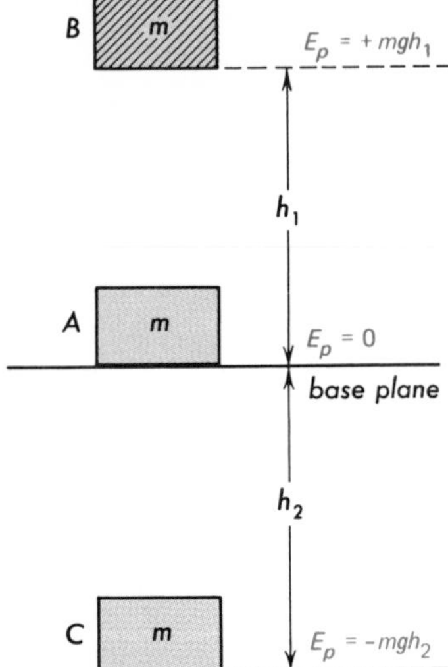

Fig. 9F. Potential energy with respect to a base plane may be plus or minus.

downhill, travel a great distance. Potential energy is measured by the amount of work that is available. It is therefore measured in *ergs,* or *joules.*

If a given mass m is raised to a specified height h, as illustrated in Fig. 9E, it then has potential energy $F \times h$ by virtue of its position above the ground level from which it has been lifted. The *work done* in lifting it has been stored up as potential energy in the block. This energy can be regained by dropping the mass back to the ground, for in so doing it can be made to perform some kind of work. By definition,

$$\text{potential energy} = F \times h$$

$$E_{\text{p}} = F \times h$$

or, in absolute units,

$$\text{potential energy} = mg \times h \tag{9f}$$

Example 4. A mass of 5.0 Kg is raised to a height of 2.50 m above the ground. Calculate its potential energy.

Solution. The known quantities are $m = 5.0$ Kg, $h = 2.50$ m, and $g = 9.80$ m/s². By direct substitution in Eq.(9f), we obtain

$$E_{\text{p}} = mgh$$

$$E_{\text{p}} = 5 \text{ Kg} \times 9.8 \frac{\text{m}}{\text{s}^2} \times 2.5 \text{ m} = 122.5 \text{ J}$$

If a body is lifted straight upward, carried up a staircase, or pulled up an inclined plane, the potential energy acquired is given by the *weight* × *vertical height* to which it is raised.

The meaning of positive, zero, or negative potential energy is illustrated in Fig. 9F. Located at any point above the *base plane* a body has positive potential energy, while at points below that line it has negative potential energy. To lift the mass m from A to B, work is done, and the mass acquires a potential energy to the amount of mgh_1.

In returning from B to A, the mass loses potential energy, performing *work* = mgh_1 on some other body. Similarly, in going from A to C, the body loses energy and ends up at C with mgh_2 less energy than it had at A. To raise it again to A, an equivalent amount of work mgh_2 will have to be done on the body.

The choosing of a *base plane* as a zero energy level is a purely arbitrary selection. In many practical applications it is customary to select the lowest point to be reached by a body as the zero level, so that all displacements from there will be positive in sign.

When a force is applied to a body to slide or roll it along the ground, the *work done* is not stored up as potential energy. Because of friction, the energy is transformed into heat, and as a practical matter is considered lost for further use. If the body ends up at the same level at which it started, all of the energy has gone into heat and the potential energy remains unchanged.

If a body is pulled up an inclined plane, on the other hand, part of the energy goes into heat and part into potential energy. The potential energy as illustrated in Fig. 9G is given by mgh, while the work done is given by $F \times s$ and the frictional energy by $f \times s$:

$$F \times s = f \times s + mgh$$

$$\text{work done} = \text{frictional energy} + \text{potential energy}$$

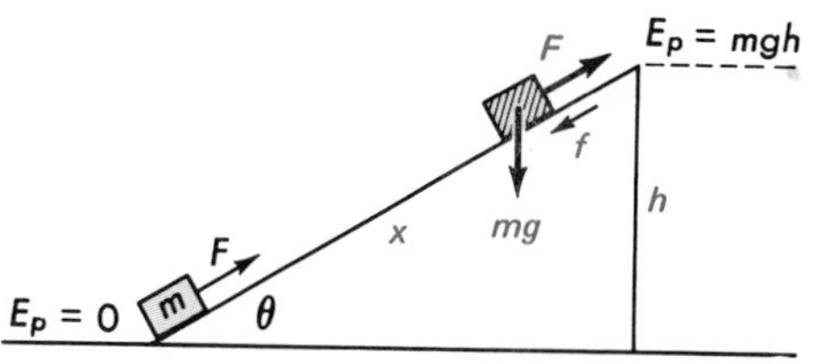

Fig. 9G. Part of the work done in sliding a mass up an incline goes into friction, and part into potential energy.

9.5. *Kinetic Energy*

The kinetic energy of a moving body is defined as its ability to do work by virtue of its motion. A car moving along the highway has kinetic energy of translation, and a rotating wheel on a machine has kinetic energy of rotation. For a given mass m, moving in a straight line with constant speed v, the kinetic energy is given by

$$\text{kinetic energy} = \tfrac{1}{2}mv^2 \tag{9g}$$

Example 5. Calculate the kinetic energy of a 20.0-Kg mass, moving with a speed of 4.0 m/s.

Solution. The known quantities are $m = 20.0$ Kg and $v = 4.0$ m/s. By direct substitution in Eq.(9g).

$$E_k = \frac{1}{2} \times 20 \text{ Kg} \times \left(4 \frac{\text{m}}{\text{s}}\right)^2 = 160.0 \frac{\text{Kg m}^2}{\text{s}^2}$$

This answer has exactly the dimensions of *work,* and *potential energy,* and can be written in the same derived units:

$$E_k = 160.0 \text{ J}$$

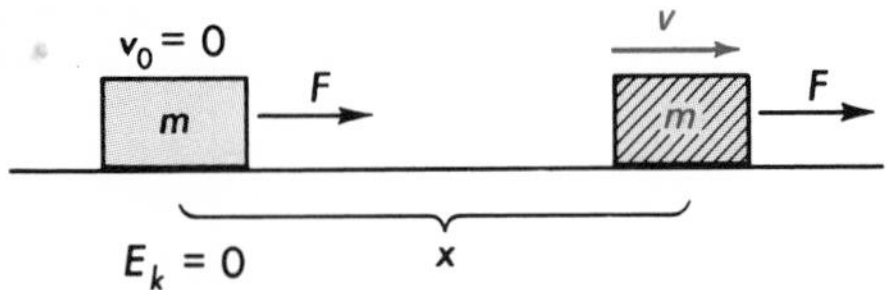

Fig. 9H. A body has kinetic energy by virtue of its motion.

A moving body has energy, because in being brought to rest it must exert a force F on some other object, and this force acting through a distance x does work. In other words, work can be done by a moving body. Conversely, by applying a constant horizontal force F on a body of mass m for a distance x, it will be given a kinetic energy $\frac{1}{2}mv^2$ (see Fig. 9H):

$$F \times x = \tfrac{1}{2}mv^2 \qquad \text{(9h)}$$

The above equation is known as the "work equation." In it, friction is entirely neglected and the body is presumed to start from rest. To derive Eq.(9h) from previous principles, Newton's second law of motion will serve as a starting point:

$$F = ma$$

Upon multiplying both sides of the equation by x,

$$F \times x = max \qquad \text{(9i)}$$

For the product ax on the right Eq.(2n) is used. The equation $v_2^2 = v_1^2 + 2ax$ is solved for ax, and gives

$$ax = m\,\frac{v_2^2 - v_1^2}{2}$$

which, substituted in Eq.(9i), gives

$$F \times x = \frac{v_2^2 - v_1^2}{2}$$

Then

$$F \times x = \frac{1}{2}mv_2^2 - \frac{1}{2}mv_1^2 \qquad \text{(9j)}$$

In the special case that the body starts from rest, $v_1 = 0$, the last term drops out, and the equation becomes Eq.(9h).

Example 6. A constant horizontal force of 250.0 N acts for a distance of 36.0 m on a 500-Kg box. If friction is neglected and the box starts from rest, what is its velocity?
Solution. The known quantities are $F = 250.0$ N, $v_1 = 0$, $m = 500$ Kg, and $x_1 = 36.0$ m. The special Eq.(9h) may be used by first

solving for v^2, and substituting the known quantities as follows:

$$v^2 = \frac{2(Fx)}{m} = \frac{2(250 \times 36)}{500}$$

$$v^2 = 36.0 \frac{m^2}{s^2}$$

$$v^2 = 6.0 \frac{m}{s}$$

9.6. Work Done by a Constant Force

The lifting of a mass m a vertical distance h is an *example of work* done by a *constant force.* In this simplest of cases, we can write

$$F = \text{constant}$$

and the work done as

$$W = F \times h$$

See Eq.(9b).

If we draw a graph with the force plotted along the y-axis and the distance along the x-axis, we will obtain the straight horizontal line shown at the top in Fig. 9I. For any specified F and h the work done, $F \times h$, is just equal to the shaded area shown in color. This idea that *work done* can be represented by the *area under a curve* is extremely useful, for it can be extended to practical cases where the force may not be constant, but varies.

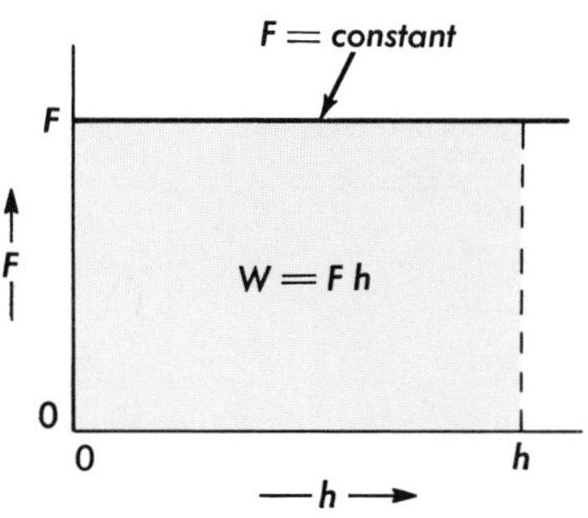

Fig. 9I. The work done by a force F acting for a distance h is given by the area under the curve.

9.7. Work Done by a Variable Force

Up to this point in the treatment of work done, and energy expended, it has been assumed that an applied force is constant at all points along the path over which it acts. While these conditions are realized in many cases, there are numerous practical examples where the force is far from constant.

Consider as an illustration the stretching of a coil spring as shown in Fig. 9J. The zero point of a meter stick is set at a marker M. A force of 2 N is then applied to the spring and the marker indicates a total stretch of 1.25 cm. A total force of 4 N is now applied and the marker shows a total stretch of 2.50 cm. Applying forces of 6 N, 8 N, and 10 N, respectively, the distances recorded in Table 9A are obtained.

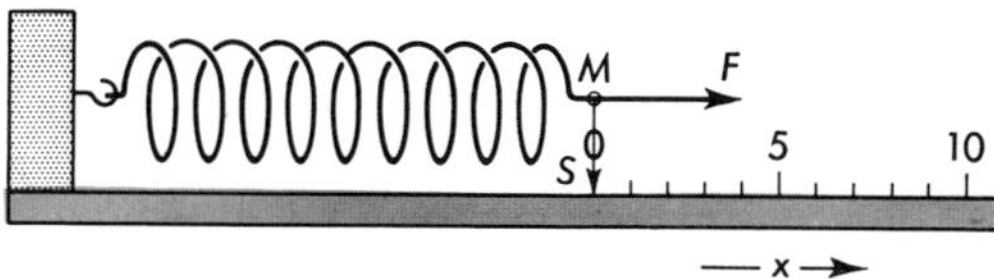

Fig. 9J. A coil spring is stretched more and more by a steadily increasing force F.

TABLE 9A
Data recorded for the stretching of a spring

F (N)	x (m)
0	0
2	0.0125
4	0.0250
6	0.0375
8	0.0500
10	0.0625

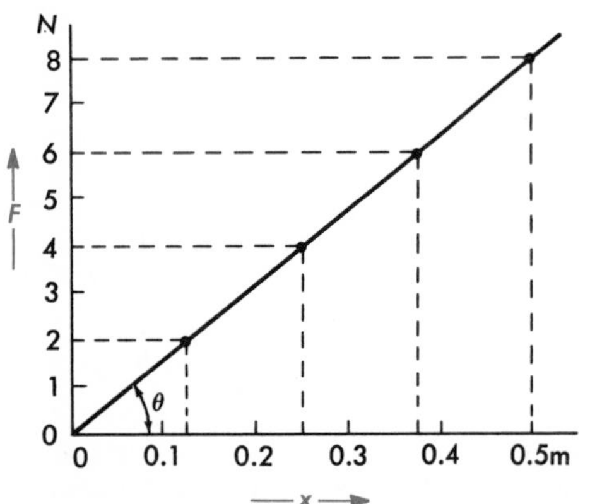

Fig. 9K. Force graph for the stretching of a spring as shown in Fig. 9J.

If these data are plotted as a graph, we obtain a straight line, inclined at an angle θ, as shown in Fig. 9K. The interpretation of this graphical result is that a direct proportionality exists between F and x, and we can write

$$F = kx \tag{9k}$$

Here k, the proportionality constant, is the slope of the line, and is a measure of what is called the *stiffness* of the spring. From the recorded data the spring constant is found to be

$$k = \frac{F}{x} = \frac{10\text{ N}}{0.0625\text{ m}}$$

$$k = 160\,\frac{\text{N}}{\text{m}}$$

The larger the value of k the stiffer the spring.

For all values of F, within the measurements of this experiment, the spring at all times exerts an equal but opposite force $-F$. For the spring then, $-F = kx$, or

$$F = -kx \tag{9ℓ}$$

The minus sign indicates that x and F are in opposite directions. This equation, and the kind of experiment it represents, is known as Hooke's law.*

A plot of the data from Table 9A is shown again in Fig. 9L to illustrate that the area under the curve from $x = 0$ up to any selected value of x, such as $x = x_1$, is just equal to $\frac{1}{2}F_1x_1$.

As a useful relation for the stretching of a spring we can write, for the work done,

$$W = \frac{1}{2}Fx \tag{9m}$$

It is well known that the elastic properties of solid bodies, such as the bending of a beam, the stretching of a wire, the compression of a rod, etc., obey Hooke's law, Eq.(9ℓ), and that Eq.(9m) can be applied to calculate energy expended and energy stored.

*Robert Hooke (1635–1703), English experimental physicist, is known principally for his contributions to the wave theory of light, universal gravitation, and atmospheric pressure. He originated many physical ideas but perfected few of them. Hooke's scientific achievements would undoubtedly have received greater acclaim had his efforts been confined to fewer subjects. He had an irritable temper, and made many virulent attacks on Newton and other men of science, claiming that work published by them was due to him.

Example 7. A coil spring is fastened at one end, as shown in Fig. 9J. If a force of 60.0 N stretches the spring 24.0 cm, find (a) the spring stretch constant, and (b) the work done.

Solution. (a) We first solve Eq.(9k) for the unknown k, and substituting known values, $F = 60.0$ N and $x = 0.240$ m, obtain

$$k = \frac{F}{x} = \frac{60.0 \text{ N}}{0.240 \text{ m}} = 250.0 \text{ N/m}$$

(b) To find the work done, which is also the potential energy stored in the spring, we substitute directly in Eq.(9m), and find

$$W = \frac{1}{2} 60.0 \text{ N} \times 0.240 \text{ m} = 7.20 \text{ J}$$

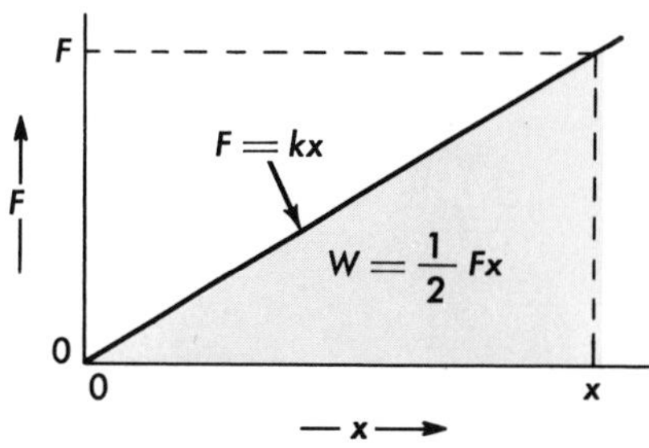

Fig. 9L. The work done by a uniformly increasing force F is seen to be given by the area under the curve.

9.8. Power

Power is defined as the rate of doing work or the rate at which work is being done:

$$\text{Power} = \frac{\text{work}}{\text{time}}$$

$$P = \frac{W}{t} \qquad \text{(9n)}$$

The faster a given amount of work is done, the greater is the power. In other words, the smaller the time t in the above equation, the greater is the fraction W/t and the power P.

In the metric system, with work measured in *joules*, power is expressed in *joules per second.* One joule per second is called the *watt,** a unit of power:

$$1 \text{ joule/second} = 1 \text{ watt} \qquad \text{(9o)}$$

The *kilowatt* is another unit of power and is equal to *1000 watts:*

$$1 \text{ kilowatt} = 1000 \text{ watts}$$

$$1 \text{ KW} = 1000 \text{ W}$$

*James Watt (1736–1819), Scottish engineer and inventor, was born at Greenock on January 19, 1736. It is appropriate that the unit of power is named after him, for he is best known for his long and tedious work of improving the efficiency of the steam engine. He also invented the centrifugal governor and the steam pump. In spite of his life long work on the steam engine, he took a dim view of its use in locomotives, and in the last years of his life, refused to countenance it. Watt also invented a press for copying manuscripts and discovered the composition of water. He was twice married, and the father of six children.

Example 8. What is the power required for a hoist to raise a total mass of 350.0 Kg a total distance of 180.0 m in a time of 40.0 s?
Solution. The known quantities are $m = 350.0$ Kg, $g = 9.80$ m/s^2, $h = 180.0$ m, and $t = 40.0$ s. Since work done in raising any mass vertically upward is given by Eq.(9c), we may substitute known quantities in Eq.(9n) and obtain

$$P = \frac{mgh}{t} = \frac{350 \text{ Kg} \times 9.80 \text{ m/s} \times 180 \text{ m}}{40 \text{ s}}$$

$$P = 15{,}440 \text{ W}$$

$$P = 15.44 \text{ KW}$$

problems

1. A concrete hoist with a mass of 4500 Kg is raised vertically upward a distance of 60.0 m. How much work is done?

2. An automobile is loaded onto the deck of a ship for transport overseas. If the car's mass is 2200 Kg, and it is hoisted a vertical distance of 15.0 m, find the work done.

3. A 3.30×10^6-Kg Saturn rocket takes off from its launching pad and acquires a vertical velocity of 1000 m/s at an altitude of 25.0 Km. Calculate (a) the potential energy, and (b) the kinetic energy. [Ans. (a) 8.085×10^{11} J, (b) 1.650×10^{12} J.]

4. A 16,000-Kg jet plane cruises at 900 Km/h at an altitude of 12.0 Km. Find (a) its potential energy, and (b) its kinetic energy.

5. A small plane with a mass of 1200 Kg cruises at 140.0 Km/h at an altitude of 1.50 Km. Find (a) its potential energy, (b) its kinetic energy, and (c) its total energy.

6. A small plane with a mass of 1500 Kg climbs to a height of 1.80 Km in 8.0 min where it levels out in straight and level flight at 180.0 Km/h. Find (a) its potential energy, (b) its kinetic energy, (c) its total energy, and (d) the power developed. [Ans. (a) 2.646×10^7 J, (b) 1.875×10^6 J, (c) 2.834×10^7 J, (d) 5.90×10^4 W.]

7. A fully loaded elevator car has a total mass of 1950 Kg. If it rises 24 floors, a distance of 96.0 m, in 15.0 s, find (a) the potential energy of the car, and (b) the power developed.

8. A 3500-Kg truck climbs to the top of a grade 550 m above the bottom in 8.0 min. Neglecting friction, what power is developed?

9. Oil is pumped from the tanks of a ship to a storage tank on land 45.0 m higher in elevation. What is the minimum power required to pump 20,000 liters an hour, if one liter of oil has a mass of 0.80 Kg. Neglect all friction. [Ans. 1.960 KW.]

10. A coil spring is stretched a distance of 10.0 cm as the result of applying a force of 25.0 N. Calculate the stored energy when it is stretched 14.0 cm.

11. A coil of steel wire has a spring constant of 120 N/cm. Calculate the stored potential energy if this spring is stretched a distance of 50.0 cm.

12. A 40.0-Kg box is pulled up a ramp 5.0 m long, inclined at 30° to the horizontal. If the applied force is parallel to the ramp, and the coefficient of sliding friction is 0.25, find (a) the force, (b) the work done, and (c) the stored potential energy. Make a diagram. [Ans. (a) 280.9 N, (b) 1404 J, (c) 980 J.]

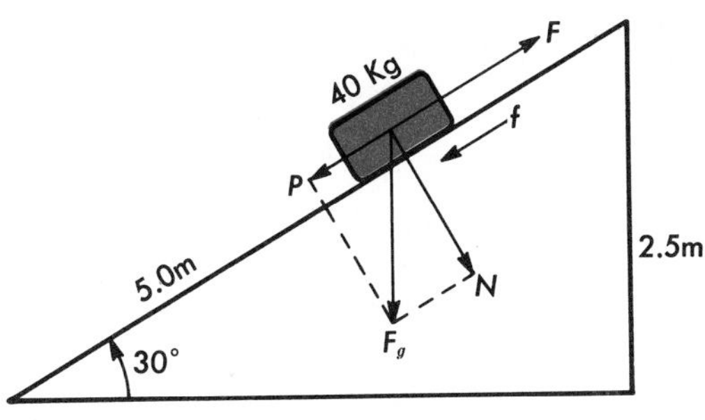

Prob. 12.

13. A trunk with a mass of 55.0 Kg is pulled up a plank lying on the stairway of a house. The plank is 6.0 m long and the coefficient of sliding friction is 0.32. If the plank makes an angle of 38° with the horizontal, find (a) the force of friction, (b) the force required to pull the trunk, (c) the work done pulling it to the top, and (d) the potential energy stored. Make a diagram.

14. A tractor pulls a 1200-Kg log up a 20% grade by sliding it along the ground. The coefficient of sliding friction for this operation is 0.55. If the log is pulled for a distance of 250 m, find (a) the force required to overcome friction, (b) the total force to pull the log, (c) the total work done, and (d) the stored potential energy in the log. Make a diagram. A 20% grade is one which rises 20.0 m for every 100.0 m measured horizontally.

10 Conservation of energy and momentum

In order to provide an accurate description of many of the events that occur in nature, the laws of conservation of energy and conservation of momentum are most important. While these two laws involve different concepts, both are implicated in many events and both are generally applied to practical problems.

Most important of all the laws of nature is the law of the conservation of energy. Although the law has been stated in almost as many different ways as there are books written on the subject, they all have in reality the same meaning. The following three examples are typical statements:

(1) *In transforming energy from one form to another, energy is always conserved.*
(2) *Energy is never created or destroyed.*
(3) *The sum total of all energy in the universe remains constant.*

Everyone should be aware of the fact that there are many forms of energy, the most important of which are:

Mechanical	**Light**
Electrical	**Atomic**
Chemical	**Molecular**
Heat	**Nuclear**

FORMS OF ENERGY

In this chapter we are concerned with the law of conservation of energy only as it applies to the two forms of mechanical energy, *potential* and *kinetic.* The law will again be encountered in connection with the other forms in the chapters on heat, electricity, and atomic structure.

10.1. Energy Levels

In the preceding chapter we have seen that *potential energy* is one of the two forms of mechanical energy and is defined as *the energy a body has by virtue of its position or state.* In terms of *work done,*

$$W = F \times h$$

Calling the potential energy E_p, we write

$$E_p = F \times h \quad (10a)$$

A simple example is that of lifting a mass m against the pull of gravity as shown in Fig. 10A. An upward force F is applied to raise the mass m to a height h_1. By definition the *work done* is equal to the force times the distance moved, $W = F \times h_1$. Since the force is equal to mg, the work done is stored as potential energy and we can write

$$E_1 = mgh_1 \quad (10b)$$

If the mass is lifted to the top level, an additional distance h_2, the work done $F \times h_2$ is stored as an additional amount of potential energy mgh_2. The total stored energy is then given by

$$E_2 = mgh \quad (10c)$$

where $h = h_1 + h_2$.

If we select a base plane, such as sea level, as a level of zero potential energy, an object may have positive potential energy $+mgh_2$, or negative potential energy $-mgh_1$ as shown in Fig. 10B. A body located at any point above the base plane has positive potential energy; at points below that level it has negative potential energy. In lifting the mass m from A to B, work is done. In returning from B to A, the mass releases energy. Similarly in going from A to C, the mass releases energy and ends up at C with less than it had at A. To raise it again to A, energy will have to be provided to do work.

From these considerations it is clear that we are free to choose the base plane of zero potential energy at any level and at the same time retain, unchanged, the energy differences between levels.

The other form of mechanical energy presented in the last chapter is called *kinetic energy. The kinetic energy of a moving*

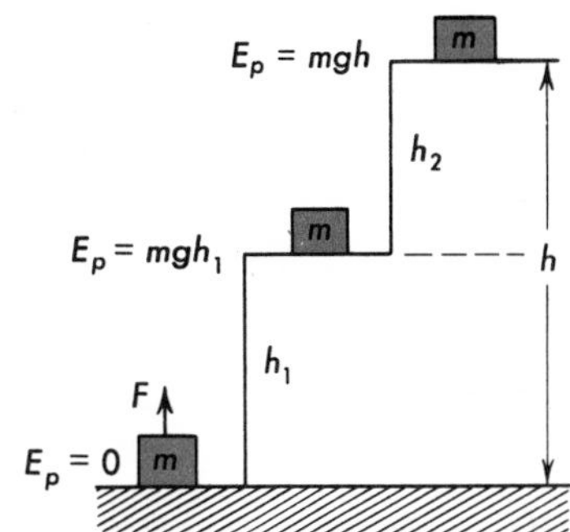

Fig. 10A. An illustration of potential energy, E_p.

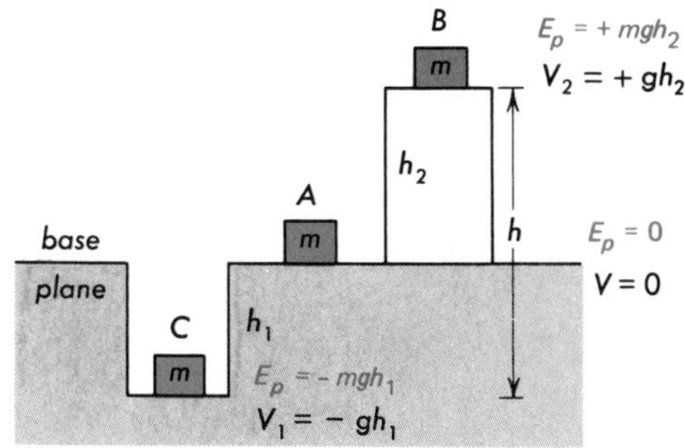

Fig. 10B. Potential energy with respect to a base plane may be plus or minus.

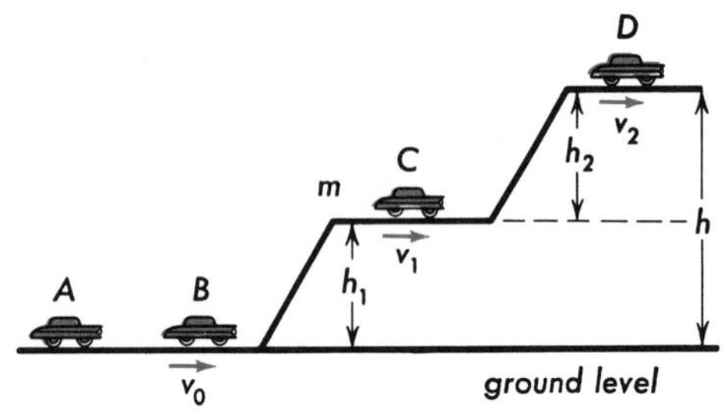

Fig. 10C. A moving car at different levels has different amounts of energy.

mass is defined as the energy a body possesses by virture of its motion. An airplane in straight and level flight has kinetic energy of translation, and a spinning wheel has kinetic energy of rotation. For a given mass m moving in a straight line with constant velocity v, the kinetic energy E_k is given by

$$E_k = \tfrac{1}{2}mv^2 \tag{10d}$$

At times it is convenient to express the kinetic energy of a body in terms of *momentum.* In Chap. 4 we have seen that the momentum p of a moving body is defined as the mass m multiplied by the velocity v:

$$p = mv \tag{10e}$$

Multiplying numerator and denominator of Eq.(10d) by m and substituting p^2 for m^2v^2, we obtain for the kinetic energy

$$E_k = \frac{p^2}{2m} \tag{10f}$$

10.2. Total Energy

When a body moves on an elevated plane, it possesses kinetic energy by virture of its motion and potential energy by virtue of its position. The total energy of such a body is the sum of its separate energies:

$$\text{Total energy} = E_k + E_p$$

$$E_t = E_k + E_p \tag{10g}$$

As an illustration consider a car moving on different floor levels in a modern auto parking building (see Fig. 10C). Starting at rest at A, where the ground level is selected as the base plane, the velocity $v = 0$, the height $h = 0$, and both E_k and E_p are zero. The total mechanical energy is therefore zero:

$$E_0 = 0$$

When the car is at B and moving with a velocity v_0 at the ground level, $h = 0$, the total energy is all kinetic:

$$E_1 = \tfrac{1}{2}mv_0^2 + 0$$

When the car is at C, moving with a velocity v_1 at a height h_1 above the ground level, the total stored energy is

$$E_2 = \tfrac{1}{2}mv_1^2 + mgh_1$$

and when the car is moving with a velocity v_2 at D on the next floor up, the total energy is

$$E_3 = \tfrac{1}{2}mv_2^2 + mgh$$

If we assign specific values to m, v, and h in these equations, we can calculate each specific energy and construct an energy-level diagram of the kind shown in Fig. 10D. Energy in joules E_t is plotted vertically upward from zero and horizontal lines are drawn at the appropriate values. The up arrows show the energy stored as the car goes up from one level to the other, while the down arrows show the energy being liberated as the car descends. Note that although the floor levels might be equally spaced the energy levels need not be.

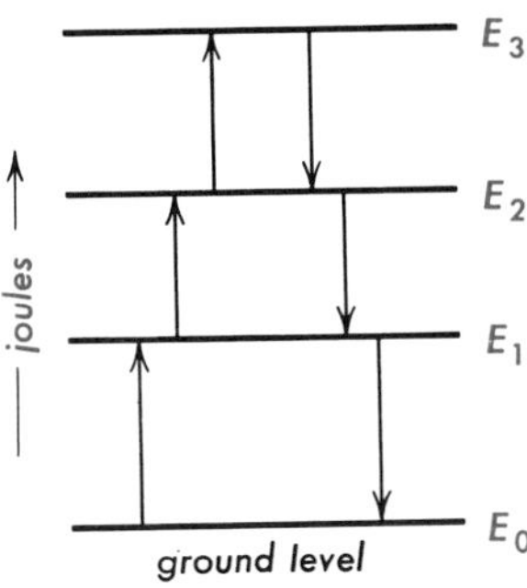

Fig. 10D. Energy-level diagram for the total mechanical energy of the car shown in Fig. 10C.

10.3. Conservation of Energy

Consider the energy involved in a waterfall as shown in Fig. 10E. The water at the top of the fall has potential energy by virtue of its position above the base. As it falls over and then downward with ever-increasing speed, the kinetic energy $\tfrac{1}{2}mv^2$ increases, while the potential energy decreases. At the bottom of the fall, the potential energy approaches zero and the kinetic energy approaches its maximum value. At the top, the energy was practically all potential, while near the bottom it is mostly kinetic. Assuming the water to start from rest at the top and that no energy is lost in falling, the E_p at the top of the falls equals the E_k at the bottom:

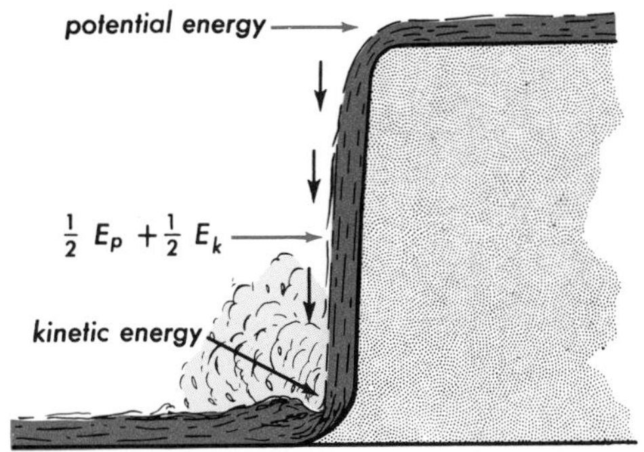

Fig. 10E. All the available energy at the top of a waterfall is potential. At the bottom it is kinetic.

$$E_p \textbf{ at top} = E_k \textbf{ at bottom}$$

$$F \times h = \tfrac{1}{2}mv^2 \qquad (10h)$$

or

$$mgh = \tfrac{1}{2}mv^2 \qquad (10i)$$

Divide both sides of the equation by m and solve for v:

$$v^2 = 2gh$$

$$v = \sqrt{2gh} \quad (10j)$$

This is the same equation that is derived for uniformly accelerated motion in Chap. 2, used for freely falling bodies in Chap. 3, and applied to projectiles in Chap. 8 [see Eqs.(3d) and (3ℓ).]. Here the equation has been derived from the law of conservation of energy.

Example 1. A mass of 25.0 Kg is dropped from a height of 5.0 m. Find (a) the kinetic energy and (b) velocity just as it reaches the ground.

Solution. Since the E_p at the top is equivalent to the E_k at the bottom,

$$E_p = 25.0 \text{ Kg} \times 9.80 \frac{\text{m}}{\text{s}^2} \times 5.0 \text{ m}$$

$$E_p = 1225 \text{ joules} = E_k$$

The velocity is found by Eq.(10j):

$$v = \sqrt{2 \times 9.80 \times 5.0} = 9.90 \text{ m/s}$$

When the falling body in the above problem is part way down, it has some E_p and some E_k. Its total energy at any point on the way down is therefore given by Eq.(10g):

$$E_t = \tfrac{1}{2}mv^2 + mgh$$

At the instant the body reaches the ground, it is suddenly stopped and all of the energy is quickly transformed into heat. The transformation of mechanical energy into heat is often demonstrated in the physics laboratory by an experiment in which a quantity of lead-shot is dropped from a height of several feet and its temperature measured before and after falling. By raising the shot and dropping it many times, the rise in temperature amounts to several degrees.

10.4. The Inclined Plane

It can be shown that a body sliding without friction down an incline of height h should acquire at the bottom a velocity $v =$

$\sqrt{2gh}$. This equation is readily derived from the law of conservation of energy.

Consider the demonstration experiment shown in Fig. 10F in which a small truck is pulled up an incline. The work done to reach the top is given by the product of force F times the distance x. By conservation of energy, this must be equal to the stored-up potential energy mgh at the top. Therefore

$$F \times x = mgh$$

Fig. 10F. Conservation of energy.

Now, if the truck is released, it will accelerate back down the incline, thereby converting the potential energy mgh into kinetic energy $\frac{1}{2}mv^2$. By conservation of energy we can write the more general form:

total E at top = total E at bottom

$$E_p + E_k = E_p + E_k \tag{10k}$$

$$mgh + 0 = 0 + \tfrac{1}{2}mv^2$$

$$mgh = \tfrac{1}{2}mv^2$$

Since the m on both sides refers to the same mass, we can divide by m and obtain

$$gh = \tfrac{1}{2}v^2,$$

$$v = \sqrt{2gh}$$

A comparison of this last equation with Eq.(10j) shows that neglecting friction, an object acquires the same speed at the bottom of an incline as that of a body falling freely from the same height. In effect, the speed at the bottom of an incline does not depend upon its steepness, but upon the height alone.

When sliding friction is not negligibly small, Eq.(10k) must include an additional term. At the top of the incline the total energy E is all potential and $E_t = mgh$. In sliding down, part of this available energy, to the amount of $f \times x$, is used up in overcoming friction, and the rest goes into kinetic energy, $\frac{1}{2}mv^2$. By conservation of energy,

$$E_p \text{ at top} = \text{frictional enegry} + E_k \text{ at bottom}$$

$$mgh = fx + \tfrac{1}{2}mv^2$$

In applying this formula to the solution of problems, the force of friction, $f = \mu N$, is found by resolving the weight mg into components.

10.5. The Law of Conservation of Momentum

When two or more bodies collide with each other, or some internal changes occur within a body or system of bodies, it is common practice to first apply the law of conservation of momentum.

The law applies to all collision phenomena whether they involve the largest astronomical bodies or the smallest atomic particles. This universal law of nature may be stated as follows: *The total momentum before impact equals the total momentum after impact.*

Consider as an example the "head-on" encounter of two balls as shown in Fig. 10G. Before impact the mass m_1 is moving with a velocity u_1 and has a momentum m_1u_1, while m_2 is moving with a velocity u_2 and has a momentum m_2u_2. The total momentum before impact is therefore equal to the sum of the two momenta, $m_1u_1 + m_2u_2$.

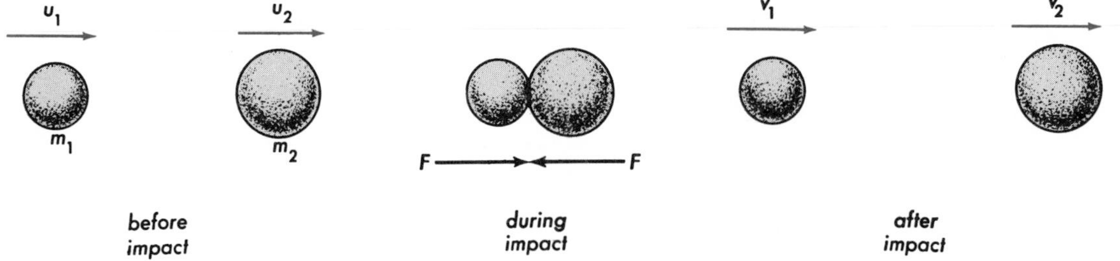

Fig. 10G. The total momentum of two bodies before impact is equal to the total momentum after impact.

By similar reasoning it is clear that after impact, m_1 and m_2, with their new velocities v_1 and v_2, have a total momentum $m_1v_1 + m_2v_2$. The law of conservation of momentum requires that

$$m_1u_1 + m_2u_2 = m_1v_1 + m_2v_2 \tag{10ℓ}$$

$$\textbf{total momentum before impact} = \textbf{total momentum after impact}$$

During impact, two equal but opposite forces are set up between the bodies, one the force exerted by m_1 on m_2, and the other the force exerted by m_2 on m_1. These two equal but opposite forces are an action and reaction pair as specified by Newton's third law of motion. Each force acts for the same short interval of time, giving equal impulses Ft to both bodies. By Newton's second law, as expressed by the impulse equation $Ft = mv - mv_0$, equal impulses produce equal changes in momentum. One body gains as much momentum as the other loses. In other words, the total momentum remains constant.

Example 2. A ball with a mass of 5.0 Kg moving with a velocity of 20.0 m/s collides with another ball with a mass of 10.0 Kg moving in the same direction along the same line with a velocity of 10.0 m/s. After impact the first mass is still moving in the same direction but with a velocity of 8.0 m/s. Calculate the velocity of the second mass after impact.
Solution. The given quantities are $m_1 = 5.0$ Kg, $m_2 = 10.0$ Kg, $u_1 = 20.0$ m/s, $u_2 = 10.0$ m/s, and $v_1 = 8.0$ m/s. By direct substitution in Eq.(10ℓ), we obtain

$$(5 \times 20) + (10 \times 10) = (5 \times 8) + (10 \times v_2)$$

$$200 = 40 + 10v_2$$

$$10v_2 = 160 \qquad v_2 = 16.0 \text{ m/s}$$

After impact, the second mass has a velocity of 16.0 m/s.

If, in the above example, the total kinetic energy after impact is calculated and compared with the total kinetic energy before impact, the two will not be found equal. Employing the equation $E_k = \frac{1}{2} mv^2$, we obtain

$$E_k = \tfrac{1}{2}(5 \times 20^2) + \tfrac{1}{2}(10 \times 10^2)$$

$$= 1500 \text{ J}$$

before impact

$$E_k = \tfrac{1}{2}(5 \times 8^2) + \tfrac{1}{2}(10 \times 16^2)$$

$$= 1440 \text{ J}$$

after impact

The difference in energy, to the amount of 60 J, has disappeared as mechanical energy and gone into heat. During impact, both basses were slightly deformed in shape due to the mutually acting forces and a small amount of heat was generated internally. This heat raised the temperature of the two colliding bodies. It is only by including this heat energy of 60 J with the mechanical energy after impact that makes it possible to retain the law of conservation of energy.

This is just another way of stating that collisions in general are not perfectly elastic. If they were perfectly elastic, conservation of mechanical energy would hold, as well as conservation of momentum.

The law of conservation of momentum can be derived from Newton's second law as shown by Eq.(4j). An unbalanced force F acting on a body for a time t changes the momentum from its initial value mv_1 to a final value mv_2,

$$Ft = mv_2 - mv_1 \tag{10m}$$

If no external unbalanced forces are applied to a body, or system of bodies, $F = 0$, and the impulse $Ft = 0$:

$$0 = mv_2 - mv_1$$

or

$$mv_2 = mv_1$$

Forces between individual parts of a system of bodies are internal forces and always exist in pairs. Each pair gives rise to equal and opposite impulses so that no resultant momentum is imparted to the system as a whole.

Another interesting experiment illustrating conservation of momentum may be performed with six or seven large balls or small marbles and a grooved board as shown in Fig. 10H. When one ball is rolled up to the others, it will be stopped by collision with the others and the one on the extreme right-hand end will roll out with the same velocity. If two balls are rolled up as indicated in the diagram, two will roll out on the other end, and if three are

Fig. 10H. Experiment with the duckpin balls, illustrating the law of conservation of momentum.

rolled up, three will roll out. (Glass or steel marbles work best in this experiment, since they are highly elastic.)

When the two balls are rolled up, why doesn't just one roll off on the other side with twice the velocity, thus conserving momentum? The answer to this question involves conservation of energy, for if only one came off with twice the velocity to conserve momentum, its kinetic energy would be twice the energy available from the original two.

10.6. Resilience, and the Coefficient of Restitution

Experimental observations show that most hard bodies in collision are highly resilient and rebound from each other quite rapidly, while many soft bodies are less resilient and rebound much more slowly. *Resilience is defined as the ability of a body to undergo a compression, or rapid deformation, without the development of permanent deformation.* The vigor with which a body restores itself to its original shape after a deformation is called *restitution.*

The coefficient of restitution r is defined as a number expressing the ratio of the velocity with which the two bodies separate after collision to the velocity of their approach before collision:

$$r = \frac{\text{velocity of separation}}{\text{velocity of approach}} \tag{10n}$$

Referring to the two bodies in Fig. 10G,

$$r = \frac{v_2 - v_1}{u_1 - u_2} \tag{10o}$$

One method of determining r for two bodies in collision is to employ spheres of the material and mount them as pendulums, as shown in Fig. 10I. With m_2 hanging freely at rest, m_1 is raised to height h_1 and released. From the rebound heights h_2 and h_1' the velocities before and after collision can be determined from the equation $v = \sqrt{2gh}$ [see Eq.(3d)]. By substitution of the calculated velocities in Eq.(10o), the value of r is found.

The simplest method of finding the coefficient of restitution for two bodies at impact is shown in Fig. 10J. Spheres of different substances are dropped successively, all from the same height, onto the smooth top surface of a large anvil and allowed to bounce to their various heights. Contrary to one's preconceived ideas of elasticity, a glass or steel marble will bounce to a greater

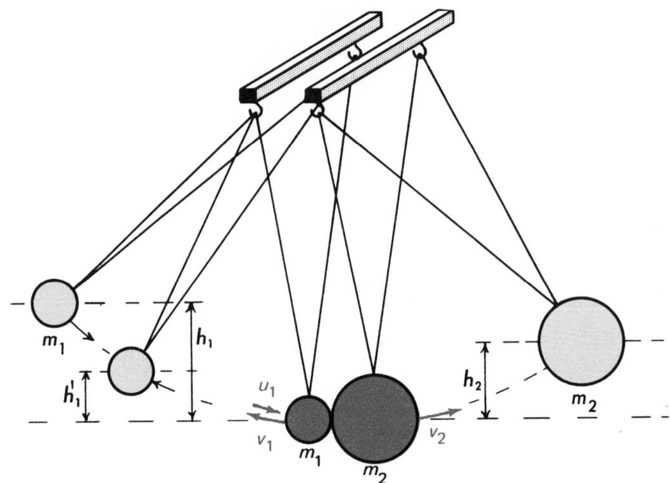

Fig. 10I. Experiment for determining the coefficient of restitution.

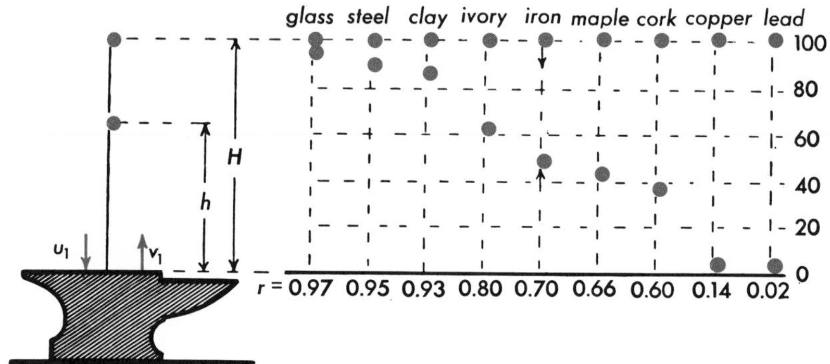

Fig. 10J. The bouncing marble experiment, illustrating the resilience of different substances.

height than will a ball made of the best Pará or India rubber. A lead ball or lead marble, on the other hand, hardly bounces at all.

If we apply Eq.(10ℓ) to these bouncing marbles, we note that the very great mass of the anvil reduces its recoil velocity v_2 to practically zero. Under these conditions we can write $u_2 = 0$ and $v_2 = 0$, and u_1 and v_1 are given by the law of freely falling bodies,

$$u_1 = \sqrt{2gH} \qquad v_1 = \sqrt{2gh}$$

Upon substitution in Eq.(10o), we obtain

$$r = \frac{\sqrt{2gh}}{\sqrt{2gH}}$$

or, simply

$$r = \sqrt{\frac{h}{H}} \tag{10p}$$

As illustrated in Fig. 10J, H is the height from which a marble falls and h is the height to which it rebounds. For a very elastic substance, like glass or steel colliding with steel, r has a value of 0.95 or better, whereas for a very inelastic substance, like lead colliding with steel, r is extremely small. It is seen from Eq.(10p) that the smallest value that r can have is zero, while the largest value is unity.

10.7. Head-on Collisions

We have seen in Sec. 10.3 that when two bodies collide head-on the law of conservation of momentum as given by Eq.(10ℓ) applies. This law is not sufficient, however, to determine the recoil velocities of each of the two bodies after impact. Different kinds of materials have different elastic properties and do not behave alike during impact, and for this reason will move apart with different velocities.

Combining Eq.(10ℓ) with the coefficient of restitution, as given by Eq.(10o), provides a means for determining the recoil velocities of all objects.

Suppose for example that the masses of two bodies, their initial velocities, and the coefficient of restitution are known. With two equations and two unknowns, the recoil velocities of the two bodies can be calculated.

By solving Eq.(10o) for v_2, and substituting for v_2 in Eq.(10ℓ), we obtain the equation

$$v_1 = u_1 - \frac{m_2}{m_1 + m_2}(u_1 - u_2)(1 + r) \tag{10q}$$

By solving Eq.(10o) for v_1 and substituting for v_1 in Eq.(10ℓ), we obtain the equation

$$v_2 = u_2 - \frac{m_1}{m_1 + m_2}(u_2 - u_1)(1 + r) \tag{10r}$$

Example 3. A 2.0-Kg steel ball moving with a velocity of 8.0 m/s collides head-on with a 5.0-Kg steel ball moving in the same direction and along the same straight line at 1.0 m/s. If the coefficient of restitution is 0.90, find the recoil velocity of the two balls.

Solution. The given quantities are $m_1 = 2.0$ Kg, $u_1 = 8.0$ m/s, $m_2 = 5.0$ Kg, $u_2 = 1.0$ m/s, and $r = 0.90$. By direct substitution in Eq.(10q), we obtain

$$v_1 = 8\,\frac{\text{m}}{\text{s}} - \frac{5\ \text{Kg}}{7\ \text{Kg}}\left(8\,\frac{\text{m}}{\text{s}} - 1\,\frac{\text{m}}{\text{s}}\right)(1 + 0.90)$$

$$v_1 = -1.50\,\frac{\text{m}}{\text{s}}$$

By direct substitution in Eq.(10r), we obtain

$$v_2 = 1\,\frac{\text{m}}{\text{s}} - \frac{2\ \text{Kg}}{7\ \text{Kg}}\left(1\,\frac{\text{m}}{\text{s}} - 8\,\frac{\text{m}}{\text{s}}\right)(1 + 0.90)$$

$$v_2 = 4.80\,\frac{\text{m}}{\text{s}}$$

As a check on the law of conservation of momentum, we can apply these values by direct substitution in Eq.(10ℓ):

$$2 \times 8 + 5 \times 1 = 2(-1.5) + 5 \times 4.8$$

$$16 + 5 = -3 + 24$$

The above equations are particularly important in atomic and molecular structure collisions where perfectly elastic impacts are the common occurrence. In this special case the velocity of separation equals the velocity of approach and the coefficient of restitution $r = 1$.

For perfectly elastic collisions that are head-on, $r = 1$, Eqs. (10q) and (10r) simplify, and the law of conservation of energy applies as well as the conservation of momentum:

$$\tfrac{1}{2}m_1u_1^2 + \tfrac{1}{2}m_2u_2^2 = \tfrac{1}{2}m_1v_1^2 + \tfrac{1}{2}m_2v_2^2 \qquad (10s)$$

total kinetic energy before impact = **total kinetic energy after impact**

It is important to note from the discussion above that, for all impact problems whether perfectly elastic or not, the law of conservation of momentum applies, and that if the bodies are perfectly elastic, then and only then does the conservation of kinetic energy apply.

10.8. The More General Problem of Impact

In general, the impact between two bodies is not a head-on collision but one in which a moving body collides with another body initially at rest, and the two bodies recoil in different directions. The diagram in Fig. 10K shows a mass m_1 moving with an initial velocity u_1 and colliding with a mass m_2 initially at rest.

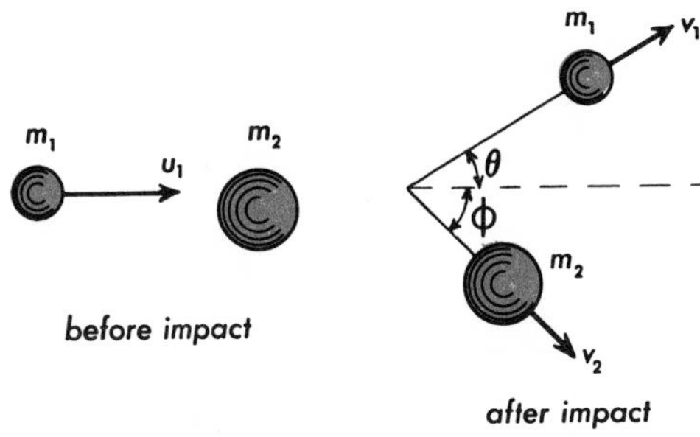

Fig. 10K. Diagram of the impact between two bodies in which the collision is not head-on.

After impact, mass m_1 recoils in a direction θ with a velocity v_1 while mass m_2 recoils in a different direction ϕ with a velocity v_2. Since momentum is a vector quantity, we can draw arrows to represent the momentum of bodies before impact and after impact as shown in Fig. 10L

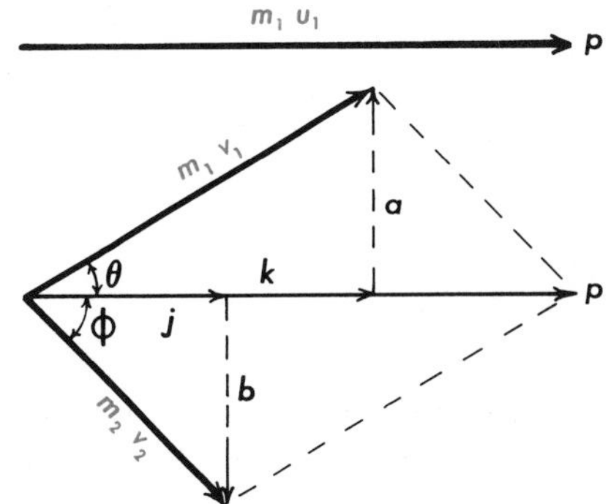

Fig. 10L. Momentum diagram for the impact of two bodies as shown in Fig. 10K.

Before impact, the total momentum p is that of the moving mass m_1 and is simply

$$p = m_1 u_1$$

After impact the total momentum p is unchanged and is composed of two parts, m_1v_1 and m_2v_2. The momentum m_1v_1 is resolved into two components, component a perpendicular to p and component k parallel to p. Similarly, the momentum m_2v_2 is resolved into two components, component b perpendicular to p and component j parallel to p.

By the conservation of momentum, the sum of the vectors j and k must be equal to the initial momentum p:

$$m_1u_1 = m_1v_1 \cos\theta + m_2v_2 \cos\phi \qquad (10t)$$

Since the initial momentum m_1u_1 has no component perpendicular to its direction of motion, the two components a and b must be equal in magnitude and opposite in direction:

$$m_1v_1 \sin\theta = m_2v_2 \sin\phi \qquad (10u)$$

Hence, in any impact between two bodies, one initially at rest, these two equations must hold.

In the special case of a gas, where the collisions between

atoms and molecules are perfectly elastic, conservation of energy also applies. If one of the particles is initially at rest, as shown in Fig. 10I, Eq.(10s) can be written

$$\tfrac{1}{2}m_1u_1^2 = \tfrac{1}{2}m_1v_1^2 + \tfrac{1}{2}m_2v_2^2 \tag{10v}$$

It can be shown that for perfectly elastic collisions, Eqs.(10t), (10u), and (10v) may be combined to obtain the relations that

$$\cos\theta = \frac{u_1^2 + v_1^2 - \dfrac{m_2}{m_1}(u_1^2 - v_1^2)}{2u_1v_1} \tag{10w}$$

$$v_2^2 = \frac{m_1}{m_2}(u_1^2 - v_1^2) \tag{10x}$$

For collisions between solid spheres of tempered steel or glass, the coefficient of restitution is so nearly unity that all five of the last equations can be assumed to hold.

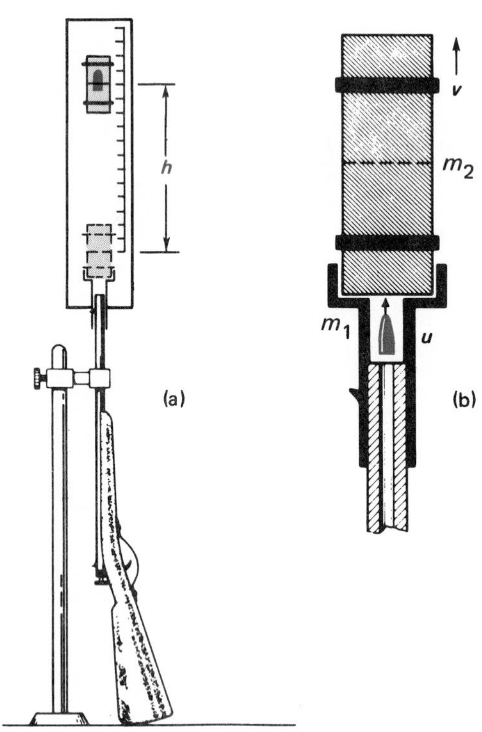

Fig. 10M. Rifle arrangement with attachments for ballistics experiment.

10.9. Ballistics

The term *ballistics* is applied to that branch of science dealing with the measurement of bullet velocities and the effects of bullets upon targets of various kinds. A major part of the activity of this science is concerned with the determination of what is called the *muzzle velocity* of guns.

One of the procedures commonly employed for small-arms measurements consists of mounting the gun in a horizontal position, with the barrel aimed directly at a large rectangular block of wood directly in front of the muzzle. The block is usually suspended as a pendulum by four long cords of equal length. As the bullet leaves the gun barrel it becomes embedded in the wood block, and the momentum of this recoiling mass causes it to swing back and up to some maximum height. By measuring the masses of the bullet and block, and the height the combined mass recoils, the muzzle velocity can be calculated.

A similar method may be employed whereby the gun is mounted with the gun barrel pointing straight upward, and the bullet is fired directly into a block of wood resting on a support as shown in Fig. 10M(a).

The penetration of the bullet into the block of wood is a collision event and the law of conservation of momentum applies. With the wood block initially at rest, the total momentum before impact is just that of the incoming bullet, m_1u [see Fig. 10M(b)]. After impact the bullet and the block, with a total mass $m_1 + m_2$, recoil upward with a velocity v, and the total momentum $(m_1 + m_2)v$. We can therefore write

$$m_1u = (m_1 + m_2)v \tag{10y}$$

Fig. 10N. Bullets, shells, and assembled cartridges for a .22-rifle.

Since u is the unknown, we divide both sides of the equation by m_1, and obtain

$$u = \frac{m_1 + m_2}{m_1} v \tag{10z}$$

The recoil velocity v can be determined from the maximum height h to which the block and embedded bullet rise. By the principle of conservation of energy applied to falling bodies, we may use Eq.(10j):

$$v = \sqrt{2gh}$$

and substitute $\sqrt{2gh}$ for v in Eq.(10z), and obtain

$$u = \frac{m_1 + m_2}{m_1} \sqrt{2gh} \tag{10aa}$$

All quantities on the right in this equation can be measured by experiment, and the substitution of any set of measurements will give the muzzle velocity u. It should be noted that since the velocity of separation between the bullet and block is zero, the coefficient of restitution $r = 0$.

A good laboratory demonstration of ballistics measurements can be performed with a wood block* as shown at the right in Fig. 10M, and a .22-caliber rifle as shown at the left. Typical bullets, shells, and assembled cartridges to be used, commonly available in sporting-goods stores, are shown in Fig. 10N. The .22-short, .22-long, and .22-high-velocity cartridges shown at the right are combinations of two bullet sizes with two shell sizes shown at the left.

* Appropriate wood blocks for this experiment may be made of hardwood, about 2 in. in diameter and 4.5 in. long, with one or two tightly fitted metal bands to prevent splitting. The same block can be used for several firings. Hardwood balls 3 in. in diameter are sometimes available in lumberyards or hardware stores, and may be used in place of cylinders.

Example 4. A rifle pointing straight upward has a 4.50-Kg block of wood resting on the muzzle end of the barrel. When the rifle fires a 25.0-g bullet into the block, it becomes embedded in the wood, and the block recoils to a height of 2.850 m before falling back. Find the bullet's muzzle velocity.

Solution. The given quantities are $m_1 = 0.0250$ Kg, $m_2 = 4.50$ Kg, $g = 9.80$ m/s², and $h = 2.850$ m. By direct substitution in Eq.(10aa), we obtain

$$u = \frac{m_1 + m_2}{m_1}\sqrt{2gh}$$

$$u = \frac{0.025\text{ Kg} + 4.5\text{ Kg}}{0.025\text{ Kg}}\sqrt{2 \times 9.8\,\frac{\text{m}}{\text{s}^2} \times 2.85\text{ m}}$$

$$u = 1353\,\frac{\text{m}}{\text{s}}$$

problems

1. A 2000-Kg car drives from the street level to the fourth floor of a car parking building. The car maintains a speed of 2.50 m/s on the ramps as well as on the first, second, and the third floor levels. All floors are spaced 3.50 m apart, with the first floor at street level. (a) Calculate the total energy at each floor level. (b) Plot an energy level diagram.

2. An elevator with a 500-Kg car goes from the subbasement 7.0 m below the street level to the fifth floor of an apartment building. All floors are 3.50 m apart. Starting from rest of the subbasement, the elevator passes all floors at a speed of 2.50 m/s, and stops at the top floor. (a) Calculate the total energy at each floor level. (b) Plot an energy level diagram for the total energy at each floor level. Assume the ground level to be the zero point.

3. A loaded jet plane with a mass of 1.20×10^5 Kg takes off from the Denver Airport, where the elevation is 1.60 Km above sea level. Climbing to a height of 8.0 Km above sea level it acquires a speed of 720 Km/h. Approaching a storm over the Midwest, it now climbs to a height of 12.0 Km above sea level, where it cruises at 810 Km/h. Approaching New York City the plane descends to 3.0 Km, where awaiting landing instructions it cruises at 360.0 Km/h. Receiving landing instructions the plane lands and comes to rest at the air terminal. Assuming the airport in New York is approximately at sea level, find (a) the total energy at each level during the flight. (b) Plot an energy level

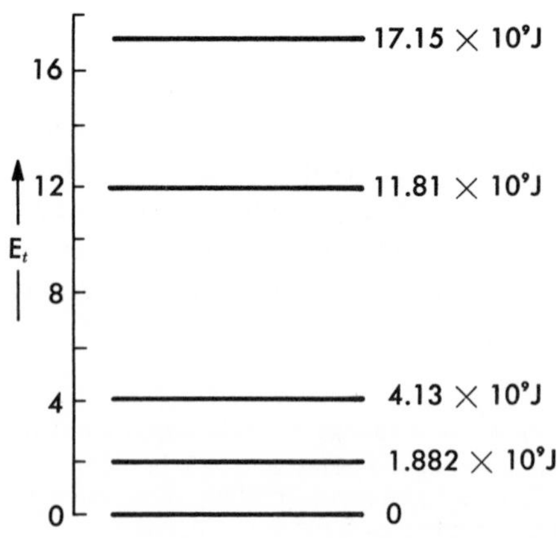

Prob. 3. Energy level diagram for jet plane.

diagram. [Ans. (a) 1.882×10^9 J, 11.81×10^9 J, 17.15×10^9 J, 4.128×10^9 J, 0.]

4. If 160.0 m^3 of water goes over a waterfall 42.0 m high every minute of time, (a) find the power in watts. What is this power in kilowatts?

5. A 4.50-Kg bowling ball is suspended from the ceiling, as a simple pendulum, by a cable. If the pendulum is 5.0 m long, and is pulled back until the cable makes an angle of 45° with the vertical, (a) what is its potential energy? (b) What will be its maximum kinetic energy, and (c) its velocity at the bottom of its swing?

6. A 5.0-Kg ball moving with a velocity of 9.0 m/s collides head-on with another ball with a mass of 2.0 Kg and initially at rest. After impact the first ball is moving in the forward direction but with a velocity of 5.0 m/s. Calculate (a) the velocity of the second mass after impact, (b) the initial kinetic energy, (c) the total kinetic energy after impact, (d) the energy converted into heat during impact, (e) the relative velocity of approach before impact, and (f) the relative velocity after impact. [Ans. (a) 10.0 m/s, (b) 202.5 J, (c) 162.5 J, (d) 40.0 J, (e) 9.0 m/s, (f) 5.0 m/s.]

7. A 2.0-Kg ball moving with a velocity of 6.0 m/s collides head-on with a 3.0-Kg ball initially at rest. After impact the velocity of the 3.0-Kg ball is 2.50 m/s in the forward direction. Find (a) the velocity of the first mass after impact, (b) the initial kinetic energy, (c) the total kinetic energy after impact, (d) the energy loss during impact, (e) the relative velocity before impact, and (f) the relative velocity after impact.

8. A rifle pointing straight upward has a 4.50-Kg block of wood resting on the muzzle end of the barrel. When the rifle fires a 60.0-g bullet into the block, it becomes embedded in the wood, and the block rises to a height of 5.20 m before falling back. Find the muzzle velocity of the bullet.

9. An 8.40-Kg wooden block hangs as a pendulum by vertical strings 4.0 m long. When a 12.0-g bullet is fired at close range into the block, and it becomes embedded in the wood, the block swings to a height where the strings make an angle of 26° with the vertical. Find (a) the recoil height of the block, (b) the recoil speed of the block, and (c) the speed of the bullet. Make a diagram. [Ans. (a) 0.405 m, (b) 2.817 m/s, (c) 1975 m/s.]

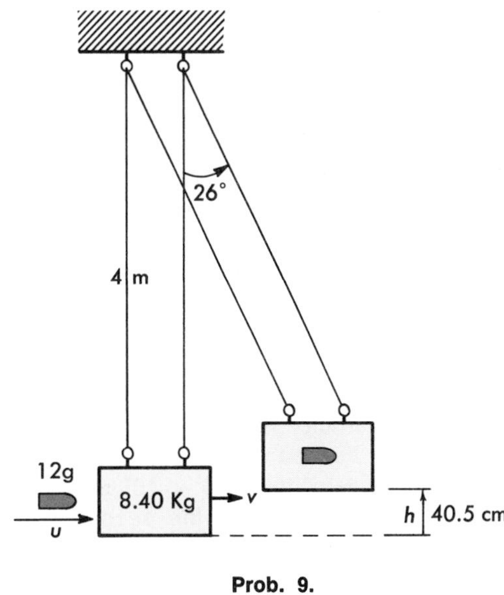

Prob. 9.

10. A 10.5-Kg block of wood hangs by cords as a pendulum 2.0 m long. A bullet enters the block causing it to swing to a height where the cords make an angle of 35° with the vertical. If the bullet has a mass of 15.0 g, find (a) the recoil height of the block, (b) the recoil velocity of the block, and (c) the bullet's velocity. Make a diagram.

11. A plastic ball with a mass of 0.80 Kg and a velocity of 2.60 m/s collides head-on with another plastic ball of the same size and mass at rest. If the coefficient of restitution is 0.70, find the velocity of each ball after collision.

12. A metal ball with a mass of 4.40 Kg, moving with a velocity of 6.0 m/s, collides head-on with another metal ball with a mass of 5.60 Kg traveling in the same direction with a velocity of 2.0 m/s. If the coefficient of restitution is 0.85, find the velocity of each ball after impact. [Ans. (a) $v_1 = 1.856$ m/s, (b) $v_2 = 5.256$ m/s.]

13.* A 5-Kg ball traveling at 8.0 m/s collides with a 6.0-Kg ball initially at rest. After impact the 5.0-Kg mass is traveling in a new direction, but with a velocity of 4.0 m/s. Assuming perfect elasticity, find (a) the angle m_1 makes with its original direction, (b) the velocity of m_2, and (c) the direction of m_2. Make a diagram.

14.* A perfectly elastic sphere with a mass of 8.0 Kg moving with a velocity of 6.0 m/s collides with another perfectly elastic sphere with a mass of 5.0 Kg initially at rest. After impact the first mass is moving away with a velocity of 4.0 m/s. Find (a) the direction of m_1, (b) the velocity of m_2, and (c) the direction of m_2. Make a diagram.

15.* An atomic particle with a mass of 7.2×10^{-28} Kg moving with a velocity of 6.0×10^7 m/s collides with a second atomic particle with exactly half the mass, and at rest. If the first particle is deflected through an angle θ, and its velocity is 5.0×10^7 m/s, find (a) the angle θ, (b) the velocity of the second particle, (c) the direction of the second particle, (d) the total kinetic energy before impact, and (e) the total energy after impact. Make a diagram. [Ans. (a) $\theta = 22.3°$, (b) 4.690×10^7 m/s, (c) 54.1°, (d) 1.296×10^{-12} J, (e) 1.296×10^{-12} J.]

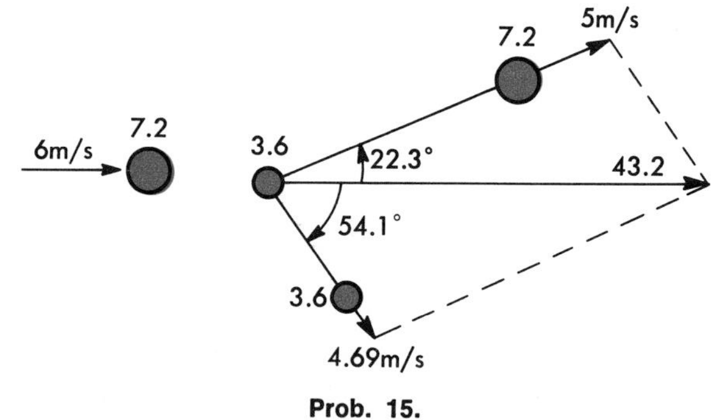

Prob. 15.

16. An ivory ball is dropped from a height of 2.0 m onto the smooth surface of a steel anvil. If the coefficient of restitution is 0.60, find the height to which it bounces on (a) the first, (b) the second, and (c) the third bounce.

17. A steel marble is dropped onto the smooth surface of a steel anvil and the coefficient of restitution is found to be 0.95. If this marble is dropped from a height of 1.0 m, how many times will it bounce higher than 0.50 m?

11 Circular motion and Kepler's laws

The universe as we know it today is a dynamic system of moving bodies. From the tiniest of atomic particles on the one hand, to the largest stars on the other, we can say that everything is in a state of motion. It can be shown that any motion we can impose upon any rigid body can be resolved into two components. One component is a simple *translation* without *rotation,* and the other is a *rotation* without *translation.*

Try moving any object from one specified position and orientation, to some other position and orientation. You will find that this same change can be brought about by a pure rotation about some axis followed by a pure translation, or the reverse.

Under the conditions of Newton's first law of motion, a body at rest remains at rest, while a body moving with constant velocity continues to move along the same straight line with constant speed. When a constant force is applied, the body is accelerated along a straight-line path, or under special conditions, as in falling bodies, along a parabolic path.

In this chapter we are concerned with motions in which a body is acted upon by what is called a *central force.* When a body moves under a central force, the path may have the shape of any one of the conic sections, a *circle, ellipse, parabola, hyperbola,* or *straight line.* The first two are the subjects of this chapter.

11.1. Rotational Speed and Angular Velocity

The speed with which a body rotates is called its rotational speed, or *frequency.* Either of these terms refers to the number of complete revolutions a body makes in unit time and is designated by the letter n:

$$n = \text{number of revolutions per second}$$

A flywheel, for example, might be said to have a rotational

speed of 10 revolutions per second (10 rps). This is equivalent to a rotational speed or frequency of 600 revolutions per minute (600 rpm), and to a speed or frequency of 36,000 revolutions per hour (36,000 rph).

In formulating the laws of mechanics it will be found convenient to express all rotation in radians, not in degrees or revolutions. *The radian* (rad) *is a unit of angular measure,* just as the centimeter is a unit of linear measure. It is defined as the angle subtended by the arc of a circle whose length is equal to the radius of the same circle. Referring to Fig. 11A, the distance x measured along the arc is equal to the radius r, and the angle $\theta = 1$ radian.

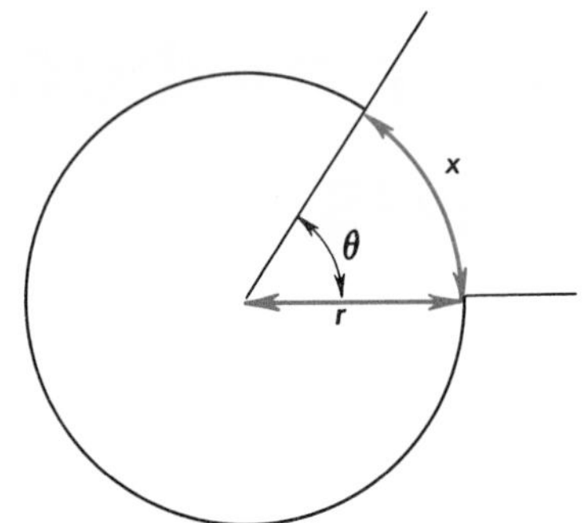

Fig. 11A. The radian is a unit of angular measure. When the arc equals the radius r, the angle θ equals one radian.

Since the entire circumference of a circle is just 2π times the radius r, there are 2π radians in one complete circle:

$$2\pi \text{ radians} = 360°$$

Since $\pi = 3.14159$,

$$1 \text{ radian} = 57.296°$$

It follows from the above relations that the angle θ in radians between any two points on the circumference of a circle is given by x, the length of the arc between the two points, divided by the radius r. In other words,

$$\text{angle in radians} = \frac{\text{arc length}}{\text{radius}}$$

or, an algebraic symbols,

$$\theta = \frac{x}{r} \qquad (11a)$$

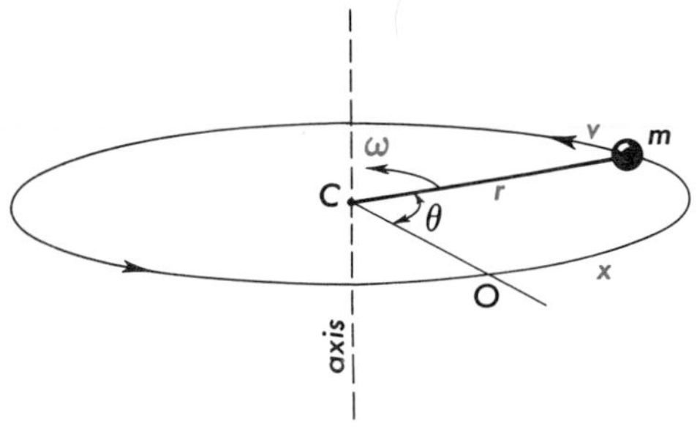

Fig. 11B. An illustration of circular motion.

The reason for measuring angles in radians is that it simplifies all formulas for rotary motion. As an illustration, consider the speed of a stone being whirled on the end of a string as shown in Fig. 11B.

The angular velocity of a rotating body is defined as the angle turned through, divided by the elapsed time:

$$\text{angular velocity} = \frac{\text{angle turned through}}{\text{elapsed time}}$$

The angle through $\Delta\theta$ is equal to $\theta_2 - \theta_1$, and the elapsed time of turning Δt is equal to $t_2 - t_1$:

$$\Delta\theta = \theta_2 - \theta_1$$

$$\Delta t = t_2 - t_1$$

In symbols, the angular velocity is defined as

$$\omega = \frac{\theta_2 - \theta_1}{t_2 - t_1}$$

or

$$\omega = \frac{\Delta\theta}{\Delta t} \qquad (11b)$$

increment notation

If we start at $\theta_1 = 0$ and $t_1 = 0$, this equation becomes simply

$$\omega = \theta/t \qquad (11c)$$

and is to be compared with the corresponding definition of linear velocity,

$$v = x/t \qquad (11d)$$

Angular velocity ω corresponds to linear velocity v, and angular displacement θ corresponds to linear displacement x. With θ measured in radians and t in seconds, the angular velocity ω has the units of radians per second (rad/s).

Example 1. A stone on the end of a string 0.50 m long makes 8.0 revolutions in 2.0 s. Find the angular velocity in radians per second.

Solution. Since 1.0 revolution $= 2\pi$ radians, 8.0 revolutions are equivalent to

$$\theta = 8 \times 2\pi = 50.3 \text{ rad}$$

Direct substitution in Eq.(11b) gives

$$\omega = \frac{\theta}{t} = \frac{50.3 \text{ rad}}{2 \text{ s}} = 25.15 \frac{\text{rad}}{\text{s}}$$

To find the linear speed of the stone along its curved path, Eqs.(11a), (11c), and (11d) can be used by combining them as follows. Solving Eq.(11a) for x, we obtain

$$x = r\theta \tag{11e}$$

Substitute $r\theta$ for x in Eq.(11d):

$$v = \frac{r\theta}{t} = r\frac{\theta}{t}$$

Replace θ/t by ω from Eq.(11c) and we obtain

$$v = r\omega \tag{11f}$$

From Example 1 of the stone on a string in Fig. 11B, we can now calculate the speed of the stone from the known values of r and ω. Since the angular velocity $\omega = 25.1$ rad/s, and the length of the string, r, is 0.50 m, then, in 1.0 s ($t = 1$ s), the angle turned through will be 25.1 rad, and the velocity will be

$$v = 0.50 \text{ m} \times 25.15 \frac{\text{rad}}{\text{s}} = 12.58 \frac{\text{m}}{\text{s}}$$

If it is required to find the distance traveled in 5.0 s, Eq.(11d) can be used as follows:

$$x = vt = 12.58 \frac{\text{m}}{\text{s}} \times 5 \text{ s} = 62.9 \text{ m}$$

To find the total angle turned through in 5.0 s, Eq.(11a) can be used:

$$\theta = \frac{x}{r} = \frac{62.9}{0.50} = 125.8 \text{ rad}$$

Likewise, Eq.(11c) can be used to find the angle turned through:

$$\theta = \omega t = 25.1 \frac{\text{rad}}{\text{s}} \times 5 \text{ s} = 125.5 \text{ rad}$$

Note that all equations are consistent with each other and that the radian as a unit has no dimensions. The radian is the ratio between two lengths and therefore has the same value in all systems of units. It is for this reason that it can be canceled out where it is not needed, or added where necessary in the above answers to give the results meaning.

11.2. Centripetal Force

When a stone is whirling on the end of a string, there is an inward force exerted by the string on the ball. This force is called the *centripetal force* (see Fig. 11C). Since the only force acting on the ball is inward, the ball is not in equilibrium but is being continually accelerated in the direction of the force, that is, toward the center.

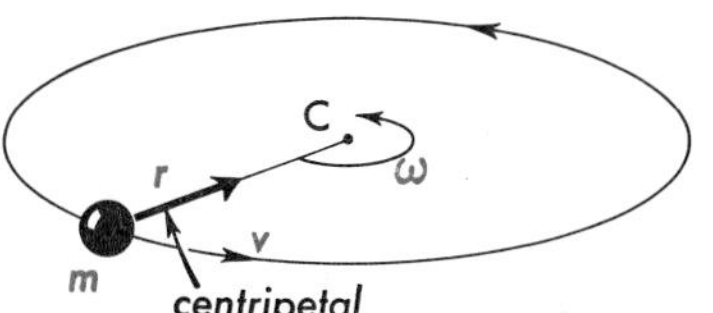

Fig. 11C. A mass *m*, moving in a circle, experiences an acceleration toward the center.

This appears to be a physical paradox, for here is a body moving with constant speed in a circle and yet being accelerated toward the center of the circle without getting any closer to it. If the string were to break suddenly, the ball would fly off on a tangent to the circle and move with constant velocity according to Newton's first law.

To obtain a clearer picture of centripetal force and acceleration toward the center, motion in a circle is to be compared with the motion of a projectile accelerated downward by the pull of gravity as shown in Fig. 8G. Due to the earth's attraction of all bodies, a projectile is continually accelerated downward, away from the straight line of its original projection. In circular motion the mass is continually accelerated toward the center, always at right angles to its instantaneous velocity and away from any straight-line tangent along which it would travel if suddenly released.

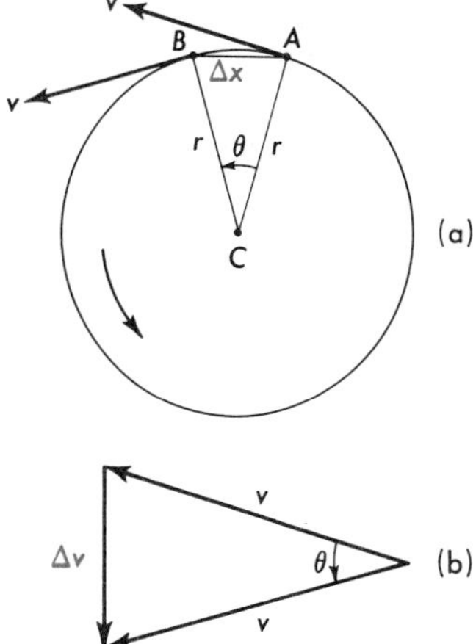

Fig. 11D. Geometry for deriving the equation for centripetal acceleration.

The instantaneous velocity is shown at two points, A and B, in diagram (a) of Fig. 11D. The velocity, as indicated by the vectors *v*, is seen to be changing in direction but not in magnitude. Diagram (b) is a velocity diagram showing Δv as the change in velocity that occurs in going from A to B. Since this velocity triangle is similar to triangle ABC in diagram (a), corresponding sides are proportional to each other, and the following can be written:

$$\frac{\Delta v}{v} = \frac{\Delta x}{r} \tag{11g}$$

or

$$\Delta v = \frac{v}{r}\,\Delta x$$

We now divide both sides of the equation by Δt, the time re-

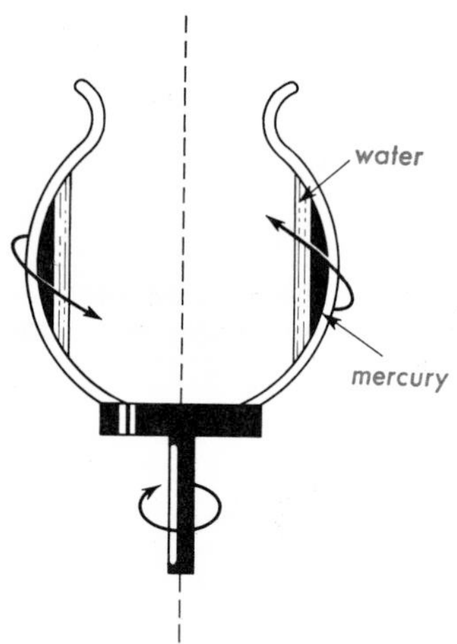

Fig. 11E. Mercury and water rotate in a dish; the water is inside the mercury. Centripetal force, like gravitational force, is greater for the denser substance.

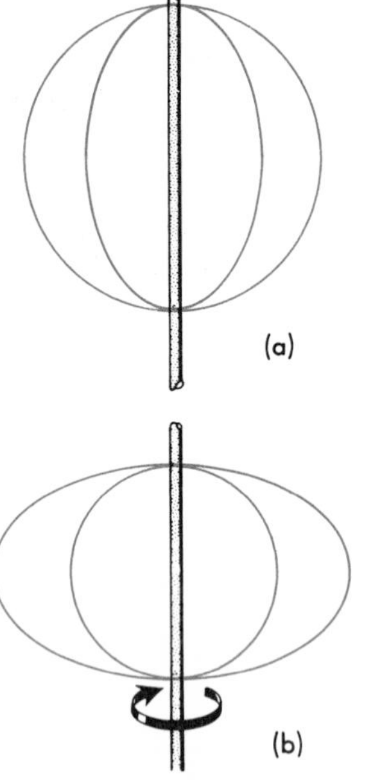

Fig. 11F. The flattening of the earth is due to its rotation about the polar axis.

quired to go from A to B, and we obtain

$$\frac{\Delta v}{\Delta t} = \frac{v}{r}\frac{\Delta x}{\Delta t}$$

As the angle θ in Fig. 11D is made smaller and smaller, the chord length Δx becomes closer and closer to the arc length AB, while the change in velocity Δv, which gives the direction of the acceleration a, becomes more nearly perpendicular to v. In the limit as $\Delta t \to 0$, $\Delta v/\Delta t$ approaches the acceleration a, $\Delta x/\Delta t$ approaches r, and

$$a = \lim_{t \to 0} \frac{v}{r}\frac{\Delta x}{\Delta t} \tag{11h}$$

giving

$$a = \frac{v^2}{r} \tag{11i}$$

This is the *centripetal acceleration.*

If we substitute $r\omega$ for v [Eq.(11f)], the centripetal acceleration can be expressed in terms of the angular velocity ω:

$$a = r\omega^2 \tag{11j}$$

Centripetal force is defined as that constant force which, acting continuously at right angles to the motion of a particle, causes it to move in a circle with constant speed. Since by Newton's second law of motion, $F = ma$, the centripetal force is given by

$$F = m\frac{v^2}{r} \tag{11k}$$

or in angular quantities by

$$F = mr\omega^2 \tag{11\ell}$$

Example 2. A mass of 5.0 Kg is moving in a circle of 1.0-m radius with an angular velocity of 2.0 rad/s. Find the centripetal force.
Solution. The known quantities substituted directly in Eq.(11ℓ) give

$$F = 5\ \text{Kg} \times 1\ \text{m} \times \left(2\ \frac{\text{rad}}{\text{s}}\right)^2 = 20.0\ \frac{\text{Kg m}}{\text{s}^2} = 20.0\ \text{N}$$

Note: Radians have no dimensions and are therefore dropped out in arriving at the force.

By Newton's third law of motion, centripetal force has a *reaction force.* This oppositely directed force is called the *centripetal force.* Referring to Fig. 11C, the centrifugal force, equal in magnitude to the centripetal force, is an outward force exerted by the ball on the string. The string in turn transmits this outward force to the center pin C. It should be emphasized, however, that the centrifugal force does not act on the ball. Only one force acts on the ball and that is the one shown, the centripetal force.

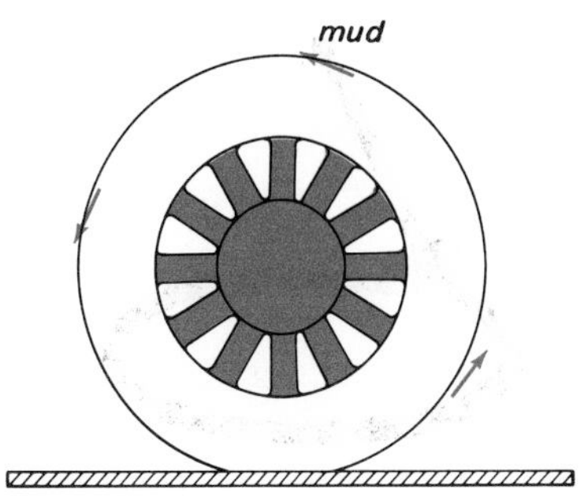

Fig. 11G. Mud or water on a fast-turning wheel flies off on a tangent.

11.3. Experiments Demonstrating Centripetal Force

Many interesting experiments can be performed to illustrate centripetal force. In Fig. 11E mercury and water have been placed in a dish and the dish set rotating rapidly about a vertical axis. Since mercury is 13.6 times as heavy as an equal volume of water, the centripetal force F on each cm^3 of mercury is 13.6 times larger than on each cm^3 of water. The mercury therefore takes the outermost position in the dish. This is the principle of the centrifuge and ultracentrifuge, a spinning device used for separating materials having different densities.

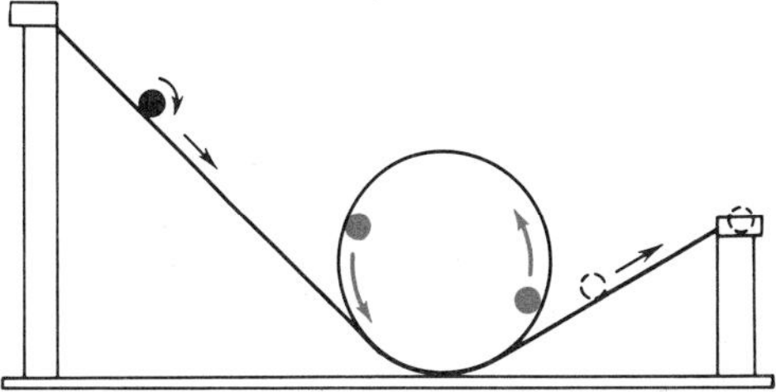

Fig. 11H. The ball will loop the loop if it starts rolling from a point high enough on the incline.

Although the earth is often said to be spherical, it is in reality an oblate spheroid; that is, a slightly flattened sphere. Accurate measurements show that the earth's diameter is 28 mi greater through the equator than it is through the poles. The cause for this flattening is illustrated in Fig. 11F by two circular metal strips. Diagram (a) shows the strips to be round when at rest, while (b) shows the flattening due to rapid rotation. The flattening of the earth is due to its own rotation of 2π rad every 24 h. It is the enormous size of the earth and its lack of greater rigidity that makes it behave as through it were soft and semiplastic.

Mud or water clings to an automobile tire until the speed becomes too high and then it flies off on a tangent, as shown in Fig. 11G. To remain with the tire the required contripetal force cannot exceed the force of adhesion.

Figure 11H shows a ball rolling down a looped track. The ball will stay with the track even at the top of the loop if the required

Fig. 11I. A lariat takes a circular form because each small part tries to fly off on a tangent, thus getting as far from the center as possible. Centripetal force is responsible for keeping it in a circle.

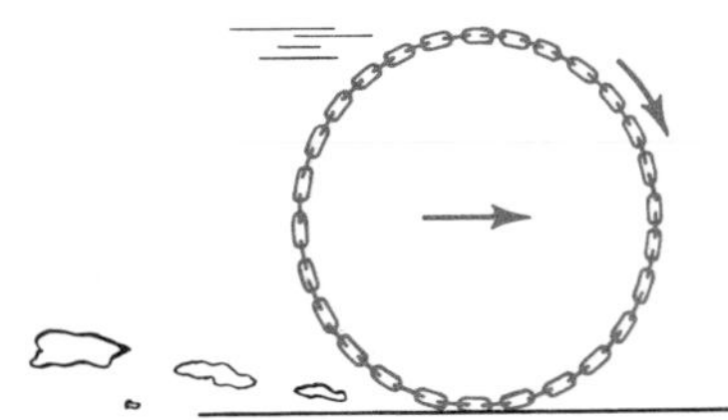

Fig. 11J. A chain turning at high speed will roll along the level as a rigid wheel.

centripetal force there is equal to or greater than the downward force of gravity. This means that the speed v must be greater than a certain critical speed or the ball will fall. Such a behavior is similar to that of whirling a bucket of water in a circle up over the head and down, at arm's length, without spilling it. To find the critical velocity at the top of the circle, the centripetal force mv^2/r is equated to the body's weight mg. This is the same as equating the centripetal acceleration v^2/r to the acceleration of gravity g. For any given radius r, the critical speed becomes fixed by the equation

$$g = \frac{v^2}{r} \tag{11m}$$

When a stone on the end of a string is whirled in a vertical circle, gravity acts downward upon it at all times. At the bottom of its path, the weight must be added to the centripetal force to obtain the tension in the string, while at the top of its path the weight must be subtracted.

When a stone on the end of a string is whirled in a horizontal circle, the stone's weight is at all times perpendicular to centripetal force, and the string describes a cone. The *centripetal force* F is the resultant of two forces, the *tension* T in the string and the *weight* F_g. The forces F and F_g are at right angles.

The opening of the loop in a lariat as whirled and thrown by a cowboy is due to centripetal force (see Fig. 11I). Because of rotation, each small section of the rope, acting as an individual mass m, tends to fly off on a tangent and thus get as far from the center of rotation as possible. The average distance from the center of all sections of the rope is a maximum when the loop takes the form of a circle rotating about an axis perpendicular to the plane of the loop.

When a small chain, as shown in Fig. 11J, is set rotating at high speed by an electric motor and then set free, it will roll along the floor as though it were a rigid metal hoop. Upon bumping into an obstacle, it will bounce into the air, and upon coming down, will retain its circular form as it rolls on. The rigidity of the hoop is due to the enormous centripetal force attained at high angular velocities.

11.4. Planetary Motion

According to astronomical history, it was the early Greek philosopher Pythagoras (530 B.C.) who said "the world is round and hangs in space." "The earth," he said, "does not stand still but revolves around a central fire, called Hestia. This fire is not the sun, for the sun is illuminated, as are the planets, by reflection from Hestia."

This idea lay dormant for 2000 years before Copernicus,* at the beginning of the 16th century, said "the sun stands still and the earth and planets move in orbits around it." The observational and mathematical proof that all the planets move in elliptical orbits was first presented in 1609 when Johannes Kepler* published a book containing two of his three laws which are now known as Kepler's Laws of Planetary Motion.

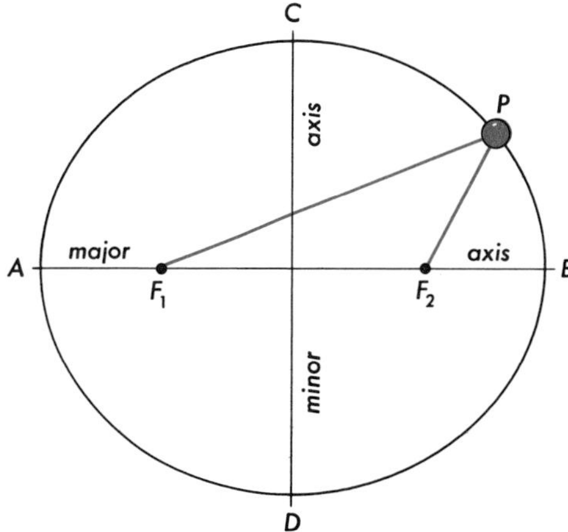

Fig. 11K. An ellipse can be drawn with two pins, a string, and a pencil.

11.5. Kepler's First Law

The planets move in elliptical orbits with the sun at one of the foci.

An ellipse can be constructed by fastening the two ends of a piece of string to two pins, F_1 and F_2, as shown in Fig. 11K. By keeping the string tight with a pencil at P, the complete arc can be swung around, much the same as one draws a circle with a compass.

If the length of the string remains unchanged, and the foci F_1 and F_2 are brought closer and closer together, the major axis AB and the minor axis CD become more and more nearly equal; in the limit when the foci coincide, the axes are equal and the ellipse becomes a circle. The real orbits of the planets are so nearly circular, however, that if they were drawn with a compass, the ellipse would differ from the circle by less than the thickness of the pencil line.

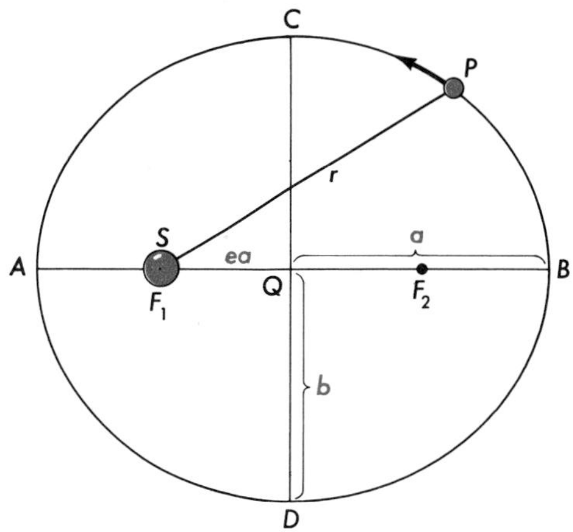

Fig. 11L. Elliptical orbit with an eccentricity $e = 0.5$.

The eccentricity e of an ellipse is defined as the ratio of the distances SQ and AQ (see Fig. 11L):

$$e = \frac{\text{SQ}}{\text{AQ}} \tag{11n}$$

where AQ is the semimajor axis a, and SQ is equal to ea. With the sun at one focus, the distance of closest approach AS is called *perihelion*, and the greatest distance BS is called *aphelion.* A little study of Fig. 11L will enable the reader to find that

* See Introduction A, for biographies of Copernicus, Tycho Brahe, and Johannes Kepler.

$$\text{aphelion} = a(1 + e)$$
$$\text{perihelion} = a(1 - e) \tag{11o}$$
$$b = a\sqrt{1 - e^2}$$

where b is the semiminor axis DQ.

These equations are readily derived by noting that if straight lines are drawn from F_1 and F_2 to the point D, the distance F_1DF_2 equals the length of the major axis $2a$, and that these two lines form right triangles with a as the hypotenuse for each.

That point of a satellite's orbit closest to the earth, moon, or Jupiter is called *perigee, perilune,* and *perijove,* respectively, while the orbital point farthest away is called *apogee, apolune,* and *apojove,* respectively.

Example 3. An ellipse is to be drawn with a major axis of 20.0 cm and a minor axis of 10.0 cm. Find the (a) eccentricity, (b) perihelion, (c) aphelion, (d) distance between foci, and (e) length of string to use in drawing this ellipse.

Solution. The known quantities are $a = 10.0$ cm and $b = 5.0$ cm. To find (a) use the third Eq.(11o), by solving first for the unknown, e:

$$e = \sqrt{\frac{a^2 - b^2}{a^2}}$$

Substituting known quantities we obtain

$$e = \sqrt{\frac{100 - 25}{100}} = 0.866$$

(b) By direct substitution in Eq.(11o), we obtain

$$\text{perihelion} = 10(1 - 0.866) = 1.340 \text{ cm}$$

(c) By direct substitution in the first Eq.(11o), we obtain

$$\text{aphelion} = 5(1 + 0.866) = 9.33 \text{ cm}$$

(d) Subtract twice the perihelion distance from the major axis:

$$20.0 - 2.68 = 17.32 \text{ cm}$$

(e) Note in Fig. 11K, that when P is at B, the string will go from F_1 to B to F_2. This is just the length of the major axis, or 20.0 cm.

11.6. Kepler's Second Law

The straight line joining the sun and any planet sweeps out equal areas in equal intervals of time.

As shown in Fig. 11M, the straight line referred to is called the *radius vector;* it varies in length from a minimum at perihelion to a maximum at aphelion. Although the orbit of the earth is nearly circular, the numbers 1, 2, 3, 4, etc., correspond to the position of the earth at the end of each 12 equal months.

To cover these unequal orbital distances in equal intervals of time, the speed must be a maximum at perihelion and a minimum six months later at aphelion. During the periods 1 to 2 and 7 to 8, for example, the areas swept out are equal.

As the earth moves along its orbit in September, October, November, etc., the attractive force of the sun causes it to speed up. Upon reaching perihelion at the end of December, its speed is a maximum, and too fast to remain at this distance r_1 from the sun. During the months of March, April, May, etc., the earth is receding from the sun, and the attractive force of the sun slows the earth down. Upon reaching aphelion at the end of June, the speed of the revolving earth is a minimum, too slow to keep it at this greater distance r_2 from the sun. The average distance from the sun is 149,000,000,000 m, while the average orbital speed of the earth is 29,800 m/s.

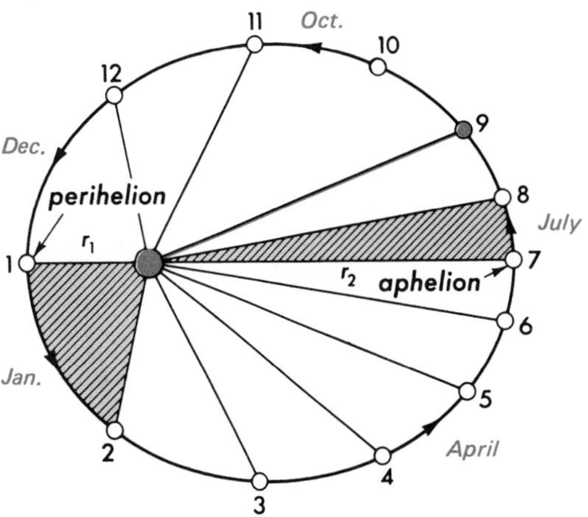

Fig. 11M. Elliptical orbit of the earth, showing equal areas swept out by the radius vector in equal intervals of time.

11.7. Kepler's Third Law

The squares of the orbital periods of the planets are proportional to the cubes of their mean distances from the sun.

The period T of a planet, or satellite, is defined as the time required to make one complete trip around its orbit; the mean

TABLE 11A
Measured characteristics of the planets

Name	*Period T* (years)	*Mean distance* (mi × 10^6)	(Km × 10^6)	$\frac{T^2}{r^3}$	*Mean radius* (mi)	(Km)	*Mass* (Kg 10^{24})
Mercury	0.241	36.0	57.9	1.245	1504.3	2421.1	0.3244
Venus	0.615	67.1	108.1	1.252	3828.2	6161.0	4.861
Earth	1.000	92.9	149.5	1.247	3958.9	6370.0	5.975
Mars	1.881	141.5	227.8	1.249	2070.5	3332.1	0.6387
Jupiter	11.862	483.3	777.8	1.246	43429.0	69892.0	1902.1
Saturn	29.458	886.1	1426.0	1.247	35748.5	57532.0	569.4
Uranus	84.015	1783.0	2869.0	1.245	14727.0	23701.0	87.1
Neptune	164.790	2793.0	4496.0	1.246	13381.0	21535.0	103.1
Pluto	247.700	3665.0	5899.0	1.246	1781.4	2867.0	0.5?

distance r is defined as the average distance away from the sun. Important data on the nine major planets of the solar system are given in Table 11A. The constant ratios in column five verify Kepler's Third Law.

While Kepler's laws were originally derived from Tycho Brahe's careful observations, they are readily derived from the basic laws of classical mechanics.

For simplicity we will assume that the orbit of the earth is circular, as shown in Fig. 11N. In this diagram, M is the mass of the sun, m is the mass of a planet like the earth, and r is the distance between their centers. The centripetal force F, as given by Eq.(11k), is just the force of gravitational attraction given by Eq.(6a). These are

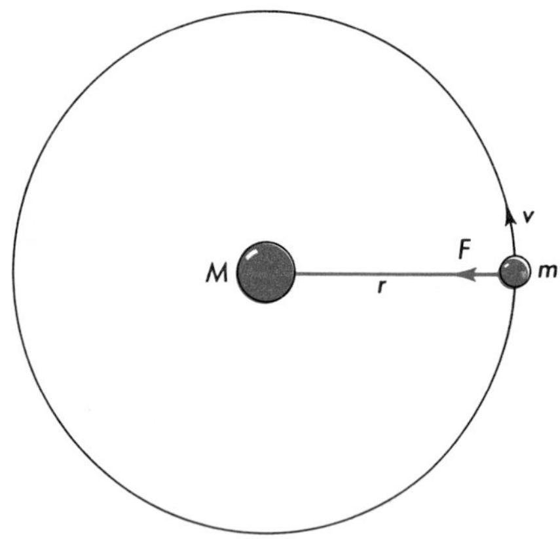

Fig. 11N. The gravitational force attraction F is the centripetal force that keeps the earth in its nearly circular orbit around the sun.

$$F = m\frac{v^2}{r} \qquad F = G\frac{Mm}{r^2} \tag{11p}$$

centripetal force **Newton's law of gravitation**

where

$$G = 6.6732 \times 10^{-11}\ \frac{\text{m}^3}{\text{Kg s}^2}$$

Since these two equations are different expressions for the same force F, the right-hand sides may be placed equal to each other, which gives

$$G\frac{Mm}{r^2} = m\frac{v^2}{r}$$

Upon simplifying, this equation becomes

$$\frac{GM}{r} = v^2 \tag{11q}$$

The orbital velocity of any planet is given, therefore, by the very simple relation

$$v = \sqrt{\frac{GM}{r}} \tag{11r}$$

orbiting velocity

In mechanics the velocity of a body is given by $v = x/t$. If we choose the distance x to be once around the orbit, the time t then becomes the period T, and we obtain

$$v = \frac{2\pi r}{T} \tag{11s}$$

By squaring both sides of this equation, and substituting the right-hand side for v^2 in Eq.(11r), we can write

$$\frac{GM}{r} = \frac{4\pi^2 r^2}{T^2} \tag{11t}$$

or

$$T^2 = \left(\frac{4\pi^2}{GM}\right) r^3 \tag{11u}$$

Since all quantities in parentheses are constants, $T^2 \propto r^3$, and Kepler's third law is consistent with the laws of classical mechanics.

problems

1. A box with a mass of 25.0 Kg rests on the floor of a merry-go-round, 4.0 m from the center. If the coefficient of sliding friction is 0.340, find (a) the force of friction, (b) the angular velocity at which the box will just begin to slide, and (c) the speed of the box at that moment.

2. A car with a mass of 2200 Kg rounds a curve of 420 m radius, at 95.0 Km/h. What is (a) its angular velocity in rad/s, (b) the centripetal acceleration, and (c) the centripetal force?

3. A motorcycle rider, going 90.0 Km/h around a curve with a radius of 100.0 m, must lean at an angle to the vertical. Find (a) the velocity in m/s, (b) the centripetal acceleration, and (c) the angle at which he leans. Make a diagram. [Ans. (a) 25.0 m/s, (b) 6.25 m/s², (c) 32.53°.]

4. A car with a mass of 2000 Kg, traveling at 81.0 Km/h, rounds a curve of 120.0 m radius. Find (a) the speed of the car in m/s, (b) the centripetal acceleration, and (c) the angle the road should be banked if there is no tendency to slip. Make a diagram.

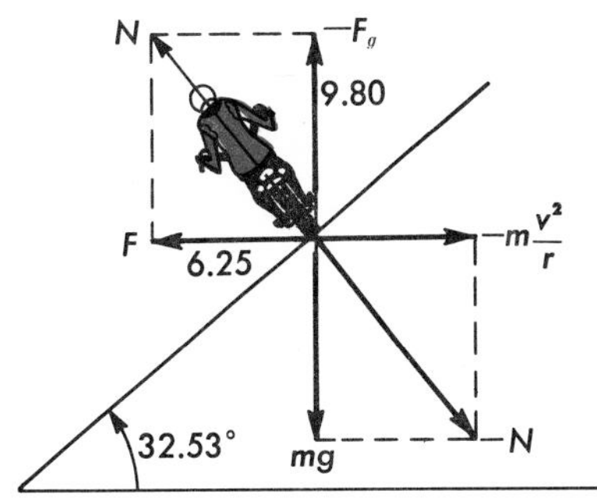

Prob. 3.

5. A man living at the equator weighs himself and finds his mass is 75.0 Kg. What correction should be made for the earth's rotation?

6. If a pail of water is swung in a vertical circle at arms' length, find (a) the minimum speed at the top to ensure that no water spills out, and (b) the corresponding angular velocity. Assume r = 1.0 m. [Ans. (a) 3.130 m/s, (b) 3.130 rad/s.]

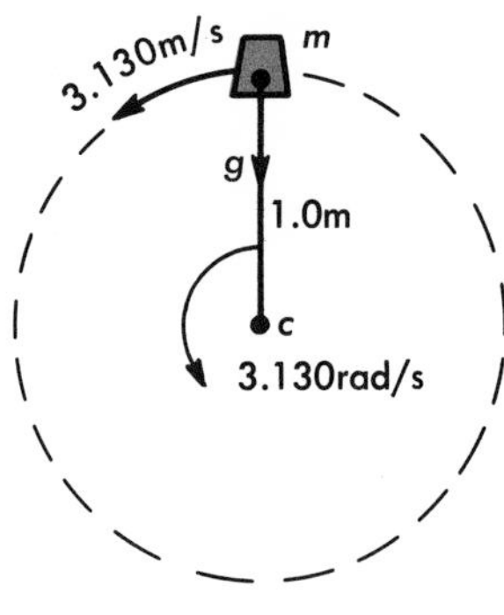

Prob. 6.

7. A 45.0-Kg stone is whirled at 60.0 rpm in a circle at the end of a wire 1.40 m long. If the plane of the circle is vertical, what is the tension in the wire, (a) at the top of the circle, and (b) at the bottom?

8. A 2.0-Kg stone is whirled in a horizontal circle at the end of a 2.0 m long cord. If the cord stands out at an angle of 30° with the vertical, find (a) the radius of the stone's circle, (b) the angular velocity, and (c) the centripetal force. Make a diagram.

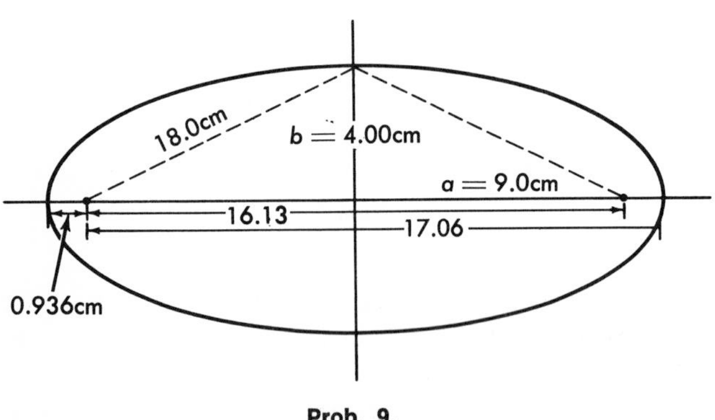

Prob. 9.

9. An ellipse is to be drawn with a major axis of 18.0 cm, and a minor axis of 8.0 cm. Find (a) the eccentricity, (b) the maximum orbital distance, (c) the minimum orbital distance, (d) the distance between foci, and (e) the length of the string required to draw this ellipse on paper. [Ans. (a) 0.896, (b) 17.06 cm, (c) 0.936 cm, (d) 16.13 cm, (e) 18.0 cm.]

10. An ellipse is drawn with two pins as focal points 6.0 cm apart. The ends of a string are tied to these pins so the string is 10.0 cm long. Find (a) the major axis, (b) the minor axis, (c) the eccentricity, (d) the maximum orbital distance, and (e) the minimum orbital distance. Make a diagram.

11.* A satellite put into orbit for relaying TV signals back to earth is at apogee 13,630 Km, and at perigee 630 Km, above the earth's surface. Find (a) the semimajor axis, (b) the semiminor axis, (c) the perigee distance, (d) the apogee distance, and (e) the eccentricity. Make a diagram.

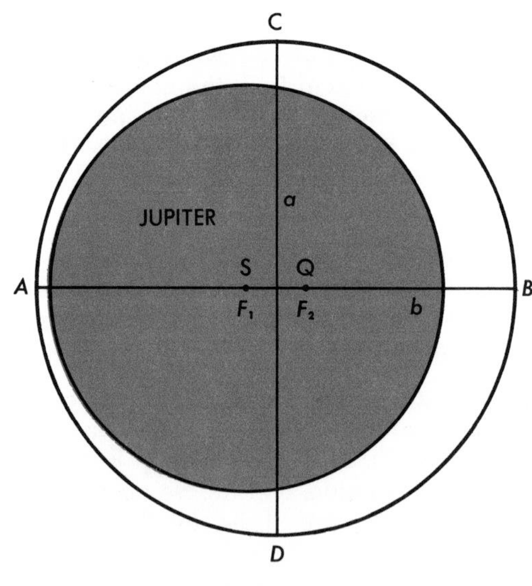

Prob. 12.

12.* A satellite orbits the planet Jupiter. If it is 5,108 Km above the surface at perijove, and 25,108 Km above the surface at apojove, find for its orbit (a) perijove, (b) apojove, (c) the semimajor axis, (d) the semiminor axis, and (e) the eccentricity. Make a diagram of the results. [Ans. (a) 75,000 Km, (b) 95,000 Km, (c) 85,000 Km, (d) 84,400 Km, (e) 0.1776.]

13.* Using Eq.(11n), and the relationship that the distance F_1C in Fig. 11L is equal to the semimajor axis a, derive the relation $b = a\sqrt{1 - e^2}$.

14. Draw straight lines from F_1 to C and from C to F_2 in Fig. 11L, and show that F_1C is equal to the semimajor axis a.

12 Gravitational fields and orbiting satellites

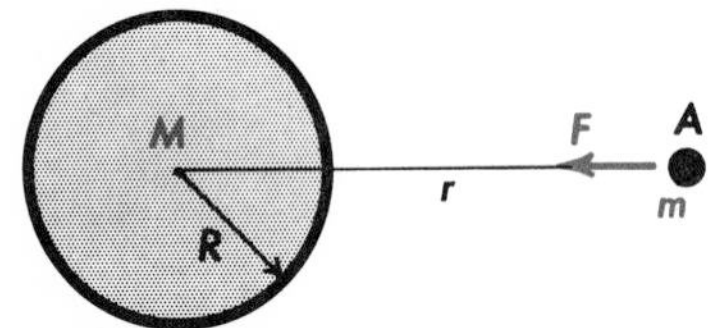

Fig. 12A. Gravitational forces are always those of attraction.

We are living today at the beginning of the space age, an age in which each planned space flight brings together, in one project after the other, all of the known science and technology at our command. Such large-scale operations illustrate not only the unity of science but the importance of understanding the basic principles of each of the separate sciences.

As each space ship leaves or approaches an astronomical body, such as the earth, the moon, or the planets, it is subject to gravitational forces of great magnitude. Since these forces vary with distance along each flight path, we find it quite necessary to take them into account, describing them in terms of what are called *gravitational fields* and *gravitational potentials.*

12.1. Gravitational Fields

The concept of a gravitational field begins with Newton's Universal Law of Gravitation (see Sec. 6.1). In Fig. 12A a mass M is shown exerting a gravitational force F on a small mass m. The magnitude of this force is

$$F = -G\,\frac{Mm}{r^2} \qquad (12a)$$

where M and m are in kilograms, r is in meters, F is in newtons, and the universal constant of gravitation G is given by

$$G = 6.673231 \times 10^{-11}\,\frac{\mathrm{m}^3}{\mathrm{Kg\ s}^2} \qquad (12b)$$

The minus sign in Eq.(12a) signifies that the force is one of attraction.

The field intensity I at any point A, in free space surrounding any mass M, is defined as the force per unit mass acting on any object placed there:

$$I = \frac{F}{m} \tag{12c}$$

The small mass is used in this definition only as a means of detecting and measuring the gravitational field at A. Whether m is large or small, the force per unit mass at the point is exactly the same. Double the mass m and F will be doubled, triple the mass m and F will be tripled, etc.

To develop an equation for the field intensity I, we obtain a value for F/m from Eq.(12a). Dividing both sides of the equation by m, we obtain

$$\frac{F}{m} = -\frac{GM}{r^2}$$

which gives

$$I = -\frac{GM}{r^2} \tag{12d}$$

gravitational field intensity

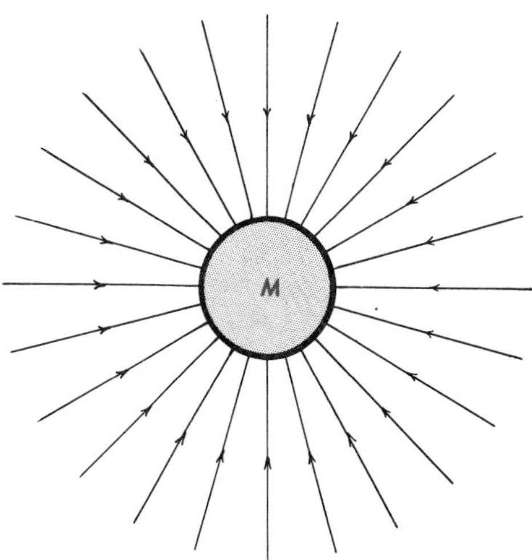

Fig. 12B. The gravitational field around a spherical mass M is radially inward.

A diagram of the gravitational field around a spherical mass M is shown in Fig. 12B. The arrows show the direction of the field as everywhere radially inward, and the spacing of the lines shows that the field is strongest at the surface. For every point at the same distance from the center, the field intensity I has the same magnitude, but as the distance increases, the field intensity decreases.

It is to be noted that as many radial lines as desired can be drawn to represent the field, but they must be equally spaced. Furthermore, the lines themselves are imaginary and do not actually exist; they are introduced here as an aid to the understanding of gravitational phenomena.

Multiplying both sides of Eq.(12c) by m, we obtain the relation that

$$F = mI \tag{12e}$$

This equation says that any mass m placed in a gravitational field of intensity I experiences a force given by the product $m \times I$.

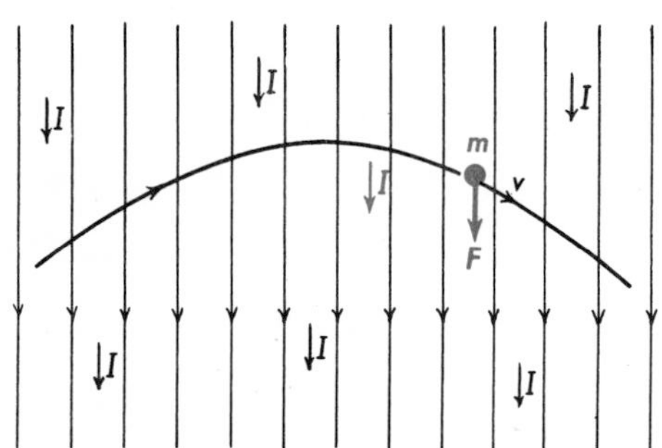

Fig. 12C. The path of a projectile in a uniform gravitational field is a parabola.

While Eqs.(12a) through (12e) apply to all masses *m*, we may use Eq.(4c) and obtain a special case for the earth. The downward force on any mass *m* at the earth's surface is given by

$$F = mg \tag{12f}$$

Since by Eq.(12e), $F = mI$, we obtain the equality

$$mI = mg$$

or

$$I = g \tag{12g}$$

at the earth's surface

Although the field intensity has the dimensions of an acceleration, it is more meaningful to express I, through Eq.(12c), as a force per unit mass:

$$1\,\frac{\text{newton}}{\text{kilogram}} = 1\,\frac{\text{meter}}{\text{second}^2} \tag{12h}$$

Over a small volume of space, the gravitational field can be assumed to be constant. Throughout the space of one cubic Km at or near the earth's surface, for example, the direction of the field at all points is practically parallel, and the magnitude of I is practically constant (see Fig. 12C). Such a field is said to be *uniform.* The path taken by a mass *m* projected through a uniform gravitational field is the result of a constant downward force F; if air friction is negligibly small, the path is a parabola, as shown in the diagram.

Example 1. The earth has a mass of 5.975×10^{24} Kg, and a radius of 6370 Km. Find the gravitational field intensity at a distance of 500 Km above the earth's surface. Express values to four significant figures.

Solution. The given quantities are $G = 6.673 \times 10^{-11}$ m³/Kg s², $M = 5.975 \times 10^{24}$ Kg, and $r = 6.870 \times 10^{6}$ m. By direct substitution in Eq.(12d), we obtain

$$I = -\frac{6.673 \times 10^{-11} \times 5.975 \times 10^{24}}{(6.870 \times 10^{6})^2}$$

$$I = 8.448\,\frac{\text{N}}{\text{Kg}}$$

When a space vehicle takes off from the ground to orbit the earth as a satellite, its initial takeoff direction is vertically upward (see Fig. 8H). As the rocket gains height, control fins or jets are set to make it turn slowly toward a horizontal trajectory. To find the velocity that a space vehicle must acquire to circle the earth, consider the details of Fig. 12D.

Imagine a tower several hundred miles high, from the top of which projectiles are launched in a horizontal direction. With a low initial velocity, the projectile will follow a nearly parabolic path as shown at A. At a somewhat higher velocity, the trajectory will be that of path B. At a still higher velocity, the projectile in falling toward the earth will follow a circular path of radius r. This particular velocity is called the *orbiting velocity.* At still higher velocities, such as shown at D, the projectile will follow an elliptical path or escape completely from the earth.

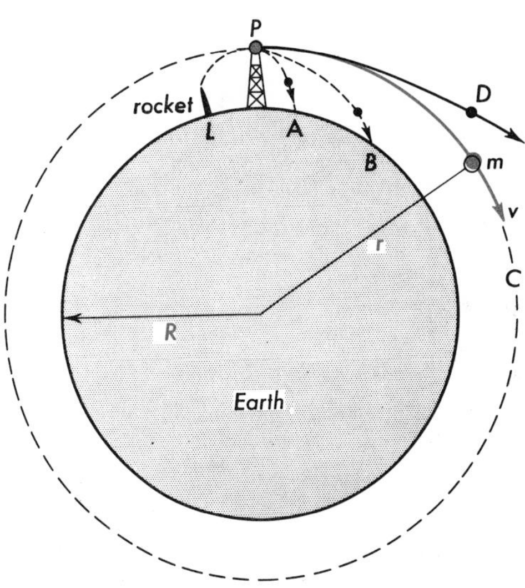

Fig. 12D. Horizontal projection from P with a high velocity v can cause a projectile m to circle the earth.

We have seen in the preceding chapter that by simply equating the centripetal force for a satellite moving in a circular orbit to the gravitational force given by Newton's universal law of gravitation, we obtain directly the orbiting velocity [see Eq.(11r)]:

$$v = \sqrt{\frac{GM}{r}} \tag{12i}$$

orbiting velocity

This equation holds for any satellite moving in a circular orbit around any astronomical body throughout the universe. In the special case of a satellite circling the earth close to the surface, the orbital radius is approximately the radius of the earth R. Under these conditions the centripetal force F is just mg, and we may write Eq.(12a) in the form

$$mg = G\,\frac{Mm}{R^2}$$

neglecting the minus sign, since in this case it only indicates an attractive force.

Solving this equation for GM, we obtain

$$GM = gR^2 \tag{12j}$$

where R is approximately 6370 Km, and

$$g = 9.80 \text{ m/s}^2 \tag{12k}$$

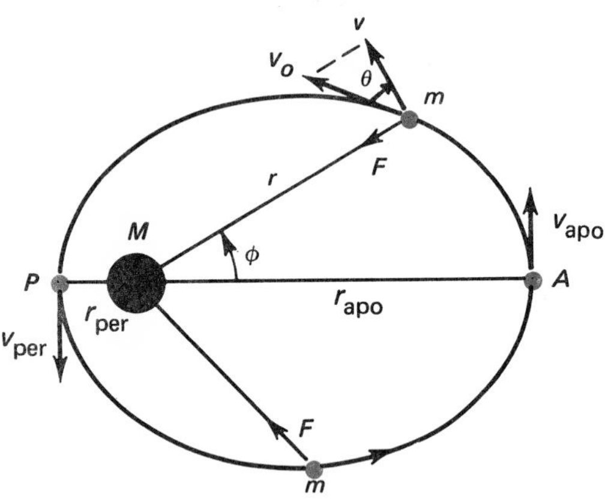

Fig. 12E. Diagrams of the elliptical orbit of a satellite showing the different orbital speeds and velocities.

If we now substitute gR^2 for GM in Eq.(12i), we find

$$v = \sqrt{g\frac{R^2}{r}} \qquad (12\ell)$$

orbiting velocity for the earth only

Example 2. A satellite orbits the earth 900 Km above the surface. Find its orbital speed in m/s to four significant figures. See Table 11A for values of constants.

Solution. To use Eq.(12i), we refer to Table 11A to obtain R = 6370 Km, $M = 5.975 \times 10^{24}$ Kg, and from Eq.(12b), $G = 6.673 \times 10^{-11}$ m³/Kg s². Direct substitution gives

$$v = \sqrt{\frac{6.673 \times 10^{-11} \times 5.975 \times 10^{24}\ \text{m}^3/\text{s}^2}{(6370 + 900)\ \text{Km}}}$$

$$v = \sqrt{\frac{39.871 \times 10^{13}\ \text{m}^3/\text{s}^2}{7.270 \times 10^{6}\ \text{m}}}$$

$$v = 7.406 \times 10^3\ \text{m/s}$$

If a satellite orbits the earth at an altitude of only 200 Km, air friction is still extremely small, and a fairly stable orbit is sustained. For such a special case we can substitute R for r in Eq.(12ℓ) and obtain the very simple relation that

$$v = \sqrt{gR} \qquad (12\text{m})$$

If the orbit of a satellite is not circular, but elliptical, the magnitude of the orbital velocity changes from one point to another. As shown in Fig. 12E, the velocity v_{per} at perigee P is a maximum.

As the satellite m recedes from its perigee position P, the backward gravitational pull of the mass M slows it down, until at apogee A the orbital speed is a minimum. As the satellite moves along the opposite side of its orbit, the gravitational pull F speeds it up again until at perigee P its speed becomes a maximum.

The general formula for the speed of a satellite is quite complicated, but for the maximum and minimum positions, where the *instantaneous velocity* is perpendicular to the radius vector r, it simplifies and gives

$$v_{\text{per}} = \sqrt{\frac{GM}{a}\left(\frac{1+e}{1-e}\right)}$$
$$v_{\text{apo}} = \sqrt{\frac{GM}{a}\left(\frac{1-e}{1+e}\right)} \qquad (12n)$$

where a is the semimajor axis, and e is the eccentricity given by Eqs.(11n) and (11o).

From the simple laws of mechanics, it can be shown for satellite motion that the angular momentum remains constant. The angular momentum p of a satellite is given by the product

$$p = mvr \qquad (12o)$$

where, as shown in Fig. 12E, r is the distance to the satellite, m is the mass, and v is the perpendicular component of the orbital velocity v_0.

Example 3. A satellite with a mass of 5000 Kg is in an elliptical orbit around the earth. If it comes down to 300 Km above the earth's surface, and then out to a maximum of 30,000 Km above the earth's surface, find (a) its perigee, (b) its apogee, (c) the orbit's semimajor axis, (d) its eccentricity, (e) its semiminor axis, (f) its velocity at perigee, (g) its velocity at apogee, and (h) its angular momentum.

Solution. The given quantities are minimum distance from earth 3.0×10^5 m, maximum distance from earth 3.0×10^7 m, $M = 5.975 \times 10^{24}$ Kg, $G = 6.673 \times 10^{-11}$ m^3/Kg s^2, $R = 6.370 \times 10^6$, and $m = 5.0 \times 10^3$ Kg.

The distance from the earth's center to perigee is given by the sum

$$r_{\text{per}} = 6.370 \times 10^6 + 3.0 \times 10^5 = 6.670 \times 10^6\text{m}$$

and the distance from the earth's center to apogee is given by the sum

$$r_{\text{apo}} = 6.370 \times 10^6 + 3.0 \times 10^7 = 3.637 \times 10^7\text{m}$$

Referring to Fig. 11L, half the major axis is $\frac{1}{2}(r_{\text{apo}} + r_{\text{per}})$, or

$$a = \tfrac{1}{2}(3.637 \times 10^7 + 0.667 \times 10^7)$$

$$a = 2.152 \times 10^7\text{m}$$

Solving the first Eq.(11o) for the eccentricity, and substituting known quantities, we find

$$e = \frac{r_{\text{apo}} - a}{a} = \frac{3.637 \times 10^7 - 2.152 \times 10^7}{2.152 \times 10^7}$$

$$e = 0.690$$

By the lower Eq.(11o), we obtain for the semiminor axis

$$b = a\sqrt{1 - e^2} = 2.152 \times 10^7 \sqrt{1 - (0.690)^2}$$

$$b = 1.558 \times 10^7 \text{m}$$

By direct substitution in Eq.(12n), we obtain (see Table 12A for value of GM)

$$v_{\text{per}} = \sqrt{\frac{GM}{a}\left(\frac{1+e}{1-e}\right)} = \sqrt{\frac{3.979 \times 10^{14}}{2.152 \times 10^7}\left(\frac{1.690}{0.310}\right)}$$

$$v_{\text{per}} = 1.004 \times 10^4 \text{m/s}$$

and

$$v_{\text{apo}} = \sqrt{\frac{GM}{a}\left(\frac{1-e}{1+e}\right)} = \sqrt{\frac{3.979 \times 10^{14}}{2.152 \times 10^7}\left(\frac{0.310}{1.690}\right)}$$

$$v_{\text{apo}} = 1.842 \times 10^3 \text{m/s}$$

By direct substitution in Eq.(12o), we obtain for the angular momentum at perigee

$$p_{\text{per}} = 5.0 \times 10^3 \times 1.004 \times 10^4 \times 6.670 \times 10^6$$

$$p_{\text{per}} = 3.348 \times 10^{14} \text{Kg m}^2/\text{s}$$

and as a check, at apogee, we obtain

$$p_{\text{apo}} = 5.0 \times 10^3 \times 1.842 \times 10^3 \times 3.637 \times 10^7$$

$$p_{\text{apo}} = 3.350 \times 10^{14} \text{Kg m}^2/\text{s}$$

12.3. Gravitational Potential

We have seen in Chap. 9 that the work done in raising a body of mass m to a height h is given by the product, force times distance:

$$W = Fh$$

where the force F is given by Newton's second law, $F = mg$,

$$W = mgh$$

As a result of doing work on a body, we have stored within it, by virtue of its new position, an equivalent amount of potential energy:

$$E_p = mgh$$

In setting up these defining equations in Chaps. 9 and 10, it was assumed that the gravitational field intensity g is constant over the distance h through which the force acts and that some horizontal plane like *sea level* is the *zero level* of potential energy.

If the distance a mass m is raised from the earth's surface is a thousand kilometers or more, the gravitational field intensity can no longer be considered constant, but varies inversely as the square of the distance from the center of the earth [see Eq.(12d)]. As one gets farther and farther away from the earth, the field becomes weaker and weaker, and approaches zero as r approaches infinity.

It is customary, therefore, to define the gravitational potential P of any point in space near a mass M in terms of work done per unit mass in carrying any object from infinity to that point (see Fig. 12F):

$$P = \frac{W}{m}$$

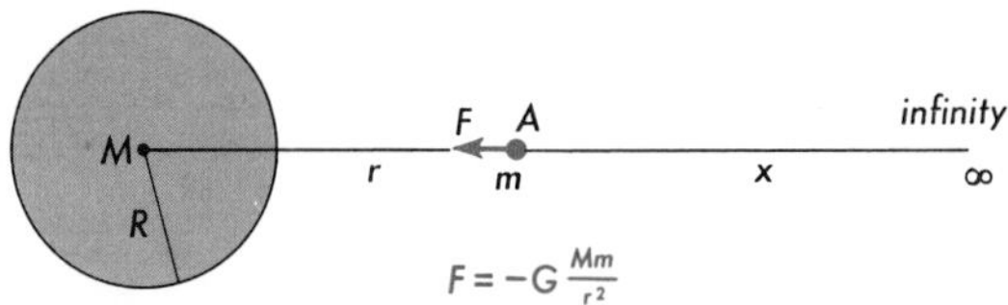

Fig. 12F. The gravitational force on the mass m is zero at infinity, and increases steadily as it approaches the mass M.

To calculate the work done by means of the defining equation, $W = F \times h$, and with a continuously changing force, imagine that we divide the distance from R to r into a number of small intervals, so that over each interval the gravitational force will be practically constant, and given by a kind of average force over that interval (see Fig. 12G). We can then calculate the work done for each interval and add them all together to get the total.

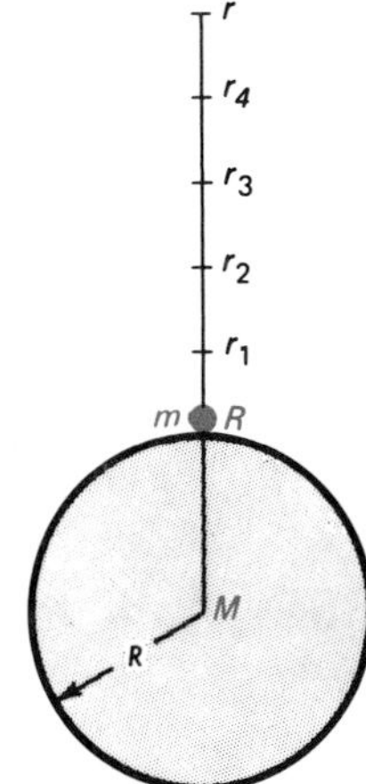

Fig. 12G. Diagram showing how to calculate the work done in lifting a mass m from the surface of a planet like the earth to a height r.

At the surface the force is $F_0 = GMm/R^2$, while at r_1 it is $F_1 = GMm/r_1^2$. We may therefore write for the average force in the first interval R to r_1

$$F_1 = G\frac{Mm}{Rr_1}$$

and for the work done

$$W_1 = G\frac{Mm}{Rr_1}(r_1 - R)$$

or, by the distributive law,

$$W_1 = GMm\left(\frac{1}{R} - \frac{1}{r_1}\right)$$

In a similar way the work done lifting the mass through the second interval r_1 to r_2 is found to be

$$W_2 = GMm\left(\frac{1}{r_1} - \frac{1}{r_2}\right)$$

and similarly for the third interval

$$W_3 = GMm\left(\frac{1}{r_2} - \frac{1}{r_3}\right)$$

If we add all these W's from R to r, all intermediate values cancel out and we obtain for the total

$$W = GMm\left(\frac{1}{R} - \frac{1}{r}\right)$$

If we now choose r bigger and bigger, and finally take r to infinity ($r = \infty$), the value $1/r = 0$, and we obtain

$$W = G\frac{Mm}{R} \tag{12p}$$

We can see from this simple result that *to carry a mass m from any point A at a distance r to infinity where r = ∞, the energy expended is given by*

$$W = G\frac{Mm}{r} \tag{12q}$$

Since the work done is stored as potential energy, the potential energy of a mass m at any point A is, therefore,

$$E_p = -G\frac{Mm}{r} \tag{12r}$$

The minus sign establishes the zero level of potential energy at infinity, that is, in free space. Lifting a mass against the pull of a gravitational field requires the expenditure of energy, and where $r = \infty$, Eq.(12r) gives $E_p = 0$.

We now define the gravitational potential P of any point in the space around a mass M as the potential energy per unit mass of any mass m located there:

$$P = \frac{E_p}{m} \tag{12s}$$

Dividing both sides of Eq.(12r) by m and substituting from Eq.(12s), we obtain

$$P = -\frac{GM}{r} \tag{12t}$$

gravitational potential

TABLE 12A
Masses and constants for the planets

	M (Kg $\times$ 10^{24})	GM (m^3/s^2)	GM/R (m^2/s^2)
Mercury	0.324	2.160×10^{13}	8.921×10^{6}
Venus	4.861	3.237×10^{14}	5.254×10^{7}
Earth	5.975	3.979×10^{14}	6.245×10^{7}
Mars	0.6387	4.254×10^{13}	1.277×10^{7}
Jupiter	1902.1	1.267×10^{17}	1.813×10^{9}
Saturn	569.4	3.792×10^{16}	6.591×10^{8}
Uranus	87.1	5.801×10^{15}	2.448×10^{8}
Neptune	103.1	6.866×10^{15}	3.188×10^{8}

$$\text{moon mass} = 7.32 \times 10^{22} \text{ Kg}$$

$$\text{moon radius} = 1.740 \times 10^{6} \text{ m}$$

Any mass m located at or near the surface of the earth M can be looked upon as being in a hole where the potential energy is negative, and to lift it out into free space (r infinite, and $E_p = 0$) requires an amount of energy W:

$$W = -mP$$

We therefore arrive at the very simple result that the force on any mass is given by

$$F = mI$$

and its potential energy is given by

$$E_p = mP$$

Moving in an elliptical orbit around the earth or the sun at one focus, the total energy of a satellite or planet remains constant. The total energy of the moving mass m is given by the sum of the kinetic energy $\frac{1}{2}mv^2$ and the potential energy $-GMm/r$ [see Eq.(12q)]:

$$E = \tfrac{1}{2}mv^2 + \left(-\frac{GMm}{r}\right) = \text{constant}$$

total energy = kinetic + potential

This equation is not to be confused with the total energy required to put a mass into orbit from the earth's surface. When starting from the earth's surface the potential energy is $-GMm/R$, and raising it to a distance r from the earth's center, the potential energy is $-GMm/r$. The difference between these two is the energy that must be supplied. This added to the kinetic energy at a distance r gives the total energy expended. This sum is

$$E = \frac{1}{2}mv^2 + \left(m\frac{GM}{R} - m\frac{GM}{r}\right)$$

Since from Eq.(12i), $v^2 = GM/r$, the relationship $\frac{1}{2}mv^2$ gives

$$E = \frac{1}{2}m\frac{GM}{r} + \left(m\frac{GM}{R} - m\frac{GM}{r}\right)$$

which can be simplified to

$$E = m\frac{GM}{R} - \frac{1}{2}m\frac{GM}{r}$$

or

$$E = mGM\left(\frac{1}{R} - \frac{1}{2r}\right) \qquad (12u)$$

total energy expended to put a satellite in orbit from earth's surface

In a circular orbit both v and r are constant, and so are the two forms of energy. In an elliptical orbit, however, the potential energy gets larger (negatively)as r decreases, and to compensate for this v increases to keep the total energy constant.

12.4. Escape Velocity

For a satellite to escape from the earth and never return, it must be launched with a velocity greater than that required to make it orbit. To find the *minimum escape velocity,* we make use of the gravitational potential as given in the preceding section.

To lift a mass m from any point at a distance r from the center of M requires the expenditure of energy in the amount given by Eq.(12q) (see Fig. 12F). If we impart this energy by giving the mass a velocity, the total energy expended will be kinetic, $\frac{1}{2}mv^2$. By direct substitution in Eq.(12q) of $\frac{1}{2}mv^2$ for W, we obtain

$$\frac{1}{2}mv^2 = m\frac{GM}{r}$$

Upon solving for v, we find

$$v = \sqrt{2\frac{GM}{r}} \qquad (12v)$$

escape velocity for all bodies

If we launch the mass m from the earth's surface, where $r = R$, we write

$$v = \sqrt{2\frac{GM}{R}} \qquad (12w)$$

If we wish to express this escape velocity in terms of g at the earth's surface, we can make use of Eq.(12j), and substitute gR^2 for GM in Eq.(12w) and obtain

$$v = \sqrt{2gR} \qquad (12x)$$

escape velocity from earth's surface

Note that the escape velocity from a point at any distance r from any body M, as given by Eq.(12v), is just $\sqrt{2}$ greater than the orbiting velocity at the same distance r, as given by Eq.(12i):

$$v_{escape} = 1.41v_{orbit} \qquad (12y)$$

This relation holds for any value of r.

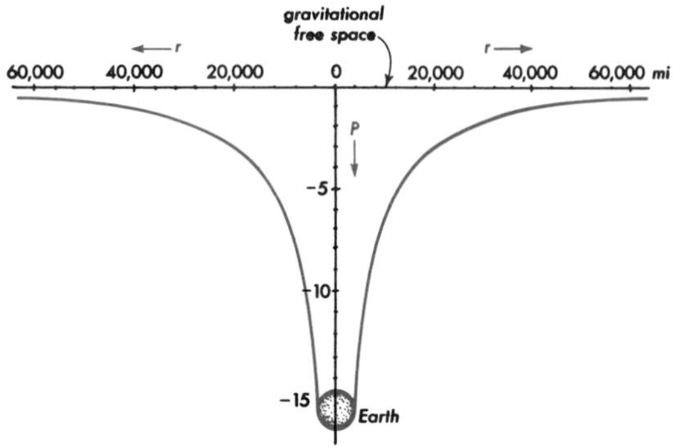

Fig. 12H. Potential-energy graph illustrating the "well" analogy of the earth's gravitational field.

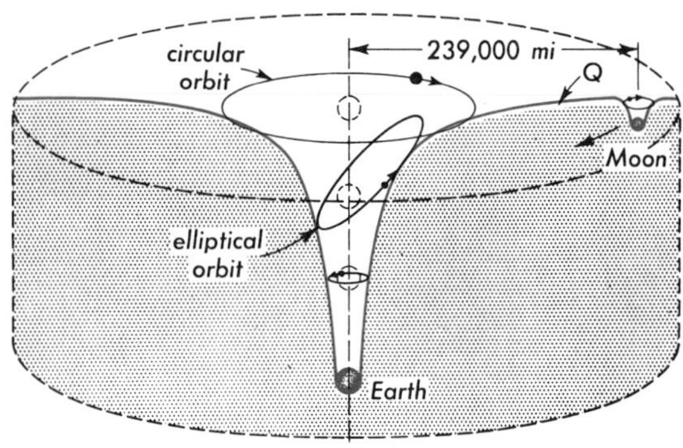

Fig. 12I. Mechanical well model for the earth and moon.

12.5. Mechanical Well Model

The preceding sections of this chapter show that we on the surface of the earth are living at the bottom of a "gravitational well" thousands of miles deep. To reach the moon, the planets, or other worlds, we must climb out of this well onto a horizontal plane we call *gravitationless free space.*

To see what is meant by a well, we plot a potential-energy graph for the gravitational field around the earth like that shown in Fig. 12H. Such a graph is obtained by using Eq.(12t) and plotting the potential P vertically and the distance from the center of the earth r horizontally.

For a distance r that is infinitely far away, $P = 0$. At smaller and smaller distances P increases, but is negative. The colored curve in the diagram comes down to the earth's surface where r has the value of the earth's radius R.

A mechanical well model for demonstrating satellite orbits is obtained by rotating this potential-energy graph around the vertical axis. In so doing, the curve describes a cone-like surface as shown in Fig. 12I. If we make a solid body of some hard material with the shape of the shaded section, a small steel or glass marble can be rolled around in the cone to describe satellite orbits.

A great variety of orbits can be generated simply by varying the initial velocity of the marbles. When viewed from directly overhead, most orbits are elliptical or circular. Orbital distortion arising from rolling friction can be held to a minimum by using hard materials with smooth surfaces.

If orbits including the moon are desirable, a small potential crater, far out on the periphery of the earth model, can be made (see Fig. 12I). The rolling of a marble toward this crater, away from the earth, is analogous to the path of an earth-based satellite on its projected trip to or around the moon. At the saddle point Q the gravitational pull of the earth and moon are equal and opposite.

12.6. Simulated Weight in Space Vehicles

Biological records on astronauts circling the earth indicate that prolonged exposure of the body to weightless conditions may cause permanent health damage. This is not surprising, when it is realized that evolutionary processes have taken place in the earth's gravitational field over millions of years, and bodily functions rely greatly upon the ever-present gravitational forces.

If, therefore, extended space travel is to become a commonplace reality, it would appear that weightlessness must be replaced by centripetal and centrifugal forces. Gravitational mass m, and weight mg, could be replaced by inertial mass m, and centripetal force mv^2/r.

Figure 12J shows two widely separated space capsules rotating around their common center of mass. After being launched close together in orbit, small rockets on each capsule may be so directed as to set the system rotating. Connecting cables are simultaneously reeled out until the two bodies are several hundred meters apart.

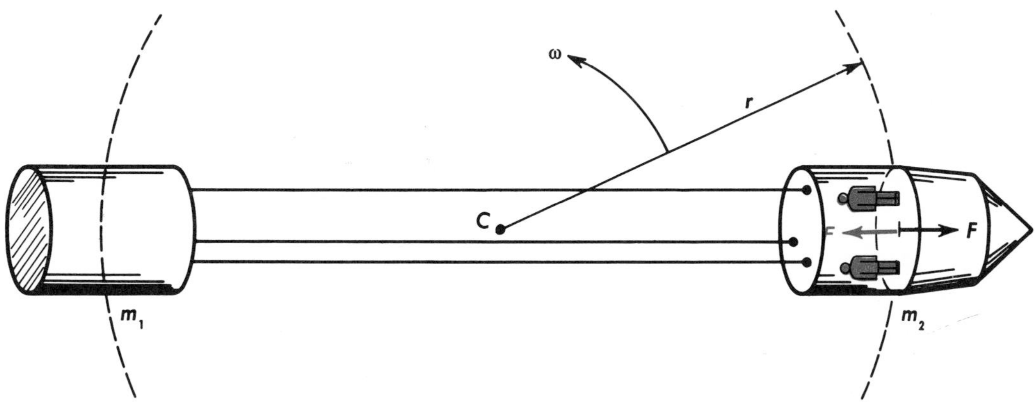

Fig. 12J. Two separated space vehicles bound together by cables, and rotating, simulate normal earth weight conditions for the astronauts.

If the centripetal force $mr\omega^2$ is to be equal to the astronauts' weight mg, we may write

$$mr\omega^2 = mg$$

where ω is the angular velocity in radians per second.

Solving for ω, we obtain

$$\omega = \sqrt{\frac{g}{r}} \tag{12z}$$

If we make $r = 39.2$ m, direct substitution in Eq.(12z) gives

$$\omega = \sqrt{\frac{9.80 \text{ m/s}^2}{39.2 \text{ m}}} = 0.50 \frac{\text{rad}}{\text{s}}$$

This is a relatively low angular speed and means that the system would make one revolution every 12.5 s. To the standing astronaut in the space vehicle the force on his body, exerted by the floor, would seem to be practically straight up. An object released from the hand of the astronaut would fall to the floor but its path would be slightly curved.

problems

1. A space ship orbits the earth 230.0 Km above the surface. Find (a) its speed, and its period in (b) seconds, (c) minutes, and (d) hours.

2. A space ship orbits the moon 90.0 Km above the surface. Find (a) its speed, and its period in (b) seconds, (c) minutes, and (d) hours.

3. A space vehicle orbits the planet Jupiter at a distance of 510 Km above the surface. Find (a) its speed in m/s, and its period in (b) seconds, (c) minutes, and (d) hours. [Ans. (a) 4.24×10^4 m/s, (b) 1.042×10^4 s, (c) 173.7 min, (d) 2.895 h.]

4. When a 18,000-Kg space station first goes into orbit, its closest approach to the earth is 500 Km and its maximum is 5000 Km. Find its (a) perigee, and (b) its apogee. Find also (c) its semimajor axis, (d) the eccentricity, (e) its velocity at perigee, (f) velocity at apogee, and (g) its total angular momentum. Make a diagram.

5. A 22,000-Kg space station is put into a highly elliptical orbit around the earth. If it comes down to 500 Km above the earth's surface at perigee, and then out to 50,000 Km at apogee, find (a) its perigee, (b) its apogee, (c) the orbit's semimajor axis, (d) its eccentricity, (e) its velocity at perigee, (f) its velocity at apogee, and (g) its total angular momentum. Make a scale diagram.

6. A space ship orbits the planet Jupiter in an elliptical orbit. If it comes to within 3.10×10^5m of the surface at closest approach, and then out to 3.0×10^8m at its greatest distance, find (a) its perijove distance, (b) its apojove distance, (c) its semimajor axis, (d) its eccentricity, (e) its velocity at perijove, and (f) its velocity at apojove. Make a scale diagram. [Ans. (a) 0.702×10^8m, (b) 3.699×10^8m, (c) 2.20×10^8m, (d) 0.681, (e) 5.51×10^4 m/s, (f) 1.046×10^4 m/s.]

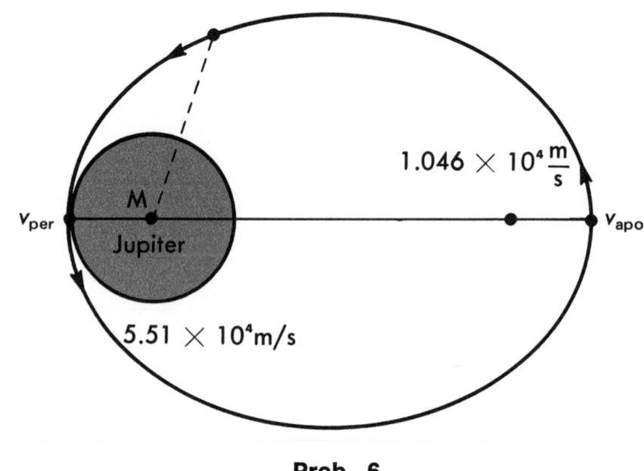

Prob. 6.

7. At what speed must a space ship, with a mass of 2500 Kg, be launched from the earth's surface (a) to escape into interplanetary space? (b) What kinetic energy would it have upon leaving?

8. With what speed must a 15,000-Kg lunar module be launched from the moon's surface (a) to escape into interplanetary space? (b) What kinetic energy would be required?

9.* A 5000-Kg space vehicle is to be put into orbit 10,000 Km above the earth's surface. Find (a) the orbital velocity, (b) the orbital kinetic energy, (c) the total energy expended, and (d) make a scale diagram. [Ans. (a) 4.93×10^3 m/s, (b) 6.077×10^{10} J, (c) 2.516×10^{11} J.]

10.* A 4500-Kg space ship takes off from the earth and goes into a circular orbit 7200 Km above the surface. Calculate (a) the orbital velocity, (b) the orbital kinetic energy, and (c) the total energy expended.

11.* A space platform with a mass of 3.50×10^4 Kg orbits the planet Mars. If at closest approach it comes to within 68.0 Km of the surface, and its greatest dis-

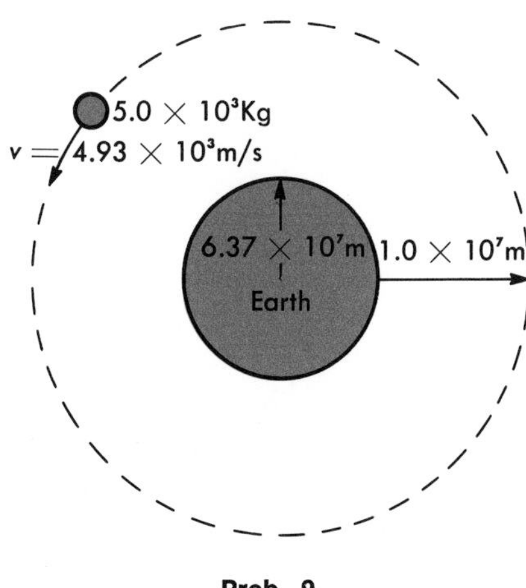

Prob. 9.

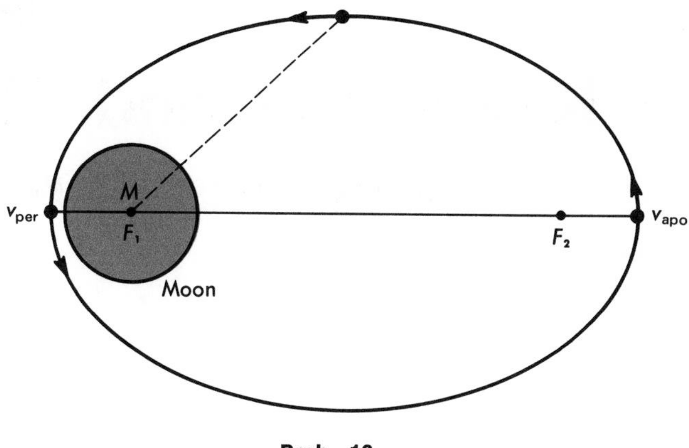

Prob. 12.

tance from the planet goes out to 6000 Km, find (a) the shortest distance it comes to the planet's center, and (b) its greatest distance. Also find (c) the semimajor axis, (d) the eccentricity, (e) the semiminor axis, (f) its maximum speed at closest approach, and (g) its lowest speed. Make a scale diagram.

12.* A space platform orbits the moon in an elliptical orbit. If at closest approach it comes to within 60.0 Km of the surface, and at its farthest point it is 10,000 Km above the surface, find (a) its perilune distance, (b) its apolune distance, (c) its semimajor axis, and (d) its eccentricity. Find also (e) its semiminor axis, (f) its maximum orbital speed, and (g) its minimum orbital speed. Neglect any effects of the earth's gravitational field. Make a scale diagram of your results. [Ans. (a) 1.80×10^6 m, (b) 11.74×10^6 m, (c) 6.77×10^6 m, (d) 0.734, (e) 3.122×10^6 m, (f) 2.169×10^3 m/s, (g) 3.326×10^2 m/s.]

13. A space vehicle on its way to Mars simulates gravity by reeling out half of its total mass 4.80×10^6 Kg, and setting the two sections rotating about the center of mass. If the distance between two sections is 20.0 m, and the centripetal acceleration is $\frac{1}{2}$ *g*, find (a) the angular velocity in rad/s, (b) its period in seconds, and (c) the centripetal force.

14. Once a space vehicle is on its way to Jupiter, it simulates gravity by extending one-third of its total mass of 5400 Kg outward 48.0 m by a long telescoping tunnel, and setting the system rotating at 4 rpm, as shown in the diagram. Neglecting the mass of this tunnel, find (a) the center of rotation, (b) the angular velocity in rad/s, (c) the period in seconds, (d) the centripetal acceleration in *g*'s on each astronaut when in the more massive section, (e) in the lighter section, and (f) the total angular momentum.

13 Kinematics and dynamics of rotation

In all of the preceding chapters, we have not found it necessary to take into account the size and shape of a body. It is frequently sufficient in the subjects of *kinematics* and *dynamics* to think of an object as though the mass were confined to a single point. Obviously, this is done for convenience only, and is justified as long as one's interests are not centered on structural details. Under certain conditions it is found necessary to take into account the structural details and still make use of the simplest forms of Newton's laws of motion.

13.1. Center of Mass

The center of mass of any given body, or system of bodies, is a point such that, if any plane is passed through it, the mass moments on one side of the plane are equal to the mass moments on the other.

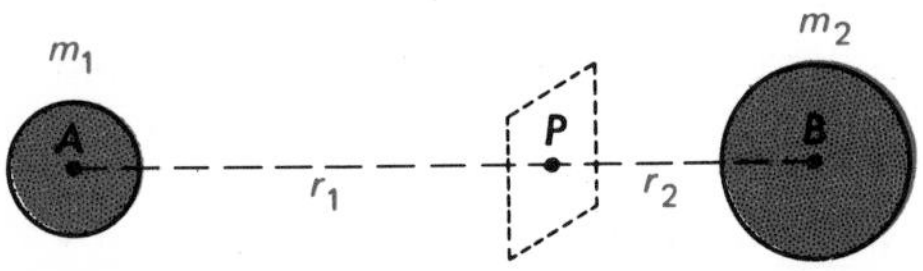

Fig. 13A. The center of mass of two bodies is located at some point on a line joining their centers of mass.

Consider, for example, two spheres of mass m_1 and m_2 as shown in Fig. 13A. The center of mass *(c of m)* P lies on a line connecting the centers of the two bodies and in such a position that

$$m_1 \times r_1 = m_2 \times r_2 \tag{13a}$$

For a vertical plane through P, perpendicular to the line AB, $m_1 \times r_1$ is the *mass moment* of m_1, and $m_2 \times r_2$ is the *mass moment* of m_2. The mass moment of a body about any chosen plane is given by the mass of the body multiplied by its perpendicular distance to the plane.

Example 1. Find the *c of m* of two bodies $m_1 = 2.0$ Kg, and $m_2 = 5.0$ Kg, placed 14.0 m apart.

Solution. Given is the distance $r_1 + r_2 = 14.0$ m, from which

$$r_2 = 14 - r_1$$

Substitute all known quantities in Eq.(13a):

$$2r_1 = 5(14 - r_1) \qquad \text{or} \qquad 2r_1 = 70 - 5r_1$$

and

$$7r_1 = 70 \qquad \text{or} \qquad r_1 = 10.0$$

The substitution of this value of r_1 in Eq.(13a) gives

$$r_2 = 4.0 \text{ m}$$

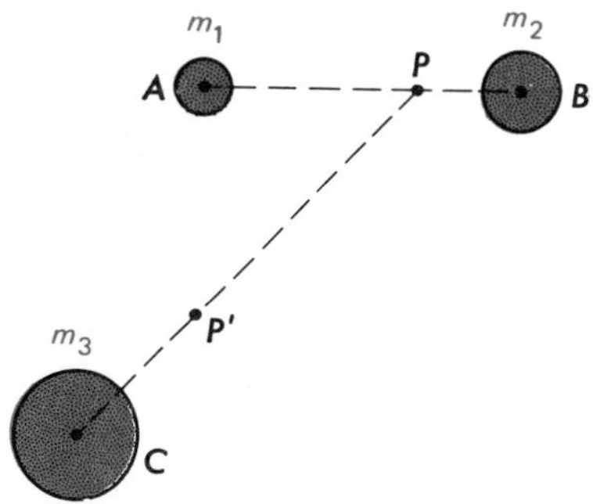

Fig. 13B. Diagram illustrating the method for finding the center of mass of a three-body system.

The *c of m* of a three-body system is found by an extension of the above principle (see Fig. 13B). To illustrate, two of the masses like A and B are first selected and their *c of m* found by use of Eq.(13a). These two bodies are then treated as though they were one body located at P. With one mass $(m_1 + m_2)$ located at P and a second mass m_3 located at C, Eq.(13a) is applied to find P′, the resultant *c of m*. If a system consists of more than three bodies, the above process is continued until all masses have been included.

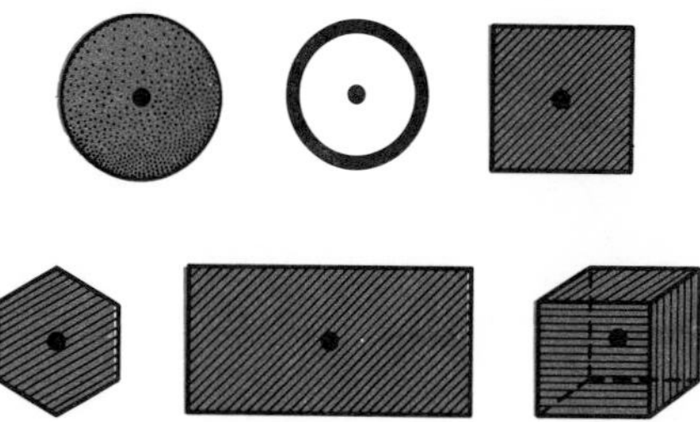

Fig. 13C. Illustrating the center of mass of regularly shaped objects.

The *c of m* of all regularly shaped bodies like those shown in Fig. 13C is at their geometrical center. A plane passed through the center of any of these figures will divide the body into two equal parts. Consider, for example, a thin ring of mass *M* as shown in Fig. 13D(a). By drawing straight lines through the geometrical center, the total mass can be divided up into pairs of small but equal masses. Since the masses *m* of each pair are equidistant from the center, their *c of m* is at their midpoint P, and this is common to all pairs.

A similar process can be applied to a long thin rod or pole of equal cross section. Dividing the rod into an equal number of parts as shown in Fig. 13D(b) permits the pairing off of equal parts at equal distances from the center. Since the geometrical center is the *c of m* of each pair, it is also the *c of m* of the entire rod. It is now clear why the distances in Fig. 13A must be meas-

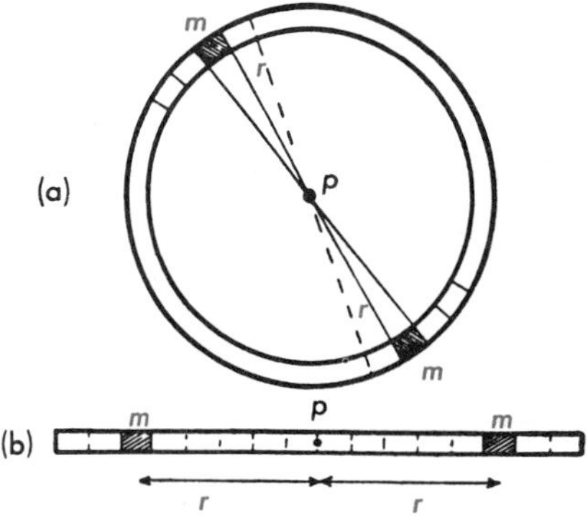

Fig. 13D. Center of mass is at the geometrical center: (a) uniform ring, (b) uniform rod.

ured from the centers of the spheres; their centers are their *c of m.*

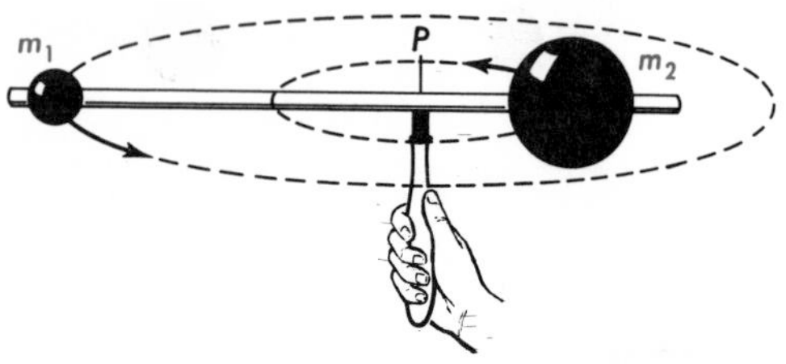

Fig. 13E. Diagram illustrating the smooth rotation of two bodies around their center of mass.

13.2. Rotation about the Center of Mass

In Fig. 13E two masses m_1 and m_2 are shown supported at the ends of a thin rod and rotating smoothly around a pin through the *c of m.* If the pin is located at any other point, for example halfway between the two masses, the experimenter will experience an unbalanced force on his hand, tending to make it "wobble."

Should the two-body system be thrown spinning into the air as shown in Fig. 13F, it will be observed to rotate about its *c of m* while the *c of m* traces out the smooth trajectory of a projectile.

The earth and the moon serve as a good illustration of two bodies rotating freely about their *c of m.* The mass of the earth is 81 times the mass of the moon, and the distance between them is approximately 3.840×10^8 m. A calculation, as in Example 1, gives $r_2 = 4.80 \times 10^6$ m; a distance nearly 4.83×10^6 m from the center of the earth and 1.61×10^6 m below the earth's surface.

In a similar manner the earth and moon, considered as a single body, rotate with the sun as the second body about their *c of m.* Relatively, the bodies are similar to those in Fig. 13B, with m_1 and m_2 rotating about P, and the point P and mass m_3 rotating more slowly around P′.

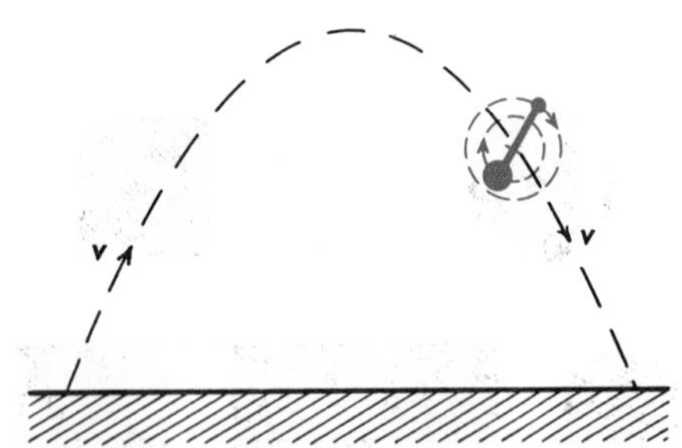

Fig. 13F. A body thrown spinning into the air rotates smoothly about its center of mass, while the center of mass traces out the smooth trajectory of a projectile.

13.3. Torque

When a single force acting on a body tends to set it in rotation about some axis, it is said to exert a *torque* or *force moment.* Torque is synonymous with force-moment and is defined as the product of force times lever arm, the lever arm being the perpendicular distance from the rotational axis to the force. In Fig. 13G a body is shown acted upon by a torque. The force F is applied at the point A while the body is pivoted at the point P. The perpendicular distance r is equal to the line PQ, and the torque L is given by

$$L = F \times r \tag{13b}$$

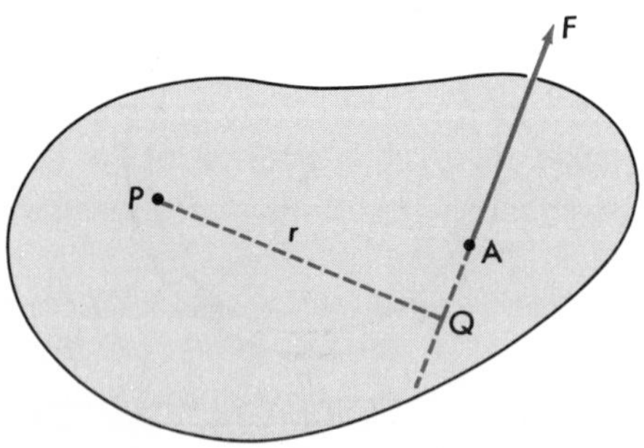

Fig. 13G. A single force acting on a rigid body pivoted at some point P exerts a torque $L = F \times r$.

If $F = 5$ N, and $r = 3$ m,

$$L = 5 \text{ N} \times 3 \text{ m} = 15 \text{ N m}$$

The dimensions *"newton meters"* should not be confused with the units of *work* and *energy*. In the calculation of work, force and distance are measured in the same direction, while in torque the two are measured at right angles.

It is customary to ascribe a positive sign to all torques acting to turn a body counterclockwise and a minus sign to all torques tending to turn it clockwise.

When a rigid body is acted upon by an unbalanced torque, it is set into rotation. Free to turn about an axis, such a body increases in angular velocity and acquires, when the torque ceases to act, some final angular velocity (see Fig. 13H).

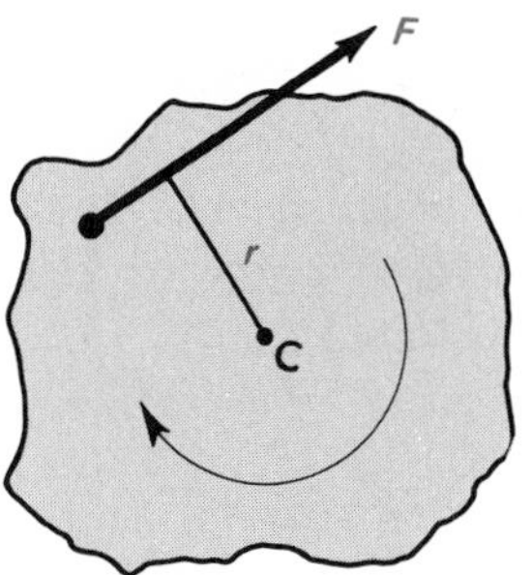

Fig. 13H. A rigid body is acted upon by a torque, $F \times r$.

13.4. Angular Acceleration

Just as the acceleration of a body in linear motion is defined as the rate of change of velocity, so the angular acceleration of a body in rotation is defined as the rate of change of angular velocity.

By comparison, this definition can be expressed the same mathematically, as Eqs.(2b) and (2c),

$$\alpha = \frac{\omega_2 - \omega_1}{t_2 - t_1} \qquad (13c)$$

$$\alpha = \frac{\Delta\omega}{\Delta t}$$

In these two relations, α represents the *angular acceleration* and is analogous to the linear acceleration a; ω_1 the *initial angular velocity* is analogous to v_1, and ω_2 the *final angular velocity* is analogous to v_2. If we let t represent the elapsed time $t_2 - t_1$, we can solve Eq.(13c) for ω_2, and obtain

$$\omega_2 = \omega_1 + \alpha t$$

Angular velocity is defined in Chap. 11 by the following relation:

$$\omega = \frac{\Delta\theta}{\Delta t} \qquad (13e)$$

The following example will illustrate the meaning, as well as an application, of the above angular formulas.

Example 2. A flywheel starting from rest acquires a speed of 240.0 rpm in 10.0 s. Find the acceleration.

Solution. Since the wheel starts from rest $\omega_1 = 0$. The other given quantities are $\omega_2 = 240.0$ rpm and $t = 10.0$ s. The final velocity in radians per second is calculated by the use of Eq.(13e). Since there are 2π radians in 1.0 revolution,

$$\omega_2 = \frac{2\pi \times 240.0}{60.0 \text{ s}} = 25.13 \frac{\text{rad}}{\text{s}}$$

Using Eq.(13c), we find that

$$\alpha = \frac{25.13 - 0}{10} = 2.513 \frac{\text{rad}}{\text{s}^2}$$

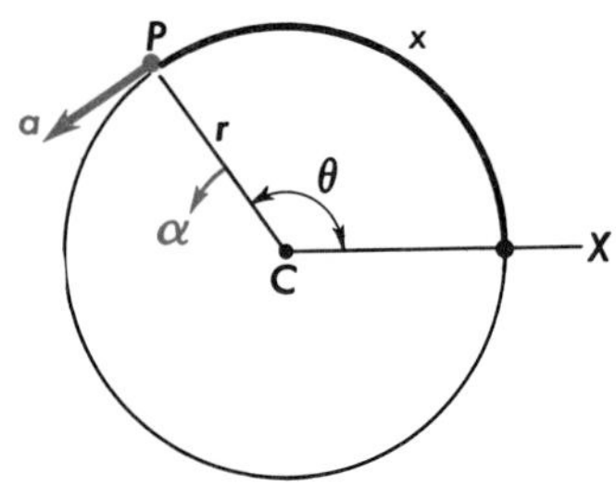

Fig. 13l. A wheel free to rotate about its center is given an angular acceleration.

It is clear from the above formulas that linear quantities x, v, and a in the linear equations have only to be replaced by the corresponding angular quantities, θ, ω, and α, to obtain the angular equations. This direct correspondence is the result of using the radian as a unit of angular measure and holds throughout all of the formulas in mechanics.

To derive a formula for the linear acceleration of a point around the periphery of an accelerated wheel, it is convenient to start with the definition of acceleration given by Eq.(13c) and substitute for the velocities v_2 and v_1 the equality given by Eq. (11f), $v_2 = r\omega_2$ (see Fig. 13l):

$$a = \frac{v_2 - v_1}{t} = \frac{r\omega_2 - r\omega_1}{t}$$

$$a = r\left(\frac{\omega_2 - \omega_1}{t}\right) = r\,\alpha$$

The result, $a = r\alpha$, is to be compared with two previous formulas, Eqs.(13e) and (13f). The similarity is more conspicuous when written together:

$$x = r\theta$$

$$v = r\omega \tag{13f}$$

$$a = r\alpha$$

These transformation equations are well worth remembering, for they are found to be quite useful in solving many problems.

13.5. Average Angular Velocity

To calculate the total angle turned through by a rigid body undergoing constant angular acceleration, use is made of the average angular velocity. By analogy with linear motion, the average angular velocity is defined as $\frac{1}{2}$ the sum of the initial and final velocities.

Symbolically, we write

$$\bar{\omega} = \frac{\omega_2 + \omega_1}{2} \tag{13g}$$

Since the angle turned through is given by

$$\theta = \bar{\omega}\, t$$

direct substitution gives

$$\theta = \frac{\omega_2 + \omega_1}{2}\, t \tag{13h}$$

Example 3. An airplane engine, while idling at 300.0 rpm, is suddenly accelerated. At the end of 3.0 s it has acquired the speed of 2400 rpm. Assuming constant acceleration, find (a) the average angular velocity, and (b) the total angle turned through.

Solution. We begin by changing the given speeds to radians per second:

$$\omega_1 = \frac{300}{60} \times 2\pi = 31.42\ \frac{\text{rad}}{\text{s}}$$

$$\omega_2 = \frac{2400}{60} \times 2\pi = 251.3\ \frac{\text{rad}}{\text{s}}$$

To find (a), direct substitution in Eq.(13g) gives

$$\bar{\omega} = \frac{251.3 + 31.42}{2} = 141.4\ \frac{\text{rad}}{\text{s}}$$

To find (b), direct substitution in Eq.(13h) gives

$$\theta = 141.4 \times 3 = 424.2\ \text{rad}$$

13.6. Kinematics of Rotation

The term "kinematics of rotation" refers to a quantitative description of motion such as that given above. By combining two of the equations already studied, Eqs.(13d) and (13h), two other useful formulas may be derived:

$$\theta = \omega_1 t + \frac{1}{2}\alpha t^2 \qquad (13i)$$

$$\omega_2^2 = \omega_1^2 + 2\alpha\theta \qquad (13j)$$

Again note that the angular quantities θ, ω, and α take the place of the corresponding linear quantities *x, v,* and *a.*

Example 4. An automobile engine running at 300.0 rpm is given an angular acceleration of 20.0 rad/s² for 10.0 s. Find (a) the angle turned through during these 10.0 s, and (b) the total number of revolutions.

Solution. First we change 300.0 rpm to radians per second:

$$\omega_1 = \frac{300}{60} \times 2\pi = 31.42\,\frac{\text{rad}}{\text{s}}$$

We now substitute the known quantities $\omega_1 = 31.42$ rad/s, $t =$ 10.0 s, and $\alpha = 20.0$ rad/s² in Eq.(13i), and obtain

$$\theta = 31.42\,\frac{\text{rad}}{\text{s}} \times 10.0\text{ s} + \frac{1}{2}\,20.0\,\frac{\text{rad}}{\text{s}^2} \times (10.0\text{ s})^2$$

$$\theta = 1314\text{ rad}$$

$$\theta = \frac{1314}{2\pi} = 209.1\text{ rev.}$$

The four basic equations most useful in dealing with the kinematics of rotational motion are placed together here in a box:

$$\omega_2 = \omega_1 + \alpha t$$

$$\theta = \frac{\omega_2 + \omega_1}{2}\,t$$

$$\theta = \omega_1 t + \tfrac{1}{2}\alpha t^2$$

$$\omega_2^2 = \omega_1^2 + 2\alpha\theta$$

13.7. Dynamics of Rotation

In the treatment of angular acceleration given in the preceding sections of this chapter, neither the torques causing the acceleration, nor the mass of the rotating body, entered into the calculations. When these two factors are introduced into the equations, the treatment is referred to as the *dynamics of rotation.*

When a specified torque is applied to a body free to rotate about some axis, the angular acceleration produced depends not only upon the size and shape of the body, but also upon the distribution of the mass with respect to the axis of rotation. To see how these factors are taken into account, consider the simplest kind of example, namely, that of a small mass m fastened to the end of a string and set into rotation as shown in Fig. 13J.

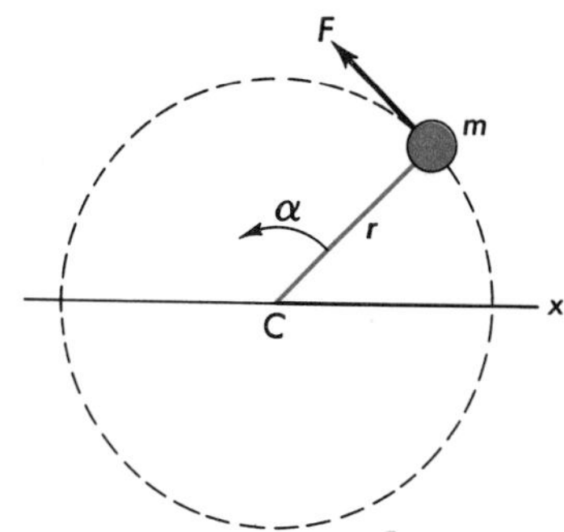

Fig. 13J. Angular acceleration depends upon torque and moment of inertia.

By Newton's second law of motion, the acceleration a of the mass around the periphery of the circle should be given by

$$F = ma$$

Multiply both sides of this equation by the radius of the circle r:

$$F \times r = ma \times r$$

The product $F \times r$ on the left side represents the applied torque L. If we replace the acceleration a on the right by its equal, $r\alpha$, from Eq.(13f), the result is

$$L = mr^2\alpha \qquad (13k)$$

Since m and r for a given body are both constants, they may be replaced by a single constant I, and the equation written

$$L = I\alpha \qquad (13\ell)$$

angular motion

where $I = mr^2$, and is called the *moment of inertia.* By comparison with the following force equation,

$$F = ma$$

linear motion

the torque L is seen to be analogous to F, the angular acceleration α analogous to a, and the moment of inertia I analogous to m.

According to Eq.(13k), the angular acceleration α is inversely proportional to r^2. An experiment illustrating this fact is shown in Fig. 13K. Two masses m threaded on light horizontal arms, free to turn about a vertical axis, are acted upon by a constant torque $L = F \times R$.

When the masses are clamped at equal distances from, and halfway out on the arms, the angular acceleration is relatively large, and the weight F_g exerting the constant torque L quickly drops from A to B. When the masses m are moved to the outer ends of the arms where their distance r is doubled, the angular acceleration is reduced to $\frac{1}{4}$ and the weight F_g takes 2 times as long to go from A to B. By measuring the distance of each mass from the center, and the time of fall of the weight F_g for each part of the experiment, the product αr^2 is found to be constant.

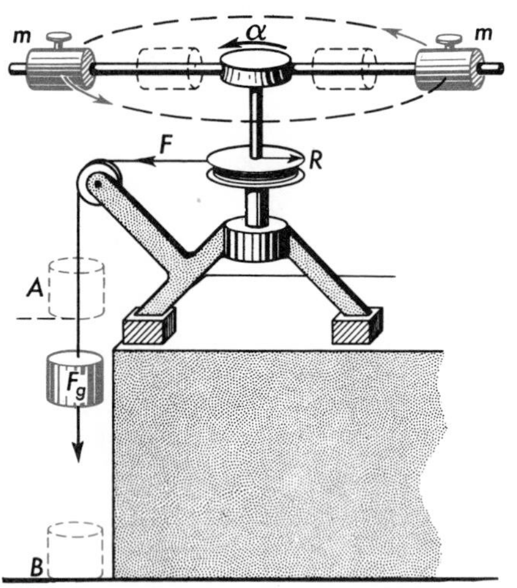

Fig. 13K. An experimental demonstration of moment of inertia.

13.8. Angular Momentum

Angular momentum and *rotational kinetic energy* are to all rotating bodies what *linear momentum* and *kinetic energy* are to all bodies moving along a straight line. By definition, the angular momentum p of a rotating body is equal to the product of its *moment of inertia* about the axis of rotation and its angular velocity:

$$p = I\omega \tag{13m}$$

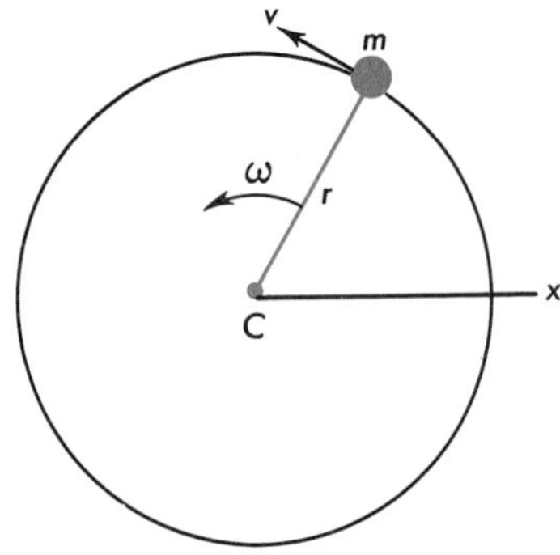

Fig. 13L. Angular momentum of a small mass m is given by mvr, or by $mr^2\omega$.

In the special case of a small mass moving in a circle, as shown in Fig. 13L, the moment of inertia equals mr^2, and

$$p = mr^2\omega \tag{13n}$$

If ω is replaced by its equivalent, v/r,

$$p = mvr \tag{13o}$$

The first two of the above equations apply to any rotating body regardless of size or shape, while the last one applies only to bodies considered small with respect to their distance from the center of rotation. To illustrate, consider the following example.

Example 5. A boy whose mass is 50.0 Kg rides at the outer edge of a merry-go-round, 12.0 m in diameter. Calculate his angular momentum if the merry-go-round is making 3.0 rpm.

Solution. Since the boy is small compared with his distance from the center of rotation, Eq.(13n) can be used. First the angular velocity ω is found by Eq.(13e):

$$\omega = \frac{3 \times 2\pi}{60} = 0.3142 \frac{\text{rad}}{\text{s}}$$

Substitution of known values in Eq.(13n) gives

$$p = 50 \text{ Kg} \times (6 \text{ m})^2 \times 0.3142 \frac{\text{rad}}{\text{s}}$$

$$p = 566 \frac{\text{Kg m}^2}{\text{s}}$$

13.9. Theoretical Considerations

To understand why angular momentum is defined as $I\omega$, return to the fundamental equation for torque, $L = I\alpha$. If in this equation the angular acceleration is replaced by its defining equation, $\alpha = (\omega_2 - \omega_1)/t$,

$$L = I \frac{\omega_2 - \omega_1}{t} \tag{13p}$$

Solving for the product Lt, we obtain an equation analogous to the impulse equation in translational motion:

$$Ft = mv_2 - mv_1$$

linear motion

$$Lt = I\omega_2 - I\omega_1 \tag{13q}$$

angular motion

In linear motion, Ft is called the impulse and $mv_2 - mv_1$ the change in momentum. By analogy, therefore, it is logical that Lt be called the *angular impulse* and $I\omega_2 - I\omega_1$ the *change in angular momentum.* $I\omega_1$ is the initial angular momentum and $I\omega_2$ the final value.

13.10. Conservation of Angular Momentum

If no external torque acts upon a body or system of bodies already in rotation, the angular momentum remains constant. Setting the torque L in Eq.(13q) equal to zero, $0 = I\omega_2 - I\omega_1$,

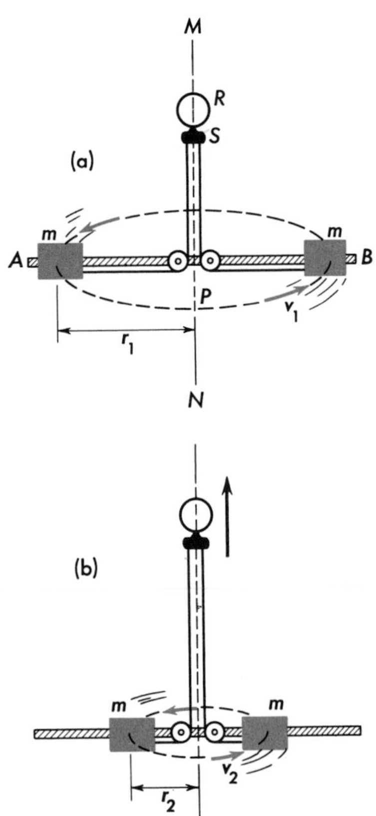

Fig. 13M. Experimental demonstration of the conservation of angular momentum.

from which

$$I\omega_2 = I\omega_1 \tag{13r}$$

In words, the final angular momentum is always equal to the initial angular momentum.

An experiment illustrating a system of bodies in rotation is diagrammed in Fig. 13M. Two equal masses m are mounted on a rod AB which is capable of rotation about a vertical axis MN. Cords fastened to each mass and leading over pulleys at P to the ring R enable the radial distance to be changed from r_1 in (a) to r_2 in (b) by simply pulling up on the ring R. The swivel S prevents the cords from twisting.

When the system is first set rotating as in (a) with an angular velocity ω_1, the angular momentum of each mass is $I\omega_1$. On pulling up on the ring R, the radius decreases to r_2 and the angular velocity ω_2 increases. Conservation of angular momentum requires that, for each mass m,

$$I_1\omega_1 = I_2\omega_2 \tag{13s}$$

In terms of speed v,

$$mv_1r_1 = mv_2r_2 \tag{13t}$$

Since the mass is not altered in value, the conservation of angular momentum requires that any decrease in r must be compensated for by an increase in speed. This is necessary to keep both sides of the above equation equal to each other.

Equation (13t) shows for example that, if r is reduced to half value, the velocity v must double. With v doubled and the circle only half as large, the angular velocity increases fourfold.

Example 6. Suppose in Fig. 13M that $m = 10.0$ g, $v_1 = 20.0$ cm/s, and $r_1 = 16.0$ cm. What will be the new speed if the radius r_1 is decreased to half value, i.e., $r_2 = 8.0$ cm?

Solution. By direct substitution in Eq.(13t),

$$10 \text{ g} \times 20 \frac{\text{cm}}{\text{s}} \times 16 \text{ cm} = 10 \text{ g} \times v_2 \times 8 \text{ cm}$$

$$3200 \frac{\text{cm}}{\text{s}} = 80\ v_2$$

$$v_2 = 40.0 \frac{\text{cm}}{\text{s}}$$

An interesting experiment illustrating the same principle is diagrammed in Fig. 13N. An observer stands on a turntable with weights in each hand. With arms fully extended horizontally, he is first set rotating slowly. Upon drawing the hands and weights in toward the chest, as shown, the angular velocity is considerably increased. This experiment is best appreciated by the turning observer who feels himself speeded up by what seems to be a mysterious force.

This principle is used by expert figure skaters on the ice. They start into a whirl with their arms and perhaps one leg extended, and then upon drawing the arms and leg in, obtain a greatly increased angular velocity.

Fig. 13N. Experiments illustrating conservation of angular momentum.

13.11. Kinetic Energy of Rotation

In a previous chapter on linear motion, kinetic energy was seen to be given by $\frac{1}{2}mv^2$. By analogy the kinetic energy of a rotating body is given by $\frac{1}{2}I\omega^2$:

$$E_{\mathrm{k\ trans}} = \tfrac{1}{2}mv^2$$

linear motion

$$E_{\mathrm{k\ rot}} = \tfrac{1}{2}I\omega^2 \qquad (13u)$$

angular motion

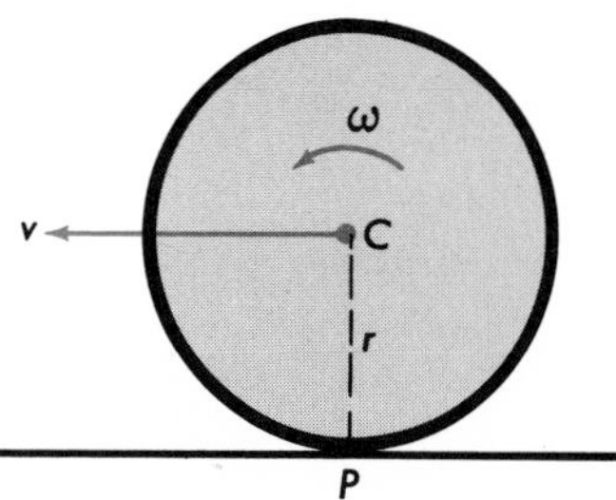

Fig. 13O. A rolling hoop has kinetic energy of rotation and kinetic energy of translation.

As a hoop rolls along a level road it has both kinetic energy of rotation and kinetic energy of translation (see Fig. 13O). In rotating about its geometrical center, it has a moment of inertia I and kinetic energy $\frac{1}{2}I\omega^2$, while the center of gravity C, moving along a straight line with velocity v, has kinetic energy $\frac{1}{2}mv^2$. The total kinetic energy is, therefore,

$$E_{\mathrm{k\ total}} = \tfrac{1}{2}I\omega^2 + \tfrac{1}{2}mv^2 \qquad (13v)$$

$$\text{Total } E_{\mathrm{k}} = \text{rotational } E_{\mathrm{k}} + \text{translational } E_{\mathrm{k}}$$

It will be observed that as a rolling wheel makes one complete turn its center moves along a straight line a distance equal to the circumference. The linear speed of the wheel's center is, therefore, equal to the speed v of a point on the rim with respect to the center.

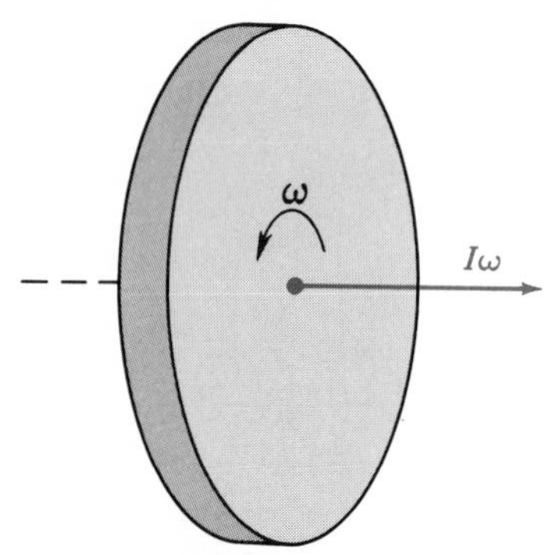

Fig. 13P. Angular momentum may be represented by a vector.

13.12. Angular Momentum as a Vector

Angular momentum, as illustrated by the rotating wheel in Fig. 13P, may be treated as a vector quantity. To obtain an angular momentum vector, imagine grasping the axis of rotation with the right hand, the fingers pointing in the direction of rotation, the thumb then pointing in the direction of the vector. The length of the vector is given by the magnitude of $I\omega$.

The advantage of representing angular momentum and angular impulse by vectors becomes apparent when attempting to determine the resultant motion of a body that undergoes rotation about two or more axes simultaneously. The gyroscope in some of its varied forms serves as a good illustration of this.

The moments of inertia of a number of regularly shaped solid bodies are given in Fig. 13Q. Diagram (b) represents a thin ring or hoop of radius R, (c) a disk of uniform density, and (h) a thin hollow sphere, with an axis through the center, etc.

In the *MKSA* system, the moment of inertia has the fundamental units of Kg m^2.

Frequently an object is set rotating around an axis that does not pass through its geometrical center. Under these conditions it would appear that any formula for calculating the moment of inertia should be quite complex. It turns out, however, that for regularly shaped objects like those shown in Fig. 17H the formulas are quite simple.

If I_0 represents the moment of inertia of a body around any axis through its center of mass, the moment of inertia I of that body around any parallel axis is given by

$$I = I_0 + Mh^2$$

13.13. Equilibrium

In Chap. 5 it was shown how *a body acted on by any number of forces is in equilibrium if the vector sum of all the forces is zero.* If each of these forces is resolved into *x* and *y components* and the conditions of equilibrium applied, the summation of all the *x components* of force must be zero, and the summation of all the *y components* must be zero. Symbolically,

$$\Sigma F_x = 0 \qquad \Sigma F_y = 0 \qquad (13w)$$

(The capital Greek sigma represents *"summation."*)

If all of the forces acting on a body lie in one plane, the fulfillment of these two conditions is all that is necessary to ensure *translational equilibrium.* These equations are commonly referred to as *the first condition of equilibrium.*

If one or more torques act upon a rigid body, tending to turn it one way or the other, the resultant rotation will depend upon the sum of all the torques. If the body is in equilibrium, the sum of all the torques must be zero:

$$\Sigma L = 0 \tag{13x}$$

It is customary to assign a *positive sign* to all torques acting in a counterclockwise direction, and a *negative sign* to all torques acting in a clockwise direction. Equation (13x) is commonly referred to as *the second condition of equilibrium.* This is the same convention used for the radius of generation of trigonometric angles.

To see how the first and second conditions of equilibrium are applied to a practical example in the field of orthopedics, consider the anatomical mechanics of the human foot (see Fig. 13R). In the flexion and extension of the whole foot, the ankle acts as a hinge or pivot about which rotation in a vertical plane takes place. The top of the *astragalus* is like a ball fitting into and free to turn in the socket formed by the ends of the *fibula* and *tibia* bones of the leg. When a person attempts to rise on tiptoe, the strong muscles, the *gastrocnemius* and *soleus* forming the calf of the leg, act as prime movers. A sufficient tightening of these muscles causes the heel to rise, and the foot to bend at C where the *phalanx* of the toes join the *metatarsals.*

A simple space diagram shown in Fig. 13S illustrates how rising on tiptoe involves the simplest type of torque action with a fixed pivot at C. The horizontal member AC represents the foot skeleton from A to C in Fig. 13R, and the vertical member (BD) the leg skeleton (BD) supporting the body. To calculate the tension required of the muscles and the load to be carried by the leg bones, the foot member A to C is drawn as a rigid body and all forces acting upon it are taken into account.

There are three forces acting on the horizontal member, an upward force at A due to tension in the muscles, a downward force at B due to the leg bones, and an upward force at C due to the floor.

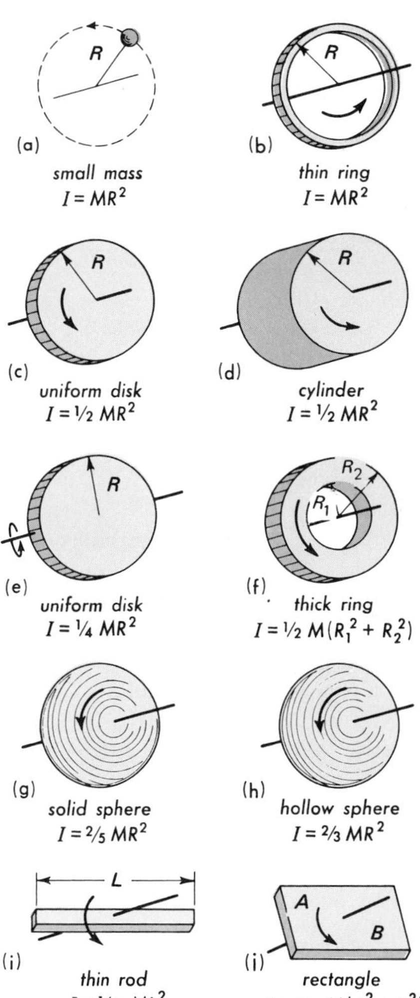

Fig. 13Q. Moments of inertia for a few common objects frequently found to be rotating.

Example 7. A 75.0-Kg man stands on one foot and then rises on tiptoe. If his foot dimensions are AB = 5.0 cm and BC = 15.0 cm,

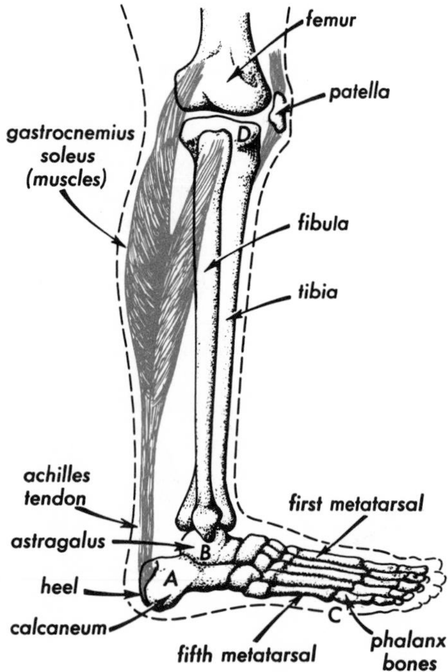

Fig. 13R. Skeleton diagram of the lower leg and foot showing the muscles and tendon used in rising on tiptoe.

calculate (a) the tension force T in the achilles tendon, and (b) the compression force P in the leg bones (see Fig. 13S).

Solution. The given quantities are AB = 0.050 m, BC = 0.150 m, and $F_g = 75.0 \text{ Kg} \times 9.80 \text{ m/s}^2 = 735 \text{ N}$. Applying the first *condition of equilibrium* to Eq.(13w), we see there are no x-components of force, so that automatically

$$\Sigma F_x = 0$$

In the y-direction there are forces and we write

$$\Sigma F_y = F_g + T - P = 0 \qquad (13y)$$

where

$$F_g = 735 \text{ N}$$

This is the man's weight in newtons, and T and P are still unknowns.

Applying the second *condition of equilibrium,* we take all torques about A as a pivot, and equate their sum to zero:

$$\Sigma L = F_g \times \text{AC} - P \times \text{AB} = 0$$

$$\Sigma L = F_g \times 0.20 \text{ m} - P \times 0.050 \text{ m} = 0$$

which upon substituting the value of F_g from above, and solving for P, gives

$$P = \frac{735 \text{ N} \times 0.20 \text{ m}}{0.050 \text{ m}}$$

$$P = 2940 \text{ N}$$

Taking force moments around B as a pivot, we obtain

$$\Sigma L = F_g \times 0.150 \text{ m} - T \times 0.050 \text{ m} = 0$$

which upon substituting for F_g, and solving for T gives

$$T = \frac{735 \text{ N} \times 0.150 \text{ m}}{0.050 \text{ m}}$$

$$T = 2205 \text{ N}$$

As a check upon these answers, the calculated values can be substituted in Eq.(13y), to obtain

$$735 \text{ N} + 2205 \text{ N} - 2940 \text{ N} = 0$$

It should be pointed out that tension is produced by a contraction of the large part or "belly" of a muscle, and not by the narrow section called the *tendon.*

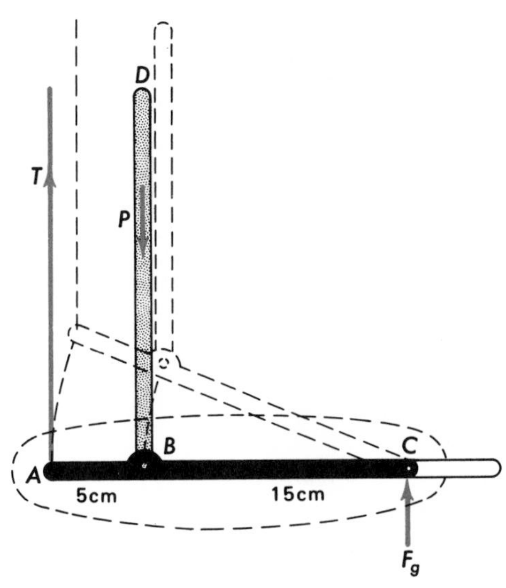

Fig. 13S. Schematic diagram showing the mechanical principle of the human foot when rising on tiptoe.

13.14. Mechanics of the Lower Jaw

The *mandible,* or lower "jawbone," is a large, strong, horseshoe-shaped bone, forming the lower third of the facial skeleton [see Fig. 13T(a)]. A pair of *condyles* at the ends fit into sockets, one on either side of the skull just in front of the auditory canal, and act as hinges about which the lower jaw pivots.

The *masseter* or "chewing muscle" is one of the strongest muscles in the body. As illustrated in the figure, it is located in the back part of the side of the face. Originating on the lower margin of the *zygoma,* the masseter passes downward to where it terminates on the lower edge of the *ramus* of the mandible.

The action of the two masseters, one on either side of the face, is such as to lift the lower jaw and at the same time draw it slightly forward. In principle, this is a torque action with a pivot at C, an upward force at B, and a load force at A introduced when chewing takes place between the teeth of the upper and lower jaws.

A schematic diagram of the torque action is shown in Fig. 13T(b), with selected values of the dimensions given in inches. When the mandible is selected as the rigid body, all of the acting forces, due to symmetry, are reduced to three, F_g, T, and P. To calculate the magnitudes of these forces, at least one of them must be known.

Example 8. A boy is chewing on a piece of dried meat and exerts a force of 200 N at the front teeth. Calculate (a) the tension T exerted by the two masseters, and (b) the force P exerted on the condyles. Assume the dimensions shown in Fig. 13T.

Solution. The known quantities are AB = 0.0850 m, DC = 0.040 m, and F_g = 200.0 N. Assuming the pivot point to be at the point C, we apply the second condition of equilibrium, and obtain

$$\Sigma L = F_g \times 0.1250 \text{ m} - T \times 0.040 \text{ m} = 0$$

Upon substituting the value of F_g = 200 N, and solving for T, we obtain

$$T = \frac{200 \text{ N} \times 0.1250 \text{ m}}{0.040 \text{ m}}$$

$$T = 625 \text{ N}$$

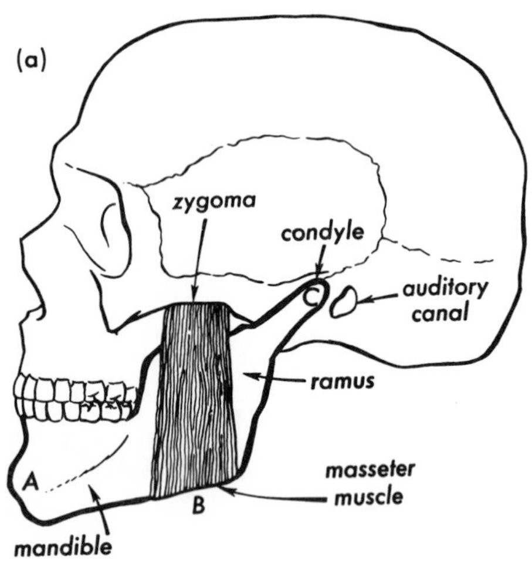

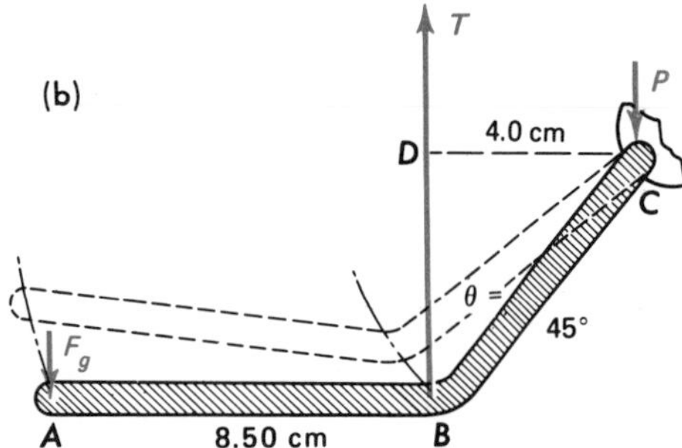

Fig. 13T. (a) Diagram of a human skull. (b) Schematic diagram showing the mechanics involved in chewing.

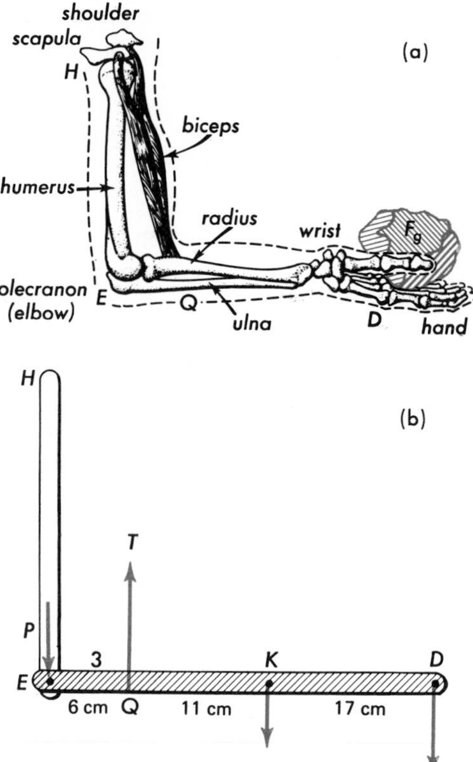

Fig. 13U. (a) Skeleton diagram of the arm and hand showing the biceps used in lifting a load. (b) Mechanics of the forearm.

Applying the first condition of equilibrium, we find

$$\Sigma F = P + F_g - T = 0$$

which, upon substituting known values, gives

$$P = T - F_g = 625 \text{ N} - 200.0 \text{ N}$$

$$P = 425.0 \text{ N}$$

Each masseter exerts $\frac{1}{2}$ of 625 N, or 312.5 N, while each condyle presses against its socket with a force of $\frac{1}{2}$ of 425.0 N, or 212.5 N.

The above procedure of solution may be applied to the muscle problem involved in the flexion of the lower arm. In Fig. 13U(a) a skeleton of the forearm is shown in a horizontal position supporting a stone in the palm of the hand. With a pivot point at the elbow joint, the forearm and hand form a compression member like the boom of a crane, while the *biceps* which assume the duty of prime mover in any flexor movement become the tension member. The biceps originate on the *scapula* or shoulder, from where they pass downward and forward to terminate on the *radius* near the elbow.

The problem to be solved resolves itself into one of calculating (a) the upward force T exerted by the biceps and (b) the downward force P exerted by the humerus on the elbow. With two unknown forces P and T, either one can be determined by eliminating one of them from torque calculations. Taking E as a pivot point and applying the second condition of equilibrium, we can calculate T. Applying the first condition of equilibrium we can calculate P. In any problem the positions and magnitudes of K and D should be indicated. Specific examples will be left as exercises for the student. See Problems 18 and 19.

problems

1. Two bodies, 24.0 Kg and 36.0 Kg, are located 8.0 m apart. Find their center of mass.

2. Three masses, 8.0 Kg, 12.0 Kg, and 8.0 Kg, respectively, are located at the corners of an equilateral triangle whose sides are 4.0 m long. Find the center of mass.

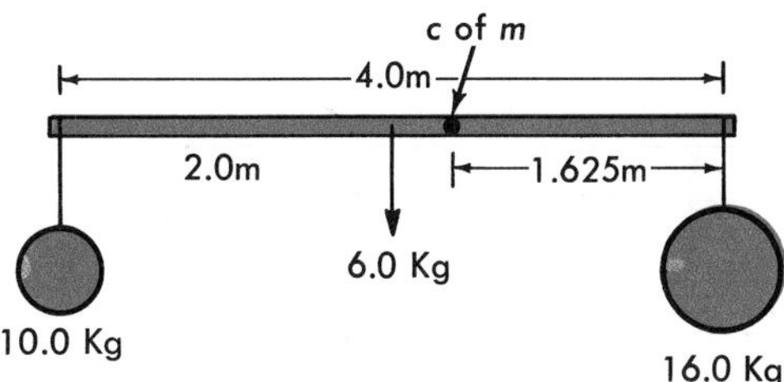

Prob. 3.

3. A uniform pole 4.0 m long has a mass of 6.0 Kg, and supports a mass at both ends. If the mass at one end is 16.0 Kg, and the mass at the other is 10 Kg, find their center of mass. Make a diagram. [Ans. 1.625 m from 16.0 Kg.]

4. The center of gravity of an empty truck with a mass of 3500 Kg is 3.0 m in front of the rear axle. The truck carries a steel box with a mass of 1200 Kg, which is placed with its center of mass 2.50 m in front of the rear axle. If the front and rear axles are 6.20 m apart, find (a) the center of mass of the system, (b) the load carried by the rear wheels, and (c) the load carried by the front wheels. Make a diagram.

5. An automobile engine is idling at 120.0 rpm. Upon constant acceleration it acquires a speed of 3600 rpm in 4.0 s. Find (a) the angular acceleration, (b) the angular velocity at the end of 4.0 s, and (c) the total angle turned through in these 4 s.

6. A 4.0-Kg stone on the end of a wire is whirled in a circle with a radius of 0.850 m, with an angular speed of 120.0 rpm. Find (a) the angular velocity, (b) the speed of a point on the rim, (c) the moment of inertia, and (d) the total kinetic energy. Make a diagram. [Ans. (a) 12.57 rad/s, (b) 10.68 m/s, (c) 2.890 Kg m^2, (d) 228.3 J.]

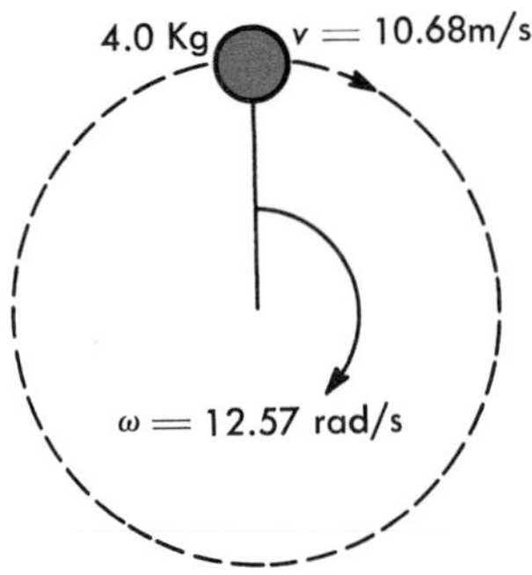

Prob. 6.

7. Two stones of 3.0 Kg and 5.0 Kg, respectively, are connected to opposite ends of a thin wire and thrown into the air to rotate around their common center of mass at 210.0 rpm. If their centers of mass are 0.80 m apart, find (a) their center of rotation, (b) their moment of inertia, (c) the angular velocity of the system, (d) the angular momentum, (e) the linear speed of each mass, and (f) the total kinetic energy of rotation.

8. An emery wheel in the form of a uniform disk, with a mass of 2.40 Kg, and a diameter of 28.0 cm, is rotating at 4500 rpm. Find (a) the moment of inertia, (b) the angular velocity, (c) the angular momentum, (d) the linear speed of the rim, and (e) the kinetic energy.

9. A thick ring with a mass of 2.40 Kg has an internal diameter of 24.0 cm, and an external diameter of 30.0 cm. This ring is welded to a thin uniform disk having a diameter of 24.0 cm, and a mass of 1.0 Kg. This wheel is set rotating about an axis through its center at 6000 rpm. Find (a) the moment of inertia of the wheel, (b) its angular velocity, (c) its angular momentum, and (d) its kinetic energy. Make a diagram. [Ans. (a) 0.0515 Kg m^2, (b) 628 rad/s, (c) 32.34 Kg m^2/s, (d) 1.016×10^4 J.]

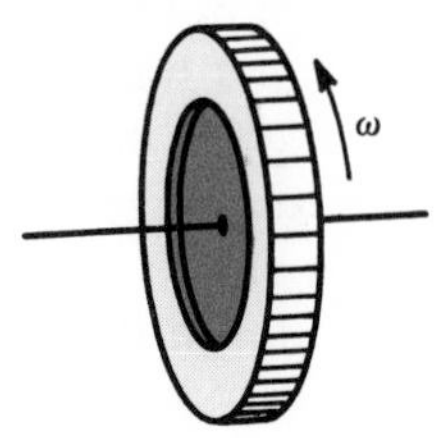

Prob. 9.

10. A thin uniform rod with a mass of 2.60 Kg, and a length of 86.0 cm, is made to rotate about an axis through one end, perpendicular to its length, at 150.0 rpm. Find (a) its moment of inertia, (b) its angular velocity, (c) its angular momentum, and (d) its kinetic energy.

11. The two atoms of a diatomic molecule each have a mass of 4.80×10^{-26} Kg. If the distance between their centers of mass is 3.60×10^{-10} m, and they rotate around their common center, like a dumbbell, with a frequency of 5.40×10^{13} rps, find (a) the angular velocity in rad/s, (b) the angular momentum, and (c) the kinetic energy. Make a diagram.

12. Two masses of 2.0 Kg and 5.0 Kg, respectively, are fastened to opposite ends of a wire so their cen-

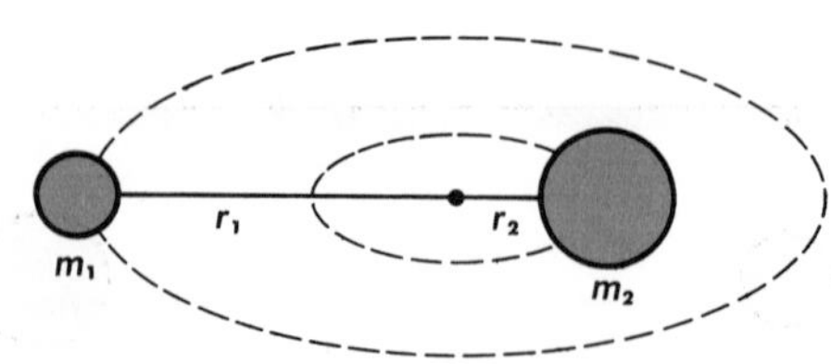

Prob. 12.

ters are 3.50 m apart. If the system is projected into space rotating at 300 rpm, calculate (a) the center of mass, (b) the moment of inertia, (c) the angular velocity, (d) the angular momentum, (e) the kinetic energy of the smaller mass, and (f) the kinetic energy of the larger mass. Make a diagram. [Ans. (a) 1.0 m from 5 Kg, (b) 17.50 Kg m^2, (c) 31.42 rad/s, (d) 550 Kg m^2/s, (e) 6170 J, (f) 2468 J.]

13. A space vehicle on a long journey to the planet Mars simulates gravity by extending one-third of its total mass of 5400 Kg outward 48.0 m by a long telescoping tube, and the system set rotating at 4.0 rpm. See diagram for Prob. 14, Chap. 12. Neglecting the mass of the connecting tunnel, find (a) the center of rotation, (b) the moment of inertia, (c) the angular velocity in rad/s, (d) the total angular momentum, and (e) the kinetic energy of each mass.

14. A uniform disk with a mass of 5.0 Kg and a diameter of 0.50 m starts from rest at the top of a 30° incline. If the incline is 20.0 m long, find (a) the initial potential energy, (b) the linear velocity at the bottom, (c) the final angular velocity, (d) its kinetic energy of translation, (e) its kinetic energy of rotation, and (f) its total energy. Make a diagram. *Note:* Apply the law of conservation of energy.

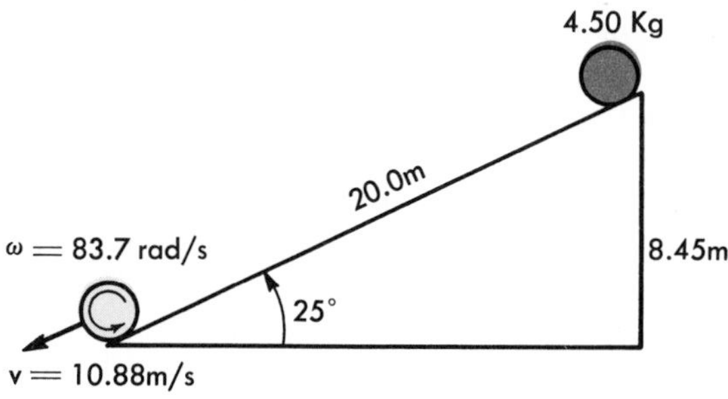

Prob. 15.

15. A bowling ball with a mass of 4.50 Kg and a diameter of 0.260 m starts from rest at the top of a 25° incline. If the incline is 20.0 m long, find (a) the initial potential energy. Upon reaching the bottom, find (b) the linear velocity, (c) the angular velocity about the center of the ball, (d) its kinetic energy of translation, (e) its kinetic energy of rotation, and (f) its total kinetic energy. Make a diagram. Apply conservation laws. [Ans. (a) 372.7 J, (b) 10.88 m/s, (c) 83.7 rad/s, (d) 266.2 J, (e) 106.5 J, (f) 372.7 J.]

16. A boy whose mass is 65.0 Kg stands on one foot and then rises on tiptoe. His foot dimensions are AB = 4.50 cm, and BC = 14.0 cm (see Fig. 13S for dimensions layout). Calculate (a) the tension in his achilles tendon, and (b) the compressional force in his leg bones.

17. A man chews on a piece of hard candy and exerts a force of 250.0 N at his front teeth. Calculate (a) the tension exerted by each of the two masseters, and (b) the force on each condyle. The dimensions of his jaw are such that AB = 9.20 cm, BC = 6.50 cm, and θ = 40° (see Fig. 13T).

18. A man with his forearm flexed in the horizontal position, as shown in Fig. 13U, holds a 5.0-Kg mass in his hand. If his arm dimensions are EQ = 6.0 cm, QK = 11.0 cm, and KD = 17.0 cm, find (a) the tension in the biceps, and (b) the compressional force in the humerus. Assume the mass of his forearm to be 1.20 Kg. [Ans. (a) 311.0 N, (b) 255.3 N.]

19. A boy with his right forearm flexed to the horizontal position, as shown in Fig. 13U, holds a 3.50-Kg mass in his hand. When his arm is measured for size it is found that ED = 36.0, EK = 20.0 cm, and EQ = 6.0 cm. Find (a) the tension in his biceps, and (b) the compression force in the humerus. Assume the mass of his forearm to be 0.950 Kg.

14 Temperature, specific heat, and thermal expansion

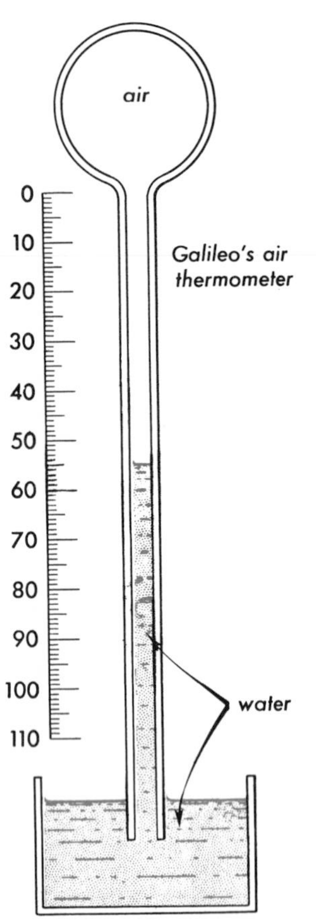

Fig. 14A. Air on heating expands and pushes the water down in the tube. On cooling, the air contracts and the water rises.

The subject of heat is that branch of knowledge dealing with the motions of molecules, whether they are in a gas, a liquid, or a solid. Adding heat to a body increases its energy. There is a significant difference between the *temperature* of a body and the *thermal energy* it contains. To make a clear distinction between these two aspects of heat, we will start with temperature.

14.1. Temperature

From a historical standpoint, the first authentic record of a thermometer dates back to the time of Galileo. Galileo's thermometer, as illustrated in Fig. 14A, consists of a narrow glass tube with an opening at one end and a bulb at the other. The open end of the tube is filled with colored water and inverted in a dish of water. When the temperature of the surrounding air rises, the air within the bulb expands, forcing the water down the tube. If the bulb is cooled, the air inside contracts, drawing the water up. To be exact, atmospheric pressure outside pushes the water up. A scale attached to the narrow tube can be calibrated to any temperature scale, low temperatures at the top and high temperatures at the bottom.

Of the many forms of temperature-measuring devices, the mercury thermometer is the most common. A mercury thermometer, as shown in Fig. 14B, consists of a narrow glass tube (called a capillary), with the bottom end sealed to a small bulb and the top end closed. The bulb and part of the capillary are filled with mercury, and the remaining section is evacuated. When the temperature rises, the mercury and the glass bulb both expand. The mercury, however, expands more than the glass, forcing a small part of the mercury up the narrow capillary. A scale is engraved on the glass to read temperature.

14.2. Temperature Scales

There are in general use today four different temperature scales. These are the Fahrenheit, Rankine, Celsius (centigrade), and Kelvin or absolute. Each scale is shown by a diagram in Fig. 14C. The thermometers are all identically made, but each has a different scale. In the United States, the Fahrenheit scale is commonly used in civil life, and the Rankine scale is used by engineers. The Celsius and Kelvin scales are used in all countries for scientific measurements.

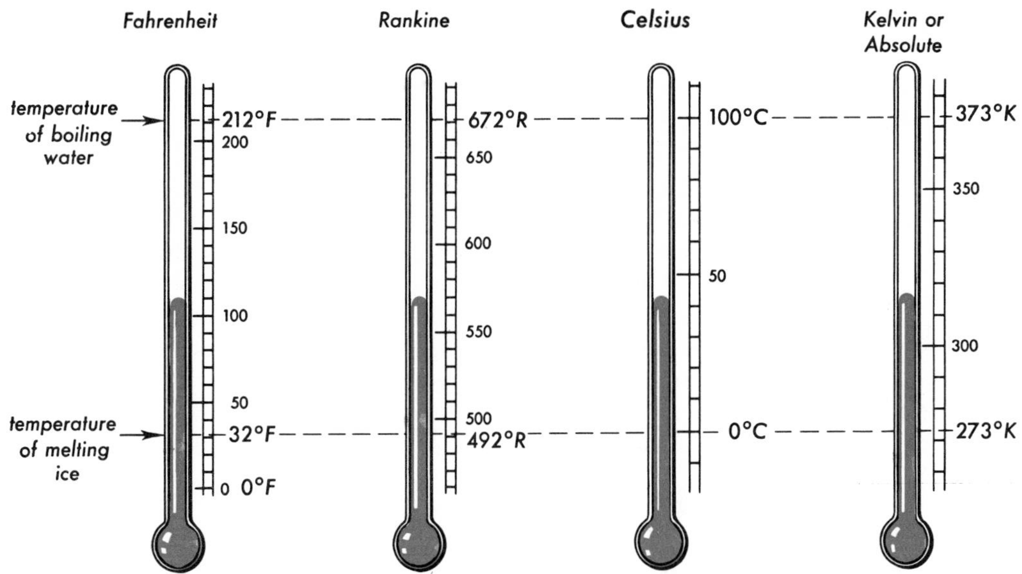

Fig. 14C. Mercury thermometers illustrating the four common temperature scales.

Most of the manufactured thermometers are calibrated to one of these four scales. To calibrate a thermometer, the bulb is first placed in a mixture of ice and water, and the height of the mercury column marked on the side of the stem. It is next placed in steam just above boiling water and again marked. These two marks then determine two points for whatever scale is to be used.

The lowest temperature ever reached is approximately $-273.16°C$, or $-459.69°F$. For reasons beyond the scope of this book, this is the lowest temperature that can ever be attained. The Kelvin and Rankine scales start with the lowest possible temperature as *absolute zero.* On the basis of the Celsius and Fahrenheit scale divisions, this locates the freezing point of

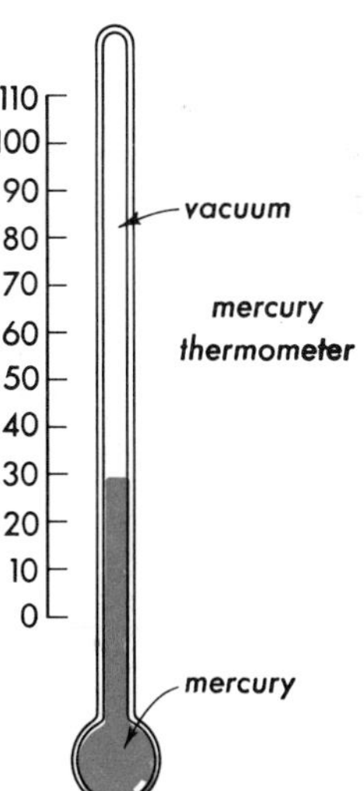

Fig. 14B. On heating a thermometer, the mercury expands more than the glass tube and the mercury level rises.

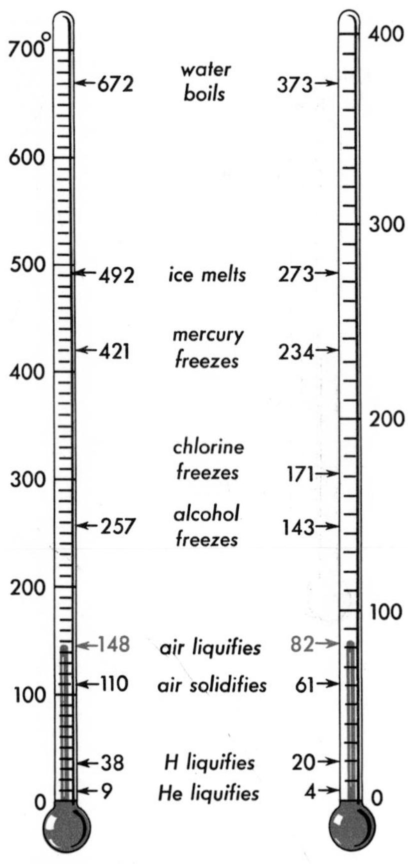

Fig. 14D. Rankine and Kelvin, or absolute, temperature scales. (Shown here on symbolic liquid thermometers, not actually realized.)

water, to the nearest whole number, at 273°K or 492°R, and the boiling point at 373°K or 672°R.

A more detailed diagram of the two absolute temperature scales in common use is given in Fig. 14D. The zero point of both these scales is called *absolute zero* and represents the temperature at which all molecular motion ceases. While all molecular motion is said to cease at absolute zero, the atoms of which some substances are composed would still have inherent motions that cannot be eliminated.

On the Kelvin scale, water boils at 373°K and ice melts at 273°K. Air becomes a liquid at 82°K and a solid at 61°K. Hydrogen gas becomes a liquid at 20°K and freezes at 14°K. Helium liquefies at 4°K.

Between the temperatures of melting ice and boiling water there are 180° on the Fahrenheit and Rankine scales, as compared with 100° on the Celsius and Kelvin scales. The ratio of these numbers is 9:5. This comparison shows that a temperature rise of 9°F, or 9°R, is equivalent to a rise of only 5°C, or 5°K.

It is frequently necessary to change temperature readings from one temperature scale to another. Rather than develop formulas for such changes, it is more convenient to work out the simple mathematical steps by the inspection of a diagram like Fig. 14C.

14.3. Electrical Thermometers

If very low or very high temperatures are to be measured, thermometers other than mercury must be employed. At temperatures below −39°C, mercury freezes and becomes a solid; at high temperatures, glass melts and becomes a liquid. For both of these temperature extremes, electrical thermometers are commonly used. These instruments operate upon the principle that the resistance a wire offers to a flow of electric current through it changes with temperature. The higher the temperature, the greater is the resistance.

A diagram of an electrical thermometer is shown in Fig. 14E. A fine piece of platinum wire is wound around a small spool made of silica. The ends of this wire are connected to a battery and an ammeter. The purpose of the battery is to supply the electric current, and the ammeter is used to determine its exact value. When the temperature of a hot body like a furnace is to be measured, the spool of platinum wire is placed inside the furnace, and the battery and ammeter outside. A rise in temperature causes the resistance of the platinum wire to increase, and the current, therefore, to decrease. When the platinum wire reaches the temperature of the furnace, its resistance reaches a constant value and the ammeter pointer indicates a steady current. In many cases the ammeter scale is calibrated to give the temperature directly in degrees.

Another form of an electrical temperature-measuring device, called a *thermocouple,* is illustrated in Fig. 14F. This device is based upon a principle, discovered in 1821 by Seebeck, known as the *thermoelectric effect.* Two pieces of wire, one copper and one iron, are joined together at the ends to form a complete loop. When one junction is heated and the other kept cool, an electric current flows around the loop in the direction indicated by the arrows. The greater the difference in temperature between the two junctions, the greater is the electric current.

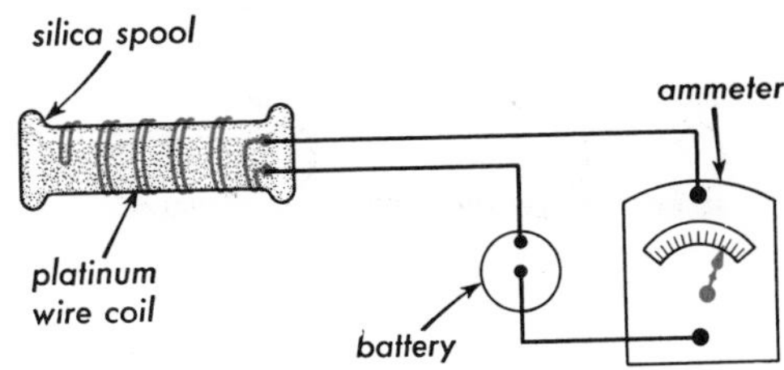

Fig. 14E. Electrical-resistance thermometer showing connections between the platinum wire coil, the battery, and the ammeter.

Diagram (b) in Fig. 14F represents a thermocouple connected by wires to an ammeter. If the junction of the thermocouple is first placed in melting ice and then in boiling water, the two scale readings of the ammeter can be marked 0°C and 100°C at the appropriate points. These determine the scale of the instrument, thus making it a direct-reading thermometer.

Thermocouples are not always made of copper and iron as shown in Fig. 14F. Any two different metals when brought into contact will exhibit a thermoelectric effect. Some combinations of two metals, however, produce larger voltages and currents than others. For very high temperature measurements, platinum and platinum–iridium alloys are used, owing to their very high melting-point temperatures.

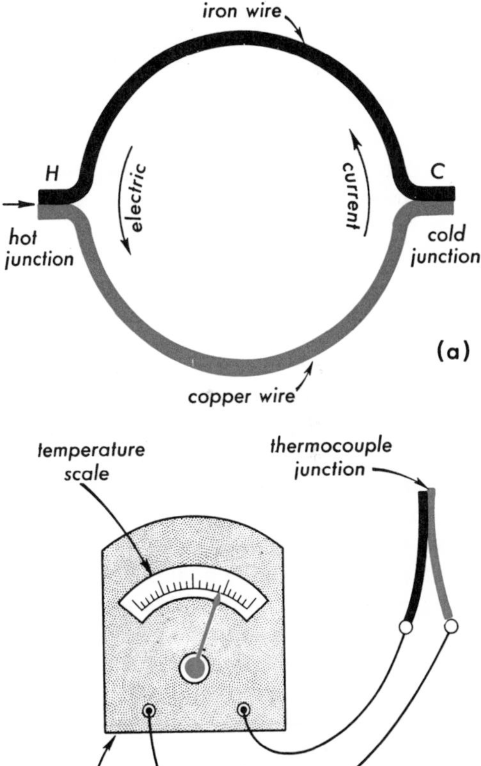

Fig. 14F. Above, a thermocouple. Below, a thermocouple thermometer circuit diagram.

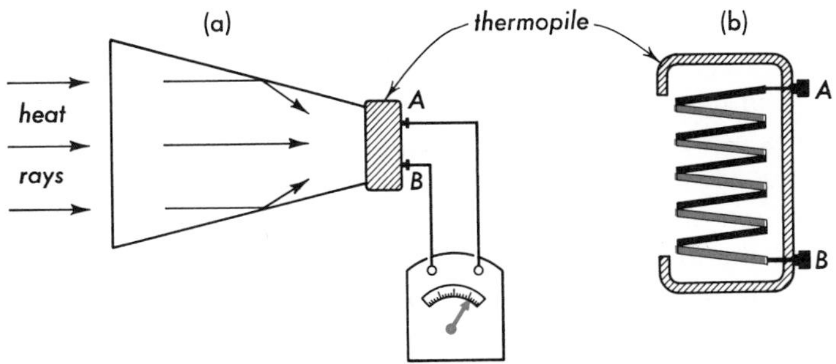

Fig. 14G. Cross section of a thermopile for measuring heat radiation from hot bodies.

A set of many thermocouples, when connected as shown in Fig. 14G, forms what is commonly called a *thermopile.* Small rods of two different metals are joined alternately as shown in diagram (b). One set of junctions is usually protected by placing them at the back of a small box container, and the other set is exposed

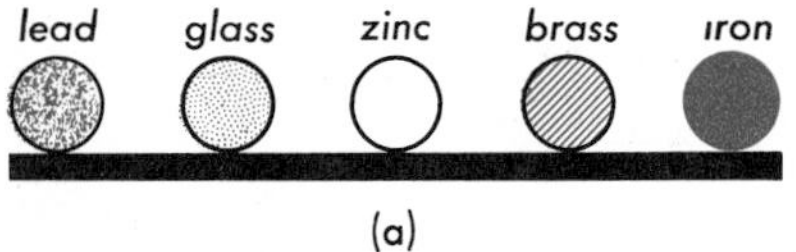

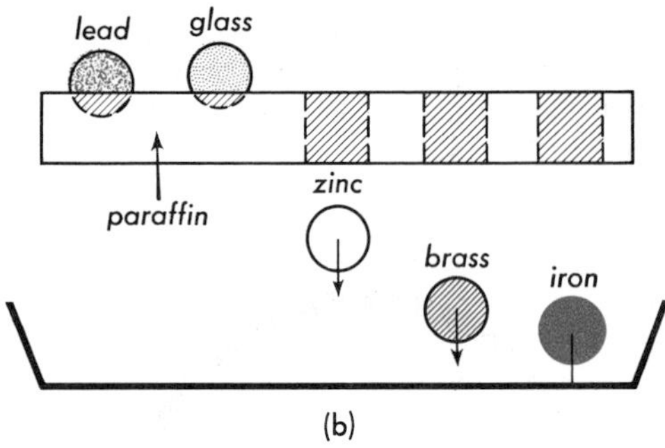

Fig. 14H. Experiment demonstrating the different heat capacities of different substances of the same size.

to heat rays through the opposite side which is left open. A funnel or horn-shaped reflector mounted over the open side will collect more heat rays from a distant hot object and thereby increase the electric current. Thermocouples containing several hundred elements can be made so sensitive that they will detect the heat of a candle flame several hundred feet away.

14.4. Specific Heat

According to the kinetic theory of matter, the individual atoms of which all substances are made are in a state of rapid motion. As a body is heated to a higher temperature, this atomic motion increases and the body expands. As a body cools, the atomic motions decrease and the body shrinks. That heat is a form of energy and is due to the kinetic energy of molecular motion was first proposed by Count Rumford in the latter part of the 18th century.*

It is not always clear to the beginning student that the temperature and the quantity of heat are different entities. The difference between the two can be illustrated by the heating of two pans of water. More gas must be burned to heat a large pan of water than a small pan. Although both are started at the same temperature and both are raised to the same boiling point, 100°C, the larger pan has required more thermal energy, called heat.

The difference between the temperature and quantity of heat is well illustrated by the following experiment (see Fig. 14H). Five marbles, all of the same size but made of different materials, are heated in boiling water to a temperature of 100°C. At a given instant they are all placed on a sheet of paraffin about 0.5 cm thick and permitted to melt their way through. The iron and brass marbles are observed to drop through first, but the lead and glass marbles never do. This illustrates the fact that the heat content of the iron and brass, even though raised to the same temperature as the others, is considerably greater than the heat content of the glass and lead.

In order to determine the exact heat capacity of a substance, we must first define the *kilocalorie* and the *calorie.*

The amount of heat required to raise 1 Kg of water 1C° is called a kilocalorie (Kcal, or Cal).

The amount of heat required to raise the temperature of 1 g of water 1C° is called the calorie (cal).

The ratio between these units is

$$1 \text{ Kcal} = 1000 \text{ cal} \qquad (14a)$$

***Benjamin Thompson (Count Rumford) was born in Woburn, Massachusetts, in 1753. He spent most of his adult life abroad, notably in Bavaria, which was then a part of the Holy Roman Empire. Among other ventures, he managed a Bavarian artillery factory. From his observations about the heat developed in boring cannon, he was able to show that heat is not a pervading fluid, but a form of internal energy of the atoms or molecules forming the substance. His own expression was that heat was a mode of motion of these particles. For these and other services, Thompson was appointed a count of the Holy Roman Empire; he chose the name of his wife's former home in New Hampshire, Rumford, as his title.**

Once the kilocalorie is defined, the amount of heat required to raise any amount of water from one temperature to another may be calculated by simply multiplying the mass of water by the rise in temperature. For example, to raise the temperature of 25 Kg of water from 10°C to 50°C requires $25 \times 40 = 1000$ Kcal.

While 1 Kcal of heat will raise the temperature of 1 Kg of water 1C°, a different number of Kcal will be required to raise the temperature of 1 Kg of some other substance 1C°. For example, to raise the temperature of 1 Kg of iron 1C° requires $\frac{1}{10}$ of a Kcal, while to raise 1 Kg of lead 1C° requires only $\frac{1}{30}$ of a Kcal. In other words, the thermal capacities of equal masses of different materials have different values.

The thermal capacity of a substance is defined as the number of kilocalories required to raise the temperature of 1 Kg of that substance through 1C°.

The ratio between the thermal capacity of a substance and the thermal capacity of water is called specific heat.

Numerically, specific heat has the same value as thermal capacity; being a ratio, however, it is like *specific gravity* and has no units.

The specific heats or thermal capacities of a few common substances are given in Table 14A.

To illustrate the use of this table, consider the calculation of the heat content of the marbles used in the above experiment. In Table 14B the measured mass of each marble is given in the second column of the following tabulation and the corresponding thermal capacity or specific heat in the next column. The product of these two quantities gives the values shown in the third column; they represent the amount of heat in Kcal required to raise that marble 1C°. Since all marbles were raised from room temperature 20°C to the boiling point of water, 100°C, the values in the third column have been multiplied by the rise in temperature 80°C to obtain the total heat values in the last column.

TABLE 14A
Specific heats, or thermal capacities in Kcal/Kg

Substance	*c*
Aluminum	0.220
Brass	0.092
Copper	0.093
Glass	0.160
Gold	0.031
Glycerine	0.60
Ice	0.50
Iron, steel	0.105
Lead	0.031
Mercury	0.033
Silver	0.056
Zinc	0.092
Steam	0.50
Water	1.000

TABLE 14B
Tabulated results of the marble experiment

Substance	*Mass* (Kg)	*Thermal capacity* (Kcal/ Kg C°)	*Heat to raise 1C°* (Kcal)	*Heat to raise 80C°* (Kcal)
Lead	0.045	0.031	0.00139	0.111
Glass	0.010	0.160	0.00160	0.128
Zinc	0.024	0.092	0.00220	0.176
Brass	0.030	0.092	0.00276	0.221
Iron	0.028	0.105	0.00294	0.235

These numbers clearly indicate that, in the experiment above, iron and brass should melt through the paraffin first. They have available within them the largest amounts of stored thermal energy, 0.235 and 0.221 Kcal, respectively.

The definition of thermal capacity and the calculation of total heat added may be summarized by a generally useful formula of the following form:

$$\Delta H = m \times c \times \Delta t \tag{14b}$$

ΔH represents the total heat added in Kcal, m the mass of the body in Kg, c the thermal capacity in Kcal/Kg C°, and Δt the rise in temperature in C°.

Example 1. How much heat is required to raise 5.0 Kg of copper from a room temperature of 27°C to the melting point of 1063°C?
Solution. With the value of the specific heat of copper from Table 14A, the known quantities are $m = 5.0$ Kg, $c = 0.0930$ Kcal/Kg, $t_2 = 1063$°C, and $t_1 = 27$°C. Direct substitution in Eq.(14b) gives

$$\Delta H = m \times c \times \Delta t$$

$$\Delta H = 5 \text{ Kg} \times 0.093 \frac{\text{Kcal}}{\text{Kg}} \times (1063 - 27)°\text{C}$$

$$\Delta H = 482 \text{ Kcal}$$

14.5. Thermal Expansion of Solids

In general, when an object is heated, whether it be a solid, liquid, or gas, it expands. There are only a few known exceptions to this. The expansion of a solid with a rise in temperature can be demonstrated by heating a long wire and measuring its overall elongation. One experimental arrangement for demonstrating this is shown in Fig. 14I. An iron wire about 2 m in length is fastened to a hook A at one end and to a weight W at the other. Between these two points the wire passes over three pulleys B, C, and D. The wire is heated by connecting it to a battery and sending an electric current through it from end to end.

As the wire is heated and lengthens, the weight slowly falls, thus turning the pulleys as well as the pointer P. When the current is turned off by opening the switch, the wire cools and at the

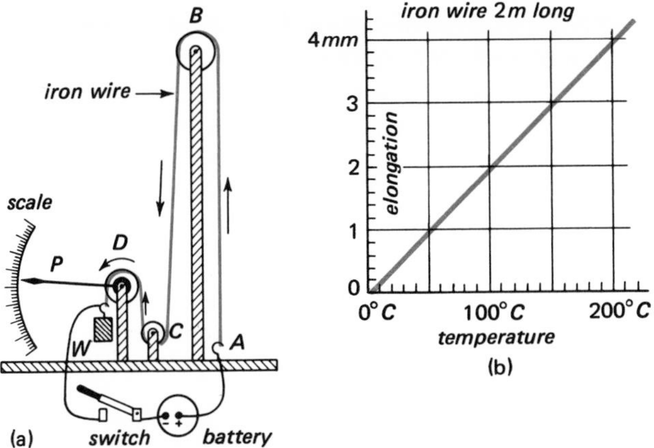

Fig. 14I. Experiment illustrating the expansion (elongation) of a wire due to a rise in temperature.

same time contracts to its original length. In the well-equipped laboratory, accurate measurements of the rise in temperature and the lengthening of a solid rod are readily made. The graph in Fig. 14I(b) illustrates the straight-line relation between the rise in temperature and the elongation. By the elongation is meant the increase in length and not the total length of the wire. For an iron wire 2 m long, a rise in temperature of 50°C produces an elongation of 1 mm, 100°C produces an elongation of 2 mm, 150°C an elongation of 3 mm, etc. The straight line means, therefore, that the elongation is directly proportional to the rise in temperature.

There are many instances in engineering where the expansion of solids is an important factor in design and construction. This is particularly true in the construction of suspension birdges and railroads. When the steel rails of the early railroads were first put in place, small gaps were left at every union. The reason for this is that in summer, when the temperature rises, the rails expand and close these gaps. If the gaps are not large enough in cold weather, the track may buckle up in summer and cause serious accidents. In winter when the rails contract and the gaps are wider, they become noisy to travel as the car wheels roll over them.

Not all substances expand by the same amount when heated through the same difference in temperature. This is illustrated by the linear coefficients of thermal expansion of a few common substances given in Table 14C.

The linear coefficient of thermal expansion α is defined as the change in length per unit length of a substance per 1° rise in temperature. Once this constant is known, the linear expansion

TABLE 14C
Linear coefficients of thermal expansion (centigrade)

Material	α per °C
Aluminum	25×10^{-6}
Brass	18×10^{-6}
Copper	17×10^{-6}
Glass (soda)	17×10^{-6}
Glass (pyrex)	3×10^{-6}
Gold	14×10^{-6}
Iron	11×10^{-6}
Platinum	9×10^{-6}
Silver	18×10^{-6}
Quartz	0.4×10^{-6}
Pine wood (along grain)	5×10^{-6}
Pine wood (across grain)	30×10^{-6}

for any sized object made of that same material can be calculated for any rise in temperature by the following formula:

$$\text{elongation} = \alpha \times \text{length} \times \text{rise in temperature}$$

$$\Delta L = \alpha L \,\Delta t \tag{14c}$$

where $\Delta t = t_2 - t_1$. In this equation t_1 is the original temperature of the body, t_2 the final temperature to which it is raised, and L its original length.*

Example 2. A pyrex glass rod is accurately ground and polished to a length of 2.0000 m when the room temperature is 20°C. If this same rod is heated to a temperature of 420°C, how much does it elongate?

Solution. The given quantities are $L = 2.0000$ m, $\alpha = 3.0 \times 10^{-6}$, and $t = 420°C - 20°C$. From the above equation we write

$$\begin{aligned}\Delta L &= 3 \times 10^{-6} \times 2 \times (420 - 20)\\ &= 3 \times 10^{-6} \times 2 \times 400 = 0.0024 \text{ m}\\ &= 2.40 \text{ mm}\end{aligned}$$

The rod thus lengthens by only 0.00240 m to give an over-all length of 2.00240 m. It should be noted that had the length of the rod been given as 2 in., the elongation would have been 0.0024 in. In other words, ΔL and L are always in the same units, so that the coefficients of thermal expansion are valid in the metric as well as the English system. The coefficients given in Table 14C, however, are for the Celsius temperature scale only. Should the known temperature be Fahrenheit or Rankine, the change in temperature should be converted to the Celsius scale.

14.6. Differential Expansion

In the previous section it was stated that all substances do not expand alike. Some metals like brass and aluminum expand twice as much as others, like iron and platinum (see Table 14C).

* It is customary in formulas to use the letter t for temperature on either the Celsius or Fahrenheit scale. When absolute temperature must be used, however, the capital letter T is used.

This difference in expansion is demonstrated by the heating of a bimetallic strip as shown in Fig. 14J. Two thin strips of different metal are placed side by side and welded together over their entire length. When heated, one metal expands more than the other, causing the strip to bend. The hotter it becomes, the more it bends. When it cools down to its original temperature, the strip becomes straight again, and if cooled still further, it bends in the opposite direction.

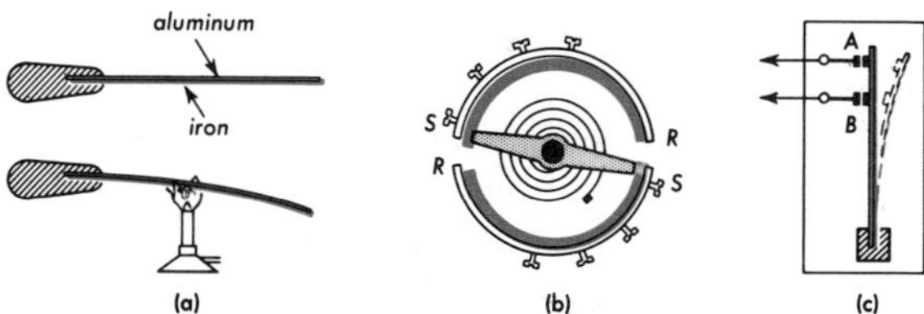

Fig. 14J. Different substances expand by different amounts. (a) Bimetallic strip, (b) balance wheel of a watch, (c) a thermostat.

Differential expansion as shown by this experiment finds many practical applications in industry. Bimetallic strips are used, for example, in the making of balance wheels for fine watches and in thermostats for refrigerators, hot-water heaters, and car radiators. When on a hot day the spokes of the balance of a watch expand, they shift the weight of the rim farther from the center, causing the balance wheel to oscillate more slowly. By making the rim of the wheel of two bimetallic strips, this can be compensated for as shown in Fig. 14J(b). With a rise in temperature the ends of the spokes S move out and the free ends R of the bimetallic strips bend in closer to the axis of rotation. One expansion compensates the other, keeping the watch running at the same rate.

Thermostats are so commonly employed in electrical devices today that their explanation will be given here. An electrical thermostat is an automatic electric switch which closes when the temperature reaches one desired temperature and opens when it reaches another. One type of switch is shown in Fig. 14J(c). If the temperature is low, the bimetallic strip is straight and makes electrical contact between the points A and B. This operates an electrical device which, for argument's sake, might open a gas valve of a furnace in the basement of a house. When the air in the house rises to the desired temperature, the bimetallic strip has bent far enough away to break the electrical contact at A and B, thus turning off the furnace. As the air cools,

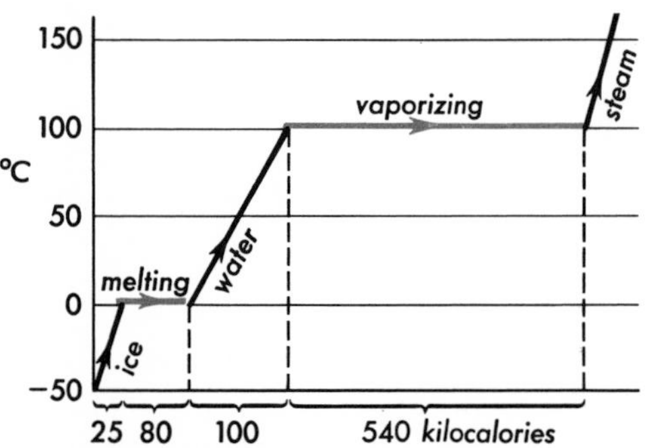

Fig. 14K. Volume–temperature graphs of the thermal expansion of liquids.

TABLE 14D
Volume coefficients of expansion for four common liquids

Liquid	*per °C*	*per °F*
Alcohol	11.0×10^{-4}	6.6×10^{-4}
Glycerine	5.3×10^{-4}	2.9×10^{-4}
Mercury	1.8×10^{-4}	1.0×10^{-4}
Turpentine	10.5×10^{-4}	5.8×10^{-4}

the strip straightens out and makes contact, again turning on the furnace.

14.7. Thermal Expansion of Liquids

Accurate measurements of the expansion of liquids with a rise in temperature are made difficult by the simultaneous expansion of the containing vessel. This difficulty can be overcome, however, and one finds that most liquids, like solids, expand by an amount which is proportional to the rise in temperature. This is illustrated by the straight-line graphs for alcohol and mercury in Fig. 14K(a).

A straight-line graph here means that with each degree rise in temperature the increase in volume due to expansion is exactly the same. If 1 m^3 of mercury at 0°C is heated to a temperature of 1°C, its volume will be 1.00018 m^3, or an increase of 0.00018 m^3. At 10° the increase will be ten times this amount, or 0.0018 m^3. Thus for each degree rise, the increase is the same and equal to 0.00018. This number is called the volume coefficient of thermal expansion of mercury. For alcohol the coefficient is 0.0011 per degree centigrade.

The volume expansion of liquids like mercury or alcohol is given by a formula of exactly the same form as the one for solids [see Eq.(14c)]:

$$\Delta v = \beta V \Delta t \tag{14d}$$

where Δv is the change in volume, β the volume coefficient of thermal expansion, V the original volume, and Δt is the difference in temperature. If the linear coefficient of thermal expansion α is known for any substance, the volume coefficient β is given by the relation

$$\beta = 3\alpha$$

14.8. Anomalous Expansion of Water

Over a large range in temperature, liquids do not expand linearly. Actually, their graphs curve slightly upward, indicating a more rapid rise at higher temperatures. The extent of the departure from a straight-line graph differs considerably with liquids. At 100°C, for example, alcohol expands about 20% more for each degree rise than it does at 0°C. Mercury, on the other hand, varies by less than one hundredth of 1% and may be assumed accurately linear between these two temperatures.

Starting at its freezing temperature of 0°C, and being slowly heated, water contracts until it reaches a temperature of 4°C and then expands. At 4°C, where it reaches its minimum volume, it has its maximum density. It might be considered fortunate that water expands on being cooled from 4°C to 0°C. If this were not the case and it contracted the way most liquids do, ice would form at the bottom of lakes instead of at the top.

When a pond of water cools toward the freezing point, the surface water next to the cold air cools first. Having cooled and contracted, it has a greater density than the water below and it sinks. This process continues until all the water reaches 4°C. Now, as the surface water cools below 4°C it expands, and, becoming less dense, floats. The water on the surface therefore reaches 0°C first and freezes. In freezing, the water expands still more to become ice. Ice floats on water because its density is less than that of water. When 1.00000 m^3 of water at 4°C is cooled down to 0°C, it expands to a volume of 1.00013 m^3, and when it freezes its new volume as a solid is 1.09051 m^3.

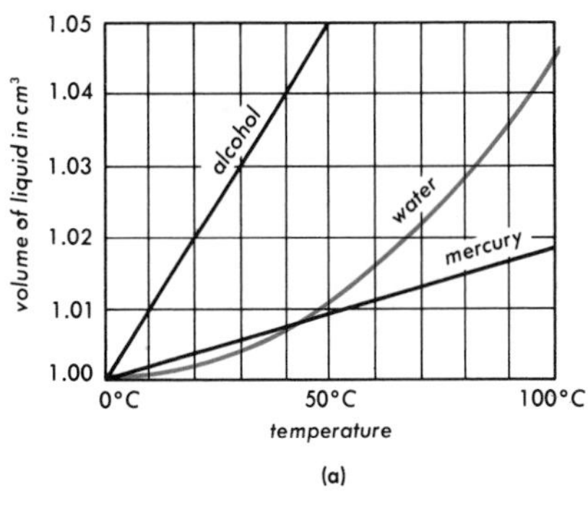

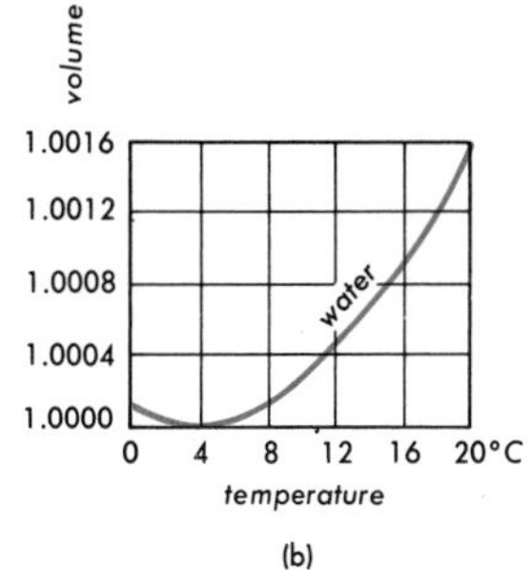

Fig. 14L. Heat–temperature graph for 1 Kg of ice starting at −50°C, illustrating the latent heat of fusion and vaporization.

14.9. Change of State

The continuous addition of heat to a solid or liquid mass will eventually bring about a change of state. The general behavior of many substances can be illustrated by a detailed description of the changes that occur with the most common of all liquids, water. If a block of ice at a temperature of −50°C is placed in a pan and put on a stove to heat, its temperature will rise slowly until it reaches 0°C.

At 0°C the temperature stops rising and the ice begins to melt. More and more ice is melted as heat is continually added; not until it has all turned to water does the temperature begin to rise. As the water becomes hotter and hotter, it eventually reaches a temperature of 100°C, where vigorous boiling sets in. Here again the temperature stops rising and, as heat is added, more and more water is boiled away to become steam. Finally, when all has become steam at 100°C, the temperature begins to rise once more.

All of these changes of temperature and changes of state are shown by a graph in Fig. 14L. The horizontal sections represent changes of state without change in temperature, while the slanted sections on either side represent changes in temperature without abrupt changes in state.

14.10. Melting, Boiling, and Vaporizing of Substances

The melting point is defined as the temperature at which a substance, under standard atmospheric pressure, changes from the solid to the liquid state, or vice versa. Every substance has its own melting point, and for water, it is 0°C or 32°F. As shown by a few common substances listed in Table 14E, some substances melt at low temperatures, some at medium temperatures, and still others at very high temperatures.

TABLE 14E
Melting Points, Boiling Points, Heats of Fusion, and Heats of Vaporization of Several Common Substances

Substance	*Melting Point* °C	*Boiling Point* °C	*Heat of Fusion* Kcal/Kg	*Heat of Vaporization* Kcal/Kg
Air	−212	−191	5.5	51
Aluminum	658	1800	77	—
Copper	1080	2310	42	—
Gold	1063	2500	16	—
Helium	−271	−268	—	6
Hydrogen	−259	−252	14	108
Iron	1530	2450	6	—
Lead	327	1525	5.9	—
Mercury	−39	357	2.8	65
Nitrogen	−210	−195	6.1	48
Oxygen	−219	−184	3.3	51
Platinum	1760	3910	27	—
Silver	962	1955	21	—
Tungsten	3400	5830	—	—
Water	0	100	80	540

The boiling point is defined as the temperature at which a substance, under standard atmospheric pressure, changes from the liquid to the gaseous state, or vice versa. These temperatures too are listed in Table 14E.

We have seen that when ice is melting, heat is continually added with no resultant rise in temperature. To melt 1 Kg of ice requires 80 Kcal. Similar heat measurements for other solids show how that they too require a definite amount of heat to melt them without a rise in temperature. To melt 1 Kg of gold at the melting point of 1063°C requires 16 Kcal. To melt 1 Kg of silver at its melting point of 962° requires 21 Kcal, etc.

Such values, called the *latent heat of fusion,* are listed in Table 14E. These constants are useful in calculating the heat necessary to change the state of any specified mass of material from the solid to the liquid state without changing its temperature. To do this we use the very simple relation

$$H_f = m\ L_f \qquad (14e)$$

where H_f is the total heat required, m is the mass in Kg, and L_f is the heat of fusion.

When water is being boiled, heat is continually added without a rise in temperature. This added heat energy is not retained by the water, but goes with the vapor in the boiling process. Vaporizing 1 Kg of water, i.e., changing its state without raising its temperature, requires 540 Kcal. This number, called the *heat of vaporization,* is useful for calculating the amount of heat needed to change any given mass of water to the gaseous state. For any given substance,

$$H_v = m\ L_v \qquad (14f)$$

where H_v is the total heat required, m is the mass of substance in Kg, and L_v is the heat of vaporization. Since L_v is difficult to determine for some substances, and is of very little practical value except in a few cases, only a few of them are known and are as listed in Table 14E.

Example 3. How much heat is required to melt 6.0 Kg of lead at its melting point of 327°C, if we start with the lead at a room temperature of 27°C?
Solution. Using the specific heat of lead from Table 14A, and the heat of fusion of lead from Table 14E, we substitute in Eqs.(14b) and (14e), add the two values, and obtain

$$H = 6 \times 0.031\ (327 - 27) + 6 \times 5.9$$

$$H = 55.8 + 35.4 = 91.2 \text{ Kcal}$$

---

problems

1. A centigrade thermometer shows the following series of temperatures: (a) 20°C, (b) 55°C, (c) 32°C, (d) 0°C, and (e) −40°C. What are the corresponding temperatures on the Fahrenheit scale?

2. A Fahrenheit thermometer shows the following series of temperatures: (a) 59°F, (b) 86°F, (c) 131°F, (d) 167°F, (e) −40°F. What are the corresponding temperatures on the centigrade scale?

3. The following temperatures are recorded with a Fahrenheit thermometer: (a) 50°F, (b) 68°F, (c) 158°F, (d) 177°F, and (e) 212°F. Find the corresponding temperatures on the Kelvin or absolute scale. [Ans. (a) 283°K, (b) 293°K, (c) 343°K, (d) 348°K, (e) 373°K.]

4. The following temperatures are recorded using a centigrade thermometer: (a) 10°C, (b) 25°C, (c) 65°C, (d) 85°C, and (e) 120°C. What are the corresponding temperatures on the Rankine scale?

5. If the temperature is 50°F, find the equivalent temperature on the (a) Rankine scale, (b) the Celsius scale, and (c) the Kelvin or absolute scale.

6. If a centigrade thermometer shows the temperature of a block of ice to be −40°C, find the equivalent temperature on (a) the Fahrenheit scale, (b) the Rankine scale, and (c) the Kelvin scale. [Ans. (a) −40°F, (b) 420°R, (c) 233°K.]

7. The temperature of a smelting furnace is found to be 1620°R. Find the equivalent temperature on (a) the Fahrenheit, (b) the centigrade, and (c) the absolute scales.

8. How much heat is required to raise the temperature of 4.0 Kg of mercury from 25°C to 300°C?

9. Calculate the heat required to raise the temperature of 20.0 Kg of gold from 20°C to 1000°C. [Ans. 608 Kcal.]

10. How much heat is required to raise the temperature of 10.0 Kg of iron from 30°C to 1500°C?

11. The iron rails used in building railroads are 18.0 m in length. If at the time they are nailed into place the temperature is 25°C, how large will the gaps between the rail ends be when the temperature drops to −50°C?

12. A copper bar 2.50 m long at 22°C is raised in temperature to 48°C. Find its increase in length in millimeters. [Ans. 1.105 mm.]

13. One of the iron towers of a suspension bridge is 210.0 m high. Find its increase in height in cm if the temperature rises from 10°C to 35°C.

14. A pine wood plank is sawed to the exact length of 4.250 m when the temperature is 24°C. Find its change in length in mm after laying in the sun and the temperature rises to 42°C.

15. A round brass plate 50.0 cm in diameter has a hole in the center that is exactly 20.0 cm in diameter, when the temperature is 15°C. Find the diameter of the hole if the temperature rises to 40°C. [Ans. 20.0090 cm. *Note:* the hole gets larger, not smaller.]

16. An aluminum tank has a volume of exactly 1.20 m^3 when the temperature is 25°C. Find its increase in volume in cm^3 when the temperature rises to 35°C.

17. An aluminum tank with a volume of exactly 2.40 m^3 when the temperature is 25°C is filled with alcohol. How much alcohol flows over the top if the temperature rises to 35°C.

18. A copper vessel with a volume of exactly 1.80 m^3 at a temperature of 20°C is filled with glycerine. If the temperature rises to 30°C, how much glycerine will spill out? [Ans. 8622 cm^3.]

19. Calculate the amount of heat required to change 5.0 Kg of ice at −20°C into steam at 100°C.

20. How much heat is required to change 4.0 Kg of mercury at −20° into mercury vapor at 357°C.

15 Heat transfer and the atmosphere

There are numerous processes in nature and in practice where various forms of matter and energy are transported or transmitted from one place to another. The blowing of powdered coal through a pipe from a source of supply to its destination, for example, is an illustration of *mass transfer.* The transfer of heat from a furnace through pipes to the rooms of a house is an illustration of *heat transfer.*

We will see in this chapter that heat may be transmitted from one place to another in many ways. Some of these methods are slow, while others are very fast and to the point. A careful study of all known methods has led to the realization that there are only three general types of heat transfer: *conduction, convection,* and *radiation.* Conduction is a slow process by which heat is transmitted through a substance by molecular activity. Convection is a more rapid process involving the motion of heated matter itself from one place to another. Radiation of heat from one place to another takes place in the same manner and with the same speed as light, 3.0×10^6 Km/s (186,000 mi/s).

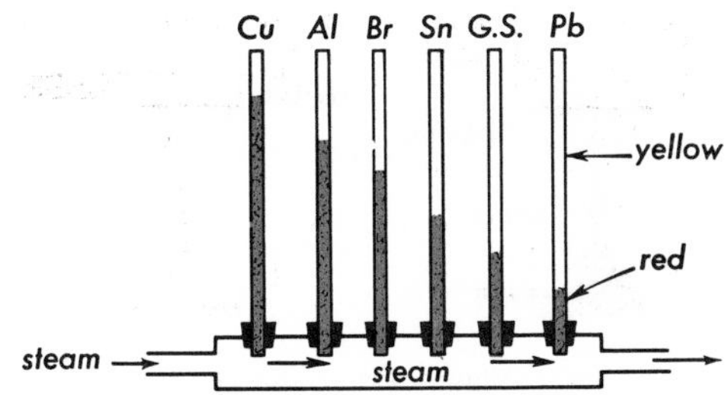

Fig. 15A. Experiment illustrating the relative heat conductivities of six different metals: copper, aluminum, bass, tin, German silver, and lead.

15.1. Conduction

Not all bodies are good conductors of heat. Metals like copper and silver are much better for this purpose than are other substances like wood, glass, paper, and water. The ability of a given substance to conduct heat is called its *thermal conductivity.*

The relative conductivities of different substances can be illustrated by an experiment performed as follows: Similar rods of six different metals such as copper, aluminum, brass, tin, German silver, and lead are coated with a special yellow paint as shown in Fig. 15A. The ends of the rods, mounted in rubber corks, project through holes in a metal tube where their lower ends are heated to 100°C by steam passing through the tube. As the heat

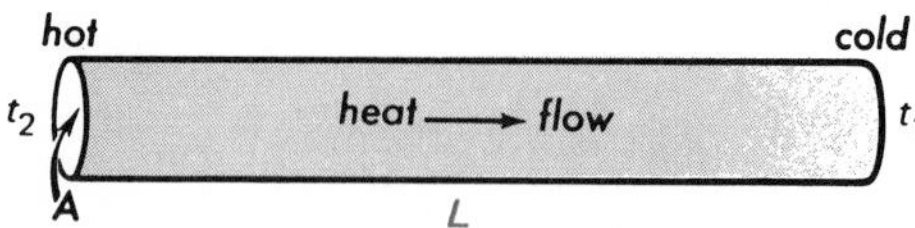

Fig. 15B. Diagram illustrating the various measurable factors involved in the flow of heat through a body by conduction.

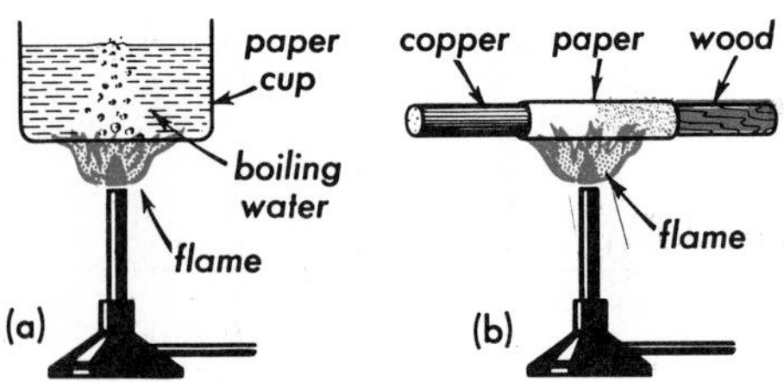

Fig. 15C. Illustration of the conduction of heat through paper.

travels slowly up each rod, the yellow paint turns to red. After 5 or 10 min of heating, the height to which the paint has turned color is approximately as shown by the stippled areas in the figure. Of these six metals, copper is observed to be the best conductor and lead the poorest.

In order to heat an object, it is customary to bring it into contact with some other body at a higher temperature. A pan of water, for example, is generally heated by placing it over an open flame. The combustion of natural gas first sets the gas molecules into rapid motion. These molecules, striking the bottom of the pan, set the molecules of the metal into rapid vibration. They in turn strike other metal molecules, thus transferring the motion through to the other side. This is called heat conduction. The metal molecules set the first layer of water molecules moving, and they in turn set others moving. Thus molecular motion, called heat, has been given to the body of water.

Laboratory experiments show that the amount of heat flowing through a rod is proportional to the time, the cross-sectional area, and the difference in temperature between the ends, and is inversely proportional to the length.

Using appropriate symbols for each of these factors and inserting a proportionality constant, we can set up the following equation:

$$H = k\,\frac{A\,\Delta t}{L}\,\Delta\tau \tag{15a}$$

where H is the amount of heat flowing through the body of length L and cross section A, k is the thermal conductivity, $\Delta\tau$ is the time interval of flow, and Δt is the temperature difference between the two ends. It is quite clear that if the temperature difference Δt, or the area A is increased, the amount of heat passing through is increased (see Fig. 15B). It is not as obvious, however, that an increase in the length L causes a decrease in the heat flow, or that a decrease in length produces an increase. The latter will be illustrated by two experiments.

Although paper is a poor conductor, the flow of heat through it can be made very great by increasing A, the cross-sectional area, and decreasing L, the distance it has to flow. Diagram (a) in Fig. 15C illustrates thermal conductivity by the boiling of water in a paper cup. Although the gas flame plays directly against the surface of the paper, the cup will not burn. The reason for this is that the heat from the lower surface of the paper is conducted through to the water fast enough to keep the temperature of the paper from rising too high. If the paper is thick, the lower surface will burn. Strange as it may seem, the thinner the paper, the less is the chance of burning.

In diagram (b) of Fig. 15C, a thin piece of paper is wrapped once around a rod made half of wood and half of copper. When the flame is brought up, as shown, the paper burns only where it is in contact with the wood, and not at all where it is in contact with the copper. Copper, being a good conductor, carries the heat into the interior of the metal and away from the metal surface. Since wood is a poor conductor it cannot conduct the heat away from the surface fast enough, and the paper heats up and soon burns.

The thermal conductivities of a few common substances are given in Table 15A.

The number k is the quantity of heat in Kcal that in 1 s will pass through a 1-m cube when two opposite faces are maintained at 1C° difference in temperature. Knowing the value of k for a given substance, it is possible to calculate, by means of Eq.(15a), the amount of heat flowing through any sized object made of that same material.

TABLE 15A
Thermal conductivities, *k*, in Kcal/m s C°

Substance	k
Silver	970×10^{-4}
Copper	920×10^{-4}
Aluminum	500×10^{-4}
Brass	260×10^{-4}
Iron	160×10^{-4}
Lead	80×10^{-4}
German Silver	100×10^{-4}
Mercury	20×10^{-4}
Tile	2×10^{-4}
Glass	2.5×10^{-4}
Water	1.4×10^{-4}
Wood	0.5×10^{-4}
Paper	0.3×10^{-4}
Felt	0.04×10^{-4}

Example 1. One end of an aluminum rod 40.0 cm long and 5.0 cm² in cross section is maintained at a temperature of 100°C, and the other end at 20°C. Find the amount of heat that will flow through the rod in 2.0 min.

Solution. Each of the given quantities converted to the *MKSA* system are $L = 0.40$ m, $A = 5.0 \times 10^{-4}$ m², $\Delta t = 100°\text{C} - 20°\text{C}$, $\Delta\tau = 120.0$ s, and $k = 500 \times 10^{-4}$ Kcal/m s C°. Substitution in Eq.(15a) gives

$$\Delta H = 500 \times 10^{-4} \frac{5 \times 10^{-4}(100 - 20)}{0.40} 120$$

$$\Delta H = 0.60 \text{ Kcal}$$

15.2. Convection

Why is it that a poor conductor of heat like water can be heated so quickly when it is placed in a pan over a hot fire? It is due to the second method of heat transfer known as *convection.* Water on the bottom of a pan is heated first. Because of a rise in temperature it expands. Being lighter than the cold water above, it then rises to the top, permitting cold water to come to the

Fig. 15D. Convection currents in a pan of water being heated over a stove burner.

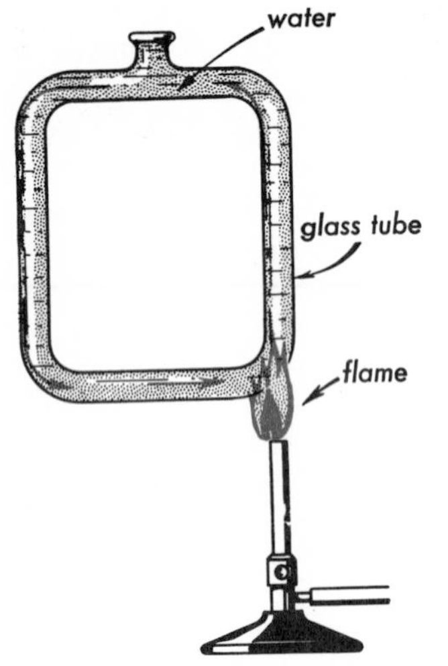

Fig. 15E. Demonstration experiment showing convection in water.

bottom from the sides. This action sets up a flow of water called *convection current* (see Fig. 15D). Convection currents thus keep the water stirred up as it heats.

A convection current set up in the heating of a vessel of water is illustrated in Fig. 15E. A glass tube in the shape of a letter O is filled with water and then heated at one of the lower corners as indicated. A drop of ink admitted at the top opening will mix with the water and quickly flow around the tube in a counterclockwise direction. This circulation is the basis of the hot-water heating systems used in some houses. As illustrated in Fig. 15F, hot water from a supply tank in a lower room or basement rises and flows through several radiators, only to return, somewhat cooled, to the tank where it is reheated.

Convection currents in the atmosphere are quite noticeable and account for the wind. Along the sea coast, cool air from over the ocean comes as a sea breeze due to convection. The sun's rays are absorbed more readily by the land than they are by water, and the warmed air over the land rises while cooler air from the ocean comes in to take its place.

At night the land cools quickly by radiation back toward the cold sky and soon the air over the water is the warmer, and in rising, causes a reversal in air movement. The wind blows from the land to the sea. These air currents are easily observed by smoke from a fire built on the seashore. During the day the smoke blows inland, and at night it blows seaward.

Pilots are well aware of rising air currents over certain local areas of ground. Solar radiation being absorbed more completely by a newly plowed field, for example, will warm the air sufficiently to cause convection. Flying into such an upward draft of air, the plane receives a sudden lift. During certain seasons these updrafts of warm air are cooled by the air layers above and water vapor is condensed to form clouds.

15.3. Radiation

When the sun comes over the horizon in the early morning, the heat can be felt as soon as the sun becomes visible. This heat, called *radiant heat* or *radiation,* travels with the speed of light, 299,792.50 m/s.

Radiant heat is only one of the many forms of energy and is readily detected by means of a radiometer, thermocouple, thermister, thermometer, etc. A Crooke's radiometer, shown in Fig. 15G, will often be found in a jewelry store window. In daylight or under a bright light the little pinwheel, made of very thin mica, will be found spinning around as if by perpetual motion.

Each vane of such a radiometer is shiny on one face, and blackened on the other. The black faces absorb more radiant energy than the polished surfaces, so that the adjacent air is heated. The faster recoiling air molecules therefore exert a larger force on the blackened sides, driving them around.

Should a radiometer be so highly evacuated that little air remains inside, light waves in bouncing off the polished surfaces will exert twice the force they do in being absorbed on the blackened side, and the pinwheel will spin the other way.

Radiant heat rays, like visible light, are electromagnetic waves and have all the general properties known to visible light. The essential difference between the two is that heat waves, sometimes called *infrared rays,* are not visible to the human eye.

A demonstration of the reflection of infrared rays is diagrammed in Fig. 15H. A candle flame acting as a source at F emits light and heat rays in all directions. Of these rays, only the ones traveling toward the concave mirror M_1 are reflected into a parallel beam. Arriving at the second concave mirror M_2, these rays are again reflected, being brought together to a focus on the exposed junctions of a thermopile T. As the junctions of the thermopile warm up, an electric current is produced, which causes the ammeter pointer P to move to the right. When the candle is removed, the pointer returns to zero.

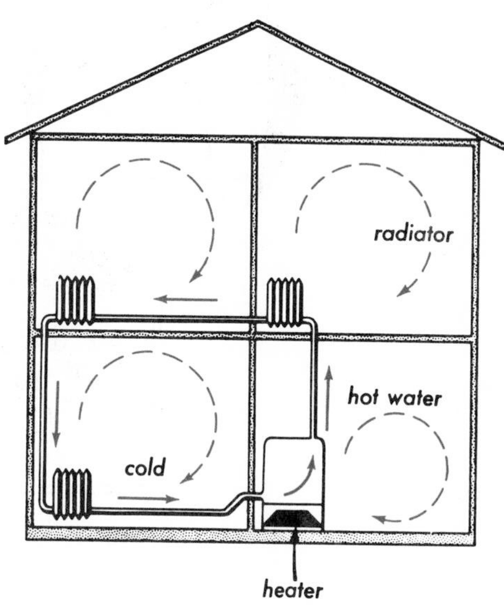

Fig. 15F. Illustrations of heat convection by the circulation of water in a pipe and air in a room.

A practical example of heat radiation is to be found in every home where a fireplace is used as a means of heating. Contrary to most beliefs, the heat entering a room from a fireplace is practically all in the form of infrared rays originating in the flames, the coals, and the hot stone or brick walls. The air that is heated within the fireplace does not enter the room but is carried up the chimney as a convection current (see Fig. 15I). This rising current of air draws fresh air into the room and into the fire, thus supplying fresh oxygen to the burning wood or coal.

Fig. 15G. A Crooke's radiometer.

A Dewar-flask or "Thermos bottle" is an example of a practical device in which the conduction, convection, and radiation of heat are reduced as much as possible. As shown by the cross-sectional diagram in Fig. 15J, a Thermos bottle consists of a double-walled glass vessel silvered on the inside. The purpose of the silvering is to reflect all radiant heat attempting to enter or leave the vessel. The space between the walls is highly evacuated to prevent convection, and the glass, being a poor conductor, minimizes conduction through the walls of the neck. With the exception of the vacuum space between walls, a calorimeter of the type commonly used in laboratories is similar to a Dewar-flask.

Another type of heating system for public buildings and private

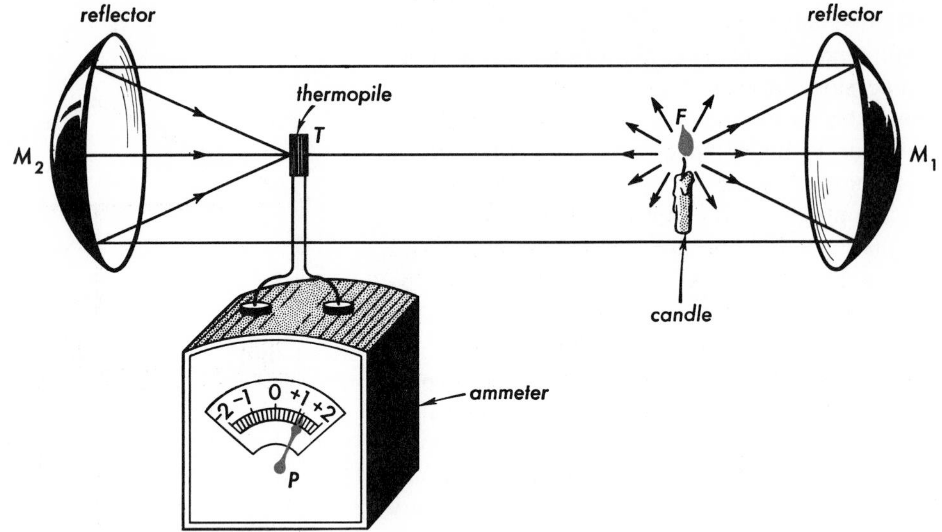

Fig. 15H. Reflection of heat rays by concave mirrors.

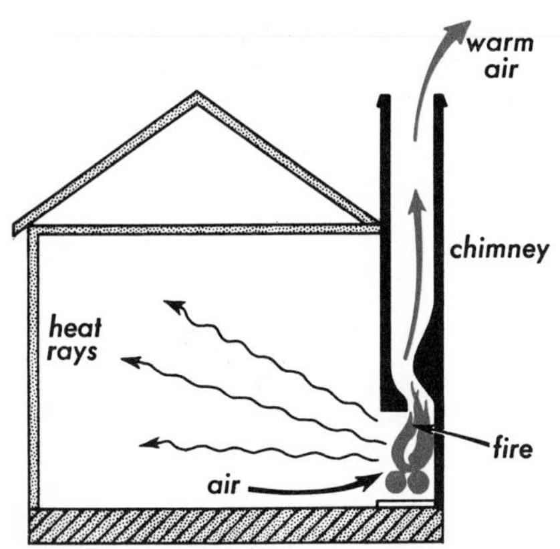

Fig. 15I. A fireplace heats a room by radiation from the flame, the coals, and the stove walls. Convection currents set up a draft and carry warm air and smoke out the chimney.

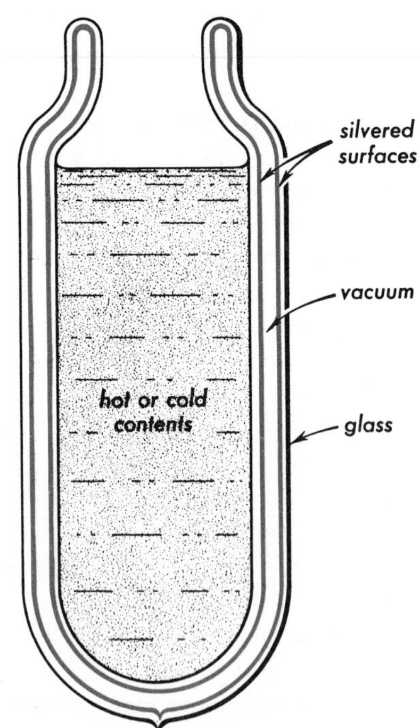

Fig. 15J. The Dewar-flask, or "Thermos" bottle, minimizes conduction by using glass, convection by evacuating, and radiation by silvering.

dwellings has recently been developed. Known to engineers as *panel heating,* this system heats the walls of the rooms by hot air or water pipes that run through them. Even though the windows are open on the coldest days, radiant heat keeps the occupants warm.

15.4. Emission and Absorption

The rate at which a body radiates or absorbs heat depends not only upon the absolute temperature, but upon the nature of the exposed surfaces as well. Objects that are good emitters of heat are also good absorbers of the same kind of radiation. This is known as *Kirchhoff's law of radiation.* A body whose surface is blackened is an excellent emitter as well as an excellent absorber. If the same body is chromium plated, it becomes a poor emitter and a poor absorber.

If the outside surface of a hot coffee cup were painted a dull black, the rate of cooling would be more rapid than if it were chromium plated. A highly polished surface, as in the Dewar-flask, would help by reflection to keep radiant heat from crossing the boundary.

Black clothes should not be worn on a hot day since black is a good absorber of the sun's radiant heat. While black is also a good emitter, the external temperature is higher than the body temperature and the exchange rate is therefore such as to heat the body. White clothes are worn in hot climates because white is a good reflector and therefore a poor absorber.

15.5. Black-Body Radiation

The relation between the radiant heat E emitted by a body and its temperature was first discovered through the extensive laboratory experiments of Josef Stefan. The same law was later derived from theoretical consideration by Ludwig Boltzmann,* and is now known as the *Stefan–Boltzmann law:*

$$E = kT^4 \tag{15b}$$

Here E represents the energy radiated per second by a body at an absolute temperature T, and k is a proportionality constant. The law applies only to so-called "black bodies:" *A black body is defined as one that absorbs all of the radiant heat that falls upon it.* Such a perfect absorber would also be a perfect emitter.

If E represents the heat in kilocalories radiated per square

***Ludwig Boltzmann (1844–1906), Austrian theoretical physicist, was educated at Linz and Vienna. At 23 he was appointed assistant at the physical institute in Vienna. Later he became professor at Graz, then at Munich, and finally back at Vienna. His first publication was on the second law of thermodynamics, and was followed by numerous papers on molecular motion, on viscosity and diffusion of gases, on Maxwell's electromagnetic theory, on Hertz's electrical experiments, and on Stefan's law for black-body radiation.**

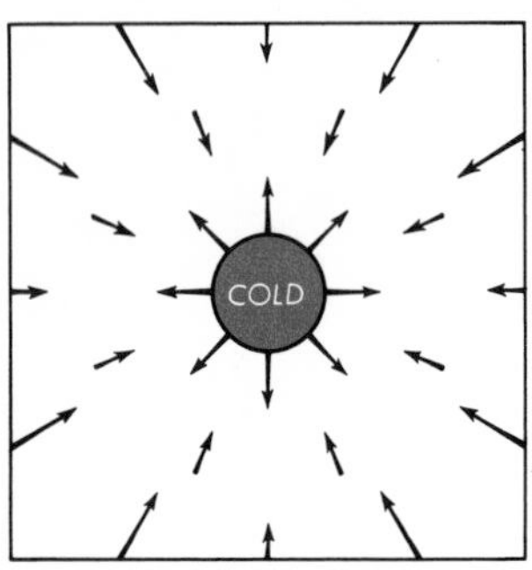

Fig. 15K. A cold body warms up to room temperature.

meter per second, then

$$k = 1.3567 \times 10^{-11} \text{ Kcal/m}^2\text{s}^\circ\text{K}^4$$

If E represents the energy in joules radiated per square meter per second, then

$$k = 5.670 \times 10^{-8} \text{ J/m}^2\text{s}^\circ\text{K}^4$$

With these definitions of k we may write the Stefan–Boltzmann law as

$$E = kT^4A\ \Delta\tau \tag{15c}$$

where A is the area in square meters, and $\Delta\tau$ is the time in seconds.

The best laboratory approach to a black-body is a hole in a blackened box. Practically all heat entering such a hole would be absorbed inside. Black velvet cloth or a surface painted dull with lampblack will absorb about 97% of the radiant heat falling on it, and may for many purposes be considered a black-body. Polished metal surfaces, however, are far from black-bodies; they absorb only about 6% of the incident energy and reflect the remainder. Most other substances have absorption ratios between these two extremes.

15.6. Prevost's Law of Heat Exchange

Laboratory experiments, as well as the Stefan–Boltzmann law, show that all bodies, whether they are hot or cold, radiate heat. The words "hot" and "cold" are only relative terms, since even ice radiates heat. The greater the absolute temperature of a body, the greater is the rate at which it radiates, and ice at 0°C is 273° above absolute zero.

If a cold block of metal is brought into a warm room, it radiates heat to the walls of the room and the walls of the room radiate heat to the block. Because the walls are at a higher temperature, they give more heat per second to the block than the block gives up in return (see Fig. 15K). Due to this unequal exchange of heat, the temperature of the cold block rises until it comes to the same temperature as the room, at which time it radiates and absorbs at exactly the same rate. *Prevost's law of heat exchange states that a body at the temperature of its surroundings is radiating and receiving heat at equal rates.*

When a person stands near a fireplace, he feels warm because his body receives more heat from the fire than he emits. If he stands next to a cold window, he feels chilly because he radiates more heat than he absorbs. The side of his body facing the window gets noticeably colder than the other.

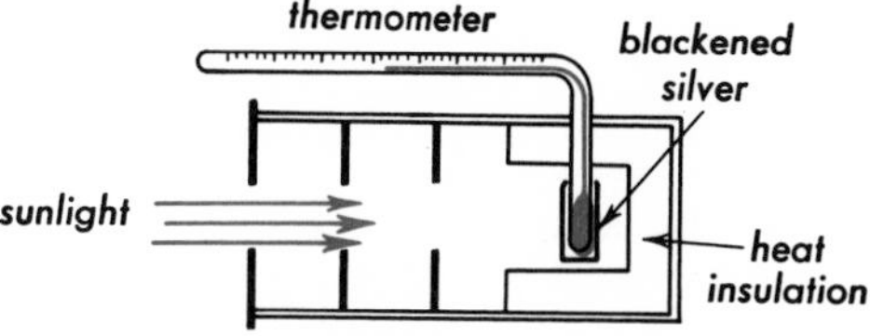

Fig. 15L. Abbot's pyroheliometer for measuring the heat radiated by the sun.

Example 2. A copper ball 20.0 cm in diameter is coated with lampblack and heated to a temperature of 727°C. (a) How much heat will this body radiate in 5.0 s? (b) If the walls of the room are at 27°C how much heat will this body absorb in the same time? Assume blackbody radiation for both (a) and (b).
Solution. Converted to the *MKSA* system the known quantities are $T = 727 + 273 = 1000°K$, $A = 4\pi r^2 = 0.1257\ m^2$, $\Delta\tau = 5.0$ s, and $k = 1.3567 \times 10^{-11}\ Kcal/m^2 s°K^4$. Substituting these quantities directly into Eq.(15c), we obtain for part (a)

$$E = kT^4 A\ \Delta\tau = 1.360 \times 10^{-11}\ (1000)^4 \times 0.1257 \times 5$$

$$E = 8.527\ \text{Kcal}$$

For part (b), we substitute the room temperature of 27°C + 273°C, or 300°K:

$$E = 1.360 \times 10^{-11} \times (300)^4 \times 0.1257 \times 5$$

$$E = 0.06924\ \text{Kcal}$$

15.7. Radiant Heat from the Sun

Instruments designed to measure solar radiation are called pyroheliometers (see Fig. 15L). A beam of sunlight of known cross-sectional area is allowed to fall upon the blackened surface of a silver disk where it is absorbed. A drill hole in the metal disk admits the narrow bulb of a sensitive mercury thermometer, the latter being bent and threaded through a hole in the heat-insulated box as shown in the diagram. Knowing the heat capacity of the metal and its rise in temperature, the total number of calories per minute can be calculated.

Measurements of this kind by various observers are in remarkable agreement with each other and give a value of 19.38 Kcal/m^2 min. This number, called *the solar constant,* is defined as the average amount of energy falling in 1 min on 1 m^2 of surface placed at right angles to the sun's rays. Multiplying the solar constant by the area of a sphere 14.95×10^{10} m in radius, we obtain the figure 9.1×10^{22} Kcal/s as the total heat radiated by the sun.

An appreciation of these figures can be gained by the following comparison. If all of the energy radiated by the sun could be used to heat the oceans of the earth, the temperature would rise from the freezing point to the boiling point in less than 2 s. Where all this heat comes from within the sun had long been a puzzle to astronomer and physicist alike. A satisfactory answer to the problem has recently been found and will be given in Sec. 62.7.

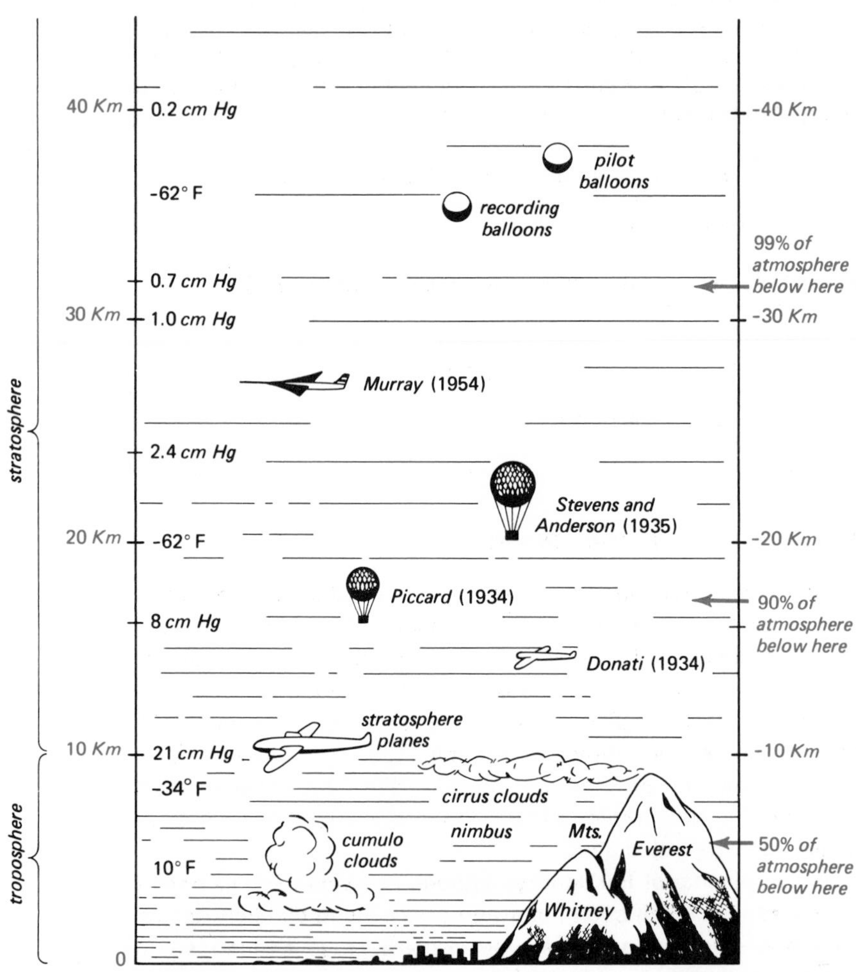

Fig. 15M. Illustration of important facts concerning the troposphere and the stratosphere and the relative heights reached by man in balloons and airplanes.

15.8. The Earth's Atmosphere

Figure 15M is a schematic cross section of the atmosphere up to a height of 40 Km. It will be noted on the right-hand side of the diagram that 50% of the earth's atmosphere lies below 5 Km, and that 99% lies below 30 Km. While this accounts for most of the atmosphere, experiments with radio waves show that the small amount of air existing at a height of several hundred miles is sufficient to reflect radio waves back to the earth.

Living as most of us do near sea level, we are constantly subjected to an enormous pressure due to the weight of the air above us. Unbelievable as it may seem, the air exerts a pressure of close to one hundred thousand newtons for every square meter of surface. This, the atmospheric pressure, is given by the weight of a column of air 1 m^2 in cross section and reaching from sea level to the top of the atmosphere.

A pressure of one atmosphere is defined as the average atmospheric pressure at sea level. This is taken to be 101,300 N/m^2.

15.9. The Density of Air

That air has weight may be shown by one of the simplest of experiments. A hollow brass ball with a volume of 1 liter (1 liter = 1000 cm^3) is first weighed when it is filled with air, and again when it is evacuated (see Fig. 15N). With the air removed, the vessel is found to be lighter than before by 1.29 g. If the scales are first balanced with the sphere evacuated, and then the air is allowed to enter, a mass of 1.29 g must be added to the opposite scale pan to restore balance. Since this is the mass of 1000 cm^3 of air, the mass of 1 m^3 will be 1.29 Kg. This is the density of air.

If the above experiment is repeated at an elevation of 5 Km, the air in the brass vessel will weigh only one-half as much as at sea level. The reason for this is that the lower pressure at a height of 5 Km admits only one-half as much air to an evacuated vessel.

If, on the other hand, air is pumped into the hollow sphere, the weight can be made to increase considerably, thus giving a greater than normal density. The density of a gas is therefore standardized and defined as the mass of 1 m^3 of the gas measured at standard pressure and temperature. Standard pressure is defined as a pressure of one atmosphere and is explained in Sec. 15.12. Standard temperature is defined as zero degrees centigrade. The densities of a few common gases are given in Table 15B. The reason for specifying temperature is that gases expand with a rise in temperature.

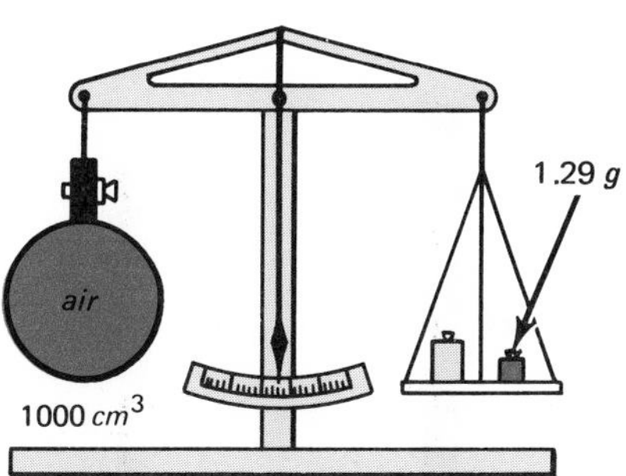

Fig. 15N. The weighing of air.

TABLE 15B
Densities of common gases

Gas, and chemical symbols		Kg/m^3 *or* g/liter
Air	N_2, O_2	1.293
Ammonia	NH_3	0.771
Butane	C_4H_{10}	2.519
Carbon dioxide	CO_2	1.980
Carbon monoxide	CO	1.250
Chlorine	Cl	3.214
Helium	He	0.180
Hydrogen	H_2	0.090
Hydrogen bromide	HBr	3.641
Krypton	Kr	3.708
Neon	Ne	0.900
Nitrogen	H_2	1.250
Nitrous oxide	N_2O	1.978
Oxygen	O_2	1.430
Sulfur dioxide	SO_2	2.927

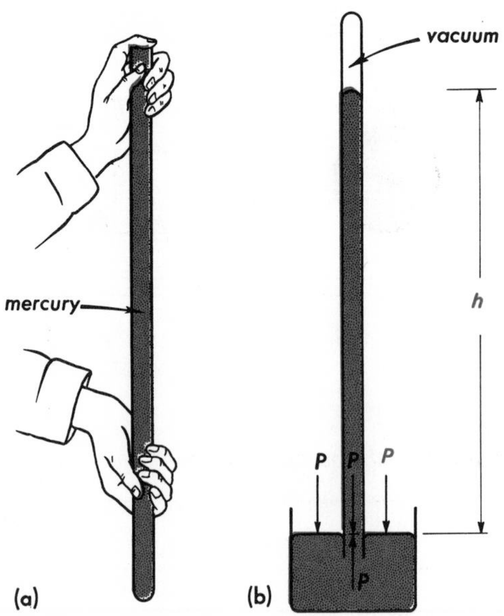

Fig. 15O. Torricelli's experiment. The making of a mercury barometer.

15.10. The Mercury Barometer

A barometer is a device for measuring the atmospheric pressure. There are in common use today two kinds of barometers—the mercury barometer and the aneroid barometer. The mercury barometer was invented by the Italian physicist, Evangelista Torricelli, some 300 years ago. Torricelli's experiment is illustrated in Fig. 15O. A long glass tube open at one end only is filled with mercury as shown in diagram (a). With one finger over the open end, the tube is inverted, the open end is immersed in a dish of mercury, and the finger is removed as in diagram (b). At the instant the finger is removed, the mercury level drops in the tube to a height *h* as shown. The mercury drops until the pressure due to its own weight inside the tube (at the level P) is equal to the atmospheric pressure outside.

At sea level the height at which the mercury column stands is about 76 cm or 30 in. This height at any given point, and any given time, will be the same regardless of the diameter of the tube or the length of the vacuum space at the top. Torricelli's experiment shows that a column of air 1 cm^2 in cross section and reaching to the top of the atmosphere is equal in weight to a column of mercury of the same cross section and 76 cm high.

It was the French philosopher and mathematician, Blaise Pascal, who first showed that when a mercury barometer is taken to a high elevation like the top of a mountain, the height of the mercury column drops considerably. It drops because there is less air above that point and hence a lesser downward pressure on the free mercury surface.

Figure 15P is a diagram of an experiment demonstrating that it is the atmosphere outside of a barometer pushing down on the exposed mercury surface which supports the mercury column inside, and not the vacuum in the space above drawing it up. An entire barometer is placed in a tall cylinder and the air removed by means of a vacuum pump. As the air slowly leaves, the mercury column drops steadily. When the cylinder is well evacuated, the level of the mercury inside the tube is the same as the level in the small reservoir outside. A return of the air forces the mercury back into the tube and up to its original height *h*.

The height of the mercury in a barometer measures directly the atmospheric pressure. Instead of specifying the pressure in N/m^2 it is customary to give the height of the mercury column in centimeters. The pressure so expressed in centimeters of Hg (the chemical symbol for mercury is Hg) is given at the left in Fig. 15M.

If a barometer were made to employ water in place of mercury, the barometer tube would have to be at least 13.6 times as high, or 10.34 m. (This is equivalent to about 34 ft.) Such an instrument would be too cumbersome to be of much practical value.

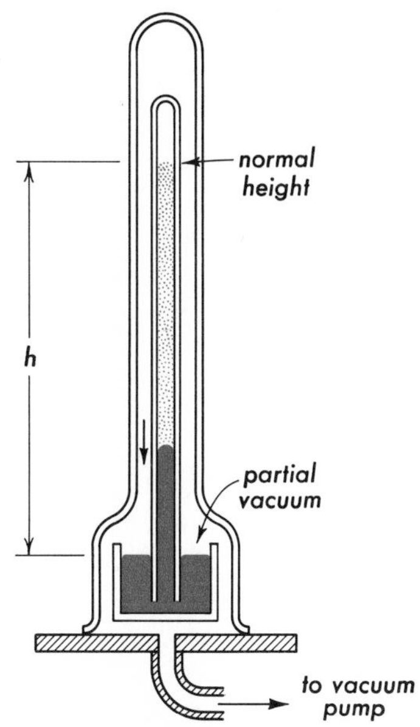

Fig. 15P. Experimental arrangement demonstrating that atmospheric pressure supports the column of mercury in a barometer tube. When the air is removed, the mercury column drops from its normal height.

15.11. The Aneroid Barometer

The desirability of a small portable pressure-measuring instrument has led to the development of the aneroid barometer. This device is frequently used as an altimeter and barometer combined. A cross-sectional diagram of such an instrument is shown in Fig. 15Q and photographs are reproduced in Fig. 15R. A small flat metal box, evacuated and with a flexible top, is attached at A to a multiplying system of levers. The end of the lever system is connected to small cable C which is wrapped around a spindle N, carrying a pointer, I. If the atmospheric pressure P increases, the flexible boxtop is pushed down at A. This lowers the end of the lever system at B, and with a pivot at D raises the point C. The cable winds up on the spindle N, turning the pointer I to the right to a scale reading of higher pressure. The scale of the aneroid is calibrated by a standard mercury barometer, so the pressure is always given in centimeters or inches of mercury.

Since the atmospheric pressure decreases as one goes to higher altitudes, a barometer is often used to determine elevation. As a matter of fact, aneroid barometers are frequently made with an altitude scale attached. Such instruments, called *altimeters,* are to be found on the instrument panel of every airplane. Some of these instruments are small enough to be carried in the pocket like a watch, and others are so sensitive that they will indicate a change in elevation of 1 meter. The altitude scale usually has its zero mark near the sea-level pressure as shown in Fig. 15Q.

15.12. Standard Atmospheric Pressure

Standard atmospheric pressure is defined as the pressure equivalent to a column of mercury 76 cm high when the temperature is 0°C.

To calculate the equivalent pressure in newtons per square meter, multiply the height by the density of mercury and the acceleration due to gravity:

$$0.76 \text{ m} \times 13{,}600 \text{ Kg/m}^3 \times 9.8 \text{ m/s}^2$$

$$1 \text{ atm} = 1.013 \times 10^5 \text{ N/m}^2$$

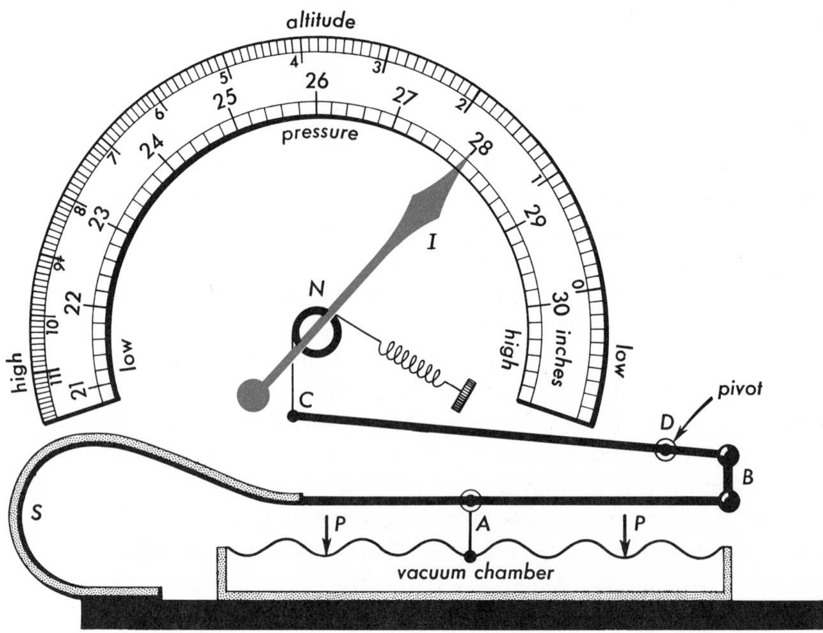

Fig. 15Q. Schematic diagram and cross section of an aneroid barometer.

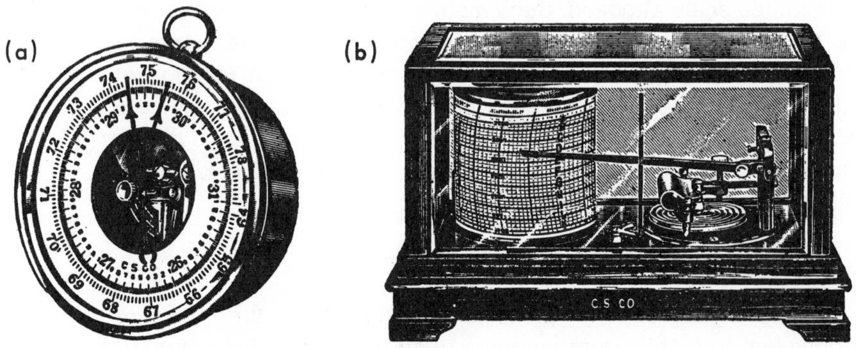

Fig. 15R. (a) Aneroid barometer used for measuring atmospheric pressure. (b) Self-recording aneroid barometer, or barograph. (Courtesy, Central Scientific Co.)

It is common practice in meteorology to measure atmospheric pressure in bars and millibars:

$$1 \text{ bar} = 100{,}000 \text{ N/m}^2$$

$$1 \text{ millibar} = 100 \text{ N/m}^2$$

On this basis,

$$1 \text{ atm} = 1.013 \text{ bars} = 1013 \text{ millibars}$$

The United States Weather Bureau obtains daily records of the barometric pressure from hundreds of weather stations over the country. These records are obtained automatically at each station by means of a specially designed aneroid like the one shown in Fig. 15R(b). A pen or stylus from the barometer itself moves up and down on a slowly rotating drum, thus recording the pressure at every instant. These records are then compiled by the United States Weather Bureau, and maps are published daily of the equal pressure areas over the country (see Fig. 15S).

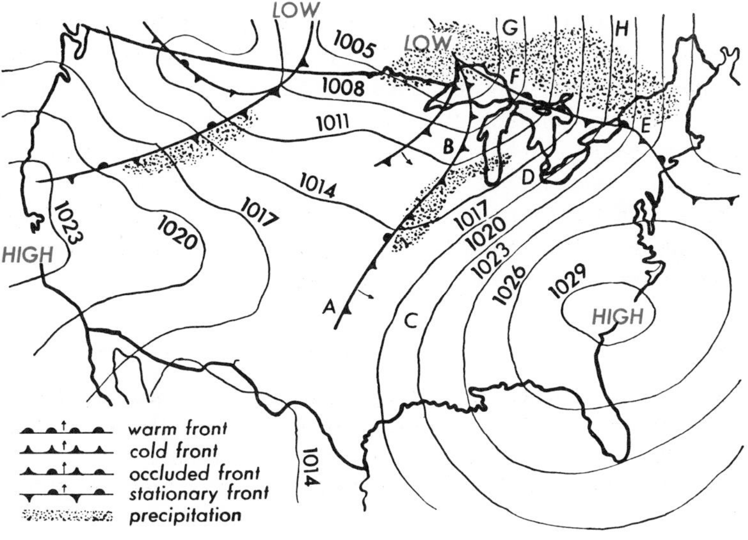

Fig. 15S. Typical daily U. S. weather map showing barometric pressures, warm and cold air fronts, and precipitation.

15.13 Experiments Illustrating Atmospheric Pressure

Normal atmospheric pressure of 1.013×10^5 N/m^2, or 14.7 lb/in.^{2}, does not ordinarily impress a person as being very great. Taken over a considerable area, however, such a pressure gives rise to a tremendous force.

In the year 1654, Otto von Guericke performed before the Emperor Ferdinand III, at Regensburg, the celebrated experiment of the "Magdeburg hemispheres." Two copper hemispheres, about 56 cm in diameter, were placed together to form a sphere

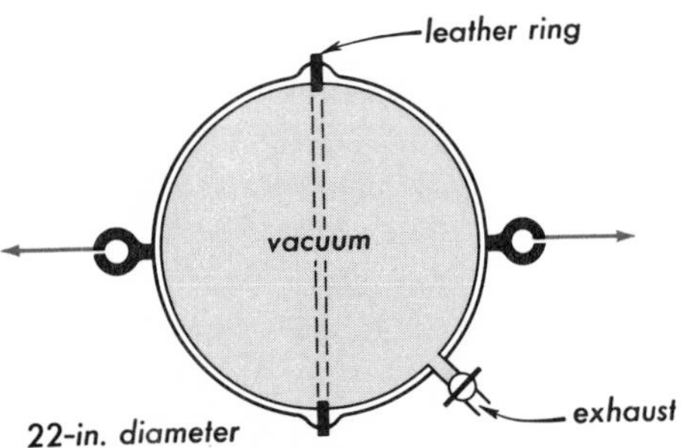

Fig. 15T. The Magdeburg hemisphere designed by Otto von Guericke.

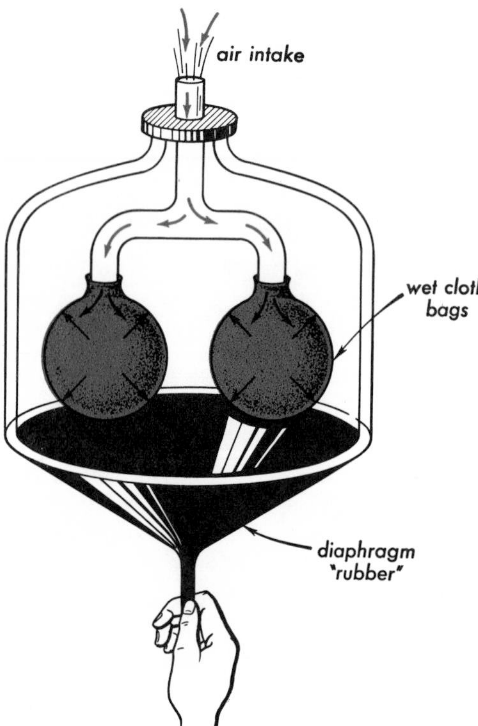

Fig. 15U. Experimental demonstration of the principles of breathing by the human body.

as shown in Fig. 15T. A ring of leather soaked in oil and wax was set between them to make an airtight joint. When the sphere was evacuated, two teams, consisting of eight horses each, were unable to pull the hemispheres apart. This is not to be wondered at, for the force required to pull them apart is easily calculated: it amounts to nearly three tons.

The principles of breathing in the human body are demonstrated in Fig. 15U. Muscular contraction in pulling down on the *diaphragm* creates a low pressure around the lungs and atmospheric pressure pushes air into the lungs. Retraction of the diaghragm raises the pressure and compresses the lungs, forcing air and carbon dioxide out.

Finally, consider the evacuated glass picture tube of the average home TV receiver. The face of a tube 50 cm by 37 cm has an area of 0.185 m^2, and hence withstands a total inward force of 1.013×10^5 N/m^2 $\times$ 0.185 m^2 $= 1.87 \times 10^4$ N. The glass walls can withstand this because the force is distributed uniformly over the whole surface. If it were all applied at one small point, the tube would surely break. A spherical or cylindrical vessel can have thin walls and yet withstand enormous pressures whereas a vessel with flat sides may not. It is for this reason that all large vessels used for storing liquids or gases, or evacuated vessels, have curved walls instead of flat ones.

Example 3. A television picture tube has a rectangular picture area 40.0 cm $\times$ 50.0 cm. Assuming this surface to be flat, find the total inward force due to atmospheric pressure.

Solution. Since total force is given by pressure $\times$ area, we obtain

$$F = P \times A$$

$$F = 1.013 \times 10^5 \text{ N/m}^2 \times 0.40 \text{ m} \times 0.50 \text{ m}$$

$$F = 2.026 \times 10^4 \text{ N}$$

---

problems

1. A brass rod with a diameter of 2.0 cm is 12.0 cm long. How much heat will flow through this rod in 1 h if one end is maintained at 5°C and the other end at 95°C.

2. A copper rod with a cross sectional area of 8.0 cm^2, and a length of 35.0 cm, is used to conduct heat from one end to the other. If one end is maintained at 6°C and the other end at 380°C, how much heat will flow through in 1 h?

3. A glass window pane has an area 1.50 m by 2.0 m and a thickness of 5.0 mm. If snow outside maintains the outer surface at −5.0°C, and the heat in the room maintains the inner surface at 0°C, how much heat will be conducted through the glass in 1.0 h? [Ans. 2700 Kcal.]

4. The bottom of an aluminum pan has a diameter of 24.0 cm and a thickness of 0.50 mm. If the gas flames keep the under surface at 52.0°C, and the upper surface is maintained at 48°C, how much heat will flow through the bottom in 1.0 min?

5. A large water tank with a bottom 1.0 m in diameter is made of iron boiler plate 4.0 mm thick. As water is being heated in the tank, the gas burner underneath is able to maintain a temperature difference of 3.50°C between the two sides of the plate. How much heat will flow through to the water in 10.0 min?

6. A silver rod 15.0 cm long has a cross-sectional area of 3.0 cm^2. If one end is maintained at 10°C and the other end at 75°C, how much heat will flow through in 5.0 min? [Ans. 3.783 Kcal.]

7. The bottom of an aluminum pan has a diameter of 20.0 cm, and a thickness of 1.20 mm. If the pan is filled with water, and the gas burner on which it is placed maintains a temperature difference of 4.5°C between the two surfaces, how much heat will flow through in 1 min?

8. The bottom of an aluminum pan has a cross-sectional area of 85.0 cm^2 and a thickness of 1.50 mm. If the pan is filled with water that is to be heated, and the hotplate on which it is placed maintains a difference of 6°C between the two surfaces, how much heat will flow through per minute?

9. A large window contains 20 panes of glass, each one of which is 20.0 cm by 30.0 cm, and 2.0 mm thick. If snow outside the house maintains the outer surface at −3.0°C, and the heat of the room maintains the inner surface at +3.0°C, how much heat will flow through in 10.0 min? [Ans. 540 Kcal.]

10. A small copper ball 4.0 cm in diameter is coated with lampblack and heated to a temperature of 827°C. How much heat is radiated from this sphere in 1 min?

11. The wooden handle of a frying pan is 3.50 cm in diameter and 15.0 cm long. If the pan temperature is 120°C, and the free end of the pan handle is at 30°C, how much heat will flow through in 10.0 min?

12. An electric hotplate has a coil heater with a surface area of 280 cm^2. When turned on high it maintains a surface temperature of 727°C. (a) How much heat will this unit give off each minute of time? (b) If the wall of the room is maintained at 27°C, how much heat will this unit absorb each minute of time? Assume all surfaces to be black bodies. [Ans. (a) 22.85 Kcal/min, (b) 0.1851 Kcal/min.]

13.* A copper ball 6.0 cm in diameter is coated with lampblack and heated to a temperature of 427°C. (a) How much heat will this body radiate each second of time? (b) If the walls of the room are maintained at 27°C, how much heat will the ball absorb each second of time? Assume black-body surfaces.

14.* The rear wall of a brick fireplace has an effective area of 0.80 m^2. Find the number of Kcal radiated per minute if this area is maintained at 327°C. Assume the surface to be a black-body

15.* A small silver metal cube 5.0 cm on a side is raised to a temperature of 927°C. Assuming black-body radiation, how much energy is radiated per second (a) in joules, and (b) in kilocalories? [Ans. (a) 1.763×10^3 J, (b) 0.423 Kcal.]

16.* A thin square sheet of iron 3.0 cm on a side is heated to a temperature of 1327°C. Assuming black-body radiation, find the energy radiated per second in (a) joules, and (b) kilocalories?

17. The tube of a small TV receiver has a picture area of 0.45 m^2. Assuming normal atmospheric pressure, find the total inward force on this face of the tube.

16 Thermodynamics and rocket engines

As we proceed from chapter to chapter in this book, we will come to realize increasingly that there are many forms of energy, and that any one form can be transformed into any other. Thermodynamics is that branch of physics dealing with the conversion of mechanical energy into thermal energy, and the reverse process, heat into work. There are numerous ways of carrying out either of these transformations. By rubbing the palms of the hands together, for example, heat is produced; by rubbing two sticks of wood together a fire may be started. If a weight falls freely from some height, heat is developed when the weight strikes the ground. The bearings of a car motor or the wheels of a freight car, if not lubricated, will get hot and either "burn out" or lock together, as in a "hot box." These are all examples of mechanical energy being transformed into heat.

Fig. 16A. Cork gun: friction heat boils water, and steam blows cork out.

The reverse process of transforming heat into mechanical energy is illustrated by present-day steam, diesel, gasoline, and jet-propulsion engines. In all of these engines, fuel is burned to produce heat and by expanding gases the heat is turned into mechanical energy. Jet propulsion is not a new idea. A simple device based upon the principle of jet propulsion is to be found in the writings of some of the ancient philosophers of Archimedes' time.

An interesting demonstration is shown in Fig. 16A. A small hollow brass tube, mounted on the shaft of an electric motor, has a few drops of water in the base and a cork driven into the open end. A wooden clamp, like the one shown in the figure, is squeezed tightly around the tube as it spins. Because of friction the tube gets hot, boils the water, and steam pressure suddenly blows the cork out as if from a gun.

16.1. The First Law of Thermodynamics

The First Law of Thermodynamics expresses the relation between two forms of energy, and is usually expressed as *the mechanical equivalent of heat.* It is to the painstaking work of Joule (1843) that we attribute this fundamental verification of the universal law of conservation of energy. With his apparatus he was able to show that, when a moving body is brought to rest, the energy that disappears is directly proportional to the amount of heat produced. In his most famous experiment, he set water into motion in a bucket by means of rotating paddles and then brought the water to rest by stationary paddles. He was able to show that, if all of the work used in churning the water goes into producing heat, then the same amount of work will always produce the same amount of heat regardless of the method used to carry out the transformation. In other words, the calorie, which is a unit of heat energy, is equivalent to a definite number of joules of mechnical energy.

The number of energy units, which upon conversion gives one heat unit, is called the mechanical equivalent of heat. By experiment

$$1 \text{ Kcal} = 4.179 \times 10^3 \text{ J} \qquad (16a)$$

As an equation,

$$\frac{\text{work}}{\text{heat}} = \text{mech. equiv. of heat}$$

$$\frac{W}{H} = J \qquad (16b)$$

Because of the fundamental importance of this relation, many experimenters have devoted considerable time and effort to obtain a more accurate value of the constant J. In 1879, the famous American physicist Henry Rowland, using an improved form of Joule's apparatus, obtained the value

$$J = 4.179 \times 10^3 \frac{\text{J}}{\text{Kcal}}$$

Since that time, simpler experiments have been devised that make use of a method first employed by Joule, namely, that of heating by electric currents. Heating effects of electric currents will be treated in Chap. 25.

16.2. Experiments on Mechanical Equivalent of Heat

There are numerous ways of transforming mechanical energy into heat. By rubbing the palms of the hands together, for example, heat is produced by friction. Again, if a weight is dropped from any height, heat is developed when it strikes the ground. A 1-Kg mass dropped from a height of 426 m will, on stopping, produce 1 Kcal of heat.

One simple laboratory method of measuring the mechanical equivalent of heat is to place a measured amount of lead shot (about 100 g) in a tube about 5 cm in diameter and about 1 m long. After reading the temperature of the shot with a thermometer, the tube is turned end around end about 50 to 200 times, stopping each time in a vertical position to allow the shot to fall the full distance and strike the bottom (see Fig. 16B). The temperature of the shot is then measured again. From the known mass of shot, m, its specific heat, c, and the rise in temperature, $t_2 - t_1$, the total *heat gained* can be calculated, $H = mc(t_2 - t_1)$. From the mass of the shot m, the acceleration due to gravity g, the number of tube inversions n, and the length of the tube ℓ, the input energy is calculated. Since *work done* equals *force times distance*, $W = mg \times n\ell$. Substituting in Eq.(16b), we obtain

$$J = \frac{W}{H} = \frac{mg\,n\ell}{mc\,\Delta t} = \frac{g\,n\,\ell}{c\,\Delta t} \tag{16c}$$

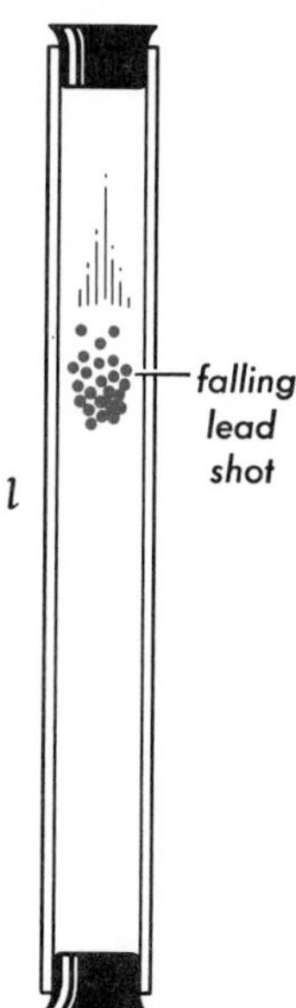

Fig.16B. Experiment for determining the mechanical equivalent of heat.

The disappearance of m is to be expected since, for example, the dropping of twice the amount of shot will produce twice as much heat, but this will be divided between twice the amount of lead.

Consider as a problem the calculation of the mechanical equivalent of heat from the following data taken in such a laboratory experiment:

Initial temperature of lead shot	23.0°C
Final temperature of lead shot	30.9°C
Length of tube	1.05 m
Number of falls	100

By substituting these values in Eq.(16c) and the specific heat of lead from Table 14A, we obtain

$$J = \frac{9.80 \times 100 \times 1.05}{0.031(30.9 - 23.0)}$$

$$J = 4.20 \times 10^3 \frac{\text{J}}{\text{Kcal}}$$

The transformation of potential energy into heat usually occurs by first changing it into kinetic energy. In the above experiment, for example, the lead shot acquired a velocity in falling and its kinetic energy $\frac{1}{2}mv^2$ was changed into heat at the bottom. Due to the impact the molecules of the colliding bodies were given additional kinetic energy.

Example 1. A 1.0-Kg hammer, moving with a velocity of 50.0 m/s, strikes a 200-g iron nail driving it into a block of wood. If half of the energy goes into heating the nail, what will be its rise in temperature?

Solution. In the *MKSA* system the given quantities are $m = 1.0$ Kg, $v = 50.0$ m/s, $m' = 0.20$ Kg, and $c = 0.1050$ Kcal/Kg C°. In order to use Eq.(16b), we first calculate the kinetic energy of the hammer since this is the energy converted into heat:

$$E_k = \frac{1}{2}\,1.0\text{ Kg}(50.0\text{ m/s})^2 = \text{W}$$

$$E_k = 1250\text{ J}$$

Substituting known quantities in Eq.(16b), we find

$$H = \frac{W}{J} = \frac{1250\text{ J}}{4.179 \times 10^3\text{ J/Kcal}}$$

$$H = 0.2991\text{ Kcal}$$

Since one-half this energy goes to heat 0.20 Kg of iron, we use Eq.(14b), solve for the rise in temperature, and obtain

$$\Delta t = \frac{\Delta H}{mc} = \frac{0.1496\text{ Kcal}}{0.20\text{ Kg} \times 0.105\text{ Kcal/Kg C°}}$$

$$\Delta t = 7.12\text{ C°}$$

16.3. Kinetic Theory of Gases

According to the kinetic theory of matter, the pressure exerted by a gas upon the walls of the containing vessel is due to the continual bombardment of the walls by the rapidly moving gas molecules. If the temperature of the gas is raised, the molecules move faster and the pressure rises, whereas if it is lowered, they move slower and the pressure decreases. The absolute temperature of a gas is proportional to the average kinetic energy of translation of the molecules.

The more gas that is pumped into a vessel of constant volume, the more molecules there are to bombard the walls per second and the greater is the resultant pressure. At any given instant of time some molecules are moving in one direction and some in another; some are traveling fast, some slow, and a few are momentarily at rest.

In any reasonably large volume of gas, there are many molecules (about 3×10^{25} molecules/m^3 at normal atmospheric pressure and room temperature) and, according to the mathematical laws of probability, some average speed can be determined which, if possessed by all the molecules, would correspond to the same temperature and would give rise to the same wall pressure. Denoting this average speed by $\bar{v}$, we shall now derive a formula for the pressure.

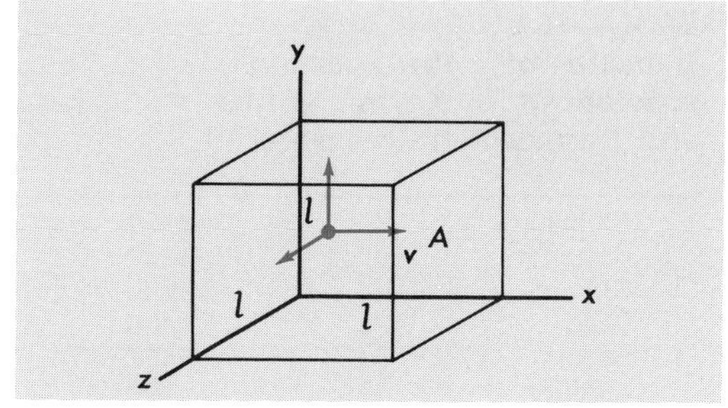

Fig. 16C. Gas molecules in a closed compartment create pressure by virtue of their impact against the walls.

Consider a cubical vessel whose volume, as shown in Fig. 16C, is ℓ^3. Because the total number n of molecules present is very large, the calculations are simplified by assuming that one-third are moving in the x direction, one-third in the y direction, and one-third in the z direction.

Select now the one-third that are moving in the x direction. Each molecule as it approaches the right-hand wall of the vessel is moving with a velocity $\bar{v}$ and after collision it rebounds with a velocity $-\bar{v}$. There has been a change in velocity of $2\bar{v}$. Since the impulse Ft exerted on the wall is given by the change in momentum, we may write

$$Ft = 2m\bar{v} \tag{16d}$$

Bouncing back and forth between opposite walls of the vessel, each molecule will make many impacts on the same wall in unit time. Now, t is the average time required for the molecule to make the round trip, 2ℓ, from the right-hand wall to the left-hand wall and back. Therefore

$$t = 2\ell/\bar{v}$$

Since the impulse Ft is given by the change of momentum, we may write

$$F \times 2\ell/\bar{v} = 2m\bar{v} \qquad \text{or} \qquad F = m\overline{v^2}/\ell$$

For $\frac{1}{3}n$ molecules, then, the force will be $n/3$ times that for one molecule, or

$$F = \frac{nm\overline{v^2}}{3\ell}$$

TABLE 16A
Densities of a few common substances, in Kg/m³, at 0°C and 1 atmosphere pressure

Substance	Density
Aluminum	2,700
Copper	8,900
Gold	19,300
Lead	11,400
Silver	10,500
Alcohol	790
Gasoline	650
Mercury	13,600
Water	1,000.000
Air	1.293
Carbon dioxide	1.980
Carbon monoxide	1.250
Helium	0.180
Hydrogen	0.090
Oxygen	1.430
Sulfur dioxide	2.927

Since pressure is the force per unit area, and the area of the wall is ℓ^2,

$$P = \frac{F}{\ell^2} = \frac{nm\overline{v^2}}{3\ell^3} \tag{16e}$$

Since the number of molecules n multiplied by the mass of a single molecule gives the total mass of the gas, and ℓ^3 gives it volume, the density ρ is given by

$$\rho = \frac{nm}{\ell^3}$$

By substituting ρ for nm/ℓ^3 in Eq.(16e), we obtain for the pressure

$$P = \tfrac{1}{3}\rho\overline{v^2} \tag{16f}$$

The average velocity of molecules in a gas of density ρ, under an absolute pressure P, is given by rearranging the terms:

$$\bar{v} = \sqrt{3P/\rho} \tag{16g}$$

In Table 16A the gas densities are given for 0°C and standard atmospheric pressure.

Example 2. Calculate the average velocity of hydrogen molecules in a gas at normal atmospheric pressure and room temperature. **Solution.** In the *MKSA* system of units, normal pressure is $P = 1.013 \times 10^5$ N/m², and the density of hydrogen gas at the normal temperature of 0°C is obtained from Table 16A as $\rho = 0.090$ Kg/m³. Upon direct substitution of these values in Eq.(16g), we find

$$\bar{v} = \sqrt{\frac{3 \times 1.013 \times 10^5 \text{ N/m}^2}{0.090 \text{ Kg/m}^3}}$$

$$\bar{v} = 1838 \ \frac{\text{m}}{\text{s}}$$

This is considerably faster than a rifle bullet or the shells from the largest guns.

The formula above shows that the greater the density of a gas, the lower is the average speed of its molecules. For a gas like oxygen, with 16 times the density of hydrogen, the molecules will be moving with only one-quarter the average speed of the hydrogen molecules. This is well illustrated by the mechanical model shown in Fig. 29D, representing the case of a mixture of two gases of different density.

It should be noted that a pressure gauge reads zero when the gas in a tank reaches atmospheric pressure. In solving problems, therefore, standard atmospheric pressure should be added to all gauge readings to obtain the true gas pressure.

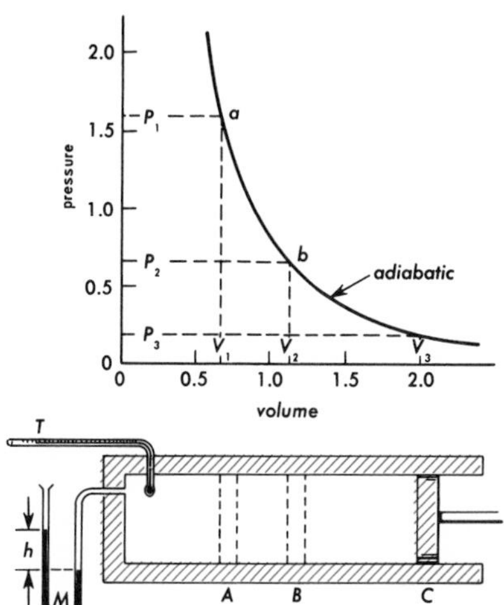

Fig. 16D. Adiabatic compression and expansion of a gas.

16.4. The General Gas Law

This is a law dealing with the compression and expansion of a gas at different temperatures. It states that the pressure of a given quantity of gas is proportional to the *absolute temperature* and inversely proportional to the *volume*. As an equation

$$P = R\frac{T}{V}$$

or

$$PV = RT \qquad (16h)$$

general gas law

The proportionality constant R is called the *gas constant,* and is given by

$$R = \frac{PV}{T}$$

An experiment illustrating the expansion or compression of a gas is shown in Fig. 16D, along with a *pressure* vs. *volume* graph of the results. A heat-insulated cylinder with a movable piston is arranged with a mercury manometer and a sensitive thermometer. The gas pressure P is determined by adding the manometer height h to the atmospheric pressure P_0, the volume by multiplying the length of the gas column and the piston cross-sectional area, and the gas temperature by reading the thermometer in °C and adding 273°.

For position A the pressure is represented by P_1, the volume by V_1, and the temperature by T_1. Moving the piston to position B is called an *adiabatic expansion:* The pressure decreases to a lower value P_2, the volume increases to a higher value V_2, and the temperature drops to T_2. A further expansion bringing the piston to C lowers the pressure to P_3, raises the volume to V_3, and lowers the temperature to T_3.

When the piston is pushed in from position C to position A, the gas undergoes an *adiabatic compression:* The volume decreases, the pressure increases, and the temperature rises. Experimentally, it is found that

$$\frac{P_1V_1}{T_1} = \frac{P_2V_2}{T_2} = \frac{P_3V_3}{T_3} \tag{16i}$$

Example 3. A balloon in a partially filled condition contains 1000 m^3 of helium gas at ground level, where the pressure is 76.0 cm of mercury and the temperature is 27°C. Calculate the gas volume when this balloon rises into the stratosphere to a height of 20.0 Km, where the pressure drops to 4.0 cm of mercury and the temperature to −50°C.

Solution. The given quantities are $P_1 = 76.0$ cm of Hg, $P_2 = 4.0$ cm of Hg, $V_1 = 1000$ m^3, $T_1 = 273° + 27°\text{C} = 300°\text{K}$, and $T_2 = 273° - 50°\text{C} = 223°\text{K}$. In using Eq.(16i) it will be observed that pressures can be expressed in any units so long as they are the same on both sides of the equation. The same is true of the volumes and temperatures. Therefore, upon direct substitution, all units but volume cancel out:

$$\frac{P_1V_1}{T_1} = \frac{P_2V_2}{T_2}$$

$$\frac{76.0\ \text{cm} \times 1000\ \text{m}^3}{(273 + 27)°\text{K}} = \frac{4.0\ \text{cm} \times V_2}{(273 - 50)°\text{K}}$$

Solving for V_2 gives

$$V_2 = \frac{76.0\ \text{cm} \times 223 \times 1000\ \text{m}^3}{4.0 \times 300} = 14{,}120\ \text{m}^3$$

The value of the gas constant R in Eq.(16h) depends upon many factors, including units of measurement. It is common practice to choose an amount of gas equal to one kilogram mole. The *kilogram mole* is defined as that mass in kilograms of a substance equal to its molecular weight. Oxygen, for example, has an atomic weight of 16.0, and a molecular weight of 32.0. One kilogram mole of oxygen has a mass of 32 Kg. For one mole of any gas

$$R = 8.3143435 \frac{\text{J}}{\text{Kg mole °K}} \tag{16j}$$

One kilogram mole of any gas at 0°C and 76 cm of Hg pressure occupies a volume of 22.4 m^3, and contains a number of molecules equal to

$$N = 6.0221694 \times 10^{26} \frac{\text{molecules}}{\text{Kg mole}} \tag{16k}$$

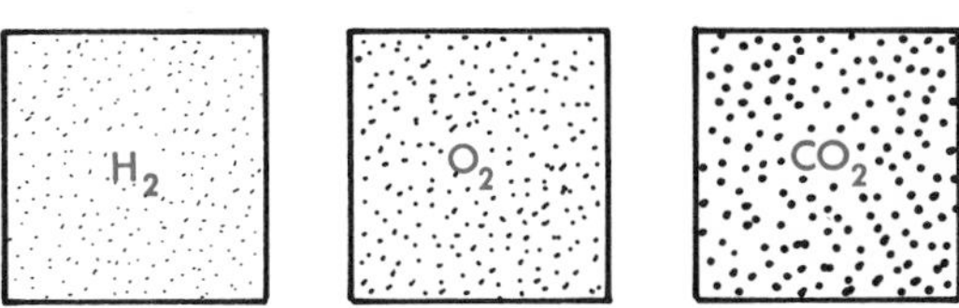

Fig. 16E. Equal volumes of different gases at the same temperature and pressure contain equal numbers of molecules.

This is called Avogadro's number and follows from Avogadro's hypothesis which states that equal volumes of different gases at the same temperature and pressure contain equal numbers of molecules (see Fig. 16E).

The ratio of the two constants, R/N, is called the *Boltzmann constant* k, and is given by

$$k = \frac{8.314343}{6.022169 \times 10^{26}}$$

$$k = 1.380623 \times 10^{-26} \frac{\text{J}}{\text{molecule °K}} \tag{16ℓ}$$

and represents the energy per molecule for each degree rise in temperature.

For most problems the values of N and k are rounded off to three or four figures.

16.5. Speeds of Molecules

The velocities of individual molecules in a gas vary over a wide range of magnitudes and over all directions. At room temperature and standard atmospheric pressure, each molecule makes about 10^9 elastic collisions per second with other molecules, and travels an average distance of 500 molecular diameters, or about 10^{-7} m. At times the speed of a molecule will be greater than the average value given by Eq.(16g), and at times it will be considerably less. The probability for extremely high speeds relative to the average value is low.

The law for the distribution of velocities of molecules in a gas was first derived from theoretical considerations by James Clerk Maxwell a little over one hundred years ago. His equation may be written

$$n\,\Delta v = 4\pi v^2 n_0 \left(\frac{m}{2\pi kT}\right)^{\frac{3}{2}} e^{-[(\frac{1}{2}mv^2)/kT]}\,\Delta v \qquad (16m)$$

In this equation n_0 represents the total number of molecules in any given container, k is the so-called Boltzmann constant, T is the absolute temperature, m is the mass of a single molecule, v is its speed, and e is the base of the natural logarithms, $e = 2.71828$. The quantity n_0 represents the number of molecules having speeds between v and $v + \Delta v$.

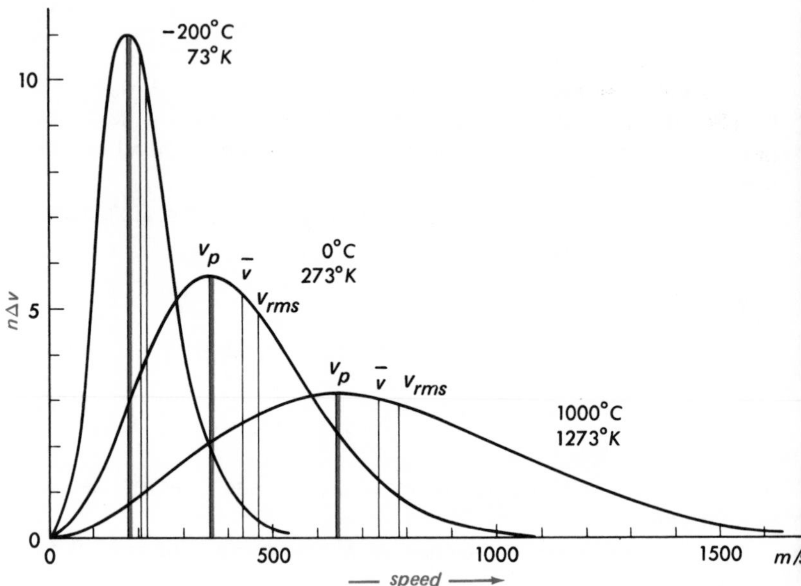

Fig. 16F. The Maxwellian distribution of the speeds of oxygen molecules at three different temperatures. Δv is taken as 1 m/s.

A graph of this Maxwellian distribution of speeds is shown in Fig. 16F for three different temperatures. At any one of the temperatures, note that the number of molecules in any given interval Δv increases from zero upward and reaches a maximum at the most probable speed v_p and then decreases asymptotically toward zero at higher speeds. It will be observed that the higher the temperature, the higher the most probable speed. Notice for each curve that the distribution is not symmetrical about the most *probable value*, and that the average value $\bar{v}$ (dividing the area under each curve equally) is somewhat larger than the most probable value v_p.

The root-mean-square speed v_{rms} is of importance because the square of its value is directly proportional to the *total kinetic energy* of the gas molecules, and directly proportional to the absolute temperature T. The total mass M of a gas is given by the product of the mass of one molecule m, and the number of molecules n_0:

$$M = n_0 m$$

The total kinetic energy of the gas can then be written as

$$\tfrac{1}{2}M\overline{v^2} \tag{16n}$$

where $\overline{v^2}$ is the sum of the squares of all speeds divided by the total number of molecules.

While the probability of finding molecules having extreme speeds is small, it is not zero. The equation shows how the speeds depend upon the mass of the molecules, as well as the absolute temperature. The larger the mass m, the lower the proportion of high-speed molecules at any given temperature.

Experimental verification of Maxwell's equation was first demonstrated by O. Stern in 1926 in a way quite similar to Fizeau's toothed-wheel experiment used for measuring the speed of light (see Chap. 32).

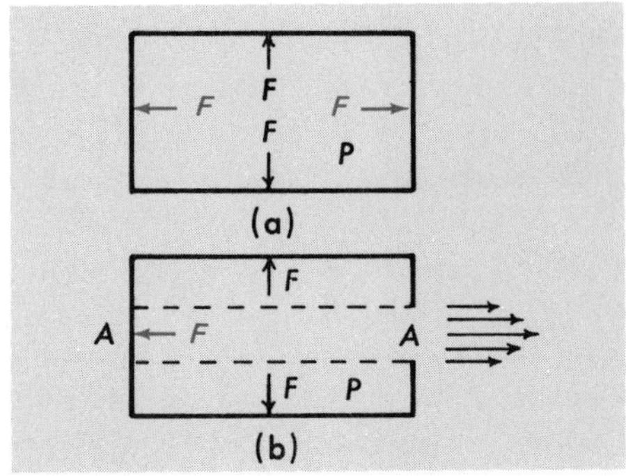

Fig. 16G. Diagram illustrating the thrust arising from the gas exhausted from a hole in a tank containing gas under pressure.

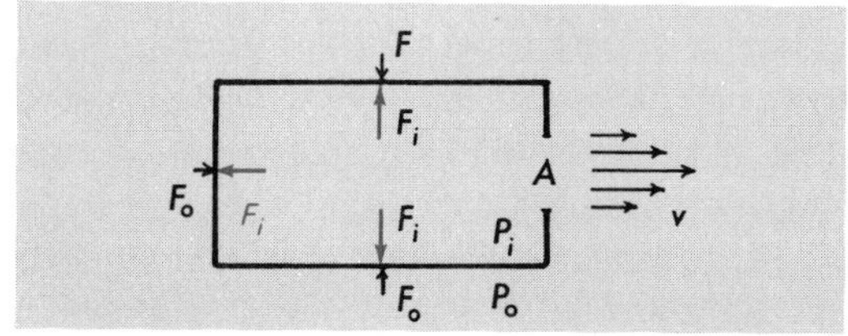

Fig. 16H. Illustration of internal and external gas pressures on the walls of a gas container and the thrust from an exhaust jet.

16.6. Rocket Engines

The thrust of a rocket engine is readily explained in terms of gas pressure and Newton's third law of motion. Consider a hollow vessel having the shape of a cylindrical tin can and containing a mixture of combustible fuels as shown in Fig. 16G(a).

When the fuel is ignited, the high pressure developed inside exerts outward forces normal to the walls as shown. The forces F on the two ends are equal and opposite, as are also the forces on opposite sides. All of these forces are balanced out and the net resultant force is zero.

Imagine that we now remove a circular section of area from the center of the right-hand end as shown in diagram (b). The container now experiences an unbalanced force F to the left, given by the product of the pressure P and the exit area A:

$$F = P \times A \tag{16o}$$

At the earth's surface the atmosphere outside the container exerts inward forces on all the walls and must be taken into account (see Fig. 16H). The pressure P in Eq.(16o) then becomes the difference between the inside pressure P_i and the outside or ambient pressure P_o. The pressure thrust on the rocket becomes, therefore,

$$F = (P_i - P_o)A \tag{16p}$$

The principal elements of a typical liquid-propellant rocket engine are shown by a cross-section diagram in Fig. 16l. Oxidizer and fuel, kept in separate tanks, are pumped into the combustion chamber where they are sprayed out of jets to form an efficient combustible mixture. Burning at a steady rate, liquid fuel and oxidizer not only expand into a gas but rise in temperature to a very high value.

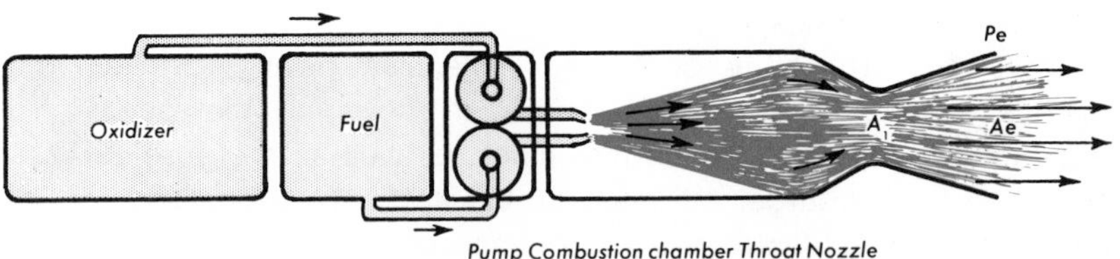

Fig. 16l. Schematic diagram of a liquid rocket motor.

The purpose of a well-designed nozzle is to accelerate the gas particles to still higher velocity and at the same time to direct their motion into a smoothly flowing exhaust stream.

As the gases approach the throat of the nozzle, the decreasing cross-sectional area causes the molecules to speed up. Once they are through the narrowest section, the low pressure of free space provides an additional acceleration.

Out in free space, far removed from all external forces, the resultant accelerating force acting upon a rocket is due entirely to the momentum change of the mass of the particles it ejects through the exhaust. Applying Newton's second law of motion to these gases, the force on them equals the rate of change of their momentum. The total thrust of the rocket engine may be written

$$F = \frac{\Delta(mv)}{\Delta t} \tag{16q}$$

Assuming steady burning of the fuel, the exhaust velocity v of the waste products is constant and Eq.(16q) may be written

$$F = -\frac{\Delta m}{\Delta t} v \tag{16r}$$

The minus sign indicates that v is oppositely directed to the force F. The velocity v is measured with respect to the rocket, and F is called the *momentum thrust.*

The exit pressure P_i of the gas from within the rocket is usually quite different from the ambient pressure P_o of the surrounding gas. Although P_i may stay fairly constant as a rocket climbs through the atmosphere, the ambient pressure P_o will decrease and become practically zero in free space.

To take these varying conditions into account, it is convenient to write for the total thrust of the rocket engine

$$F = -\frac{\Delta m}{\Delta t} v_{\text{eff}} \tag{16s}$$

total thrust

where v_{eff} is called the *effective exhaust velocity.* As the rocket climbs through the atmosphere where the ambient pressure P_o decreases and becomes zero, the effective velocity v_{eff} increases and approaches v, while the thrust F increases and becomes constant in free space.

16.7. Specific Impulse

Specific impulse is the term applied to the performance of a rocket engine, and is given by the total thrust divided by the weight of the propellant consumed per second:

$$I_s = \frac{F}{\Delta w/\Delta t} \tag{16t}$$

Since F and w are both measured in newtons, specific impulse is in seconds. Since total thrust varies with altitude, the value of F given by Eq.(16s) may be substituted in Eq.(16t):

$$I_s = \frac{\Delta m/\Delta t}{\Delta w/\Delta t} v_{\text{eff}}$$

By Newton's law, weight = mass × acceleration due to gravity, $\Delta w = \Delta m \times g$. Direct substitution gives

$$I_s = \frac{\Delta m/\Delta t}{\Delta m/\Delta t} \times \frac{v_{\text{eff}}}{g}$$

$$I_s = \frac{v_{\text{eff}}}{g} \tag{16u}$$

specific impulse

TABLE 16B
Performance of liquid propellants calculated for expansion from 20 atm to 1 atm pressure

Propellant	*Exhaust velocity v* (Km/s)	*Specific impulse I_s* (s)
Oxygen and hydrogen	4.18	426
Oxygen and ethyl alcohol	2.34	240
Oxygen and kerosene	2.43	248
Nitric acid and analine	2.00	204
Hydrogen and fluorine	3.80	388
Hydrogen and ozone	3.60	368
Hydrazine and oxygen	2.60	265

The value of g is assumed to be a constant and equal to 9.80 m/s^2, wherever the rocket is located. Specific impulse can be found either by dividing the thrust by the fuel consumption, or by dividing the exhaust velocity by the constant g.

Another relation for the specific impulse can be derived from the kinetic theory of gases Eq.(16g), and the general gas law Eq.(16h). Since $P = RT/V$, and the density $\rho = M/V$, direct substitution in Eq.(16g) gives

$$\bar{v} = \sqrt{3R\frac{T}{M}}$$

Assuming this relation gives the theoretical gas velocity from the rocket nozzle, direct substitution in Eq.(16t) gives

$$I_s = k\sqrt{\frac{T}{M}}$$

where T is the absolute temperature of combustion, M is the mass of the exhaust particles or molecules, and

$$k = \frac{\sqrt{3R}}{g}$$

The higher the temperature reached through combustion, and the lower the mass of the propellant molecules, the greater will be the exhaust velocity v, and the greater will be the specific impulse I_s.

Typical values of these two quantities for a number of liquid propellants are given in Table 16B.

These are theoretical values only and are not fully realized in practice. A specific impulse of 240 means a thrust of 240 N per newton of propellant consumed per second. A mass of 1 Kg has a weight of 9.8 N. (For the description of a nuclear reactor rocket engine, see Sec. 63.12 and Fig. 63R.)

Example 4. Liquid hydrogen and liquid oxygen are used as a propellant to lift a 2.0×10^7-Kg rocket from its launching pad. Assuming a specific impulse of 426 s, (a) find the effective velocity of the gases in the exhaust and (b) the rate at which fuel is consumed, when the initial acceleration reaches 1.0 m/s^2.
Solution. The given quantities are $m = 2.0 \times 10^7$ Kg, $g = 9.80$ m/s^2, and $I = 426$ s. For the answer to part (a) solve Eq.(16u) for v_{eff} and substitute the appropriate given quantities:

$$v_{\text{eff}} = I_s\,g = 426 \times 9.80\,\frac{\text{m}}{\text{s}^2}$$

$$v_{\text{eff}} = 4180\,\frac{\text{m}}{\text{s}}$$

For part (b) we note that the thrust of the motors must not only lift the rocket but give it an acceleration of 1.0 m/s^2. Therefore, the thrust F must be

$$F = mg + ma = m(g + a)$$

$$F = 2.0 \times 10^7\ \text{Kg}(9.80 + 1.0)\,\frac{\text{m}}{\text{s}^2}$$

$$F = 2.160 \times 10^8\ \text{N}$$

We now solve Eq.(16s) for $\Delta m/\Delta t$ and substitute known quantities:

$$\frac{\Delta m}{\Delta t} = \frac{F}{v_{\text{eff}}} = \frac{2.16 \times 10^8\ \text{N}}{4180\ \text{m/s}} = 5.17 \times 10^4\,\frac{\text{Kg}}{\text{s}} \tag{16v}$$

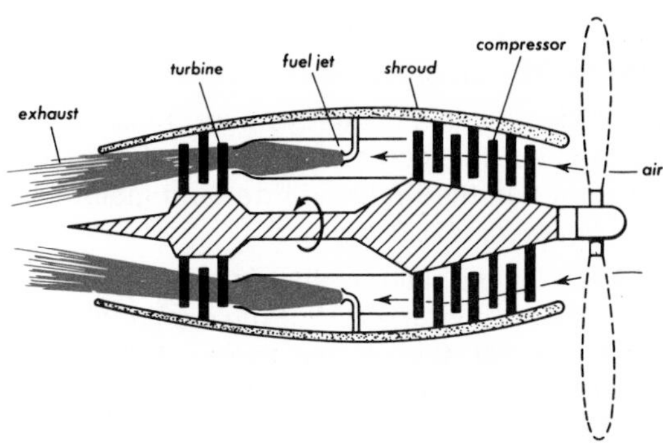

Fig. 16J. Cross-sectional diagram of a turbojet engine used principally in aircraft (propeller optional). Top speed about 600 mi/h.

16.8. The Turbojet

This engine, used extensively in high-speed aircraft, is shown schematically in Fig. 16J. Air needed for combustion enters the nose of the *shroud* where it is compressed by a fan-like centrifugal *compressor.* This air, along with the fuel to be burned, is injected into a *combustion chamber* and there the mixture is ignited. The rapidly expanding gases drive a fan-like *turbine* wheel and at the same time create a forward thrust on the walls by exhausting through the rear as shown. The principal function of the turbine is to drive the compressor and small auxiliary equipment like fuel pumps, generators, etc.

problems

1. The water in a waterfall drops 500 m to the canyon below. Assuming that all the energy goes into heat, find the rise in temperature of the water.

2. A 6.0-Kg block of copper is dropped from a tower 100.0 m high. Assuming that three-quarters of the heat developed, as it hits the ground, goes into the copper, find (a) the heat that goes into the copper, and (b) the temperature rise.

3. A train weighing 5.0×10^6 Kg and traveling 72.0 Km/h is brought to a stop by applying the brakes Find the total heat developed. [Ans. 2.393×10^5 Kcal.]

4. A horizontal force of 450 N is required to pull a

100.0-Kg box across the floor of a room. How much heat is developed for each 10.0 m it slides?

5. A boy riding a motorcycle at 108.0 Km/h applies the brakes and comes to a stop. How much heat is developed in the brakes if rider and motorcycle have a total mass of 225.0 Kg.

6. A 50-g steel bullet is shot into a target with a velocity of 700 m/s. If one-half of the expended energy goes into the bullet, find (a) the energy in Kcal, and (b) the rise in temperature of the bullet. [Ans. (a) 2.931 Kcal, (b) 279.2C°.]

7. Calculate the average velocity of oxygen molecules in the air at a normal temperature of 0°C, and a normal pressure of 76 cm of mercury.

8. Calculate the average velocity of oxygen molecules in a tank of compressed gas, where the pressure is 10.0 atmospheres and the temperature is 0°C.

9. A tank of hydrogen gas at 25.0 atmospheres pressure and at 27°C has a volume of 0.60 m^3. When this gas is allowed to expand into a much larger vessel where its pressure is 1.0 atmosphere and its temperature is 0°C, find its new volume. [Ans. 13.65 m^3.]

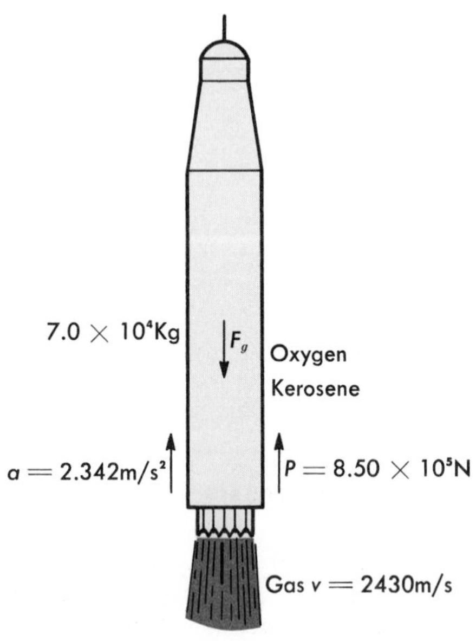

Prob. 12.

10. An automobile tire shows a gauge pressure of 2.0×10^5 N/m^2 when the temperature is 27°C. After the car runs for some time on the hot pavement the temperature of the tire rises to 60°C. Find the gauge pressure. Assume the volume has not changed. *Note:* When a tire is flat a gauge will show zero, even though the pressure is 1.0 atmosphere; therefore, add 1 atmosphere to all gauge pressure readings.

11.* A rocket engine using liquid oxygen and liquid hydrogen as propellant develops a specific impulse of 320 s. If the propellant is consumed at the rate of 95.0 Kg/s, find (a) the effective exhaust velocity, and (b) the total thrust in newtons.

12.* A rocket engine using liquid oxygen and kerosene as a propellant has a total mass of 7.0×10^4 Kg. If the propellant is consumed at the rate of 350.0 Kg/s, what is (a) the effective exhaust velocity, (b) the total thrust, and (c) the vertical acceleration as it leaves the ground? Assume the specific impulse to be that given in Table 16B. [Ans. (a) 2430 m/s, (b) 8.50×10^5 N, (c) 2.351 m/s^2.]

13.* A rocket using liquid oxygen and hydrazine as propellant has a total weight of 5.0×10^4 Kg. If this fuel is consumed at the rate 250.0 Kg/s, and the specific impulse is 265 s, find (a) the effective exhaust velocity, (b) the total thrust, and (c) the vertical acceleration as the rocket leaves the launching pad.

14.* Liquid oxygen and hydrogen as propellant are used to lift a 3.0×10^5-Kg rocket from its launching pad. Assuming a specific impulse of 426 s, what is (a) the effective velocity of the exhaust gases, and (b) at what rate is fuel consumed if the initial acceleration is 1.0 m/s^2?

15.* Liquid hydrogen and liquid fluorine as propellant are used to lift a 4.50×10^5-Kg rocket from its launching pad. Assuming a specific impulse as given in Table 16B, (a) what is the effective velocity of the exhaust gases, and (b) at what rate must fuel be consumed if the initial acceleration is 1.20 m/s^2? [Ans. (a) 3.802×10^3m/s, (b) 1.303×10^3 Kg/s.]

17 Vibrations and waves

The concepts of vibrations and waves are important to all present-day theories of the world around us. They both appear in a very fundamental way in the subjects of light, sound, heat, micro-waves, and in the ultramicroscopic world of atoms and nuclei and their phenomena.

Any motion, simple or complex, which repeats itself in equal intervals of time, is called *periodic motion.* There are many examples in everyday life which give rise to a special kind of periodic motion called *simple periodic motion.* The swinging of the clock pendulum, the turning of the balance wheel of a watch, or the vibration of a tuning fork are good examples of such motions. The term "simple periodic motion" applies to these because each can be described in terms of one of the simplest known types of periodic motions—namely, *uniform circular motion.*

17.1. Simple Harmonic Motion

Simple harmonic motion (SHM) is the linear motion duplicated by

(1) constructing a reference circle whose radius is equal to the amplitude of the given SHM,
(2) causing a point to move uniformly in this circular path such that its period (time to go around once) is the same as the known period (single vibration time) of the given SHM, and
(3) then projecting this point onto any straight line in the plane of circle.

This may be visually demonstrated by casting on a vertical screen the shadow of an upright peg on the rim of a rotating record turntable.

This motion is illustrated in Fig. 17A. The point p moves around the circle of radius r with uniform speed v. If at every instant a

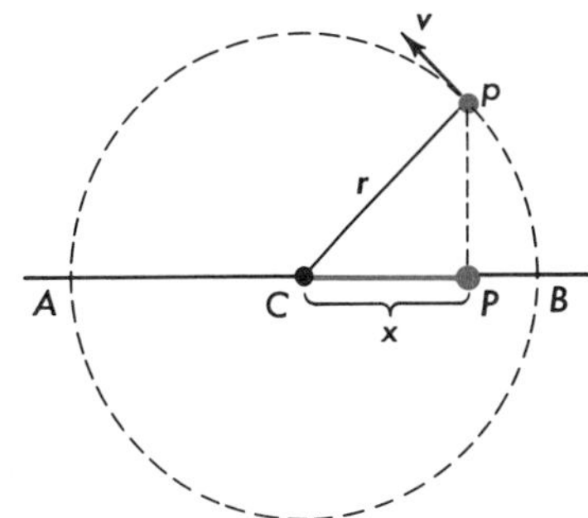

Fig. 17A. Diagram illustrating simple harmonic motion along a straight line.

perpendicular is drawn from p to the diameter AB, the intercept P will move with simple harmonic motion. Moving back and forth along the straight line from A to B, the velocity v_x is continually changing. At the center point C it has its greatest velocity, while at A and B it is momentarily at rest. Starting from either end of its path, the velocity increases until it reaches C; from there it slows down again, coming to rest at the opposite end of its path.

The *displacement* of a simple harmonic motion is defined as the distance from the center C to the point P. As shown in Fig. 17A, the displacement x varies in magnitude from zero at C up to r, the radius of the *circle of reference*, at A or B.

The *amplitude* r is defined as the maximum value of the *displacement* x, and the *period* is defined as the time required to make one complete vibration.

If a vibration starts at A, it is not completed until the point moves across to B and back again to A. If it starts from C and moves to B and back to C, only half a vibration has been completed. It is not completed until the point moves to A and back to C again. The amplitude r is usually measured in centimeters and the period T in seconds.

The frequency of a harmonic motion is defined as the number of complete vibrations per second. For example, if a particular vibrating object completes one vibration in one-half second (the period $T = \frac{1}{2}$ s), then it will make two complete vibrations in 1 s (the frequency $\nu = 2$ vib/s). If again a body completes one vibration in one-tenth of a second, $T = \frac{1}{10}$ s, it will make ten vibrations in 1 s, $\nu = 10$ vib/s. In other words, ν and T are reciprocals of each other:

$$\text{period} = \frac{1}{\text{frequency}}$$

or

$$\text{frequency} = \frac{1}{\text{period}}$$

In algebraic symbolism,

$$T = \frac{1}{\nu} \qquad \nu = \frac{1}{T} \tag{17a}$$

When describing the vibration of a body in terms of motion in a circle, the vibration frequency is equivalent to the number of *revolutions per second* or *cycles per second:*

$$1\ \frac{\text{vibration}}{\text{second}} = 1\ \frac{\text{cycle}}{\text{second}} \tag{17b}$$

As a result of international meetings of the appropriate technical societies not many years ago, the unit of frequency is called the *hertz,* abbreviated Hz. The unit is named in honor of Heinrich R. Hertz,* a German physicist who became famous the latter part of the 19th century for his outstanding discovery of radio waves:

$$1\ \frac{\text{cycle}}{\text{second}} = 1 \text{ hertz}$$

or abbreviated:

$$1\ \frac{\text{vib}}{\text{s}} = 1\ \frac{\text{c}}{\text{s}} = 1 \text{ Hz}$$

All three of these abbreviations are commonly used, the latter increasing in its use in newer books.

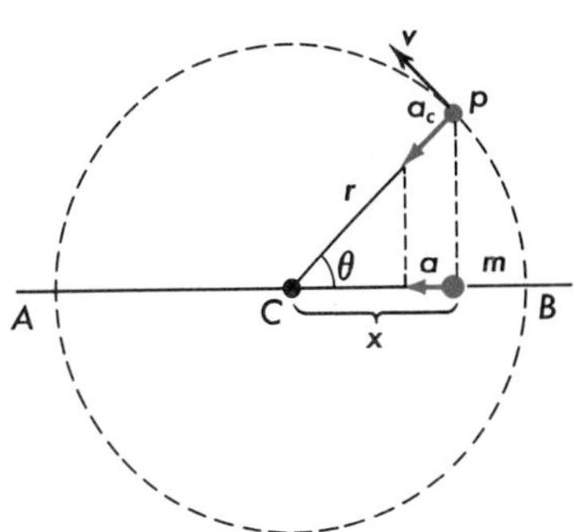

Fig. 17B. In any simple harmonic motion, the acceleration is always toward the central equilibrium position.

17.2. Theory of Simple Harmonic Motion

It is intended here to derive a general formula for the period of vibrating bodies executing simple harmonic motion.

In Fig. 17B it can be seen that the displacement x is given by

$$x = r \cos \theta \tag{17c}$$

Since the graph point p moves with constant speed, the radius vector rotates with constant angular velocity ω, and the angle θ is changing at a constant rate, giving

$$x = r \cos \omega t \tag{17d}$$

Referring to Fig. 17B, the point p, moving with a speed v, will travel once around the circle of reference, a distance $2\pi r$, in a time T. Applying the relation that *time equals distance divided by velocity,* we get

$$T = \frac{2\pi r}{v} \tag{17e}$$

In terms of the period of vibration T, the angualr velocity ω of the graph point is given by

$$\omega = \frac{2\pi}{T} \tag{17f}$$

*Heinrich Rudolf Hertz (1857–1894), German physicist, was born at Hamburg, February 22, 1857. He studied physics under Helmholtz in Berlin, at whose suggestion he first became interested in Maxwell's electromagnetic theory. His researches with electromagnetic waves which made his name famous were carried out at Karlsruhe Polytechnic between 1885 and 1889. As professor of physics at the University of Bonn, after 1889, he experimented with electrical discharges through gases and narrowly missed the discovery of X rays described by Röntgen a few years later. By his premature death, science lost one of its most promising disciples.

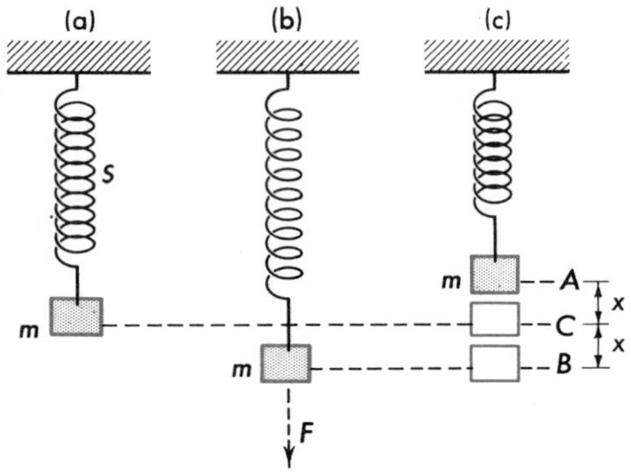

Fig. 17C. A mass on the end of a spring executes simple harmonic motion.

We have seen in Sec. 11.2 that an object moving in a circle with uniform speed v has a constant acceleration toward the center given by Eq.(11i) as

$$a_c = \frac{v^2}{r} \tag{17g}$$

As this acceleration a_c changes in direction, its component a along the x axis changes in magnitude and is given by $a_c \cos \theta$. Making this substitution, we obtain

$$a = \frac{v^2}{r} \cos \theta$$

Since $\cos \theta = x/r$

$$a = \frac{v^2}{r} \cdot \frac{x}{r} \qquad a = \frac{v^2}{r^2} x$$

Multiplying both sides of the equation by r^2/av^2 and taking the square root, we obtain

$$\frac{r^2}{v^2} = \frac{x}{a} \qquad \text{and} \qquad \frac{r}{v} = \sqrt{\frac{x}{a}}$$

Substituting $\sqrt{x/a}$ for r/v in Eq.(17e) gives

$$T = 2\pi \sqrt{\frac{x}{a}} \tag{17h}$$

When the displacement is $+$, the acceleration a is toward the center and therefore $-$. Conversely when x is $-$, a is $+$. For this reason the period should be written

$$T = 2\pi \sqrt{-\frac{x}{a}} \tag{17i}$$

This is a useful equation because it gives the period of vibration in terms of the displacement x and the corresponding acceleration a.

17.3. Vibrating Spring

Any elastic body may be set into a state of vibration by first distorting it in some way and then releasing it. This is demonstrated by a weight on the end of a spring as shown in Fig. 17C.

In diagram (a), the spring S and mass m hang in a state of equilibrium. At (b) a force F has been applied to stretch the spring, displacing the mass a distance x. After being released, the mass m moves up and down with simple harmonic motion. In diagram (c) the spring is shown compressed with m at its highest point. The maximum displacement x of the vibration is determined by the original distance to which the spring is stretched, and the period T is given by the algebraic equation

$$T = 2\pi\sqrt{m/k} \qquad (17j)$$

where m is the mass of the vibrating body in Kg and k a number expressing the stiffness of the spring. The constant k is the force in newtons required to stretch the spring 1 m. This formula shows that, if m is made larger, the period is increased and that, when a stiffer spring is used (k being in the denominator), the period is decreased.

In accordance with Hooke's law [see Eq.(9ℓ)], the stretch of a spring is given by the relation

$$F = -kx \qquad (9\ell)$$

where F is the restoring force, x the displacement, and k the same as above. Since a force of magnitude F acts to accelerate the mass m, $F = ma$ gives

$$ma = -kx \qquad \text{or} \qquad -x/a = m/k$$

The substitution of m/k for $-x/a$ in Eq.(17i) gives Eq.(17j).

Example 1. When a 5.0-Kg mass is suspended from the lower end of a coil spring, it stretches the spring 12.0 cm. If the spring with this mass is then set vibrating up and down, what will be (a) the spring constant, (b) the period, and (c) the frequency of vibration?

Solution. The given quantities expressed in the *MKSA* system are $m = 5.0$ Kg, $g = 9.80$ m/s^2, and $x = 0.120$ m. For the answer to part (a) we can use Eq.(9ℓ), solve for the spring constant k, and substitute the known quantities:

$$k = \frac{-F}{x} = \frac{5 \times 9.80}{0.12} = 408 \text{ N/m}$$

(b) To find the *period of vibration*, we substitute directly in

Eq.(17j):

$$T = 2\pi\sqrt{m/k}$$

$$T = 2\pi\sqrt{5/408}$$

$$T = 0.696\ \text{s}$$

(c) The reciprocal of the period is the *frequency:*

$$\nu = \frac{1}{T} = \frac{1}{0.696\ \text{s}} = 1.437\ \text{Hz}$$

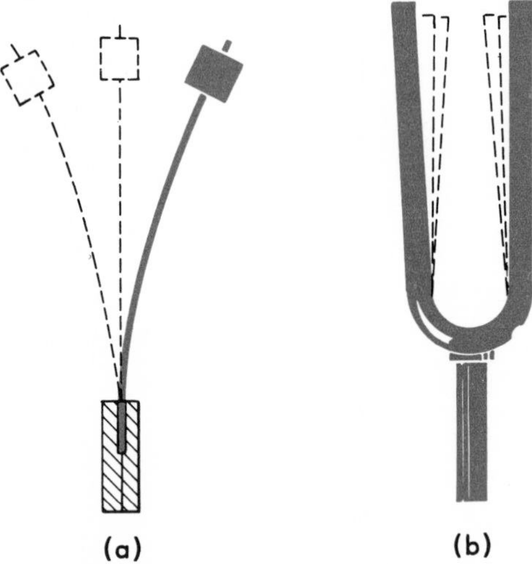

Fig. 17D. A weighted leaf spring, or reed, and a tuning fork vibrate with simple harmonic motion.

17.4. Vibrating Strips

If a strip of wood or metal is clamped tightly at one end, as shown in Fig. 17D(a), it may be set into a natural state of vibration. Pulled to one side and then released, the free end of the strip will move back and forth with simple harmonic motion. If the mass m clamped to the free end is increased, the frequency of vibration will decrease; whereas, if the strip is made stiffer either by increasing its thickness or decreasing its length, the frequency will increase.

Shown in diagram (b) is a tuning fork used by musicians to determine pitch. Striking one prong of a fork against some object sets both prongs vibrating simultaneously in opposite directions. The thinner the prongs of the fork, the lower is the frequency of vibration; the shorter the prongs of the fork, the higher is the frequency of vibration.

Besides being used as standards of pitch by musicians, tuning forks are used for scientific purposes. As scientific instruments they perform one very useful function of marking off short but equal intervals of time. A common fork used for this purpose has a frequency of 1000, $\nu = 1000$ Hz, and is frequently kept vibrating by means of an electrical circuit similar to that of a doorbell.

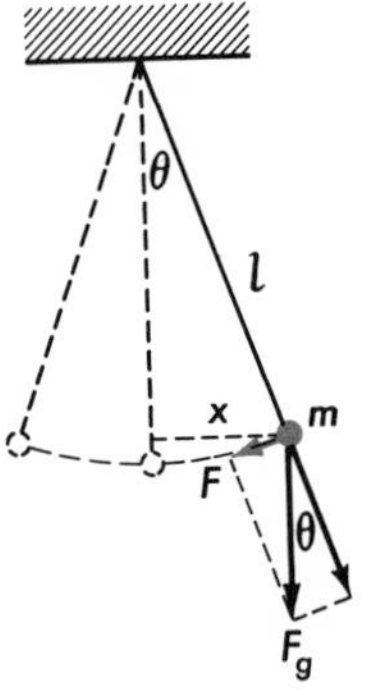

Fig. 17E. A pendulum bob executes simple harmonic motion along a curved path.

17.5. The Simple Pendulum

If a simple pendulum, as shown in Fig. 17E, is set swinging in an arc that is not too big (approximately 6°), its period T is given by the following formula:

$$T = 2\pi\sqrt{\frac{\ell}{g}} \tag{17k}$$

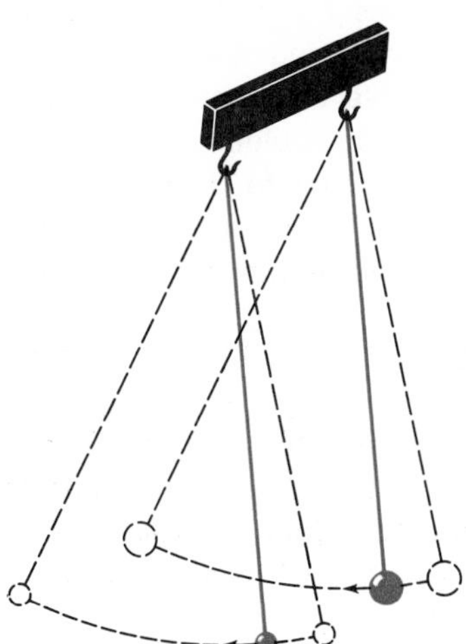

Fig. 17F. Two simple pendulums of the same length but different mass have the same period of vibration.

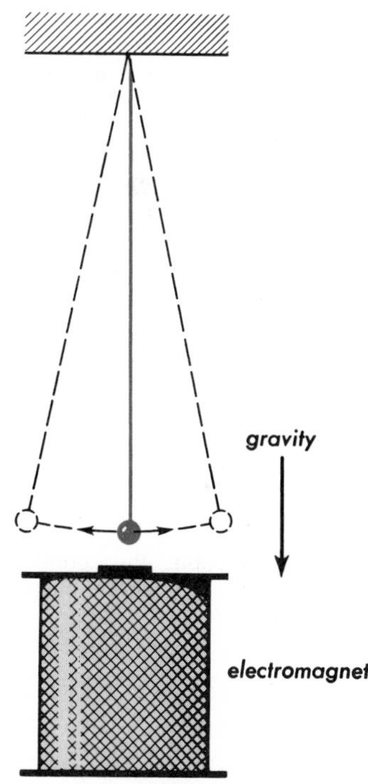

Fig. 17G. An increase in gravitational attraction, like the downward pull of the magnet, will shorten the period of a simple pendulum.

where T is the time of one complete vibration, ℓ is the length of the pendulum, and g is the acceleration due to gravity. If the angle of swing is much greater than 6°, the period will be slightly increased.

The statement can now be made that the bob of a simple pendulum moves along its arc with *simple periodic motion.* At the ends of its swing the velocity is momentarily zero and at the center is a maximum. The driving force which starts the bob at one end of its path and accelerates it until it reaches the center and then decelerates it, bringing it to rest at the other end, is the component F of the force of gravity F_g.

The fact that the mass of a pendulum bob does not appear in Eq.(17k) signifies that pendulums of equal length but different mass should have the same period T. Started together, and with small amplitudes, simple pendulums of different mass will swing in synchronism (see Fig. 17F).

The effect of the acceleration of gravity g on the period is illustrated in Fig. 17G. If the pull of gravity could be increased, the period of all pendulums would decrease, that is, they would swing faster. If gravity could be decreased, the periods would be greater, that is, they would swing more slowly. In the diagram

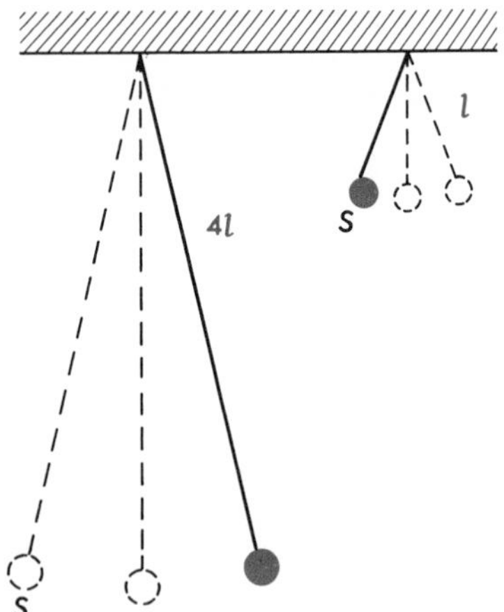

Fig. 17H. To double the period of a simple pendulum, the length must be increased fourfold.

the pull of gravity is imitated by means of an electromagnet. When the magnet is turned on, it pulls down on the iron bob and makes it swing more quickly.

The effect of the length ℓ on the period is shown in Fig. 17H. Two pendulums of lengths ℓ and 4ℓ are shown at the same instant a short time after having started simultaneously at their respective origins S. While the pendulum of length ℓ has made one complete swing, the pendulum of length 4ℓ has made only half a swing. This shows that to double the time of swing the length must be made four times as large. This is in agreement with Eq.(17k) in which the length occurs under the square-root sign.

A derivation of Eq.(17k) can be obtained from Fig. 17E as follows. The downward pull of gravity on the bob of mass m is F_g, and this has been resolved into two components, one parallel to the support ℓ and the other F perpendicular to it. Because of equal angles θ in the two right triangles and the theorem that corresponding sides of similar triangles are proportional, we may write

$$\frac{F}{F_g} = \frac{x}{\ell}$$

Since the force F accelerates the mass m in the direction opposite to x, and the weight F_g is equal to mg, substitution in the above proportionality gives

$$\frac{ma}{mg} = \frac{-x}{\ell} \qquad \text{or} \qquad -\frac{x}{a} = \frac{\ell}{g}$$

Substituting ℓ/g for $-x/a$ in Eq.(17i), we obtain

$$T = 2\pi\sqrt{\ell/g}$$

Example 2. Find the length of a simple pendulum that has a period of exactly 1 s.

Solution. The known quantities are $T = 1.0$ s and $g = 9.80$ m/s^2. Squaring both sides of Eq.(17k), and solving for the unknown ℓ, we obtain

$$\ell = \frac{T^2\, g}{4\pi^2}$$

and upon substituting the known quantities, we find

$$\ell = \frac{1.0^2 \times 9.80}{4 \times (3.142)^2}$$

$$\ell = 0.2482 \text{ m}$$

17.6. Sources of Waves

The motion of any material object may be considered as a source of waves. A board striking the water, the snap of a finger, or a bowed violin string are examples of this.

Suppose that the far end of a rope is fastened to a post, as shown in Fig. 17I, and that the other end (a), which is held in the hand, is given a sudden flip up and down. The disturbance sent out along the rope travels down the rope to the post, as shown, and is then reflected back again toward the hand. This kind of wave is called a *single-wave pulse.* If instead of a sudden pulse the hand is moved up and down with simple harmonic motion, a *train of waves,* like that shown in diagram (b), travels down the rope.

When the prongs of a tuning fork are made to vibrate, they set the surrounding air into periodic motions. Each prong periodically strikes the air molecules next to it and these molecules in turn strike others, thus transmitting the disturbance outward. Traveling outward in all directions, such periodic disturbances constitute sound waves.

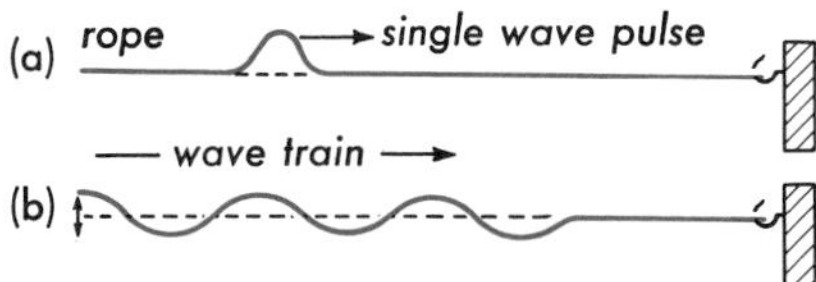

Fig. 17I. Examples of transverse waves sent out along a rope.

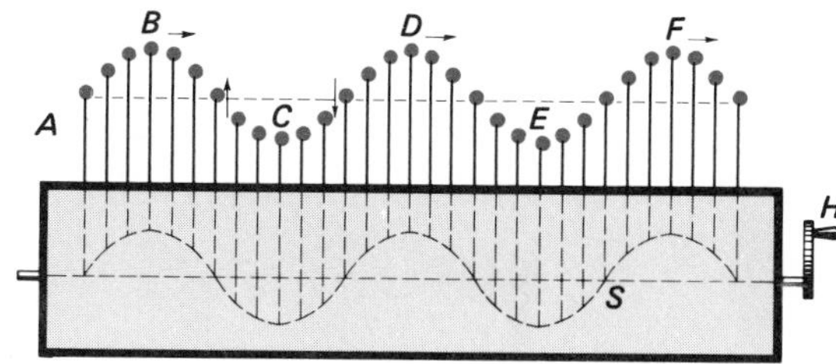

Fig. 17J. Diagram of a wave machine for demonstrating transverse waves.

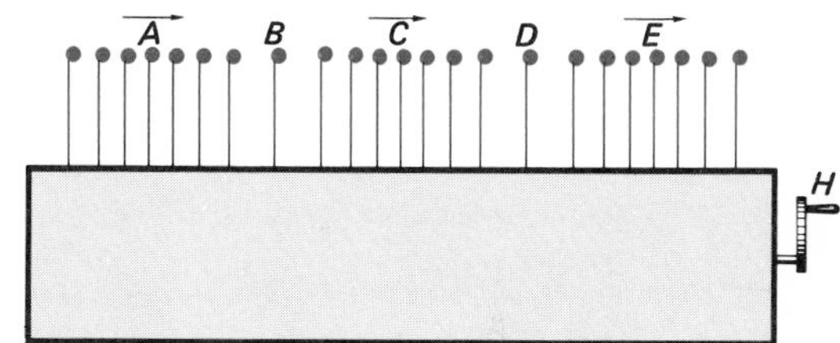

Fig. 17K. Diagram of a wave machine for demonstrating longitudinal waves.

17.7. Transverse Waves

Transverse waves are those in which each particle vibrates along a line perpendicular to the direction of propagation. Along any one line of travel all particles are vibrating in only one plane. Such waves are illustrated in Fig. 17J by means of a wave machine designed for this purpose. As the handle H is turned one way or the other, the small round balls at the top move up and down with simple harmonic motion. As they move up and down, each along its own line, the wave form ABCDEF will move to the right or to the left. Light is an example of transverse wave motion.

17.8. Longitudinal Waves

Longitudinal waves are those in which the vibrations of the particles are along straight lines parallel to the direction of propagation. This type of wave is illustrated in Fig. 17K by another wave machine. As the handle is turned, each small ball moves horizontally and in the plane of the page with simple harmonic motion. In so doing, the regions of rarefaction B and D and the regions of condensation A, C, and E move to the right, always keeping their same relative distances.

Sound waves in air are examples of longitudinal waves. Each air molecule vibrates back and forth about some equilibrium position as the wave train passes by.

17.9. Standing Waves

Nearly all sounds emanating from musical instruments are the result of standing waves. Standing waves may be produced in any substance, whether it is a solid, liquid, or gas, by two wave trains of the same frequency traveling in the same medium in opposite directions. One of the ways in which this is done is illustrated in Fig. 17L. One end of a rope is fastened to a post, and the other end, held taut, is moved up and down with simple harmonic motion. As the waves reach the fixed end of the rope, they are reflected back to meet succeeding waves just coming up. If the waves have just the right frequency, the rope will sustain both wave trains by dividing into sections as shown. The points L_1 to L_5, where the rope has a maximum up and down motion, are called *antinodes*, and the points of no motion halfway between are called *nodes.* The heavy line represents the rope at one instant and the other lines represent it at other instants. The entire wave section between two consecutive nodes is called a *loop.*

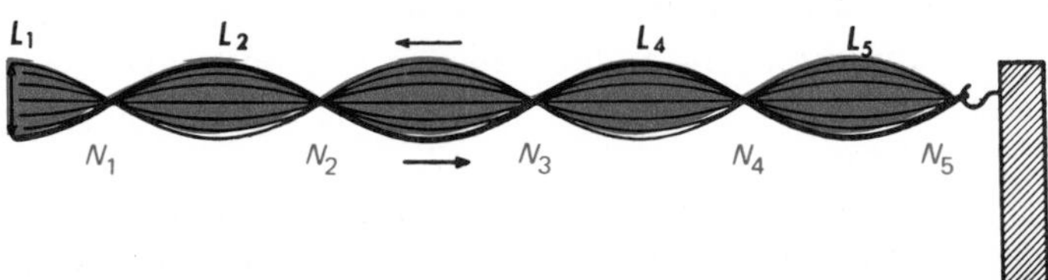

Fig. 17L. Standing waves produced by reflecting a train of transverse waves from the fixed end of a rope.

Standing waves with longitudinal vibrations may be demonstrated with a long flexible spring as shown in Fig. 17M(a). The right-hand end of the spring is fixed and the left-hand end is moved back and forth with simple harmonic motion. If the impressed vibration has the proper frequency, the waves traveling to the right, in meeting the reflected waves traveling to the left, set up *nodes* and *antinodes.* The nodes N correspond to points where there is no motion, and the antinodes L to points where the motion is a maximum. The dots in diagram (b) show the relative positions and motions of each individual coil of the spring at nine different times during one complete vibration. The dots at the nodes remain fixed at all times while those at the antinodes move back and forth as shown by the arrows in diagram (c). At one instant (3), compressions are formed at the odd-numbered nodes N_1, N_3, and N_5 and rarefactions at the even-numbered nodes N_2, N_4, and N_6. Half a vibration later (7), they change; the nodes of compression become nodes of rarefaction, and vice versa.

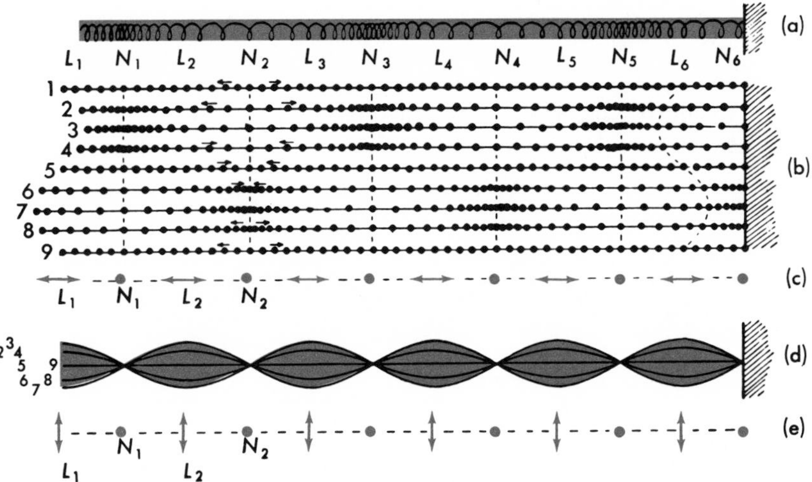

Fig. 17M. Illustration of standing waves as they are produced with (a) the longitudinal waves of a spring, (b) the longitudinal waves of sound in the air, and (d) the transverse waves of a rope; (c) and (e) indicate the direction of vibration at the antinodes.

A direct comparison of standing transverse and standing longitudinal waves is given by diagrams (b), (c), (d), and (e) in Fig. 17M. The numbers (1), (2), (3), etc., indicate the corresponding states in the vibrations of each. Diagram (c) indicates the amplitudes of the longitudinal motions at the antinodes of the spring, and diagram (e) the transverse motions of the antinodes of the rope.

It should be explained that the dots in diagram (b) also represent the motions of air molecules when sound waves are reflected from a flat wall, back on themselves, to produce standing waves. As we shall see in the next chapter, these are like the sustained vibrations of the air in an organ pipe, a flute, or some other musical wind instrument.

While sound waves in air are longitudinal vibrations, it is customary, for convenience only, to draw them as transverse waves. It is for this reason that the comparisons in Fig. 17M are made here. In the following two chapters, therefore, sound waves will usually be drawn as though they were transverse.

17.10. Wavelength

When a vibrating object sends out waves through a homogeneous medium, the waves travel with constant velocity. If the source vibrates with simple harmonic motion and the waves are transverse, they have the general appearance of the waves shown in Fig. 17N. The *wavelength* is defined as the distance between two similar points of any two consecutive waves, and is represented by the Greek letter lambda, λ. The distance between two consecutive wave crests, for example, is equal to one wavelength.

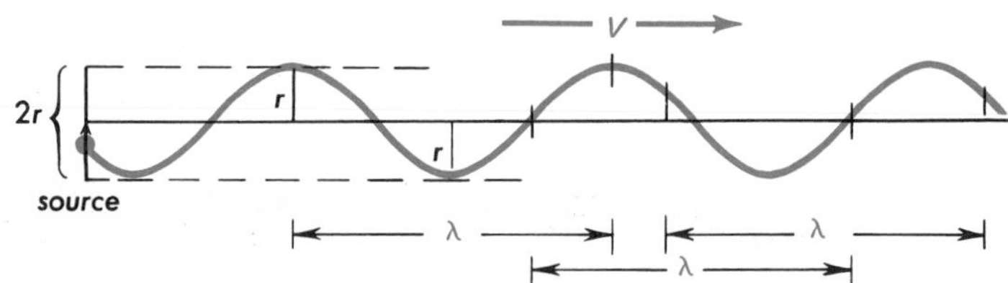

Fig. 17N. Illustration of the wavelength λ as the distance between corresponding points on two consecutive waves, and the amplitude r as the maximum displacement.

The amplitude of a wave is defined as the maximum value of the displacement. This is illustrated by r in Fig. 17N, the amplitude of the waves being proportional to the amplitude of the source. The frequency of a train of waves is defined as the number of waves passing any given point per second. This is equal to the frequency of the source and is usually designated by ν. It is customary to express frequency in *vibrations per second,* in *cycles per second,* or in *hertz.*

From the definitions of velocity, frequency, and wavelength, the following very simple relation exists among them:

$$V = \nu\lambda \qquad (17\ell)$$

The length of one wave, λ, times the number of waves per second, ν, equals the total distance traveled in 1 s, V.

Since the period is defined as the time required for one wave to pass by a given point, the relation between frequency and period given for vibrating sources in Eq.(17b) also applies to waves.

Example 3. If a train of waves moves along a rope with a speed of 100.0 m/s, and the wavelength is 20.0 m, what is (a) the frequency, and (b) the period of vibration?

Solution. The given quantities are $V = 100.0$ m/s and $\lambda = 20.0$ m. To find the answer to part (a) we use the wave equation, Eq.(17ℓ). Solving for the frequency ν, and substituting the known quantities, we find

$$\nu = \frac{V}{\lambda} = \frac{100.0 \text{ m/s}}{20.0 \text{ m}} = 5.0 \text{ Hz}$$

Using Eq.(17a), we find

$$T = \frac{1}{\nu} = \frac{1}{5.0} = 0.20 \text{ s}$$

17.11. Vibrational Energy

When an object or medium is set into vibration, energy is not only expended in setting up the vibration, but the motion of each element of mass constitutes a form of stored energy. As an illustration, consider the simple case of a mass vibrating back and forth between two identical springs as shown in Fig. 17O.

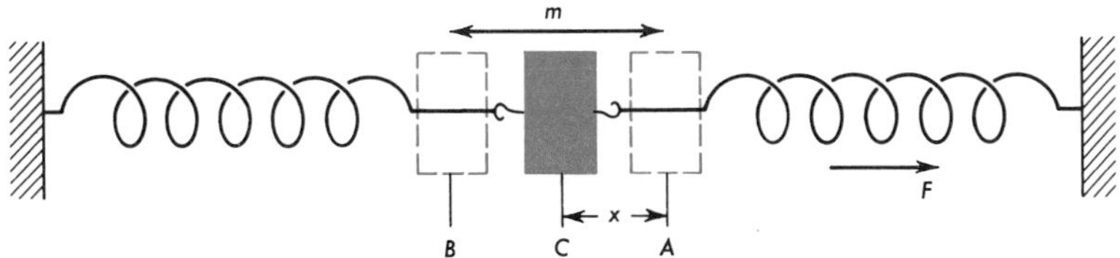

Fig. 17O. Illustration of a mass m between two identical springs, vibrating with simple harmonic motion.

Starting from its equilibrium position at C, a force F is applied to move the mass m a distance x to the right. Since the stretching and compressing of each spring obeys Hooke's law, the required

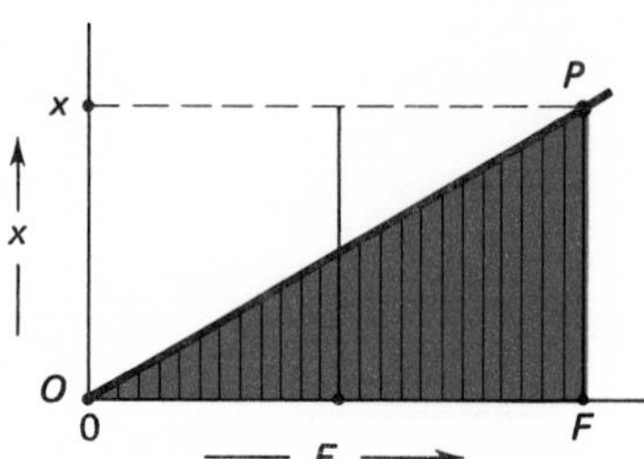

Fig. 17P. Graph showing Hooke's law and the work done in stretching and compressing of two identical springs.

force is proportional to the distance x. Hooke's law graphically leads to a straight line as shown in Fig. 17P, and analytically to the equation

$$F = kx \tag{17m}$$

Here k represents the constant for the two springs together.

The stretching of springs is treated in detail in Chap. 9. There it is shown that the work done in stretching a spring is given by

$$W = \tfrac{1}{2}Fx \tag{17n}$$

The value $\frac{1}{2}F$ is the average force, which multiplied by the distance through which it acts represents work done (see Fig. 9L).

If we now substitute the value of F from Eq.(17m) in Eq.(17n), we obtain

$$W = \tfrac{1}{2}kx^2 \tag{17o}$$

This work done is stored in the spring as potential energy, and when the mass is released it vibrates back and forth with simple harmonic motion.

As the mass passes through its equilibrium position C, the stored energy is all kinetic and we can write

$$E = \tfrac{1}{2}kr^2 = \tfrac{1}{2}mv^2 \tag{17p}$$

where r is the maximum displacement x, and is called the *amplitude*. This derived equation is basic in principle to all kinds of waves and vibrations, for it shows that *vibrational energy is proportional to the square of the amplitude.* Doubling the amplitude increases the vibrational energy fourfold:

$$E \propto (\text{amplitude})^2 \tag{17q}$$

problems

1. The amplitude of a particle executing simple harmonic motion is 15.0 mm, and the period is 0.220 s. Calculate (a) its maximum acceleration, and (b) its maximum speed.

2. The maximum speed of a particle moving with simple harmonic motion is 0.420 m/s. If its period of vibration is 0.50 s, what is (a) the amplitude, and (b) the maximum acceleration?

3. A particle moves with simple harmonic motion with an amplitude of 6.0 cm, and a period of 0.250 s. Find (a) its maximum speed, and (b) its maximum acceleration. [Ans. (a) 1.508 m/s, (b) 37.90 m/s^2.]

4. When a mass of 25.0 g is suspended from a spring as shown in Fig. 17C, it stretches the spring a distance of 12.0 cm. If the 25.0-g mass is now replaced by a mass of 100.0 g, and then set vibrating up and down, what is (a) the spring constant, and (b) the frequency of vibration?

5. When a 25.0-Kg mass is suspended from a spring as shown in Fig. 17C, the spring stretches 20.0 cm. An additional 25.0-Kg mass is then added to the lower end and the entire mass set vibrating up and down. Find (a) the spring constant, and (b) the frequency of vibration.

6. A mass of 0.350 Kg when fastened to the lower end of a lightweight spring and set vibrating up and down is found to have a frequency of 1.450 Hz. Calculate its frequency when the mass is decreased to 0.18 Kg. [Ans. 2.022 Hz.]

7.* A clock pendulum swings with a period of 1.21000 s at sea level where $g = 9.810\ m/s^2$. Find (a) its new period to seven significant figures when it is taken to a high mountain where $g = 9.800\ m/s^2$? (b) How many seconds will the clock lose in 24.0 h?

8. A simple pendulum is to have a period of 0.250 s. How long should it be if $g = 9.820\ m/s^2$?

9. A pendulum has a length of 50.80 cm where $g = 9.806\ m/s^2$. Find (a) its period and (b) its frequency to four significant figures. [Ans. (a) 1.430 s, (b) 0.6992 Hz.]

10.* A clock pendulum has a period of 1.2550 s where $g = 9.8150\ m/s^2$. (a) Find its new period to seven significant figures when it is taken to the top of a mountain where $g = 9.7950\ m/s^2$. (b) How many seconds will it lose in 24.0 h?

11. A train of waves moves along a cable with a wavelength of 0.420 m, and a velocity of 24.0 m/s. Find (a) the period, and (b) the frequency of the source.

12. A TV station broadcasts on a wavelength of 2.00 m. What is its frequency in MHz if the velocity of radio waves is 3.0×10^8 m/s? [Ans. 150 MHz.]

13. A radio station broadcasts on a frequency of 1056 MHz. What is the wavelength if the velocity of the waves is 3.0×10^8 m/s.

14. A mass of 5.0 Kg stretches a coil spring a total of 0.125 m. Find (a) the spring constant, and (b) the energy stored in the spring when it is stretched a distance of 0.250 m.

15. A spring hanging from the ceiling is stretched a distance of 8.0 cm when a mass of 12.50 Kg is suspended from its lower end. Calculate (a) the spring constant, and (b) the energy stored in joules. If the mass is pulled down, stretching the spring another 6.0 cm, and then released to vibrate up and down, find (c) the period and (d) the maximum velocity. [Ans. (a) 1531 N/m, (b) 4.90 J, (c) 0.568 s, (d) 2.711 m/s.]

18 Sound: its transmission and detection

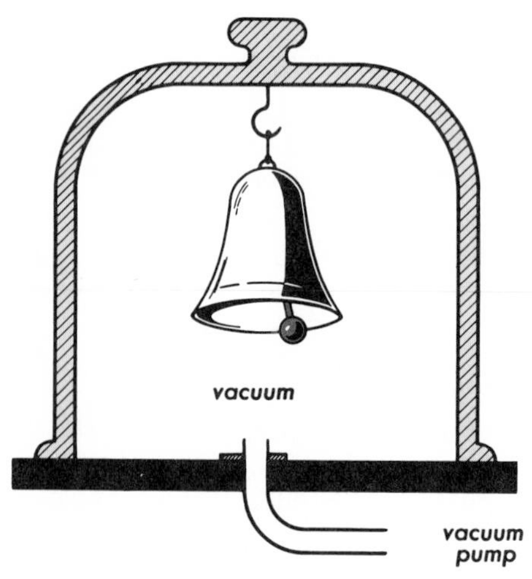

Fig. 18A. A bell ringing in a vacuum cannot be heard.

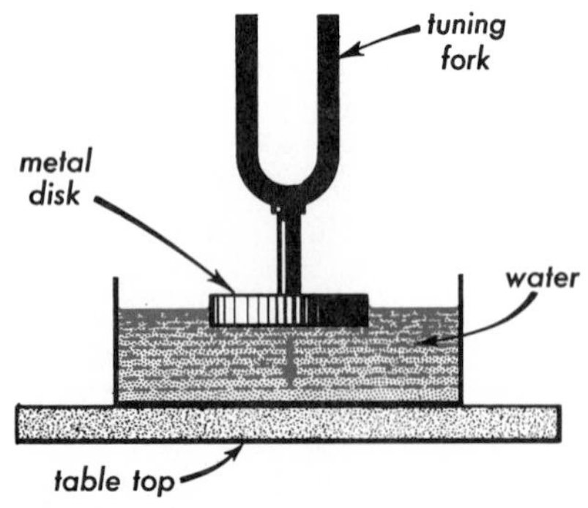

Fig. 18B. Demonstration of sound waves traveling through water.

Our present knowledge and treatment of *sound* may be divided into three subheadings: *sources, transmission,* and *detection.* Sources of sounds are too numerous to mention, but we can classify all sounds as either *noises* or *musical sounds.*

This chapter is confined principally to the transmission of sound and its *speed of travel, reflection, refraction,* and *intensity.* For sound to be transmitted from one place to another, a material medium (solid, liquid, or gas) is required to transport the waves. The medium itself is not transported from source to receiver, but only the waves themselves.

18.1. Sound Transmission

That sound is transmitted by air, or any other gas, may be demonstrated by placing a small bell in an evacuated jar (Fig. 18A). As the air is slowly removed from the jar, the ringing of the bell grows fainter and fainter until, when a good vacuum is obtained, no sound can be heard. As soon as the air is admitted, however, the ringing becomes clearly audible again. The vibrating bell strikes air molecules, knocking them away from the metal surface. These fast-moving molecules strike the adjacent air molecules and they in turn strike others. Upon reaching the side of the jar, the glass walls are periodically bombarded by the molecules and set vibrating. The walls in turn set the outside air vibrating. Arriving at the observer's ear, the disturbance strikes the eardrum, setting it into motion. Without air to transmit the vibrations from the bell to the inside surface of the glass jar, no sound could ever leave the jar.

The transmission of sound by liquids may be illustrated by an experiment shown in Fig. 18B. A tuning fork with a disk attached to its base is set vibrating and then touched against the surface of a dish of water. The vibrations of the fork and disk travel through the water to the bottom of the dish and to the table top. The table top itself is set into vibration with the same frequency as the fork, thus acting like a *sounding board* to make the sound louder.

The transmission of sound by solids is illustrated in Fig. 18C. A vibrating tuning fork is brought into contact with the end of a long wooden rod. The longitudinal vibrations travel down the length of the rod, which causes the hollow wooden box at the other end to vibrate. Sound is clearly heard coming from the box.

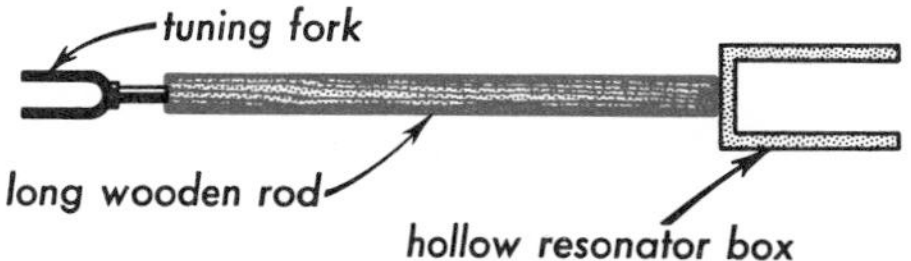

Fig. 18C. Demonstration of sound waves traveling through wood.

Sound waves, whether they travel through solids, liquids, or gases, are longitudinal in character. In Fig. 18D the prongs of a tuning fork are shown vibrating back and forth with simple harmonic motion. By collisions with air molecules, each one sends out longitudinal waves through the atmosphere.

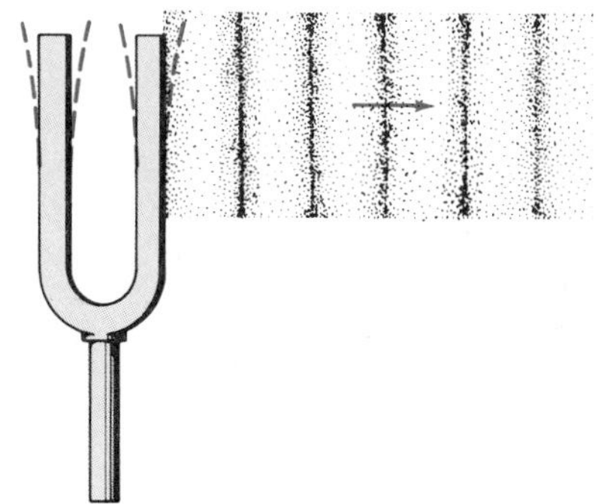

Fig. 18D. Sound waves are longitudinal waves.

18.2. Speed of Sound

Although light and sound both travel with a finite speed, the speed of light is so great in comparison that an instantaneous flash may be regarded as taking no time to travel many miles. When we see the light of a distant lightning flash and hear the thunder later, we know that the difference in time is due to the relatively low speed of sound. Knowing that sound requires 5 s to travel 1 mi, the distance of a passing thunderstorm can be noted by the second hand of a watch. Similarly, when a distant train starts up and we watch for the first puff of smoke as it starts out, the arrival of the accompanying sound is not heard until an appreciable time afterward.

The earliest successful attempts to measure the speed of sound in air were made in 1640 by Marin Mersenne, a French physicist, and in 1656 by Giovanni Borelli and Vincenzo Viviani, Italian physicists. Since that time many experimenters have improved upon these earliest measurements by using various different methods and devices. The most recent and probably the most accurate measurements are those made in 1934 by Miller.* With coast defense guns as a source of sound and a set of receivers located at certain distances apart, very accurate speed determinations were made. The results gave a speed of 331 m/s at a temperature of 0°C. This is equivalent to 1192 Km/h, or 741 mi/h.

As a general rule, sound travels faster in solids and liquids than it does in gases. This is illustrated by the measured speeds for a few common substances given in Table 18A.

***Dayton C. Miller (1866–1940), American physicist, noted for his experiments on the quality of musical sounds and on the ether drift. He collected and had in his possession the largest collection of flutes in the world. These instruments he turned over to the Smithsonian Institute in Washington, D.C., where they are now on exhibit. A member of the National Academy of Sciences, and one-time president of the American Physical Society, he was awarded the Elliott Cresson Medal and the Cleveland Distinguished Service Medal.**

TABLE 18A
Speed of sound in different substances

Substance	*Speed* (m/s)
Air (at 0°C)	331
Carbon dioxide	258
Carbon monoxide	337
Hydrogen	1,269
Alcohol	1,213
Benzine	1,166
Turpentine	1,326
Water	1,435
Aluminum	5,104
Copper	3,560
Glass	5,500
Iron	5,130
Ivory	3,013
Nickel	4,973
Oak (w/grain)	3,850

It is well known that the temperature has a small but measurable effect upon the speed of sound. For each degree centigrade rise in temperature, the speed in air increases by 61 cm/s. Written as an equation,

$$V = V_0 + 0.610t \tag{18a}$$

centigrade

where V_0 is the speed in m/s at 0°C, and t is the temperature in °C.

Example 1. An explosion in a factory is observed in a small midwestern town 15.0 Km away. If it is winter and the temperature is −40°C, (a) what is the speed of the sound, and (b) how long does it take the sound to reach the city?

Solution. The given quantities are $x = 15{,}000$ m and $t = -40$°C. To find the speed of sound we use Eq.(18a), and substitute the temperature −40°C:

$$V = 331 + 0.610\ (-40)$$

$$V = 331 - 24.4 = 306.6 \text{ m/s}$$

Using Eq.(1e), and solving for the time t, we obtain upon substitution

$$t = \frac{x}{v} = \frac{15{,}000 \text{ m}}{306.6 \text{ m/s}} = 48.9 \text{ s}$$

18.3. Pitch

The pitch of a musical note refers to its position on a musical scale, and is determined by the frequency of the sound impulses sent out by the vibrating source. The dependence of pitch upon frequency can be demonstrated in many ways. Diagram (a) of Fig. 18E represents a toothed wheel (called Savart's wheel) rotating at high speed. A small card held against the teeth is set into vibration, giving out a musical note. As the wheel slows down, the vibration frequency of the card decreases and the note lowers in pitch.

Diagram (b) is a siren similar to those commonly used as factory whistles. The energy as well as the sound is derived from

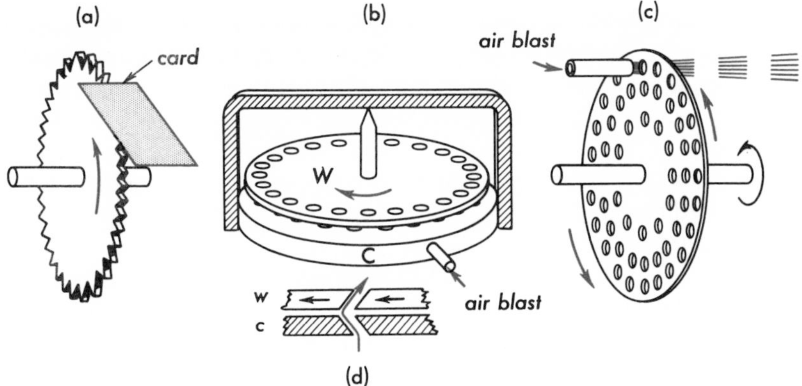

Fig. 18E. Sound demonstrations illustrating the relation between pitch and frequency.

compressed air which is blown through small holes in the hollow container C. The air issuing from these jets passes through similar holes in a rotating disk W. With the holes drilled at an angle as shown in detail in (d), the air blasts from the stationary holes below exert a force on one side of the holes in W, causing the disk to turn. As the disk turns, each blast of air is momentarily cut off until another hole arrives just above it. The intermittent pulses of air issuing from the disk give rise to a musical note.

Diagram (c) in Fig. 18E represents a siren in which a single blast of air is interrupted by a rotating disk containing several rings of holes. Detailed experiments with many musically trained and untrained observers alike show that pitch and frequency are not identical.

Pitch is a *subjective* measurement and is therefore a sensory magnitude depending upon the individual, while frequency is a *physical* measurement of the number of vibrations per second. As the intensity of a pure tone of 300 Hz is increased, for example, it appears to most observers to change in quality and at the same time to decrease slightly in pitch. Conversely, at a high frequency, an increase in the intensity seems to increase the pitch.

18.4. Detection of Sound

By far the most important instrument by which sound is detected is the ear. This hearing mechanism, which is sensitive to very faint as well as loud sounds and to very high as well as low frequencies, is treated in detail in Sec. 18.8.

Various electrical devices, commonly called microphones, have been invented for detecting sound waves and transforming them into varying electric currents. These currents may then be amplified, transmitted long or short distances, and then reconverted into sound. Sometimes they are fed into an oscilloscope for a study of wave motion, a "cutting head" for recording a light source for sound recording on film, or an electromagnet for recording on wire or tape. Some of these devices are considered in detail in later chapters.

Sound may also be detected by a rather interesting but impractical device known as the sensitive flame. This detector, as illustrated in Fig 18F, consists of a tall, thin gas flame produced by gas issuing from a small nozzle. As sound waves pass by the tip of the nozzle, the gas stream is disturbed and the flame becomes unstable and drops in height. This action is particularly noticeable with high-pitched sounds like those from a blowing whistle, or those from a jingling bunch of keys.

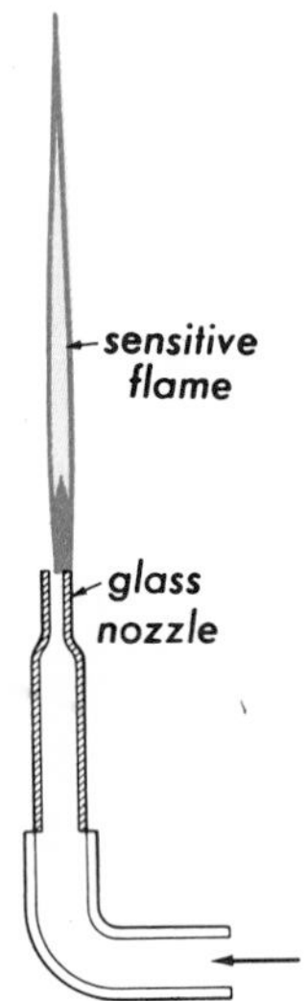

Fig. 18F. Diagram of a gas flame, sensitive to high-pitched sound waves. As the waves pass the tip of the nozzle, the flame dips down.

18.5. Reflection of Sound

The reflection of sound waves may be demonstrated in various ways. One arrangement is shown in Fig. 18G in which a Galton whistle sounding a high-pitched note acts as a source of sound and a sensitive flame as the receiver. A solid screen between the two casts a "sound shadow," thus permitting only the reflected waves from the wall of the room to reach it.

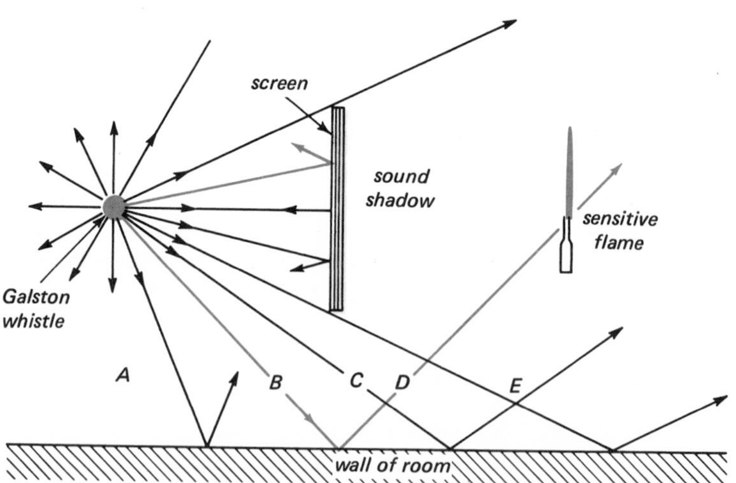

Fig. 18G. Experiment demonstrating the reflection of sound waves from the wall of a room.

When the whistle, blown by compressed air, is sounded continuously, the flame will remain unstable. If, under these conditions, the experimenter walks beside the wall through the sound path, the flame will be quite unstable when he reaches A, C, or E, but will burn smoothly when he intercepts the beam at B or D.

Sound shadows of the kind shown in this experiment are characteristic of high-pitched notes only and demonstrate that short waves tend to travel in straight lines. The longer waves of low-pitched sounds, however, tend to bend around corners. This latter effect, known as *diffraction,* is quite noticeable where a carillon of large bells is being played. On walking around the corner of a nearby building, one notices that the sharp cutoff in the intensity of the high-pitched bells is quite marked, while the low-pitched bells continue in good strength. It should be pointed out that high-pitched notes also show diffraction, but to a lesser degree. This phenomenon is due to the wave nature of sound, and will be explained in principle in the case of light waves in another chapter.

18.6. Refraction of Sound Waves

The bending of sound waves in layers of air at different temperatures is called *refraction.* The phenomenon, which can be observed in various ways, is due to the greater speed of sound in warm air than in cold (see Sec. 18.2).

A good illustration is found in the frequent observation, while boating on a lake or river, of being able to hear the music from a quite distant radio or phonograph at night but not in the daytime. The reason for this is shown in Fig. 18H. At night, the air near the water is colder than it is higher up, so that the higher speed in the warmer air bends the waves back down. During the day, the air close to the water is warmer and the waves bend up away from the water as shown.

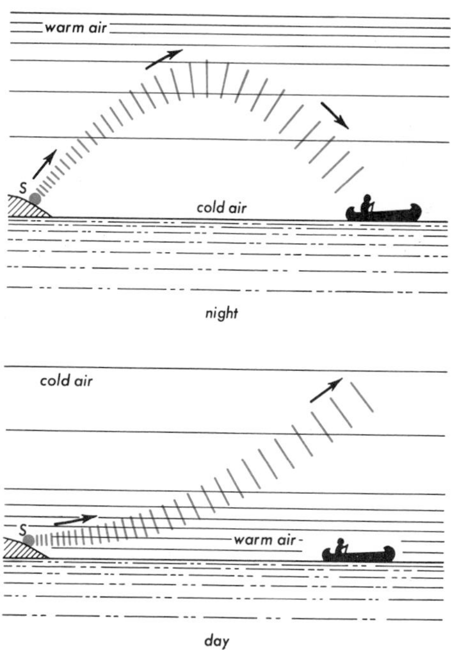

Fig. 18H. The higher velocity of sound waves in warm air causes sound waves to be refracted down at night and up in the daytime.

Recent experiments of this kind have been performed with the very loud sounds from big guns. Sound waves refracted back from high up in the stratosphere indicate with some degree of certainty the existence of very warm layers of air at altitudes of 40 to 64 Km. Refraction in such cases as this is similar to reflection from a mirror surface, since the waves travel in more or less straight lines, going up and back, but bend over when they enter, more or less abruptly, a warmer layer.

18.7. Intensity of Sound

There are three fundamental characteristics of all sounds:

Objective	Subjective
intensity	loudness
frequency	pitch
wave form	tone quality

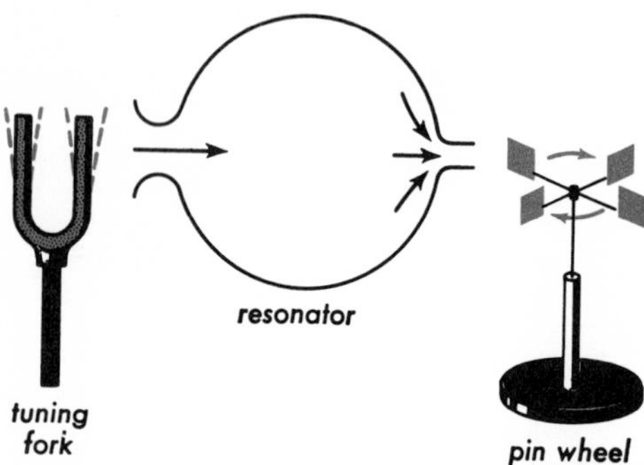

Fig. 18I. A pin wheel may be set rotating by sound waves from a tuning fork, demonstrating that sound waves have energy.

The intensity of sound is characterized by its loudness and is measured scientifically by the amount of energy in a given volume of the space through which the sound is traveling. In other words, sound waves constitute a flow of energy through matter. This may be demonstrated by an experiment, arranged as shown in Fig. 18I. A vibrating tuning fork is placed near one opening at a Helmholtz* resonator, and a very lightly constructed pinwheel is placed near the other. Air pulses from the vibrating prongs of the fork traveling through the resonator come out reinforced at the other opening and strike the vanes of the pinwheel. When the fork is removed the pinwheel stops rotating. *Loudness is a subjective measurement of sound power and is therefore a sensory magnitude. Intensity, on the other hand, is an objective measurement of the sound power being delivered.*

One method of specifying the intensity of a sound is to state the amount of energy flowing through unit area per second. Since the rate of flow of energy in most common sounds is extremely small, the ordinary unit of power, the *watt,* is too large to be practical. Consequently, a unit one million times smaller, the *microwatt* (μW), is used (see Fig. 18J):

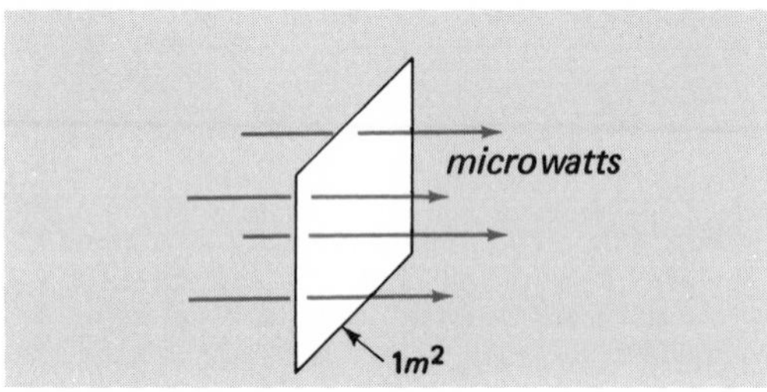

Fig. 18J. Sound intensity is measured in microwatts flowing through 1 m^2 of area.

$$\begin{aligned} 1 \text{ microwatt} &= 10^{-6} \text{ watt} \\ 1 \text{ microwatt} &= 10^{-6} \text{ joules/second} \end{aligned} \tag{18b}$$

Sound intensity is defined as the power flowing through one square meter of area, taken normal to the direction of the waves. A common method of specifying intensity is to compare the power in a given sound with the power in another. *When the power in one sound is ten times that in another, the ratio of intensity is said to be 1 bel.* The *bel* is so called in honor of Alexander Graham Bell, the inventor of the electric telephone. According to this definition, an intensity scale in bels is a logarithmic scale of power:

$$B = \log_{10} \frac{P_1}{P_2} \tag{18c}$$

***B* in bels**

***Hermann Helmholtz (1821–1894), noted German physicist, who during his lifetime made outstanding contributions to the subjects of light, sound, and electricity. Probably his greatest contribution was his explanation of tone quality in musical notes. He demonstrated that quality depends upon the number and intensity of the overtones or harmonics present in the musical tone.**

where P_1 is the intensity, or power, of one sound and P_2 that of another. The following tabulation will illustrate this equation.

The numbers at the right are just the logarithms of those at the left. According to these figures, a sound with 1000 times the power of another is 3 bels louder.

Because the *bel* represents large differences in intensity, a smaller unit, the *decibel* (db), has been introduced and used by telephone and radio engineers, as well as by physicians (ear specialists). According to this smaller unit, the bel is divided into ten equal ratios by the following equation:

$$b = 10 \log \frac{P_1}{P_2} \qquad (18d)$$

b in decibels

Table 18C will illustrate specific values from this equation. Each power ratio in the left column is 26% greater than the preceding value. Because such a change is just detectable by the human ear, the decibel is considered a practical unit. The sounds from several common sources are compared in different units in Table 18D.

Example 2. The sound intensity received from a nearby jet plane is 12.6 μW/m², and that from another plane some distance away is 0.45 μW/m². Find the relative loudness of the two in decibels.
Solution. The given quantities are $P_1 = 12.60\ \mu\text{W/m}^2$ and $P_2 = 0.450\ \mu\text{W/m}^2$. By direct substitution in Eq.(18d), we obtain

$$b = 10 \log_{10} \frac{12.6}{0.45}$$

$$b = 10 \log_{10} 28.0$$

Using the log table in Appendix IX we look up the mantissa for 28.0 and find 4472. Since the characteristic of a common logarithm of a number greater than 1 is one less than the number of integral figures, and 28 has two integral figures, we obtain

$$b = 10 \times 1.4472$$

to four figures $\qquad b = 14.47$ db

TABLE 18B
Sound intensity scale in bels

Relative Power *(P_1/P_2)*	*Relative Intensity* *(bels)*
1	0
10	1
100	2
1000	3
10000	4

TABLE 18C
Sound intensity scale in decibels

Relative power *(P_1/P_2)*	*Relative intensity* *(b)*
1.00	0
1.26	1
1.58	2
2.00	3
2.51	4
3.16	5
3.98	6
5.01	7
6.31	8
7.94	9
10.00	10

TABLE 18D
Common sound levels

	Intensity *(μW/m²)*	*Sound level* *(B)*	*Sound level* *(b)*
Threshold of hearing	10^{-6}	0	0
Rustling leaves	10^{-4}	2	20
Talking (at 3 ft)	10^{-2}	4	40
Noisy office or store	1	6	60
Subway car	10^{4}	10	100
Threshold of pain	10^{6}	12	120

18.8. Human Audiogram

An audiogram for the normal human ear is given in Fig. 18K. The lower curve gives the faintest sounds that can be heard, and the upper curve the loudest that can be heard without pain. It will be noted that the ear is most sensitive to frequencies between 2000 and 4000 Hz and that the sensitivity diminishes rapidly at higher and lower frequencies.

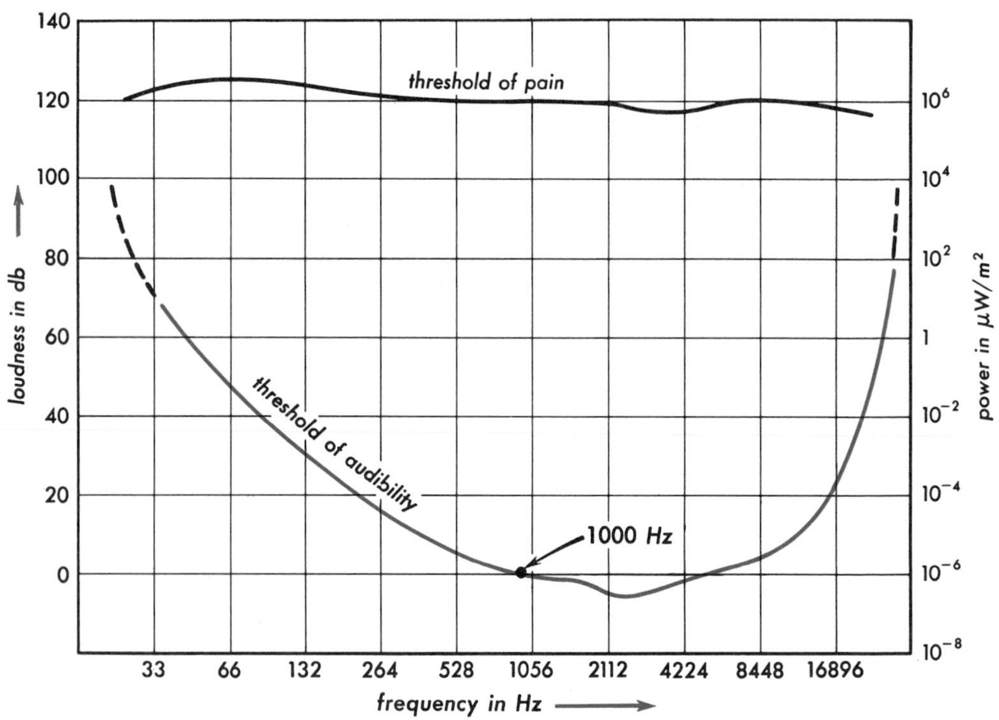

Fig. 18K. Audiogram of the average human being, showing the threshold of hearing for different frequencies of sound.

As a practical matter, sound experts have adopted as a zero level of sound intensity, $P_0 = 10^{-6}$ μW/m² at a frequency of 1000 Hz. This is the limit of audibility of the average human being for a 1000 Hz note.

To see how intensity affects the frequency limits of audibility, consider the horizontal line at 20 db. At this intensity level, with a flow of energy 100 times that necessary to hear the faintest 1000 Hz note, frequencies below about 200 Hz and above 15,000 Hz cannot be heard. At 40 db with a flow of energy 10,000 times the threshold of audibility at 1000 Hz, the lowest frequency to be heard is about 100 Hz, whereas the upper limit may be as high as 20,000 Hz.

The amplitude of the sound waves at the threshold of audibility at 1000 Hz has been determined and found to be about 1×10^{-10} m. This is about the diameter of a hydrogen atom and gives some idea of the enormous sensitivity of the human ear. When a sound becomes so loud that it is painful to the ear, the amplitude is of the order of 1–2 mm.

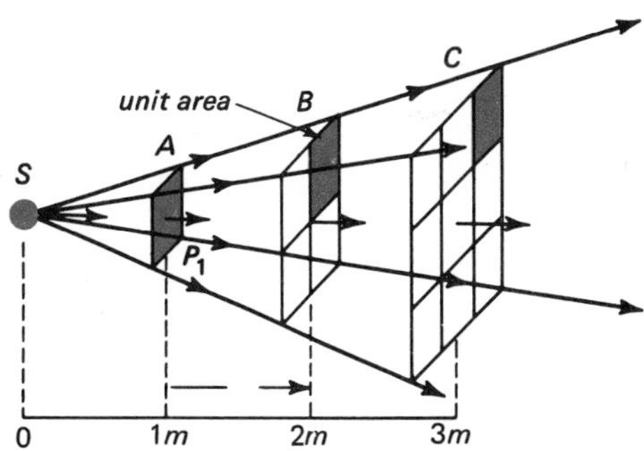

Fig. 18L. Illustration of the inverse square law.

18.9. Inverse Square Law

Theory indicates, and experiments prove, that the intensity of sound is inversely proportional to the square of the distance from the source. As an equation,

$$\frac{P_1}{P_2} = \frac{d_2^2}{d_1^2} \tag{18e}$$

where P_1 and P_2 are the intensities of the same sound at the two different distances d_1 and d_2, respectively. This is called the *inverse square law.*

If S in Fig. 18L represents a source of sound, the waves travel outward in straight lines. Whatever sound energy flows through area *A* at 1 m, the same energy will flow through area *B* at 2 m, and area *C* at 3 m. Since these areas have the ratios 1:4:9, the energy flow per second, through unit area at each distance, will be P_1, $\frac{1}{4}P_1$, and $\frac{1}{9}P_1$, respectively.

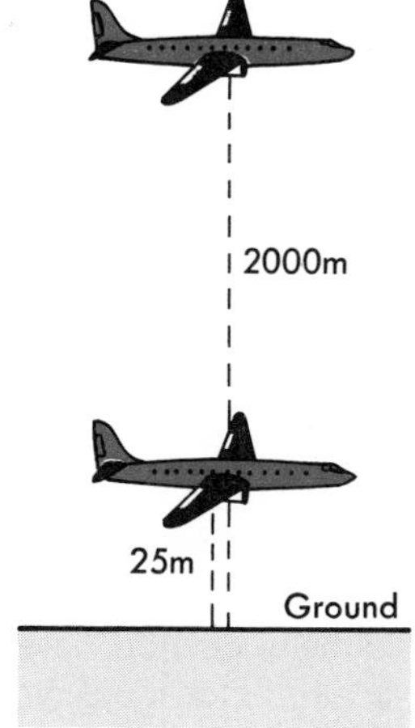

Fig. 18M. Diagram for the solution to Example 3.

Example 3. The noise from an airplane engine 25.0 m from an observer is found to have an intensity of 45.0 db. What will be the intensity in decibels when the plane flies overhead at an altitude of 2.0 Km? See Fig. 18M.

Solution. The given quantities are $P_1 = 45.0$ db, $d_1 = 25.0$ m, and $d_2 = 2{,}000$ Km. We first substitute the distance in Eq.(18e) to find the ratio of the powers as follows:

$$\frac{P_1}{P_2} = \frac{d_2^2}{d_1^2} = \frac{(2000 \text{ m})^2}{(25 \text{ m})^2} = 6400$$

Using the log table in Appendix IX we look up the mantissa for 6400 and find 8062. Since the number 6400 has four integral figures, the characteristic is one less, or 3, and substituting in Eq.(18d), we obtain

$$b = 10 \log_{10} 6400$$

$$b = 10 \times 3.8062$$

which, to four significant figures, is

$$b = 38.06 \text{ db}$$

Subtracting this value from the intensity of 45.0 db at 25.0 m gives

$$45.0 - 38.06 = 6.94 \text{ db}$$

problems

1. On a hot day in the middle of July the temperature is 42°C. Find the speed of sound.

2. What is the speed of sound at the south polar region of the earth when the temperature is −60°F?

3. What is the speed of sound in air on a hot day when the temperature is 113°F? [Ans. 358.4 m/s.]

4. To an observer standing in front of a flight of steps, a sharp clap of the hands will produce a sound that is reflected back to the observer from each step. If the step treads are 30.0 cm deep, and the temperature is 27°C, find (a) the speed of sound, and (b) the frequency of the sound heard by the observer.

5. A sharp clap of the hands in front of a flight of steps will produce a pitched note as the result of the reflection from each individual step. If the step treads are 25.0 cm deep, and the temperature is 32°C, find (a) the speed of sound, and (b) the pitch of the reflected sound.

6. If one sound is 15.0 db louder than another, what are their relative powers? [Ans. 31.62 to 1.]

7. If one sound is 46.0 db louder than another, what are their relative powers? [Ans. 39,810 to 1.]

8. A low pitched note of 66.0 Hz is on the threshhold of hearing for a man with average hearing capabilities. If a sound of this same power is produced at 528 Hz, what would be its intensity in db. Using Fig. 18K, give your answer to two significant figures. [Ans. 42 db.]

9. An observer hears a 1000 cycle note at an intensity of 60.0 db. What would be this observer's low and high frequency threshholds if other frequencies with the same absolute power were sounded? Use Fig. 18K and give your two answers to one significant figure. [Ans. 40 Hz and 20,000 Hz.]

10. Three meters from a radio the average sound level is found by experiment to be 6.40×10^{-2} μW/m^2. What would the intensity be at a distance of 12.0 m? [Ans. 1.60×10^{-3} μW/m^2.]

11. When a jet plane is flying at an elevation of 1000 m the sound level on the ground is 4.0 db. What would be the intensity on the ground when its elevation is as low as 50.0 m? [Ans. 30.0 db.]

12. At the ground the noise level coming from a jet engine 100.0 m overhead is recorded at 78.0 db. What wil be its recorded intensity when it flies overhead at 1200 m. See Fig. 18M. [Ans. 56.4 db.]

13. The volume level of an outdoor public address system is adjusted to 55.0 db for people 5.0 m away. What will be its intensity for people at a distance of 45.0 m? [Ans. 35.9 db.]

14. The sound level from a radio playing classical music is adjusted to 40.0 db at a distance of 54.0 m. Find its intensity for people in the audience only 4.50 m away. [Ans. 28.42 db.]

19 Resonance, beats, Doppler effect, and interference

When sound waves from one or more sources fall on the ears of an observer the resultant sound that is heard depends upon many factors. The source of sound or the observer may be moving, two or more sources may have the same or different frequencies, or one train of waves may interfere with another. These are the subjects to be considered in this chapter.

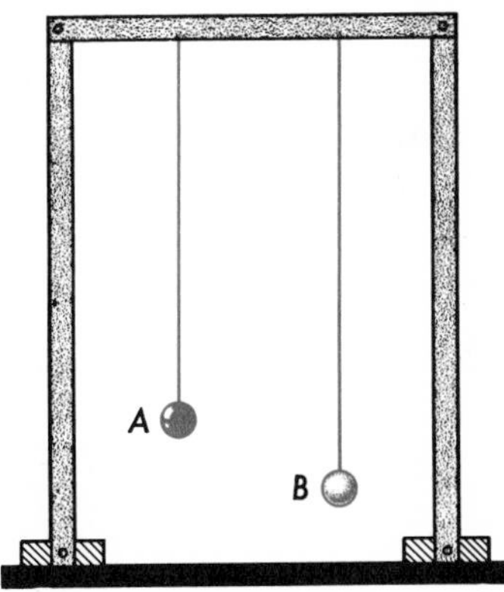

Fig. 19A. A demonstration of resonance can be performed with two pendulums.

19.1. Resonance

An experimental demonstration of resonance is easily set up, as shown in Fig. 19A. Two simple pendulums are suspended from a flexible support. One, A, has a heavy bob made of metal, and the other, B, a bob made of wood.

The heavy bob A is pulled to one side and released to swing freely. The horizontal support responds to the motion and, in swaying back and forth in step with A, acts to set the other pendulum swinging. The response of pendulum B to these forced vibrations depends upon the relative lengths of the two pendulums. If there is considerable difference in their lengths, the response is ever so slight, and the closer they are to the same length the greater is the response.

When A and B have the same length, their natural periods become equal, and B responds to the swaying support and swings with a large amplitude. It responds in sympathy, or resonance, to the driving pendulum A.

If two violin strings are tuned to the same frequency and one is set vibrating, the other stationed some distance away will soon pick up the vibrations and give out the same note. This too is a case of resonance, a phenomenon which occurs only if two objects have the same natural frequency of vibration.

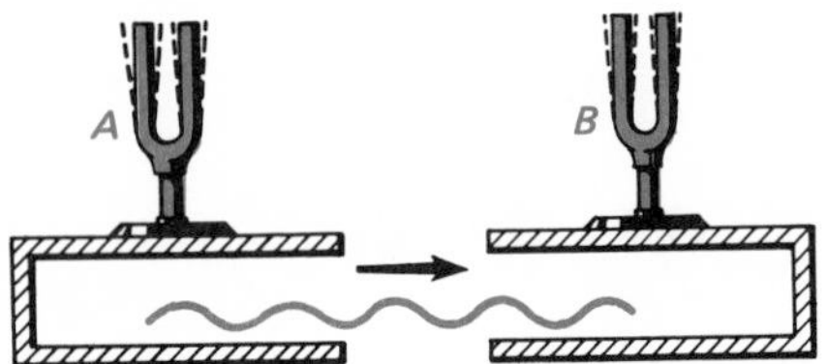

Fig. 19B. Tuning forks mounted on resonator boxes for demonstrating resonance.

Another experimental demonstration of resonance is illustrated in Fig. 19B. Two tuning forks with exactly the same pitch are mounted on separate hollow boxes as shown. Fork A is first set vibrating for a moment and then stopped by touching the prongs with the fingers. Fork B will then be found vibrating. If we take into account the hollow boxes, whose purpose it is to act as sounding boards and thus intensify the sound, we find that the explanation is quite simple. Each sound pulse that emerges from the box with each vibration of fork A passes into the other box, pushing out the sides at just the right time to make the prongs of fork B move in the proper direction.

By singing a sustained note directly at the strings of a piano, and then listening in all possible quietness, one of the strings can be heard faintly sounding forth with sympathetic vibrations of the same frequency.

Occasionally it has been shown in a motion picture that by singing a sustained note into a drinking glass or vase, sympathetic vibrations will cause it to break or explode. This is a hoax has never been demonstrated in any laboratory. Sound waves contain too little energy to do this.

19.2. Beat Notes

When two notes of slightly different pitch are sounded at the same time, beats are heard. This phenomenon is used in organ pipes to produce the familiar vibrato effect. Two pipes tuned to slightly different frequencies are used for every note.

The phenomenon of beats may be demonstrated by two tuning forks mounted as shown in Fig. 19B. One fork is made slightly out of tune with the other by looping rubber bands *tightly* around the prongs. If the two forks are sounded simultaneously, the intensity of the sound rises and falls periodically. This is illustrated by means of vibration graphs as shown in Fig. 19C. The upper curve

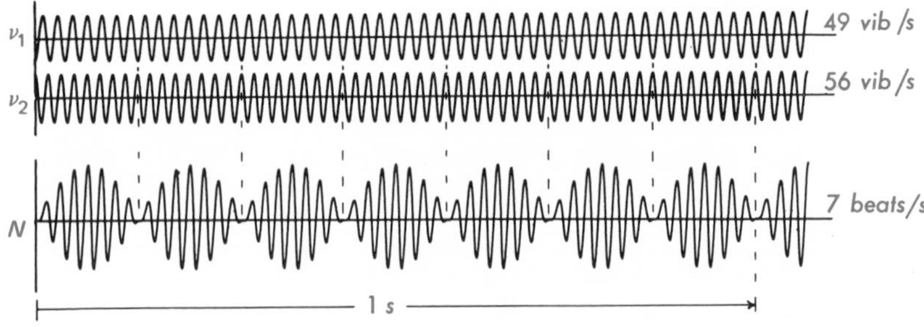

Fig. 19C. Wave graphs illustrating how beat notes are produced by two different frequencies.

represents the sound vibrations arriving at the ear from one fork, and the second curve the vibrations from the other. Both waves arriving at the ear are first in phase, i.e., in step with each other, then out of phase, then in phase, then out of phase, etc.

The resultant action of these two waves on the eardrum is represented by the third line. When the waves are in phase, the resultant has a large amplitude equal to the sum of the amplitudes of the two. When they are out of phase the amplitude becomes zero. The number of beats per second, N, is determined by the difference between ν_2 and ν_1, the respective frequencies of the two sources producing the sound:

$$\text{beat frequency } N = \nu_2 - \nu_1 \tag{19a}$$

When the beat frequency lies between about 1 and 6 vib/s, the ear perceives a single intertone halfway between the two sounded, but periodically waxing and waning in intensity. As the beat frequency increases, the smooth rise and fall gives way to a succession of pulses, then to a sensation of roughness, and finally to two clearly perceived tones.

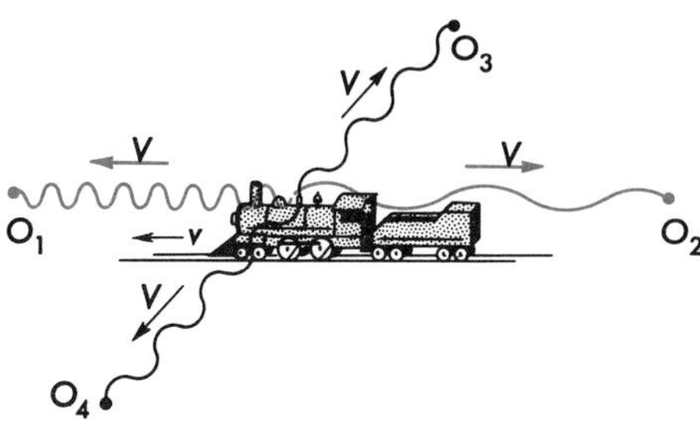

Fig. 19D. The Doppler effect: the pitch of a whistle on a fast-moving train sounds higher to an observer in front of the train, lower to an observer in back, and normal to observers off at the sides.

19.3. The Doppler Effect

Nearly everyone has at some time, perhaps without realizing it, observed the *Doppler effect.* The sounding horn of a car passing at high speed on the highway exhibits the phenomenon. The pitch of the horn, as the car goes by, drops as much as two whole notes on the musical scale. A similar observation can be made by listening to the roar of the motor of a racing car as it approaches and recedes from an observer at the race track. The motor seems to slow down as it passes by. Again, the pitch of the whistle on a fast-moving train sounds higher as the train approaches the observer than it does after the train has passed by.

This change in pitch is due to the relative motions of the source of sound and the observer. To see how this produces the effect, consider the following example. When the whistle on a train at rest is blown, it sends out waves traveling with the same velocity in all directions. To all stationary observers, no matter in what direction they are located, the true pitch of the whistle is heard, since just as many waves arrive at the ear per second as there are waves leaving the whistle.

If, on the other hand, the train is moving as shown in Fig. 19D, the whistle is moving away from the waves traveling to the rear and toward the waves traveling forward. The result is that the waves behind are considerably drawn out while those in front are crowded together. With each new wave sent out by the source, the train is farther from the preceding wave sent out to the rear and nearer to the one sent out ahead. Since the velocity of sound is the same in all directions an observer at O_1 therefore hears more waves per second and an observer at O_2 hears fewer.

To an observer O_3 or O_4, at right angles and at some little distance from the moving source, the pitch remains unchanged. For these side positions the source is neither approaching nor receding from the observer, so that approximately the same number of waves are received per second as there are waves leaving the source.

The general relations for the Doppler effect are given by the following single equation:

$$\frac{\nu_o}{V - v_0} = \frac{\nu_s}{V - v_s} \tag{19b}$$

where ν_s is the frequency of the source, ν_o is the frequency heard by the observer, V is the velocity of sound, v_s the velocity of the source, and v_o the velocity of the observer. *The direction of the velocity of sound V at the observer is positive, and its direction is taken as the positive direction for all velocities.* Either v_o or v_s is positive if it is directed along the positive direction, and negative if it is oppositely directed.

Case 1. If the source and observer are approaching each other, v_s is $+$, and v_o is $-$.

Case 2. If the source and observer are moving in the same direction, v_s and v_o are both $+$.

Case 3. The observer is at rest and the source is approaching at a velocity $v_s = 2V$. Here $v_o = 0$ and v_s is $+$. This is an interesting case since ν_o is the negative of ν_s. The observer hears the sound backward, as if played backward on a tape recorder, and it is heard after the source has passed him.

Example 1. A racing car passes the grandstand at a speed of 75.0 m/s. If the noise from the exhaust has a frequency of 540 Hz, what frequency is heard by each person as the car approaches the grandstand? Assume the speed of sound to be 342.0 m/s. **Solution.** The given quantities are $V = 342.0$ m/s, $v_s = 75.0$ m/s, and $\nu_s = 540$ Hz. Since each observer is stationary $\nu_o = 0$. In order to use the Doppler formula we first solve for the unknown:

$$\nu_o = \frac{\nu_s(V - v_o)}{(V - v_s)}$$

With the source of sound moving in the same direction as the sound waves arriving at the grandstand, v_s and V are both positive. Upon substituting the known quantities, therefore, we obtain

$$\nu_o = \frac{540(342 - 0)}{(342 - 75)} = 692 \text{ Hz}$$

19.4. Interference

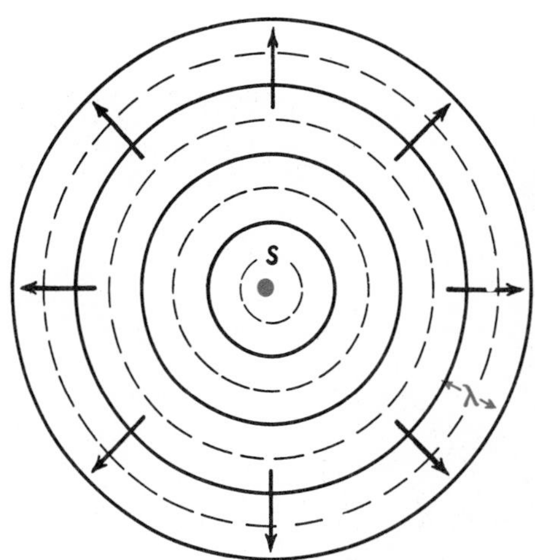

Fig. 19E. Concentric waves traveling outward from a single source S.

Everyone has at one time or another dropped a stone in a still pond of water and watched the waves spread outward in ever-widening circes. Such waves are represented by concentric circles as shown in Fig. 19E. The solid-line circles represent crests of waves and are therefore one wavelength apart, while the dotted-line circles represent the troughs of the waves, which are also one wavelength apart.

If two stones are dropped simultaneously into the water, two sets of waves will spread outward as shown in Fig. 19F. As these waves cross each other, they act one upon the other, producing what is called an *interference pattern.* Where the crests of two waves come together at the dotted intersections, they are *in step,* or in phase, and the amplitude of the water surface is increased. Where the crest of one wave and the trough of another come together, they are out of step, or out of phase, and the amplitude of the water surface is reduced. The *in-phase* regions of the waves move outward along the dotted lines, such as x, y, and z, and we have what is called *constructive interference.* The *out-of-phase* regions move outward along the solid lines, such as a and b, and we have what is called *destructive interference.*

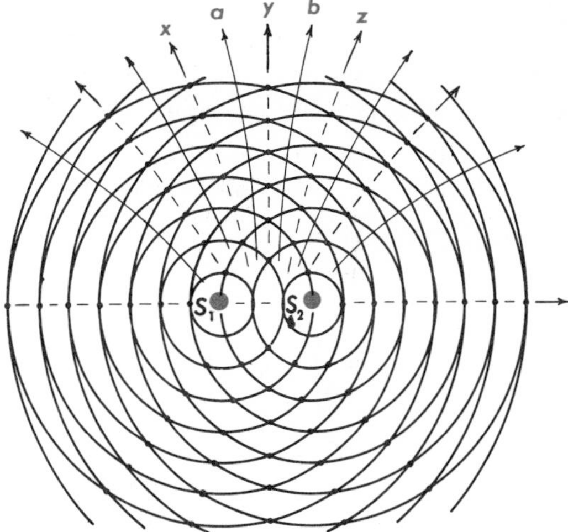

Fig. 19F. Concentric waves traveling outward from a double source, producing what is called an interference pattern.

An instantaneous photograph of such a wave pattern is shown in Fig. 19G. Note how clearly the interference regions of the waves stand out. Photographs of this kind, as well as direct observations of such wave patterns, are readily made as follows. A glass tray for maintaining a shallow water layer can be made from a piece of window glass and a wooden frame.

A thin metal strip, clamped at one end and set vibrating up and down over the water, is used as a source. A piece of wire, fastened to the vibrating end of this strip, should have one wire end dipping into the water for a single-wave source, and both ends dipping into the water for a double source. Intermittent viewing of the waves through a slotted disk, or illumination by means of a *stroboscopic light source*, enables one to make the wave pattern appear to stand still, or to progress in *slow motion.*

An experiment for demonstrating the interference of sound waves is shown in Fig. 19H. Two small radio loudspeakers S_1 and S_2 are mounted, about 150 cm apart, in a hollow box. The box is free to pivot about a vertical axis midway between the speaker centers. When both speakers are connected to an electronic sound generator, G, the speakers vibrate in phase and send out identical waves into the surrounding air. A microphone, M, about 2 m away, is an excellent detector, and an oscilloscope connected to it will indicate the relative amplitudes of the resultant sound waves arriving at M.

As the box is turned slowly in one direction, the amplitude of the oscilloscope signal P rises and falls periodically, indicating constructive and destructive interference. As it is turned slowly back, maxima and minima are again observed at the same angle positions.

Fig. 19G. Ripple-tank photograph of the interference of water waves from two sources. (Courtesy, Physical Sciences Study Committee Project.)

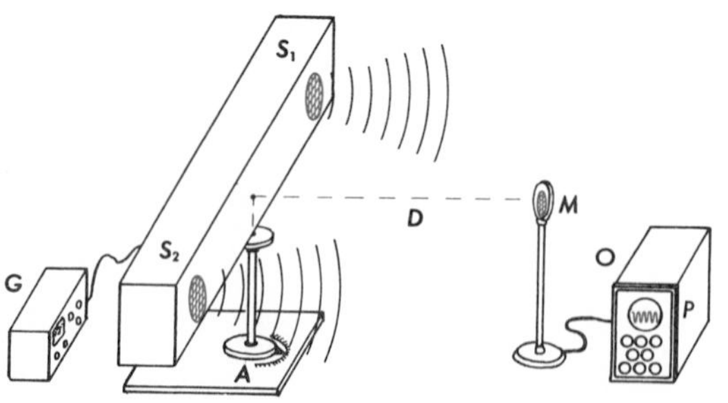

Fig. 19H. Experiment for demonstrating the interference of sound waves from two sources.

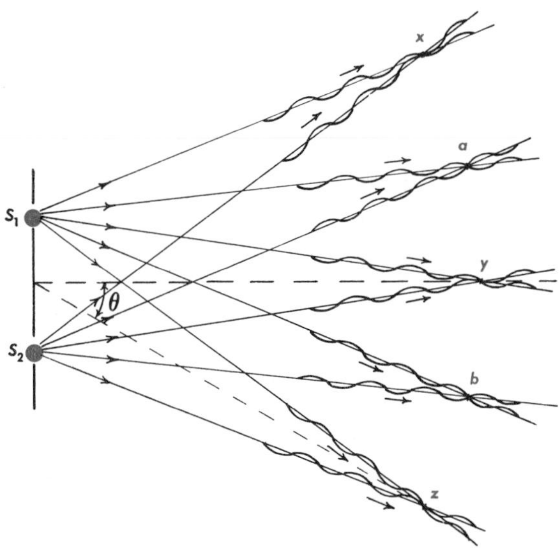

Fig. 19I. Diagram showing the in-phase and out-of-phase of waves at certain points.

An instructive diagram showing the arrival of pairs of waves at the microphone, for maximum and minimum response positions, is shown in Fig. 19I. Points *x*, *y*, and *z* correspond to points *x*, *y*, and *z* in Fig. 19F, where the waves arrive in phase, while points *a* and *b* correspond to those where they arrive out of phase.

By measuring the angles, θ, at which maximum response occurs for the experiment shown in Fig. 19H, as well as the distance d between S_1 and S_2, and the distance D, the wavelength of the sound waves can be calculated. The geometry for this calculation is shown in Fig. 19J.

When the line between the two speakers makes an angle of 90° with the perpendicular bisector D, the sources are equidistant from M, the waves arrive in phase, and we have point y of Figs. 19F and 19I. When the sources are turned to position z, the line between the speakers has been turned through an angle θ, the waves arrive in phase again, but the path x_1 is exactly one wavelength longer than the path x_2.

At some greater angle θ, the path x_1 can be made exactly two wavelengths longer than x_2, and at some still greater angle it can be made three wavelengths longer, etc. For all these particular angles where the waves are in phase, we can write the single equation

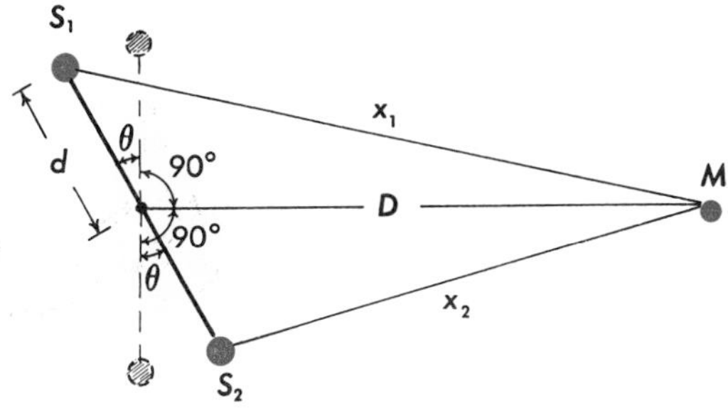

Fig. 19J. Geometrical relations for finding the wavelength of sound waves from a double source.

$$x_1 - x_2 = n\lambda \tag{19c}$$

where $$n = 0, 1, 2, 3, \ldots \tag{19d}$$

We can now apply the law of cosines to the two large triangles in Fig. 19J, and calculate the distances x_1 and x_2.

For the upper triangle, we write

$$x_1^2 = d^2 + D^2 - 2d\,D\cos(90° + \theta) \tag{19e}$$

and for the lower triangle, we write

$$x_2^2 = d^2 + D^2 - 2d\,D\cos(90° - \theta) \tag{19f}$$

By substituting the measured values of D, d, and θ in these two equations, the values of x_1 and x_2 can be calculated. Substituting these values in Eq.(19c), along with the appropriate value of n, makes it possible to calculate the wavelength λ.

If the intensities for the sound waves arriving at the microphone in Fig. 19J are plotted for a large number of angles θ, we obtain a graph of the kind shown in Fig. 19K. The maxima and minima are seen to be special points of a smooth and continuous curve. The central solid line represents the intensity graph one would expect if both sources were sounded and interference did not occur. The effect of interference, therefore, is seen to give rise to an angular redistribution of sound energy. The shaded areas above the dotted line fit exactly into the unshaded spaces below. The intensity at the peaks is double the average of the sum of the two.

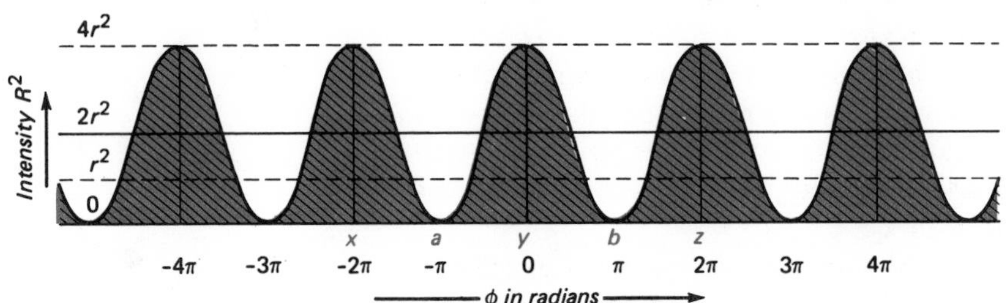

Fig. 19K. Interference pattern for two waves of equal amplitude as produced in an experiment like that shown in Fig. 19H.

Example 2. Two radio loudspeakers sounding the same frequency are 1.50 m apart as shown in Fig. 19H. A microphone is located 4.0 m away on the perpendicular bisector. As the box is slowly turned the first intensity maximum, $n = 1$, is measured and θ is found to be exactly 15°. If the speed of sound is 350 m/s, find (a) the wavelength of the sound, and (b) the frequency.

Solution. The given quantities are $D = 4.0$ m, $d = 0.750$ m, $\theta = 15°$, and $V = 350.0$ m/s. Using Eqs.(19e) and (19f), we first find the distances x_1 and x_2:

$$x_1^2 = (0.75)^2 + (4)^2 - 6(-0.2588)$$

$$x_2^2 = (0.75)^2 + (4)^2 - 6(+0.2588)$$

$$x_1^2 = 18.115 \qquad x_2^2 = 15.010$$

$$x_1 = 4.256 \text{ m} \qquad x_2 = 3.874 \text{ m}$$

Inserting these values in Eq.(19c), we obtain

$$4.256 - 3.874 = 0.382 \text{ m} = n\lambda$$

Since $n = 1$, we obtain

$$\lambda = 0.382 \text{ m}$$

To find the frequency of the sound we use the wave equation, Eq.(17ℓ), and solve for ν:

$$\nu = \frac{V}{\lambda} = \frac{350 \text{ m/s}}{0.382 \text{ m}}$$

$$\nu = 916 \text{ Hz}$$

19.5. Phase Angles

The instantaneous displacement and direction of motion of an object vibrating with simple harmonic motion are readily described by specifying the position of a graph point on a circle of reference (see Fig. 17B). The angle θ specifying the position is called the *phase angle,* and the maximum possible displacement r is called the *amplitude.*

Consider as another example an object vibrating up and down along the y axis as shown in Fig. 19L. The instantaneous position of the mass point m is given by the projection of the graph point P on the y axis. From the right triangle PQO in the figure,

$$y = r \sin \theta \tag{19g}$$

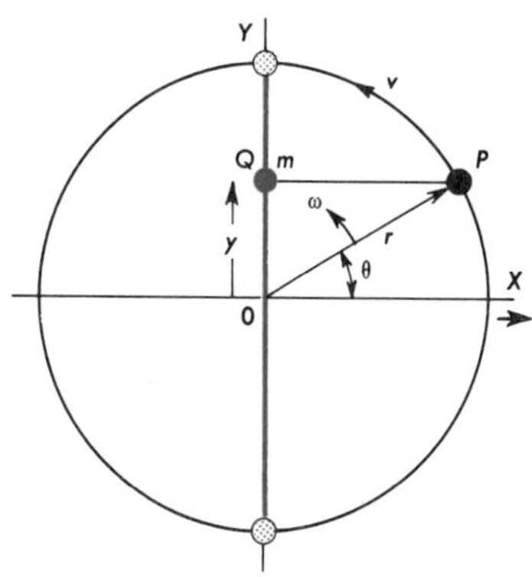

Fig. 19L. Circle of reference for a simple harmonic motion along the y axis.

Here again the phase angle θ is measured from the $+\ x$ axis. Since the graph point is moving with constant speed v, and constant angular velocity ω, we can write for any angle θ,

$$\theta = \omega t$$

By substituting ωt for θ in Eq.(19g), we obtain

$$y = r \sin \omega t \tag{19h}$$

This equation assumes that at time $t = 0$ the graph point is at + X, and the mass point is at O. If we start counting time when the mass point is at Q, and the graph point is at P, Eq.(19h) must be modified by adding the starting angle θ as follows:

$$y = r \sin (\omega t + \theta_1) \tag{19i}$$

The angle θ_1 is a constant and is called the *initial phase angle.* As the point P moves around the circle, the angle ωt increases uniformly and is always measured from the starting angle θ_1. The total quantity in parentheses represents the total angle measured from the $+\ x$ axis.

Although ω can be given in degrees per second, and θ in degrees, it is customary to express both in radian measure.

Example 3. An object vibrating with simple harmonic motion has a period of 4 s, an amplitude of 5 cm, and an initial phase angle of $\pi/6$ rad. ($\pi/6$ rad = 30°.) Find (a) the initial displacement, and after a time of 6 s, (b) the phase angle, and (c) the displacement. **Solution.** Since the graph point of this motion makes one revolution in 4 s, the angular velocity ω is 2π rad in 4 s, or $\pi/2$ rad/s. See Eq.(17f). At time $t = 0$, direct substitution in Eq.(19i) gives

$$y = 5 \sin \left(\frac{\pi}{2} 0 + \frac{\pi}{6}\right)$$

$$y = 5 \sin \frac{\pi}{6} = 5 \times 0.500$$

$$y = +2.50 \text{ cm}$$

At time $t = 6$ s, substitution in Eq.(19i) gives

$$y = 5 \sin \left(\frac{\pi}{2} 6 + \frac{\pi}{6}\right)$$

$$y = 5 \sin \left(3\pi + \frac{\pi}{6}\right)$$

This phase angle of $3\pi + \pi/6$ is equivalent to 570°, and measured from the $+x$ axis places the graph point 30° below the $-x$ axis on the circle of reference. This angle gives

$$\sin \theta = -0.500,$$

$$y = 5 \times (-0.5)$$

or

$$y = -2.5 \text{ cm}$$

A graphical representation of this example is shown by the sine curve in Fig. 19M. The displacement y is plotted vertically and time t is plotted horizontally for the first two complete vibrations, or 8 s. On such a time graph the up and down motion is

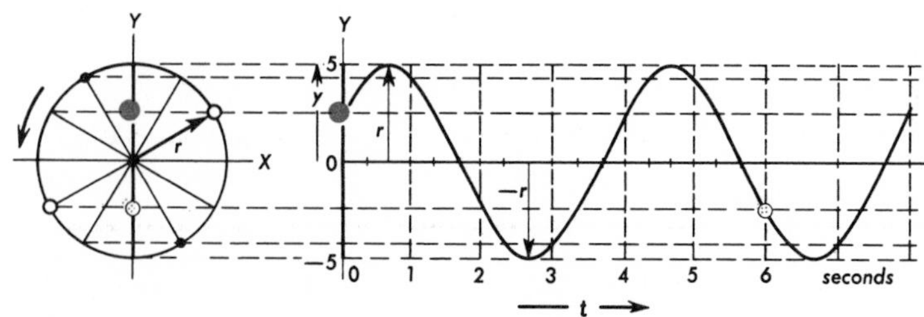

Fig. 19M. Time graph for the vibration of a point along the vertical line, the y axis.

traced out to show the starting point, the times at which each reaches its maximum displacement, and when it crosses the center point. The amplitude r at the right is seen to be the radius of the circle of reference even though the mass point starts at +2.5 cm.

19.6. Superposition of Two Vibrations

We have seen in the last chapter that the intensity of sound, in any medium through which the waves are traveling, is proportional to the flow of energy per unit area per unit time. When a number of waves of the same frequency fall on a receiver or a detector, the resultant intensity depends upon the amplitudes of all of the individual waves, and upon the phase differences between them.

In Sec. 17.11 it is shown that *the energy of a vibrating mass is proportional to the square of the amplitude.* Combining all these relations we find that the resultant intensity due to any number of waves falling on a detector of any kind is proportional to the square of the resultant amplitude:

$$\text{intensity} \propto (\text{amplitude})^2$$

$$I = kR^2 \tag{19j}$$

where k is a proportionality constant. The resultant amplitude is given by the vector sum of all the individual amplitudes.

Consider as a practical example the coming together of two sound waves of the same frequency at regions along a smooth line drawn through $x\ a\ y\ b\ z$ as in Fig. 19I. To find the resultant amplitude R, due to the two vibrations they produce at any given point, we add their respective amplitudes as shown in Fig. 19N. The equation of motion at that point, due to the two waves separately, may be written

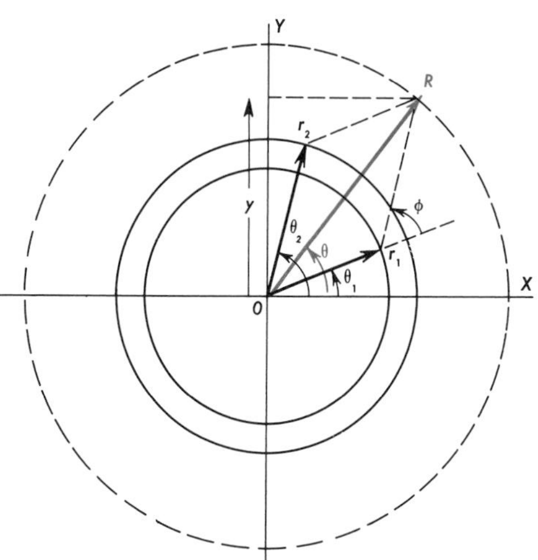

Fig. 19N. Graphical composition of two amplitudes as vectors.

$$\begin{aligned} y_1 &= r_1 \sin (\omega t + \theta_1) \\ y_2 &= r_2 \sin (\omega t + \theta_2) \end{aligned} \tag{19k}$$

where r_1 and r_2 are the two amplitudes, and θ_1 and θ_2 their respective initial phase angles. Together they produce the resultant amplitude R, and give rise to a resultant vibration along the y axis given by

$$y = R \sin (\omega t + \theta)$$

where ω is the same for the two individual vibrations, and the maximum value of y is R.

From the graph it can be seen that θ represents the initial phase angle of the amplitude R, and that the phase difference ϕ between the two separate vibrations is given by

$$\phi = \theta_2 - \theta_1 \tag{19\ell}$$

Since the two vibrations have the same frequency, we can visualize the vector diagram rotating around the center point O, unchanged in shape, and with the tips of the arrows tracing out their respective circles of reference.

To find R analytically we make use of the lower right triangle of the vector parallelogram, and from the law of cosines write

$$R^2 = r_1^2 + r_2^2 + 2r_1r_2 \cos \phi \tag{19m}$$

In most practical cases the amplitudes r_1 and r_2 are equal and Eq.(19m) simplifies. Replacing r_1 and r_2 by r, we obtain

$$R^2 = 2r^2(1 + \cos \phi)$$

From an often used relation in trigonometry, $1 + \cos \phi = 2 \cos^2 (\phi/2)$, we obtain

$$R^2 = 4r^2 \cos^2 \frac{\phi}{2} \tag{19n}$$

If the phase difference is such that $\phi = 0, 2\pi, 4\pi, \ldots, \cos^2 (\phi/2) = +1$, and $R^2 = 4r^2$. This means that *the resultant intensity is four times r^2, the intensity of either wave alone.* If $\phi = \pi, 3\pi, 5\pi, \ldots, \cos^2 (\phi/2) = 0$, and the intensity is zero. For intermediate values, the intensity varies between these limits according to the square of the cosine. This is well illustrated by the intensity graph in Fig. 19K.

Two cases of the superposition of two vibrations of the same frequency and same amplitude are shown in Fig. 19O. The top graph is drawn for a phase angle difference $\phi = 45°$, and the second is for $\phi = 135°$. In the right-hand graphs it will be seen that at any instant of time t the sum of the vertical displacements of the two separate vibrations is just equal to the displacement of the resultant.

Furthermore, the resultant vibration is a smooth curve having the same frequency as the separate vibrations. As the angle ϕ approaches $0, 2\pi, 4\pi, \ldots$ rad, R approaches $2r$, and as ϕ approaches $\pi, 3\pi, 5\pi, \ldots$ rad, A approaches zero.

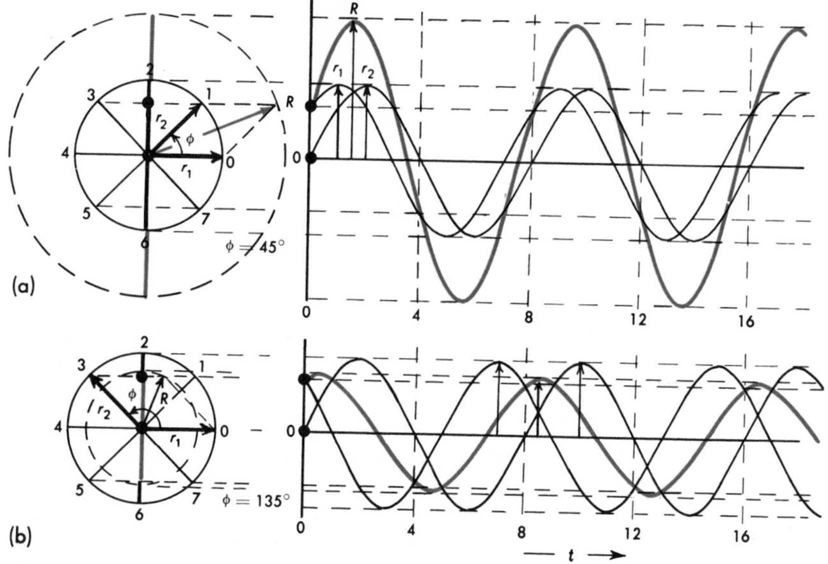

Fig. 19O. Superposition graphs for two vibrations of equal amplitude and the same frequency, (a) with a phase difference of $\pi/4$ or 45°, and (b) $3\pi/4$ or 135°.

19.7. Coherent Sources

If two sources of waves vibrating with the same frequency maintain a constant relative phase angle, they are said to be *coherent.* If they both start at time $t = 0$, and then keep exactly the same frequency, they may be represented by the equations

$$y_1 = r_1 \sin \frac{2\pi}{T} t$$
$$y_2 = r_2 \sin \frac{2\pi}{T} t \qquad (19o)$$

The amplitudes r_1 and r_2 may be equal or different, but the period must be the same for both. In other words, they may have different intensities, but they must have the same frequencies.

If one of two sources starts 90° or $\pi/2$ rad behind the other in phase, they would still be coherent, but represented by different functions:

$$y_1 = r_1 \sin \frac{2\pi}{T} t$$
$$y_2 = r_2 \sin \left(\frac{2\pi}{T} t - \frac{\pi}{2}\right) \qquad (19p)$$

problems

Unless otherwise specified assume the speed of sound to be 350.0 m/s in the following problems.

1. The four strings of a violin are designated G, D, A, and E. If these strings are properly tuned their frequencies will be G = 198 Hz, D = 297 Hz, A = 440 Hz, and E = 660 Hz. What are the beat note frequencies produced if these strings are sounded in pairs?

2. The following musical tetrad is sounded by four violins, C = 264 Hz, F = 352 Hz, A = 440 Hz, and C′ = 528 Hz. What are the frequencies of all the beat notes produced?

3. A car traveling at 25.0 m/s on a highway sounds its horn as it approaches an intersection. If the frequency heard by an observer standing at the intersection is 380 Hz, what is the actual frequency of the horn? [Ans. 352.9 Hz.]

4. A train going 32.0 m/s sounds its horn, pitched to a frequency of 320 Hz. What frequency would be heard by a stationary observer (a) ahead of the train, and (b) behind the train?

5. The siren at a fire station when sounded has a top frequency of 860 Hz. What is the top frequency heard by motorists traveling at 90.0 Km/h along the highway if they are (a) approaching, and (b) receding from the station. Assume the speed of sound is 348.0 m/s.

6. A car traveling at 28.0 m/s on the highway sounds its horn as it overtakes and passes another car traveling at 13.0 m/s in the same direction. If the horn frequency is 500 Hz, what is the frequency heard by the driver in the slower car (a) before passing, and (b) after passing? [Ans. (a) 523 Hz, (b) 480 Hz.]

7.* Automobile A traveling at 25.0 m/s on the highway sounds its horn as it overtakes and passes another car B as it sounds its horn while traveling at 15.0 m/s in the opposite direction. If the horn frequencies are both 500 Hz, what is the frequency heard by the driver in car A (a) before passing B, and (b) after passing B? What is the frequency received by the driver in car B (c) before passing A, and (d) after passing car A.

8.* Airplane A traveling at 150.0 m/s passes another plane B traveling in the opposite direction at 50.0 m/s. If the sounds of the motors both have a frequency of 500 Hz, what is the frequency heard by the pilot in A (a) before passing B, and (b) after passing B? What is the frequency heard by the pilot in B (c) before passing A, and (d) after passing A?

9. Two radio loudspeakers sounding the same frequency are 2.0 m apart. A microphone is located 5.0 m away on a perpendicular bisector as shown in Fig. 19H. As the speaker cabinet is turned, the first intensity maximum is found to be at an angle $\theta = 12.0°$. Find (a) the wavelength, and (b) the frequency of the sound. [Ans. (a) 0.408 m, (b) 858 Hz.]

10.* Two loudspeakers in a hi-fi record player are located 1.60 m apart. An observer is located 5.0 m away from the center of the cabinet and at an angle of 30° with the perpendicular to the front. What frequencies between 0 and 2000 Hz sounded by both speakers with the same intensity will not be heard?

11. The end of a rope is vibrating transversely as represented by the equation

$$y = 3.60\ \text{cm} \times \sin\left(\pi t + \frac{\pi}{4}\right)$$

If the speed of the waves along the rope is 6.20 m/s, find (a) the amplitude, (b) the initial phase angle in degrees, (c) the phase angle at the end of 10.0 s, (d) the period, and (e) the wavelength.

12. Two trains of waves coming together at a point are represented by the respective equations

$$y_1 = 8.0\ \text{mm} \times \sin\left(12\pi t + \frac{\pi}{6}\right)$$

$$y_2 = 8.0\ \text{mm} \times \sin\left(12\pi t + \frac{\pi}{3}\right)$$

Find (a) the amplitude of each vibration, (b) the initial

phase angles, (c) the resultant amplitude, (d) the initial phase angle of the resultant, and (e) the equation of the resultant vibration. [Ans. (a) both 8.0 mm, (b) 30° and 60°, (c) 15.45 mm, (d) 45°, (e) $y = 15.45$ mm $\times$ sin $(12\,\pi t + \pi/4)$.]

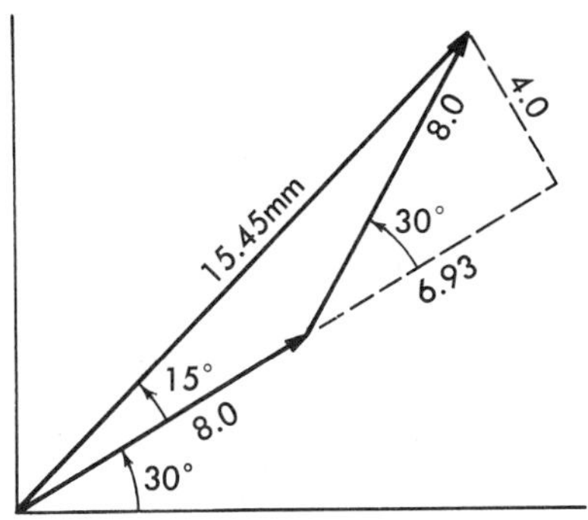

Prob. 12.

13. Two coherent waves coming together at a point are represented at that point by the equations

$$y_1 = 2.50 \text{ mm} \times \sin\left(\frac{2\pi}{8}t\right)$$

$$y_2 = 2.50 \text{ mm} \times \sin\left(\frac{2\pi}{8}t + \frac{\pi}{2}\right)$$

Find (a) the amplitude of each vibration, (b) the initial phase angles, (c) the resultant amplitude, (d) the initial phase angle of the resultant, and (e) the equation of the resultant motion.

14. Two waves coming together at a given point are represented at that point by the equations

$$y_1 = 5.0 \text{ mm} \times \sin\left(8\pi t + \frac{\pi}{6}\right)$$

and

$$y_2 = 4.0 \text{ mm} \times \sin\left(8\pi t + \frac{\pi}{3}\right)$$

respectively. Find (a) the amplitude of each vibration, (b) the initial phase angles, (c) the resultant amplitude, (d) the initial phase angle of the resultant, (e) the equation of the resultant vibration, (f) the period, and (g) the frequency.

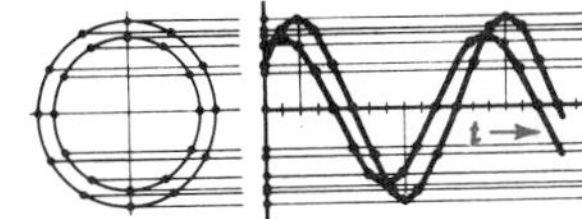

Prob. 14. Graph of two vibrations.

20 Sources of musical sounds

From the subjective point of view, music is based upon the relative pitch and timbre, or quality, of sound waves produced by the voice and musical instruments. From the scientific point of view the pitch of a note depends upon the vibration frequency of the source, and the timbre or quality depends upon the complexity of the vibration mode.

The frequencies of notes are usually chosen so that they produce the greatest amount of melody or harmony. Two or more notes are said to be harmonious or concordant if they are pleasing to the ear. If they are not pleasant to hear, they are discordant.*

Musical instruments are often classified under one of the following headings: *strings, winds,* and *percussions.* These terms apply to the material part of the instruments set into vibration when the instrument is played, or to the method by which it is set into vibration. It is the purpose of this chapter to consider these sources and the various factors governing the frequencies of their musical notes.

20.1. Stringed Instruments

There are two principal reasons why stringed instruments of different kinds do not sound alike as regards *tone quality*—first, the design of the instrument, and second, the method by which the strings are set into vibration. The violin and cello are bowed with long strands of tightly stretched horsehair, the harp and

* The essential difference between *melody* and *harmony* is quite generally recognized by everyone. Melody consists of a succession of notes and conveys the idea of motion that should go on and on, while harmony consists of the simultaneous and often sustained sounding of several notes like a chord, followed by other similar combinations of notes. The latter seems to stand still, each chord of notes being more or less complete in itself.

guitar are plucked with the fingers or picks, and the piano is hammered with light felt mallets.

Under very special conditions a string may be made to vibrate with nodes at either end as shown in Fig. 20A. In this state of motion the string gives rise to its lowest possible note, and it is said to be vibrating with its *fundamental frequency.*

Every musician knows that a thick heavy string has a lower natural pitch than a thin one, that a short strong string has a higher pitch than a long one, and that the tighter a string is stretched the higher is its pitch. The G string of a violin, for example, is thicker and heavier than the high-pitched E string, and the *bass* strings of the piano are longer and heavier than the strings of the *treble.*

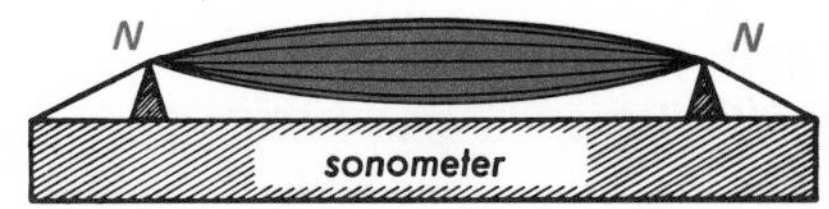

Fig. 20A. Single string vibrating with its fundamental frequency.

20.2. Harmonics and Overtones

When a professional violinist plays "in harmonics" he touches the strings lightly at various points and sets each one vibrating in two or more segments, as shown in Fig. 20B. If a string is touched at the center, a node is formed at that point and the vibration frequency becomes double that of the fundamental. If the string is touched lightly at a point one-third the distance from the end, it will vibrate in three sections and have a frequency three times that of the fundamental.

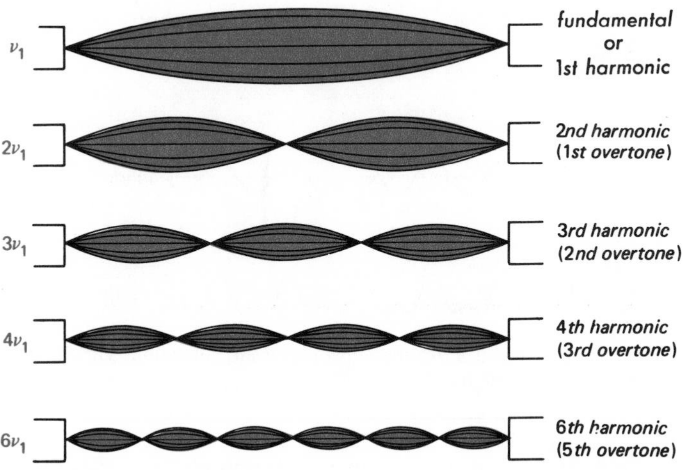

Fig. 20B. Vibration modes for strings of musical instruments.

In the elementary theory of string instruments, it is assumed

TABLE 20A
Harmonic frequencies of a piano string

Mode number	*Meas. freq.*	*Harmonic freq.*	*Ratio*
1	32.70	32.70	1.000
2	65.52	65.40	2.003
3	98.39	98.10	3.008
4	131.4	130.8	4.018
5	164.7	163.5	5.038
6	198.4	196.2	6.066
7	232.4	228.9	7.106
8	266.8	261.6	8.159

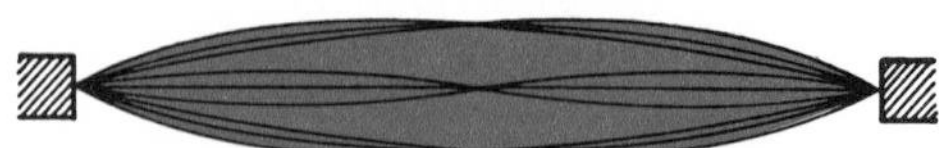

Fig. 20C. String vibrating with its first and second harmonics simultaneously.

that each string is thin, uniform, and highly flexible, and that it vibrates with small amplitude between unyielding supports. For such an ideal string, the above vibration modes have frequencies exactly equal to whole number multiples of the fundamental frequency ν_1, and are called *harmonics.*

The frequencies ν of all harmonics of a given string are given by the relation

$$\nu = n\nu_1 \tag{20a}$$

where

$$n = 1, 2, 3, 4, \ldots$$

To show how closely a real string meets these ideal conditions, the measured frequencies of a piano string whose fundamental frequency is 32.70 vib/s are given in Table 20A.

It is not difficult to set a string vibrating with its fundamental and several of its higher modes at the same time. This is accomplished by plucking or bowing the string vigorously. As an illustration a diagram of an ideal string vibrating with two normal modes at the same time is shown in Fig. 20C. As the string vibrates in two loops with a frequency $2\nu_1$, it also moves up and down as a single loop with the fundamental frequency ν_1.

The sound wave sent out by such a vibrating string, as shown in Fig. 20D, is composed of two frequencies, the fundamental or first harmonic of frequency ν_1, diagram (a), and the second harmonic or first partial with the frequency $2\nu_1$, diagram (b). The sound waves combine as they travel through the air, and upon their arrival at the ear, set the eardrum vibrating as shown in diagram (c).

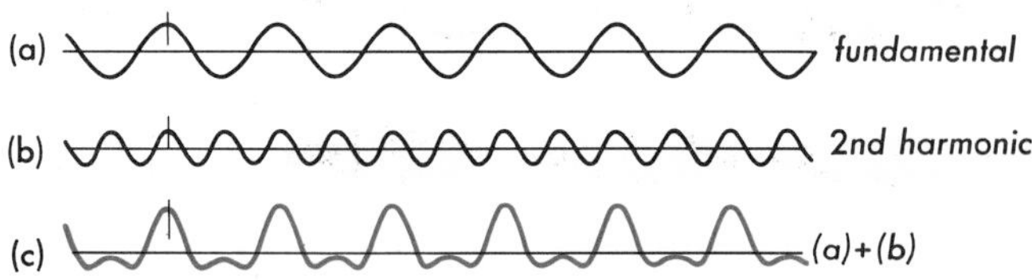

Fig. 20D. Sound wave vibrations from a string vibrating with its fundamental and the second harmonic.

An interesting experiment with a vibrating string is diagrammed in Fig. 20E. Light from an arc lamp is focused on the central section of stretched steel string, which, except for a small vertical slot, is masked by a screen. An image of the slot and the string section seen through it is focused on a screen by a second lens, after reflection from a rotating mirror. As the string vibrates up and down, only a blurred image of the short section of string is seen, but when the mirror is rotated the wire section draws out a clearly visible curve W.

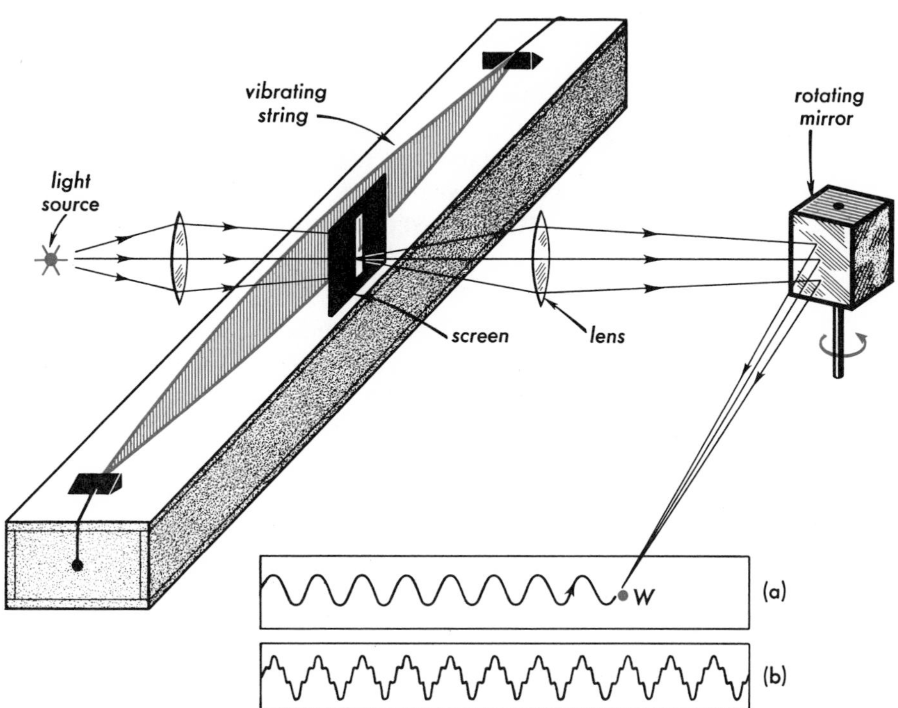

Fig. 20E. Experiment for observing the detailed vibrations of a stretched string.

If the string is plucked gently near the center, a smooth wave form (a) is drawn out on the screen, but, if it is plucked hard near the end to produce a harsh-sounding note, the wave form is more complex as shown in (b). In the first case, the string is vibrating only with its fundamental mode, while in the second case various harmonics, called *overtones* or *partials,* are also present.

As a string vibrates with *transverse waves,* it strikes air molecules all around it, sending periodic impulses through the air as *longitudinal waves.*

20.3. The Theory of Vibrating Strings

A string set into vibration with nodes and loops is but an example of standing waves (see Fig. 17L). A disturbance produced at one end, as in the plucking or bowing of a string, sends a wave or train of waves along the string to be reflected back and forth from end to end. When traveling in one direction the wave is on top and, upon reflection, it flips to the under side. Because the wave is always on top when moving to the right, and on the bottom when moving to the left, a flipping up and down of the string results.

Since the fundamental frequency of vibration is equal to the number of times per second that the wave arrives at the same end, the pitch will depend upon the velocity of the waves and the distance they have to travel.

The velocity of transverse waves along a rope or string under tension is given by

$$V = \sqrt{F/m} \tag{20b}$$

where F is the tension and m is the mass per unit length of string. When standing waves are produced, the distance L between any two consecutive nodes is just equal to half a wavelength, $\frac{1}{2}\lambda$. Accordingly,

$$\lambda = 2L$$

To obtain an equation for the fundamental frequency of a vibrating string, the general wave equation $V = \nu\lambda$ is used [see Eq.(17ℓ)]. If we solve this equation for ν, and then substitute the above values for V and λ, we obtain

$$\nu = \frac{1}{2L}\sqrt{F/m} \tag{20c}$$

Accurate measurements with vibrating strings and musical instruments confirm this equation.

Example 1. A piano string that sounds three octaves below middle C is 1.10 m long. Calculate the tension on the string when, in proper tune, its frequency is 33.0 Hz. Assume the mass of the string to be 160 g.

Solution. The *mass per unit length* of string is $m = 0.16$ Kg/1.1 m $= 0.1454$ Kg/m. Solve Eq.(20c) for F and the frequency equation becomes $F = 4\nu^2L^2m$. The given quantities are $\nu = 33.0$ Hz, $L = 1.10$ m, $m = 0.1454$ Kg/m. By direct substitution,

$$F = 4 \times (33)^2 \times (1.10)^2 \times 0.1454 = 766 \text{ N}$$

The vibration of a string brought about by bowing is associated with friction. Because starting friction is greater than sliding friction, the resinous bow periodically engages the string, pushing or pulling it to one side. During one-half the vibration the string clings to the bow and is carried along by it. When the tension becomes too great and exceeds starting friction, the string slips back to the opposite side of its vibration. There it stops and upon reversal in direction is grabbed again by the bow.

20.4. Wind Instruments

Musical instruments often classified as "wind instruments" are usually divided into two subclasses, "wood winds" and "brasses." Under the heading of wood winds, we find such instruments as the *flute, piccolo, clarinet, bass clarinet, saxophone, bassoon,* and *contrabassoon;* and under the brasses such instruments as the *French horn, cornet, trumpet, tenor trombone, bass trombone,* and *tuba* (or *bombardon*).

The fundamental principles involved in the vibration of an air column are demonstrated by means of an experiment shown in Fig. 20F. A vibrating tuning fork which acts as a source of sound waves is held over the open end of a long hollow tube containing water. Traveling down the tube with the velocity of sound in air, each train of sound waves is reflected from the water surface back toward the top. If the water is raised or lowered to the proper level, standing waves will be set up and the air column will resonate to the frequency of the tuning fork.

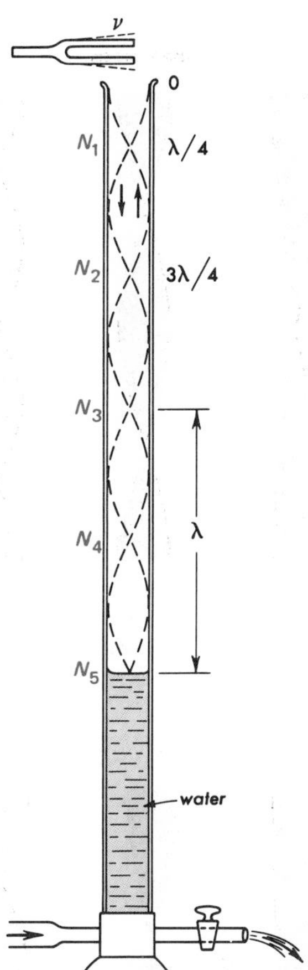

Fig. 20F. Sound waves from tuning fork set up standing waves in an air column which has been adjusted to the proper length.

The first resonance occurs at N_1 when the water level is only a short distance from the top. The second resonance occurs at N_2, three times the distance of N_1 below the top, and the third N_3 at five times the distance, etc. The reason for these odd fractions is that only a *node* can form at the closed end of the pipe, i.e., at the water surface, and an *antinode* at the open end.

Standing waves in air are longitudinal in character, and they are difficult to represent in any drawing (see Fig. 17M). For convenience only, it is quite customary to indicate the positions of nodes and loops as if they were transverse standing waves (dotted lines in the diagram).

If the frequency of the tuning fork used in the above experiment is known, the velocity of sound in air can be calculated. The distance between consecutive nodes is equal to $\lambda/2$, so that λ is equal to the length of two segments $N_3 - N_1$, $N_4 - N_2$, or $N_5 - N_3$, as shown in the diagram. In an actual experiment when the temperature is 27°C, and a tuning fork is sounding 512 Hz, the nodes are 0.340 m apart. Substitution of these values in the general

open pipes

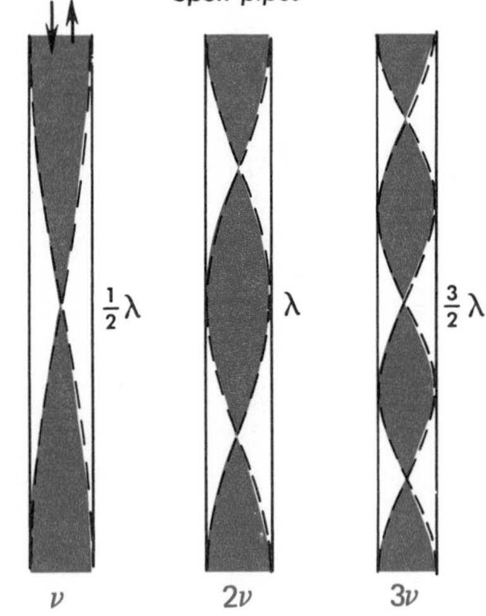

fundamental or 1st harmonic — 2nd harmonic — 3rd harmonic

closed pipes

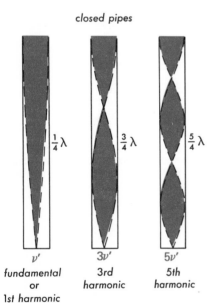

$\frac{1}{4}\lambda$ — $\frac{3}{4}\lambda$ — $\frac{5}{4}\lambda$

ν' fundamental or 1st harmonic — $3\nu'$ 3rd harmonic — $5\nu'$ 5th harmonic

Fig. 20G. Air columns in open and closed pipes have definite frequencies of vibration.

wave equation, Eq.(17ℓ), gives

$$V = \nu\lambda = 512 \times 0.680 \text{ m} = 348.2 \text{ m/s}$$

20.5. Vibrating Air Columns

The various modes in which air columns may vibrate in open or closed pipes are shown in Fig. 20G. Starting at the left, a pipe open at both ends may vibrate with (1) a single node at the middle and an antinode at both ends, (2) two nodes and three antinodes, or (3) with three nodes and four antinodes, etc. On the other hand, a pipe closed at one end and open at the other may vibrate with (1) one node and one antinode, (2) two nodes and two antinodes, or (3) three nodes and three antinodes, etc. *In all vibrating air columns, an antinode always forms at an open end and a node at a closed end.*

The various possible frequencies to which a pipe may resonate are definite and fixed in value, and depend only upon the length of the pipe and the velocity of sound in air. If, for example, the pipes in Fig. 20G are all 60 cm long and the velocity of sound in air is 336 m/s, $V = \nu\lambda$ shows that they will vibrate with the following respective frequencies:

ν	2ν	3ν	ν'	$3\nu'$	$5\nu'$
280	560	840	140	420	700

With an open pipe, the lowest possible vibration frequency is called the *fundamental;* the others, with whole-numbered multiples of the fundamental frequency, 2ν, 3ν, 4ν, etc., are called *harmonics.* With closed pipes, the lowest frequency is again the fundamental and the others with odd multiples, $3\nu'$, $5\nu'$, $7\nu'$, etc., are harmonics.

All these vibration modes are referred to as natural modes and their corresponding frequencies as natural frequencies. *The fundamental is also called the first harmonic.* It should be noted that with one end of a pipe closed, all even-numbered harmonics cannot be sounded.

The existence of standing waves in a resonating air column may be demonstrated by a long hollow tube filled with illuminating gas as shown in Fig. 20H. Entering through an adjustable plunger at the left, the gas escapes through tiny holes spaced at regular intervals in a row along the top. Sound waves from an organ pipe enter the gas column by setting into vibration a thin paper sheet, stretched over the right-hand end.

When resonance is attained by sliding the plunger to the correct position, the small gas flames will appear as shown. The nodes and antinodes are then clearly delineated for the height contours formed by the yellow flame tips.

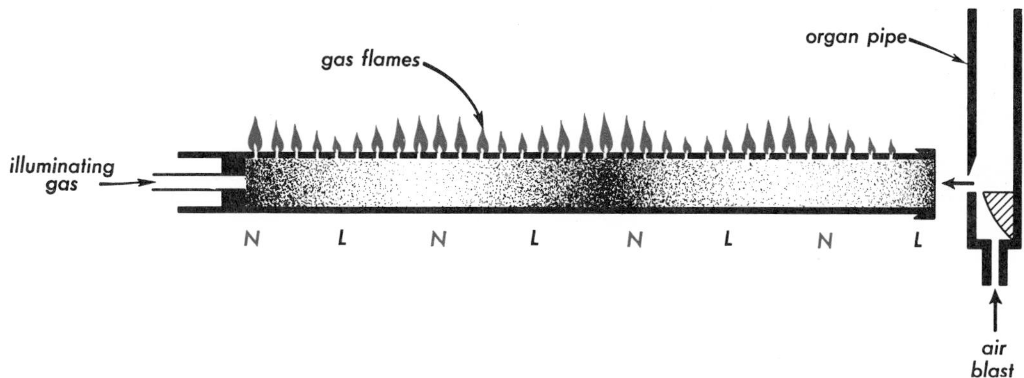

Fig. 20H. Standing waves in a long tube containing illuminating gas.

In many of the wind instruments of the orchestra, the vibrating air columns are not entirely uniform and the far open end is considerably flared. Because of this nonuniformity, the nodes are not equally spaced nor are the possible frequencies exactly harmonics of the fundamental. As an example of how nearly the various normal modes come to being harmonics of a fundamental, the following measured frequencies of the *open notes* of a B♭ cornet are given in Table 20B ($\nu_1 = 116.7$ Hz). Open notes are those for which all valves are open and the entire air column is vibrating.

TABLE 20B
Harmonic frequencies of a B♭ cornet

Mode number	*Meas. freq.*	*Harmonic freq.*	*Ratio*
1	116.7	116.7	1.000
2	233.4	233.4	2.000
3	349.8	350.1	2.998
4	467.5	466.8	4.007
5	587.7	583.5	5.037
6	706.2	700.2	6.058
8*	948.6	933.6	8.130

*The seventh harmonic was not sounded.

20.6. Theory of Vibrating Air Columns

The various notes produced by most wind instruments are brought out by varying the length of the vibrating air column. This is illustrated by the organ pipes in Fig. 20I. The longer the pipe, the lower the fundamental frequency or pitch of the note. In a regular concert organ, the pipes vary in length from about 15 cm for the highest note to almost 5 m for the lowest. For the middle octave of the musical scale, the open-ended pipes vary from .6 m for middle C to .3 m for C^1, one octave higher. In the wood winds, like the flute, the length of the column is varied by openings in the side of the instrument; and in many of the brasses, like the

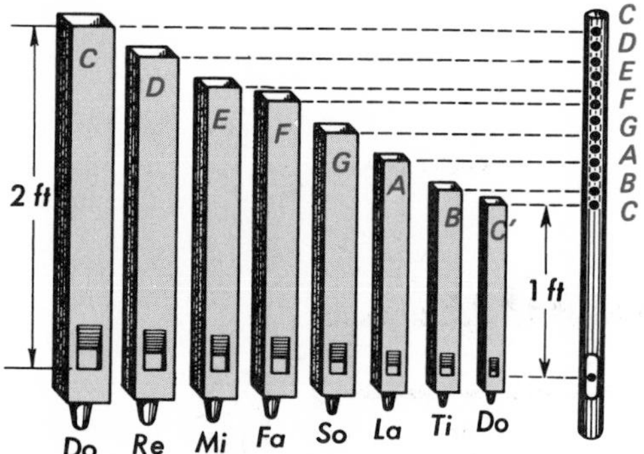

Fig. 20I. Organ pipes arranged in a musical scale. The longer the pipe, the lower is its fundamental frequency and pitch. The vibrating air column of the flute is terminated at various points by openings along the tube.

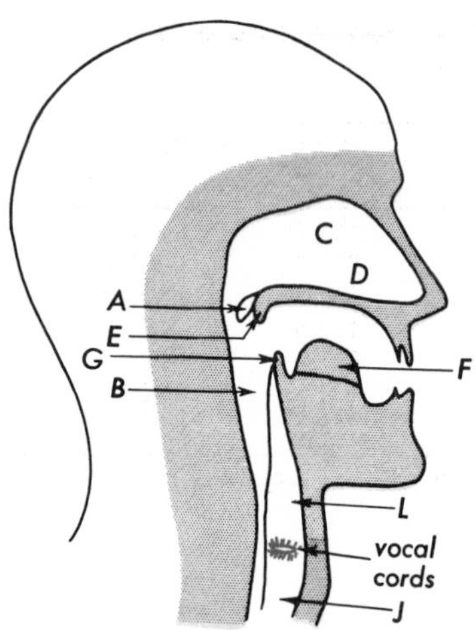

Fig. 20J. Cross-sectional diagram showing the vocal chords in the larynx: (A) soft palate, (B) pharynx, (C) nasal cavity, (D) hard palate, (F) tongue, (G) epiglottis, and (J) windpipe.

trumpet, by means of valves. A valve is a piston which, on being pressed down, throws in an additional length of tube.

Since a vibrating air column is a condition of standing waves, the frequency of vibration will depend upon two factors, the length of the pipe and the velocity of waves through it. The velocity of longitudinal waves in a gas is given by Newton's formula as modified by Laplace:

$$V = \sqrt{K\frac{P}{\rho}} \tag{20d}$$

where K is a number representing the compressibility of a gas, P is the gas pressure in N/m^2, and ρ its density in Kg/m^3.

Gases	K
Monatomic	1.667
Diatomic	1.400
Triatomic	1.333

For all standing waves, the distance L between any two consecutive nodes, that is, the length of one segment, is just equal to half a wavelength, $\lambda/2$. Accordingly,

$$\lambda = 2L$$

By substituting this relation and the velocity above in the general wave equation, Eq.(17ℓ), we get the general formula

$$\nu = \frac{1}{2L}\sqrt{K\frac{P}{\rho}} \tag{20e}$$

Measurements with resonating pipes confirm this relation.

The effect of the density of a gas on the pitch of a note may be demonstrated by a very interesting experiment with the human voice. Voice sounds originate in the vibrations of the vocal cords in the larynx (see Fig. 20J). This source of vibration, which determines the fundamental pitch of the speaking or singing voice, is controlled by muscular tension on the cords. The quality of the voice is determined by the size and shape of the throat, the mouth, and the nasal cavities.

If a gas lighter than air is breathed into the lungs, the above equation shows that the voice quality should change. The demonstration can be best and safely performed by exhaling completely, and then filling the lungs with helium gas (hydrogen is unsafe). Upon speaking, the experimenter will be observed to have a very peculiar high-pitched voice, which must be heard to be appreciated. The peculiarities arise from the fact that the fundamental pitch, due to the vocal-cord frequency, remains practically normal, while the harmonics from the resonating mouth, throat, and nasal cavities are raised by about $2\frac{1}{2}$ octaves.

Example 2. A straight piece of pipe 2.0 m long and open at both ends is filled with carbon dioxide gas at standard temperature and pressure. Find (a) the speed of sound in carbon dioxide, and (b) the fundamental frequency of the pipe.

Solution. To find the speed use Eq.(20d). Since CO_2 is a triatomic molecule, $K = 1.33$. From Table 16A, the density of CO_2 gas is 1.980 Kg/m³. By direct substitution in Eq.(20d) of the given quantities, $K = 1.333$, $P = 1.013 \times 10^5$ N/m², and $\rho = 1.980$ Kg/m³, we obtain

$$V = \sqrt{\frac{1.333 \times 1.013 \times 10^5 \text{ N/m}^2}{1.980 \text{ Kg/m}^3}}$$

$$V = \sqrt{6.820 \times 10^4 \text{ m}^2/\text{s}^2}$$

$$V = 261.3 \text{ m/s}$$

(b) To find the fundamental frequency, use Eq.(17ℓ). Since an antinode forms at the open end of a pipe, the pipe length is equal to $\frac{1}{2}\lambda$, and this is equal to L, the length of one loop. By substitution in Eq.(17ℓ), we obtain

$$\nu = \frac{1}{2 \times 2 \text{ m}} 261.3 \frac{\text{m}}{\text{s}}$$

$$\nu = 65.3 \frac{\text{vib}}{\text{s}}$$

20.7. Edge Tones

Although the pitch of the note sounded by any wind instrument is determined by the vibration of an air column according to principles of resonance, the method by which the air is set into vibration varies widely among instruments. In instruments like the saxophone, clarinet, oboe and bassoon, air is blown against a

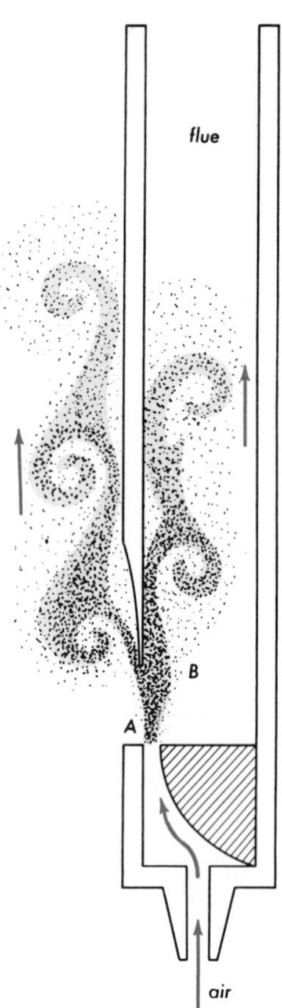

Fig. 20K. A steady stream of air blown across the lip of an organ pipe sets up whirlwinds along both sides of the partition.

thin strip of wood called a reed, setting it into vibration. In most of the brasses the musician's lips are made to vibrate with certain required frequencies, while in certain wood winds, like the flute and piccolo and in organs and whistles, air is blown across the sharp edge of an opening near one end of the instrument, setting the air into vibration. A brief discussion of these source vibrations is therefore important here.

When wind or a blast of air encounters a small obstacle, little whirlwinds are formed in the air stream behind the obstacle. This is illustrated by the cross section of a flue organ pipe shown in Fig. 20K. Whether the obstacle is long, or a small round object, the whirlwinds are formed alternately on the two sides as shown (see Fig. 7H). The air stream at B waves back and forth, sending a pulse of air first up one side and then the other. Although the wind blows through the opening A as a continuous stream, the separate whirlwinds going up each side of the obstacle become periodic shocks to the surrounding air. Coming at perfectly regular intervals, these pulses give rise to musical notes often described as "edge tones."

The number of whirlwinds formed per second, and therefore the pitch of the edge tone, increases with the wind velocity. When the wind howls through the trees, the pitch of the note rises and falls, its frequency at any time denoting the velocity of the wind. For a given wind velocity, smaller objects give rise to higher-pitched notes than large objects.

A fine-stretched wire or rubber band, when placed in an open window or in the wind, will be set into vibration and will give out a musical note. Each whirlwind shock to the air reacts on the obstacle (the wire or rubber band), pushing it first to one side and then the other. These are the pushes that cause the rope of a flagpole to flap periodically in the breeze, while the waving of the flag at the top of a pole shows the whirlwinds that follow each other along each side.

The air column in an organ pipe, flute, or piccolo has its own natural frequency of vibration which may or may not coincide with the frequency of an edge tone. If it does coincide, resonance will occur, the air column will vibrate with a large amplitude, and returning pulses of air down the tube with each vibration will force the air stream out at just the right moment, thus aiding in building up the natural frequency of the pipe. If the edge tone has a frequency different from the fundamental of the string, or air column, vibrations will be set up but not as intensely as before. If the frequency of the edge tone of an organ pipe, for example, comes close to double that of the fundamental, and this can be obtained by a stronger blast of air, the pipe will resonate to double its fundamental frequency and give out a strong note one octave higher.

By blowing more sharply against the opening in a piccolo or flute, the entire scale of notes can be raised one octave above normal playing range of the instrument. In all instruments like those mentioned above where air is blown across the sharp edge of an opening to make it sing, as in the organ pipe of Fig. 20K, an antinode is formed at that end. Whether an antinode or node forms at the other end depends upon whether it is open or closed, respectively.

20.8. Percussion Instruments; Vibrating Rods

If a number of small sticks are dropped upon the floor, the sound that is heard is described as a noise. If one stick alone is dropped, one would also describe the sound as a noise, unless, of course, a set of sticks of varying lengths were arranged in order of length and each one dropped in its order. If this is done, one notices that each stick gives rise to a rather definite musical note and that the set of sticks could be cut to the proper length to form a musical scale. The use of vibrating rods in a musical instrument is found in the *xylophone,* the *marimba,* and the *triangle.* Standing waves in a rod, like those in a stretched string, may be any one of three different kinds—transverse, longitudinal, and torsional. Only the first two of these modes of vibration will be treated here.

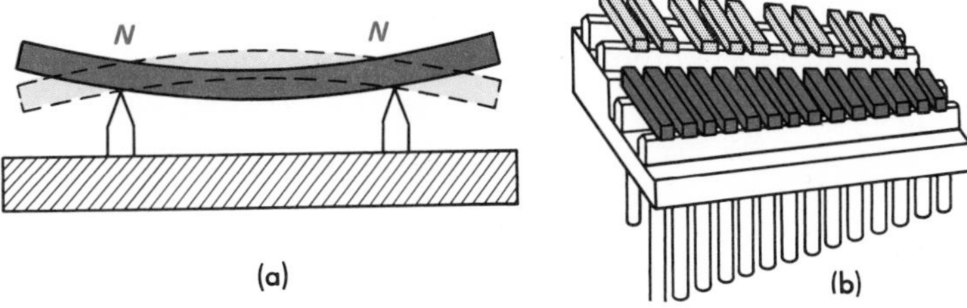

Fig. 20L. The bars of the marimba or xylophone vibrate transversely with nodes near each end.

Transverse waves in a rod are usually set up by supporting the rod at points near each end and striking it a blow at or near the center. As illustrated in Fig. 20L(a), the center and ends of the rod move up and down, forming nodes at the two supports. Like a stretched string of a musical instrument, the shorter the rod the higher is its pitch; and the longer and heavier the rod, the lower is its frequency of vibration and pitch.

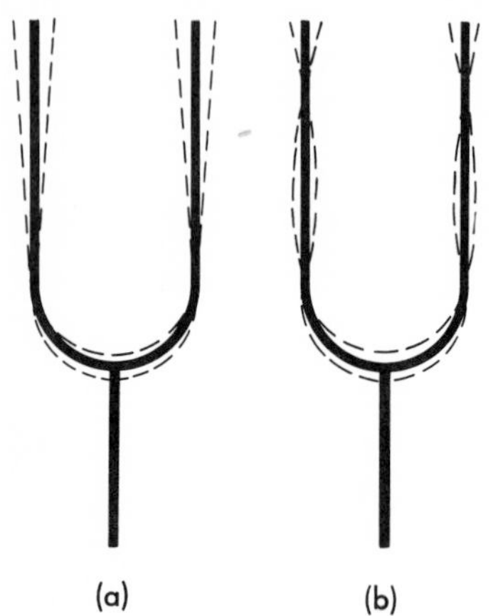

Fig. 20M. Vibration nodes of a tuning fork show (a) fundamental and (b) first overtone.

The xylophone is a musical instrument based upon the *transverse vibrations* of wooden rods of different lengths. Mounted as shown for the marimba in Fig. 20L(b), the longer rods produce the low notes and the shorter ones the higher notes. The marimba is essentially a xylophone with a long straight hollow tube suspended vertically under each rod. Each tube is cut to such a length that the enclosed air column will resonate to the sound waves sent out by the rod directly above. Each resonator tube, being open at both ends, forms a node at its center.

The tuning fork depends for its pitch upon the transverse vibrations of a bar. Sounding its fundamental as shown in Fig. 20M, an antinode forms at both ends. Due to the bend in the center, the two nodes are closer together than in a straight bar, and the antinode at the center transmits forceful vibrations of small amplitude through the shaft to any surface on which it is rested.

20.9. Vibrating Plates

Although the drum or the cymbals should hardly be called musical instruments, they are classified as such and are used in nearly all large orchestras and bands. The sound given out by a vibrating drumhead or cymbal plate is in general due to the high intensity of certain characteristic overtones. These overtones in turn are due to the very complicated modes of vibration of the source.

Cymbals consist of two thin metal disks with handles at the centers. Upon being struck together, their edges are set into vibration with a clang. A drumhead, on the other hand, is a stretched membrane of leather held tight at the periphery, and is set into vibration by being struck a blow at or near the center.

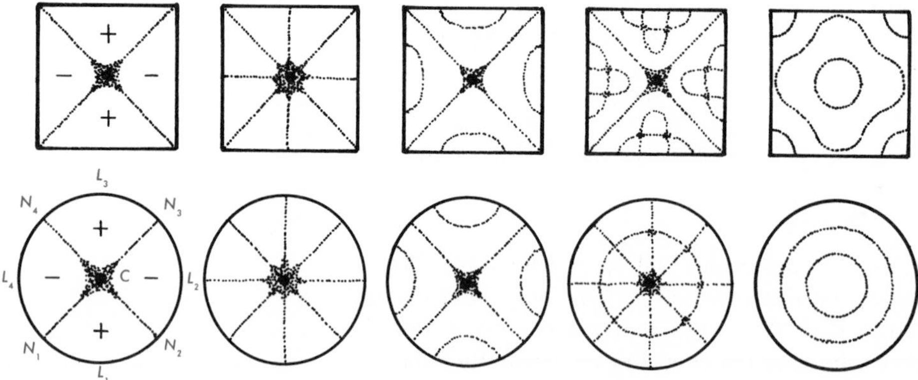

Fig. 20N. Chladni's sand figures showing the nodes and loops of vibrating plates; all but the last two on the right are clamped at the center; the last two are clamped at the periphery.

To illustrate the complexity of the vibrations of thin metal plates, ten typical sand patterns are shown in Fig. 20N. The sand-pattern method of studying the motions of plates was invented in the eighteenth century by Chladni, a German physicist. A thin square or circular metal plate is clamped at the center C and sand is sprinkled over the top surface. Then, while touching the rim of the plate at two separated points N_1 and N_2, a cello bow is drawn down over the edge at a point L. Nodes are formed at the stationary points N_1 and N_2, and antinodes in the regions of L_1 and L_2. The grains of sand bounce away from the loops and into the nodes, the regions of no motion. At one instant the regions marked with a (+) sign all move up, while the regions marked with a (−) sign all move down. Half a vibration later, the + regions are moving down and the − regions up. Such diagrams are called *Chladni's sand figures.*

With cymbal plates held tightly at the center by means of handles, a node is always formed there, and antinodes are always formed at the periphery. With a drumhead, on the other hand, the periphery is always a node and the center is sometimes, but not always, an antinode. Such vibrations constitute *two dimensional standing waves.*

20.10. Bells

In some respects a bell is like a cymbal plate, for when it is struck a blow by the clapper, the rim in particular is set vibrating with nodes and loops distributed in a symmetrical pattern over the whole surface. The vibration of the rim is illustrated by a diagram in Fig. 20O(a) and by an experiment in diagram (b).

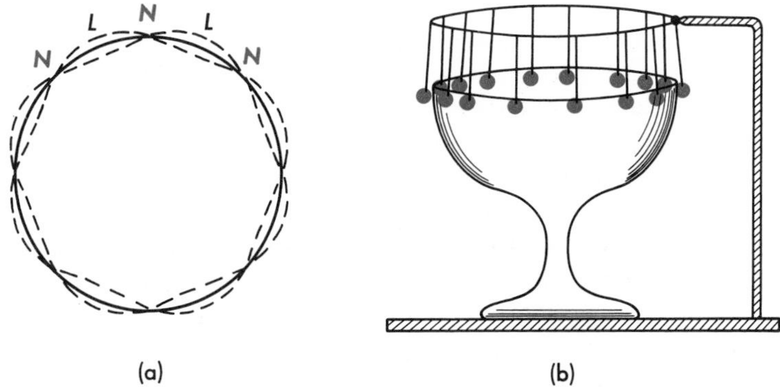

Fig. 20O. Experiment illustrating how the rim of a bell or glass vibrates with nodes and loops.

Small cork balls are suspended by threads around, and just touching, the outside rim of a large glass bowl. A violin bow drawn across the edge of the bowl will set the rim into vibration with nodes at some points and loops at others. The nodes are always even in number just as they are in cymbal plates and drumheads, and alternate loops move in while the others move out.

Strictly speaking, a bell is not a very musical instrument. This is due to the very complex vibrations of the bell surface which give rise to so many loud overtones. Some of these overtones harmonize with the fundamental, while others do not.

problems

Unless otherwise specified, assume the speed of sound to be 350.0 m/s in the following problems.

1. Find the mass of a piano string 80 cm long if under a tension of 2000 N it has a frequency of 150.0 Hz.

2. The string of a musical instrument is 32.0 cm long, and when sounded has a frequency of 198.0 Hz. If the string is weighed its mass is found to be 15.80 g. What is the tension in the string?

3. A harp string with a length of 52.0 cm is tuned to a frequency of 660 Hz. Find the wavelength of the fifth harmonic (a) on the string, and (b) of the sound waves it produces. Make a diagram. [Ans. (a) 20.80 cm, (b) 10.61 cm.]

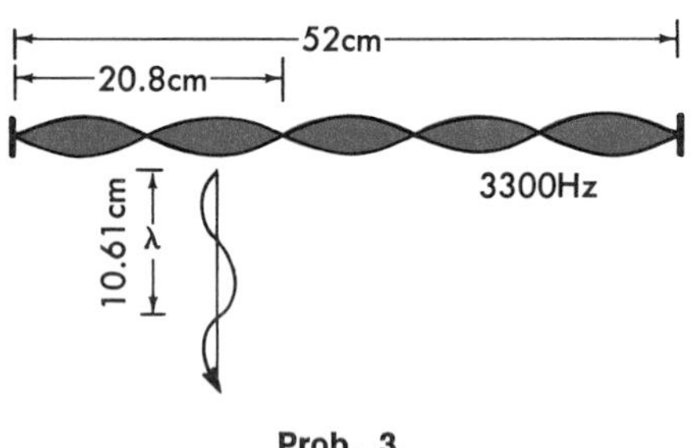

Prob. 3.

4. A steel wire 2.40 m long has a mass of 80.0 g. If this wire is fastened at both ends and then put under a tension of 1600 N, what will be the frequency of the fourth harmonic? Make a diagram.

5. The A string of a violin is 32.0 cm long and has a frequency of 440 Hz. If the mass of this length of string is 6.40 g, find the tension in the string.

6. A straight section of gas pipe is 3.50 m long and open at both ends. What is the frequency of the fifth harmonic of the enclosed air column? Make a diagram. [Ans. 250.0 Hz.]

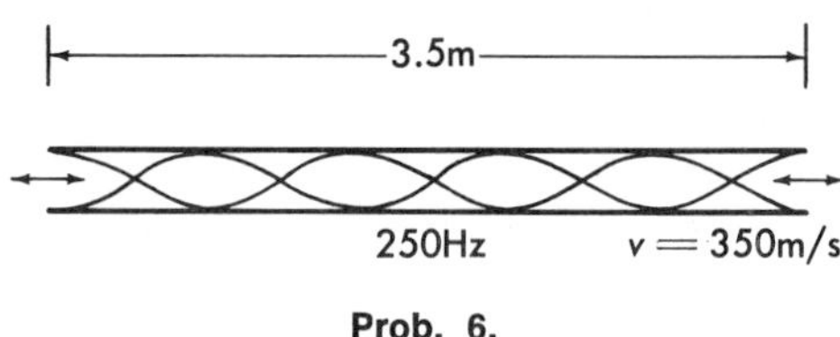

Prob. 6.

7. What is the shortest length of pipe, closed at one end and open at the other, that will resonate to a tuning fork with a frequency of 440 Hz?

8. A large organ pipe is 2.20 m long and open at both ends. Find its fundamental frequency.

9. A woodwind musical instrument has an overall length of 66.3 cm. When it is played, both ends behave as though they were open. What is the lowest frequency that can be produced? [Ans. 264.0 Hz.]

10. If a bugle were straightened into one straight tube its length would be 2.651 m long. Calculate the frequencies of the first six harmonics, assuming both ends are open.

11. A whistle has a frequency of 2000 Hz. If antinodes are formed at both ends, what is the length of the whistle?

12. An organ pipe is tuned to a frequency of 440 Hz when the temperature is 27°C. Find its frequency when the temperature drops to 0°C. Assume both ends of the pipe open. [Ans. 419 Hz.]

13.* A woodwind musical instrument has a length of 66.3 cm. When it is played, both ends behave as though they were open. If the instrument were filled with carbon monoxide at 0°C, what would be (a) the speed of sound in the instrument, and (b) the lowest frequency it could produce?

14.* A hollow pipe 90.0 cm long, open at both ends, is filled with sulfur dioxide gas at 0°C and standard pressure. Find (a) the speed of sound in sulfur dioxide, and (b) the fundamental frequency to which this pipe will respond.

Electricity 21 at rest

It is impossible to say when electricity was first discovered. Records show that as early as 600 B.C. the attractive properties of amber were known. Thales of Miletus (640–546 B.C.), one of the "seven wise men" of ancient Greece, is credited with having observed the attraction of amber for small fibrous materials and bits of straw. Amber was used by these people, even as it is now, for ornamental purposes. Just as the precious metals had their names of gold and silver, so amber had its name "electron."

Although the electrification of amber by friction was handed down from one writer to another, nothing new about the phenomenon was discovered for more than 2000 years. It was not until the beginning of the 17th century that Sir William Gilbert* announced the discovery that many substances could be electrified by friction. Gilbert named this effect "electric" after the word "electron." It is now well established that all bodies when rubbed together become electrified and that amber is just one of a number of substances which show the effect most strongly.

*Sir William Gilbert (1540–1603) was court physician to Queen Elizabeth and a noted philosopher and experimental physicist. In 1600 he published a book on magnetism, *De Magnete.* This book was full of valuable facts and experiments on electricity and magnetism, and among other things contained many criticisms of his contemporaries, predecessors, and the early philosophers. In his preface he wrote: "Why should I submit this new philosophy to the judgment of men who have taken oaths to follow the opinions of others, to the most senseless corrupters of the arts, to lettered clowns, grammatists, sophists, spouters, and the wrong-headed rabble. To you alone true philosophers, ingenious minds, who not only in books but in things themselves look for knowledge, have I dedicated these foundations of magnetic science." So strongly does he advocate here, and carry out, himself, the experimental method, that he is to be classed as a scientist with his contemporary Galileo, "the father of modern physics."

21.1. Electrostatic Attraction

The word "electrostatic" means electricity at rest, and the word "attraction" refers to the force exerted by one body upon another at a distance. To demonstrate electrostatic attraction, one can use a rubber or amber rod and rub it with a piece of flannel or fur. This electrifies the rod, so that, when the rod is held close to some small bits of paper, they jump up to the rod and hold fast.

The attraction of an electrified rubber rod for wood is illustrated in Fig. 21A. A small arrow cut from a piece of dry wood is mounted so that it is free to turn as shown. When the electrified rubber rod is brought near the pointed end of the arrow it attracts the wood, turning the arrow until it points toward the rod. Brought near the opposite end, the wood is again attracted, turning the arrow to point away from the rubber rod.

An ordinary hard-rubber comb when drawn through the hair becomes charged with electricity and will attract light objects in the same way. Sometimes the electrical charges produced in a comb are so great that tiny sparks can be seen to jump between the comb and hair. This is particularly noticeable in a darkened room. These sparks are the reason for the crackling noise so often heard when hair is being combed.

A spectacular effect is produced by bringing a charged rubber rod close to one side of a smoothly running stream of water from a faucet. As shown in Fig. 21B, the stream is diverted to one side and even into the horizontal before it falls again.

An ordinary sheet of writing paper, placed on the panel of a door or other similar flat surface and rubbed, will hold fast and remain there for some little time without falling down.

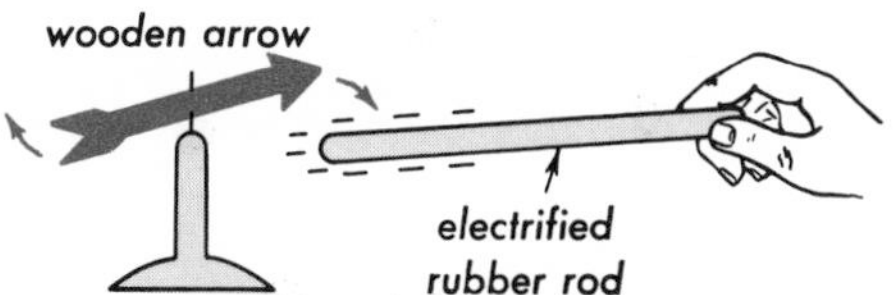

Fig. 21A. A rubber rod, electrified by rubbing against a piece of fur, attracts wood, as shown by the turning of the arrow.

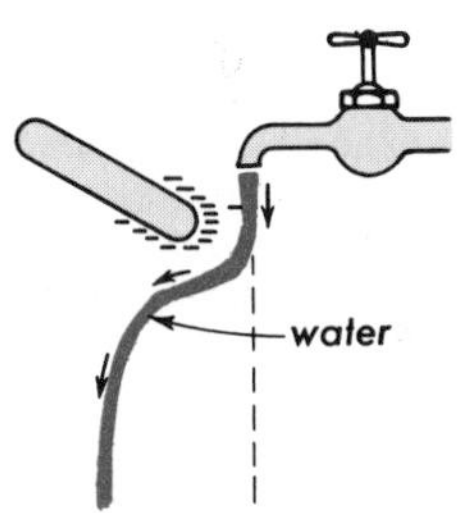

Fig. 21B. A thin stream of water is easily deflected by an electrified rod or comb.

21.2. Electricity + and −

When two different substances are rubbed together and then separated, both are found to be electrified, one with one kind of electricity and the other with another. To illustrate this, one end of a rubber rod is charged by rubbing with fur and is then suspended in a small wire stirrup, as shown in Fig. 21C.

When the electrified end of a similarly charged rod is brought close by, as shown in diagram (a), the suspended rod turns away, showing repulsion. If the fur is brought close by, in place of the

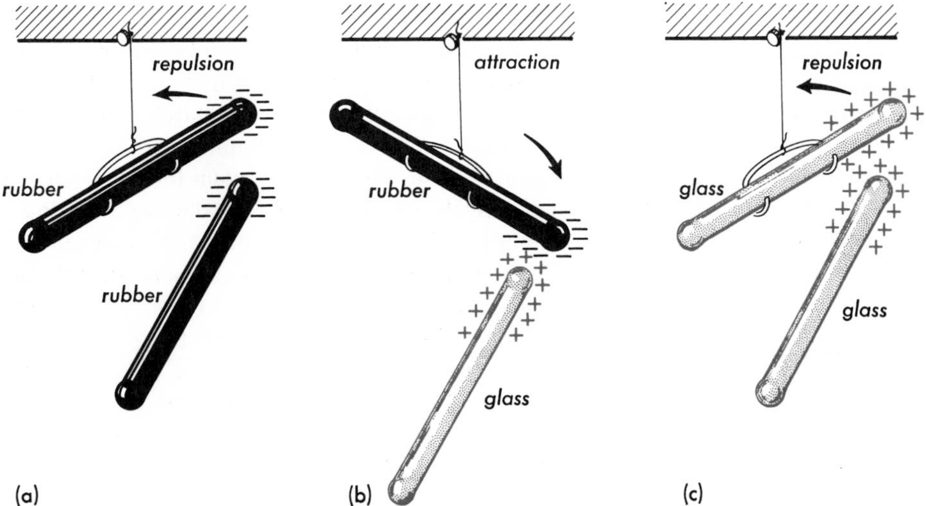

Fig. 21C. Like charges of electricity repel each other and unlike charges attract.

rubber, the suspended rod is attracted and turns toward the fur. When a glass rod, previously rubbed with silk, is brought close by, as in diagram (b), there is attraction, and when the silk is brought up there is repulsion.

Since the fur, as well as the glass, attracts the electrified rubber rod, they each have the same kind of electrification: they are said to be *positively charged.* By similar notation the rubber and silk by their actions are said to be *negatively charged.* Positive charges are designated by a (+) sign and negative charges by a (−) sign.

Not only do the above experiments indicate the existence of two kinds of electrification, but they also demonstrate a rule concerning the action of one kind of electrification on another. Diagram (a), illustrating a negatively charged rubber rod repelling a similar rod, shows that two negative charges repel each other. Diagram (b) shows that positive and negative charges attract each other, and diagram (c) that two positive charges repel each other. The general law can therefore be stated that: *Like charges repel and unlike charges attract.*

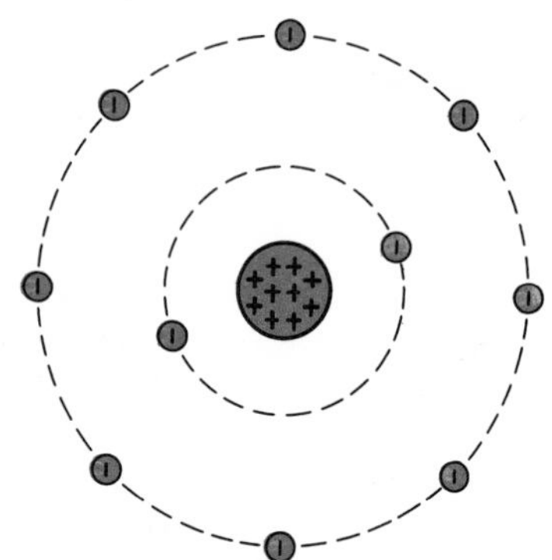

Fig. 21D. Schematic diagram of a neon atom showing its nucleus at the center with ten positive charges (called protons) surrounded on the outside by ten negative charges (called electrons).

21.3. Theory of Electrification

Historically there have been two outstanding theories of electrification: the one-fluid theory of Benjamin Franklin* and the two-fluid theory of Charles Du Fay. According to the two-fluid theory, all objects contain equal amounts of two fluids. When two different substances are rubbed together, one kind of fluid (positive) is spread over one object and the other kind of fluid (negative) over the other.

According to the one-fluid theory of Franklin, all bodies contain a certain specified amount of an "electric fire" or fluid to keep them in an uncharged or neutral state. When two objects are rubbed together, one accumulates an excess of fluid and becomes positively charged while the other loses fluid and becomes negatively charged. To Franklin we owe the terms "plus" and "minus," "positive" and "negative" electricity.

Both of these theories are in part correct, for now we know the mechanism by which bodies become electrified by friction. The modern theory is based upon the principle already put forward —that all substances are made of atoms and molecules. Each atom contains a nucleus having a known amount of positive charge (see Fig. 21D). This positive charge is due to the presence in the nucleus of a certain number of *protons.* All protons are alike and have the same mass and positive charge. Around every

***Benjamin Franklin (1706–1790) grew from printer's apprentice as a youth to a man of unusual powers, not only in politics and diplomacy but also in scientific research. His most famous scientific achievement was the discovery of the electrical nature of lightning. This he did by flying a kite into the clouds on a stormy day and noting the electrical sparks at the ground end of the kite string (a copper wire). Among his many practical applications of scientific discoveries, he invented the lightning rod and made the first pair of bifocal eyeglasses.**

atomic nucleus there are a number of negatively charged particles, called *electrons.*

Normally each atom of a substance is electrically neutral; in other words, it has equal amounts of negative and positive charge. Since each electron has the same amount of charge as every other electron, and the same amount as every proton but of opposite sign, there are just as many protons in every nucleus as there are electrons around the outside.

While protons are much smaller than electrons in size, they contain the bulk of the mass of every atom. One proton, for example, weighs nearly two thousand times as much as an electron. The electrons therefore are light particles or objects around a small but relatively heavy nucleus.

Individual atoms or large groups of atoms and molecules have an *affinity,* or an *attraction,* for additional electrons over and above the exact number which will just neutralize the positive charges of the nuclei. This attraction of the atoms for more than a sufficient number of electrons varies considerably from atom to atom and substance to substance. When, therefore, two different substances are brought into contact, the substance with greater electron affinity seizes nearby electrons from the other, and thus acquires a net negative charge. Such is the case, for example, with rubber and amber when rubbed with fur. Having a strong affinity for electrons, both of these solids become strongly negative, whereas the fur becomes deficient of electrons and thereby positively charged.

21.4. The Electroscope

An electroscope is an instrument for measuring the electrical potential of a charged body. A thin strip of gold leaf is fastened to the side of a long narrow rod of metal and mounted in a metal and glass box (see Fig. 21E). The gold-leaf support, which will here be called the "stem," is insulated from the box with amber. When the metal knob N is touched by a charged rubber rod, some of the charge flows onto and distributes itself over the gold leaf and support. Since like charges repel each other, the gold leaf is pushed out as shown in the diagram. When the source of charge is taken away the electroscope retains its acquired charge, which, distributing itself more or less uniformly over the stem, causes the leaf, as shown in diagram (b), to stand out at a somewhat smaller angle. The more charge given the electroscope, the higher the gold leaf is repelled.

If an electroscope is first charged negatively as shown in Fig.

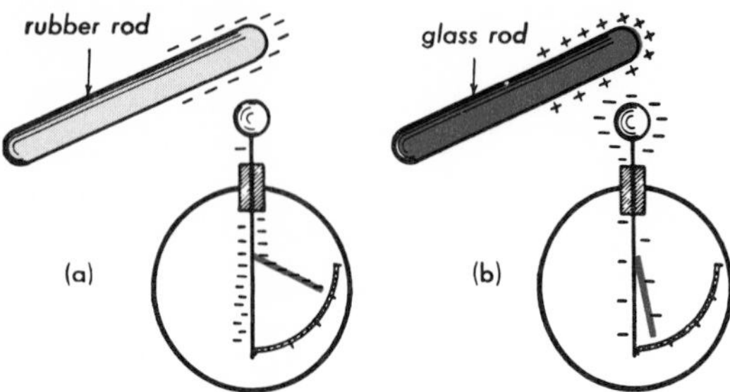

Fig. 21F. Brought near a negatively charged electroscope, (a) a negatively charged body causes the gold leaf to rise, and (b) a positively charged body causes the gold leaf to fall.

TABLE 21A
Examples of substances that are good electrical conductors and others that are nonconductors or insulators

Conductors	*Nonconductors*
Aluminum	Amber
Copper	Glass
Gold	Mica
Iron	Paper
Mercury	Porcelain
Nickel	Rubber
Platinum	Silk
Silver	Sulfur

21E(b), and then a negatively charged body is brought close to but not touching the knob, as shown in Fig. 21F(a), the gold leaf will rise as indicated. This happens because the electrons are repelled away from the knob to the far end of the stem, causing the gold leaf to rise still higher. As long as the two bodies do not touch each other, allowing more negatives to go to the electroscope, the gold leaf will fall back to its original angle when the negatively charged rod is taken away.

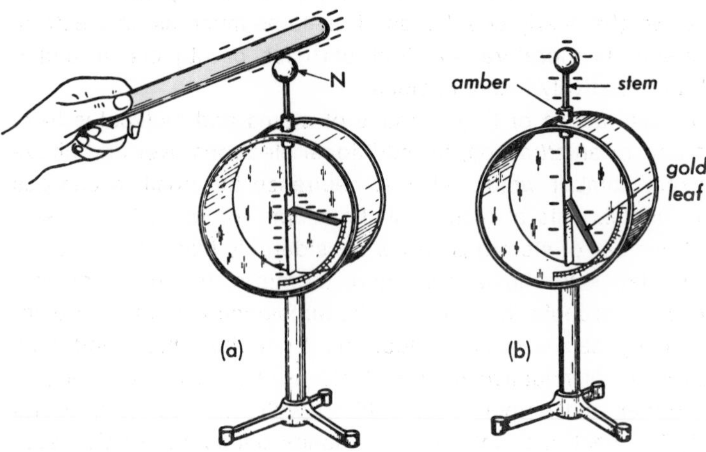

Fig. 21E. Diagram of an electroscope showing how such an instrument may be given a negative charge.

If a positively charged body is brought up as shown in Fig. 21F(b), negatives from the stem and gold leaf are attracted to the knob, causing the gold leaf to fall. *Thus, with a negatively charged electroscope, a positive charge brought nearby causes the gold leaf to drop, and a negatively charged body causes it to rise.* If the electroscope is positively charged, the reverse action will take place: a positive charge causes it to rise and a negative causes it to fall.

21.5. Conductors and Insulators

Not all substances are good conductors of electricity. As a general rule, metals are good conductors whereas nonmetals are poor conductors. The poorest of conductors are commonly called *insulators,* or *nonconductors.* Several examples of conductors and nonconductors are listed in Table 21A.

The property of electrical conduction is illustrated by an experiment in Fig. 21G. One end of a long thin copper wire is connected to an electroscope and the other end to a small brass knob mounted on a glass pedestal. When a charged rubber rod is touched to the knob as shown, the gold leaf of the distant electroscope rises immediately. Electrons have been conducted along the wire. If a positively charged rod contacts the knob, electrons flow away from the electroscope, leaving the gold leaf with a positive charge.

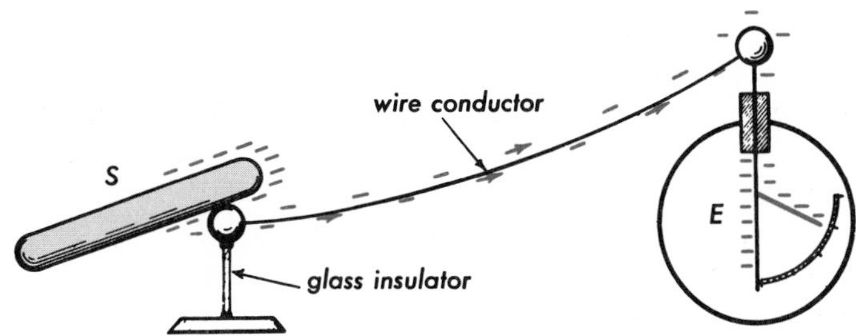

Fig. 21G. Experiment illustrating an electric current as the flow of electrons along a wire conductor.

If the copper wire in the above experiment is replaced by a nonconductor, like a silk thread, the electroscope cannot be charged by the rod contacting the distant knob. Poor conductors, such as glass and amber, are used to support metal parts of electrical apparatuses for the purpose of insulating them from unnecessary losses of electricity. An electroscope, for example, will retain its electric charge well if the gold leaf and stem are insulated from the electroscope case with amber, as shown in Fig. 21E.

The difference between a conductor and an insulator, or dielectric, is that in a conductor there are free electrons, whereas in an insulator all of the electrons are tightly bound to their respective atoms. In an uncharged body, there are an equal number of positive and negative charges. In metals a few of the electrons are free to move from atom to atom, so that when a negatively charged rod is brought to the end of a conductor, it repels nearby free electrons in the conductor, causing them to move. They in turn repel free electrons in front of them, thus giving rise to a flow of electrons all along the conductor. Hence in Fig. 21G it is not necessarily the electrons from the charged rubber rod that actually reach the electroscope leaf, but rather the electrons from the end of the wire where it touches the electroscope knob.

There are a large number of substances that are neither good conductors of electricity nor good insulators. These substances are called *semiconductors.* In them, electrons are capable of being moved only with some difficulty, i.e., with considerable force.

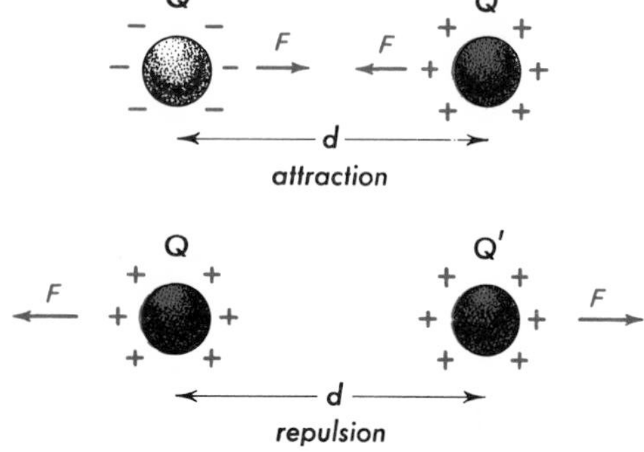

Fig. 21H. Coulomb's law: two like charges repel each other, or two unlike charges attract each other, with a force proportional to the product of their charges and inversely proportional to the square of the distance between them.

21.6. The Law of Electrostatic Force

It has already been demonstrated that like charges repel and unlike charges attract. Nothing that has thus far been said, however, has indicated just how strong the repulsion or attraction might be, nor how it depends on the magnitude of the charges and the distance between them.

The first quantitative measurements of the force between two charged bodies were made by Coulomb* in 1780. He proved experimentally that: *The force acting between two charges is directly proportional to the product of the two charges and inversely proportional to the square of the distance between them.*

Symbolically, this law is usually written as an algebraic equation,

$$F = k\,\frac{QQ'}{d^2} \qquad (21a)$$

where F is the force, Q and Q' are the charges, and d is the distance between them (see Fig. 21H). The constant of proportionality k has a value that depends upon the units chosen.

In the *MKSA* system of units, *force* is given in newtons, *distance* in meters, *charge* in coulombs, and

$$k = 9.0 \times 10^9\,\frac{\text{newton meters}^2}{\text{coulombs}^2} \qquad (21b)$$

Observe that the charges are assumed to be uniformly distributed over the spheres, that the distance d is measured between sphere centers, and that the forces F are mechanical in nature, are vector quantities, and are directed toward or away from the sphere centers.

It is customary to define the coulomb (C) in terms of the *ampere*—the practical unit of electric current. Along with the kilogram, meter, and second, the ampere is to be considered as the fourth fundamental unit, defined later in Sec. 22.2, and all other electrical units are derived units.

The coulomb is defined as that quantity of electrical charge which passes by any point in a wire each second when a current of one

***Charles Augustin Coulomb (1736–1806), French physicist, was born in Angouleme on June 14, 1736. He was a military engineer and spent nine years in the West Indies before returning to his homeland. In poor health, he retired to a small estate at Blois and devoted himself to scientific research. He designed a very sensitive torsion balance, and with it established the inverse square law for electrically charged bodies and for magnetic poles. He also showed that an electric charge is confined to the surface of a conductor and stated that in the case of action at a distance the intervening medium played no part. He is best remembered for the inverse square law known as "Coulomb's law."**

ampere is flowing:

$$1 \text{ coulomb} = 1 \text{ ampere second}$$

$$1 \text{ ampere} = 1 \, \frac{\text{coulomb}}{\text{second}}$$

From here on we will use almost exclusively the *MKSA* system of units.

Since the unit of charge in the *MKSA* system is measured in terms of electric currents, the numerical value of k in Eq.(21a) must be determined experimentally. The best value to date is $k = 8.98755 \times 10^9$. For most practical purposes, however, the approximation $k = 9.0 \times 10^9$ is used. In abbreviated symbols

$$k = 9.0 \times 10^9 \, \frac{\text{N m}^2}{\text{C}^2}$$

Experiments described in later chapters show that electrons are all alike and that each carries a charge

$$e = 1.6021917 \times 10^{-19} \text{ coulomb} \tag{21c}$$

This means that, when a body has a unit negative charge of one coulomb, it has an excess of 6.24×10^{18} electrons and that a body charged positively with one coulomb has a deficiency of 6.24×10^{18} electrons:

$$1 \text{ coulomb} = 6.241450 \times 10^{18} \text{ electrons} \tag{21d}$$

To simplify some of the equations that are derived from Coulomb's law, it is convenient to introduce a new constant, ϵ_0, in place of k:

$$k = \frac{1}{4\pi\epsilon_0} \tag{21e}$$

and write Coulomb's law

$$F = \frac{1}{4\pi\epsilon_0} \cdot \frac{QQ'}{d^2} \tag{21f}$$

Using the numerical value of k from above it follows that

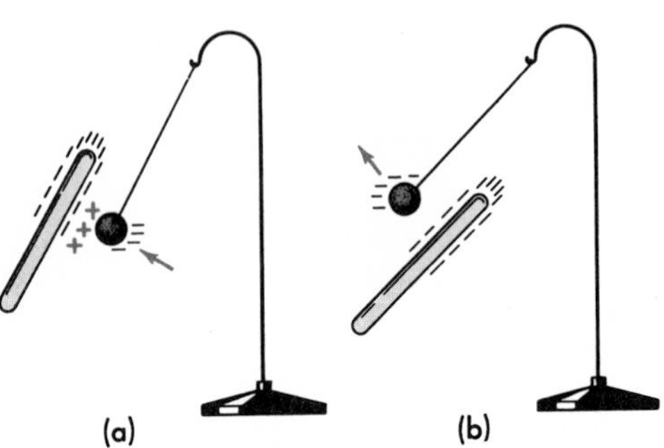

Fig. 21l. (a) A metallic-coated pith ball is attracted by a charged rod; (b) after contact, the pith ball is repelled.

$$\epsilon_0 = \frac{1}{4\pi \times 8.9855 \times 10^9}$$

$$\epsilon_0 = 8.8562 \times 10^{-12} \frac{C^2}{Nm^2} \qquad (21g)$$

This is the so-called rationalized *MKSA* system of units.*

Example 1. A charge of $+25.0 \times 10^{-9}$ C is located 6.0 cm from a charge of -72.0×10^{-9} C. Calculate the force between them.

Solution. The given quantities are $Q = 25.0 \times 10^{-9}$ C, $Q' = -72.0 \times 10^{-9}$ C, $k = 9.0 \times 10^9$ Nm²/C², and $d = 0.060$ m. Direct substitution in Eq.(21a) gives

$$F = 9 \times 10^9 \frac{(25 \times 10^{-9})(-72 \times 10^{-9})}{(0.06)^2 \text{ m}^2}$$

$$F = -4.50 \times 10^{-3} \text{ N}$$

The minus sign indicates attraction.

In the *cgs* system of units, force is measured in *dynes,* distance in *centimeters,* and *unit charge* is chosen so that $k = 1$. Coulomb's law with $k = 1$ then defines unit charge, called the *electrostatic unit* or the *statcoulomb.* One electrostatic unit, or one statcoulomb, is defined as that charge which when placed one centimeter from an equivalent charge exerts upon it a force of one dyne.

Experimental measurements give as the best probable value: 1 coulomb = 2.9979×10^9 statcoulombs. For most practical uses it is assumed that

$$1 \text{ coulomb} = 3 \times 10^9 \text{ statcoulombs}$$

21.7. Attraction of Neutral Bodies

An interesting demonstration of electrostatic attraction is shown in Fig. 21l. A tiny ball cut from the pithy core of a corn cob is coated with tin foil or metallic paint and suspended by a silk thread. When a charged rod is brought nearby as in (a), the pith ball is attracted to the rod and upon contact bounces away. As

* Some books define ϵ_o by the equation $\epsilon_o = 1/k$ instead of $1/4\pi k$. Coulomb's law becomes $F = QQ'/\epsilon_o d^2$, where $\epsilon_o = 1.11 \times 10^{-10}$. This is the so-called nonrationalized *MKSA* system. One must be careful in reading other texts to determine which system is being used.

the rod is now moved toward the ball, it avoids the rod and keeps as far away as possible.

To explain this result, assume the rod to be negatively charged in the position shown in (a). Free electrons on the sphere are repelled to the opposite side, leaving an equal number of positives on the near side unneutralized. Attraction now takes place, because the positive charges are closest and the attractive force acting on them is greater than the repelling force on the negatives. When contact is made, negatives on the rod neutralize all the positives and the ball, with its negative charges, moves away by mutual repulsion.

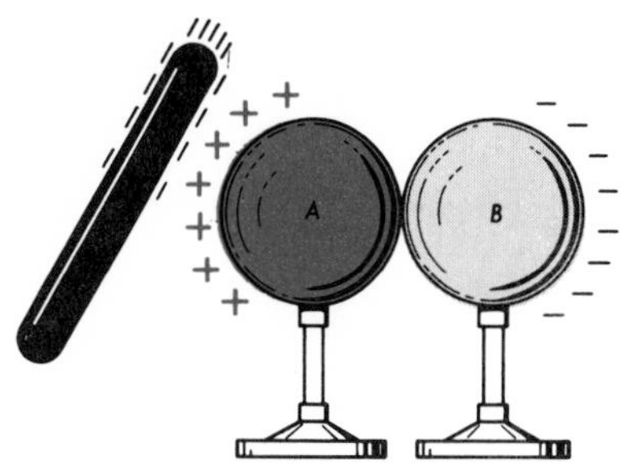

Fig. 21J. Experiment showing how bodies may be charged by induction.

21.8. Charging by Induction

To charge a body by induction is to give it a charge without touching it. One method of inducing a charge is illustrated in Fig. 21J. Two metal spheres A and B, insulated by glass standards, are touching each other when a charged rubber rod is brought close to one of them. If sphere B is now moved away, and then the rod is removed from the vicinity, both spheres are found to be charged, sphere A positively and sphere B negatively.

The explanation is similar to that of the pith ball in the preceding section: the close proximity of the charged rod repels free electrons from sphere A to the far side of sphere B leaving unneutralized positives behind. Separated under these conditions, both spheres are left with their respective charges. This is called *charging by induction.*

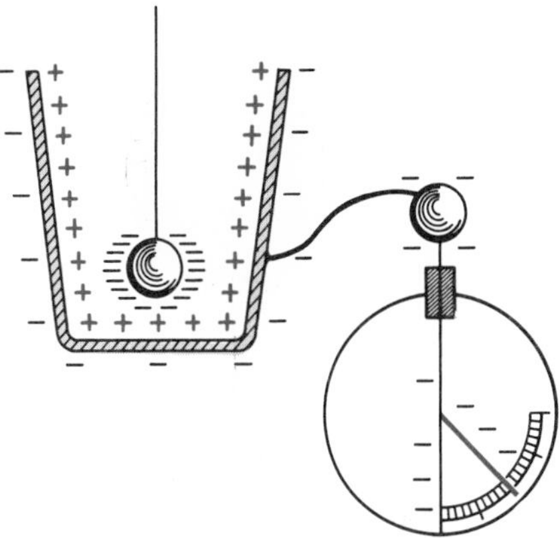

Fig. 21K. Diagram illustrating Faraday's ice-pail experiment.

21.9. Faraday Ice-Pail Experiment

The distribution of charge over a metallic conductor can in part be demonstrated by an experiment first performed by Michael Faraday in 1810. This demonstration, known as *Faraday's ice-pail experiment,* involves a small metal ball, a hollow metal container like a tin pail, and an electroscope, as shown in Fig. 21K.

If the ball is charged from another source and then lowered into the pail, the leaf of the electroscope rises. Upon moving the ball inside the pail, and even touching the inside surface with it, no change in the potential is shown by the electroscope leaf. After the ball has been removed, the inner surface of the pail and the ball are found to be completely free of charge.

To explain what happens, let the ball be charged negatively and lowered to the position shown. Free electrons in the metal pail are repelled to the outer surface and to the connecting electroscope, leaving positives on the inside unneutralized. When the ball touches the pail, all negatives leave the ball and neutralize an equal number of positives. The fact that the electroscope leaf remains fixed when the ball is removed shows (1) that there is no redistribution of the negative charges on the outer pail surface, and (2) that the number of induced positives within the pail was equal to the number of negatives on the ball.

When static charges are acquired by a nonconductor like hard rubber, glass, or amber, they remain where they were first located. When a conductor like copper, silver, or gold acquires a charge, however, the charge quickly spreads over the entire surface. With a metallic sphere, whether solid or hollow, the charge spreads uniformly over the surface as shown in Fig. 21L. On other shaped conductors the charge distributes itself according to surface curvature, concentrating more at points and less where the walls are more nearly straight.

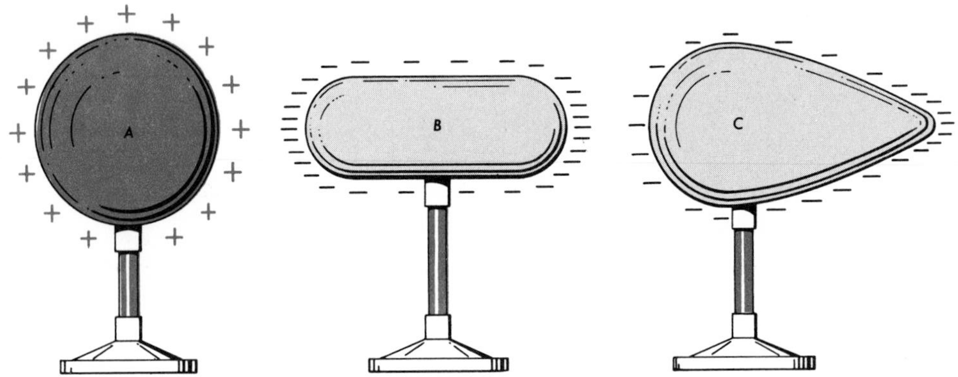

Fig. 21L. Charge density on conductors is greatest in regions of greatest curvature.

problems

1. Two like charges of -2.40×10^{-7} C each are located 6.0 cm apart. What is the force on each charge?

2. Two small spheres 15.0 cm apart, and having equal but opposite charges, attract each other with a force of 6.0×10^{-3} N. Find the charge on each particle.

3. A charge of $+8.0 \times 10^{-8}$ C is located 10.0 cm from another charge of -20.0×10^{-8} C. Calculate the

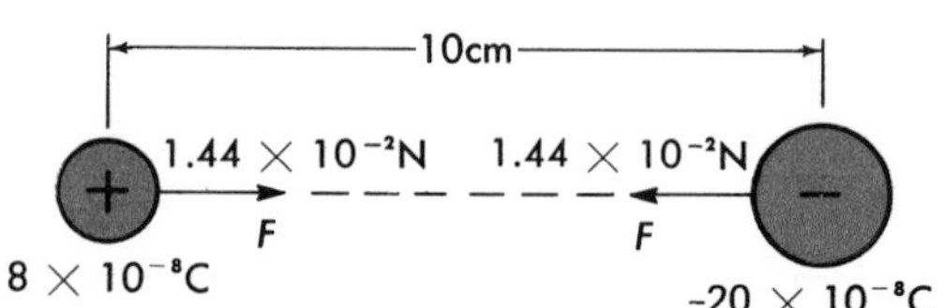

Prob. 3.

force exerted by each charge on the other. [Ans. 1.440×10^{-2} N.]

4. What charge Q placed 12.0 cm from a charge of -30.0×10^{-8} C will produce an attractive force of 0.180 N?

5. Two negative charges of -20.0×10^{-7} C each are located diagonally opposite each other on the corners of a square 5.0 cm on a side. Two positive charges of the same magnitude are located at the other two corners. Calculate the resultant force on each charge, and show the resultant on a diagram drawn to scale.

6. Three equal charges of $+4.0 \times 10^{-7}$ C are located at the corners of a right triangle whose sides are 6.0 cm, 8.0 cm, and 10.0 cm, respectively. (a) Find the force exerted on the charge located at the 90° angle. (b) Make a diagram. [Ans. (a) 0.459 N repulsion at 29.4°.]

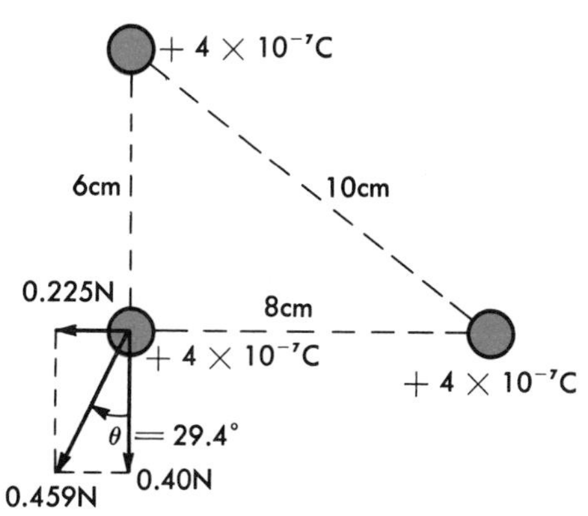

Prob. 6.

7. Three equal charges of $+5.0 \times 10^{-7}$ C are equally spaced 10.0 cm apart on a straight line. Calculate the force on each of the two end charges.

8.* Four charges are placed 8.0 cm apart along a straight line. Starting at one end they have the following charges: $+4.0 \times 10^{-7}$ C, -8.0×10^{-7} C, $+12.0 \times 10^{-7}$ C, and -16.0×10^{-7} C, respectively. Find the resultant force on each of the two end charges.

9.* Four charges are located 6.0 cm apart on a straight line. Starting at one end they lie in the following order: -3.0×10^{-7} C, $+6.0 \times 10^{-7}$ C, -9.0×10^{-7} C, and $+12.0 \times 10^{-7}$ C, respectively. Find the resultant force on each of the two end charges. [Ans. 0.3813 N inward on the -3.0×10^{-7} C, and 2.350 N inward on the $+12.0 \times 10^{-7}$ C.]

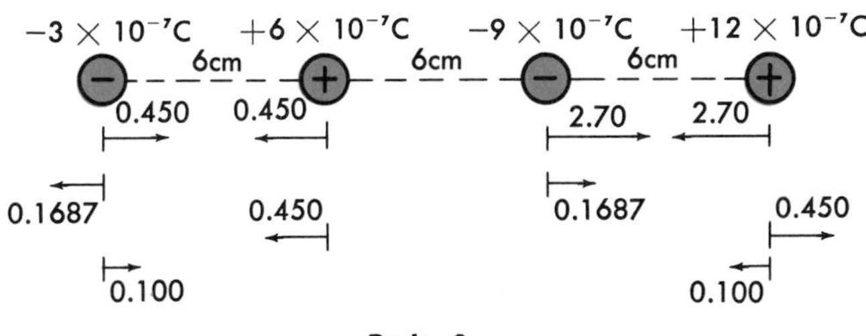

Prob. 9.

10. Three equal charges of 1.80×10^{-6} C each are located at the corners of an equilateral triangle whose sides are 6.0 cm long. Calculate the resultant force on each charge.

Electricity in motion

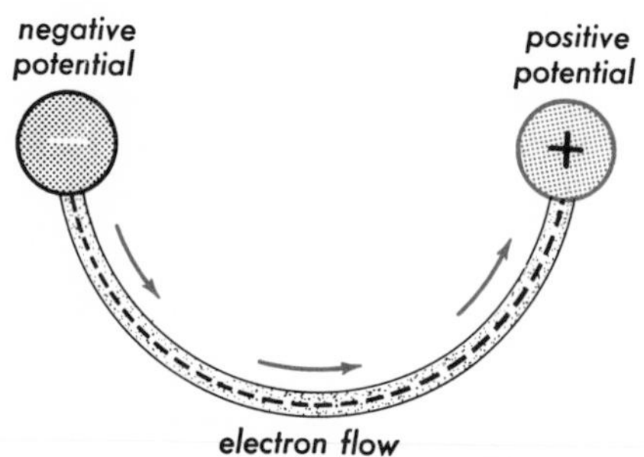

Fig. 22A. Two terminals at different potentials and connected by a conductor give rise to an electron current.

The importance of electricity in our everyday lives is never so well demonstrated as when a city light and power house shuts down. Hospitals, hotels, office buildings, food storage plants, and research laboratories maintain standby motor generator units that automatically start the instant of a city power plant failure. For these and many other reasons everyone should have some knowledge of electricity, how it is connected to common devices, and the basic principles upon which these devices operate.

When an electric charge is at rest it is spoken of as *static electricity,* but when it is in motion it is referred to as an *electric current.* In most cases, an electric current is described as a flow of electric charge along a conductor. Such is the case, for example, in the experiment of charging an electroscope from a distant point by means of a long copper wire and a charged rubber rod (see Fig. 21G). This experiment is explained by stating that electrons already in the wire are pushed along toward the electroscope by the repulsion of electrons from behind. No sooner does this current start, however, than the negative charge of the rod is dissipated and the current stops flowing.

22.1. Electron Current

To make an electron current flow continuously along a wire, a continuous supply of electrons must be available at one end and a continuous supply of positive charges at the other (see Fig. 22A). This is like the flow of water through a pipe: to obtain a continuous flow, a continuous supply of water must be provided at one end and an opening for its escape into some receptacle at the other. The continuous supply of positive charge at the one end of a wire offers a means of escape for the electrons. If this is not provided, electrons will accumulate at the end of the wire and their repulsion back along the wire will stop the current flow.

Many years ago, before it was known which of the electric charges, (+) or (−), moved through a wire, there seemed to be some evidence that it was the positive charge and not the negative. This notion soon became so thoroughly entrenched in the minds of those interested in electrical phenomena that in later years, when it was discovered that the negatives move in solid conductors and not the positives, it became difficult to change.

There are two general methods by which a continuous supply of electrical charge is obtained: one is by means of *a battery* and the other by means of *an electric generator.* The battery is a device by which chemical energy is transformed into electrical energy; the generator is a device by which mechanical energy is transformed into electrical energy.

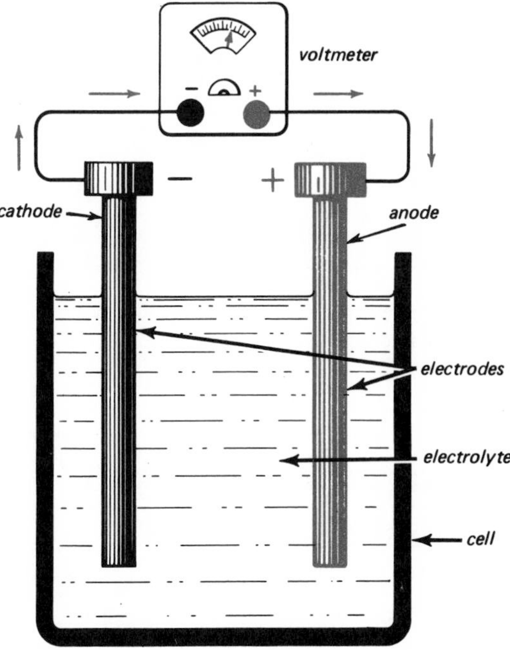

Fig. 22B. The emf of a voltaic cell is measured with a voltmeter.

22.2. Batteries and Electromotive Force

Batteries as continuous sources of electrical energy are the result of a long series of experiments which started with the discoveries of Alessandro Volta* more than one hundred years ago. Today battery cells are manufactured in two common forms: (1) dry cells, as used in flashlights, portable radios, etc., and (2) wet cells, as used in automobiles, airplanes, boats, etc.

Every battery is composed of one or more cells. A battery cell, like the earliest "voltaic cell," is composed of three different parts; a pair of dissimilar plates or rods called *electrodes,* an acid in the form of a liquid or paste called an *electrolyte,* and a nonconducting container called the *cell* (see Fig. 22B).

Due to chemical action between the metals and the acid, one electrode obtains a positive charge and is called the *anode,* while the other obtains a negative charge and is called the *cathode.* When a voltmeter is connected to the two terminals of the cell, the pointer indicates the *difference of potential* in *volts,* and this is called the *electromotive force* (emf). The volt is the unit of *potential difference* in the *MKSA* system, and is abbreviated V. If two or more cells are connected together as shown in Fig. 22C, they form what is called a battery. In this diagram the battery is composed of four dry cells connected *in series.* By series connections it is meant that the (+) terminal of one cell is connected to the (−) terminal of the next.

The purpose in connecting two or more cells in series is to obtain a higher emf than that available with one cell alone. The potential difference between the extreme end terminals A and E of any battery is just the sum of those for the individual cells. Each dry cell produces an emf of 1.50 V, so that if the voltmeter is connected to two points, it will indicate 1.50 V between

***Alessandro Volta (1745–1827), Italian scientist, was for more than twenty years professor of physics at Pavia. Traveling considerably throughout Europe, he became acquainted with many celebrities. In 1801 he was awarded the Copley medal of the Royal Society of London, and then was called to Paris and awarded a medal by Napoleon. In 1815 the emperor of Austria made him director of the philosophical faculty of the University of Padua. A statue now stands in his memory at Como, his birthplace.**

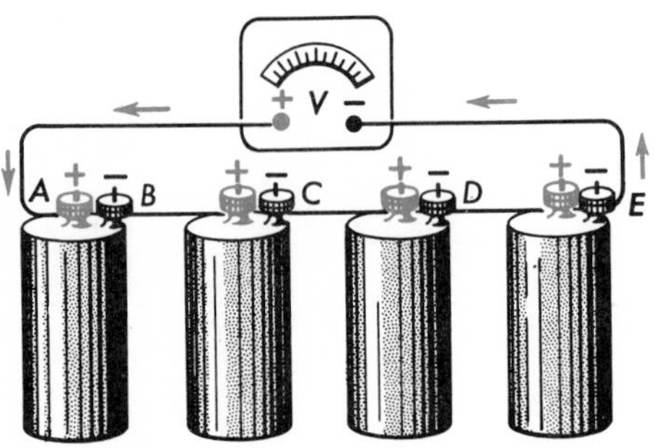

Fig. 22C. Four dry cells connected in series form a 6-volt battery.

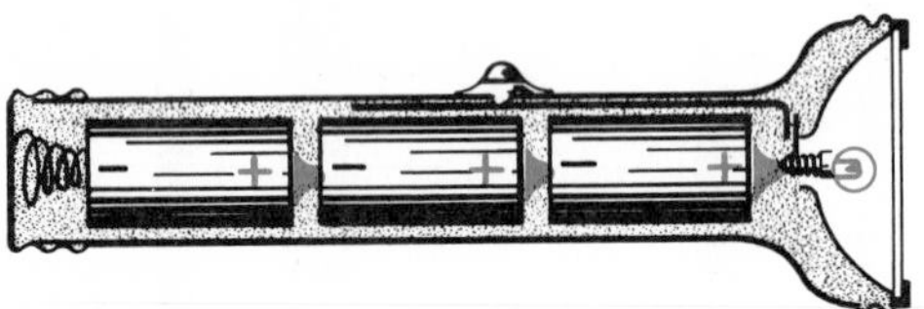

Fig. 22D. Cross section of a 3-cell flashlight.

A and B, 3.0 V between A and C, 4.50 V between A and D, and 6.0 between A and E.

The common flashlight contains several dry cells connected in series as shown in Fig. 22D. When new cells are inserted, they are all turned in the same direction so that the (+) terminal at the center of each cell makes good contact with the (−) case of the next cell. The closing of the switch shown in the figure applies the end terminal voltage of 4.50 V to the light bulb.

The storage battery commonly used in automobiles contains six wet cells of 2 V each, connected in series as shown in Fig. 22E. Note how the heavy crossbars connect the (−) terminal of any one cell with the (+) terminal of the next. With six cells in series the end terminals produce a resultant of 12 V, hence its name of *twelve-volt battery.*

It is customary in circuit diagrams to represent battery cells as shown in Fig. 22F. The (+) and (−) terminals of each cell are indicated by long and short lines, respectively. The first four diagrams shown represent one, two, three, and four cells, respectively, connected in series. If many cells are to be represented, four or five can be drawn and the over-all terminal voltage written beneath it as shown by $V = 45.0$ V.

22.3. *The Ampere*

We have seen in the preceding chapter that electron current is measured in units called *amperes.* The ampere, named in honor of the French physicist Ampère,* is one of the four fundamental units in the *MKSA rationalized system,* and was used in Sec. 21.6 to define the unit of electric charge called the *coulomb.* Although the ampere will be defined precisely in Sec. 26.8, its meaning may be described as follows: one coulomb of electric charge flowing past any given point in a conductor in one second constitutes a current of one ampere:

$$1 \text{ ampere} = \frac{1 \text{ coulomb}}{1 \text{ second}}$$

$$1 \text{ A} = \frac{1 \text{ C}}{1 \text{ s}} \qquad (22a)$$

If two coulombs pass by in one second, the current is 2.0 A. Thus electron current is analogous to the rate of flow of water through a pipe:

*André M. Ampère (1775–1836), French physicist and mathematician, began his career as professor of physics and chemistry at Bourg at the early age of 26. He later established the relation between electricity and magnetism, and helped to develop the subject he called electrodynamics. His only son, Jean J. Ampère, also became famous; he was a philologist, lecturer, and historian.

$$\text{current} = \frac{\text{quantity of charge}}{\text{time}}$$

$$I = \frac{Q}{t} \tag{22b}$$

As stated in Sec. 21.6,

$$1 \text{ coulomb} = 6.241450 \times 10^{18} \text{ electrons}$$

so that a current of 1 A means a flow of 6.241450×10^{18} electrons per second past any given point. This enormous number does not mean that the electrons are flowing with high speed through the conductor. In a good conductor like copper, for example, there are approximately 1×10^{23} electrons per cubic centimeter free to move as an electric current. This means that for a current of 1.0 A flowing through a wire 1 mm^2 in diameter (18-gauge wire), the average drift velocity of the electrons is approximately 4 m/h.

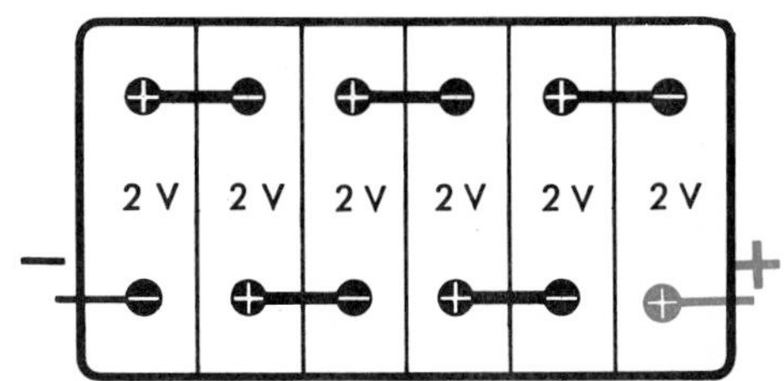

Fig. 22E. Series connections for a 12-volt storage battery.

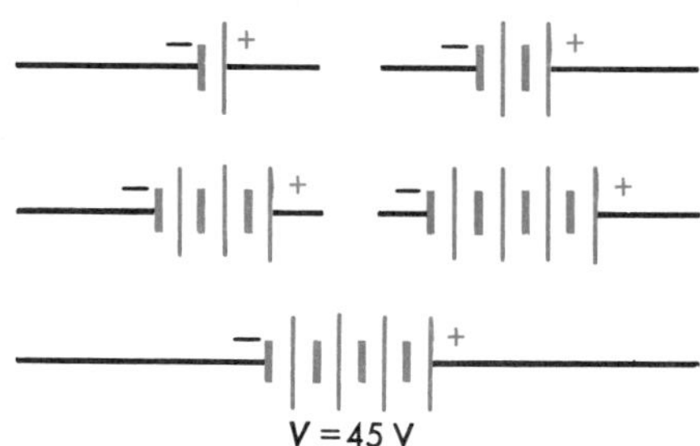

Fig. 22F. Circuit diagrams indicating the cells of a battery.

22.4. Resistance

Every material object offers some resistance to the flow of an electron current through it. Good conductors like the metals copper, silver, and aluminum offer very little resistance, while nonconductors such as glass, wood, and paper offer a very high resistance. The unit by which resistance is measured is called the *ohm,* in honor of the German physicist G. S. Ohm.*

In the MKSA system of units the ohm is defined as the resistance of a conductor which carries a steady current of 1 ampere when a steady potential difference of 1 volt is impressed across its terminals. The ohm is abbreviated Ω.

There are several factors that determine the electric resistance of any wire: (1) the material of which it is composed, (2) the size of the wire, and (3) its temperature. If the length of a wire is doubled, its resistance is likewise doubled; if the cross-sectional area is doubled, the resistance is halved. In more general terms, the resistance of a wire is proportional to its length and inversely proportional to its cross-sectional area. Symbolically,

$$R = \rho \frac{L}{A} \tag{22c}$$

*George Simon Ohm (1787–1854), German physicist, was born at Erlavgen and educated at the university there. After teaching mathematics in Cologne for 16 years, and in Nuremberg for 16 more, he became professor of experimental physics in the high school at Munich. His writings were numerous and, but for one exception, were not of the first order. This single exception consists of a pamphlet on electric currents, the most important part of which is summarized in what is now called "Ohm's law." For this work he was awarded the Copley Medal of the Royal Society of London in 1841 and made a foreign member of the society one year later.

TABLE 22A
Resistivity of metals, ρ, in ohm meters

Aluminum	$\rho = 3.2 \times 10^{-8}$
Bismuth	$\rho = 119 \times 10^{-8}$
Copper	$\rho = 1.72 \times 10^{-8}$
Iron	$\rho = 15 \times 10^{-8}$
Mercury	$\rho = 94.1 \times 10^{-8}$
Silver	$\rho = 1.05 \times 10^{-8}$
Tungsten	$\rho = 5.5 \times 10^{-8}$
Platinum	$\rho = 11 \times 10^{-8}$

where R is the resistance, L the length, A the cross-sectional area, and ρ the resistivity of the material in question. Resistivity is defined as the resistance of a wire 1 m long and 1 m^2 in cross section. Values of this constant are given for several common metals in Table 22A. The smaller the constant ρ, the better is the substance as a conductor.

To find the resistance of any size of wire made of one of these metals, the value of ρ is inserted in Eq.(22c) along with the length and cross-sectional area, and the value of R is calculated. To illustrate the method, consider the following example.

Example 1. Find the resistance of a copper wire 1.0 mm in diameter and 300.0 m long.
Solution. If we use Eq.(22c) and remember that there are 1000 mm in 1.0 m, and area equals πr^2, we find on substitution

$$R = \rho \frac{L}{A} = 1.72 \times 10^{-8}\ \Omega\text{m}\ \frac{300.0\ \text{m}}{\pi \times 0.25 \times 10^{-6}\ \text{m}^2}$$

$$R = 6.57\ \Omega$$

The greater the resistivity of a wire, the poorer it is as an electrical conductor. Because of this, a term called the *conductivity* is sometimes used to specify the current-carrying ability of a material: it is defined as the reciprocal of the resistivity:

$$\sigma = 1/\rho \tag{22d}$$

What makes a material a good electrical conductor or not depends upon the number of free electrons within, and upon how easily these can move between the atoms from place to place. The free electrons in a metal behave a little like the molecules in a gas; they move about at random, with velocities that have a relatively high average value. In the *MKSA* system of units, resistance in ohms has the units m^2Kg/s^3A^2.

22.5. Ohm's Law

This is the well-known and fundamental law in electricity which makes it possible to determine the current flowing through a conductor when the resistance of the conductor and the potential difference applied to it are known. What Ohm discovered was that the ratio of the potential difference between the ends of a metallic conductor and the current flowing through the metallic conductor is a constant. The proportionality constant is called the electrical *resistance*:

$$\text{resistance} = \frac{\text{potential difference}}{\text{current}}$$

Symbolically, Ohm's law is often written

$$R = \frac{V}{I} \tag{22e}$$

In electrical units,

$$1 \text{ ohm} = \frac{1 \text{ volt}}{1 \text{ ampere}}$$

Transforming this equation, one obtains two other useful forms of the same basic law:

$$I = \frac{V}{R} \tag{22f}$$

$$V = IR \tag{22g}$$

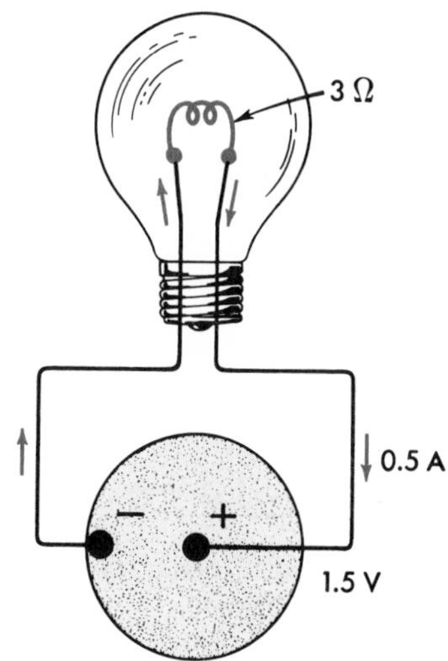

Fig. 22G. A dry cell connected to a small light bulb.

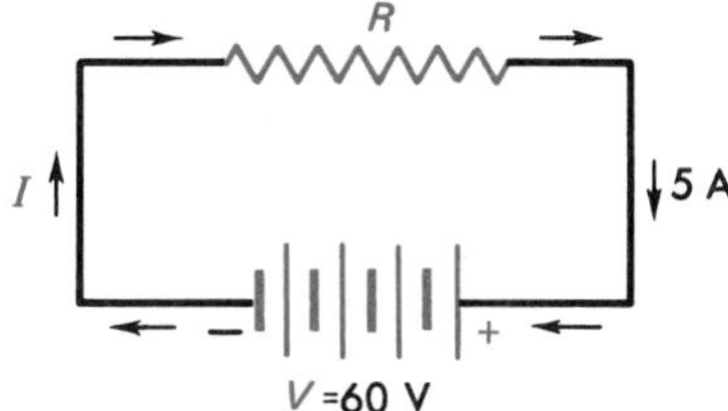

Fig. 22H. Circuit diagram of a resistor *R* connected to a 60-volt battery.

The law is of great importance because of its very general application to so many electrical phenomena. One of its simplest applications is illustrated in Fig. 22G. A dry cell is directly connected by wires to a small light bulb. The battery maintains a potential difference of 1.50 V across the lamp. If the electron current flowing through the lamp is 0.50 A, the resistance of the lamp is

$$R = \frac{1.50 \text{ V}}{0.50 \text{ A}} = 3.0 \ \Omega$$

Although the resistance as found here is assumed to be the resistance of the light bulb, it really includes the resistance of the connecting wires. In practice one usually uses wires of such low resistance that they can be neglected in most calculations. If they are not small, they cannot be neglected and must be added in as part of the *R* in Ohm's law.

Consider the illustration shown in Fig. 22H, where a battery of

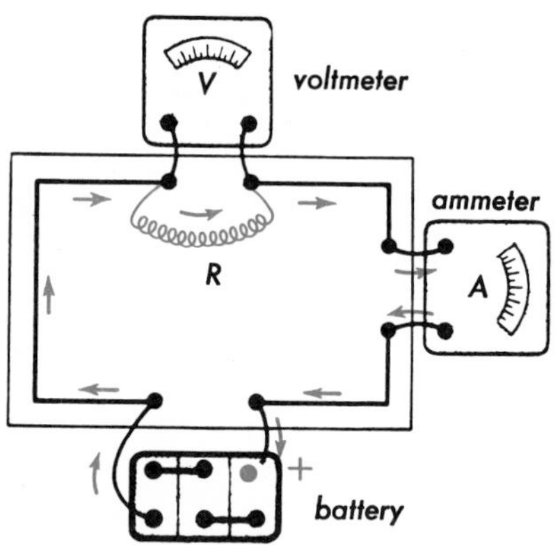

Fig. 22l. Connector board for determining electrical resistance.

TABLE 22B
Recorded data

Element	V	A
Toaster	6.3	2.3
Waffle iron	6.2	1.6
Iron	6.1	1.8

many cells maintains a potential difference of 60.0 V across a conductor and a current of 5.0 A through it. By Ohm's law the resistance of the conductor is given by Eq.(22e) as

$$R = \frac{V}{I} = \frac{60.0\ \text{V}}{5.0\ \text{A}} = 12.0\ \Omega$$

Resistance in circuit diagrams is represented by a saw-toothed line as shown.

To determine the resistance of any electrical circuit it is common practice to use a voltmeter and an ammeter. The voltmeter is applied across the resistance to measure the potential difference, and the ammeter is connected in series to measure the current.

Figure 22l represents a connector board arranged for measurements of this kind. An appliance, or unknown resistor R, is connected between two terminals at the top, so the current supplied by the battery below must pass through it as well as the ammeter. The voltmeter is connected across R to measure the potential difference between its ends.

Suppose that three heating elements, commonly used as replacement elements for electrical kitchen utensils, are connected in turn to the two terminals at the top of the board and a 6-V storage battery is applied to the terminals below. The voltage V and the current I from a sample set of measurements give the following results.

By Ohm's law, Eq.(22e), the resistance of each element can be calculated. This will be left as an exercise for the student.

When a switch is first closed to complete an electric circuit, there are essentially three velocities involved in the flow of an electron current: first, there is the electric impulse that travels along the wire with essentially the speed of light; second, the average random velocity of the electrons; and third, the *average drift velocity* of the electrons in the direction of the current, and this is relatively slow.

22.6. Series Circuits

When several electrical devices are connected in series, the resistance R of the combination is equal to the sum of the resistances of the individuals. Symbolically,

$$R = R_1 + R_2 + R_3 + R_4 + \text{etc.} \qquad (22h)$$

series resistors

This, *the law of series resistances,* is illustrated by an application of Ohm's law to the external electric circuit in Fig. 22J. Three resistors $R_1 = 5.0\ \Omega$, $R_2 = 1.0\ \Omega$, and $R_3 = 3.0\ \Omega$ are connected in series with a battery capable of supplying a terminal voltage of 18.0 V.

To calculate the current supplied by the battery, we first find the equivalent resistance of the entire series circuit. By Eq.(22h)

$$R = 5 + 1 + 3 = 9.0\ \Omega$$

In other words, if the three resistors R_1, R_2, and R_3 are replaced by a single resistor R of 9.0 Ω, the electron current supplied by the battery will be the same. To find this current we note that the potential difference maintained by the battery $V = 18.0$ V. Applying Ohm's law in the form of Eq.(22f), the electron current flowing through the circuit is

$$I = \frac{18\text{ V}}{9\ \Omega} = 2.0\text{ A}$$

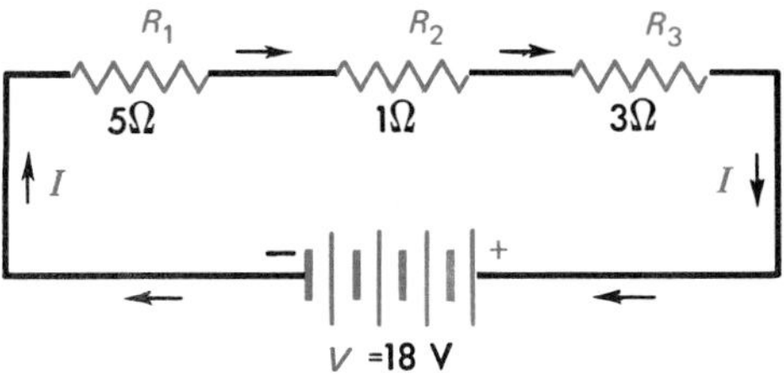

Fig. 22J. The same electron current flows through all resistors when connected in series.

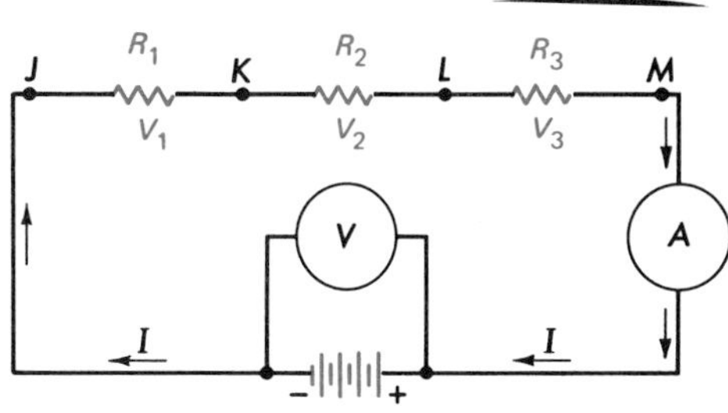

Fig. 22K. Circuit diagram of three resistors in series.

This electron current of 2 A flows through the high resistance as well as the low. Like water flowing through pipes of different sizes connected one after the other, just as much water passes through one pipe per second of time as through any other, and none can accumulate at any point.

A circuit diagram showing how an ammeter and a voltmeter are connected to a series circuit to measure current and voltage is given in Fig. 22K.

If the two leads of the voltmeter are connected to the two points J and K, the potential difference across R_1 is measured. Knowing the resistance of R_1 and the current I through it, one can calculate this potential difference by using Eq.(22g):

$$V_1 = I_1R_1$$

$$V_1 = 2.0\text{ A} \times 5.0\ \Omega = 10.0\text{ V}$$

Because the potential differs by 10 V, from one side of the resistor to the other, this potential difference is commonly called the *IR drop.* In a similar way the IR drop across R_2 or R_3 can be measured by connecting the voltmeter to K and L, or L and M, or computed by means of Eq.(22g):

$$V_2 = 2.0\text{ A} \times 1.0\ \Omega = 2.0\text{ V}$$

$$V_3 = 2.0\text{ A} \times 3.0\ \Omega = 6.0\text{ V}$$

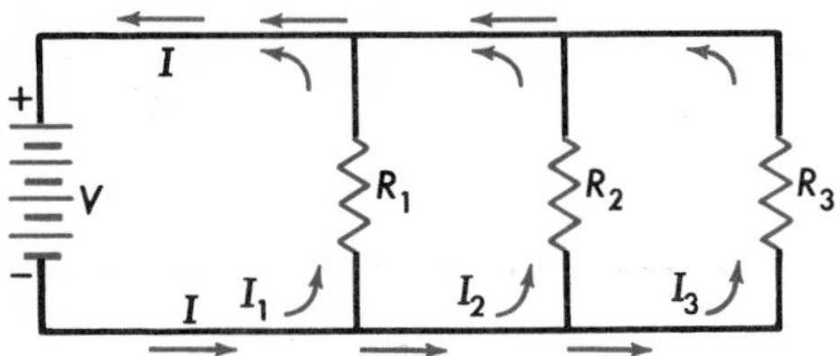

Fig. 22L. Parallel circuit for three resistors R_1, R_2, and R_3.

If we find the sum of all the IR drops around the circuit, we obtain

$$10.0 + 2.0 + 6.0 = 18.0 \text{ V}$$

This is known as Kirchhoff's law and is written in the general form*

$$V = V_1 + V_2 + V_3 + \dots \tag{22i}$$

Kirchhoff's First Law

The construction and operation of any electrical device, whether it is simple or complex, should always be preceded by a certain amount of planning and calculation. The procedure involves a knowledge of the properties of the various electrical components required to accomplish the objective, the drawing of a circuit diagram, and the calculation of the currents that will flow through various parts of the circuit.

It should be noted that in this chapter we will be concerned with circuits involving steady-state currents and voltages, i.e., conditions generally referred to as *direct currents*, or dc.

22.7. Parallel Circuits

A circuit diagram showing three resistors R_1, R_2, and R_3 connected in parallel is shown in Fig. 22L. The electron current I, leaving the battery at the lower left, divides at the first junction; part I_1 goes through R_1, and the remainder goes on the next junction. Part of this current I_2 goes through R_2, and the remainder goes on and through R_3. These three currents recombine at the top junctions and form, finally, the same total electron current I returning to the battery.

It is clear from this explanation that for any number of resistors in parallel

$$I = I_1 + I_2 + I_3 + \dots \tag{22j}$$

Kirchhoff's Second Law

where I is the total current and I_1, I_2, I_3, etc., are the separate currents through the resistors. Equation (22j) is the second of Kirchhoff's laws.

An excellent demonstration of the second law is shown in Fig.

***Gustave Robert Kirchhoff (1824–1887), German physicist, was born March 12, 1824, at Königsberg, Prussia. During his lifetime, he served as professor at the Universities of Breslau, Heidelberg, and Berlin. His contributions to experimental and mathematical physics were numerous and important. He extended Ohm's law to conductors in networks and generalized the relations in two laws known at Kirchhoff's laws. He demonstrated that an electrical disturbance is propagated along a wire with the speed of light in free space, founded the science of chemical analysis by spectra with R. W. von Bunsen, and established a relationship between the emission and absorption of light known as Kirchhoff's law of radiation.**

22M, where four ordinary tungsten-filament light bulbs are connected in parallel to a house lighting circuit of 120 V. The lamps used in this experiment are all different and are rated as 25, 50, 75, and 100 W, respectively. We begin the experiment with all of the lamps sufficiently loose in their screw bases to be disconnected. Each lamp in turn is tightened in its socket, the ammeter current is read and recorded, and then that lamp loosened again to disconnect it. The recorded currents are those shown at the left in Table 22C.

As the second step, each lamp in turn is tightened in its socket without loosening any, and as each new lamp comes on, the current is recorded. This second set of recorded currents is shown at the right in Table 22C.

A careful examination of the current sums in the second set of observations will be seen to confirm Kirchhoff's law, as given by Eq.(22j).

Another type of diagram frequently drawn for parallel circuits is shown in Fig. 22N. Three resistors R_1, R_2, and R_3 are connected in parallel to a 90-V battery. To find the total current through such a circuit, we proceed to find a single resistance R which, when substituted for the parallel combination of R_1, R_2, and R_3, will result in the same current. This equivalent resistance is given by *the law of parallel resistances* as

$$\frac{1}{R} = \frac{1}{R_1} + \frac{1}{R_2} + \frac{1}{R_3} + \cdots \tag{22k}$$

parallel resistors

To illustrate its use, let $R_1 = 8.0\ \Omega$, $R_2 = 12.0\ \Omega$, and $R_3 = 24.0\ \Omega$, as shown in Fig. 22N. By direct substitution in Eq.(22k)

$$\frac{1}{R} = \frac{1}{8} + \frac{1}{12} + \frac{1}{24}$$

Since the common denominator is 24,

$$\frac{1}{R} = \frac{3}{24} + \frac{2}{24} + \frac{1}{24} = \frac{6}{24}$$

from which

$$R = \frac{24}{6} = 4\ \Omega$$

If we now imagine the parallel combination of three resistors replaced by a single resistor $R = 4.0\ \Omega$, the circuit will have the

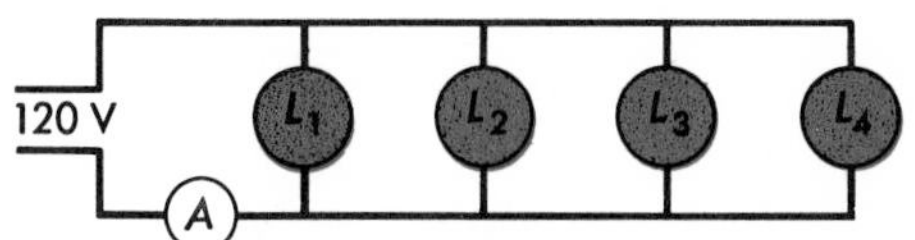

Fig. 22M. Parallel circuit of four light bulbs.

TABLE 22C
Recorded data

$I_1 = 0.24$ A	$I_1 = 0.24$ A
$I_2 = 0.44$ A	$I_1 + I_2 = 0.68$ A
$I_3 = 0.65$ A	$I_1 + I_2 + I_3 = 1.33$ A
$I_4 = 0.85$ A	$I_1 + I_2 + I_3 + I_4 = 2.18$ A

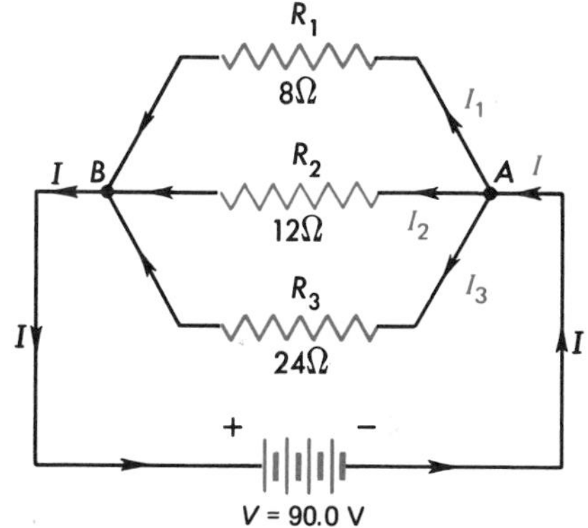

Fig. 22N. Three resistors in parallel, illustrating Kirchhoff's law.

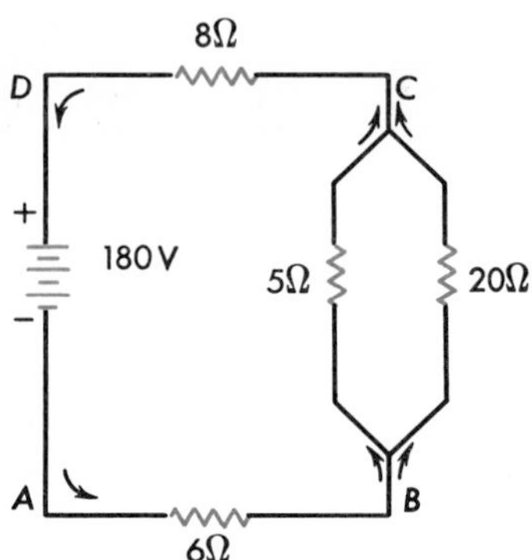

Fig. 22O. Series and parallel resistances in the same circuit.

general form as Fig. 22H, and the current I will be given by Ohm's law as follows:

$$I = \frac{V}{R} = \frac{90 \text{ V}}{4 \ \Omega} = 22.5 \text{ A}$$

This is the total current I supplied by the battery to the parallel circuit of Fig. 22N.

To find how this current divides at A into three parts I_1, I_2, and I_3, we note that the full 90.0 V are directly applied to each resistor. Therefore, Ohm's law can be applied to each resistor separately as follows:

$$I_1 = \frac{90 \text{ V}}{8 \ \Omega} = 11.25 \text{ A}$$

$$I_2 = \frac{90 \text{ V}}{12 \ \Omega} = 7.50 \text{ A}$$

$$I_3 = \frac{90 \text{ V}}{24 \ \Omega} = 3.75 \text{ A}$$

If we now apply Kirchhoff's law, Eq.(22j), we find

$$I = 11.25 + 7.50 + 3.75 = 22.5 \text{ A}$$

and this is a check upon the previous total current. Note that the largest of the three currents, $I_1 = 11.25$ A, flows through the smallest resistance, and the smallest current I_3 flows through the highest resistance.

Kirchhoff's law of currents is frequently stated as follows: *The sum of all the currents flowing into any junction point is equal to the sum of all the currents flowing out.* An inspection of junction A or junction B in Fig. 22N will show how this definition gives us Eq.(22j).

Example 2. A battery supplies a potential difference of 180 V to the ends of a circuit containing four resistors of 5.0, 6.0, 8.0, and 20.0 Ω as shown in Fig. 22O. Calculate (a) the equivalent resistance of the 5- and 20-Ω parallel combination, (b) the electron current supplied by the battery, and (c) the electron current through each resistor.

Solution. (a) Apply the law of parallel resistances, Eq.(22k):

$$\frac{1}{R} = \frac{1}{5} + \frac{1}{20} = \frac{4}{20} + \frac{1}{20} = \frac{5}{20}$$

from which, by inverting, we obtain

$$R = 20/5 = 4.0\ \Omega$$

(b) Since the parallel combination of 5.0 and 20.0 Ω is equivalent to 4.0 Ω, and it is in series with the other two of 6.0 and 8.0 Ω, respectively, the three are added by the law of series resistance, Eq.(22h):

$$R = 6.0 + 4.0 + 8.0 = 18.0\ \Omega$$

Apply Ohm's law, Eq.(22f):

$$I = \frac{V}{R} = \frac{180\ \text{V}}{18.0\ \Omega} = 10.0\ \text{A}$$

(c) The electron current of 10.0 A flows through the 6.0-Ω resistor and divides at B of the parallel circuit. Combining again at C, the total electron current flows through the 8.0-Ω resistor. To find how the current divides in the parallel circuit, the IR drop across that circuit is found:

$$IR = 10.0\ \text{A} \times 4.0\ \Omega = 40.0\ \text{V}$$

This value of 40.0 V is the potential difference between B and C. If we apply Ohm's law to each of the two resistors separately, we obtain

$$I = \frac{40\ \text{V}}{5\ \Omega} = 8.0\ \text{A} \qquad \text{and} \qquad I = \frac{40\ \text{V}}{20\ \Omega} = 2.0\ \text{A}$$

Hence 8.0 A flows through the 5.0-Ω resistor, and 2.0 A through the 20.0-Ω resistor. Note that these currents are in inverse ratio to their resistances.

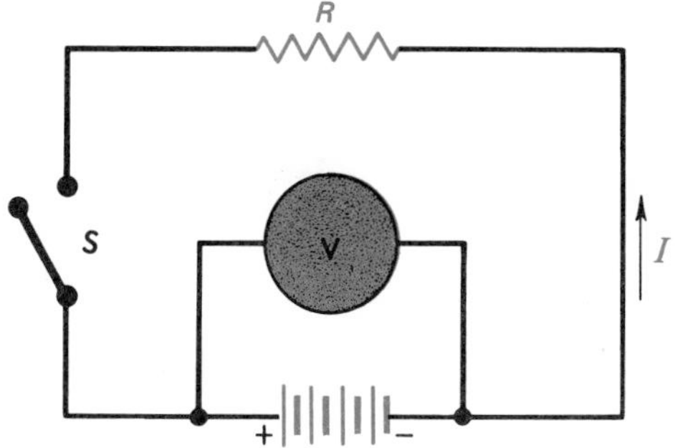

Fig. 22P. The measured voltage V changes when the switch is closed.

22.8. Internal Resistance

Although the terms *electromotive force* and *potential difference*, as applied to electrical circuits in general, are both measured in *volts*, there is a recognized distinction between them. This difference may be illustrated by a demonstration experiment shown by circuit diagram in Fig. 22P.

A battery of four dry cells is connected to a resistor R of 3.0 Ω. When the switch S is open, no current will flow around the circuit. The voltmeter, however, with its very high resistance of several

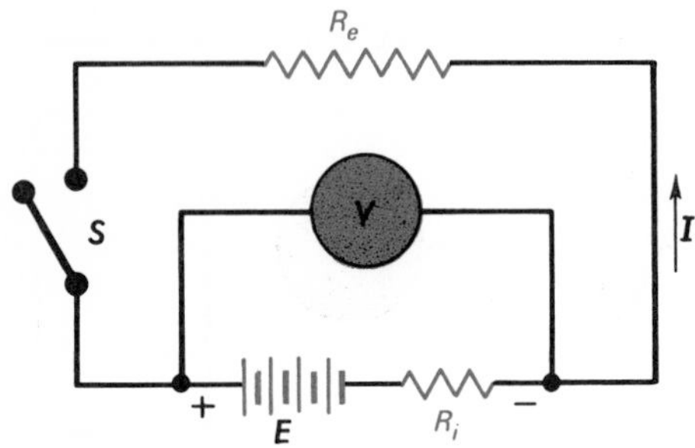

Fig. 22Q. Batteries have an internal resistance R_i.

thousand ohms will draw a negligibly small current from the battery, yet one that will indicate the electromotive force E. For the four dry cells it would read 6.0 V.

When the switch S is closed to complete the electric circuit, a current I of about 2.0 A will flow around and through R, and the voltmeter will show a potential difference V between the battery terminals of about 5.4 V.

The drop in battery voltage from 6.0 V on open circuit to 5.4 V on closed circuit is due to the *internal resistance* of battery cells. This internal resistance behaves as though it were in series with the battery and may be illustrated circuitwise as shown in Fig. 22Q. The total resistance of this circuit is composed of the external resistance R_e in series with the battery's internal resistance R_i. When the switch is closed, the current I flowing through the circuit is given by Ohm's law as

$$I = \frac{E}{R} \tag{22ℓ}$$

where

$$R = R_e + R_i \tag{22m}$$

and E is the internal electromotive force of the battery (E = 6.0 V).

If the internal resistance $R_i = 0.30\ \Omega$, and $R_e = 2.70\ \Omega$, the total resistance $R = 3.0\ \Omega$, and a current of 2.0 A will flow through the circuit. The IR drop across R_i will be $2 \times 0.30 = 0.60$ V, and the voltmeter will indicate $V = 5.4$ V instead of the 6.0 V it indicates on open circuit.

The emf E may be thought of as the driving force of the battery acting on the electrons in the circuit conductors. A voltmeter always measures the potential difference between the two points to which it is connected. This is true whether they are battery terminals or two points anywhere in the circuit. We see therefore that the effective V across a battery will depend upon the battery emf, the current being drawn from that battery, and the internal resistance.

Instead of applying Eq.(22ℓ) to a circuit, it is customary to measure or specify V, the terminal voltage, on closed circuit and then apply Ohm's law in the form

$$I = \frac{V}{R} \tag{22n}$$

where R is the external resistance only.

problems

1. A battery of 28.0 V supplies a current of 20.0 A when the starter of a motorboat engine is turned on. What is the resistance of the starter motor?

2. A storage battery supplies 12.0 V to the headlights of an automobile. If the total current to the two lights is 8.50 A, what is the circuit resistance?

3. A battery of six dry cells is used in a flashlight with a bulb of 24.0 Ω. What current does it draw when it is turned on? [Ans. 0.3750 A.]

4. A copper wire is 2.0 mm in diameter and 5.0 Km long. What is its resistance?

5. A fine tungsten wire 0.80 mm in diameter is 20.0 m long. Find its resistance.

6. Three resistors, R_1 = 2.0 Ω, R_2 = 6.0 Ω, and R_3 = 30.0 Ω, are connected in series to each other and to a battery of 12 dry cells. If the internal resistance is R_i = 2.0 Ω, calculate (a) the current supplied by the battery, and (b) the *IR*-drop across each resistor. [Ans. (a) 0.450 A, (b) V = 0.90 V, V = 2.70 A, V = 13.50 V.]

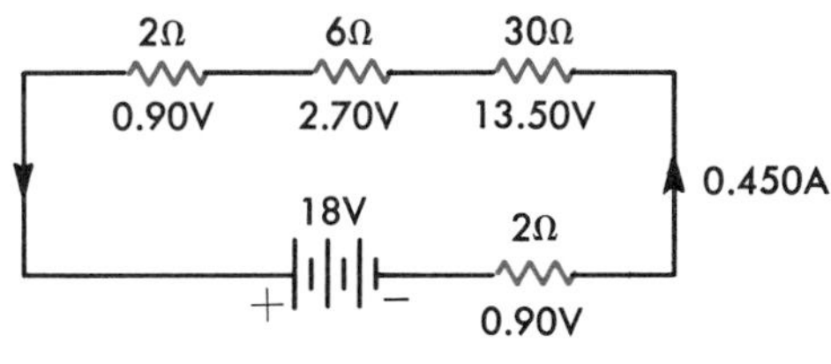

Prob. 6.

7. Three resistors, R_1 = 6.0 Ω, R_2 = 9.0 Ω, and R_3 = 15.0 Ω, are connected in series, and this combination is connected to a 120-V house lighting circuit. Calculate (a) the current through the circuit, and (b) the *IR*-drop across each resistor.

8. Four resistors, R_1 = 4.0 Ω, R_2 = 5.0 Ω, R_3 = 6.0 Ω, and R_4 = 10.0 Ω, are connected in series with each other, and the combination connected to a house lighting circuit of 120 V. Find (a) the current flowing in the circuit, and (b) the voltage across each resistor.

9. Four resistors, R_1=2.50 Ω, R_2 = 5.0 Ω, R_3 = 7.50 Ω, and R_4 = 10.0 Ω, are connected in series to a 120-V house lighting circuit. Find (a) the current flowing in the circuit, and (b) the *IR*-drop across each resistor. [Ans. (a) 4.80 A, (b) V_1 = 12.0 V, V_2 = 24.0 V, V_3 = 36.0 V, V_4 = 48.0 V.]

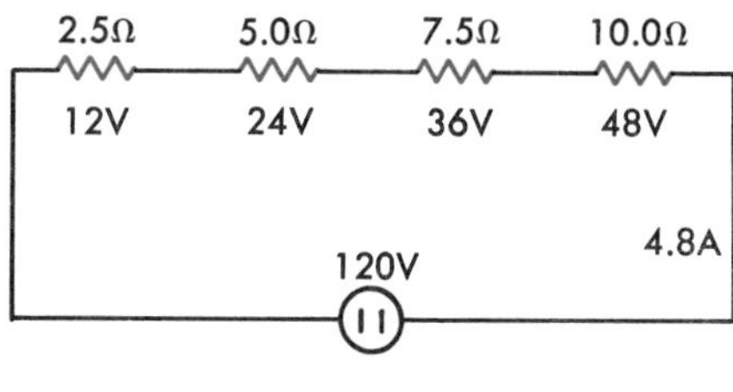

Prob. 9.

10. Three resistors, R_1 = 12.0 Ω, R_2 = 18.0 Ω, and R_3 = 36.0 Ω, are connected in parallel, and this combination connected to a 70.0-V battery with an internal resistance of R_i = 1.0 Ω. Find (a) the current supplied by the battery, (b) the current through each resistor, and (c) the voltage across the battery.

11. Three resistors, R_1 = 40.0 Ω, R_2 = 50.0 Ω, and R_3 = 200.0 Ω, respectively, are connected in parallel. This combination is connected to a 110-V battery with an internal resistance of 2.0 Ω. Find (a) the resistance of the parallel circuit, (b) the current supplied by the battery, (c) the voltage across the battery, and (d) the current through each of the three resistors.

12. Four resistors are connected as shown in Fig. 22O: 2.0 Ω at the top, 3.0 Ω at the bottom, and 8.0 Ω and 24.0 Ω forming the parallel circuit. If a battery with an emf of 30.0 V, and an internal resistance of 1.0 Ω, is applied, find (a) the resistance of the entire circuit,

(b) the current supplied by the battery, (c) the voltage across the battery, and (d) the current through the parallel resistors. [Ans. (a) 12.0 Ω, (b) 2.50 A, (c) 27.5 V, (d) 0.625 A and 1.875 A.]

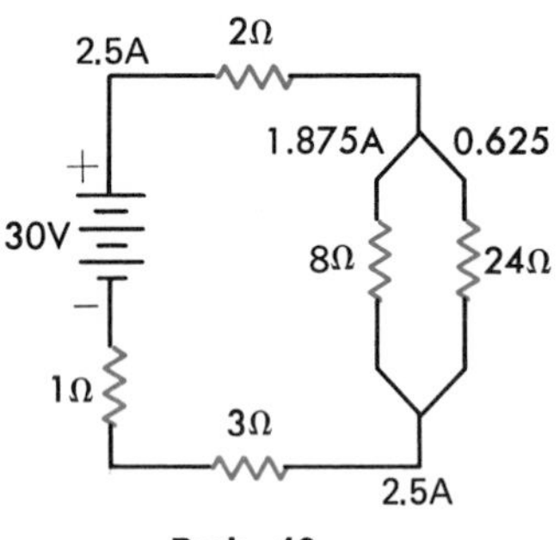

Prob. 12.

13.* Two resistors of 10.0 Ω and 40.0 Ω are connected in parallel. Two other resistors of 8.0 Ω and 24.0 Ω are connected in parallel. These two combinations are connected in series with a 120-V battery having an internal resistance of 1.0 Ω. Calculate (a) the resistance of the circuit, (b) the current supplied by the battery, (c) the voltage across the battery, and (d) the current through the four resistors.

14.* Three resistors 6.0 Ω, 8.0 Ω, and 24.0 Ω are connected in parallel. Two additional resistors of 5.0 Ω and 20.0 Ω are connected in parallel. These two combinations are connected in series with a 40-V battery having an internal resistance of 1.0 Ω. Calculate (a) the resistance of the circuit, (b) the current supplied by the battery, (c) the voltage across the battery, and (d) the current through each of the five resistors.

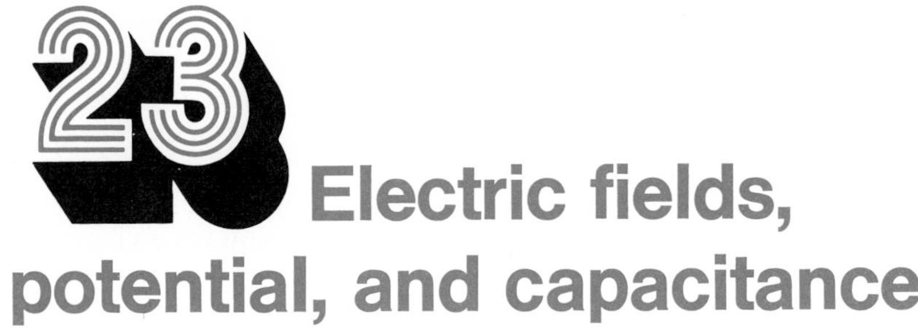

Electric fields, potential, and capacitance

It is common knowledge among students of science that bodies with like kinds of electric charge repel each other, and those with unlike charges attract. The *inverse square law* for calculating the magnitudes and directions of these forces is introduced in Chap. 21 and is known as *Coulomb's law.*

Although we say that charging a body positively means the removal of electrons from it, and charging it negatively means adding electrons, no one knows what an electric charge really is. Whatever this thing we call charge is, we do know that it can exert forces on objects at a distance, even though there appears to be nothing in the intervening space.

In order to describe these electrostatic forces acting across free space, an imaginary invisible medium, called an *electric field,* has been invented.

23.1. Electric Fields

As an introduction to the concept of an electric field, we will start with Coulomb's law: *The force acting between two charges is directly proportional to the product of the two charges, and inversely proportional to the square of the distance between them.* As an equation

$$F = k\frac{QQ'}{r^2} \tag{23a}$$

In the *MKSA* system of units, F is in newtons, Q and Q' are the charges in coulombs, r is the distance between them in meters, and k is a proportionality constant:

$$k = 9 \times 10^9 \frac{\text{Nm}^2}{\text{C}^2} \tag{23b}$$

See Eqs.(21a) and (21b).

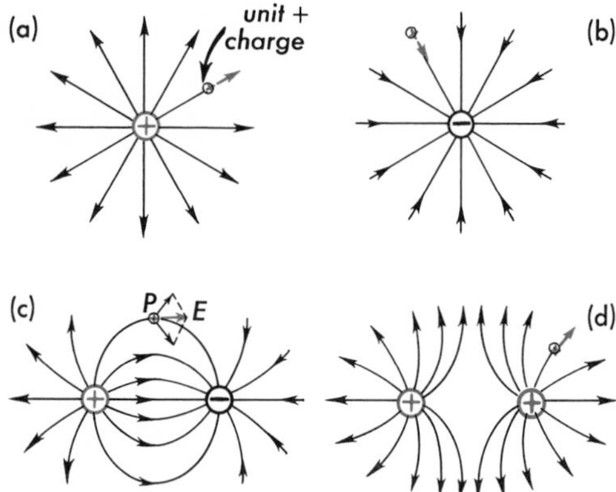

Fig. 23A. Diagrams of the electric field around charged bodies.

The electric field around isolated charged bodies is shown diagrammatically in Fig. 23A(a) and (b). *The intensity of the electric field at any point in the region around a charged body is equal to the force per unit charge exerted on any charge placed at that point.*

To obtain a quantitative expression from this definition, let Q represent the charge on a sphere whose electric field $\mathcal{E}$ is to be determined at all points in the surrounding space. Let q represent a small positive test charge which we imagine placed at any point P in that field. By definition it follows that

$$\mathcal{E} = \frac{F}{q} \tag{23c}$$

where F is the force on the charge q, exerted by the body Q, and is given by

$$F = k\,\frac{Qq}{r^2} \tag{23d}$$

In the *MKSA* system of units the electric-field intensity $\mathcal{E}$ is in newtons per coulomb (*abbr.* N/C).

This concept is analogous to gravitational-field intensity as given by Eq.(12c) in Sec. 12.1. Since force is a vector quantity, an electric field has magnitude and direction. The field about a positive charge is described as radially outward as shown in diagram (a) of Fig. 23A. The direction is an arbitrary assignment and is based upon the custom of finding the direction in which a force would act upon a positive test charge $+q$.

By similar reasoning the field about a negative charge is radially inward as shown in diagram (b). These lines are sometimes called *electric lines of force.* It is to be noted that as many lines as desired can be drawn and that no two lines ever cross. Furthermore, *the lines are imaginary* and do not actually exist. They were first introduced by Michael Faraday about 1820 as an aid to the understanding of various electrical phenomena.

Since $\mathcal{E}$, the electric-field intensity, is defined as the force per unit charge for any charge placed there, Eq.(23c), Coulomb's law, may be used to obtain a formula for the field intensity at any point near a body having a charge Q. Dividing both sides of Eq.(23d) by q gives

$$\frac{F}{q} = k\,\frac{Q}{r^2}$$

or

$$\mathcal{E} = k\,\frac{Q}{r^2} \tag{23e}$$

If the charge Q is in coulombs, and the distance r is in meters, the field intensity $\mathcal{E}$ is in newtons per coulomb. Since F represents the force on any charge q placed at that point,

$$F = q\mathcal{E} \tag{23f}$$

$$1 \text{ newton} = 1 \text{ coulomb} \times 1 \frac{\text{newton}}{\text{coulomb}}$$

$$1 \text{ N} = 1 \text{ C} \times \frac{1 \text{ N}}{1 \text{ C}}$$

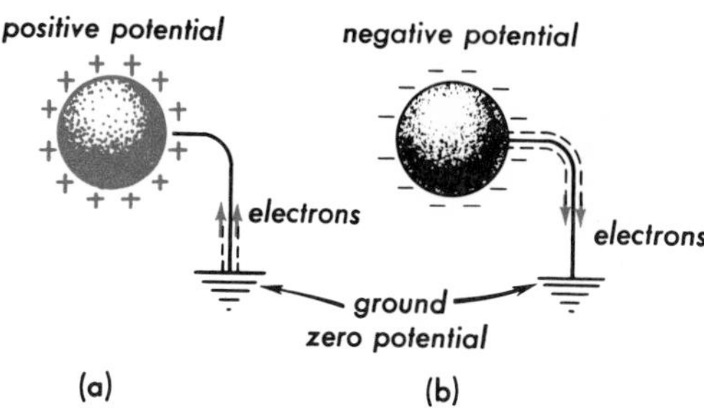

Fig. 23B. Showing the direction of the flow of electrons when a positively or negatively charged body is connected to the ground by a wire conductor.

Example 1. Alpha rays are atomic particles, each having a mass of 6.64×10^{-27} Kg and a positive charge of $+3.204 \times 10^{-19}$ C. Calculate the force on an alpha particle in an electric field $\mathcal{E}$ having an intensity of 8000 N/C.

Solution. The given quantities are $q = +3.204 \times 10^{-19}$ C, $\mathcal{E} =$ 8000 N/C, and $m = 6.64 \times 10^{-27}$ Kg. In this problem the mass of the particle is not needed. By direct substitution in Eq.(23f)

$$F = 3.204 \times 10^{-19} \text{ C} \times 8000 \frac{\text{N}}{C}$$

$$F = 2.563 \times 10^{-15} \text{ N}$$

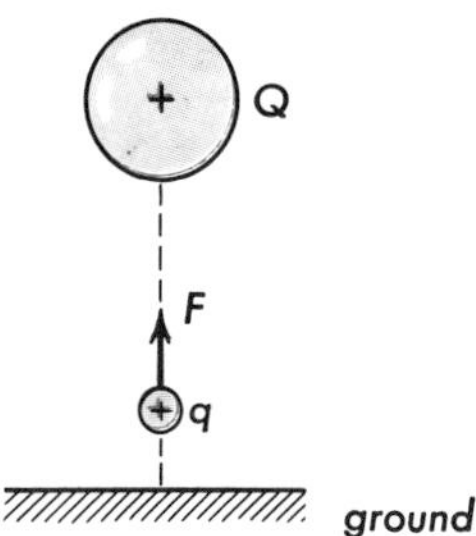

Fig. 23C. Diagram illustrating the expenditure of energy in transporting a positive charge q from the ground to a positively charged body Q.

23.2. Electric Potential of a Charged Body

If the connection of a charged body to the ground by a metallic conductor would cause electrons to flow to that body from the ground, the body is at a positive potential [see Fig. 23B(a)]. Conversely, if the connection of a body to the ground would cause electrons to flow from that body into the ground, the body is at a negative potential [see Fig. 23B(b)].

In these definitions it is assumed that the earth is at zero potential. The bodies therefore have positive and negative potentials, respectively, before they are grounded, because after they are grounded, the flow of electrons to or from the ground will bring them to zero potential.

Electrical potential is analogous to gravitational potential in mechanics [see Sec. 12.3 and Eq.(12r)]. The electrical potential V of a body is equal to the amount of work done W, or potential energy stored, E_p, per unit positive charge in carrying any small amount of charge q from the ground up to the body (see Fig. 23C):

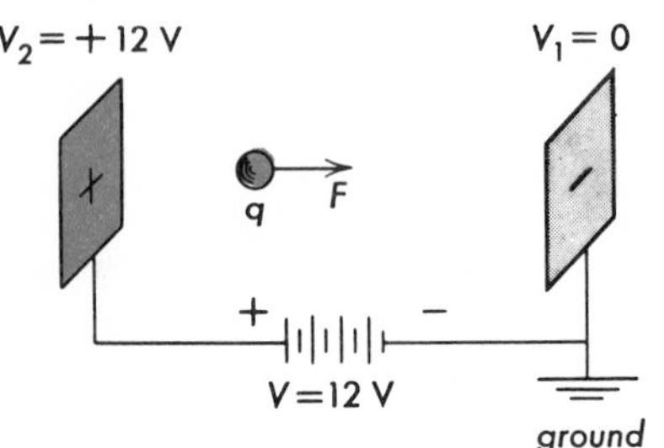

Fig. 23D. Energy is expended or liberated when a charge q is transported through a difference of potential V.

$$V = \frac{W}{q} \tag{23g}$$

or

$$V = \frac{E_p}{q} \tag{23h}$$

In the *MKSA* system of units, E_p and W are in joules, q is in coulombs, and V is in volts:

$$1 \text{ volt} = 1 \frac{\text{joule}}{\text{coulomb}}$$

If Q is positive, energy is stored in carrying a positive charge q up to the body, and the potential V is positive. If Q is negative, energy is liberated in carrying a positive charge q to the body, and the potential is negative. It must be pointed out that potential as here defined applies to the body of charge Q before the small test charge q arrives at the surface; the instant that contact is made, the total charge Q has been altered by an amount q.

The difference of potential V between two bodies having potentials V_1 and V_2, respectively, is defined as the energy expended per unit positive charge in carrying any charge from one body to the other:

$$V = V_2 - V_1 \tag{23i}$$

For example, the difference of potential between the two terminals of a car storage battery is 12 V. This means that the energy expended per unit positive charge in carrying a charge q from one terminal to the other is 12 J/C.

Solving Eq.(23g) for work done, we obtain

$$W = qV \tag{23j}$$

If we connect the negative terminal of a 12-V battery to the ground, this brings that terminal to zero potential, and the positive terminal to +12 V. If the positive terminal is grounded, that terminal will come to zero potential and the negative terminal to −12 V. The difference of potential between the two terminals will be the same in either case: it is 12 V.

Consider an example in which a 12-V battery is connected to two metal plates V_1 and V_2 as shown in Fig. 23D. The grounding of V_1 maintains that plate at zero potential and the battery maintains V_2 at +12 V. If we now carry a negative charge $-q$ from V_2 to V_1, an amount of energy $W = qV$ is consumed, but in carrying it back again from V_1 to V_2 the same amount of energy is liberated.

In carrying a charge $+q$ from V_2 to V_1, an amount of energy qV is liberated, but in carrying it from V_1 to V_2, the same amount is consumed. If V_1 and V_2 are connected by a metallic conductor, electrons will flow toward V_2 and the liberated energy will be converted into heat.

The volt may be defined as the steady potential difference across a conductor which carries a current of 1 ampere and which dissipates thermal energy at the rate of 1 watt:

$$1 \text{ volt} \times 1 \text{ ampere} = 1 \text{ watt}$$

In mechanics we have seen that the watt is the *MKSA* unit of power, where power is in joules per second. We wi.l again see in Chap. 25 that the watt is also the electrical unit of power. The volt has been the legal standard of potential difference since 1950. In the *MKSA* system the volt has the dimensions $m^2 \text{ Kg/s}^3 \text{ A}$.

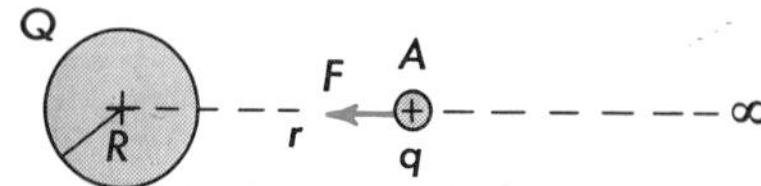

Fig. 23E. The electrical potential at a point *A* at a distance *r* from the center of charge *Q* is given by kQ/r.

23.3. Potential of a Point in Space

Just as every point in the space around a mass *M* has a gravitational potential *P*, so every point in the space around a charge *Q* has an electrical potential *V* (see Fig. 12F). The electrical potential at any point in an electric field may be defined as the work done *W*, or potential energy stored E_p, per unit positive charge in carrying any charge from infinity up to that point (see Fig. 23E):

$$V = \frac{E_p}{q} \tag{23k}$$

Following the same procedure used in Sec. 12.3 to derive an equation for the gravitational potential at a point in space, it can be shown that the stored electrical energy under the analogous electrical conditions is given by [see Eq.(12r)]

$$E_p = k\frac{Qq}{r} \tag{23ℓ}$$

For a mass *m* in a gravitational field the force is one of attraction and the equation carries a minus sign, while for like charges the force is one of repulsion and the equation carries a plus sign.

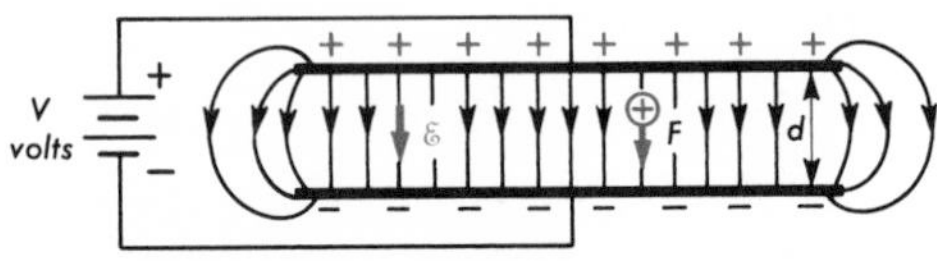

Fig. 23F. The electric field between two parallel charged plates is uniform.

From the concept of electrical potential as given by Eq.(23j), we can divide both sides of Eq.(23ℓ) by q, and obtain

$$V = k\,\frac{Q}{R} \tag{23m}$$

If q is close to the charge Q, the distance r is small and the magnitude of V is large. For positive Q, V is positive; for negative Q, V is negative. Note that by definition of electrical potential the charge q is positive. As r gets larger and approaches infinity, the potential V approaches zero.

Mathematically then, the ground, referred to in the preceding section as having zero potential, is the same as the potential of a point infinitely far away.

If the charge Q is located on a spherical conductor of radius R, the potential at all points outside the sphere is the same as though the charge Q were concentrated at the geometrical center. At the surface where $r = R$ the potential will be

$$V = k\,\frac{Q}{r}$$

while inside the sphere it will remain the same as at the surface.

23.4. Uniform Electric Field

In many experimental studies of atomic structure, a great deal of knowledge can be obtained by observing the behavior of charged atomic particles traversing a uniform electric field. To obtain such a field, that is, a field constant in magnitude and direction over a specified volume of space, two flat metal plates are set up parallel to each other as shown in Fig. 23F.

When the terminals of a battery are connected to these plates as indicated in the diagram, a uniform electric field $\mathcal{E}$ is produced between the plates. Outside the plates and near the ends, the field is not uniform.

Suppose we now wish to calculate the energy required to carry a small charge $+q$ from the upper plate to the lower plate. In mechanics, work done is given by force times distance, $W = F \times d$. The electrical equivalent of this equation can now be obtained by using Eq.(23j) for the energy W, and Eq.(23f) for the applied force F:

$$Vq = q\mathcal{E} \times d$$

giving

$$\mathcal{E} = \frac{V}{d} \quad (23n)$$

between parallel plates

If V is in volts and d is in meters, $\mathcal{E}$ is in volts/meter:

$$1\ \frac{\text{volt}}{\text{meter}} = 1\ \frac{\text{newton}}{\text{coulomb}} \quad (23o)$$

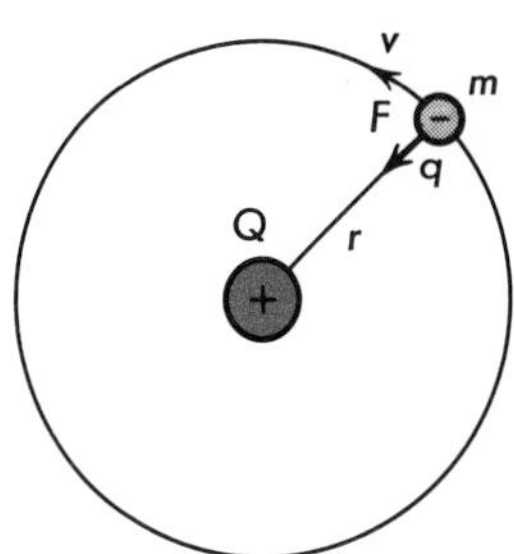

Fig. 23G. A mass m of charge $-q$ is shown moving in a stable orbit in the radial electric field of the fixed body of charge $+Q$.

Example 2. Two flat metal plates 2.0 cm apart are connected to a 1000-V battery. A proton with a positive charge of 1.602×10^{-19} C is located between these plates. Find (a) the electric field intensity between the plates and (b) the force on the proton in newtons.

Solution. The given quantities are $d = 0.020$ m, $V = 1000$ V, and $q = 1.602 \times 10^{-19}$ C. By direct substitution of given quantities in Eq.(23n), we obtain for (a)

$$\mathcal{E} = \frac{1000\text{ V}}{0.020\text{ m}} = 50{,}000\ \frac{\text{V}}{\text{m}}$$

By a direct substitution in Eq.(23f), we obtain for (b)

$$F = 50{,}000\ \frac{\text{V}}{\text{m}} \times 1.602 \times 10^{-19}\text{ C}$$

$$F = 8.01 \times 10^{-15}\text{ N}$$

Just as the path of a mass m moving in a uniform gravitational field is a parabola, so the trajectory of a charge q moving in a uniform electric field is a parabola. This behavior is considered in detail in Chap. 41.

23.5. Total Energy

Consider the illustration in Fig. 23G of a small charge $-q$ moving in a circular orbit of radius r around a fixed charge $+Q$.

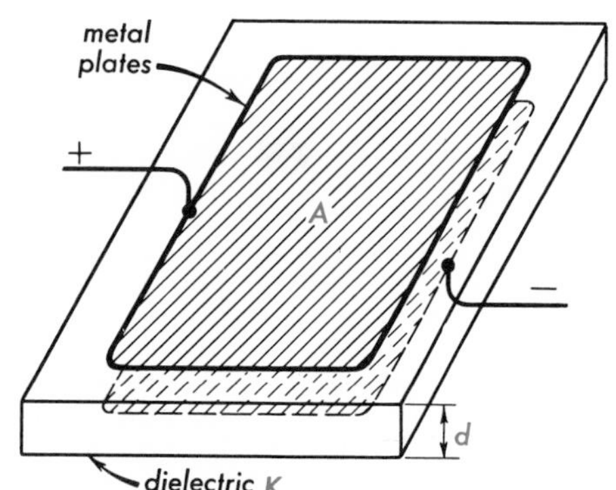

Fig. 23H. Diagram of the principal elements of a capacitor.

The motion of this charge $-q$, moving in the radial electric field of Q, is analogous to the motion of a satellite of mass m moving in the radial gravitational field of a planet (see Fig. 12D).

The total energy E_t of the moving charge $-q$ is composed of two parts: the kinetic energy of the mass m, given by $\frac{1}{2}mv^2$, and the electrical potential energy $-k\,\frac{Qq}{r}$ given by Eq.(23ℓ). Adding these two energies

$$E_t = \frac{1}{2}\,mv^2 - k\,\frac{Qq}{r} \tag{23p}$$

If the orbit is mechanically and electrically stable, the required centripetal force $m\,\frac{v^2}{r}$ keeping the mass m in its orbit is none other than the electrostatic force of attraction given by Coulomb's law. We can therefore write

$$m\,\frac{v^2}{r} = k\,\frac{Qq}{r^2}$$

Multiplying both sides by r, we obtain

$$mv^2 = k\,\frac{Qq}{r}$$

The term $k\,\frac{Qq}{r}$ can be substituted for mv^2 in Eq.(23p), and we obtain

$$E_t = \frac{1}{2}\,k\,\frac{Qq}{r} - k\,\frac{Qq}{r}$$

which simplifies to

$$E_t = -\,\frac{1}{2}\,k\,\frac{Qq}{r} \tag{23q}$$

23.6. The Capacitor

A capacitor is an electrical device for storing quantities of electricity in much the same way that a reservoir is a container for storing water or a steel tank is a container for storing gas. The general form of a capacitor is that of two parallel conducting plates as shown in Fig. 23H.

Such plates are of relatively large area, close together, and contain between them a nonconducting medium called the *dielectric.* Common dielectrics are *air, glass, mica, oil,* and *waxed paper.*

Quantitatively, the capacitance of a capacitor is a measure of its ability to store-up electricity. To increase the capacitance of a capacitor, one or more of the following changes can be made: first, the area of the plates can be increased; second, the plates can be brought closer together; and third, a more suitable dielectric can be inserted between the plates. If the plates of a capacitor are small in area and at the same time relatively far apart, the capacitance is small. If the area is large and the plates close together, the capacitance is large.

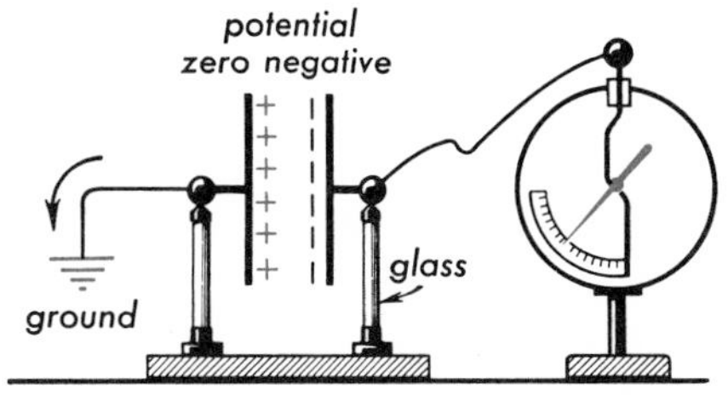

Fig. 23l. Demonstration of the principles of a capacitor.

The principles of the capacitor are illustrated in Fig. 23l. One plate of this capacitor is grounded, and the other is insulated but connected to an electroscope or electrometer. If the right-hand plate is now given a negative charge as shown, electrons in the other plate are repelled into the ground, leaving that plate positively charged. If the insulated plate is given a positive charge (not shown), electrons from the ground are attracted to the other plate and it acquires a negative charge.

In either case the grounded plate is, by definition, at *ground potential,* or *zero potential.* The right-hand plate is at negative potential, since, if connected to the ground, its electrons would escape into the ground. As shown in the diagram, however, the capacitor is charged.

If, while in the charged condition, the two plates of a capacitor are suddenly connected by a conductor, the negatives can flow through the conductor to the positives, thus neutralizing the charges. The capacitor has thus been discharged.

During the time a capacitor is being charged, the plates acquire a greater and greater difference of potential. If in Fig. 23l more electrons are added to the right-hand plate, the potential difference is increased. The amount of charge stored up in this way is limited only by the breakdown of the dielectric between the two plates. When the charge becomes too great, a spark will jump between the plates, thus discharging the capacitor.

Capacitance is not determined by the amount of charge a capacitor will hold before sparking occurs; it is defined as the amount of charge Q on one plate necessary to raise the potential V of that plate 1 V above the other. Symbolically,

$$C = \frac{Q}{V} \tag{23r}$$

The unit of capacitance, the *farad,* named in honor of Michael Faraday,* is defined as the capacitance of a capacitor of such dimensions that *a charge of one coulomb on each plate will give the plates a difference of potential of one volt:*

$$1 \text{ farad} = \frac{1 \text{ coulomb}}{1 \text{ volt}} \tag{23s}$$

Whether one plate of a 1-farad capacitor is grounded or not, the potential difference between the plates will be 1 V when one plate has a positive charge of 1 coulomb and the other plate has a negative charge of 1 coulomb. Grounding simply brings that plate to zero potential without changing its charge. The charge stays with the grounded plate because of its strong attraction from the oppositely charged plate.

A capacitance of 1 farad, abbreviated F, is very large and for practical purposes is seldom used. The *microfarad* is more convenient. This smaller unit is one-millionth of the farad and is abbreviated μF. In other words, 1,000,000 microfarads are equivalent to 1 farad. A still smaller unit, the *micromicrofarad,* or *picofarad,* is sometimes used. One picofarad is one-millionth of 1 microfarad and is abbreviated $\mu\mu$F, or pF:

$$1\ \mu\text{F} = 10^{-6}\ \text{F} \tag{23t}$$

$$1\ \text{pF} = 10^{-12}\ \text{F} \tag{23u}$$

The charging of a capacitor until the difference of potential is 1 V is analogous to raising the level of water in a tank to 1 m, whereas the charging of the same capacitor to the point where it sparks over is like filling a tank until water runs over the top. A large capacitance is like a tank of large cross-sectional area, and a small capacitance is like a tank of small area. It takes more charge to raise the potential of a large capacitance 1 V, and it takes more water to raise the level in a large tank 1 m.

Capacitors in common use today are of various kinds, sizes, and shapes. Perhaps the most common is the so-called "paper capacitor," used commonly in radios and the ignition system of automobiles. Two long strips of tin foil are glued to the two faces of a strip of thin paper. This paper is then soaked in paraffin or oil and rolled up with another paraffin-soaked strip of paper into a small compact unit. Each sheet of tin foil becomes one plate of the capacitor, and the paper becomes the dielectric separating them.

* See Introduction, Chapter A, for biography and photo.

Another type of capacitor is the variable capacitor commonly used in tuning radios (see Fig. 23J). The capacitance of such a device can be varied in amount at will by the turning of a knob. The turning of a knob moves one set of plates between the other set, thus increasing or decreasing the effective plate area, and hence, the capacitance. The capacitance of such variable air capacitors is from zero to about 4000 pF.

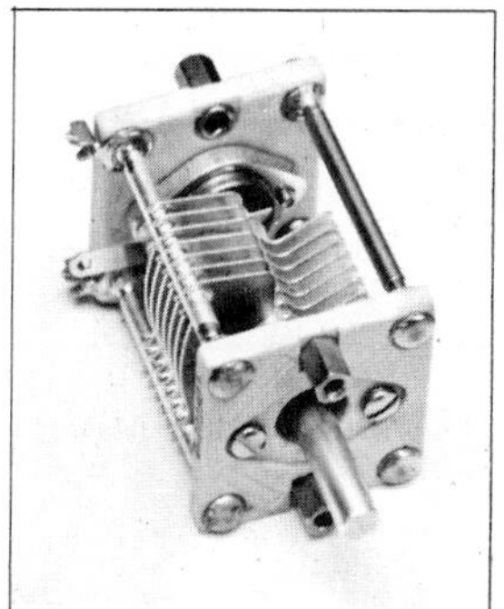

Fig. 23J. Variable capacitor commonly used in radio sets. (Courtesy, Hammarlund Manufacturing Co.)

23.7. Calculation of Capacitance

A general formula for calculating the capacitance of a parallel-plate capacitor is the following:

$$C = \epsilon \frac{A}{d} \tag{23v}$$

where, as shown in Fig. 23H, A is the area of either of the parallel plates in m^2, d is the distance between them in m, ϵ a constant of the separating medium, and C is the capacitance in farads.

The constant ϵ, called the *permittivity,* is the product of the constant

$$\epsilon_0 = 8.8562 \times 10^{-12} \text{ F/m}$$

and K the *dielectric constant,* or *dielectric coefficient:*

$$\epsilon = \epsilon_0 K \tag{23w}$$

Values of the dielectric constant of a few substances are given in Table 23A.

In the *MKSA* system, permittivity has the units of $A^2s^4/Kg\ m^3$ or, what is the equivalent, C^2/Jm.

TABLE 23A
Dielectric constants

Dielectric	*K*
Vacuum	1.0000
Air	1.0006
Glass	5–10
Rubber	3–35
Mica	3–6
Glycerine	56
Petroleum	2
Water	81

Example 3. Two rectangular sheets of tinfoil 20.0 cm × 25.0 cm are stuck to opposite sides of a thin sheet of mica 0.10 mm thick. Calculate the capacitance if the dielectric constant is 5.0.

Solution. The given quantities are $K = 5.0$, $d = 1.0 \times 10^{-4}$ m, and $A = 0.200 \times 0.250 = 0.050\ m^2$. By substituting in Eqs. (23v) and (23w), we obtain

$$C = 5 \times 8.86 \times 10^{-12} \frac{0.05}{1 \times 10^{-4}}$$

$$= 221.5 \times 10^{-10} \text{ farad} = 0.02212\ \mu\text{F}$$

---

parallel capacitors

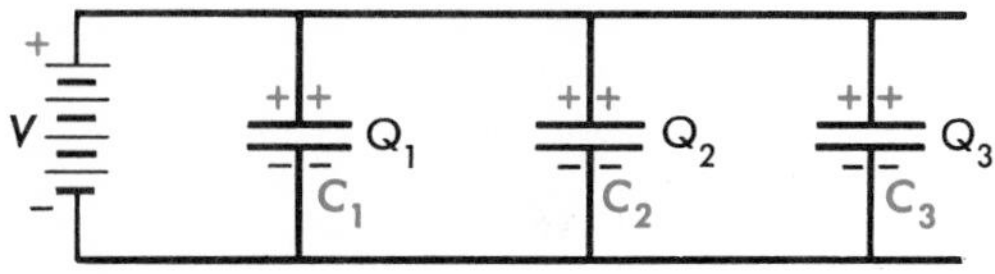

Fig. 23K. Circuit diagram of parallel capacitors.

series capacitors

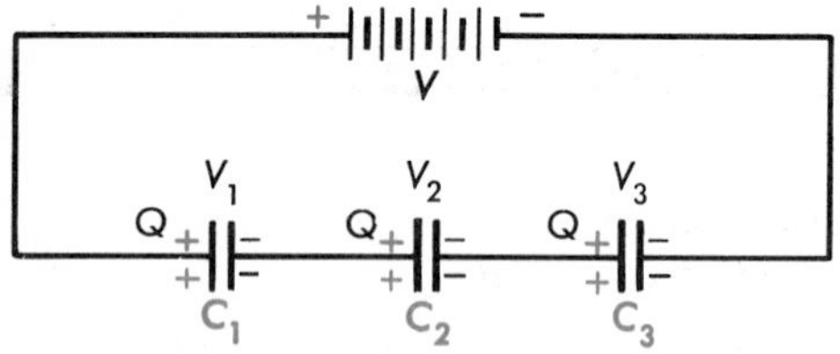

Fig. 23L. Circuit diagram of capacitors connected in series.

When capacitors are connected in parallel, as shown in Fig. 23K, their combined capacitance is just the arithmetic sum of the individual capacities:

$$C = C_1 + C_2 + C_3 + \ldots \quad (23x)$$

parallel capacitors

When capacitors are connected in series, as shown in Fig. 23L, the combined capacitance is given by the reciprocal of the sum of the reciprocals:

$$\frac{1}{C} = \frac{1}{C_1} + \frac{1}{C_2} + \frac{1}{C_3} + \ldots \quad (23y)$$

series capacitors

The first formula is derived from the principle that capacitors in a parallel combination each have the same potential difference V given by $V = Q/C$, while $Q = Q_1 + Q_2 + Q_3 +$ etc. The second of these formulas is derived from the principle that capacitors in a series combination acquire the same charge Q given by $Q = CV$, while $V = V_1 + V_2 + V_3 +$ etc.

It should be noted with care that these two formulas are just the reverse of those for series and parallel resistors. Their derivation is left as a student exercise.

problems

1. A hollow metal sphere, with a negative charge of -8.0×10^{-8} C, is supported on the end of an insulating rod. What is (a) the electric field intensity, and (b) the potential at a point 25.0 cm from the center of the sphere?

2. A spherical conductor 0.60 m in diameter has a charge of 7.0×10^{-7} C. Calculate the potential of (a) the surface of the spherical conductor, and (b) at a point 1.0 m from the center.

3. A charge of -4.50×10^{-7} C is carried from a distant point up to a charged metal sphere. What is the electrical potential of that body if the work done is 1.80×10^{-3} J. [Ans. -4.0×10^4 V.]

4. A hollow metal ball 8.0 cm in diameter is given a charge of -5.0×10^{-8} C. What is (a) the electric field intensity, and (b) the electric potential at a point 15.0 cm from the center of the ball?

5. Two metal spheres 30.0 cm apart have charges of -6.0×10^{-7} C and $+6.0 \times 10^{-7}$ C, respectively. Calculate (a) the electric field intensity, and (b) the potential at a point 30.0 cm from the center of each sphere.

6. Two insulated spheres 50.0 cm apart each have a charge of -9.0×10^{-7} C. Calculate (a) the electric field intensity, and (b) the potential at a point on a straight line through the centers of the spheres and

1.0 m beyond either of the spheres. [Ans. (a) -11.70×10^3 N/C, (b) -13.50×10^3 V.]

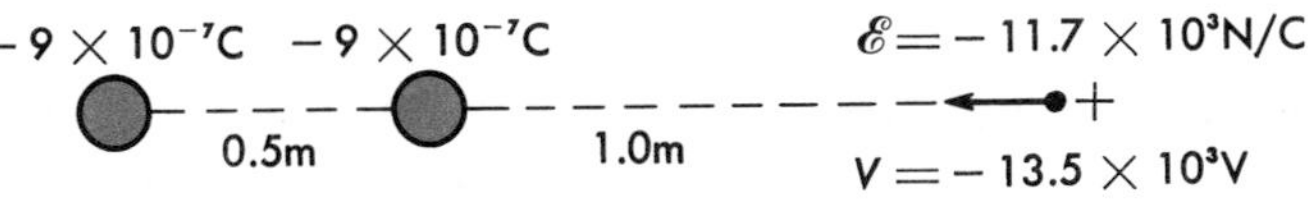

Prob. 6.

7. Two metal spheres 50.0 cm apart have charges $+6.0 \times 10^{-6}$ C and -6.0×10^{-6} C, respectively. Calculate (a) the electric field intensity, and (b) the potential at a point on a straight line through their centers and 50.0 cm beyond the negative charge.

8. A 6000-V battery is connected to two parallel metal plates 3.0 cm apart. A small drop of oil with a charge of 9.60×10^{-19} C is falling between the plates (see Fig. 23F). Find (a) the electric field intensity between the plates in N/C, and (b) the force on the oildrop. Neglect gravitational forces.

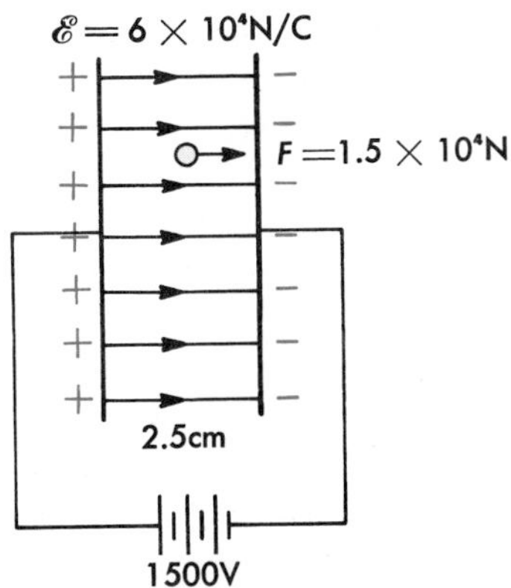

Prob. 9.

9. Two flat metal plates 2.50 cm apart are connected to a 1500-V battery, as shown in Fig. 23F. A small positively charged body with 2.50×10^{-9} C is located between the plates. Find (a) the electric field intensity between the plates, and (b) the force on the charged body. [Ans. (a) 6.0×10^4 N/C, (b) 1.50×10^{-4} N.]

10.* A metal sphere 8.0 cm in diameter has a charge of 1.50×10^{-8} C. What is the electric field intensity at a distance from the center of (a) 30.0 cm, (b) 20.0 cm, (c) 10.0 cm, (d) 5.0 cm? (e) Plot a graph of the field intensity $\mathcal{E}$ versus the distance r. Show the curve from $r = 0$ to $r = 40.0$ cm.

11. A 450-V battery is connected to a 15.0 μF capacitor. How much charge does each pole hold?

12. A battery of 7000 V is applied to two metal plates 2.50 cm apart. What is the force on an electron of charge -1.60×10^{-19} C when it passes through the uniform electric field between the plates? [Ans. 4.48×10^{-14} N.]

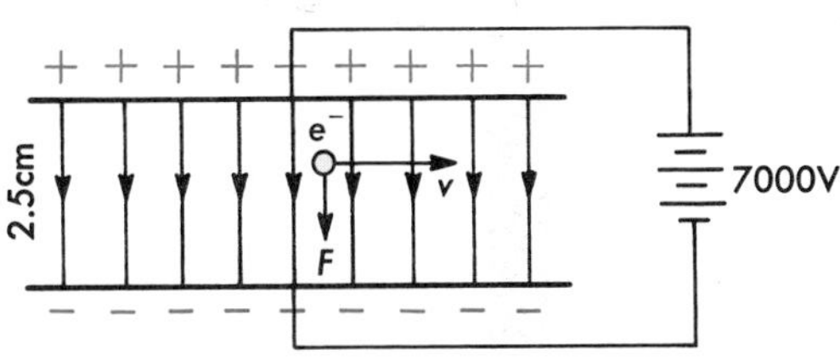

Prob. 12.

13. Three capacitors, (a) 6.0 μF, (b) 12.0 μF, and (c) 36.0 μF, respectively, are connected in series. Find their combined capacitance.

14.* An electronics repair man has three capacitors, $C_1 = 4.0$ μF, $C_2 = 6.0$ μF, and $C_3 = 12.0$ μF. Taking these one, two, or three at a time, and connecting them in all possible ways, how many different capacitances can he obtain?

Magnetism 24

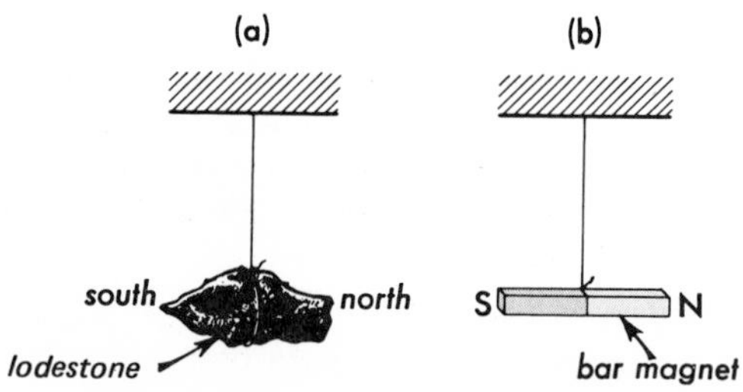

Fig. 24A. Magnetized bodies, when free to turn, come to rest in a north–south direction.

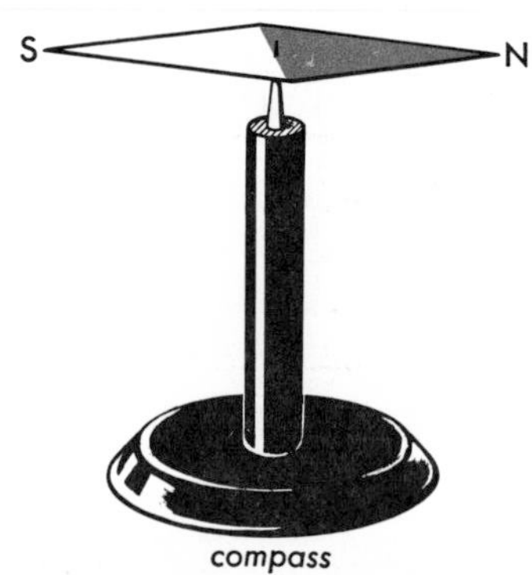

Fig. 24B. A compass needle is a magnet.

Some physics textbooks introduce the subject of magnetism as one of the effects of electric currents flowing through circular loops of wire. This then leads to magnetism as the result of orbital and spinning electrons in atoms, molecules, and solids. Other textbooks begin with permanent magnets and their attraction for iron, with the justification that it is better to introduce a subject using concepts and experiences familiar to everyone. This approach leads to a more direct and better understanding of magnetic dipole moments.

From the time we were very young we played with small permanent magnets and discovered their magical powers of attraction for iron. From a historical standpoint, the attractive powers of a natural magnetic material called *lodestone* were known to the early Greek philosophers. Lodestone, sometimes called *magnetite,* is a solid natural ore composed of nearly 100% pure iron, found in many parts of the world. A piece of lodestone attracts iron in much the same way as a permanent magnet.

That lodestone can be used as a compass is a very old idea. A Chinese author writing as early as the beginning of the 12th century explains that a needle, when rubbed with lodestone and suspended free to turn, will point toward the south. This appears to be the first evidence that a piece of iron could be magnetized by a lodestone and used as a compass. The action of a lodestone or a bar magnet when suspended free to turn about a vertical axis is illustrated in Fig. 24A.

A compass, as it is often made for demonstration purposes, usually consists of a straight steel needle which has been magnetized and mounted free to turn on a sharp pointed rod as shown in Fig. 24B. In the early days of the mariner's compass, it was common to float several small magnetic needles on water by mounting them on a block of wood or other light material. In more recent designs a compass needle with a jewel in its center is set upon the sharp point of a hard metal rod, much shorter than that shown in Fig. 24B, and placed in a small brass box with a glass top. Such compasses are familiar in appearance to everyone.

24.1. Magnets

Until recent years, magnets have been made of hardened steel and molded or rolled into many shapes. Perhaps the most common of these is the horseshoe magnet shown in Fig. 24C, or the straight bar magnet shown in Fig. 24D. The strongest magnets are now made of an alloy containing aluminum, cobalt, nickel, and iron. Small magnets of this alloy are strong enough to lift hundreds of times their own weight.

Pure iron (sometimes called soft iron), when magnetized, will not retain its magnetism and is therefore useless in making what are called permanent magnets. Soft iron is used, however, in the construction of electromagnets. These devices will be discussed and demonstrated in another chapter. Of the many practical applications of permanent magnets, the compass, the telephone receiver, and the radio loudspeaker are perhaps the most common.

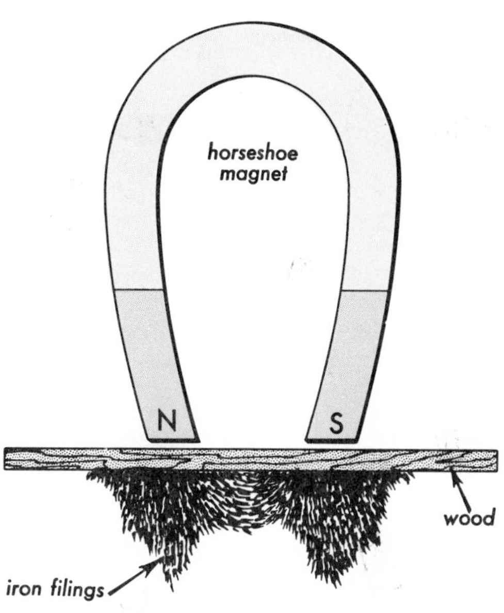

Fig. 24C. The attraction of a magnet for iron acts through all substances.

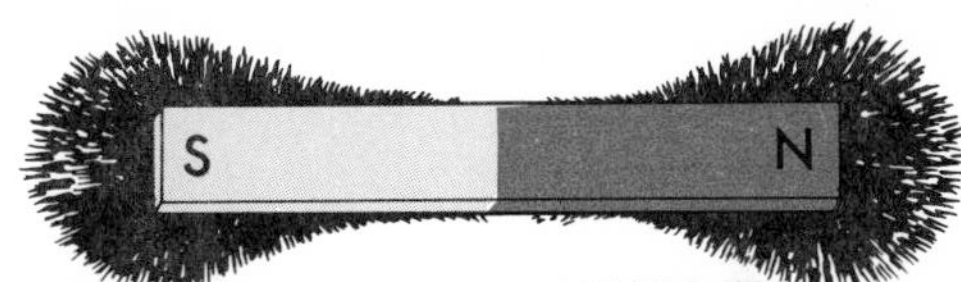

Fig. 24D. The attraction of iron filings by a straight bar magnet is greatest near the ends. These regions of greatest attraction are called *magnetic poles.*

24.2. The Power of Attraction

Nearly everyone has at some time or another played with a small horseshoe magnet and discovered for himself that it attracted only things containing iron. Upon drawing the same magnet through the dry sand or dirt, you probably discovered that it will pick up small grains of iron ore.

If more extensive experiments are carried out, a magnet can be shown to attract magnetic substances at a distance even though matter lies in the intervening space. In other words, magnetic attraction acts right through matter of all kinds. This can be demonstrated as shown in Fig. 24C by picking up iron filings on one side of a thin wooden board by holding a magnet close to the other side. If a sheet of copper, or brass, or, as a matter of fact, any substance, is placed over the magnet, the power of attraction is not destroyed. A small region of space can be partially shielded from magnetic fields if it is entirely surrounded by layers of soft iron.

While a few metals are known to be feebly attracted by a magnet, most substances like aluminum, copper, silver, gold, wood, glass, paper, etc., do not exhibit any noticeable effect. Of those weakly affected, nickel and cobalt are the most important. These two metals, as mentioned above, when alloyed together with other metals in the proper proportions, are found to exhibit stronger magnetic susceptibility than the best grades of iron or steel. As a pure element, however, iron is by far the most strongly magnetic metal.

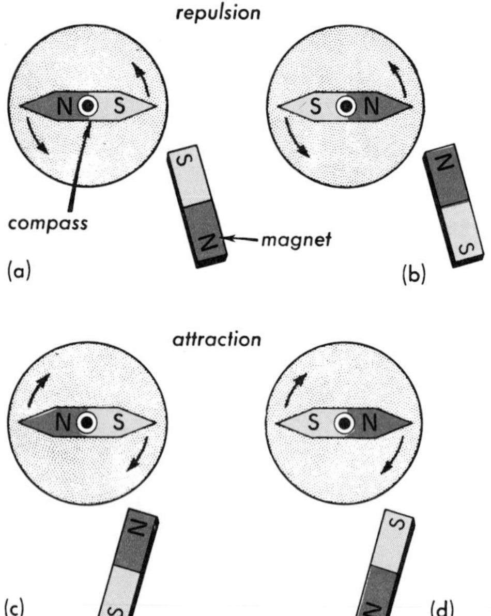

Fig. 24E. When the pole of one magnet is brought close to the pole of another magnet, it is found that like poles repel each other and unlike poles attract.

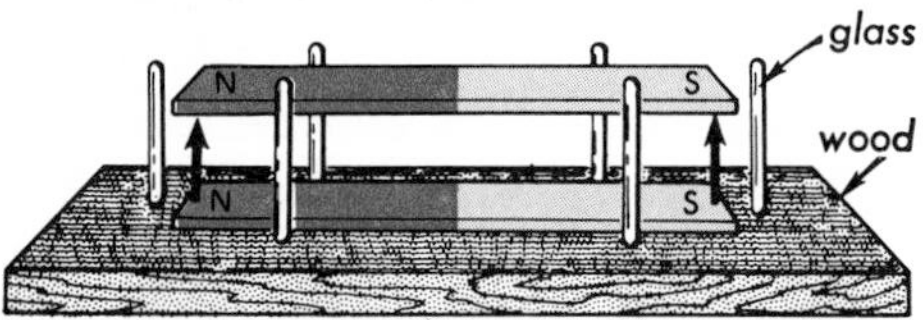

Fig. 24F. One magnet may be suspended in mid-air by the strong repulsion of like poles of another magnet.

24.3. Magnetic Poles

When an ordinary straight bar magnet is dipped into a box of iron filings, the tiny bits of iron are observed to cling to the ends as shown in Fig. 24D. These preferred regions of attraction are called *magnetic poles.* If this same magnet is suspended by a thread as shown in Fig. 24A, it will come to rest in a position close to the north-south direction. The end toward the north is therefore called the N or *north-seeking pole,* and the other end the S or *south-seeking pole.*

That the N and S poles of a magnet are different may be shown by bringing the magnet close to a compass needle. Such an experiment is illustrated in Fig. 24E. When the S pole of the magnet is brought close to the S pole of the compass needle as in diagram (a), there is a force of repulsion acting, and the compass needle turns away as shown. A similar repulsion occurs between the two N poles as shown in diagram (b). If the N and S poles are brought near to each other, however, a very strong attraction arises and the compass needle turns toward the other, as shown in diagrams (c) and (d). These experiments show, therefore, that *two kinds of magnetic poles exist* and that *like poles repel and unlke poles attract.*

Permanent magnets can now be made so strong that one magnet can be lifted by the repulsion of another. This is illustrated in Fig. 24F. Unless guide rods of glass or some other substance are used, however, the floating bar will move to one side and then fall. In other words, the forces of repulsion are such that the upper bar is not in stable equilibrium. If the floating magnet is turned end for end, opposite poles become adjacent and the two magnets attract each other. Although the forces may be great enough, no one has ever succeeded in floating a magnet in mid-air by means of permanent magnets, against the pull of gravity, without guide rods.

It should be pointed out that each magnetic pole in a magnetized body is not confined to a single point, but extends over a finite region. From a distance, however, each polar region acts as though it were concentrated at a point, similar to that of the center of mass in mechanics.

24.4. Poles Exist in Pairs

If a magnet is broken in the middle in an attempt to separate the poles, one finds new poles formed at the broken ends. If one of these pieces is again broken, each piece is again found to contain two poles of opposite kind. As long as this process is repeated, the same result is obtained—a magnetic pole of one kind is always accompanied by a pole of opposite polarity. This is conveniently illustrated by magnetizing a hack-saw blade and breaking it successively into smaller and smaller pieces as shown in Fig. 24G. Each time a piece is broken, each fragment, upon being tested with a compass, is found to have an N pole on one side and an S pole on the other. A hack-saw blade is readily magnetized by stroking it from one end to the other with one of the poles of a magnet.

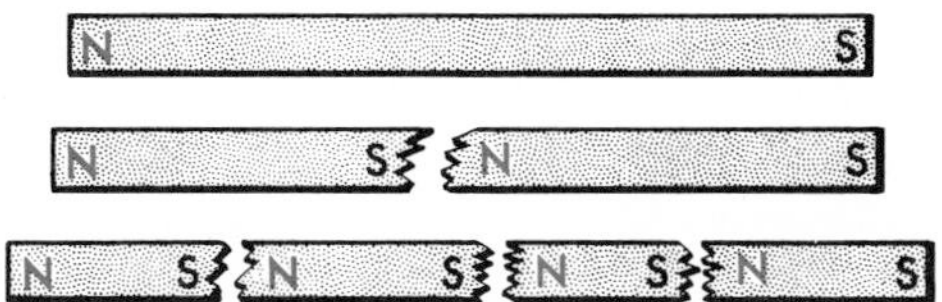

Fig. 24G. The poles of a magnet cannot exist alone. When a bar magnet is broken, poles appear on either side of the break, such that each piece has two opposite poles.

It is possible to magnetize a bar of steel so that it has three or more polar regions. This is illustrated in Fig. 24H where a hack-saw blade has been magnetized with an N pole at each end and an S polar region in the center. The combined strength of the N poles is seen by the quantity of iron filings to be equal to the S pole strength in the center. We might say, therefore, that the magnet has four poles: an N pole at either end and two S poles at the center.

Fig. 24H. Diagram of a bar magnet with iron filings showing the three polar regions.

24.5. The Magnetic Field

In the space surrounding every magnet, there exists what is called a magnetic field. Although this field cannot be seen, it can be demonstrated and mapped out in the following way.

If a very small compass is placed at some point near the N pole of a straight bar magnet, and then moved always in the direction the compass is pointing, the center of the compass will trace out a smooth line called a magnetic line of force. Starting at various points, many such lines may be drawn as shown in Fig. 24I. Each line starts at some point near the N pole and ends at a corresponding point near the S pole.

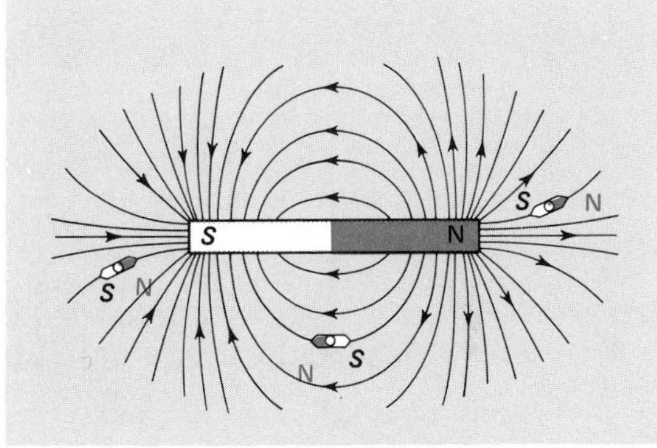

Fig. 24I. Diagram of the magnetic field and magnetic lines of force about a straight bar magnet, as obtained with a small compass needle.

These magnetic *lines of force,* as they are called, do not really exist; they are but useful devices that may be used in describing the many different magnetic phenomena to be taken up in later chapters. It should be noted that, where the magnet exerts its strongest attraction near the poles, the lines are closest together and that each line points away from the N pole and toward the S pole. This latter is an arbitrary assignment, being the direction indicated by the N pole of the compass.

A close examination of the iron filings that cling to a magnet (Figs. 24D and 24H) shows that each tiny needle-like piece of iron lines up in the direction of the magnetic lines of force. The reason for this is that each filing has become magnetized by the magnet, and having its own N and S poles, acts like a compass. An excellent demonstration of the field and its direction can be performed by laying a plate of glass or a sheet of paper over a magnet and then sprinkling iron filings over the top. By gently tapping the glass or paper, the filings turn and line up as shown in the photographic reproduction given in Fig. 24J.

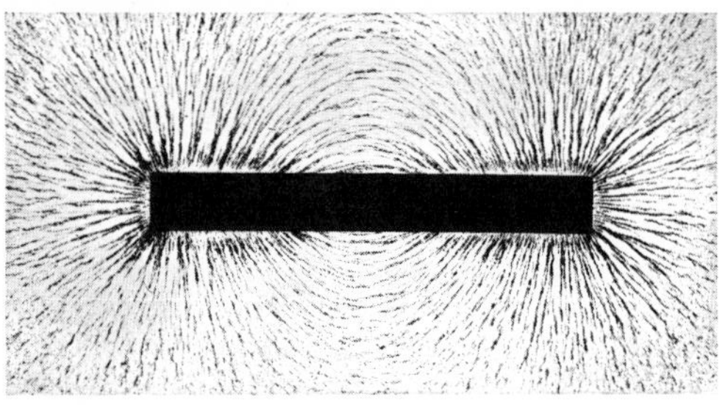

Fig. 24J. Photograph of the iron filings lined up by the magnetic field of a permanent straight bar magnet.

24.6. The Field about Separated Magnets

When two magnets are brought close together as shown in Fig. 24K, the mutual action of the two is such as to produce a complicated magnetic field. This is illustrated by compass-made drawings at the top and by photographic reproductions of the iron-filing method of observation at the bottom.

A simplified explanation of many electric and magnetic phenomena can be given by assuming that these imaginary *lines of force* are endowed with certain real but simple properties. *Lengthwise along the lines they act as though they were stretched rubber bands under constant tension, whereas sideways they act as if they repelled each other.* Both of these properties are illustrated in Fig. 24K. When the two poles are of different polarity as in diagram (a), the lines of force acting like stretched rubber bands tend to pull the poles together. In diagram (b) where the poles are alike, the lines repel each other, pushing the poles apart.

Observe how closely the magnetic field around two magnetic poles resembles the electric field around two charged bodies of like or unlike kinds. Compare Fig. 23A with Fig. 24K.

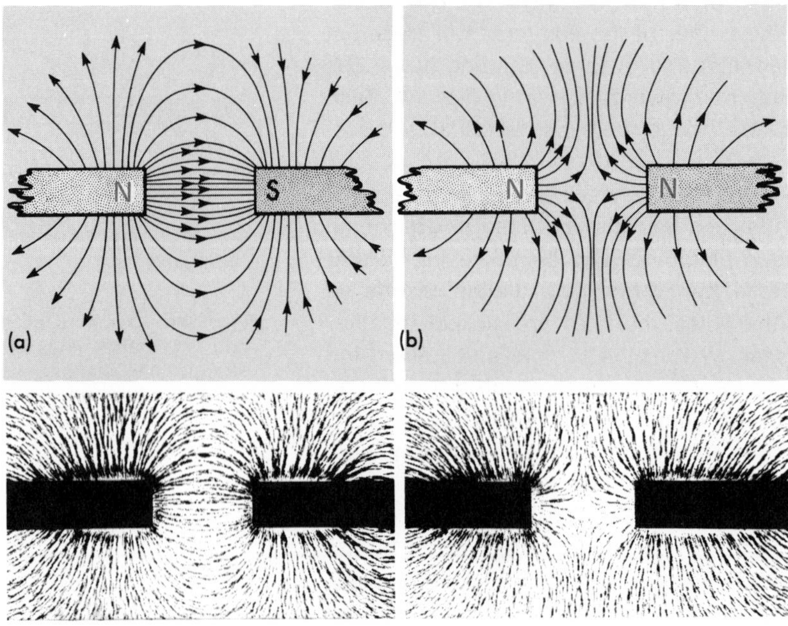

Fig. 24K. Diagrams and photographs illustrating the magnetic fields around pairs of magnetic poles.

24.7. The Earth's Magnetic Field

To Sir William Gilbert we owe the view that the earth is a great magnet. To prove his theory, Gilbert shaped a lodestone into a sphere and demonstrated that a small compass placed at any spot of the globe always pointed, as it does on the earth, toward the North Pole.

The earth, therefore, has been schematically pictured in Fig. 24L as a large magnetized sphere of iron, or as though it contained a huge permanent magnet. Since the magnetic axis is at an angle with the polar axis, the earth's magnetic poles are not at the *true North* and *true South Poles.* The true North and true South Poles are points located on the earth's rotational axis.

The *North Magnetic Pole* is located in far northern Canada, while the *South Magnetic Pole* is located almost diametrically opposite in the Southern Hemisphere. As for polarity, the North Magnetic Pole is an S pole and the South Magnetic Pole is an N pole. This becomes apparent from the magnetic lines of force which always start from an N pole and are directed toward, and end, at an S pole.

Although the cause for the earth's magnetism is not completely understood, several reasonable theories have been proposed. The earth is known to contain large iron ore deposits, some of these deposits being almost pure iron. One theory proposes that, during the ages past, all these iron deposits gradually became magnetized, in very nearly the same direction, and that together they act like one huge permanent magnet. Another theory, and a very plausible one, is that the magnetism is due to large electric currents which are known to be flowing around the earth, not only in the earth's crust but also in the air above. These electric earth currents seem to be connected in some direct way with the earth's rotation. This appears to be corroborated by the fact that the earth is magnetized in a direction almost parallel to the earth's polar axis.

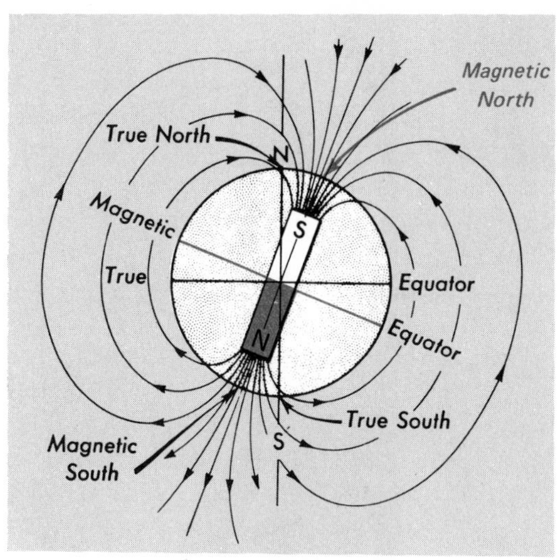

Fig. 24L. Schematic diagram illustrating the earth as a huge magnet surrounded by a magnetic field extending far out into space.

24.8. Magnetic Declination

Since the earth's magnetic and polar axes do not coincide, a compass needle does not in general point toward True North. Because of the influence of the irregular iron deposits near the earth's surface, the magnetic field is not as regular as it is pictured in Fig. 24L and a compass needle may deviate considerably from magnetic north. The angle that a compass needle deviates from True North is called the *angle of declination.*

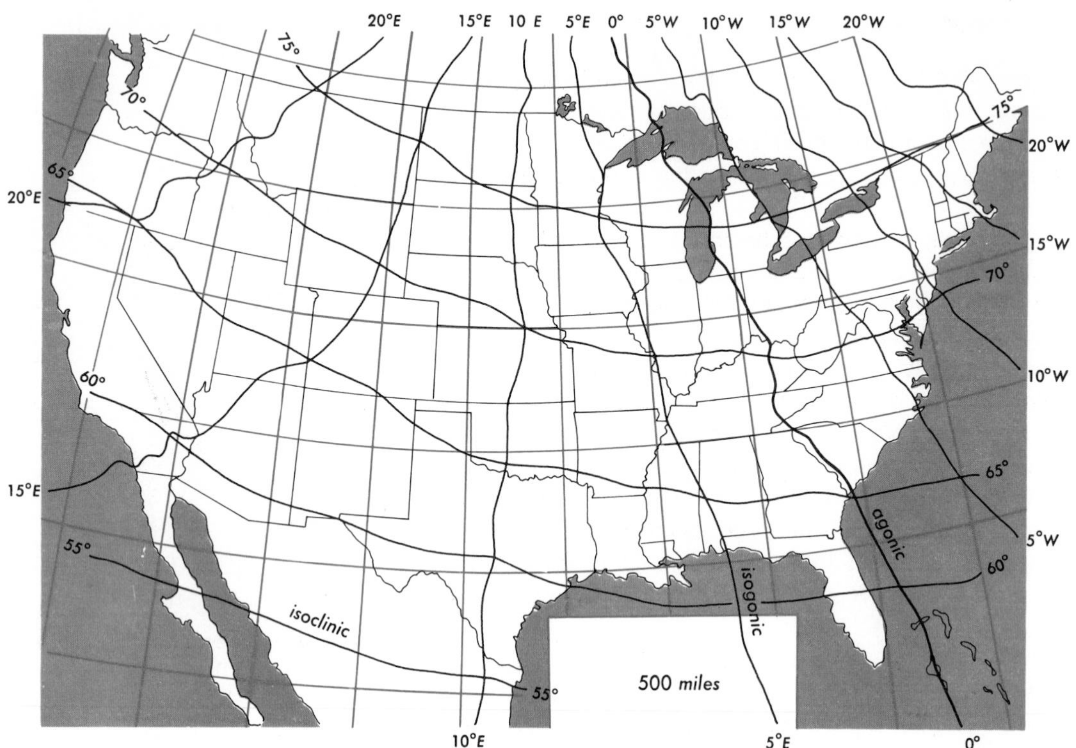

Fig. 24M. A magnetic map of the United States for the year 1970 showing the declination of a compass from true north and the angle of dip of a dip needle. Such maps are drawn from data assembled by the U.S. Coast and Geodetic Survey.

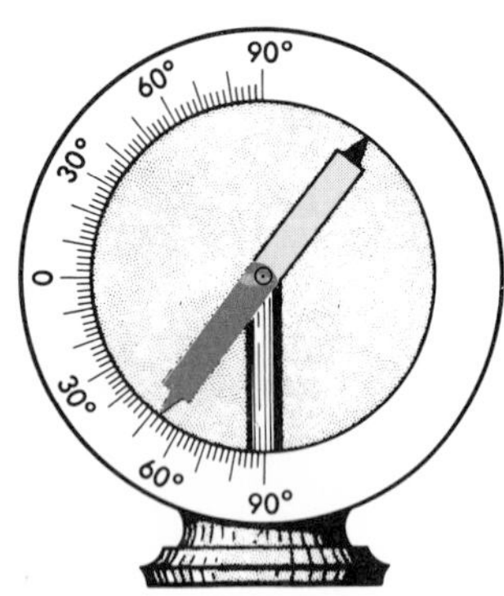

Fig. 24N. A magnetic dip needle.

A map showing the angle of declination for the United States during the year 1954 is shown in Fig. 24M. The more-or-less vertical set of irregular lines are lines of equal declination and are called *isogonic lines.* At every point along the line marked 20°E, for example, a compass needle actually points 20° east of True North. In the region of San Francisco the declination is seen to be about 18°E, while in the region of New York it is about 11°W. The line through points where a compass points True North, 0°, is named the *agonic line.*

24.9. Magnetic Dip

If a compass needle is mounted free to turn about a horizontal axis as shown in Fig. 24N, it will not come to rest in a horizontal position but will dip down at some angle with the horizontal as shown. This direction, called the *dip,* is the angle the earth's field makes with the earth's surface at the point in question. Referring to Fig. 24L, it is seen that in the far north and south the angle of dip is quite large, whereas near the equator it is quite small. Figure 24O indicates the approximate dip at different latitudes for one cross section of the entire globe.

At a region on the Boothia Peninsula just north of Hudson Bay and 20° from True North, a dip needle points straight down, perpendicular to the earth's surface, and locates the North Magnetic Pole. At a region about 18° from the true South Pole a dip needle points straight up, at 90° from the horizontal, and locates the South Magnetic Pole.

On maps of terrestrial magnetism, all points that have equal dip angles are connected by a line called an *isoclinic* line. Such lines for different angles form a set of nearly parallel lines as shown on the map of the United States in Fig. 24M.

Careful and accurate measurements of the *declination* and *dip* show that the earth's magnetic field is continually changing. Although these changes are extremely small, they are somewhat periodic and at times quite erratic.

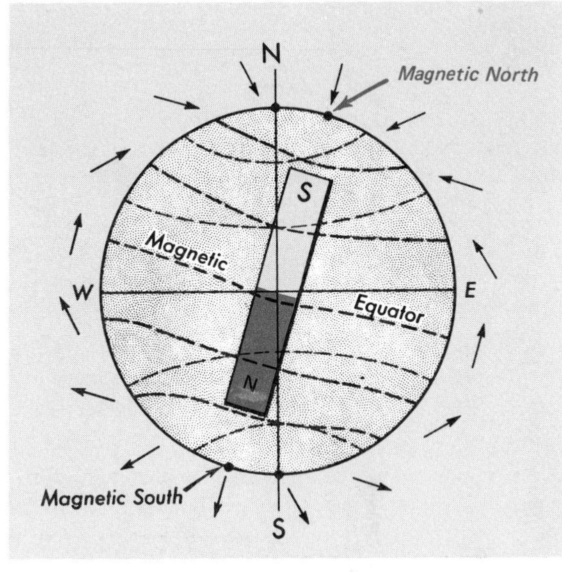

Fig. 24O. Arrows show the direction a dip needle takes at different parts of the earth's surface.

24.10. Magnetization

When a strong magnet is brought close to a piece of soft iron, the iron takes on all the properties of a new but somewhat weaker magnet. This phenomenon, called *magnetization,* is illustrated in Fig. 24P(a). As long as the permanent magnet is held close to the soft iron bar, the iron filings cling to the end as shown. When the permanent magnet is removed, however, the soft iron immediately loses its magnetism and the iron filings drop off.

When a piece of iron is magnetized, a pole of opposite sign is created at the points of closest approach as shown in the diagrams. If a common iron nail is brought up to the N pole of a permanent magnet, it will become magnetized with an S pole at the point of contact and an N pole at the other end, as shown in diagram (b). Having two poles, the nail is thus magnetized and will attract another nail and magnetize it in the same way. With a good strong magnet, this process can be repeated by adding one nail after the other.

It is now clear how iron filings line up with the lines of force of a magnet. Each filing becomes magnetized and, like a small compass, turns parallel to the field in which it is located.

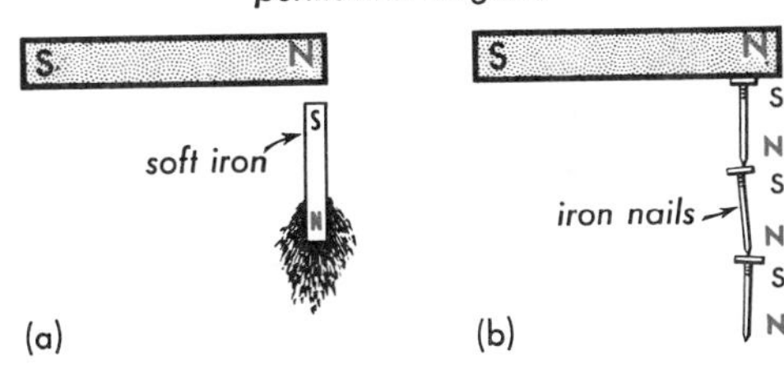

Fig. 24P. Soft iron may be magnetized by induction at a distance or by contact.

24.11. Coulomb's Law for Magnetic Poles

For a study of the law of force between magnetic poles, specially designed magnets have been used. The necessity for this is realized when it is remembered that single magnetic poles cannot be isolated by breaking a magnet in two. Furthermore, a magnetic pole is not a geometrical point but seems to be somewhat distributed over the surface of the material of which it is made.

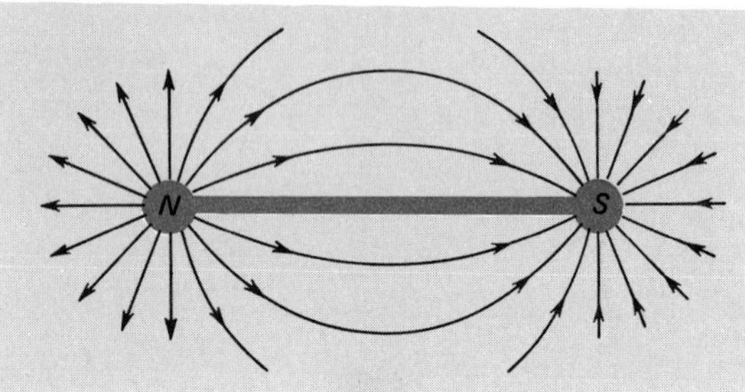

Fig. 24Q. Map of the magnetic field around a special type of permanent magnet.

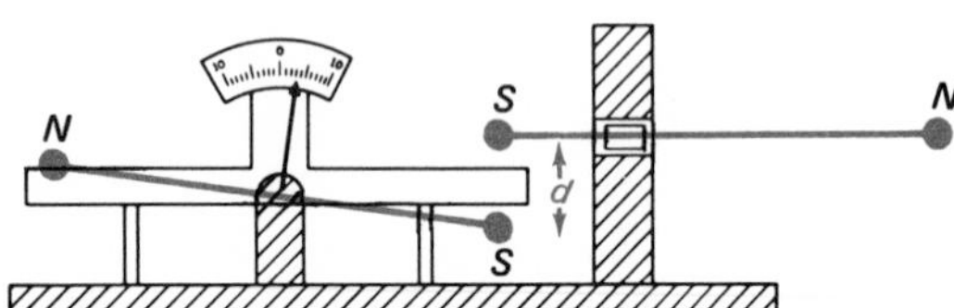

Fig. 24R. Diagram of the Hibbert magnetic balance for measuring the force between two magnetic poles.

The special magnets consist of thin steel rods about 46 cm long, with a small steel ball on either end. When magnetized, the N and S poles become concentrated in the steel balls as shown in Fig. 24Q.

As used in the Hibbert balance* shown in Fig. 24R, one magnet is balanced on a special set of scales and another is held tightly in an adjustable clamp stand. If the two adjacent poles, when they are brought together, are alike, the repulsion will throw the one magnet off balance. The weight that must then be added to the left-hand side to restore balance again is a direct measure of the force of repulsion. Carrying out experiments of a similar nature, Coulomb was the first to find that *the force acting between two magnetic poles is inversely proportional to the square of the distance between their centers.* Having discovered this relation, he compared the pole strengths of different magnets with each other and found that *the force between two poles is proportional to the product of the pole strengths.* Combining these two relations, Coulomb proposed as a general law for magnetic poles,

$$F = \kappa \frac{Mm}{d^2} \tag{24a}$$

for magnetic poles

where F is the force, M and m are the strengths of the poles, and d is the distance between them. In the rationalized *MKSA* system used in this text, F is in *newtons,* M and m are in *ampere meters,* and κ, the proportionality constant, is

$$\kappa = 10^{-7} \frac{\text{newton}}{\text{amperes}^2}$$

$$\kappa = 10^{-7} \frac{\text{N}}{\text{A}^2} \tag{24b}$$

Example 1. Two magnetic S poles are located 4.0 cm apart (see Fig. 24S). If the poles of each magnet have a strength of 8.0 Am,

* Magnetic balance made by W. G. Pye & Co., Cambridge, England.

and are 20.0 cm apart, find (a) the force exerted by one S pole on the other, and (b) the force of one N pole on the S pole of the other magnet.

Solution. For part (a) use Coulomb's law, Eq.(24a), and substitute the given quantities for the two S poles, $m_1 = m_2 = 8.0$ Am and $d = 4.0 \times 10^{-2}$ m:

$$F = k\frac{Mm}{d^2} = \frac{10^{-7} \times 8 \times 8}{16 \times 10^{-4}}$$

(a) $$F = \frac{10^{-7} \times 64}{16 \times 10^{-4}} = 4.0 \times 10^{-3} \text{ N}$$

To find the answer to part (b), again substitute the known quantities in Eq.(24a), $m_1 = m_2 = 8.0$ Am, and $d^2 = 400 \times 10^{-4} + 16 \times 10^{-4}$ m:

(b) $$F = \frac{10^{-7} \times 8 \times 8}{400 \times 10^{-4} + 16 \times 10^{-4}}$$

$$F = 1.538 \times 10^{-4} \text{ N}$$

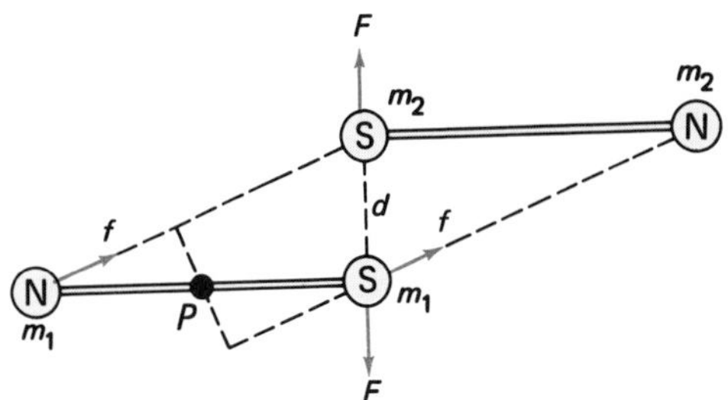

Fig. 24S. Geometry of the forces and torques involved in the Hibbert balance.

As we will see later, magnetism is due to the motions of electrons in atoms and molecules. Acting like tiny current loops, the magnetic field strengths are directly proportional to the equivalent current in amperes. Hence the measurement of pole strengths is in ampere meters.

When two magnets are arranged in the configuration shown in Fig. 24S, the two poles nearest each other will exert by far the strongest forces on each other. These forces, represented by F in the diagram, are an *action* and *reaction pair.*

To measure the force F exerted on the lower S pole, the lower magnet is initially balanced carefully on a pivot P at its center of mass. Under these conditions the two attractive forces f, due to the poles of the upper magnet, will cancel out since they exert equal and opposite torques.

If the magnets are long and the distance d relatively small, the force of repulsion between the extreme end poles will be exceedingly small. To a first approximation, this force and the torque it exerts can be neglected.

24.12. Magnetic Induction B

It is quite common practice to refer to the strength or the intensity of a magnetic field as the *magnetic induction.*

The magnetic induction B at any point in space may be defined as the force per unit N pole acting on any pole placed at that point. Algebraically,

$$B = \frac{F}{m} \tag{24c}$$

Note the similarity of this definition of magnetic field intensity with the definition of electric field intensity, Eq.(23c), and the definition of gravitational field intensity, Eq.(12c).

Suppose, for example, that when a unit pole of *1 ampere meter* is placed at a given point in space it experiences a force of 5 *newtons.* The magnetic induction B at that point is then said to have a magnitude of 5 *newtons per ampere meter* (5 N/Am). If a pole with a strength of m_1 ampere meters is placed at this same point where the magnetic induction is known to be B newtons per ampere meter, the force acting on the pole in newtons is

$$F = m_1 B \tag{24d}$$

From the above definition that $B = F/m$, and Coulomb's law, a relation for the magnetic induction at any point near a single pole of strength M may be obtained. When Eq.(24a) is solved for F/m, we obtain

$$\frac{F}{m} = \kappa \frac{M}{d^2}$$

or

$$B = \kappa \frac{M}{d^2} \tag{24e}$$

where d is the distance from the field producing pole M to the point in question.

While the magnetic induction, as given by either Eq.(24c) or Eq.(24e), is in N/Am, it is customary to express B in teslas.* In other words

$$1 \frac{\text{newton}}{\text{ampere meter}} = 1 \text{ tesla}$$

$$1 \frac{\text{N}}{\text{Am}} = 1 \text{ T} \tag{24f}$$

*Nikola Tesla (1857–1943), American electrician and inventor, was born at Smiljan, Yugoslavia. He studied at the Realschule in Karlstadt in 1873, the Polytechnic School in Graz in 1876, and the University of Prague in 1879. After coming to the United States in 1884, he first worked for the Edison Co. at Orange, N.J., and then left to found his own research laboratory. There he did a great deal of research on alternating current electricity. In 1888 he invented and patented the induction motor. He invented the principle of a rotating magnetic field, and did significant research on capacitors. He is best known for his development of a high voltage, high frequency impulse transformer known as a "Tesla coil."

This means that the constant κ can be expressed in fundamental units as

$$\kappa = 10^{-7}\ \text{Kg m/s}^2\ \text{A}^2 \tag{24g}$$

or in derived units as

$$\kappa = 10^{-7}\ \text{Tm/A} \tag{24h}$$

The direction of the magnetic field at any point is the direction of the force acting on an N pole placed at that point, or the direction a small compass would point if placed there. This is another way of determining or plotting magnetic lines of force. As illustrated in Fig. 24T, an N pole placed in a position (a), equidistant from the two poles of the magnet, is repelled by the N pole with the same force that it is attracted by the S pole. The resultant of these two forces is the horizontal force to the right and parallel to the magnet. If an S pole were located at the same point, the resultant force would be just oppositely directed. It is therefore clear why a compass placed at (a) turns parallel to the magnet, and why at other points like (b) it turns in another direction. Forces acting on each pole of the compass needle turn it into the equilibrium positions found and plotted as the magnetic field in Fig. 24I.

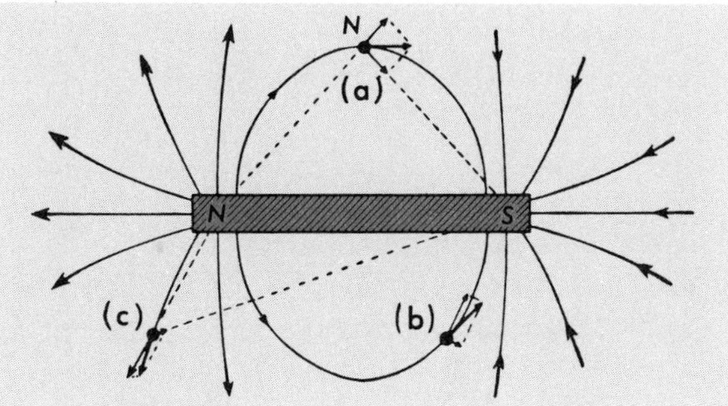

Fig. 24T. The force acting on a unit N pole placed in a magnetic field gives the magnitude and direction of the magnetic field at that point.

Example 2. Two poles of a bar magnet are 6.0 cm apart, and each has a strength of 25.0 Am. Find the magnitude and direction of the magnetic induction B, at a point in line with the two poles, and 8.0 cm beyond the N pole.

Solution. Referring to Fig. 24T, and substituting known quantities in Eq.(24a), we find for each pole separately

$$B = k\frac{M}{d^2} = \frac{10^{-7} \times 25}{(8 \times 10^{-2})^2} = 3.906 \times 10^{-4}\ \text{T}$$

$$B = k\frac{M}{d^2} = \frac{10^{-7} \times 25}{(14 \times 10^{-2})^2} = -1.276 \times 10^{-4}\ \text{T}$$

Since B is a vector quantity, and these two values are oppositely directed,

$$B = 2.630 \times 10^{-4}\ \text{T outward}$$

directed along the axis, away from the N pole.

24.13. Molecular Theory of Magnetism

The modern theory of magnetism, which is now quite firmly established, is that a piece of iron consists of myriads of tiny elementary magnets. These tiny ultramicroscopic magnets consist of individual atoms. How single atoms can act as magnets will be explained later.

Before a piece of iron or steel has been magnetized, these elementary magnets may be thought of as being oriented more or less at random throughout the metal as shown in Fig. 24U(a).

During the time a piece of iron is being magnetized, the elementary magnets are turned around and lined up parallel to each other and to the magnetizing field. This is shown by the schematic representation in diagram (b). Lined up in this way, the small N and S poles are adjacent to each other and cancel each other's effect on external objects. At one end there are many free N poles, and at the opposite end an equal number of free S poles.

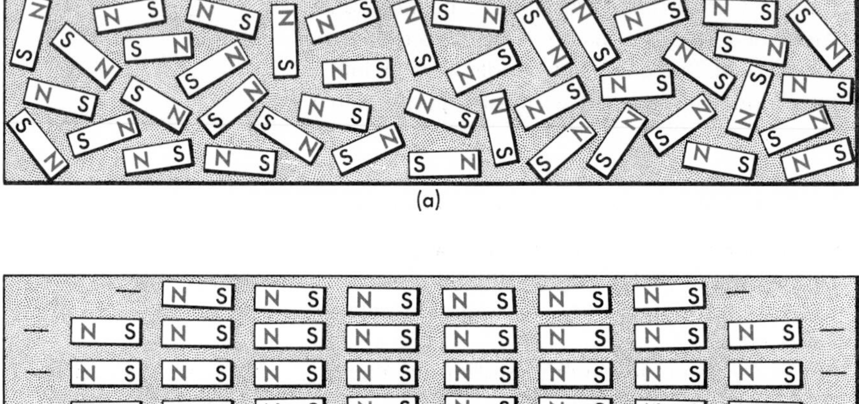

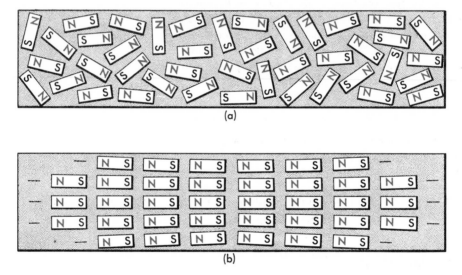

Fig. 24U. Schematic diagrams of the elementary magnets within a piece of iron: (a) unmagnetized, and (b) magnetized.

When a magnet is broken at any point, *free* S *poles* are exposed at one side of the break and *free* N *poles* at the other. It is therefore clear why poles always exist in pairs and that, no matter how many times a magnet is broken, each piece will contain an N pole at one end and an S pole at the other.

When soft iron is magnetized by induction and the permanent magnet is taken away, the elementary magnets return to their original random orientations, but, when hardened steel becomes magnetized, they remain lined up after the magnetizing field is taken away.

problems

1. Two magnetic poles with a strength of 15.0 Am are of opposite sign and located 5.0 cm apart. What is the force acting on each pole?

2. Two magnetic N poles are located 8.0 cm apart, as shown in Fig. 24S. If the poles of each magnet have a strength of 12.0 Am and are 10 cm apart, find (a) the force of one S pole on the other, (b) the force of one N pole on the S pole of the other magnet, and (c) the force of one N pole on the other N pole.

3. Two S poles of separate magnets are located 5.0 cm apart, as shown in Fig. 24S. If the poles of each magnet have a strength of 25.0 Am and are 15.0 cm apart, find (a) the force exerted by one S pole on the other S pole, (b) the force of one N pole on the S pole of the other magnet, and (c) the force of one N pole on the other N pole. [Ans. (a) 2.50×10^{-2} N, (b) 2.50×10^{-3} N, (c) 6.76×10^{-4} N.]

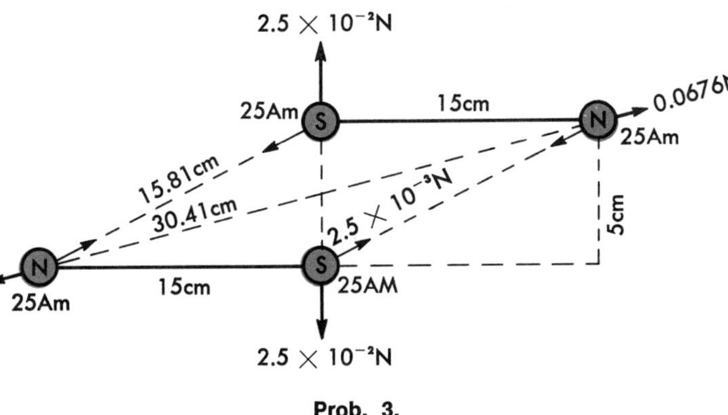

Prob. 3.

4.* Two magnets of the type shown in Fig. 24Q have poles 12.0 cm apart and each with a strength of 16.0 Am. If the poles are located at the four corners of a tetrahedron, find the direction and magnitude of the force on each pole. Neglect the force between the two poles of the same magnet.

5. The two poles of a bar magnet have a strength of 75.0 Am each and are 8.0 cm apart. Find the magnetic induction at a point in line with the two poles, (a) 6.0 cm beyond the S pole, and (b) 20.0 cm beyond the N pole.

6. A straight bar magnet has two poles of 15.0 Am each, spaced 5.0 cm apart. Find the magnetic induction at a point in line with the poles, (a) 5.0 cm from the N pole, (b) 10.0 cm from the N pole, and (c) 20.0 cm from the N pole. (d) Make a diagram. [Ans. (a) 4.50×10^{-4} T, (b) 8.33×10^{-5} T, (c) 1.350×10^{-5} T.]

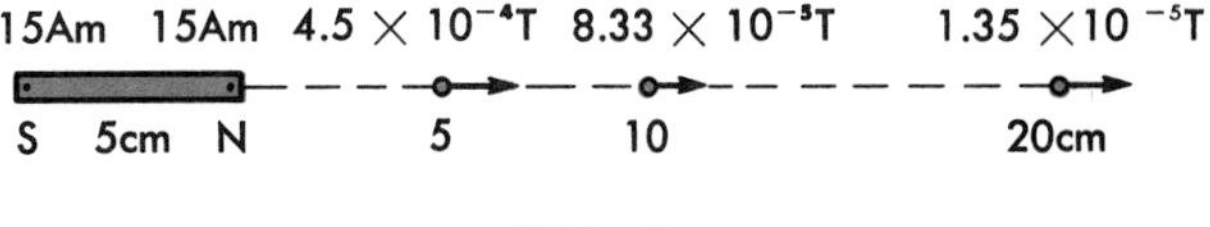

Prob. 6.

7.* A magnet of the type shown in Fig. 24Q has two poles of 40.0 Am each which are located 10.0 cm apart. Find the magnetic induction at a point in line with the poles and a distance beyond the N pole of (a) 5.0 cm, (b) 10.0 cm, (c) 15.0 cm, (d) 20.0 cm, and (e) 25.0 cm. Plot a graph of B versus x, where x is the distance from the center of the magnet.

8.* A magnet of the type shown in Fig. 24Q has two poles each of 5.0 Am. If the poles are located 20.0 cm apart, find the magnetic induction along the line through the center of the magnet perpendicular to the magnet axis and at a distance from the center of (a) 5.0 cm, (b) 10.0 cm, (c) 15.0 cm, (d) 20.0 cm, and (e) 25.0 cm. Plot a graph of B versus x, where x is the distance from the center of the magnet.

9. A bar magnet with two poles, each with a strength

of 50.0 Am, is located in a magnetic field of 0.80 T. Find the magnitude of the force on each pole. [Ans. 40.0 N on each pole.]

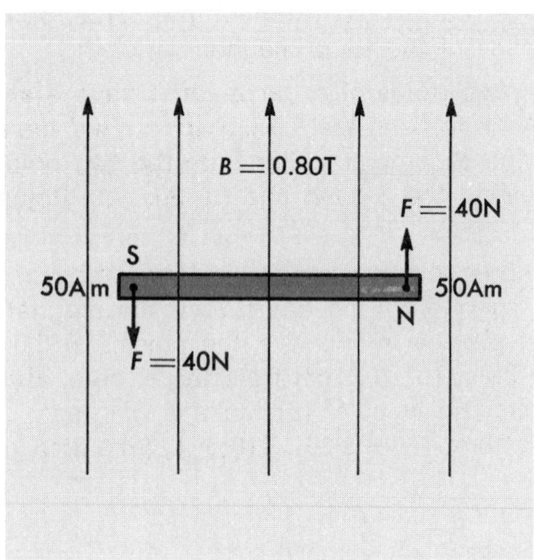

Prob. 9.

10. When an N pole of 18.0 Am is placed 12.0 cm from another pole of unknown strength, it experiences a repulsive force of 6.0×10^{-4} N. Find (a) the magnetic induction at the point, and (b) the unknown pole strength.

11. A small magnet of the kind shown in Fig. 24Q has two poles 3.20 cm apart, and each of 23.50 Am. If this magnet is located in a uniform magnetic field of 1.40 T, with its axis at right angles to B, find (a) the force on each pole, and (b) the torque acting on the magnet.

12. A compass needle has two poles 2.0 cm apart, and each pole has a strength of 0.50 Am. (a) Find the force on each pole when the compass is located in the earth's magnetic field of 5.40×10^{-5} T. (b) What is the torque on the needle when its axis is at right angles to B? [Ans. (a) 2.70×10^{-5} N, (b) 5.40×10^{-7} Nm.]

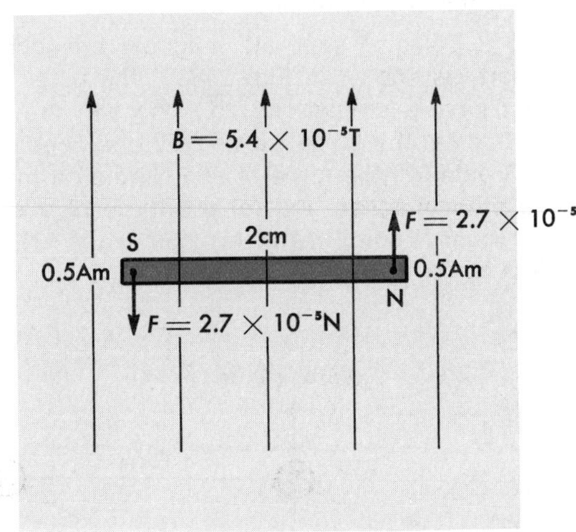

Prob. 12.

Effects of electric currents

Everyone is more or less familiar with the electrical appliances of the modern household: the electric lights, electric toaster, iron, refrigerator, vacuum cleaner, washing machine, etc. All of these devices depend for their operation upon one or more of five general effects produced by electric currents; these are

heating effect
magnetic effect
mechanical effect
chemical effect
lighting effect

It is the purpose of this chapter to consider the first three of these different effects and to take up in some detail the important principles involved.

25.1. Electric Energy

When the householder pays his monthly electricity bill, he pays according to the amount of electric energy consumed. To calculate electric energy, a general formula involving *current, voltage,* and *time* is usually employed. A battery or generator, in supplying current to any electric system, maintains a constant difference of potential between two ends of the circuit.

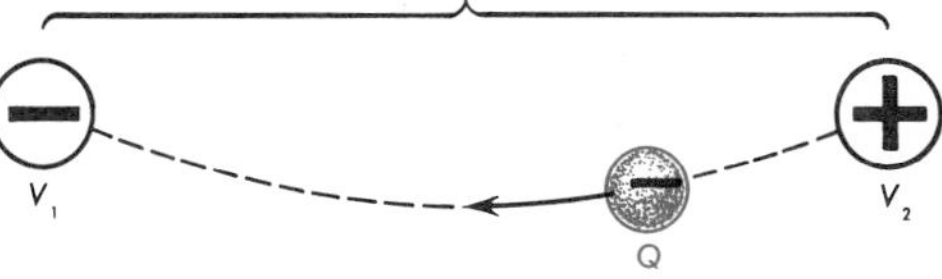

Fig. 25A. The work done per unit charge in carrying any charge Q from one terminal to the other is called the difference of potential V.

Consider the two terminals of a battery as shown in Fig. 25A and the mechanical work that would be required to move a negative charge from the (+) terminal to the (−) terminal. *The amount of work done per unit charge in carrying any charge Q from one terminal to the other is called the difference of potential.* Symbolically,

$$V = \frac{W}{Q} \tag{25a}$$

where V is in volts, W in joules, and Q in coulombs.

If, instead of carrying a charge from one terminal to the other and thereby doing work, we connect the two terminals with a conductor, a current I will flow and the battery will be doing work for us in creating heat. *The current I is given by the amount of charge Q flowing per second of time:*

$$I = \frac{Q}{t} \tag{25b}$$

If we solve this equation for Q,

$$Q = It$$

and substitute It for Q in Eq.(25a), we obtain

$$V = \frac{W}{It}$$

Upon solving for W, we find

$$W = VIt \tag{25c}$$

joules = volts × amperes × seconds

If V is in volts, I is in amperes, and t is in seconds, the energy W is in joules. By Ohm's law, $I = V/R$, direct substitution for I or for V gives two other useful forms of the same equation:

$$W = I^2Rt \qquad W = \frac{V^2}{R}t \tag{25d}$$

25.2. *Electric Power*

Power is defined in mechanics, as well as in electricity, as the rate at which energy is developed or expended. $P = W/t$. Dividing each of the above energy equations by t, we find that

$$P = I^2R \qquad P = V^2/R$$

and

$$P = VI \tag{25e}$$

where P is in watts. These are practical equations since with most electrical equipment the *voltage, current,* and *resistance* are usually known from voltmeter and ammeter readings. The last equation is well worth memorizing: *"Power in watts is equal to potential difference in volts times current in amperes."* The other two follow by a direct substitution from Ohm's law.

The *watt* is abbreviated W. One thousand watts are called the *kilowatt,* which is abbreviated KW:

$$1000 \text{ W} = 1 \text{ KW}$$

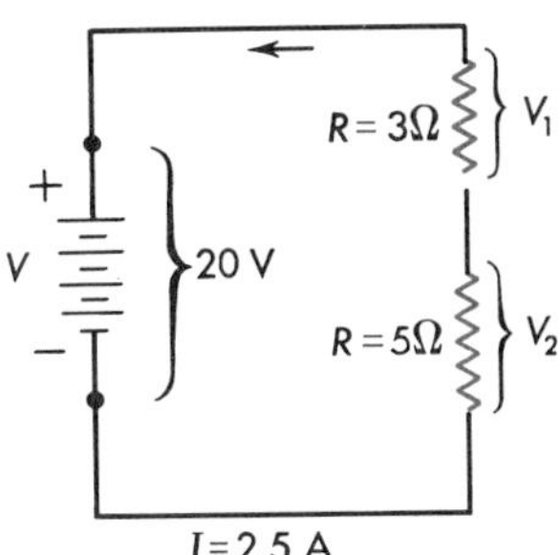

Fig. 25B. The power consumed by any resistance is given by the voltage across it multiplied by the current.

Energy as expressed in Eq.(25c) is power VI multiplied by the time t. *Power in kilowatts multiplied by the time in hours gives the energy in kilowatt-hours.* The kilowatt-hour is the unit of electric energy by which all electric energy is calculated for payment.

The watt-hour meter placed on the premises of every consumer is a slowly revolving motor, having a low resistance winding which is in series with the line and which therefore conducts the current in the line, and a high resistance winding which is across the line and which therefore conducts a small current proportional to V. The time factor t is accounted for by the automatic recording of the total number of rotations of the armature by a small clock-like mechanism with dials and pointers.

Example 1. Two resistors of 3.0 Ω and 5.0 Ω, respectively, are connected in series with a battery of 20.0-V terminal voltage (see Fig. 25B). Calculate (a) the electron current through the circuit, (b) the potential difference across each resistor, (c) the power consumed by each resistor, (d) the total energy consumed in 2.0 h of operation, and (e) the total cost of operation for 40.0 h at 3.0 cents per KW-h.

Solution. Connected in series, the two resistors $R_1 = 3.0\ \Omega$ and $R_2 = 5.0\ \Omega$ have a total resistance of $R = 8.0\ \Omega$.

(a) If we apply Ohm's law, the electron current through the circuit is found to be

$$I = V/R = 20/8 = 2.5 \text{ A}$$

(b) The drop in potential across any resistor is given by IR:

$$V_1 = I_1R_1 = 2.5 \times 3 = 7.5 \text{ V}$$

$$V_2 = I_2R_2 = 2.5 \times 5 = 12.5 \text{ V}$$

(c) The power consumed is given by VI, the potential drop across each resistor multiplied by the electron current through it:

$$P_1 = V_1 I = 7.5 \times 2.5 = 18.75 \text{ W}$$

$$P_2 = V_2 I = 12.5 \times 2.5 = 31.25 \text{ W}$$

(d) The power supplied by the battery is VI, the voltage across its terminals multiplied by the total electron current in amperes:

$$P = VI = 20 \times 2.5 = 50.0 \text{ W}$$

in agreement with the sum of the two values in (c).

To find the energy, multiply by the time in seconds:

$$W = 50.0 \text{ W} \times 7200 \text{ s} = 360{,}000 \text{ J}$$

(e) The power 50.0 W should next be expressed in KW and multiplied by the time in hours, to give

$$W = 0.050 \text{ KW} \times 40.0 \text{ h} = 2.0 \text{ KW-h}$$

At 3 cents per KW-h, the total cost will be 6 cents.

25.3. The Heating Effect of an Electric Current

When an electron current is sent through a wire, heat is generated and the temperature of the wire rises. If the current is increased, the rate at which heat it generated increases rapidly until the wire itself glows a deep red. A still further increase in current will heat the wire to a yellow or white heat. Beyond this point, if it has not already done so, the wire will reach a temperature where it will melt and become a liquid.

Whether a wire is only warmed by an electron current or heated to incandescence depends upon a number of factors, the two principal ones being the current and the resistance. Experiment shows that the energy expended in a wire is given by Eq.(25c):

$$W = VIt$$

where V is in volts, I is in amperes, and t is in seconds. Electrical energy, like mechanical energy, is measured in joules. Heat energy is measured in kilocalories.

By the law of conservation of energy, each kilocalorie of heat produced will require the expenditure of a definite amount of electrical energy. As an equation we can therefore write

$$W \propto H$$

or

$$W = JH \tag{25f}$$

where J is a proportionality constant and, as in mechanics, is found to have the value

$$J = 4.19 \times 10^3 \frac{\text{joules}}{\text{kilocalorie}} \tag{25g}$$

If we solve Eq.(25f) for H, we obtain

$$H = \frac{1}{J} W$$

and substituting W from Eq.(25c),

$$H = \frac{1}{J} VIt$$

or

$$H = 2.393 \times 10^{-4}\ VIt$$

If Ohm's law is introduced in the form $V = IR$, we can substitute IR for V and obtain

$$H = 2.393 \times 10^{-4}\ I^2Rt \tag{25h}$$

This is known as *Joule's law.*

Example 2. If the heating element of an electric toaster has a resistance of 22.0 Ω and is connected to an ordinary house lighting circuit of 110.0 V, how much heat will be generated in 1.0 min?
Solution. From Ohm's law, $I = V/R$, the electron current is first calculated:

$$I = 110.0/22.0 = 5.0\ \text{A}$$

We can now make use of Joule's law by substituting in Eq.(25h):

$$H = 2.393 \times 10^{-4} \times (5)^2 \times 22 \times 60$$

$$H = 7.90\ \text{Kcal}$$

For some electric appliances, heating is a desired effect, while in others it is a source of trouble and even danger. In an electric

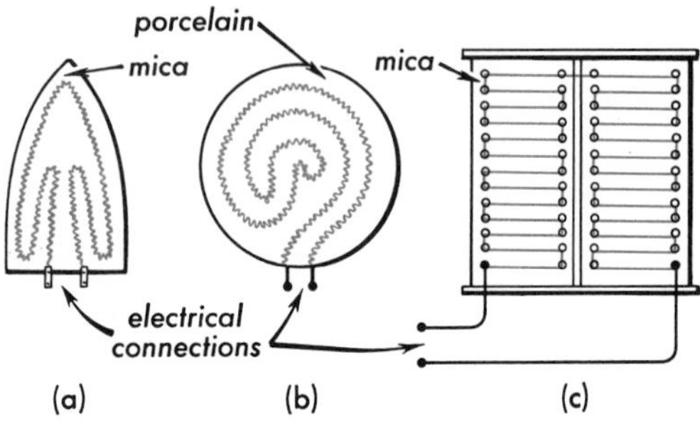

Fig. 25C. Diagrams of the heating elements of various electrical appliances found in many modern homes: (a) electric iron, (b) electric stove, and (c) electric toaster.

iron, hot plate, or toaster, for example, heat is the main objective of the device. In such appliances a relatively large current of several amperes is sent through a coil or element of special wire having a resistance of several ohms. As a rule the wire is of some alloy, such as nichrome, and of such a size that the heat developed will not raise the temperature higher than red hot. Diagrams of typical heating elements used in three different household appliances are shown in Fig. 25C.

25.4. Magnetic Effect, Oersted's Experiment

The first discovery of any connection between electricity and magnetism was made by Oersted* in 1820. Often, during his lectures at the University of Copenhagen, Oersted had demonstrated the nonexistence of a connection between electricity and magnetism. His usual procedure was to place a current-carrying wire at right angles to, and directly over, a compass needle to show that there was no effect of one on the other. On one occasion, at the end of his lecture, when several members of the audience came up to meet him at the lecture room desk, he placed the wire parallel to the compass needle and, not the least expecting it, saw the needle move to one side (see Fig. 25D). Upon his reversing the current in the wire, the needle, to his amazement and perplexity, deviated in the opposite direction. Thus this great discovery was made quite by accident, but, as Lagrange once said of Newton on a similar occasion, "such accidents come only to those who deserve them."

25.5. The Left-Hand Rule

Oersted's experiment is interpreted as demonstrating that *around every wire carrying an electric current there is a magnetic field.* The direction of this field at every point, like that around a bar magnet, can be mapped by means of a small compass or by iron filings. If a wire is mounted vertically through a hole in a plate of glass or other suitable nonconductor, and then iron filings are sprinkled on the plate, there will be a lining-up of the filings parallel to the magnetic field. The result shows that the magnetic lines of force or *lines of induction* are concentric circles whose planes are at right angles to the current. This is illustrated by the circles in Fig. 25E.

The left-hand rule used in electromagnetism can always be relied upon to give the direction of the magnetic field due to an electron current in a wire. Derived from experiment, the rule states: *If the current-carrying wire were to be grasped with the left*

***Hans Christian Oersted (1777–1851), Danish scientist, was born the son of an apothecary. Oersted spent part of his boyhood teaching himself arithmetic. At the age of 12, he assisted his father in his shop and there became interested in chemistry. Passing the entrance examinations at the University of Copenhagen at the age of 17, he entered the medical school, and graduated six years later with his doctorate in medicine. At age 29 he returned to the university, this time as professor of physics. It was at one of his demonstration lectures on chemistry and metaphysics that he discovered the magnetic effect bearing his name. The discovery not only brought him many endowments and prizes, but also made him one of the most eminent personalities in his own country.**

hand, the thumb pointing in the direction of the electron current, (−) to (+), the fingers will point in the direction of the magnetic induction.

25.6. Magnetic Properties of a Solenoid

Not long after the announcement of Oersted's discovery of the magnetic effect of a current-carrying wire, Ampère found that a loop or coil of wire acted as a magnet. This is illustrated by a single loop of wire in Fig. 25F, and by a coil of several turns of wire in Fig. 25G. A coil of wire of this kind is sometimes referred to as a *solenoid,* or as a *helix.* In either case, the magnetic lines of force are such that one side or end of the coil acts like an N magnetic pole and the other side or end like an S magnetic pole.

At all points in the region around a coil of wire carrying a current, the direction of the magnetic field, as shown by a compass, can be predicted by the left-hand rule. Inside each loop or turn of wire, the lines point in one direction, whereas outside they are oppositely directed.

Outside the coil, the lines go from N to S in quite the same way they do about a permanent bar magnet, whereas inside they go from S to N.

Not only does one coil of wire act like a magnet but two coils may be used to demonstrate the repulsion and attraction of like and unlike poles.

Another *left-hand rule,* which must not be confused with the one in the preceding section, but which follows directly from it, is the following: *If the solenoid were to be grasped with the fingers pointing in the direction of the electron current, around the coil from (−) to (+), the thumb would point in the direction of the internal field as well as the N pole.*

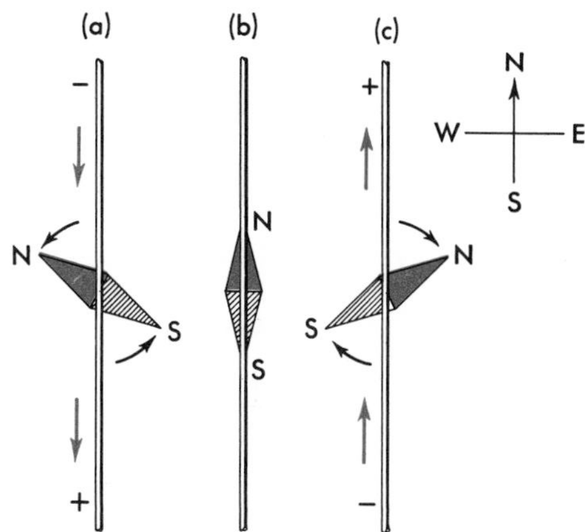

Fig. 25D. Diagram of Oersted's experiment illustrating the effect of an electron current upon a compass needle.

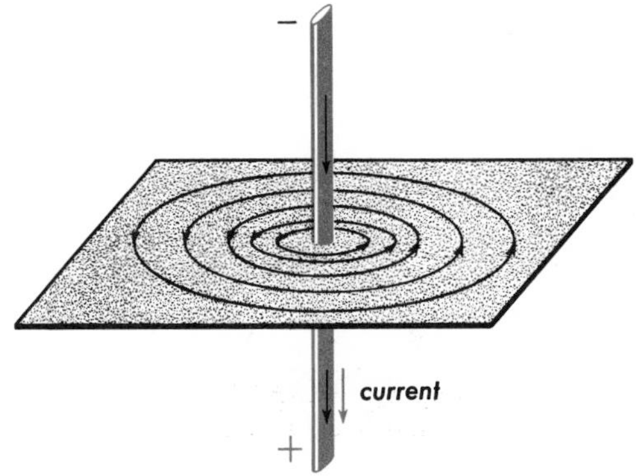

Fig. 25E. Experiment demonstrating the magnetic field about a straight wire carrying an electron current.

25.7. The Electromagnet

Five years after Oersted's discovery and Ampère's demonstration of the magnetic properties of a solenoid, William Sturgeon filled the center of a coil of wire with soft iron and thereby produced a powerful magnet. This is illustrated in Fig. 25H. As long as the electron current continues to flow, the addition of the iron core produces a magnet hundreds of times stronger than does the solenoid alone. A nearby compass needle, if set oscillating, will demonstrate this effect by vibrating quickly with the iron core in place, and slowly with it removed.

Again, with the iron core in the solenoid, a nearby rod of soft iron, magnetized by induction as shown in Fig. 25P, will attract iron fillings much more strongly than when the iron core is removed.

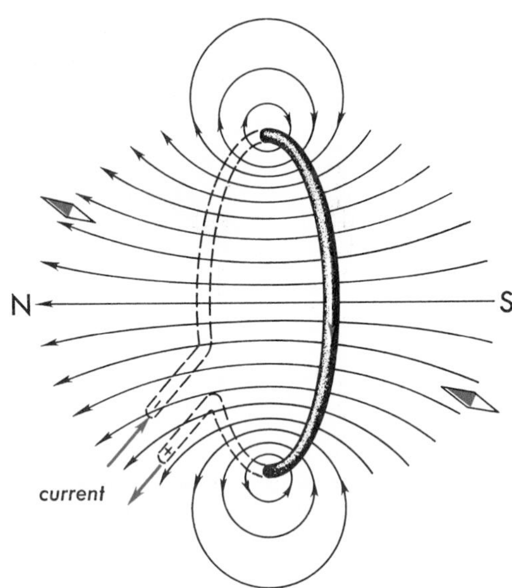

Fig. 25F. Diagram of the magnetic field through and around a single loop of wire carrying an electron current.

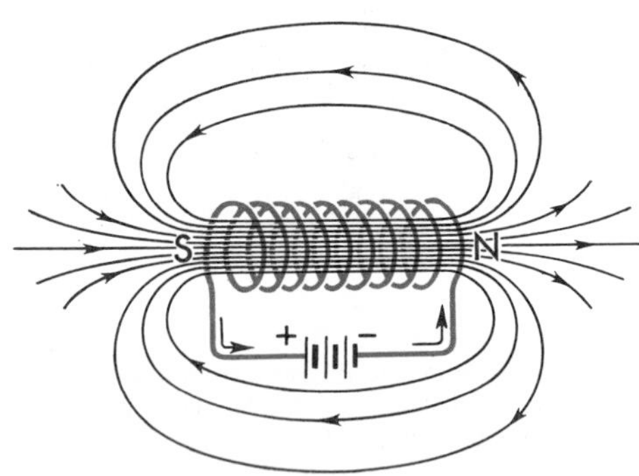

Fig. 25G. Diagram of the magnetic field around a solenoid carrying an electron current.

25.8. Mechanical Effects of Electric Currents

In 1821, Michael Faraday discovered that, when a wire carrying a current is placed in the field of a magnet, a mechanical force is exerted on the wire. This is the principle upon which the modern electric motor is based.

A demonstration of Faraday's discovery is shown in Fig. 25I, where a flexible copper wire about one meter long is suspended from a support. A U-shaped magnet straddles the wire somewhere near the middle.

Upon closing the switch K, an electron current flows up through the wire and the wire moves to the left. If the battery connections are reversed, thereby reversing the electron current, the deflection of the wire will be to the right.

If the magnet is turned over, thereby interchanging N and S poles, the deflection of the wire will again reverse. In other words, the reversing of either the magnetic field or the direction of the electron current will reverse the direction of the force acting on the wire. The reversal of both will make it the same.

The existence of a mechanical force may be demonstrated by another simple experiment as shown in Fig. 25J. Two parallel brass bars fastened to a board are placed over the N pole of a magnet and then connected to a battery. When a round metal rod is laid across the bars, thus allowing an electron current to flow in the direction shown, the rod experiences a force and rolls to the left. A reversal of either the electron current or the polarity of the magnet will cause the rod to roll to the right. A reversal of both will cause it to roll to the left.

It should be emphasized here that this force is exerted on the electrons, the moving charges in the wire, and that they, being confined to the wire, cause it to move. An electron at rest in a magnetic field experiences no force from the magnet. An electron moving across magnetic lines of force experiences a force at right angles to both the field and the direction of motion.

25.9. Interaction between Magnetic Fields

To gain some understanding of this mysterious invisible force acting on a current-carrying wire in a magnetic field, consider the diagrams in Fig. 25K.

The circles in diagram (a) represent the circular magnetic lines of force around a straight wire carrying a current. The directions of the arrows are given by the left-hand rule, shown here for an electron current up and out of the page. The lines of force in diagram (b) represent the magnetic field between two opposite poles of a magnet.

If we now place the current-carrying wire between the poles of the magnet, the two fields interact on each other. The interaction is such that a newly formed field like that shown at the right in Fig. 25L is obtained. Imagining that the magnetic lines of force act like stretched rubber bands, one can predict from this diagram that the wire should experience a force *F* to the left.

To understand how such a field can arise out of two interacting symmetrical fields, it should be remembered that the field direction at any point is that taken by a small magnet placed there. Consider as examples the points A, B, C, and D of diagram (a). At A the field due to the current in the wire is to the right, and that due to the magnet poles is down. If the two fields exert equal torques on the tiny compass needle, it will point along a direction half-way between the two.

At B the field due to the wire is down, and so is the field due to the magnet. A compass at this point would point down. At C the fields are again at right angles, and the compass points down and to the left. At D the fields are oppositely directed and, if they are equal in magnitude, cancel each other's effect. This process repeated for many other points will lead to the field shown in diagram (b).

It is important to note that the direction of the current *I* in the wire, the direction of the magnetic field *B* at the wire due to the magnet, and the direction of the force *F* acting on the wire are all at right angles to each other. Furthermore, the direction of the force *F* can be quickly ascertained by applying the left-hand rule to the electron current in the wire. If the wire were to be grasped with the left hand, the thumb pointing in the direction of the electron current (− to +), the force is toward the weakened field, that is, toward the region where the fingers are oppositely directed to the field of the magnet.

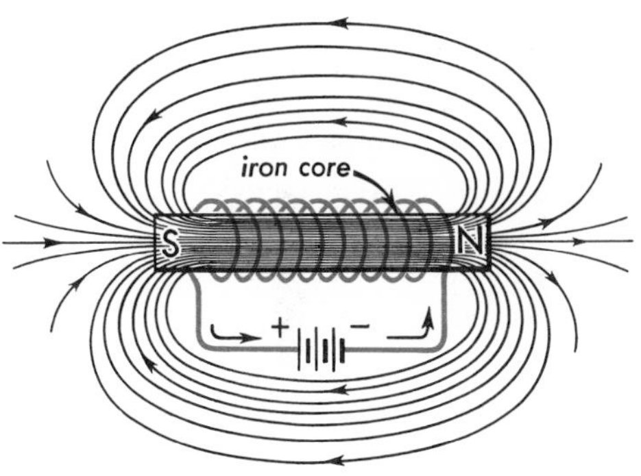

Fig. 25H. Diagram of an electromagnet and the field surrounding it when a current flows through the coil.

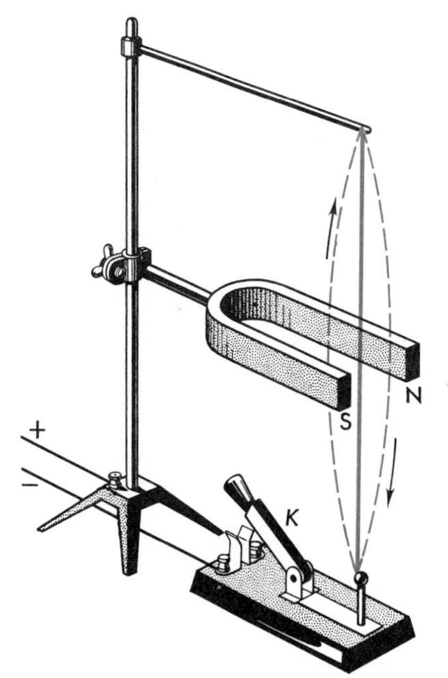

Fig. 25I. Demonstration of the mechanical effect of an electron current in a magnetic field.

25.10. The Electric Motor

An electric motor is a device by which electrical energy in the form of an electron current is transformed into mechanical energy. The principle of the motor is illustrated in Fig. 25M. A wire carrying an electron current is bent into a loop and placed between two magnetic poles as shown in Fig. 25N. In this horizontal position, the resultant magnetic field is warped, which forces one wire down and the other up. Mounted free to turn about an axis, the

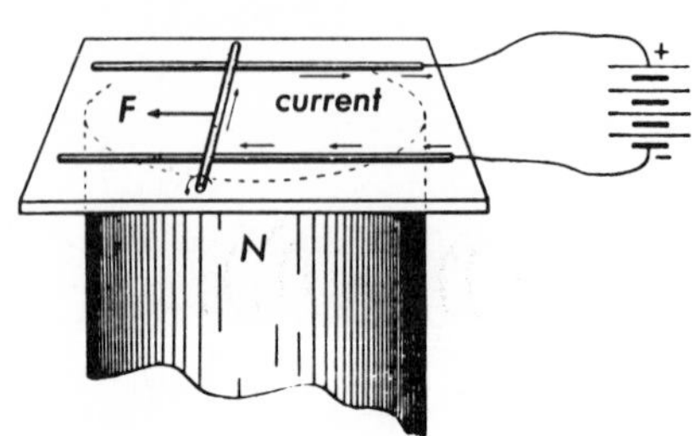

Fig. 25J. An experimental arrangement for demonstrating that a wire carrying a current in a magnetic field experiences a force tending to move it across the field at right angles to the current, and at right angles to the field.

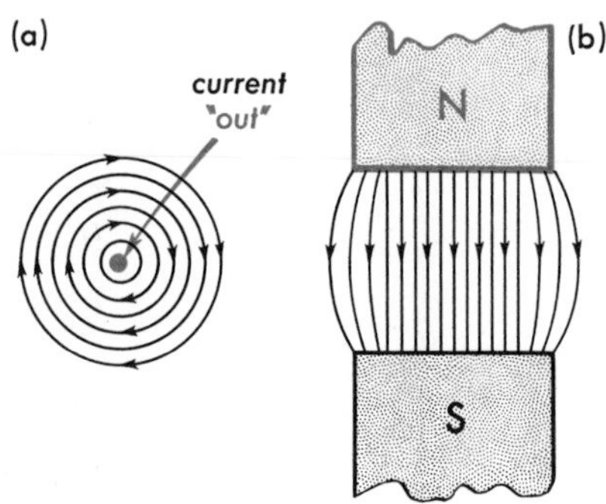

Fig. 25K. Magnetic fields (a) due to an electron current and (b) due to magnetic poles.

loop rotates until it is in a vertical plane. At this point, the current in the loop is reversed in direction by means of *sliding contacts* and a *split-ring commutator.* The reversal of the electron current reverses the forces so that the side of the loop which was previously pushed up is now pushed down, and the side previously pushed down is now pushed up. The loop therefore rotates through half a turn more, where the current again reverses. A repetition of this reversing process at each half turn gives rise to a continuous rotation, the left side of the coil or loop always moving down and the right side always moving up.

25.11. Ammeters and Voltmeters

Electrical instruments designed to measure an electric current are called *ammeters,* and those designed to measure potential difference are called *voltmeters.* The principle upon which both of these devices operate is essentially the same as that of the electric motor as shown in Fig. 25M. They differ from the motor, however, in the delicateness of their construction and the restrained motion of the rotating armature.

A coil of fine copper wire is so mounted between the two poles of a permanent magnet that its rotation, as shown in Fig. 25O, is restrained by a hairspring. The farther the coil is turned from its equilibrium or zero position, the greater is the restoring force. To this coil is fastened a long pointer, at the end of which is a fixed scale reading amperes if it is an ammeter, or volts if it is a voltmeter. Upon increasing the current through the moving coil of an ammeter or voltmeter, the resultant magnetic field between the coil and the magnet is distorted more and more. The resulting increase in force therefore turns the coil through a greater and greater angle, reaching a point where it is just balanced by the restoring force of the hairspring.

Photographs of two small panel instruments are shown in Fig. 25P. The two connections necessary in each instrument are on the back and are not shown. On each instrument they lead to the moving coil by means of flexible connections near or through the armature pivots.

Whenever an ammeter or voltmeter is connected to a circuit to measure electron current or potential difference, the ammeter must be connected in series and the voltmeter in parallel. As illustrated in Fig. 25Q, the ammeter is so connected that all of the electron current passes through it. To prevent a change in the electron current when such an insertion is made, all ammeters must have a low resistance. Most ammeters therefore have a low-

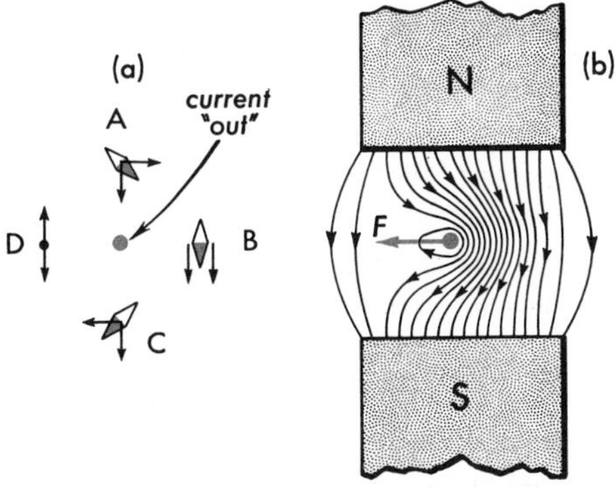

Fig. 25L. Diagrams of two interacting magnetic fields.

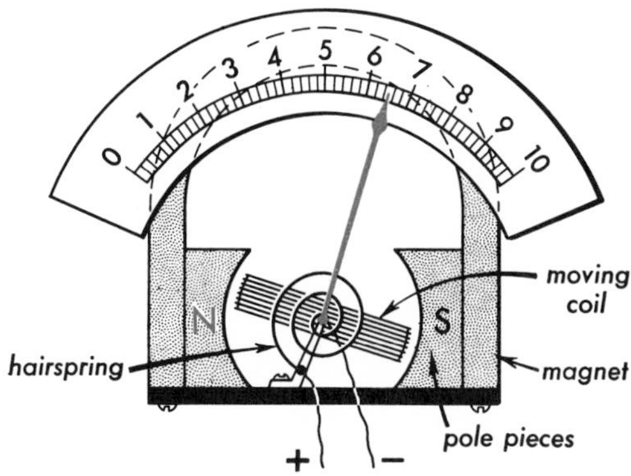

Fig. 25O. Diagram of the essential parts of an ammeter or voltmeter.

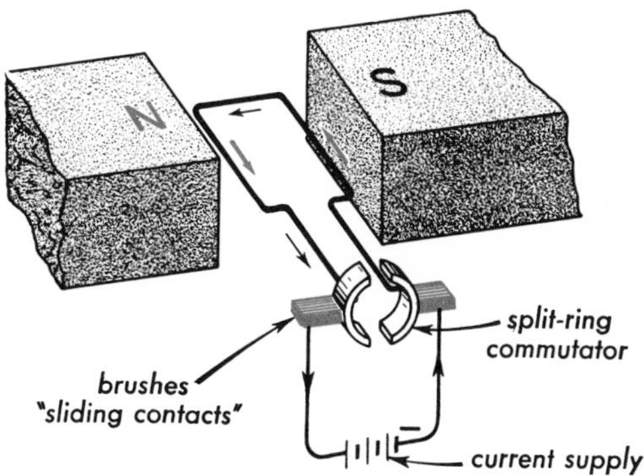

Fig. 25M. Principal elements for demonstrating the principles of an electric motor.

Fig. 25P. Photographs of the front face of a typical voltmeter and ammeter. The two electrical connections to each of these instruments are on the back and are not shown. (Courtesy, General Electric Co.)

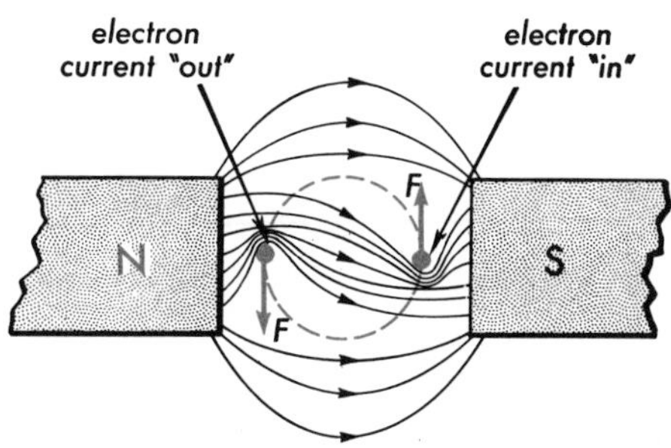

Fig. 25N. Magnetic field lines in an electric motor with two poles.

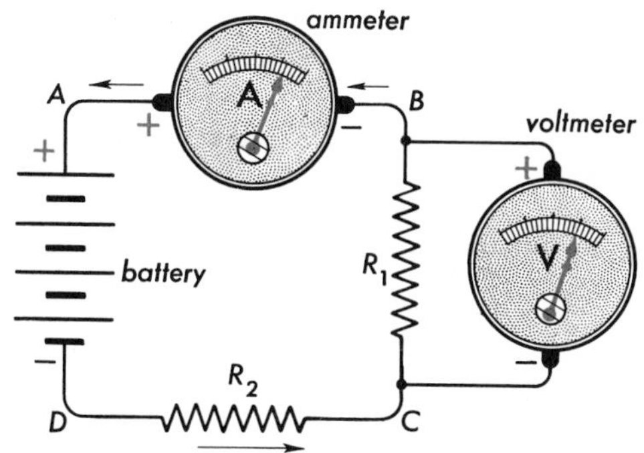

Fig. 25Q. Circuit diagram showing the connections for an ammeter and voltmeter.

resistance wire, called a *shunt,* connected across the armature coil.

A voltmeter, on the other hand, is connected across that part of the circuit for which a measurement of the potential difference is required. If the potential difference between the ends of the resistance R_1 is wanted, the voltmeter is connected as shown. If the potential difference across R_2 is desired, the voltmeter connections are made at C and D, whereas, if the potential difference maintained by the battery is desired, the connections are made at A and D. In order that the connection of a voltmeter to a circuit does not change the electron current in the circuit, the voltmeter must have a high resistance. If the armature coil does not have a large resistance of its own, additional resistance is added in series.

Very delicate ammeters are often used for measuring very small currents. A meter whose scale is calibrated to read thousandths of an ampere is called a *milliammeter.* One whose scale is calibrated in millionths of an ampere is called a *micro-ammeter* or *galvanometer.*

problems

1. Two resistors, 4.50 Ω and 6.85 Ω, respectively, are connected in series with a 120-V house lighting circuit. Calculate (a) the electron current through the circuit, (b) the power consumed by each resistor, (c) the energy consumed by each resistor in 1.0 min, and (d) the cost of operation for 1 h at 2.60 cents per KW-h.

2. Two resistors of 8.0 Ω and 12.0 Ω, respectively, are connected in series to a house lighting circuit of 120 V. Calculate (a) the electron current through the circuit, (b) the power consumed by each resistor, (c) the energy consumed by each resistor per minute, and (d) the total cost of operation per hour at 3.40 cents per KW-h.

3. Three resistors of 4.0 Ω, 6.0 Ω and 12.0 Ω, respectively, are connected in parallel to a 12.0-V battery. Find (a) the electron current through each resistor, (b) the power consumed by each resistor, (c) the energy consumed by each resistor per hour, and (d) the total cost of operating for 1 h at 4.2 cents per KW-h. [Ans. (a) 3.0 A, 2.0 A, 1.0 A, (b) 36.0 W, 24.0 W, 12.0 W, (c) 12.96×10^4 J, 8.64×10^4 J, 4.32×10^4 J, and (d) 0.3024 cents.]

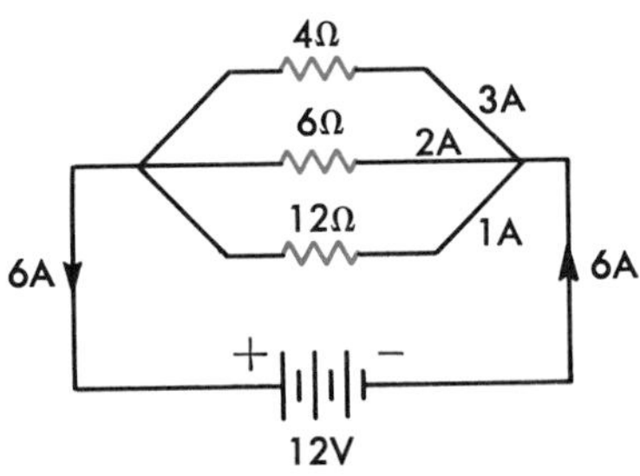

Prob. 3.

4. When a certain coffee pot is plugged into a 120-V outlet it draws an electron current of 3.60 A. How much heat is produced per minute?

5. An electric hot-plate draws a current of 6.50 A when

plugged into a house lighting circuit of 115.0 V. (a) How much energy is expended in 1 h, and (b) how much heat is produced in this time?

6.* When an electric coffee pot is plugged into a 120-V outlet, it draws an electron current of 2.7 A. If the pot contains 1.50 Kg of water, and 75% of the heat goes into the water, how long will it take to raise the temperature of the water from 20°C to 100°C? [Ans. 34.4 min.]

7.* A pan containing 2.50 Kg of water is placed on a hot-plate. When plugged into a house lighting circuit of 115 V, the unit draws a current of 7.20 A. If 80% of the heat goes into the water, how long will it take to raise the temperature of the water from 30°C to 100°C?

8. An electric toaster with a resistance of 24.0 Ω draws an electron current of 3.80 A when connected to a house lighting circuit. If it takes 1.5 min to make light toast, (a) what is the line voltage, and (b) how many Kcal were developed?

9. An electric iron having a resistance of 18.0 Ω is connected to a 120-V line. Find the heat developed in 10.0 min. [Ans. 114.9 Kcal.]

10.* A teakettle containing 3.0 Kg of water at a temperature of 20°C is heated on an electric stove. If the heating element draws an electron current of 3.50 A from a 208-V line, and one-half of the heat generated goes to heat the water, how long will it take to reach the boiling point?

11.* A boiler containing 25.0 Kg of water at a temperature of 25°C is heated on an electric stove. If the heating element draws an electron current of 5.50 A from a 208-V line and 70.0% of the heat generated goes into the water, how long will it take to reach the boiling point?

12.* An electric coffee maker containing 8.0 Kg of water at 25°C is connected to a 208-V outlet. If the electron current drawn is 6.40 A, and 80% of the heat developed goes into the water, how hot will the water be in 15.0 min? [Ans. 53.7°C.]

13. A voltmeter with a resistance of 200 Ω shows a full scale reading when 10.0 V is applied to its terminals. What resistance connected to this instrument will give it a full scale reading when 500 V is connected?

14. A voltmeter with a resistance of 150.0 Ω shows a full scale reading when 5.0 V is applied to its terminals. What resistance connected to this instrument will give it a full scale deflection when connected to 600 V?

15.* A voltmeter having a resistance of 800 Ω shows a full scale reading when connected to 400 V. (a) What current flows through this instrument at full scale? (b) What shunt resistance across this instrument will enable it to be used as an ammeter with 5.0 A as a full scale reading? [Ans. (a) 500 mA, (b) 88.9 Ω.]

16.* A voltmeter with a resistance of 1600 Ω shows a full scale reading of 160 V. What resistance should be connected as a shunt for this instrument if it is to be converted to an ammeter showing a full scale reading of 10.0 A?

26 Magnetic induction

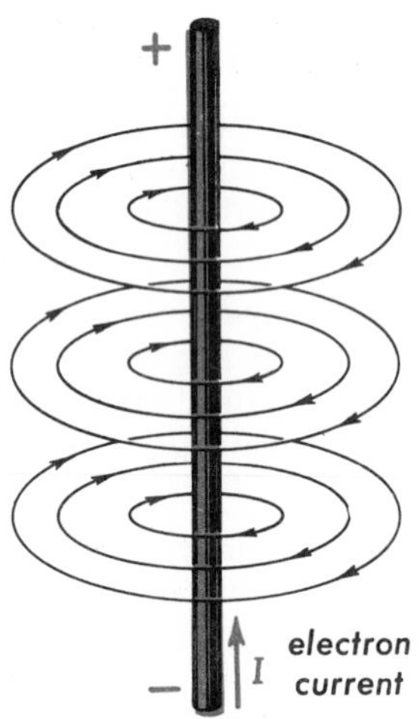

Fig. 26A. The magnetic field around a long, straight conductor.

We have seen in the preceding lessons how an electron current gives rise to a magnetic field surrounding the conductor, and also how a current-carrying wire placed in a magnetic field experiences an unbalanced force tending to move it across the field. The mathematical formulation of the principles involved in these magnetic and mechanical effects depends primarily upon a quantitative account of the magnetic field strength.

The strength of the magnetic field at any point in and around any electrical equipment is represented by the letter B and is called the *magnetic induction.* As a simple illustration, the magnetic induction around a long, straight wire is everywhere perpendicular to the wire, and the magnetic lines of force representing B are drawn as concentric circles as shown in Fig. 26A. While the direction of B, as represented by the arrowheads, is given by the left-hand rule, the magnitude of B at any point is given by *Ampère's theorem*, a fundamental principle connecting electric currents with the magnetic fields they produce.

26.1. *Ampère's Theorem*

Consider a wire of any shape carrying an electron current. The current in each small part of the wire contributes to the magnetic induction at all points around the wire. In Fig. 26B, for example, the small element of wire of length $\Delta \ell_1$ at a distance r_1 from any chosen point P produces its own magnetic induction contribution at P which, by the left-hand rule for electron currents, is "out" from the page. Similarly, the small element of wire $\Delta\ell_2$, at a distance r_2 from the same point P, produces another contribution at P which is out from the page. The resultant magnetic induction at P is, therefore, the vector sum of the contributions from all elements of the wire.

The magnitude of the magnetic induction due to a small current element was first proposed by Biot and Savart in 1820, and later formulated by Ampère, to be given by

$$B = \kappa \frac{I \sin \theta}{r^2} \Delta \ell \qquad (26a)$$

where, as shown in Fig. 26C, B is the magnetic induction at a point P, $\Delta \ell$ is the length of a current element of the wire, r is the distance from ℓ to P, θ is the angle between r and ℓ, and κ is a proportionality constant:

$$\kappa = 10^{-7} \frac{\text{tesla meters}}{\text{ampere}}$$

Equation(26a) is called *Ampère's theorem.*

This is the same constant given in Eq.(24b), since

$$\frac{\text{N}}{\text{A}^2} = \frac{\text{Tm}}{\text{A}}$$

The magnitude of the constant κ, like the constant κ in Coulomb's law [see Eq.(24a)], depends on the choice of units for the other factors.

In applying Ampère's theorem to straight wires and circular coils of various kinds, the factor 4π enters so frequently into the formulas that it is convenient to express κ in terms of another constant μ_0, as follows,

$$\kappa = \frac{\mu_0}{4\pi} \qquad (26b)$$

This is analogous to replacing k in Coulomb's law for electric charges by $1/4\pi\epsilon_0$. See Eqs.(21a) and (21e).

Ampère's theorem, therefore, becomes

$$B = \frac{\mu_0}{4\pi} \cdot \frac{I \sin \theta}{r^2} \Delta \ell \qquad (26c)$$

If I is in amperes, and r and $\Delta \ell$ are in meters, B is in teslas and the constant

$$\mu_0 = 4\pi\kappa$$

$$\mu_0 = 12.5664 \times 10^{-7} \frac{\text{Tm}}{\text{A}}$$

From a study of Eq.(26a) and Fig. 26C, it seems reasonable

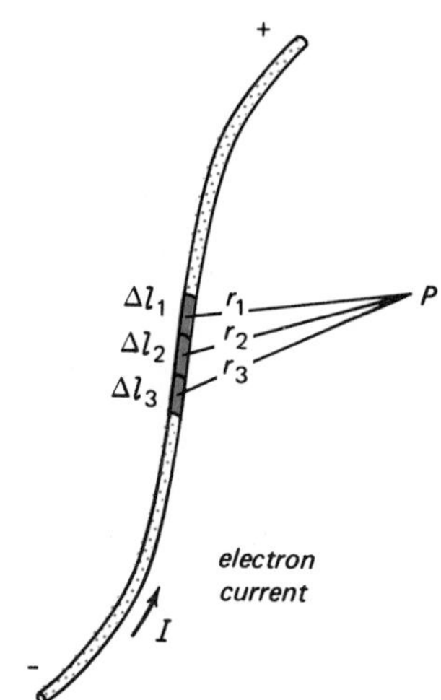

Fig. 26B. The magnetic induction at any point P is due to all current elements of the conductor from one end to the other.

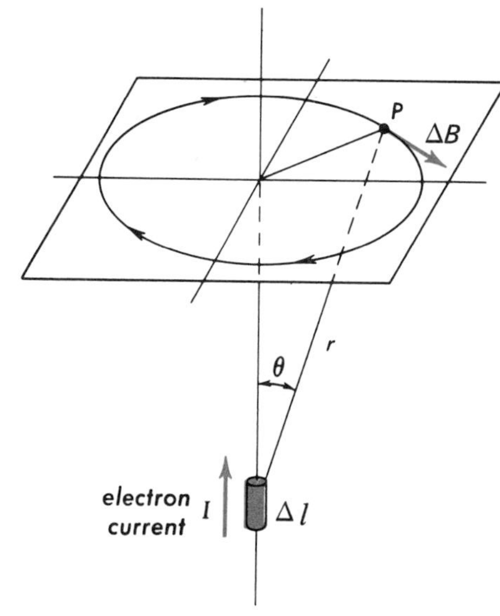

Fig. 26C. Ampère's theorem.

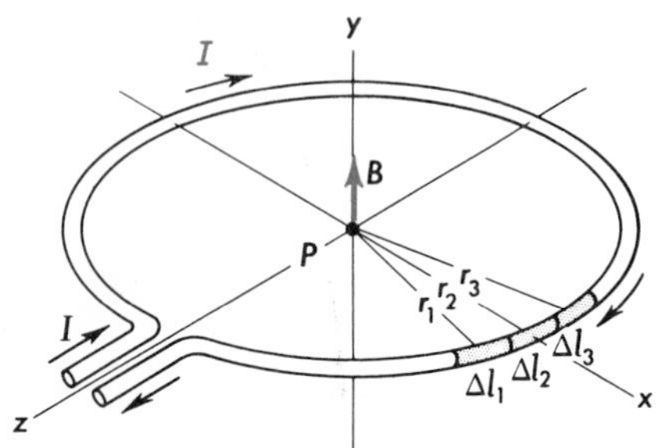

Fig. 26D. Ampère's theorem applied to a single loop of wire.

that doubling the electron current I, or doubling the length of the element $\Delta\ell$, would double the magnetic induction. It is also reasonable by comparison with the field around magnetic poles, and Coulomb's law, that the magnetic induction should vary inversely as the square of the distance. That the magnetic induction varies as sin θ, however, was first proved experimentally by Ampère.

To obtain the resultant value of B at any specified point near a current-carrying wire, the contributions from all small elements $\Delta\ell$ of the entire circuit must be added together. To do this, a summation process, the *integral calculus*, is usually required. With the calculus, many different calculations are readily carried out, but without it they are, except for the following simple case, difficult.

26.2. The Magnetic Induction at the Center of a Circular Turn

Consider a circular loop of wire, as shown in Fig. 26D, where each small element $\Delta\ell$ of the wire is perpendicular to the radial distance r, and equidistant from the center P. Since $\theta = 90°$, and $\sin\theta = 1$, Eq.(26c) becomes the same for each element $\Delta\ell$:

$$B_1 = \frac{\mu_0}{4\pi} \cdot \frac{I}{r_1^2}\,\Delta\ell_1$$

$$B_2 = \frac{\mu_0}{4\pi} \cdot \frac{I}{r_2^2}\,\Delta\ell_2$$

$$B_3 = \frac{\mu_0}{4\pi} \cdot \frac{I}{r_3^2}\,\Delta\ell_3, \text{ etc.}$$

If we sum up the mutually parallel contributions from all elements of the wire, the resultant magnitude of B becomes

$$B = \frac{\mu_0}{4\pi}\left(\frac{I\Delta\ell_1}{r^2} + \frac{I\Delta\ell_2}{r^2} + \frac{I\Delta\ell_3}{r^2} + \ldots\right)$$

or

$$B = \frac{\mu_0 I}{4\pi r^2}\,(\Delta\ell_1 + \Delta\ell_2 + \Delta\ell_3 + \ldots)$$

Since the sum $\Delta\ell_1 + \Delta\ell_2 + \Delta\ell_3 + \ldots$ must equal the circumference of the wire loop, the above parentheses can be replaced by $2\pi r$. When this is done, we obtain

$$B = \mu_0 \frac{I}{2r} \qquad (26d)$$

for single turn

where I is in amperes, r is in meters, and B is in teslas. Note that B is the magnetic induction at the center only and that its direction is perpendicular to the plane of the loop. For the general shape of the field, see Fig. 26E.

For a wire conductor that is wound in the form of a flat circular coil having a number of turns N, and a radius r, the magnetic field in and around the coil is greatly increased over that produced by a single turn (see Fig. 26F). Along the axis of the coil the magnetic induction B is perpendicular to the plane of the coil and its magnitude is given by

$$B_x = \mu_0 \frac{NIr^2}{2d^3} \qquad (26e)$$

any point on axis of flat coil

where N is the number of turns, r is their radius in meters, I is the current in amperes, and

$$d = \sqrt{r^2 + x^2} \qquad (26f)$$

Here x is the distance from the coil center to the axial point where B_x is to be calculated.

At the coil center, where $x = 0$, $d = r$, Eq.(26e) simplifies to

$$B_0 = \mu_0 \frac{NI}{2r} \qquad (26g)$$

center of a flat coil

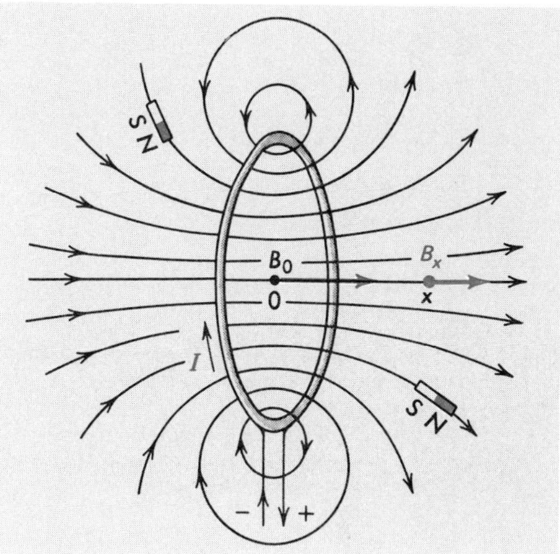

Fig. 26E. Diagram of the magnetic field through and around a flat circular coil carrying an electron current I.

26.3. Uniform Magnetic Fields

While there are numerous ways of producing uniform magnetic fields, the methods commonly employed in the research laboratory are few in number. One of these is shown in Fig. 26F. Here, two identical flat coils of radius r, placed a distance r apart, form what are called *Helmholtz coils.* The magnetic induction B at the geometrical center of this arrangement, and over a considerable volume of space around this center, is given by

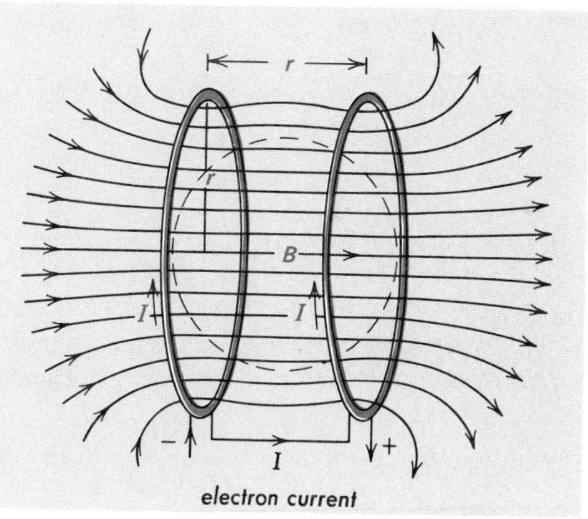

Fig. 26F. Diagram of the magnetic field around Helmholtz coils, showing the uniformity of field over the large central volume of space.

$$B = 1.43\ \mu_0 \frac{NI}{2r}$$

Helmholtz coils

where N is the number of turns in one of the two identical coils.

This equation is derived from Eq.(26e) by setting $x = r/2$ and doubling the result, since the two coils contribute equal amounts to the field at the center.

Example 1. A pair of Helmholz coils, 24.0 cm in diameter and 40.0 turns each, are 12.0 cm apart and carry a current of 2.50 A. Find the magnetic induction at a point on the common axis (a) at the very center midway between the coils, and (b) at the center of one coil.

Solution. For the answer to part (a) we use Eq.(26h), and substitute the given quantities, $N = 40.0$ turns, $I = 2.50$ A, $r = 0.120$ m, and $\mu_0 = 12.57 \times 10^{-7}$ Tm/A:

$$B_1 = \frac{1.431 \times 12.57 \times 10^{-7} \times 40.0 \times 2.50}{2 \times 0.120}$$

$$B_1 = 7.49 \times 10^{-4}\ \text{T}$$

For part (b) we calculate the field contributed to the point in question by the two coils separately, and add the two. For one coil we use Eq.(26f), and substitute the given quantities, $r = 0.120$ m and $x = 0.120$ m:

$$d = \sqrt{r^2 + x^2} = 0.1697\ \text{m}$$

Upon substitution in Eq.(26e), we obtain

$$B_x = \frac{12.57 \times 10^{-7} \times 40.0 \times 2.50 \times 144 \times 10^{-4}}{2 \times (0.1697)^3}$$

$$B_x = 1.852 \times 10^{-4}\ \text{T}$$

For the second coil, we use Eq.(26g), and substitute directly:

$$B_0 = \frac{12.57 \times 10^{-7} \times 4.0 \times 2.50}{2 \times 0.120}$$

$$B_0 = 5.238 \times 10^{-4}\ \text{T}$$

Adding $B_x + B_0$, we obtain

$$B = 7.090 \times 10^{-4}\ \text{T}$$

A second experimental arrangement frequently employed to produce uniform magnetic fields is shown in Fig. 26G. The field is produced by sending a steady current through a long straight solenoid. As indicated by the lines of induction drawn in the figure, the number of lines per square meter of cross section is fairly constant over a considerable volume of space at the center.

The magnetic induction at the center of such a solenoid is given by

$$B = \mu_0 \frac{NI}{\ell} \tag{26i}$$

long solenoid

where N is the number of turns, I is the current in amperes, and ℓ is the length of the coil in meters.

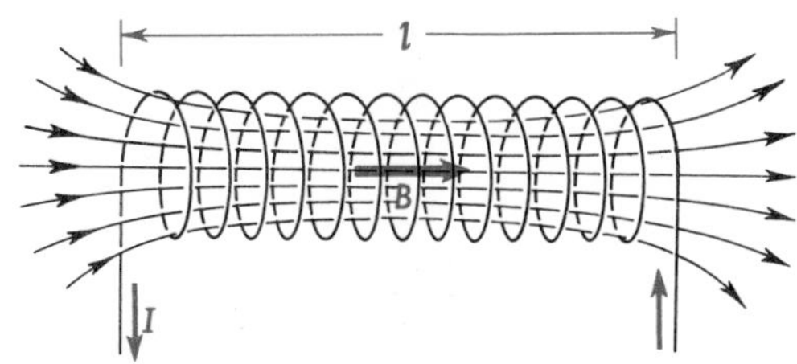

Fig. 26G. A solenoid of N turns of wire.

Example 2. If the magnetic induction at the center of a solenoid 10.0 cm in diameter and 60.0 cm long is to be 4.0×10^{-2} T, when an electron current of 5.0 A is flowing, how many turns of wire must it have?

Solution. For the answer to this problem we use Eq.(26h), solve for N, and substitute the given quantities $\ell = 0.60$ m, $I = 5.0$ A, $B = 4.0 \times 10^{-2}$ T, and $\mu_0 = 12.57 \times 10^{-7}$ Tm/A. Note that the diameter of the coil is not needed:

$$N = \frac{B\ell}{I\mu} = \frac{4 \times 10^{-2} \times 0.6}{5 \times 12.57 \times 10^{-7}}$$

$$N = 3819 \text{ turns}$$

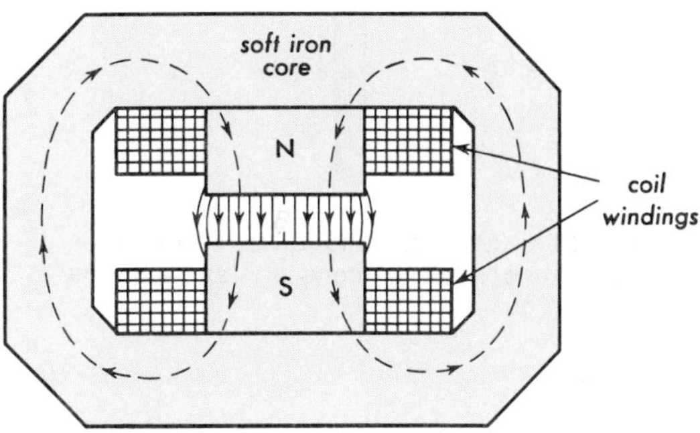

Fig. 26H. Diagram of an electromagnet for producing strong uniform magnetic fields.

When uniform fields of great strength are required, electromagnets are commonly employed (see Fig. 26H). As in any electromagnet, the soft iron core increases the magnetic induction to several thousand times that produced by the coils alone. Fields up to approximately 1.5 T are produced by this means. Since the resultant field strengths thus produced depend a great deal upon the nature of the iron core itself, the magnitude of B between the poles is usually measured by experimental methods.

26.4. *Field near a Straight Conductor*

The magnetic induction around a straight wire is shown in Fig. 25E to be everywhere perpendicular to the wire, and the lines of force to be concentric circles. The magnitude of the induction at any point P, close to a long, straight wire, is found from Ampère's theorem to be given by

$$B = \frac{\mu_0}{4\pi} \cdot \frac{2I}{r} \qquad (26j)$$

for straight wire

where, as shown in Fig. 26I, r is the perpendicular distance to the point P in meters, and I is the electron current in amperes.

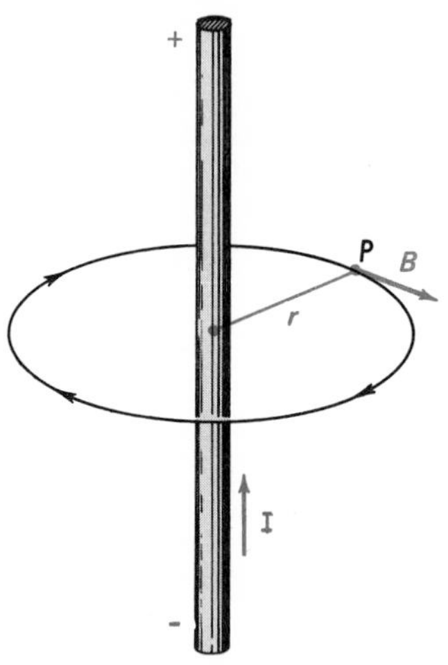

Fig. 26I. Magnetic induction B around a straight conductor carrying an electron current.

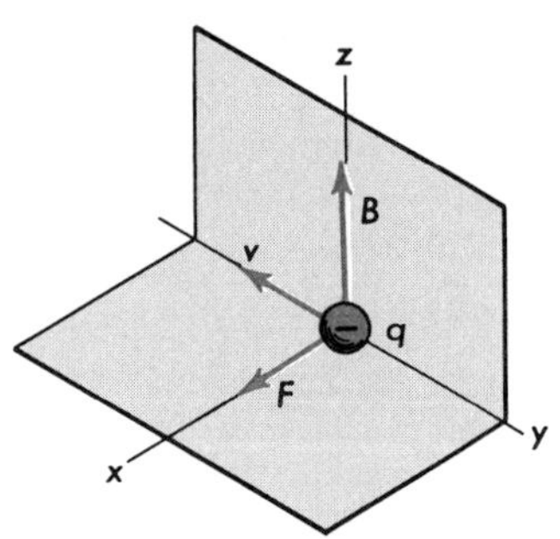

Fig. 26J. Force on a negative charge moving across a magnetic field.

26.5. Total Magnetic Flux and Flux Density

In Chaps. 24 and 25 the magnetic field over a region of space is graphically represented by what are called *lines of force.* Since lines of force are frequently used as graphical representations of the variations in the magnetic induction from point to point, they are also called *lines of induction.*

The direction of the magnetic induction B at any point is tangent to the line of induction passing through that point, and its magnitude is given by the number of lines per unit area. The unit area is so chosen that it includes the point in question and is everywhere perpendicular to all lines passing through it.

In the *MKSA* system of units, a line of induction is called a *weber* (abbr. Wb). The total number of lines of induction passing through a surface is called the magnetic flux and is represented by ϕ. In a region where the field is uniform and the surface area A is normal to the lines of induction,

$$\phi = BA \qquad (26k)$$

In the *cgs* system of units, each line of induction is called a *maxwell*, and B is given in *maxwells/cm*^{2}, or *gauss* (G). For convenience of comparison with some of the older books, note that

$$1 \text{ maxwell/centimeter}^2 = 1 \text{ gauss}$$

and that

$$1 \text{ weber/meter}^2 = 1 \text{ tesla}$$

$$1 \text{ Wb/m}^2 = 1 \text{ T}$$

where

$$1 \text{ tesla} = 10{,}000 \text{ gauss} \qquad (26\ell)$$

26.6. Force on a Moving Charge

In Sec. 25.9 it was shown how a current-carrying wire, when placed in a magnetic field, experiences a mechanical force tending to move it across the field. This mechanical force is due directly to the force exerted by the magnetic induction upon the individual moving electrons within the conductor (see Fig. 26J).

A charge q, moving with a velocity v through a magnetic field at right angles to B, experiences a force F given by

$$F = Bqv \tag{26m}$$

In the *MKSA* system, F is in *newtons*, B is in *teslas*, v is in *meters/second*, and q is in *coulombs*. The vectors B, v, and F are all mutually perpendicular to each other.

If the velocity vector v makes an angle θ with B, as indicated in Fig. 26K, the magnitude of the force F is proportional to the component of the velocity perpendicular to B:

$$F = Bqv \sin \theta \tag{26n}$$

If the charge q in Fig. 26K is positive, the force F is opposite in direction to the one shown. When a charged particle moves parallel to the field, that is, along the magnetic lines, $\sin \theta = 0$, there is no force.

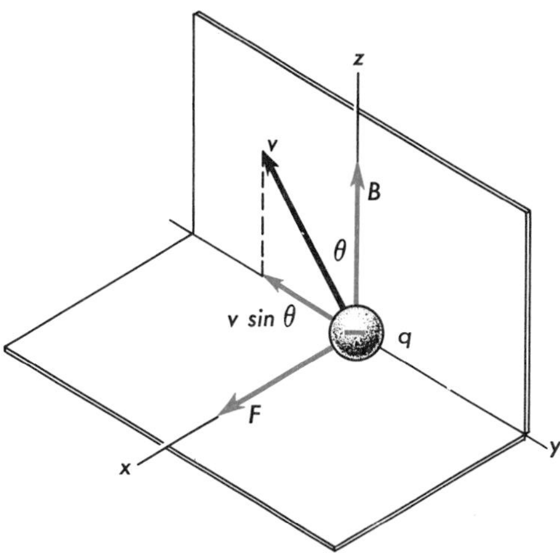

Fig. 26K. Force on a negative charge moving at an angle to a magnetic field.

26.7. Force on a Current-Carrying Wire

To find the force on a current-carrying wire in a magnetic field, we make use of the above Eq.(26n), $F = Bqv$ (see Fig. 26L). A single moving charge q constitutes a current $I = q/t$. Moving with a velocity v it will, in a time t, travel a distance $\ell = vt$. Substituting It for q and ℓ/t for v in Eq.(26n), we obtain

$$F = B \times It \times \frac{\ell}{t} \quad \text{or} \quad F = BI\ell \tag{26o}$$

In the *MKSA* system, F is in *newtons*, B is in *teslas*, I is in *amperes*, and ℓ is in *meters*.

Like a moving charge in Fig. 26K, a current-carrying wire that makes an angle θ with the field B experiences a force proportional to $\sin \theta$:

$$F = BI\ell \sin \theta \tag{26p}$$

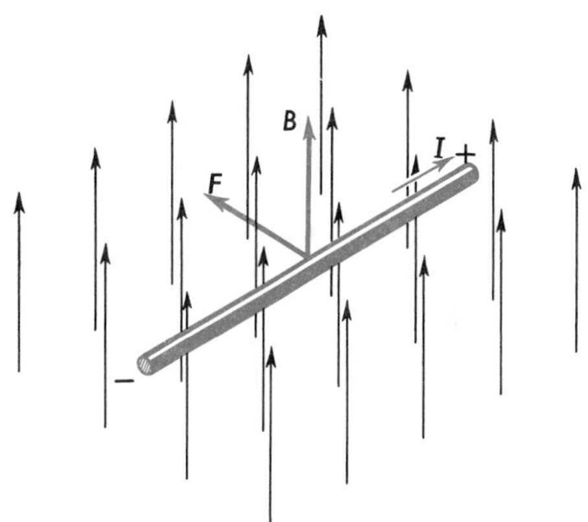

Fig. 26L. The force on a current-carrying wire in a magnetic field.

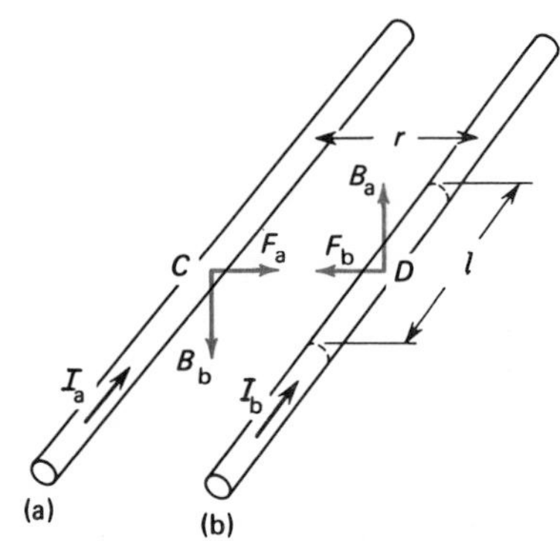

Fig. 26M. Parallel wires carrying currents exert forces on each other. This arrangement is used to define the ampere.

Example 3. A wire 40.0 cm long and carrying a current of 2.50 A is located in a uniform magnetic field in which $B = 1.0 \times 10^{-2}$ T. Calculate the force on the wire when it makes an angle of 60° with the field direction.

Solution. The given quantities are $B = 1.0 \times 10^{-2}$ T, $I = 2.50$ A, $\ell = 0.40$ m, and $\theta = 60°$. Direct substitution of these quantities in Eq.(26p) gives

$$F = 1.0 \times 10^{-2} \times 2.50 \text{ A} \times 0.40 \text{ m} \times 0.866$$

$$F = 8.66 \times 10^{-3} \text{ N}$$

26.8. Forces on Parallel Current-Carrying Wires

When two long parallel wires are each carrying a current, each gives rise to a magnetic field, and the interaction of the fields gives rise to mechanical forces acting on both wires. If the currents are in the same direction, the wires attract each other, as shown in Fig. 26M. If the two currents are oppositely directed, the wires repel each other.

The magnetic induction B_a at the point D, due to the current I_a, is given by the left-hand rule as "up." The magnitude of B_a is given by Eq.(26j) as

$$B_a = \frac{\mu_0}{4\pi} \frac{2I_a}{r} \tag{26q}$$

Since all points along the wire (b) lie in a field of this same intensity and direction, and wire (b) is carrying a current I_b, each length of the wire ℓ will experience a force given by

$$F_b = B_a I_b \ell \tag{26r}$$

By direct substitution of Eq.(26q) for B_a in Eq.(26r), we obtain

$$F_b = \frac{\mu_0}{4\pi} \frac{2I_a I_b \ell}{r}$$

Dividing both sides of this equation by ℓ, we obtain the force per unit length of either wire on the other:

$$\frac{F}{\ell} = \frac{\mu_0}{4\pi} \frac{2I_a I_b}{r}$$

or

$$\frac{F}{\ell} = 2 \times 10^{-7} \frac{I_a I_b}{r} \frac{\text{newton}}{\text{meter}} \tag{26s}$$

This force of attraction between long parallel wires has been used since 1950, by international agreement, to define the fundamental unit of current, the *ampere. The ampere is defined as that current which, when flowing in two very long straight parallel wires, 1 meter apart in free space, will produce a force of 2.000 × 10^{-7} newtons per unit length on each wire.*

One virtue of the rationalized *MKSA* system of units is that nearly all electrical quantities expressed in it, such as the volt, the ampere, the ohm, the farad, and the henry, are natural units around which all practical electrical measuring instruments have been designed and used since the turn of this century.

problems

1. A long straight wire carries a current of 8.50 A. Calculate the magnetic induction at a distance of (a) 2.0 cm, and (b) 5.0 cm from the wire.

2. Two long straight parallel wires are 7.0 cm apart. If each wire carries an electron current of 15.0 A, calculate the magnetic induction at a point between the wires, 2.0 cm from one wire and 5.0 cm from the other, when the currents are (a) in the same direction, and (b) in opposite directions.

3. A copper wire 28.0 m long is wound into a flat circular coil 8.0 cm in diameter. If an electron current of 4.50 A flows through the coil, (a) how many turns does the coil have, and (b) what is the magnetic induction at the center? [Ans. (a) 111.4 turns, (b) 7.88 × 10^{-3} T.]

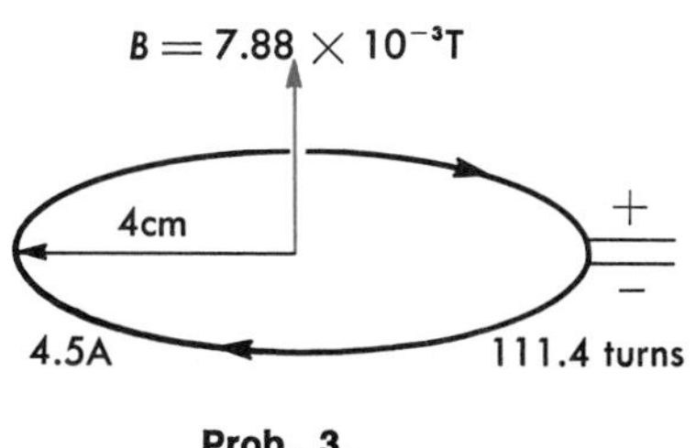

Prob. 3.

4. A wire 30.0 m long is wound into a flat coil 6.0 cm in diameter. If an electron current of 5.0 A flows through the coil, what is (a) the number of turns, and (b) the magnetic induction at the center?

5. A flat circular coil of 62.0 turns has a diameter of 20.0 cm, and carries an electron current of 6.50 A. Find the magnetic induction at the center.

6. A flat circular coil with a diameter of 10.0 cm has 40.0 turns and carries an electron current of 8.0 A. Find the magnetic induction at (a) the geometric center, and (b) at a point on the axis 12.0 cm from the center. [Ans. (a) 4.02 × 10^{-3} T, (b) 2.888 × 10^{-4} T.]

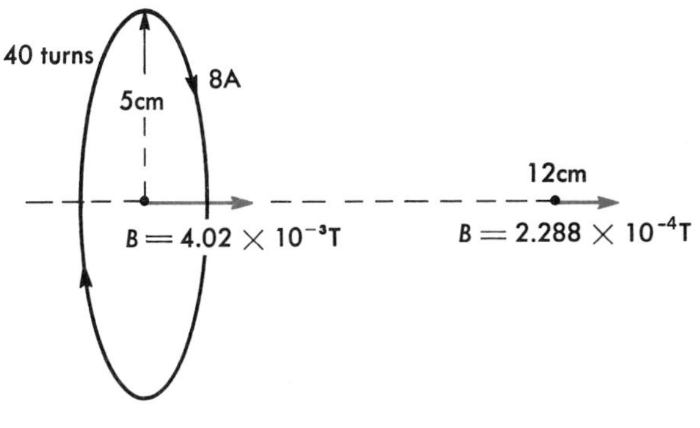

Prob. 6.

7.* A pair of Helmholtz coils, each containing 30.0 turns, are 40.0 cm in diameter and carry an electron current of 4.60 A. Find the magnetic induction at (a) the center of the combination, and (b) at the center of one of the coils.

8.* Helmholtz coils with a diameter of 40.0 cm each have 25.0 turns of wire. If each carries an electron current of 2.80 A, calculate the magnetic induction on the axis and (a) at the center point, and (b) at the center of each coil.

9. A long solenoid containing 450 turns carries an electron current of 3.70 A. If the length of the coil is 45.0 cm, what is the magnetic induction at the center? [Ans. 4.65×10^{-3} T.]

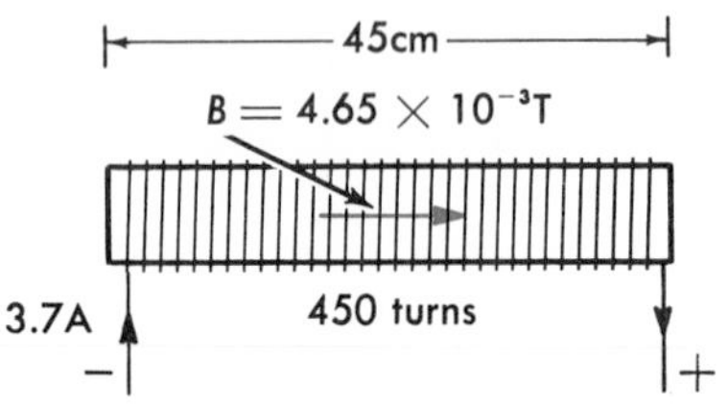

Prob. 9.

10. A straight wire 18.0 cm long carries an electron current of 12.0 A. If this wire is located in a magnetic field at right angles to *B*, where the magnetic induction is 1.0 T, find the force on the wire.

11. A solenoid 80.0 cm long is to be used in a laboratory experiment where a uniform magnetic field of 1.5×10^{-3} T is needed. If the electron current is equal to 2.50 A, how many turns of wire are required?

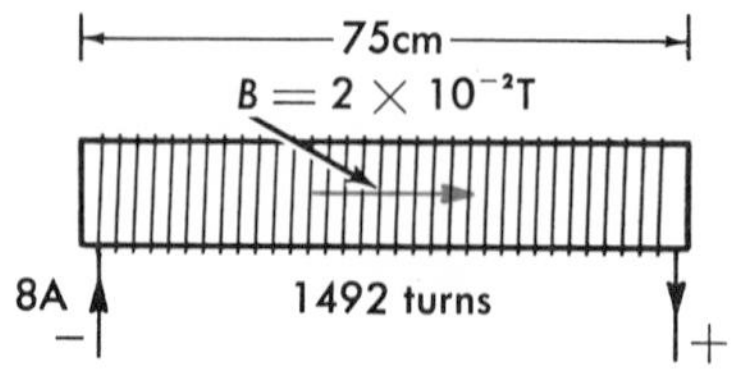

Prob. 12.

12. A coil 75.0 cm long carries an electron current of 8.0 A. How many turns must the coil have if the magnetic induction at the center is 2.0×10^{-2} T? [Ans. 1492 turns.]

13. A copper wire 100.0 m long is wound into a uniform solenoid 12.0 cm in diameter and 60.0 cm long. What is the induction at the center if an electron current of 2.50 A flows through the wire?

14. Two long straight wires, each carrying a current of 4.50 A, are placed parallel to each other 6.50 cm apart. Find the force each wire exerts on the other.

15.* A pair of Helmholtz coils, each containing 50.0 turns, are 20.0 cm in diameter and carry an electron current of 2.0 A. (a) Find the magnetic induction *B* at 1.0-cm intervals along the axis between the coil centers. (b) Plot a graph of the field *B* against the distance along the axis. [Ans. (a) (0, 10 cm) 8.51×10^{-5} T, (1, 9 cm) 8.77×10^{-5} T, (2, 8 cm) 8.92×10^{-5} T, (3, 7 cm) 8.98×10^{-5} T, (4, 6 cm) 8.99×10^{-5} T, (5 cm) 9.00×10^{-5} T. (b) See graph.]

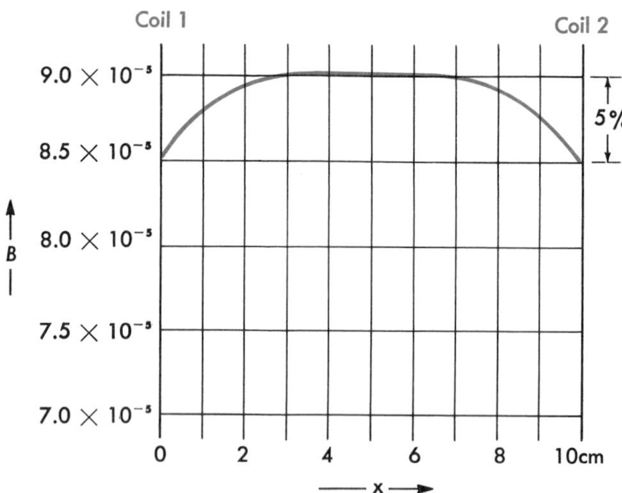

Prob. 15. Graph showing the uniformity of the magnetic induction *B*.

27 Induced electric currents

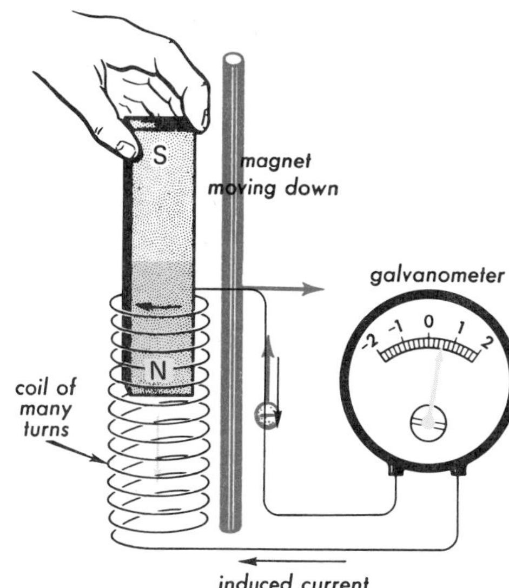

Fig. 27A. Diagram of Faraday's experimental discovery of induced electric currents.

In 1831 Michael Faraday* made the important discovery that a magnet plunged into a coil of wire gives rise to an electric current. The experiment he performed is shown in Fig. 27A. As the N pole of the magnet moves down into the coil, the needle of a sensitive current-reading instrument, such as a galvanometer, deflects to the right; and when the N pole is withdrawn, the needle deflects to the left. When the S pole is moved down into the coil, the needle deflects to the left; as it is withdrawn, the deflection is to the right.

If the magnet is held still and the coil is moved, a similar deflection of the needle demonstrates an induced current. It is the relative motion of the coil and the magnet that produces the effect, for when the relative motion ceases, the current stops. A technically correct way to describe this action is to say that when the total magnetic flux linking a closed electrical circuit is changing there is an induced emf. To demonstrate this concept, a simple experiment like that shown in Fig. 27B may be performed.

A flexible wire connected to an ammeter, and held in the hands, is moved in various ways across the pole of a magnet. When a straight section of the wire is held over the N pole and moved to the right, an electron current flows in the direction shown by the arrows. If the wire is moved in the opposite direction, the induced emf and current reverses direction. If the wire is moved vertically upward or downward, parallel to the magnetic induction, no current flows. In other words, *there is an induced emf only when the total number of lines of induction through the closed circuit is changing.*

The fact that a current is produced means that electrical energy has been created. It has been created at the expense of mechanical work, for, in moving the wire across the field, a force F had to be exerted for a distance ℓ. The faster the wire moves, and the

*See Introduction, Chapter A, at front of text for biography.

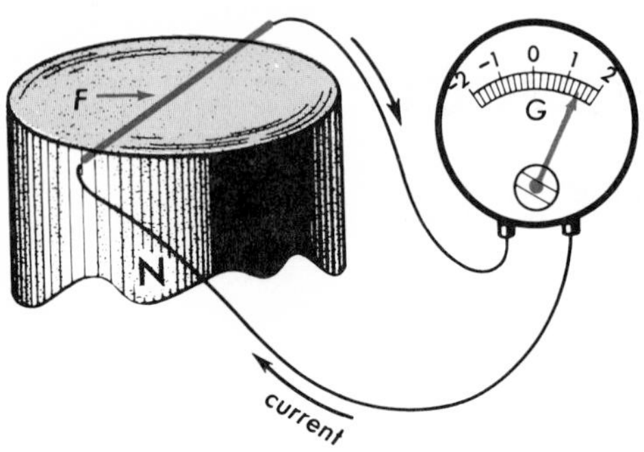

Fig. 27B. Experimental arrangement for demonstrating induced electric currents.

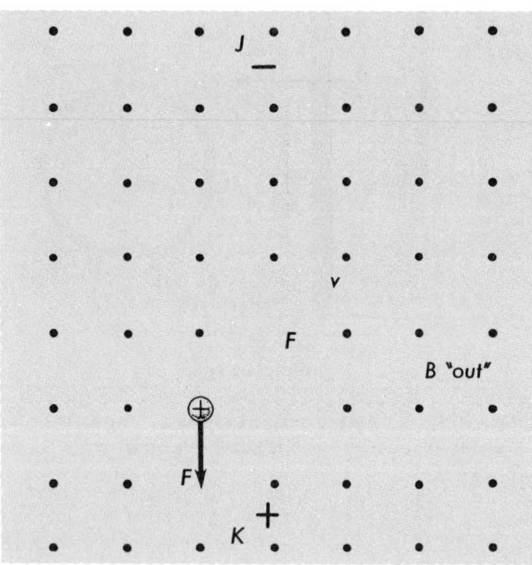

Fig. 27C. Forces on the charges in a conductor moving through a magnetic field.

stronger the field through which it moves, the greater is the required force and the greater is the induced emf and the resultant electron current. If the wire stops moving in mid-field, the emf drops to zero. These are the essential principles of the electric generator.

The *left-hand rule* may be used to predict the direction of the induced emf in any section of wire. Imagine grasping the wire in the left hand, with the fingers pointing in the direction of the magnetic induction immediately in front of the wire. Then, as the wire moves through the magnetic field, the thumb will point in the direction of the flow of electrons.

27.1. Induced Electromotive Force

It was shown in Sec. 26.5 that an electric charge $+q$, moving with a constant velocity v through a magnetic field where the flux density is B, experiences a force F upon it, given by

$$F = Bqv \tag{27a}$$

where F, B, and v are all mutually perpendicular.

When a single wire is made to cross magnetic lines of induction, as shown in Fig. 27C, every atomic charge within the metal experiences a force upon it, parallel to the conductor. The direction of the force on the + charges is from J to K, while the force on the − charges is from K to J. Since only the electrons are free to move in a metallic conductor, the negative charges migrate along the wire, building up a negative potential at one end and a positive potential at the other. If the conductor is a liquid or a gas, negative ions move in one direction and positive ions in the other.

Consider the straight metallic conductor sliding along a U-shaped conductor to form a closed circuit as shown in Fig. 27D. The potential difference, created between the ends, forces electrons through and around the circuit in the direction indicated. In other words, the moving conductor becomes the source of an *electromotive force.*

The electromotive force developed within a moving conductor of length ℓ is defined as the work per unit charge done in carrying any charge from one end to the other. From mechanics, we draw upon the principle that work done W is equal to *force times distance* moved. With the force given by Eq.(27a) and the distance moved by ℓ, the work done on a charge q is

$$W = Bqv\ell$$

If we now divide both sides of the equation by q, the work per unit charge becomes

$$E = Bv\ell \tag{27b}$$

where E is the emf, or work per unit charge done on the charges in this section of the moving conductor. Here the electromotive force E and difference of potential V are equal and are given by W/q [see Eq.(23j)].

In the *MKSA* system, B is in teslas, v is in meters/second, ℓ is in meters, and E is in volts. It should be pointed out that it makes no difference in the above treatment whether the wire moves through a stationary magnetic field or whether the field moves across a stationary conductor. It is the relative motion giving rise to the crossing of lines of induction that produces the emf.

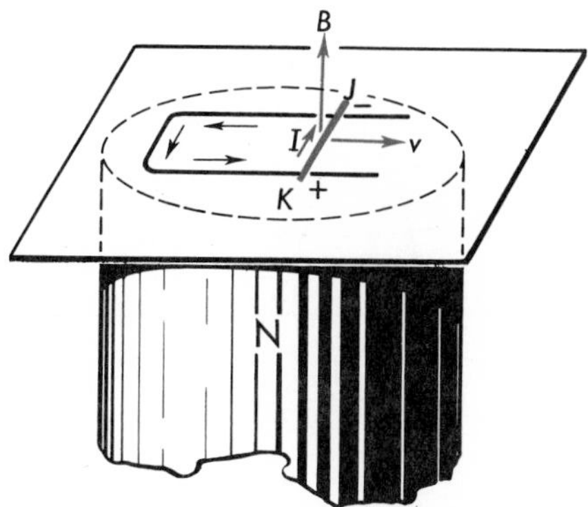

Fig. 27D. A current is induced by the motion of a conductor.

Example 1. A wire 25.0 cm long moves with a velocity of 45.0 m/s through a uniform magnetic field where the magnetic induction is 0.180 T. If the wire field and motion are at right angles to each other, what is the value of the induced electromotive force?

Solution. The given quantities in the *MKSA* system of units are $B = 0.180$ T, $v = 45.0$ m/s, and $\ell = 0.250$ m. Direct substitution of these quantities in Eq.(27b) gives

$$E = Bv\ell = 0.18 \times 45 \times 0.25$$

$$E = 2.025 \text{ V}$$

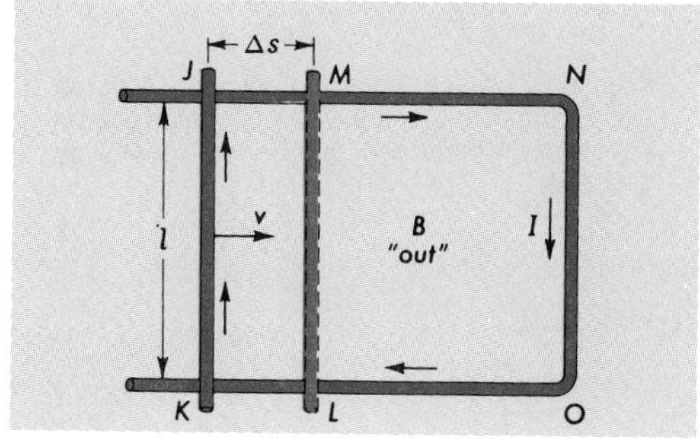

Fig. 27E. Demonstration of changing the magnetic flux linking a circuit.

27.2. Faraday's Law

Faraday's law states that *the electromotive force generated in a conductor is equal to the rate of change of magnetic flux through the circuit.* For example, as the magnet in Fig. 27A is plunged down into the coil, the number of lines of induction threading through the coil increases, and an induced electron current results. When the magnet is removed, the total flux linking the coil decreases, and again an electron current flows.

Consider again a U-shaped conductor with a slide wire moving with a velocity v across a uniform magnetic field B, as shown in Fig. 27E. At one instant the total flux ϕ_1 linking the circuit JKON is BA_1 [see Eq.(26k)]. In times Δt, the wire reaches the position

ML, where the total flux ϕ_2 linking the circuit MLON has decreased to BA_2. The change in flux, therefore, is

$$\phi_1 - \phi_2 = -\Delta\phi \tag{27c}$$

and the time rate of change of flux, which by Faraday's law gives the emf, may be written

$$E = -\frac{\Delta\phi}{\Delta t} \tag{27d}$$

The change in flux $\Delta\phi$ is given by B times the change in area ΔA:

$$\Delta\phi = B \times \Delta A \tag{27e}$$

where

$$\Delta A = \ell\Delta s \tag{27f}$$

If the area is decreasing, the total flux threading through the circuit is decreasing and the electron current flows in the direction shown by the arrows. If the wire moves in the opposite direction, thereby increasing the area as well as the total flux through the circuit, the induced current and emf will be reversed.

Here we have formulated Faraday's law from Eq.(26k), for the particular case in which there is relative motion between a conductor and a magnetic field. However, the law is equally valid for the case in which the change in flux is due to a change in the strength of the magnetic field.

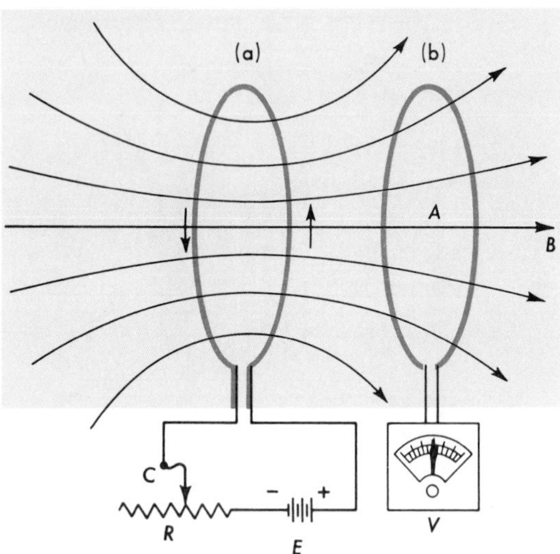

Fig. 27F. A changing current in a loop (a) changes the magnetic flux linking loop (b), and induces an emf in (b) given by Eq.(27d).

Figure 27F shows a single loop of wire (a) connected to a battery E, and a variable resistance R. A second nearby loop (b) is connected to voltmeter V. The electron current through (a) sets up a magnetic field whose magnitude is everywhere proportional to the current I. Part of this flux passes through loop (b).

If the current through (a) is now increased by sliding the contact C, the flux produced by (a) and the flux through (b) will increase. The changing flux through (b) will give rise to an emf as shown by the voltmeter. If the current is decreased in (a), a decreasing flux will induce an oppositely directed emf in (b). Only when the flux is changing will the voltmeter show an induced emf.

Since Eq.(27d) represents the flux change in a single turn of wire of area A, then an equal flux change in a coil of N turns of wire will induce an over-all emf N times as great:

$$E = -N\frac{\Delta\phi}{\Delta t} \tag{27g}$$

In the *MKSA* system, $\Delta\phi$ is in webers, Δt is in seconds, and E is in volts. [Note: Eq.(27g) gives the *average* emf.]

Example 2. A U-shaped conductor of the kind shown in Fig. 27E is located in a uniform magnetic field where the magnetic induction is 0.450 T. If the loop is 18.0 cm wide, and a straight rod slides across the loop at a speed of 6.50 m/s, find (a) the rate of change of flux linking the circuit, and (b) the induced emf.
Solution. The given quantities in the *MKSA* system are $\ell = 0.180$ m, $B = 0.450$ T, and $v = 6.50$ m/s. To find the change in flux per second we assume $\Delta t = 1$ s, and find the change in area during this time [see Eq.(27f)]:

$$\Delta A = \ell \Delta s = 0.180 \text{ m} \times 6.50 \text{ m}$$

$$\Delta A = 1.170 \text{ m}^2$$

The change in flux during this time is given by Eq.(27e):

$$\Delta\phi = B\Delta A = 0.450 \times 1.17 \text{ m}^2$$

$$\Delta\phi = 0.527 \text{ Wb}$$

from which

$$\frac{\Delta\phi}{\Delta t} = 0.527 \frac{\text{Wb}}{\text{s}}$$

We now use Eq. (27d) and write

$$E = -\frac{\Delta\phi}{\Delta t} = -0.527 \text{ V}$$

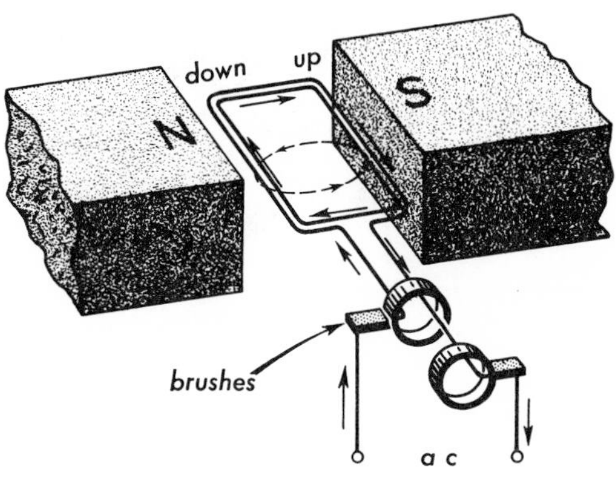

Fig. 27G. Illustration of the principles of the electric generator.

27.3. The Electric Generator

An electric generator is constructed in the same way as an electric motor, with a rotating armature containing coils of wire, pole pieces, field windings, brushes, and a commutator. Instead of supplying an electron current to obtain mechanical rotation, mechanical work is done to turn the armature, thus producing an electron current.

If, in the construction of a generator, two solid rings are used as a commutator, as shown in Fig. 27G, the current delivered to the brushes flows first in one direction, then in the other. The

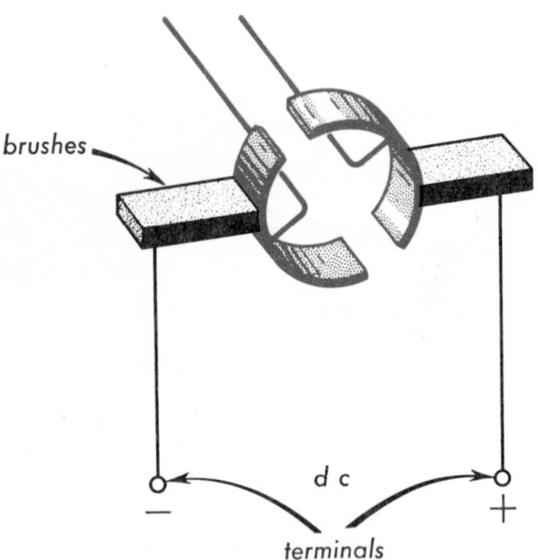

Fig. 27H. Split-ring commutator for a direct-current generator.

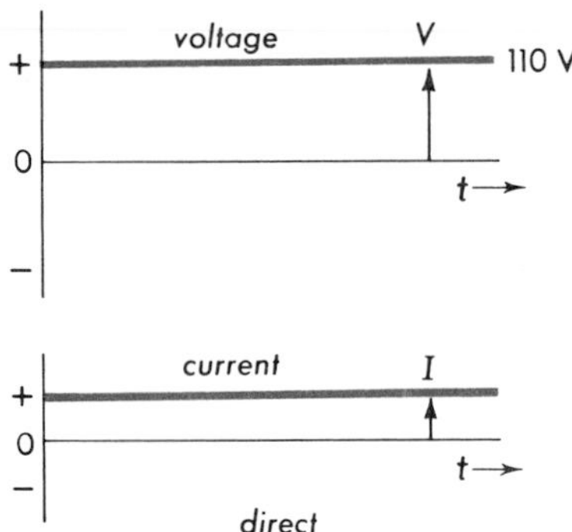

Fig. 27I. Graphs of 110-volt direct voltage and current.

reversal of current with each half-turn of the armature is due to the fact that each wire moves up across the field at one instant and down at the next. At one instant, the one terminal is positive and the other negative; at the next instant the first terminal is negative and the second positive. This periodically reversing emf produces what is called an *alternating emf.*

If a direct current is desired, the commutator of the generator must be of the split-ring type illustrated in Fig. 27H. It can be seen with this arrangement that one brush is at all times in contact with wires moving up across the field, while the other is in contact with wires moving down across the field. This produces a unidirectional electron current and the whole machine is called a *direct-current* (dc) *generator.*

It is important to note that a generator does not make electricity. The electricity, or electric charge, is always in the wire, and a generator sets it into motion. A generator produces an electron current.

27.4. Direct and Alternating Currents

The difference between a direct and an alternating current is that a direct current always flows in one direction, while an alternating current reverses its direction periodically. To send a direct current through an electric circuit, a source capable of developing a constant electromotive force is necessary. For this purpose, a battery or direct-current generator is used.

To send an alternating current through a circuit, on the other hand, a source capable of reversing its emf is required. To do this, an alternating-current generator is generally used.

Graphical representations of both direct and alternating currents are given in Figs. 27I and 27J for purposes of comparison. The lower curves in each figure permit a comparison of the *electron currents* through a circuit, while the upper curves permit a comparison of the *emf,* or *voltage,* of the source. The horizontal scale on all diagrams represents the *time.*

Within the short time of one second, the generators in most power plants reverse the emf many times. For example, the power supplied to private homes, public buildings, factories, etc., in the United States is in the form of alternating current at 25, 50, or 60 cycles per second (Hz), and 110 to 220 volts. A 60-cycle, 110-volt alternating emf, for example, is one in which the potential difference reverses direction 120 times per second. The rating of 110 volts specifies an effective voltage called the *root-mean-square* emf and not the so-called *peak* emf, which would be 155 volts.

The magnitude of the emf induced in a coil rotating at uniform speed, as shown in Fig. 27K, may be computed either from the vertical velocities of the wires forming the sides of the coil or by the rate of change of flux through the coil. In either case, we find

$$E = NBA\omega \sin \omega t \tag{27h}$$

where N is the number of turns in the coil, B is the magnetic induction in teslas, A is the coil area in *meters*^{2}, ω is the angular speed in *radians/second,* and t is the time in *seconds.* If f represents the *frequency of rotation,*

$$\omega = 2\pi f \tag{27i}$$

The top curve in Fig. 27I represents the electromotive force E, or the output emf V, at any instant, where $E_{\max}$ and $I_{\max}$ are constants and represent the amplitude or *peak emf* and *peak current,* respectively. From Eq.(27h), the emf is a maximum when the plane of the coil is parallel to the field and zero when it is perpendicular to the field. In the parallel position the coil sides are cutting across the lines of induction, while in the perpendicular position they are moving along the lines of induction. Equation (27h) is a maximum when $\sin \omega t = 1$. This gives

$$E_{\max} = NBA\omega \tag{27j}$$

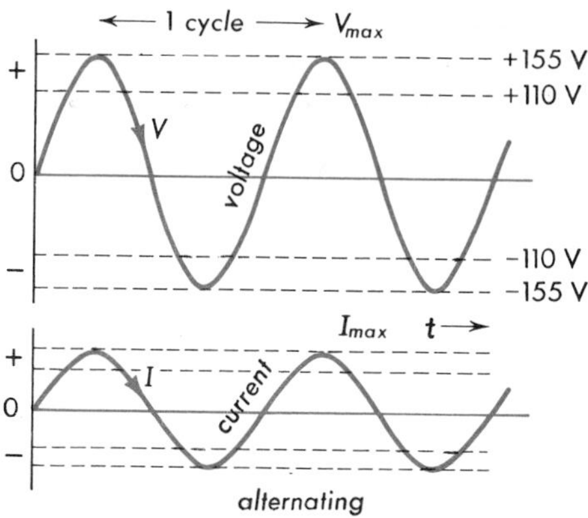

Fig. 27J. Graphs of 110-volt alternating voltage and current.

Example 3. A rectangular coil of wire having 60.0 turns with the dimensions 10.0 cm by 20.0 cm is set rotating at a constant speed of 1800 rpm in a uniform magnetic field of flux density $B = 0.50$ T. The axis of the coil is perpendicular to the field. Find the maximum emf produced.

Solution. The given quantities in *MKSA* units are $N = 60.0$ turns, $A = 0.10 \text{ m} \times 0.20 \text{ m} = 0.020 \text{ m}^2$, $B = 0.50$ T, and $\omega = 2\pi f = 2\pi \times 1800/60 = 188.5$ rad/s. Direct substitution in Eq.(27j) gives

$$E_{\max} = NBA\omega = 60 \times 0.02 \times 0.5 \times 188.5$$

$$E_{\max} = 113.1 \text{ V}$$

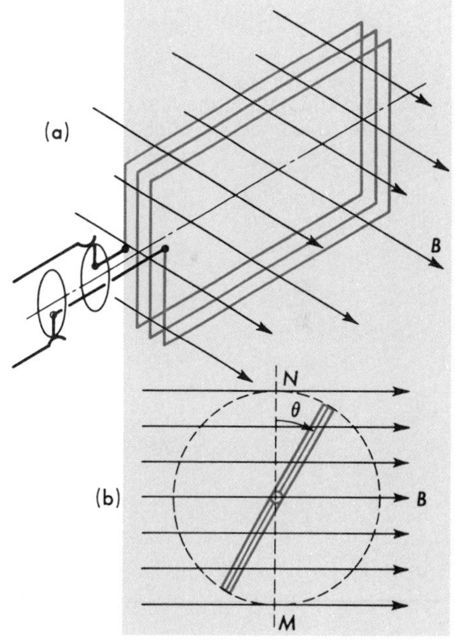

Fig. 27K. Principles of the electric generator.

Since the power dissipated as heat in any resistor at any instant is I^2R, where I is the magnitude of the current at that instant, the average power dissipated when an alternating current flows through the resistor is the average of I^2R (not the square of the

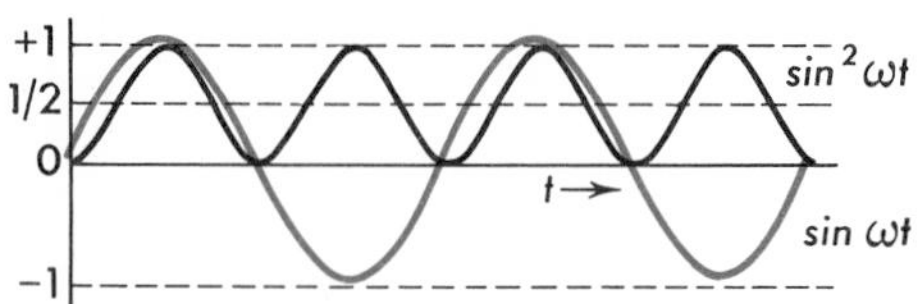

Fig. 27L. The average value of $\sin^2 \theta$ is $\frac{1}{2}$.

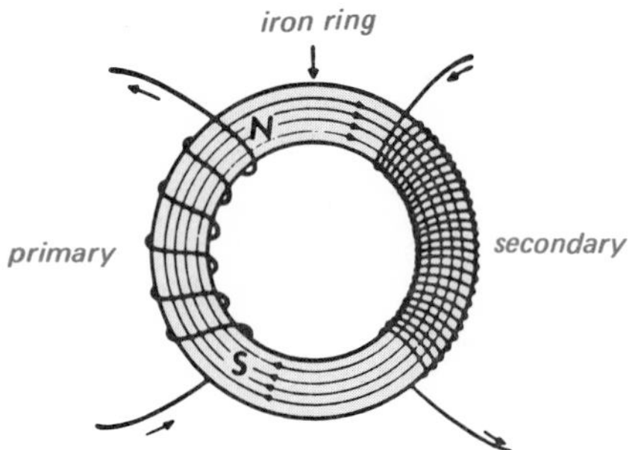

Fig. 27M. Diagram of the first closed-core transformer designed by Michael Faraday.

average I) over each cycle. Since the average of $\sin^2 \omega t$, as ωt varies from 0 to 2π, is $\frac{1}{2}$ (see Fig. 27L), the average value of I^2 is $\frac{1}{2}(I_{max})^2$. Calling the square root of this average I_{rms}, we have

$$I_{rms} = 0.707\ I_{max} \qquad (27k)$$

In a similar averaging process the *root mean square emf* is given by

$$E_{rms} = 0.707\ E_{max} \qquad (27\ell)$$

For an rms value of 110 volts, the maximum is 155 volts.

If an alternating current is applied to circuits containing inductance and capacitance, Ohm's law, as it is used with resistance and direct current, does not apply. In such instances, the current and voltage are not in phase with each other, that is, they do not rise to a maximum at the same time or fall to zero at the same time, and more complicated formulas must be used. Such circuits will be treated in Chap. 28.

Alternating-current circuits for which the direct-current relations of Ohm's law do hold true are those in which all of the circuit elements are pure resistances. Most electric lights and many heating units are of this class. In applying Ohm's law to pure resistance circuits, it is common practice to use the rms voltage E_{rms} and calculate the rms current I_{rms}. These values can be used in Eqs.(25c), (25d), and (25e) to calculate energy or power.

27.5. Transformers

A transformer is an electrical device for changing the voltage of an alternating current power source to a higher or lower voltage. Such devices are relatively inexpensive, have a very high efficiency, and are used in radio transmitters, television, telephones, long-distance power transmission, etc.

Historically, the first transformer was made by Michael Faraday in 1831. Two coils of wire were wound around opposite sides of an iron ring as shown in Fig. 27M. When a current is started in the primary winding, the magnetic field set up is confined almost entirely to the iron core. In other words, the lines of induction that develop in the primary, as a result of the growing primary current, also thread through the secondary, inducing an electromotive force and current. The iron acts like a good conductor of magnetic lines of induction, guiding them through the secondary winding.

When an alternating current is connected to the primary of a transformer, the current rises and falls periodically, satisfying the conditions for a changing magnetic field and induced currents.

Most modern transformers are of the closed-core type, as illustrated in Figs. 27N and 27O. Nearly all transformers come under one of the two following classes: (a) *step-up,* or *step-down transformers.* As shown in Fig. 27N, the step-up transformer is one in which the secondary winding has more turns of wire than the primary. In the step-down transformer the reverse is true. The importance of this distinction is based upon the general and well-established principle that the ratio of the number of turns of wire in the primary and secondary windings is the same as the ratio of the respective voltages in each. This may be stated as an equation:

$$\frac{\text{number of primary turns}}{\text{number of secondary turns}} = \frac{\text{primary voltage}}{\text{secondary voltage}}$$

$$\frac{N_{\mathrm{P}}}{N_{\mathrm{S}}} = \frac{E_{\mathrm{P}}}{E_{\mathrm{S}}} \qquad \text{(27m)}$$

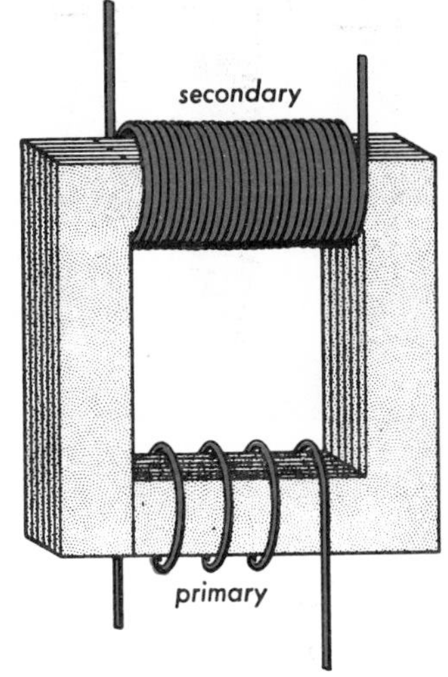

Fig. 27N. A step-up transformer with a closed core.

Thus, if a transformer has 100 turns in the primary and 100,000 turns in the secondary, the voltage delivered at the secondary terminals will be 1000 times the voltage impressed upon the primary. If this same transfomer were connected to the ordinary house lighting circuit of 110 volts ac, the voltage at the secondary terminals would be 110,000 volts ac.

The step-down transformer is just the reverse of this: The secondary voltage is lower than the primary voltage. As an illustration, suppose the primary of a transformer has 2000 turns of fine wire and the secondary has 100 turns. Having a turn-ratio of 20:1, this transformer when connected to the 110-volt ac line will deliver at its secondary a difference of potential of $\frac{1}{20}$ of 110 volts, or 5.5 volts. Such transformers are used in electric welding, for the ringing of doorbells, for the operation of toy electric trains, for lighting the filaments in radio tubes, etc.

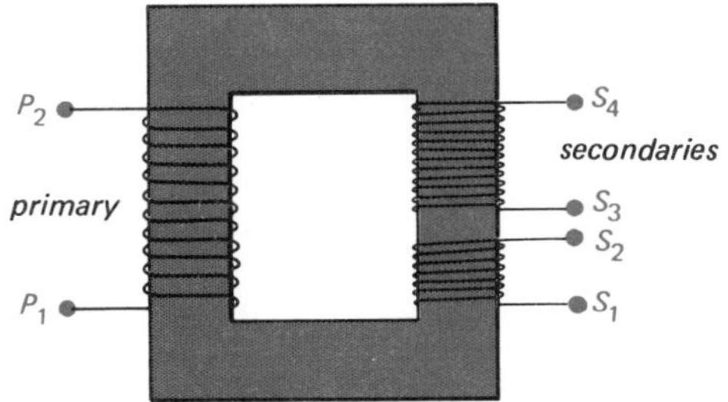

Fig. 27O. Transformer with two secondaries.

A type of transformer in widespread use today has two or more independent secondary windings (see Fig. 27O). Electrically insulated from each other, these secondaries produce their own voltage as given by Eq.(27m). Transformers used in the construction of modern radio and television receivers and transmitters are of the *shell type* shown in Fig. 27P.

27.6. Power

The increase in voltage of an alternating current by means of a step-up transformer appears at first sight to be a violation of the law of conservation of energy, i.e., it appears as though a large

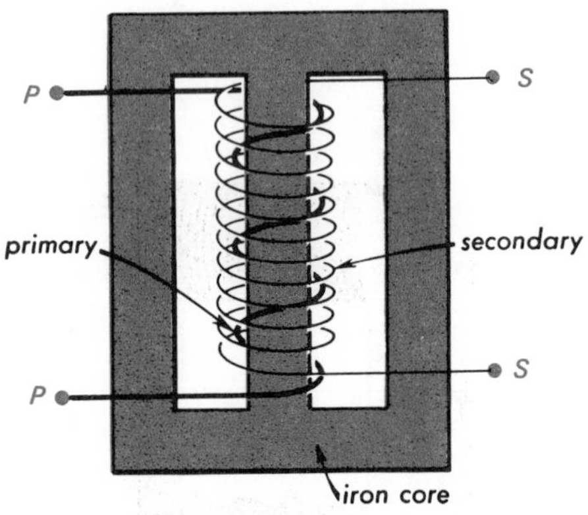

Fig. 27P. Shell-type transformer.

amount of energy could be obtained at the expenditure of a smaller amount. This is really not the case, for, when the voltage is increased, the current is simultaneously decreased by the same proportion.

When, for example, a transformer is used to step up the voltage to 100 times that supplied to the primary, the current in the secondary becomes only $\frac{1}{100}$ of the current in the primary. Therefore the power ($E_P I_P$) supplied at the primary is just equal to that delivered at the secondary ($E_S I_S$). In general, when the voltage is stepped up by a transformer, the current is stepped down by the same proportion:

$$E_P I_P = E_S I_S \tag{27n}$$

In practice this is not exactly true, because a transformer is not quite 100% efficient. A small amount of electrical energy is continually expended, principally in the form of heat. In a well-designed transformer, such losses do not exceed 2 or 3%, so that a transformer is often considered to be almost 100% efficient.

Example 4. The primary of a step-up transformer is connected to a 208-V ac line. The secondary with 10,500 turns delivers 12.0 KV and a current of 25.0 mA. Calculate (a) the number of turns in the primary, and (b) the electron current drawn from the 208-V line.

Solution. The given quantities are $E_P = 208.0$ V, $N_S = 10{,}500$ turns, $V_S = 12{,}000$ V, and $I_S = 0.0250$ A. To find the answer to part (a) we use Eq.(27m). Solving for N_P, and substituting known quantities, we obtain

$$N_P = \frac{N_S E_P}{E_S} = \frac{10{,}500 \times 208.0 \text{ V}}{12{,}000}$$

$$N_P = 182.0 \text{ turns}$$

For the answer to part (b) solve Eq.(27n) for the primary current I_P, and substitute the known quantities:

$$I_P = \frac{E_S I_S}{E_P} = \frac{0.025 \text{ A} \times 12{,}000 \text{ V}}{208.0}$$

$$I_P = 1.442 \text{ A}$$

---

problems

1. A wire 1.50 m long moves with a speed of 24.0 m/s through a uniform magnetic field where the magnetic induction is 5.0×10^{-2} T. If the wire, field, and motion are all mutually perpendicular to each other, what emf is induced in the wire?

2. A wire 8.0 m long is located in the wing of an airplane flying at 720 Km/h. If the magnetic induction due to the earth's field has a value of 5.20×10^{-4} T, what is the maximum possible emf?

3. A wire 80.0 cm long moves with a speed of 16.5 m/s through a uniform field where the magnetic induction is 0.20 T. If the wire, field, and motion are mutually perpendicular to each other, what emf is produced in the wire? [Ans. 2.640 V.]

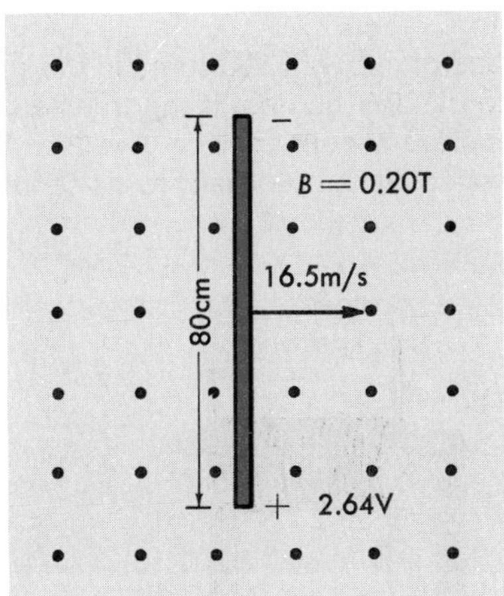

Prob. 3.

4. A wire 10.0 long is located in the wing of an airplane flying at 2400 Km/h. If the magnetic induction of the earth's field thas a value of 4.80×10^{-5} T, and makes an angle of 90° with the plane's motion, find the emf. Assume wire, field, and motion to be mutually perpendicular.

5. A U-shaped conductor 22.0 cm wide is located in a uniform magnetic field where the magnetic induction is 5.0×10^{-2} T (see Fig. 27E). If a straight rod across the loop moves with a speed of 6.0 m/s, find (a) the rate of change of magnetic flux linking the circuit, and (b) the magnitude of the emf produced.

6. A flat circular coil 14.0 cm in diameter, containing 90.0 turns of wire, is rotated at 1200 rpm, in a field where the magnetic induction is 0.250 T. Find (a) the maximum emf developed, and (b) the root-mean-square voltage. [Ans. (a) 43.5 V, (b) 30.78 V.]

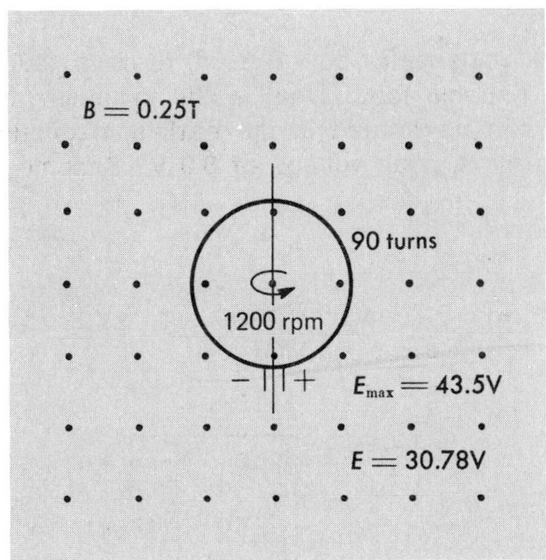

Prob. 6.

7. A flat rectangular coil 15.0 cm wide by 18.0 cm long, and containing 55.0 turns of wire, is rotating at 25.0 rps in a field where the magnetic induction is 0.650 T. Calculate (a) the maximum emf produced, and (b) the root-mean-square voltage.

8. A resistance of 8.0 Ω is connected to an ac generator whose internal resistance is 1.0 Ω. If the rms current in the circuit is 6.30 A, find (a) the rms voltage of the generator on closed circuit, and (b) the peak emf of the generator on open circuit.

9. An ac generator has a peak emf of 160.0 V when connected to a resistance of 22.5 Ω. If the internal resistance of the generator is 1.20 Ω, what is (a) the rms voltage across the terminals, (b) the rms current on closed circuit, (c) the rms voltage on open circuit, and (d) the peak voltage on open circuit? [Ans. (a) 113.1 V, (b) 5.03 A, (c) 119.1 V, (d) 168.4 V.]

10. An electric iron with a resistance of 16.0 Ω is connected to a 208-V ac line. Find (a) the peak voltage, and (b) the peak electron current.

11. An electric toaster with a resistance of 18.5 Ω is connected to a 120.0-V ac line. Find (a) the peak voltage, (b) the peak electron current, and (c) the rms current.

12. A rectangular coil of 200.0 turns is 12.0 cm wide and 18.0 cm long. What is the minimum speed this coil can be rotated in the earth's magnetic field to generate a peak voltage of 8.0 V? Assume the magnetic induction to be 5.0×10^{-5} T. [Ans. 5.895×10^3 rps.]

13.* Two resistors of 5.0 Ω and 20.0 Ω, respectively, are connected in parallel, and the combination in series with a resistor of 6.0 Ω. The ends of this circuit are connected to a generator supplying an rms emf of 208.0 V ac at its terminals. Find (a) the peak voltage across the 6.0 Ω resistance, and (b) the peak electron current through each resistor.

14. A flat circular coil 12.0 cm in diameter contains 40.0 turns of copper wire. If an rms voltage of 24.0 V at a frequency of 1000 Hz is to be obtained by rotating this coil in a uniform magnetic field, what must be the magnetic induction?

15. The primary of a step-down transformer has 260.0 turns and is connected to a 120-V line. If the secondary is to supply 2.5 V ac at its terminals, and an electron current of 200.0 A, find (a) the number of turns in the secondary, and (b) the electron current in the primary. Assume 100% efficiency. [Ans. (a) 5.42 turns, (b) 4.17 A.]

16. A transformer with 560 turns in the primary is connected to a 120-V ac line. If the transformer is to have three separate secondaries to give 2.50 V, 7.50 V, and 500 V, respectively, how many turns should each have?

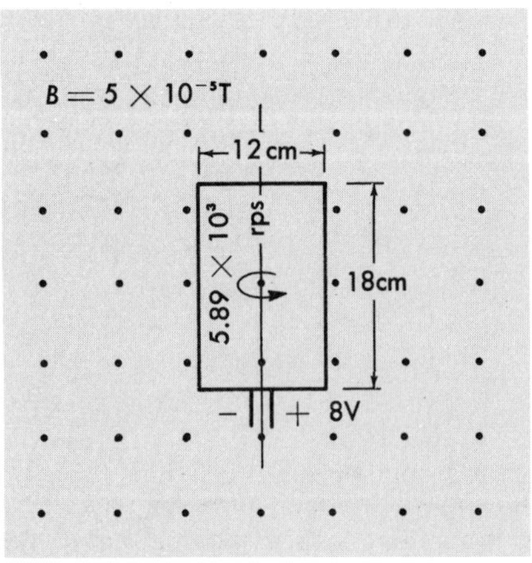

Prob. 12.

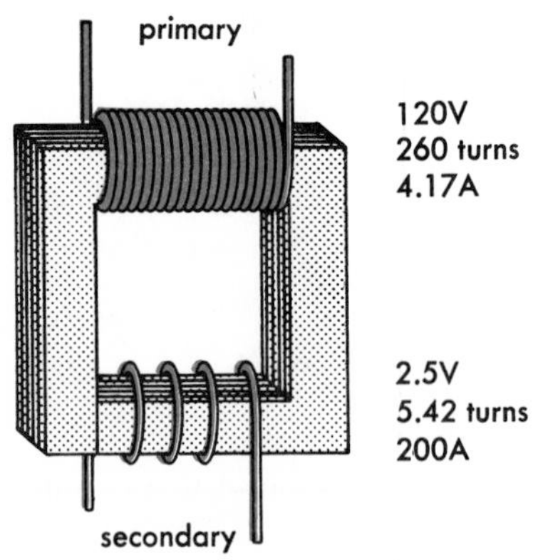

Prob. 15.

28 Dipole moments and magnetism

In order to obtain a better understanding of the principles of electricity and magnetism, we will consider in this chapter the principles of electric and magnetic dipoles. We will then see how magnetic dipoles are used to explain the phenomena of ferromagnetism, paramagnetism, and diamagnetism, and in later chapters how these concepts are carried over to atomic and nuclear structure.

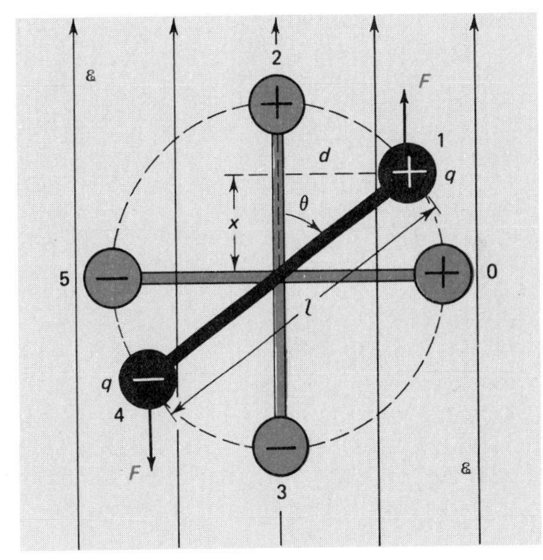

Fig. 28A. An electric dipole in a uniform electric field experiences a torque, and work must be done to turn it against this torque.

28.1. Electric Dipoles

An electric dipole may be described as two electric charges with their centers separated by a finite distance. Figure 23A shows the electric field around a dipole of like charges on the right, and unlike charges on the left.

Imagine two small metallic spheres with equal but opposite charges, $+q$ and $-q$, held a fixed distance apart by a nonconducting rod as shown in Fig. 28A. If the distance between the charge centers is ℓ, and the dipole is free to move in an electric field of intensity $\mathcal{E}$, forces will be exerted on the charges tending to turn the dipole counterclockwise about the center as shown. If the charges are equal and of the same sign, the two forces will be in the same direction and the system will not turn but move bodily in the direction of the forces.

For the dipole shown in Fig. 28A, the force on each charge is given by Eq.(23f). For each charge q we obtain for the force

$$F = q\mathcal{E}$$

where q is in coulombs, and $\mathcal{E}$ is in volts per meter. For the negative charge the force is *down*, and for the positive charge the force is *up*.

To find the total torque exerted by the field, we multiply each force F by its perpendicular lever arm d, and add:

$$L = d \times q\mathcal{E} + d \times q\mathcal{E}$$

Since $d = \frac{1}{2}\ell \sin\theta$, we substitute and obtain

$$L = \ell q \mathcal{E} \sin\theta$$

The product ℓq is called the *electric dipole moment* of the doublet, and is a quantity frequently designated by δ:

$$\delta = \ell q \tag{28a}$$

electric dipole moment

Making this substitution, we may write for the torque

$$L = \delta\mathcal{E} \sin\theta \tag{28b}$$

electric dipole torque

where θ is the angle between the dipole axis and the field $\mathcal{E}$, and the torque axis is at right angles to both.

If the dipole is free, the torque will cause it to turn and line up with its axis parallel to the field, with $+q$ in position (2), and $-q$ in position (3). To turn the dipole away from this equilibrium position will require work, and in so doing potential energy will be stored.

To find the potential energy of an electric dipole in an electric field we may select any angle for zero energy. If we assume zero energy when the dipole axis is at 90° with the field direction, $+q$ in position (2) corresponds to negative energy, and $+q$ in position (3) corresponds to positive energy.

To move the $+q$ charge from position (0) to any position such as (1), the *work done* will be

$$W = F \times x$$

$$W = -q\mathcal{E} \times \tfrac{1}{2}\ell \cos\theta$$

The minus sign signifies the liberation of energy in turning counterclockwise. Since the same energy is required to move the $-q$ charge to the corresponding position (4), the potential energy is given by

$$E_p = -q\mathcal{E}\ell \cos\theta$$

or

$$E_p = -\delta\mathcal{E} \cos\theta \tag{28c}$$

electric dipole energy

Note that in position (0), $\theta = 90°$, $\cos 90° = 0$, and $E_p = 0$. This establishes the zero potential-energy position at (0).

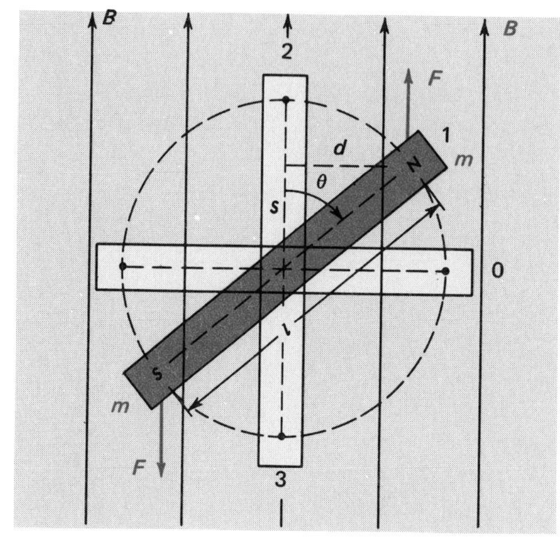

Fig. 28B. A magnetic dipole in a uniform magnetic field experiences a torque, and work must be done to turn it against this torque.

Example 1. An electric dipole is composed of two charges, $+5.0 \times 10^{-8}$ C, and -5.0×10^{-8} C, 10.0 cm apart. If this electric dipole is placed in an electric field of 100,000 V/m, find (a) the electric dipole moment, (b) the torque when at right angles to the field, and (c) the potential energy when in its equilibrium position.
Solution. The given quantities are $q = 5.0 \times 10^{-8}$ C, $\ell = 0.10$ m, $\mathcal{E} = 1.0 \times 10^5$ V/m, and $\theta = 0°$ and $90°$. To find the electric dipole moment we use Eq.(28a), and substitute the appropriate known values as follows:

$$\delta = \ell q = 0.10 \times 5 \times 10^{-8}$$

$$\delta = 5.0 \times 10^{-9} \text{ Cm}$$

To find the torque, direct substitution in Eq.(28b) gives for $\theta = 90°$

$$L = \delta\mathcal{E} \sin\theta = 5 \times 10^{-9} \times 1 \times 10^5 \times 1$$

$$L = 5.0 \times 10^{-4} \text{ Nm}$$

To find the energy we substitute directly in Eq.(28c) to find for $\theta = 0°$

$$E_p = -\delta\mathcal{E} \cos\theta = -5 \times 10^{-9} \times 1 \times 10^5 \times 1$$

$$E_p = -5.0 \times 10^{-4} \text{ J}$$

28.2. Magnetic Dipoles

When a straight bar magnet is located in a uniform magnetic field as shown in Fig. 28B, it is acted upon by a torque which tends to line it up with the field. The force acting on each pole is given by Eq.(24d) as

$$F = mB$$

where m is the strength of either pole in ampere meters, and B is the strength of the field in which it is located, in teslas. Assuming the distance between pole centers to be ℓ, each of these oppositely directed forces has a lever arm

$$d = \tfrac{1}{2}\ell \sin\theta$$

The total torque, therefore, is given by the sum of the two separate torques:

$$L = mB \times \tfrac{1}{2}\ell \sin\theta + mB \times \tfrac{1}{2}\ell \sin\theta$$

which simplified becomes

$$L = m\ell B \sin\theta$$

The product $m\ell$ is a property of the magnet alone, and by analogy with *mass moment* and *force moment* in mechanics, and electric dipole moment in electricity, is called the *magnetic dipole moment*:

$$\mu = m\ell \qquad (28d)$$

magnetic dipole moment

The torque may therefore be written as

$$L = \mu B \sin\theta \qquad (28e)$$

magnetic dipole torque

By analogy with the derivation of Eq.(28c), from Eq.(28b) we can derive the equation for the energy of a magnetic dipole in a magnetic field. Such a derivation gives

$$E_p = -\mu B \cos\theta \qquad (28f)$$

magnetic dipole energy

28.3. Magnetic Moment of a Current Loop

We have seen in Sec. 25.10 that a current-carrying loop, or coil, located in a uniform magnetic field experiences a mechanical torque (see Fig. 25N).

This torque is in such a direction as to line up the magnetic field of the loop with the applied external magnetic field B. The loop comes to rest when the field along its central axis, created by the loop current, is parallel to the external field. To turn the loop away from this equilibrium position will also require a torque, and hence work to be done.

Since the behavior of a current-carrying loop in a magnetic field is similar to that of a bar magnet, acting as though it had an N pole on one side and an S pole on the other, we can explain the action by ascribing to the loop a *magnetic dipole moment.*

By applying the current-force equation, Eq.(26o), to a current-carrying loop, located in a uniform magnetic field B, as shown in Fig. 28C, the torque acting upon the wire is found to be given by

$$L = IAB \sin \theta \tag{28g}$$

where L is the torque in newton-meters, I is the current in amperes, A is the loop area in meters^2, B is the external field strength in teslas, and θ is the angle between the axial field direction of the loop and the direction of B.

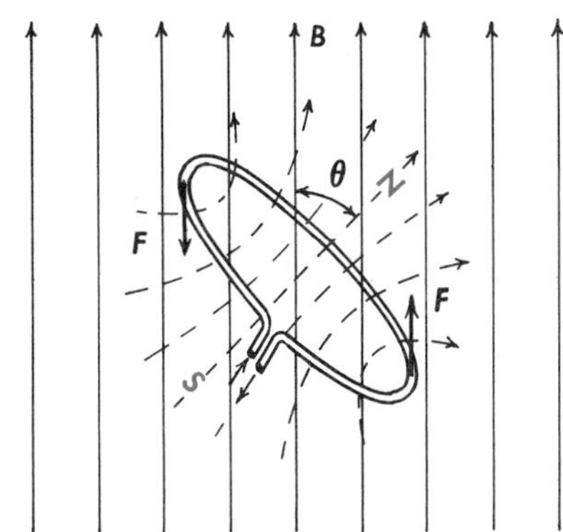

Fig. 28C. A current-carrying loop of wire in a magnetic field is acted upon by a torque.

By comparing Eq.(28g) with Eq.(28e), we observe that the product IA is analogous to the dipole moment of a bar magnet and that we can define the magnetic dipole moment of a loop by the relation

$$\mu = IA \tag{28h}$$

With this definition we may then use Eq.(28e) to determine torque, and Eq.(28f) to find the interaction, i.e., the stored energy E_p, for any current-carrying loop in a uniform magnetic field B. Since the dipole moment depends on the area, a loop may have any shape. It may be round, square, oval, rectangular, elliptical, etc.

If a flat coil of N turns is located in a magnetic field, each turn experiences a torque given by Eq.(28h) and the total torque will be just N times greater:

$$L = NIAB \sin \theta \tag{28i}$$

and the magnetic moment by

$$\mu = NIA \tag{28j}$$

Example 2. A flat circular coil of wire 8.40 cm in diameter has 28.0 turns of copper wire, and carries an electron current of 3.60 A. If this coil is placed in a uniform magnetic field where the magnetic induction is 0.250 T, (a) what is the magnitude of the magnetic dipole moment, and (b) how much energy is required to turn the coil from its stable equilibrium position through an angle of 180°?

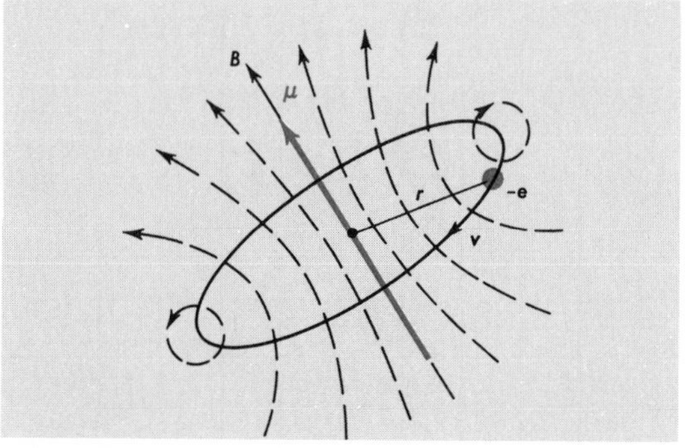

Fig. 28D. An electron of charge $-e$ moving in a circular orbit produces a magnetic field B, and a magnetic dipole moment μ.

Solution. The given quantities in *MKSA* units are $N = 28.0$ turns, $I = 3.60$ A, $B = 0.250$ T, $A = \pi r^2 = 3.142\ (0.0420\text{ m})^2 = 5.54 \times 10^{-3}\text{ m}^2$, and $\Delta\theta = 180°$. By direct substitution of quantities N, I, and A in Eq.(28j), we obtain

$$\mu = NIA = 28.0 \times 3.60\text{ A} \times 5.54 \times 10^{-3}\text{m}^2$$

$$\mu = 0.558\text{ Am}^2$$

Since the angle changes from 0° to 180°, we can substitute 2.0 for cos θ in Eq.(28f), and the values of B and μ, and obtain

$$E_p = -\mu B \cos\theta$$

$$E_p = 0.558\text{ Am}^2 \times 0.250\text{ T} \times 2.0$$

$$E_p = 0.2790\text{ J}$$

28.4. The Origin of Magnetic Moments

The magnetic properties of all substances, whether in the solid, liquid, or gaseous state, are due entirely to the motions of electrons within the atoms, and magnets of all kinds are the result of the lining up of electron loops and spinning electrons.

According to the classical theory set forward by H. A. Lorentz in 1897, the electrons in all matter move in circular orbits. Since every electron has a negative charge, these orbits are like current-carrying loops of wire and have magnetic dipole moments. The charge on every electron is

$$e = 1.60219 \times 10^{-19}\text{ coulombs}$$

It is now known that electrons also spin around an axis through their center of mass and behave as a tiny gyroscope. Because of their charge the spin too gives rise to a *spin magnetic moment.*

According to the Bohr theory, which will be taken up in detail in Chap. 44, the single electron in every normal hydrogen atom moves in a circular orbit of radius $r = 5.2918 \times 10^{-11}$ m, with a velocity of $v = 2.188 \times 10^6$ m/s (see Fig. 28D).

To find the magnetic moment of each such orbit, we can use Eq.(28h). While the area of the orbit is calculated from the radius,

$$A = \pi r^2 \qquad (28k)$$

the current equivalent of the orbiting electron is determined from the relation $I = Q/t$ as given by Eq.(22a). In words, the current is equal to the charge in coulombs passing any given point per second.

The frequency of revolution n will therefore give the number of times per second the charge e passes a given point. The frequency is given by the velocity v, divided by the circumference $2\pi r$, and when multiplied by the charge e will give the current in amperes:

$$I = \frac{v}{2\pi r} e \tag{28ℓ}$$

Combining Eqs.(28ℓ) and (28k) gives

$$\mu = IA = \frac{v}{2\pi r} e \times \pi r^2 = \frac{ver}{2} \tag{28m}$$

By direct substitution of the known values given above, we obtain

$$\mu = \tfrac{1}{2}(2.188 \times 10^6 \times 1.602 \times 10^{-19} \times 5.29 \times 10^{-11})$$

$$\mu = 9.27 \times 10^{-24} \text{ ampere meters}^2 \tag{28n}$$

As we will see in Chap. 45, this is also the value of the magnetic moment of a spinning electron, and is called the *Bohr magneton.*

The magnetic dipole moment of a bar magnet, a coil of wire, or a charge moving in a circular path is a vector quantity. The magnitude of the vector is given by the value of μ, and the direction is taken to be that of the axial field it produces.

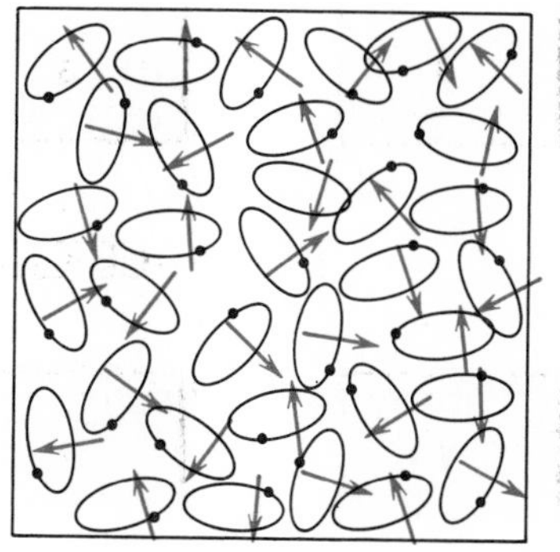

Fig. 28E. Schematic diagram showing the random orientation of electron orbits and their magnetic dipole moments in a diamagnetic substance like bismuth.

28.5. Diamagnetism

Diamagnetism was discovered by Michael Faraday in 1846 when he placed a small piece of bismuth metal near the pole of a magnet and found it was repelled instead of being attracted. Such a behavior is so unlike a substance like common iron, which is strongly attracted, that he called the phenomenon *diamagnetic.*

Diamagnetism is a weak response to magnetism, yet, with but few exceptions, is common to most elements and their alloys and compounds. According to the Lorentz theory of matter we may visualize all the electrons in a substance as though they were moving in circular orbits as described in the preceding section. Each electron has a charge $-e$, and a magnetic moment μ. In most substances these orbits are randomly oriented so that there is no net magnetic effect (see Fig. 28E). With billions of magnetic dipoles, just as many will point in one direction as any other.

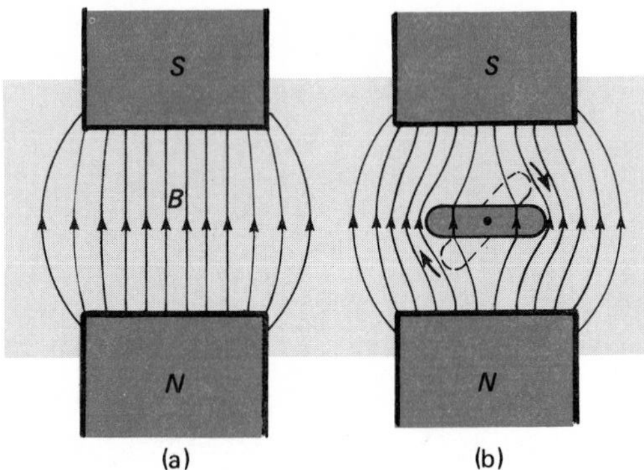

Fig. 28F. Diagram of the magnetic field between two magnet poles, (a) before a specimen is inserted, and (b) after a diamagnetic specimen is inserted. The diamagnetic rod comes to rest with its axis at right angles to original field *B*.

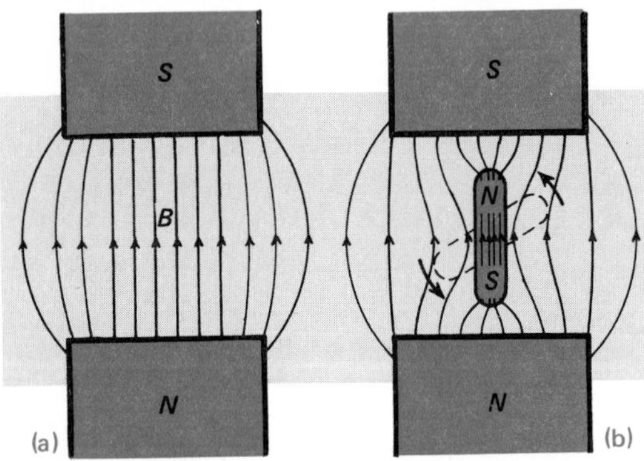

Fig. 28G. Diagram of the magnetic field between two magnet poles, (a) before a specimen is inserted, and (b) after a paramagnetic specimen is inserted. Paramagnetic rod comes to equilibrium when its axis is parallel to the original field *B*.

Suppose we now move such a diamagnetic specimen into a magnetic field. Although each dipole will experience a torque tending to line it up with the magnetic field, all of them are rigidly bound in their positions in the crystal lattice.

As the number of magnetic lines through each orbit increases, however, the induced current effect, treated in Chap. 27, gives rise to a force on each electron [see Eq.(27a)]. This force, which in a loop of wire causes electrons to flow around the loop, is in such a direction as to increase the speeds of electrons rotating in one direction and reduce the speeds of others rotating in the opposite direction.

It can be shown from basic principles of electricity that the size of the orbits remains unchanged, with the result that for electrons that are speeded up the magnetic moment increases, while for those that are slowed down the magnetic moment decreases. The net effect is to produce a resultant magnetic moment for the entire specimen. In other words the specimen behaves as though it had a north and a south pole.

When we employ the left-hand rule for induced electron currents, the induced magnetic moment is found to be opposite in direction to the applied magnetic field *B*. This means that if a small rod is placed in a strong magnetic field, as shown in Fig. 28F, the net induced magnetic moment points opposite to *B*. Thus the end of the rod closest to the magnet N pole acts like an N pole and is repelled by the magnet. Similarly the end nearest the magnet S pole acts like an S pole and is repelled. The repelling forces cause the rod to turn and come to rest at right angles to the field.

This behavior is just opposite to that of a bar of iron which when placed in a similar field experiences strong forces lining it up parallel to *B* (see Fig. 28G).

28.6. Paramagnetism

According to modern theory of atomic structure, the orbits and spins of the electrons in most atoms are such that the magnetic moments cancel each other. For an electron moving in one direction around an orbit, another will be moving in a similar orbit in the opposite direction, and for one spinning one way, the other will have opposite spin.

In some substances, however, the magnetic moments of the electrons do not all cancel out so that the atom as a whole has a magnetic moment μ. This is the case for several of the transition elements in the periodic table like manganese, the rare earths, and actinide elements, as well as for their alloys and compounds.

If a bar specimen of such material is placed free to move in a magnetic field, it will turn and line up with its axis parallel to the external field B (see Fig. 28G). The bar behaves like a permanent magnet with an N pole at one end and an S pole at the other.

In the field B each elementary atomic dipole tends to line up with the field. Perfect alignment, however, is hindered by the temperature vibrations of the atoms so that a partial alignment produces a small but net magnetic moment. The degree of alignment is specified by what is called the *magnetization.* The magnetization M of any specimen is defined as the magnetic moment per unit volume:

$$M = \frac{\mu}{V} \tag{28o}$$

In 1895 Pierre Curie discovered experimentally that the magnetization of a paramagnetic substance is proportional to the external field strength B, and inversely proportional to the absolute temperature T:

$$M = C\frac{B}{T} \tag{28p}$$

where C is called the *Curie constant.* This relation is known as *Curie's law.* Increasing B provides stronger forces tending to align the elementary magnets, while increasing the temperature increases the thermal vibrations to interfere with the alignment.

Experimentally Curie's law is found to hold true as long as B does not become too large. As B increases and alignment increases, there comes a time when nearly all dipoles have aligned themselves with the field, and the specimen approaches saturation.

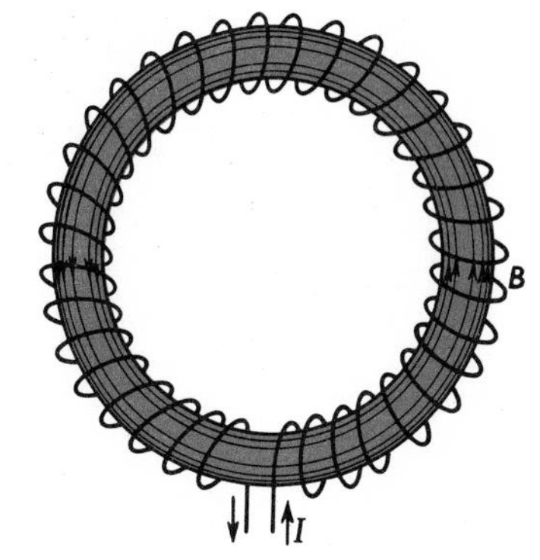

Fig. 28H. Toroidal solenoid, or "Rowland ring."

28.7. Ferromagnetism

For a few of the chemical elements such as iron, cobalt, and nickel, and for some of their alloys and compounds, a very strong magnetic alignment of the elementary atomic dipoles is found to exist. The abnormally large effect these elements exhibit, called *ferromagnetism*, is attributed to a strong coupling between adjacent atoms.

Consider a long solenoid, with or without a core, bent into a ring as shown in Fig. 28H. Such a coil with a uniform and closely spaced winding is called a Rowland ring, named after H. A. Rowland who first made use of it in his work on electricity and magnetism.

Assume, to start with, that the core is absent and that a vacuum prevails inside and outside the solenoid. When an electron current is sent through the winding, the magnetic lines of induction B are continuous, and confined entirely within the space enclosed by the winding. If ℓ is the circumference of the ring, the magnetic induction inside is given by Eq.(26h):

$$B_0 = \mu_0 \frac{NI}{\ell} \tag{28q}$$

for a vacuum

where μ_0 is the permeability of free space, and is given by

$$\mu_0 = 12.57 \times 10^{-7} \frac{\text{Tm}}{\text{A}}$$

This constant is not to be mistaken for μ used in this chapter to represent magnet dipole moment.

If the solenoid is now assumed to contain a uniform core of material, and a steady current is flowing in the winding, the field within the coil is increased or decreased. This change in B, over and above the field there previously, is to be ascribed to the field set up by the thousands of tiny magnetic dipoles that turn part way or all the way around to line up with or against the magnetizing field B_0. For para- and diamagnetic materials the induced magnetic induction B_M is proportional to the magnetizing field, and we can write

$$B_M = \chi \frac{NI}{\ell} \tag{28r}$$

where the proportionality constant χ is positive in value and is called the *magnetic susceptibility.* For diamagnetic substances χ is negative, while for paramagnetic substances it is positive. Adding Eqs.(28q) and (28r) we find the total magnetic induction inside the core is given by

$$B = B_0 + B_M \tag{28s}$$

or

$$B = \mu_0 \frac{NI}{\ell} + \chi \frac{NI}{\ell}$$

The quantity NI/ℓ is called the *magnetic intensity* and is designated by H:

$$H = \frac{NI}{\ell} \tag{28t}$$

By direct substitution, we obtain

$$B = \mu_0 H + \chi H \tag{28u}$$

or

$$B = (\mu_0 + \chi)H \tag{28v}$$

If the core of the solenoid is composed of a ferromagnetic material, the magnetic susceptibility χ is not constant. It not only varies with different specimens and with the magnetic intensity *H*, but it has very large positive values.

For iron, χ may go as high as 7×10^{-3} Tm/A, and permalloy (Ni 78.5%, Fe 21.5%) as high as 7×10^{-2} Tm/A.

Figure 28l shows a typical magnetization curve for silicon steel, a relatively common material used in motors, transformers, and other electrical equipment. As characteristic of all magnetic substances, the curve rises slowly at first (a to b), then rapidly and uniformly (b to c), and finally turns and flattens out (d to e). The flattened section represents a saturation condition in which *B* rises very little as *H* increases. In other words, when the tiny elementary magnets are all lined up, *B* increases only by the amount *H* contributes by the electron current in the winding.

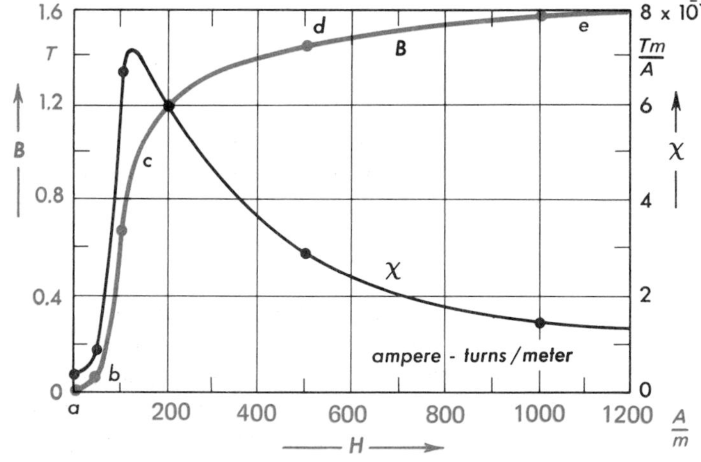

Fig. 28l. Typical magnetization and permeability curves (for silicon steel).

Values of the important magnetic properties of silicon steel are given in Table 28A.

It can be seen from the graph, as well as the values in the table, that when *H* is small, between 0 and 200 A/m, χ is very large, and practically all of the field is due to the magnetization of the iron. Beyond $H = 160$ A/m, X decreases and levels off to decrease very slowly beyond H = 1000.

TABLE 28A
Magnetic constants of silicon steel

H $\left(\frac{A}{m}\right)$	$\mu_0 H$ (T)	χ $\frac{Tm}{A}$	κ —	χH (T)	B (T)
0	0	0.310×10^{-3}	248	0	0
50	6.3×10^{-5}	0.860×10^{-3}	685	0.043	0.043
100	12.6×10^{-5}	6.700×10^{-3}	5330	0.670	0.670
200	25.2×10^{-5}	6.000×10^{-3}	4770	1.200	1.200
500	62.8×10^{-5}	2.880×10^{-3}	2290	1.440	1.440
1,000	125.7×10^{-5}	1.580×10^{-3}	1260	1.580	1.580
2,000	251.4×10^{-5}	0.780×10^{-3}	644	1.620	1.620
5,000	628.5×10^{-5}	0.320×10^{-3}	264	1.660	1.660
10,000	1257.0×10^{-5}	0.170×10^{-3}	136	1.720	1.720

Since X varies widely with H, it is customary to write Eq.(28r) in the form

$$B_M = \kappa\mu_0 H \tag{28w}$$

where κ is the permeability number. Values of this constant are given in the fourth column of Table 28A. For air or a vacuum $\kappa = 1.00$.

Since the quantity XH, as given by Eq.(28u), is a direct measure of the magnetic dipole alignment within the core, it can be shown that

$$XH = \mu_0 M \tag{28x}$$

where M, as given by Eq.(28o), is the *magnetic moment per unit volume,* and is called the *magnetization.* The above equations and values of B, given in Table 28A for a Rowland ring, also hold approximately for the field inside, as well as very close to the end outside, of a long thin electromagnet like that shown in Fig. 25H.

Example 3. A silicon steel rod 5.0 cm in diameter and 50.0 cm long is wound with a single layer of copper wire. If the solenoid contains 125.0 turns, and an electron current of 0.80 A is sent through it, find (a) the magnetic intensity, H, (b) the value of X from Table 28A, (c) the magnetic induction B, (d) the permeability number, and (e) the magnetization.

Solution. The given quantities in the *MKSA* system of units are $r = 2.0 \times 10^{-2}$ m, $N = 125.0$ turns, $I = 0.80$ A, and $\ell = 0.50$ m. By direct substitution of these quantities in Eq.(28t), we obtain

$$H = \frac{125 \times 0.8}{0.5} = 200.0 \text{ A/m}$$

From Table 28A, $H = 200$ A/m gives $\chi = 6.0 \times 10^{-3}$ Tm/A. By direct substitution in Eq.(28v),

$$B = (12.57 \times 10^{-7} + 6.0 \times 10^{-3})\ 200$$

$$B = 1.200 \text{ T}$$

By solving Eq.(28w) for κ, and substituting these values, we obtain

$$\kappa = \frac{B}{\mu_0 H} = \frac{1.20}{12.57 \times 10^{-7} \times 200}$$

$$\kappa = 4770$$

By solving Eq.(28x) for M, and substituting known quantities, we obtain

$$M = \frac{\chi H}{\mu_0} = \frac{6.0 \times 10^{-3} \times 200}{12.57 \times 10^{-7}}$$

$$M = 9.55 \times 10^5 \text{ A/m}$$

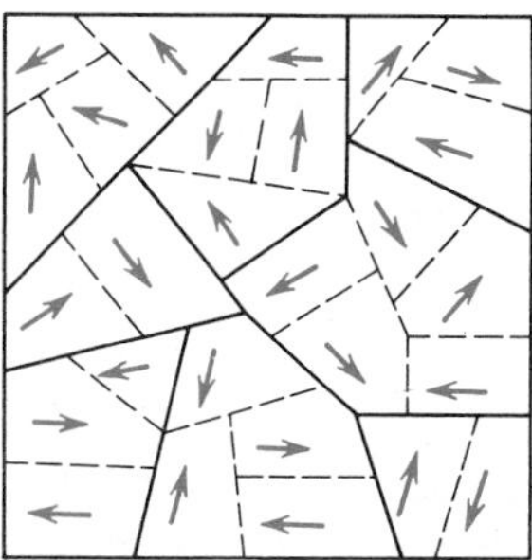

Fig. 28J. Cross-sectional diagram of the irregular-shaped crystals and magnetic domains in an unmagnetized ferromagnetic material. Thick lines represent crystal boundaries, while dotted lines within each crystal represent domain boundaries.

The most modern theory of ferromagnetism, and the explanation of a magnetization curve like that shown in Fig. 28I, is based upon magnetic domains. This theory assumes that a solid specimen like iron is composed of tiny crystal-like regions, odd in shape and microscopic in size, that fit together as in a mosaic [see Fig. 28J and Fig. 30Q(d)].

Within each crystal there are one or more domains, and within each domain there is essentially perfect alignment of the elementary magnetic moments. Each arrow in the diagram represents the net magnetic moment of that domain, and the random orientation of the arrows represents conditions existing in an unmagnetized ferromagnetic material like iron.

Within each domain strong exchange forces between atoms bind adjacent magnetic dipole moments together. Because they are all parallel, that is, saturated, they provide a large net magnetic moment.

TABLE 28B

Symbol	*Name*	*Units*
H	magnetic intensity	A/m
B	magnetic induction	T
B_M	induced magnetic induction	T
χ	magnetic susceptibility	Tm/A
μ_0	permeability of free space	Tm/A
M	magnetization	A/m
κ	permeability number	—
μ	magnetic dipole moment	Am^2

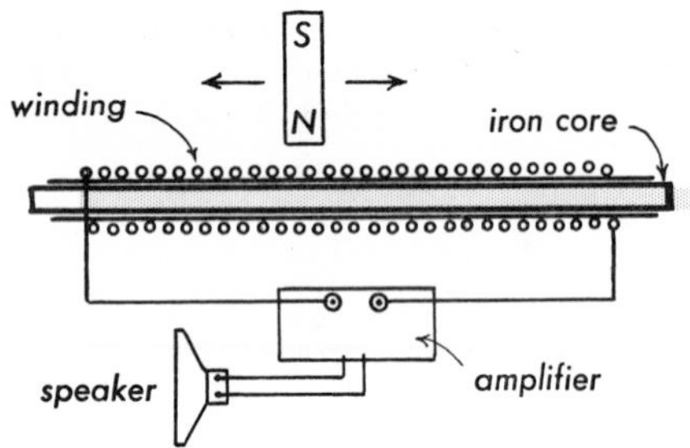

Fig. 28K. Diagram of experimental arrangement for demonstrating the Barkhausen effect.

When a piece of iron is subjected to an increasing field, two changes are found experimentally to take place. First, the orientation of the tiny atomic dipoles within a domain may suddenly swing around to line up with the external field, or an already aligned domain may grow in size at the expense of an adjacent domain adversely oriented. In other words, a common boundary between two adjacent domains in the same crystal will move.

As the field grows stronger, more and more domains flip around suddenly to line up, while others grow in size, until all domains are aligned.

If the temperature of a ferromagnetic specimen is heated above a certain temperature, called its *Curie point*, the exchange coupling disappears and the specimen becomes paramagnetic.

The contribution of each elementary magnetic dipole to the total dipole moment of a given specimen is supplied by the projection of each dipole moment on the magnetizing field direction H. The total dipole moment of the specimen is then seen to be given by the sum of all the components within it. This total dipole moment, divided by the volume, is the magnetization M.

The dipole moment of an iron atom in a solid is approximately one Bohr magneton [see Eq.(28n)]. When a soft iron specimen is fully magnetized, all of these dipoles are aligned with the field H, and the iron is said to be saturated. This condition corresponds in Fig. 28l to regions to the right of point e.

28.8. Special Demonstrations

The sudden flipping over of the magnetization of domains in a ferromagnetic material, as the magnetic field is increasing or decreasing, was discovered by H. Barkhausen in 1919. The following experiment is an effective demonstration of the phenomenon.

A plastic tube about 15 cm long is slipped over a soft iron rod about 20 cm long and 5 to 10 mm diameter. Several hundred turns of the fine insulated copper wire are wrapped in one or more layers around the tube, and the ends connected to an audio amplifier or public address system (see Fig. 28K).

When a permanent magnet is held near the coil, a hissing noise will be heard from the speaker only when the magnet is in motion. As the magnet moves quickly along, the flipping over of the magnetization of each domain induces an emf in the coil and these very small pulses to the amplifier are heard as a noise.

Another demonstration, developed recently by C. H. Harvey, involves the equilibrium suspension of a diamagnetic solid in a paramagnetic liquid, placed between the like poles of two permanent magnets. A solid plastic sphere of polystyrene about 5 cm in diameter is placed in a glass jar containing a solution of ferric chloride, $FeCl_3$. The concentration of the solution is varied until the sphere has a slightly greater density and slowly sinks to the bottom. (If the solution becomes too dark, a few drops of hydrochloric acid, HCl, will improve the visibility.)

The jar is then placed between the N poles of two strong alnico (aluminum-nickel-cobalt) magnets as shown in Fig. 28L. The left-hand diagram shows the shape of the field without the diamagnetic sphere, and the right-hand diagram the field when the sphere is centrally located.

When the jar is first placed between the poles, the sphere is at the bottom and close to the lower N pole. In this strong divergent field the net magnetic force on the sphere is up, toward the weaker field. If the pole of a third magnet is brought in on one side of the jar, the sphere will move to one side. When this third magnet is removed the sphere will move back to the center where it is in stable equilibrium.

The net force from strong to weak field is readily understood by employing the principle presented earlier that magnetic lines of force act like stretched rubber bands and at the same time repel each other laterally. Furthermore, magnetic lines prefer to follow paramagnetic materials rather than free space or a diamagnetic material. Figuratively speaking, ferromagnetic and paramagnetic materials act like better conductors of magnetic lines of force than do diamagnetic materials.

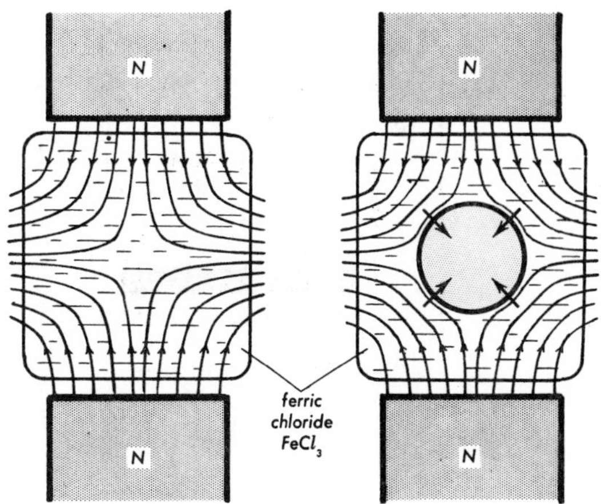

Fig. 28L. Diagram of the equilibrium suspension of diamagnetic sphere in a paramagnetic liquid.

problems

1. An electric dipole is composed of two equal charges of opposite sign, $\pm$ 3.60 $\times$ 10^{-8} C, and spaced 5.0 cm apart. If this dipole is placed in a uniform electric field of 4.50 $\times$ 10^4 V/m, find (a) the electric dipole moment, (b) the potential energy in its equilibrium position, and (c) the energy required to rotate the dipole through 180°. Make a diagram.

2. Two equal charges of opposite sign $\pm$ 4.0 $\times$ 10^{-19} C are located 3.20 $\times$ 10^{-10} m apart. If this dipole is located in a uniform electric field of 8.0 $\times$ 10^5 V/m, find (a) the electric dipole moment, (b) the potential energy in its equilibrium position, and (c) the energy required to rotate it through 180°. Make a diagram.

3. A bar magnet has two equal but opposite poles at the ends. Each pole has a strength of 24.50 Am and they are 4.80 cm apart. If this magnet is placed in a uniform magnetic field of 8.20 $\times$ 10^{-2} T, find (a) the magnetic dipole moment, (b) the torque on the magnet when it is at right angles to the field, and (c) the energy it gives up in turning to its equilibrium position. Make a diagram. [Ans. (a) 1.176 Am^2, (b) 9.64 $\times$ 10^{-2} Nm, (c) 9.64 $\times$ 10^{-2} J.]

4. A bar magnet has two equal poles at the ends. The poles are of opposite sign, have a strength of 6.0 Am, are 9.0 cm apart, and are located in a uniform magnetic field where B = 3.0 $\times$ 10^{-3} T. Find (a) the magnetic dipole moment, (b) the torque on the magnet when it makes 90° with the field, and (c) the energy required to turn it from its equilibrium position through 180°. Make a diagram.

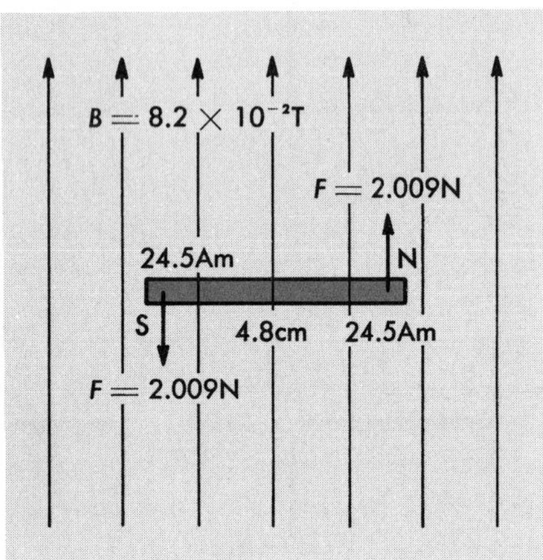

Prob. 3.

5. A flat circular coil with a diameter of 12.0 cm, containing 42.0 turns of wire, and carrying an electron current of 3.80 A, is located in a uniform magnetic field where $B = 8.60 \times 10^{-2}$ T. Find (a) the magnetic dipole moment of the coil, (b) the maximum torque exerted on the coil, and (c) the energy required to turn the coil from its equilibrium position through 180°. Make a diagram.

6. A flat circular coil with a diameter of 8.0 cm, containing 24.0 turns of wire, and carrying an electron current of 2.50 A, is located in a uniform magnetic field of 0.60 T. Find (a) the magnetic dipole moment of the coil, (b) the maximum torque exerted on the coil, and (c) the energy required to turn it from its equilibrium position through 180°. Make a diagram. [Ans. (a) 0.3016 Am², (b) 0.1810 Nm, (c) 0.3620 J.]

7. A flat rectangular coil 5.20 cm by 10.50 cm contains 34.0 turns of wire. If the coil is placed in a uniform magnetic field of 6.40×10^{-2} T, and an electron current of 2.60 A is sent through it, find (a) the magnetic dipole moment, (b) the maximum torque exerted on it, and (c) the energy required to turn it from its equilibrium position through 180°. Make a diagram.

8.* A Rowland ring like the one shown in Fig. 28H has a circumference of 48.0 cm, and contains 180.0 turns of copper wire. If an electron current of 2.20 A is sent through the coil, find (a) the magnetic intensity, (b) the magnetic susceptibility from Fig. 28I, (c) the magnetic induction at the center, (d) the permeability number, and (e) the magnetization. Make a diagram.

9. A silicon steel rod 40.0 cm long is bent into a ring

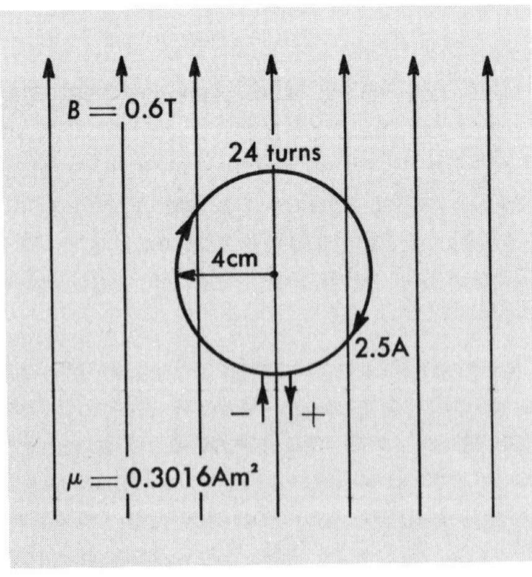

Prob. 6.

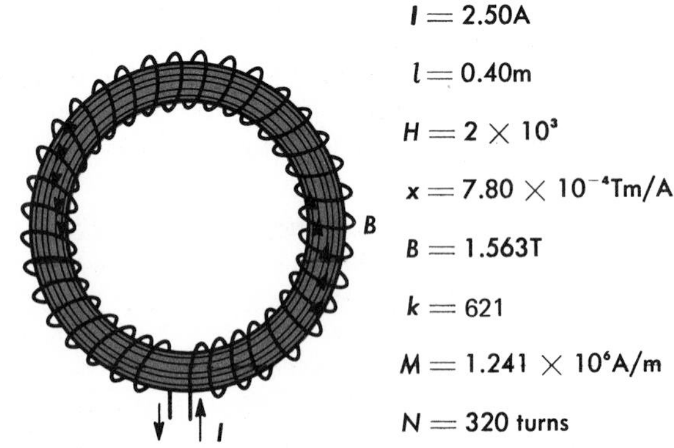

Prob. 9.

and welded to make it continuous. It is wound with 320.0 turns of insulated wire to form a Rowland ring. If an electron current of 2.50 A is sent through the coil, find (a) the magnetic intensity, (b) the magnetic susceptibility from Table 28A, (c) the magnetic induction, (d) the permeability number, and (e) the magnetization. Make a diagram. [Ans. (a) 2000 A/m, (b) 0.780 $\times$ 10^{-3} Tm/A, (c) 1.563T, (d) 621, (e) 1.241 $\times$ 10^{6} A/m.]

10.* A permalloy steel rod 60.0 cm long is wound from one end to the other with 300.0 turns of wire. If an electron current of 2.50 A through the winding produces a magnetic induction of 1.80 T, find (a) the magnetic intensity, (b) the permeability number, (c) the magnetic susceptibility, and (d) the magnetization. Make a diagram.

11.* A Rowland ring like the one shown in Fig. 28H has a diameter of 35.0 cm and contains 2000 turns of copper wire. If an electron current of 2.750 A flows through the coil, find (a) the magnetic intensity, (b) the magnetic susceptibility from Table 28A, (c) the magnetic induction, (d) the permeability number, and (e) the magnetization. Use Table 28A. Make a diagram.

12*. A steady electron current in the winding of a long solenoid gives rise to a magnetic intensity of 8000 A/m and a magnetic induction of 0.80 T. Find (a) the permeability number, (b) the magnetic susceptibility, and (c) the magnetization. If the iron in the core has a density of 7.90 g/cm^3, and each iron atom has a mass of 9.6 $\times$ 10^{-23} g, find (d) the number of atoms in 1.0 m^3 of iron. If the magnetic moment of each atom is equivalent to one Bohr magneton, and these are all aligned with H, what is (e) the total magnetic moment per cubic meter? Compare this value with M. See Eq. (28n). Make a diagram. [Ans. (a) 79.6, (b) 9.87 $\times$ 10^{-5} Tm/A, (c) 6.28 $\times$ 10^{5} A/m, (d) 8.23 $\times$ 10^{28} atoms, (e) 7.63 $\times$ 10^{5} A/m.]

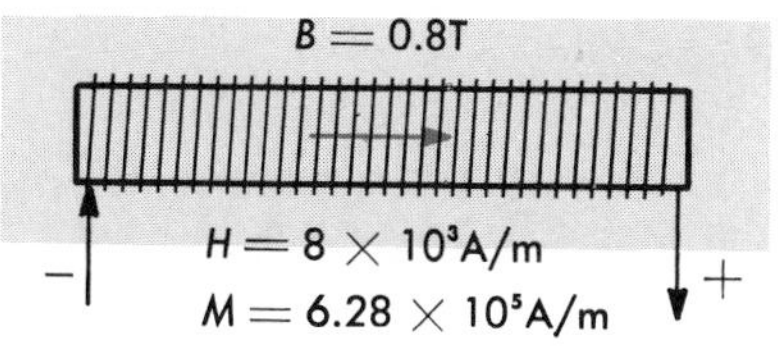

Prob. 12.

13.* A solenoid with 250 turns of wire has a silicon steel core 20.0 cm long. If an electron current of 0.80 A flows in the winding, find (a) the magnetic intensity, (b) the magnetic susceptibility from Table 28A, (c) the magnetic induction, (d) the permeability number, and (e) the magnetization. If the iron in the core has a density of 7.90 g/cm^3, and each iron atom has a mass of 9.60 $\times$ 10^{-23} g, find (f) the number of atoms in 1.0 m^3 of iron. If the magnetic moment of each atom is equivalent to one Bohr magneton, and these are all aligned with H, what is (g) the total magnetic moment per cubic meter? Use Table 28A. Make a diagram.

14. Three identical bar magnets, each with a strength of 8.0 Am and a length of 8.0 cm, are placed in a uniform magnetic field where B = 4.0 $\times$ 10^{-2} T. Find (a) the dipole moment of each magnet, and (b) the maximum torque that can be exerted on each. If the three magnets are fastened end to end with opposite poles touching each other, find (c) the maximum torque, and (d) the resultant dipole moment.

29 Alternating currents

When a battery is first connected to the ends of a long straight copper wire, the electron current rises quickly to the value given by Ohm's law. When the same wire is wound into a coil or solenoid, however, the current rises more slowly as shown by curve (b) in Fig. 29A. If an iron core is inserted to make the solenoid an electromagnet, the current rises much more slowly, as shown in curve (c).

The cause of this lagging of the current is an emf induced in the wire which is opposed in direction to the rising current. This *back emf*, as it is sometimes called, is extremely small if the wire is straight, is large if it is a coil, and still larger if a soft-iron core is inserted. To explain the existence of a back emf, consider a small section of one turn of wire in a solenoid of many turns. As the current rises in this section, the growing magnetic induction which develops around it threads through the neighboring loops of wire, inducing in them an emf. These induced emf's and their corresponding currents run counter to the impressed emf and current. This property is called *self-induction.*

29.1. Self-Induction

The unit by which one measures the self-induction of a coil is called the *henry* in honor of the American scientist, Joseph Henry*: *A coil having an inductance of one henry is one in which a change in the current of one ampere per second produces a back emf of one volt.*

A coil with a large number of turns is one that has a large inductance L, whereas one with only a few turns has a small inductance. The higher the inductance, the more slowly does the current rise or fall within the coil.

The establishment of a steady current in an inductance requires work, since the back emf must be overcome. Not all of the

***Joseph Henry (1797–1878), American physicist and scientific administrator, was born in Albany, New York, in 1797. He attended a country school, but quit at the age of thirteen. Later he attended the Albany Academy. Becoming interested in electricity and magnetism, he invented the magnetic telegraph and the electric relay, and discovered the phenomenon of self-induction. In 1832 he became professor of natural philosophy at Princeton, and in 1842 was elected by Congress as first secretary of the Smithsonian Institution in Washington, D.C. In this capacity, he founded the U. S. Weather Bureau and inaugurated the idea of distributing scientific publications to libraries and scientific bodies all over the world. He was the principal figure in the organization of the National Academy of Sciences, of which he was the second president. By general consent, Henry was the foremost American physicist of his time.**

electrical energy expended in reaching the steady current state is lost. Some is stored up in the form of a magnetic field. When the source emf is disconnected from the circuit, the magnetic induction decreases, thereby inducing an oppositely directed emf and corresponding electron current.

Two experiments demonstrating the property of self-induction are illustrated in Fig. 29B. In diagram (a), a solenoid of many turns of wire is connected in parallel with an electric light to a 120-V battery. When the switch S is closed, the light flashes bright for an instant and then becomes dim. When the switch is opened, the light again flashes bright for a moment and then goes out. When the switch is closed, the back emf in the inductance prevents the current from building up rapidly through the inductance. The inductance therefore acts as though it had a very high resistance so that practically all of the current goes through C. When the current becomes steady, there is no back emf in L, and part of the current flows through C and part through L. When the switch is opened, the magnetic field falls off, inducing a current in L. This current flowing through the lamp C causes it to light up momentarily to full brightness.

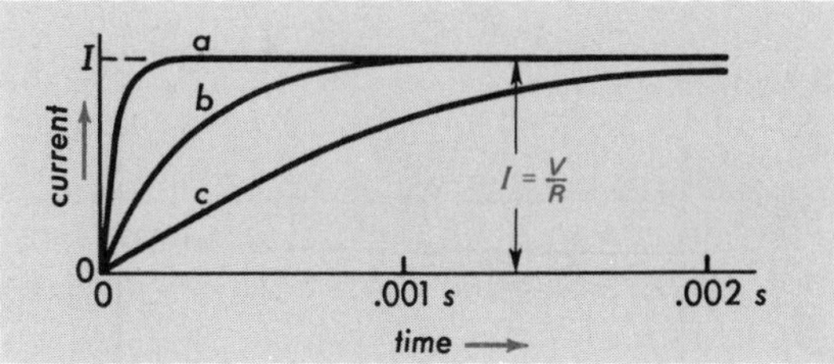

Fig. 29A. Current–time graph for a long copper wire in the form of (a) a straight wire, (b) a coil, and (c) a coil with an iron core.

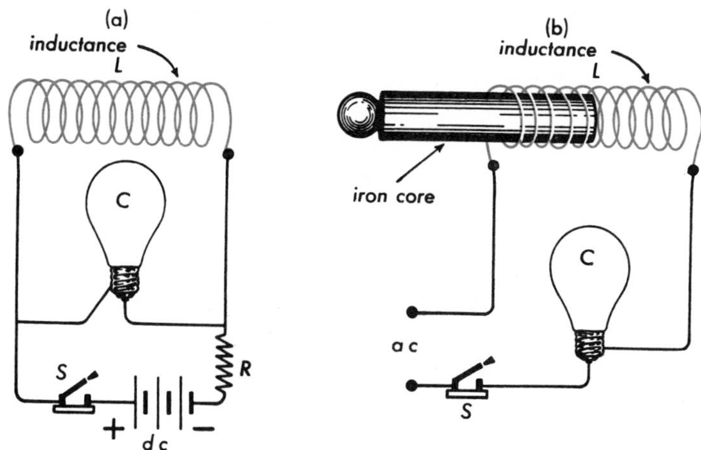

Fig. 29B. Two experiments illustrating the self-induction of a coil of wire. The circuit (b) is commonly used as a dimmer for electric lights.

The second experiment, as illustrated in diagram (b), demonstrates an increase in the self-induction of a coil due to a soft-iron core. Connected to an alternating emf, the light is bright when the iron core is out and dim when it is in place inside the sole-

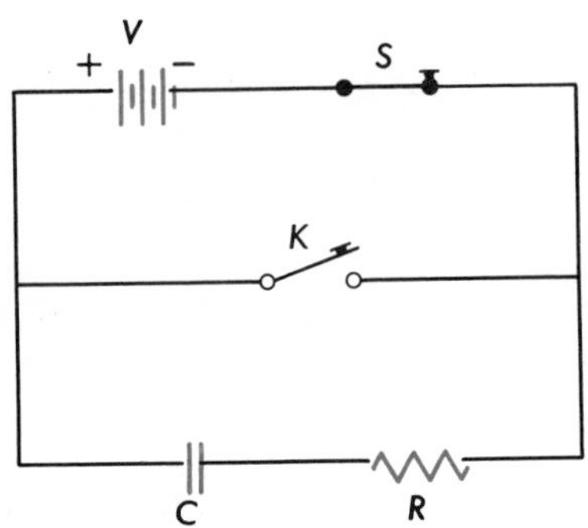

Fig. 29C. Series circuit containing capacitance and resistance.

noid. When the iron is inside, the back emf induced in the coil at each rise and fall of the current is very much greater than before, since the waxing and waning magnetic field is strengthened by its presence. The increased inductance therefore prevents the current's reaching a very high value before the current stops again and reverses its direction. The effect on the brightness of the lamp is the same as if the inductance were replaced by a variable resistance whose value is greatest when the iron core is inside the solenoid.

When a current is started in an electromagnet, the tiny elementary magnets within the iron core (these are the elementary magnets referred to in Sec. 28.7) turn around from their random orientations and line up with each other to make a single magnet of the entire core. In turning around, the field of each elementary magnet threads through the coil windings, inducing an emf opposing the rising current. This is another way of accounting for the back emf of self-induction.

29.2. Calculation of Inductance

In many instances, the inductance of a solenoid can be calculated from its geometry. For a long solenoid of uniform cross section, or a Rowland ring as shown in Fig. 28H, the inductance L, in *henries*, is given by

$$L = \kappa\mu_0 \frac{N^2A}{\ell} \tag{29a}$$

where N is the number of turns of wire, A is the cross-sectional area of the core in *square meters*, κ is the permeability number for the core, μ_0 is the permeability of free space, which is 12.57×10^{-7} Tm/A, and ℓ is the length of the coil in meters [see Eq. (28w)].

Example 1. A round bar 4.0 cm in diameter and 20.0 cm long is wrapped with one layer of copper wire to form a solenoid. The coil has 200 turns, and the permeability number of the iron is 1590. Find the inductance.

Solution. The given quantities are just those occurring on the right in Eq.(29a): $N = 200$, $\mu_0 = 12.57 \times 10^{-7}$ T, $\ell = 0.20$ m, and $A = \pi r^2 = 12.57 \times 10^{-4}$. Direct substitution in Eq.(29a) gives

$$L = \kappa\mu_0 \frac{N^2 A}{\ell}$$

$$L = \frac{1590 \times 12.57 \times 10^{-7} \times (200)^2 \times 12.57 \times 10^{-4}}{0.2}$$

$$L = 0.502 \text{ henry}$$

Without the iron core, the solenoid above would have a very much smaller inductance. For an air core, μ would be equal to $\mu_0 = 12.57 \times 10^{-7}$, and the inductance would be only 0.3160 millihenry. *The millihenry* (mH) *is a smaller unit of inductance and is equal to one-thousandth of a henry; while a still smaller unit, the microhenry* (μH), *is equal to one-millionth of a henry.*

It should be noted that, if the core is air or a vacuum, L is a constant independent of the electron current and magnetizing field H. If the core is a ferromagnetic material, however, L will vary because the permeability varies.

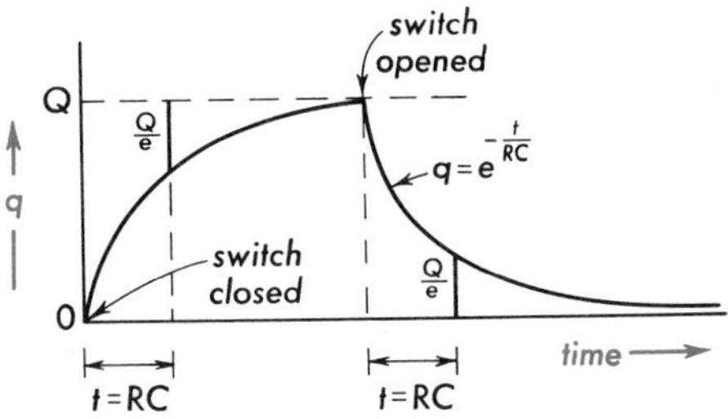

Fig. 29D. Capacitance time constant.

29.3. Time Constants

When a capacitance C is connected in series with a resistance R and a battery emf V (see Fig. 29C), an electron current flows for a short period of time because it takes time for the plates of the capacitor to acquire their full charge Q. The rate at which a capacitor charges up is shown graphically in Fig. 29D. If now the switch S is opened, disconnecting the battery, and then the switch K is closed, the capacitor will discharge, and again an electron current will flow through R.

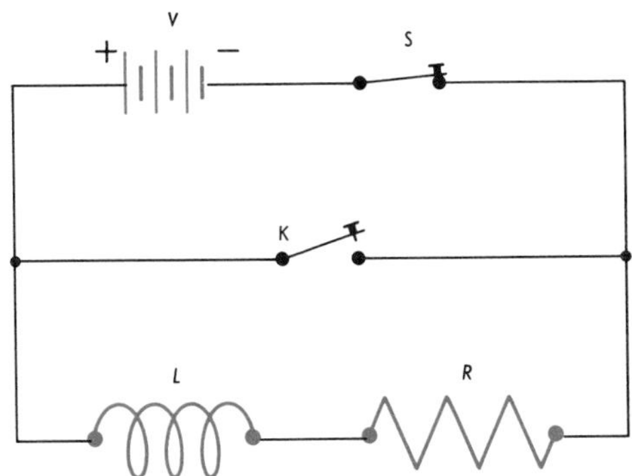

Fig. 29E. Series circuit containing inductance and resistance.

The time taken for the charge on the capacitor to reach within 1/eth of its full charge Q while charging, and the time taken to drop to 1/eth of its full charge while discharging, is called the circuit *time constant:*

$$\text{time constant} = RC \tag{29b}$$

The constant e equals 2.71828 ($1/e = 0.367880$), and is the base of natural logarithms. The greater the resistance and the larger the capacitance, the greater is the time required to charge or discharge a capacitor.

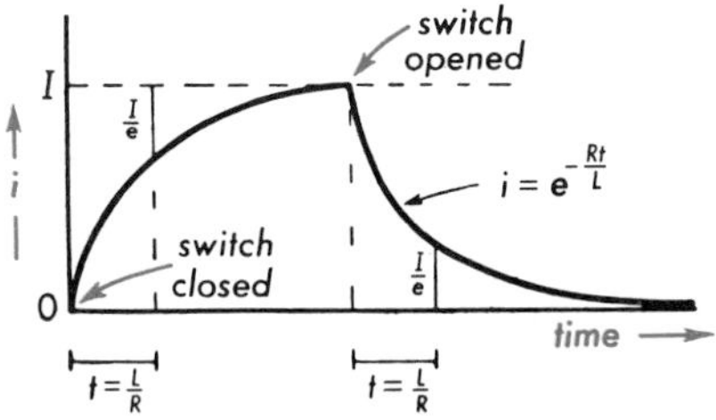

Fig. 29F. Inductance time constant.

When an inductance L is connected in series with a resistance R and a battery of emf V (see Fig. 29E), it takes time for the electron current I and the accompanying magnetic field to build up to a steady state. When the switch S is opened and the switch

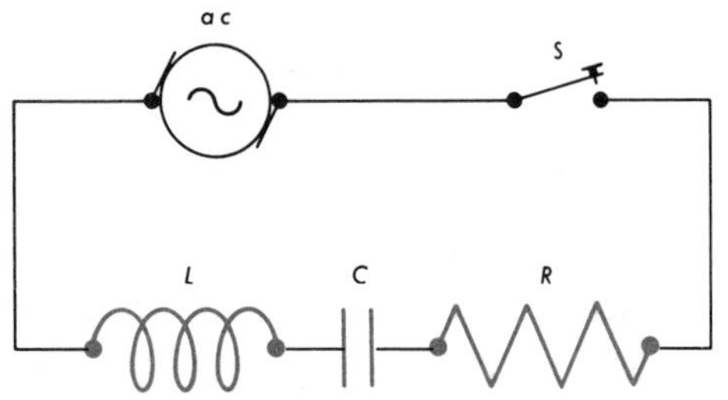

Fig. 29G. Series circuit containing inductance, capacitance, and resistance.

K closed, the field decreases and the electron current falls, approaching zero as t approaches infinity. The time constant of the circuit, that is, the time for the electron current to rise within $1/e$th of its final value (see Fig. 29F), is given by

$$\text{time constant} = \frac{L}{R} \qquad (29c)$$

29.4. Stored Electrical Energy

When a capacitor like that shown in Fig. 29C is fully charged, electrical energy is stored in the form of an electric field. If W represents the stored energy in *joules,*

$$W = \tfrac{1}{2}CV^2 \qquad (29d)$$

where C is in farads and V is in volts.

Similarly, when a steady electron current is maintained in an inductance L, as shown in Fig. 29E, electrical energy is stored up in the surrounding magnetic field to the amount

$$W = \tfrac{1}{2}LI^2 \qquad (29e)$$

where L is in *henries,* I is in *amperes,* and W is in *joules.*

29.5. Inductive and Capacitive Reactance

All electrical devices connected to a source of alternating emf contain a certain amount of *resistance, inductance,* and *capacitance.* If the total inductance and capacitance of the circuit are small compared with the resistance, Ohm's law can be applied to find the current in the various parts.

If the inductance and capacitance are not relatively small, they will introduce phase differences, or time lags, between current and voltage, so that Ohm's law will not apply in the ordinary way. Such a circuit is shown schematically in Fig. 29G.

Since an emf suddenly applied to an inductance requires a certain time for the electron current to build up to a fixed value (see Fig. 29A), the application of an *alternating* emf finds the current lagging behind the voltage in its rapid changes and reversals. Furthermore, if the frequency is very high, there is not enough time for the electron current to rise very far from zero toward its Ohm's law value.

Because the inductance effect reduces the electron current, it may be thought of as something analogous to a resistance. The measure of this effect is called *inductive reactance,* to distinguish it from a true resistance where electrical energy is converted into heat:

$$X_L = 2\pi fL \tag{29f}$$

inductive reactance

where f is the frequency in Hz or cycles per second.

Example 2. Find the inductive reactance to a solenoid with an inductance of 1.20×10^{-3} H, when connected to an alternating circuit having a frequency of 60.0 Hz.
Solution. The given quantities in *MKSA* units are $L = 1.20 \times 10^{-3}$ H and $f = 60.0$ Hz. By direct substitution in Eq.(29f), we obtain

$$X_L = 2\pi fL = 2\pi \times 60.0 \times 1.20 \times 10^{-3}$$

$$X_L = 0.452\ \Omega$$

When a capacitor is inserted into a *dc circuit,* the plates charge up, and the electron current drops to zero. The capacitor thereafter acts as though it were an infinite resistance. Connected to an alternating emf, however, it may act quite differently. As the frequency f rises in an *ac circuit*, the resistive effect of a capacitor decreases. The reversing of the emf reverses the flow of electrons to and from the plates of the capacitor, and the alternating flow of charge constitutes an *alternating current.* Because a capacitor differs from a pure resistance, in that it stores electrostatic energy, its resistive effect is called *capacitive reactance*:

$$X_C = \frac{1}{2\pi fC} \tag{29g}$$

capacitive reactance

Example 3. A capacitor is connected to a circuit in which an alternating current with a frequency of 1000 Hz is flowing. If it has a capacitance of 2.50×10^{-3} F, calculate the capacitive reactance.

Solution. The given quantities in *MKSA* units are $f = 1000$ Hz and $C = 2.50 \times 10^{-3}$ F. By direct substitution in Eq.(29g), we obtain

$$X_C = \frac{1}{2\pi fC} = \frac{1}{2\pi \times 1000 \times 2.50 \times 10^{-3}}$$

$$X_C = 0.0637\ \Omega$$

29.6. AC Series Circuit

When an inductance L, capacitance C, and a resistance R are connected in series to an ac generator as shown in Fig. 29G, the electron current in the circuit can be determined by the following equation:

$$I = \frac{V}{\sqrt{R^2 + (X_L - X_C)^2}} \tag{29h}$$

where I and V are the electron current and voltage, respectively. The quantity $X_L - X_C$ in this equation is often called the *reactance* and is represented by X:

$$X = X_L - X_C \tag{29i}$$

so that

$$I = \frac{V}{\sqrt{R^2 + X^2}} \tag{29j}$$

The whole denominator is called the *impedance* and is represented by Z:

$$Z = \sqrt{R^2 + (X_L - X_C)^2} \tag{29k}$$

and

$$I = \frac{V}{Z} \tag{29\ell}$$

Note the identical form of this last equation to Ohm's law for direct currents. The resistance R in Ohm's law has here been replaced by the impedance Z.

The relations between R, X_L, and X_C and the resultant impedance Z of a series circuit containing them may be represented graphically by treating all quantities as vectors. As shown in Fig. 29H, the resistance R is represented by a vector along the x axis, the reactances X_L and X_C by vectors up and down on the y axis, and the impedance Z as the vector resultant of all three. In practice, R includes the resistance of the inductance winding as well as all the connecting wires of the circuit.

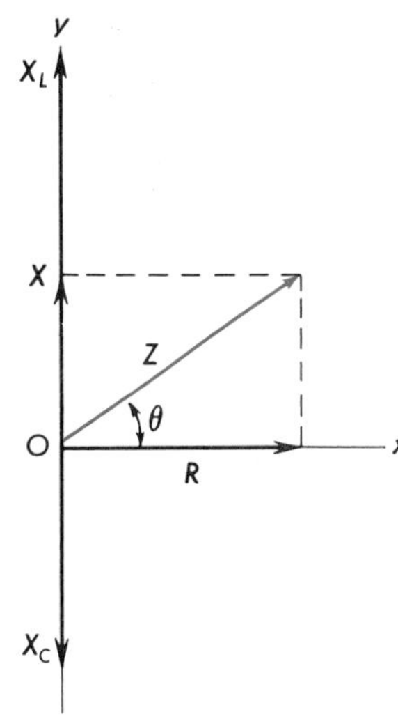

Fig. 29H. Impedance diagram for ac circuit.

Example 4. A 20.0-Ω resistor is connected in series with an inductance of 0.180 H, a capacitance of 60.0 μF, and an ac generator delivering an rms voltage of 120 V at 60.0 Hz. Calculate (a) the inductive reactance, (b) the capacitive reactance, (c) the impedance, and (d) the rms current.

Solution. The given quantities in *MKSA* units are $R = 20.0\ \Omega$, $L = 0.180$ H, $C = 60.0\ \mu$F, $V = 120.0$ V, and $f = 60.0$ Hz. For part (a) we substitute in Eq.(29f) to obtain

$$X_L = 2\pi fL = 2\pi \times 60 \times 0.180$$

$$X_L = 68.0\ \Omega$$

For part (b) we substitute directly in Eq.(29g), and find

$$X_C = \frac{1}{2\pi fC} = \frac{1}{2\pi \times 60 \times 60 \times 10^{-6}}$$

$$X_C = 44.2\ \Omega$$

For part (c), substitute in Eq.(29k), and obtain

$$Z = \sqrt{R^2 + (X_L - X_C)^2} = \sqrt{(20)^2 + (23.8)^2}$$

$$Z = 31.01\ \Omega$$

For part (d), we substitute in Eq.(29ℓ) to find

$$I = \frac{V}{Z} = \frac{120.0\ \text{V}}{31.01\ \Omega}$$

$$I = 3.870\ \text{A}$$

29.7. *Phase Relations between I and V*

The effect of an inductance and a capacitance on an *ac series circuit* is such as to alter the phase of the electron current I with

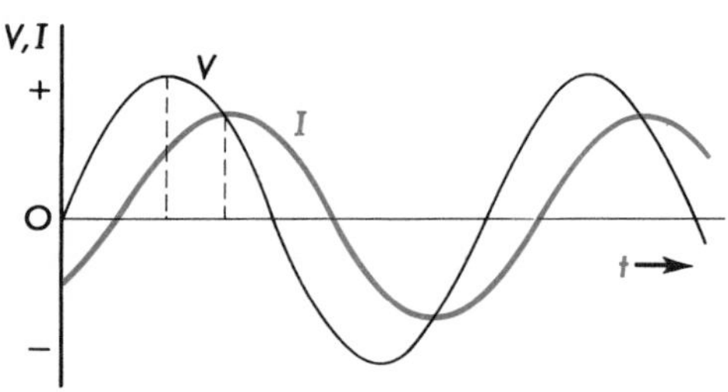

Fig. 29I. Graph showing current lagging 45° behind voltage.

respect to the applied alternating emf or voltage. If the inductive reactance X_L is greater than the capacitive reactance X_C, the impressed voltage will lead the electron current, while if X_C is greater than X_L, the impressed voltage will lag behind the electron current.

The amount the electron current lags or leads is given by the phase angle θ, where θ is given by

$$\tan\theta = \frac{X}{R} \tag{29m}$$

In Fig. 29H, θ is seen to be the angle between Z and R. In one complete cycle of either the current or voltage, the phase angle has changed by 2π rad, so that a phase lag of 45° means that the electron current is $\frac{1}{8}$ of a cycle behind the voltage. A graphical representation of this example is given in Fig. 29I.

29.8. Power Factor

With direct-current circuits, the power is given by the product $V \times I$, and is measured in *volt-amperes,* or *watts.* In alternating-current circuits, the instantaneous rate at which energy is supplied is equal to the product of the instantaneous voltage and the instantaneous current. Since both of these are sometimes zero, it is clear that the power consumption varies over each cycle and that some sort of average power must be taken.

The average power supplied to any ac circuit is equal to the rms voltage times the rms electron current multiplied by the cosine of the angle of lag:

$$P = VI\cos\theta \tag{29n}$$

The quantity $\cos\theta$ is called the *power factor.* A low power factor in *ac circuits* is to be avoided, since, for a given supply voltage V, a large current would be needed to transmit appreciable electrical energy. The I^2R heat losses in the lines should be held to a minimum by making the power factor as near unity as possible. This means that θ should be as near zero as possible, thus allowing the smallest current for the power delivered. When $\theta = 0$ the voltage and current are in phase, both reach a maximum, zero, and a reverse maximum together.

Examination of the impedance diagram, Fig. 29H, will show that a circuit containing a relatively large inductive reactance should contain an equally large capacitive reactance to make $\theta = 0$, and the power factor $\cos\theta = 1$.

The power expended in a circuit containing inductance and capacitance cannot be measured with a voltmeter and ammeter. To measure power, one uses a *wattmeter.* Such an instrument takes the emf, current, and power factor into account and reads the power directly. By reading a wattmeter, an ammeter, and a voltmeter, the power factor of a circuit can be determined by Eq.(29n):

$$\text{power factor} = \cos\theta = \frac{P}{VI} \qquad (29o)$$

If a circuit consists of a pure resistance only, connected to an alternating emf, we find from Eq.(29k), that $Z = R$. A pure resistance has no reactance so that $X = 0$, and from Eq.(29m), $\tan\theta = 0/R$, which means that $\theta = 0$. We can therefore write

$$Z = R \qquad X = 0 \qquad \theta = 0 \qquad (29p)$$

and draw Fig. 29J(a). This diagram shows that the voltage and electron current are in phase.

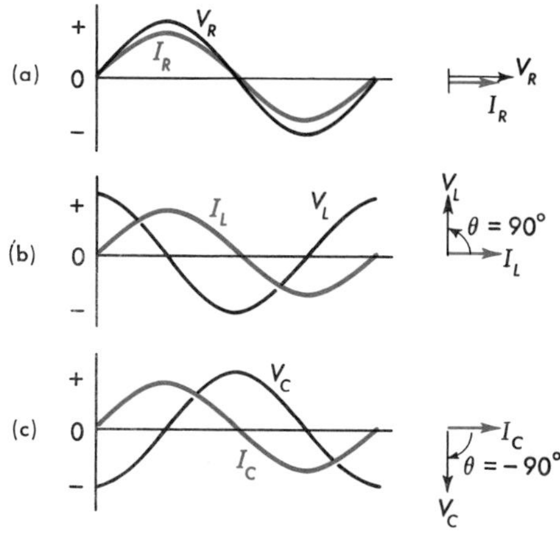

Fig. 29J. Phase relations between voltage and current for the separate elements of an ac circuit.

When a circuit consists of an inductance only, connected to an alternating emf, and we assume the connecting wires have no resistance, $R = 0$. By Eq.(29k) we obtain $Z = X_L$, and from Eq.(29m), find $\tan\theta = X/0 = \infty$. The angle whose tangent is ∞ is 90°. We can therefore write

$$Z = X_L \qquad R = 0 \qquad \theta = +90° \qquad (29q)$$

which means that the voltage *leads* the current by 90°, as shown in Fig. 29J(b).

If a circuit contains a capacitance only, connected to an alternating emf, we may assume the connecting wires have no resistance, and that $R = 0$. By Eq.(29k) the impedance $Z = \sqrt{-1}X_C$. It can be shown from advanced mathematics that $\sqrt{-1}$ means a phase difference of −90°, so that

$$Z = X_C \qquad R = 0 \qquad \theta = -90° \qquad (29r)$$

which means that the voltage *lags* behind the current by 90°, as shown in Fig. 29J(c).

Example 5. A 60.0-ohm resistor is connected in series with a 0.250-henry inductor, a 50.0-μF capacitor, and an ac generator delivering 110 V (rms) at a frequency of 60.0 Hz. Find (a) the reactance, (b) the impedance, (c) the rms electron current, (d) the power factor, and (e) the power consumed.

Solution. The given quantities in *MKSA* units are $R = 60.0\ \Omega$, $L = 0.250$ H, $C = 50.0\ \mu$F, $V = 110.0$ V, and $f = 60.0$ Hz. For the answer to part (a), we substitute in Eqs. (29f) and (29g):

$$X_L = 2\pi fL = 2\pi \times 60 \times 0.25 = 94.2\ \Omega$$

$$X_C = \frac{1}{2\pi fC} = \frac{1}{2\pi \times 60 \times 50 \times 10^{-6}} = 53.1\ \Omega$$

Substituting these two values in Eq.(29i), we find

$$X = X_L - X_C = 94.2 - 53.1$$

$$X = 41.1\ \Omega$$

For part (b) we use Eq.(29k) to find the impedance:

$$Z = \sqrt{R^2 + X^2} = \sqrt{(60)^2 + (41.1)^2}$$

$$Z = 72.7\ \Omega$$

For part (c) we substitute directly in Eq.(29ℓ) to find

$$I = \frac{V}{Z} = \frac{110.0 \text{ V}}{72.7\ \Omega}$$

$$I = 1.513 \text{ A}$$

We now refer to Fig. 29H which was drawn for part (d) of this specific example. Using Eq.(29m), we find

$$\tan\theta = \frac{X}{R} = \frac{41.1}{60.0} = 0.685$$

Using the table on the inside back cover of the book to find the angle θ, we obtain

$$\theta = 34.41^\circ$$

The cosine of 34.41°, which is equal to the power factor, is

$$\text{power factor} = \cos 34.4^\circ = 0.825$$

For part (e) we use Eq.(29n), and obtain finally

$$P = VI \cos \theta = 110 \times 1.513 \times 0.825$$

$$P = 137.3 \text{ W}$$

For drawings and graphs of this example, see Fig. 29K.

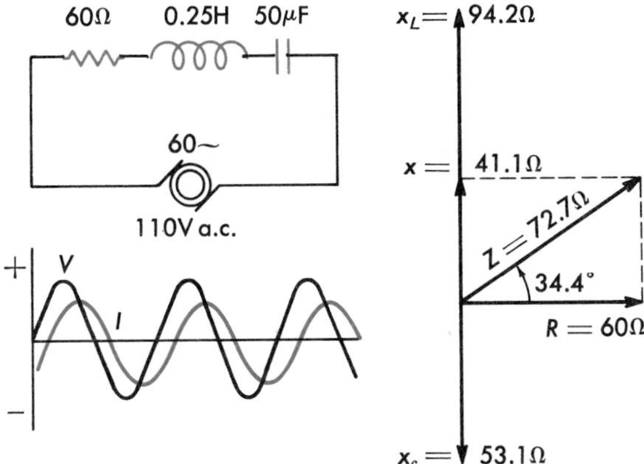

Fig. 29K. Diagrams for the solution to Example 5. The current lags behind the voltage by 34.4°.

29.9. *Voltage across Separate Parts of an AC Circuit*

The electron current in all parts of a series circuit has the same phase. When the current is a maximum in the inductor, it is also the same maximum in the resistor and capacitor. When the current is zero in the resistor, it is also zero in the inductor and capacitor.

The potential difference across the inductor, however, will not be a maximum or zero at the same instant it is a maximum or zero in either the resistor or capacitor. The voltage across any element of a series circuit is given by the product of the electron current and the impedance of that particular element:

$$V_i = IZ_i \tag{29s}$$

The phase angle between the voltage and electron current for any single element is given by

$$\tan \theta = \frac{X_i}{R_i} \tag{29t}$$

In Fig. 29G, for example, the impedance Z_R of the resistance is

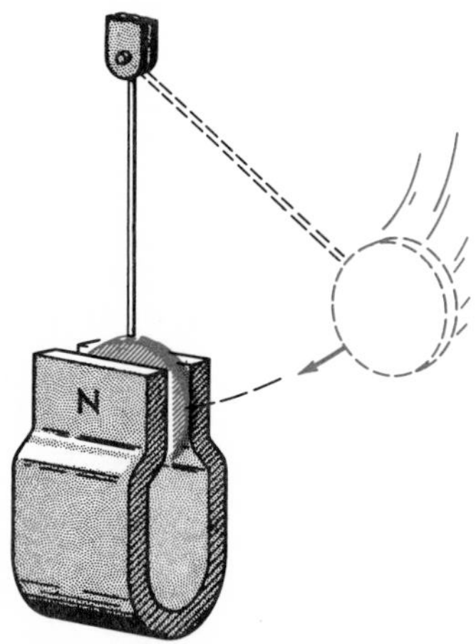

Fig. 29L. Induced currents in the copper-disk pendulum quickly stop it from swinging through.

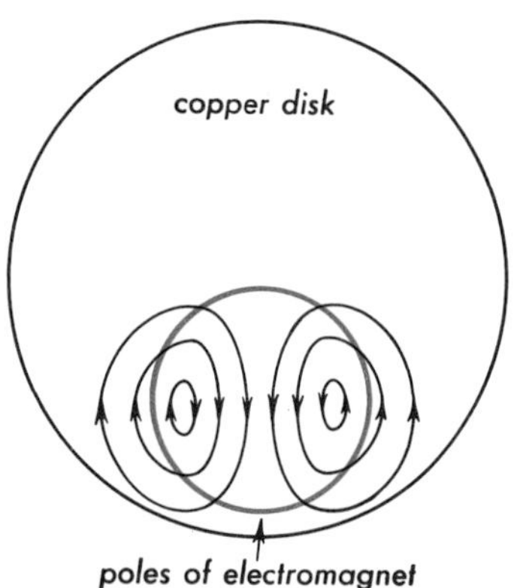

Fig. 29M. Eddy currents in a moving plate conductor.

just R, so that $V_R = IR$. Since the reactance of a pure resistance is zero, conditions of Eq.(29p) hold and *the potential difference across a pure resistance is in phase with the electron current and is given by IR.*

Across the inductance, $Z_L = X_L$, so that $V_L = IX_L$, and the conditions of Eq.(29q) hold. This means that *the potential difference across the inductance leads the electron current by 90° and is given by IX_L.*

Across the capacitance, $Z_C = X_C$, so that $V_C = IX_C$, and the conditions of Eq.(29r) hold. This means that *the potential difference across the capacitance lags the electron current by 90° and is given by IX_C.*

Example 6. Assume the series circuit given in Example 5 and find the voltage across each of the three components.

Solution. The given elements are $R = 60.0\ \Omega$, $X_L = 94.2\ \Omega$, and $X_C = 53.1\ \Omega$. By Eq.(29q), we obtain

$$V_R = IR = 1.513\text{ A} \times 60.0\ \Omega = 90.8\text{ V}$$

with V and I in phase.

$$V_L = IX_L = 1.513\text{ A} \times 94.2\ \Omega = 142.5\text{ V}$$

where V leads I by 90°.

$$V_C = IX_C = 1.513\text{ A} \times 53.1\ \Omega = 80.3\text{ V}$$

where V lags behind I by 90°.

These are the three rms voltages one would read on an ac voltmeter when connected across each element separately. Although the sum of the three voltages is 313.6 V, the same voltmeter connected across the entire circuit would read the impressed emf of 110 V. If a vector diagram like Fig. 29H is made for the three separate voltages, the resultant will be 110 V.

29.10. Lenz's Law

When a conductor moves through a magnetic field, the induced current in the wire is in such a direction that its own magnetic field generated by that current acts on the original magnetic field in a way opposing the motion. Stated for the first time by H. Lenz in 1833, this is known as Lenz's law. The action of the two magnetic fields upon each other is always such as to oppose the motion or any change in conditions already existing, for if they assisted the change we would have perpetual motion and a violation of the law of conservation of energy.

If the N pole of a straight bar magnet is approaching a solenoid (see Fig. 27A), the induced electron current in the coil is in such a direction as to produce an N pole at the nearest face of the coil. The two N poles therefore repel each other, tending to stop the motion. To keep the current flowing, a force F must continually be supplied to the moving magnet. It is this force F, moving through a given distance, that determines the amount of mechanical work done in producing a given current. If now the N pole is withdrawn from the solenoid, the induced current in the coil reverses in direction and produces an S pole at the nearest face. The opposite poles therefore attract each other, tending to stop the motion. Again, to keep the current flowing, a force F must be continually supplied; thus work is done.

There are numerous ways of demonstrating Lenz's law. One common experiment is to move a flat copper or aluminum plate rapidly through a strong magnetic field as shown in Fig. 29L. As each part of the plate enters the field, a strong opposing force tends to stop it. What happens electrically is that strong eddy currents of electricity are produced in the metal as shown in Fig. 29M. The magnetic field arising from these eddy currents opposes the field through which it is moving. If the plate is held in the hand, the sensation is that of movement through thick molasses.

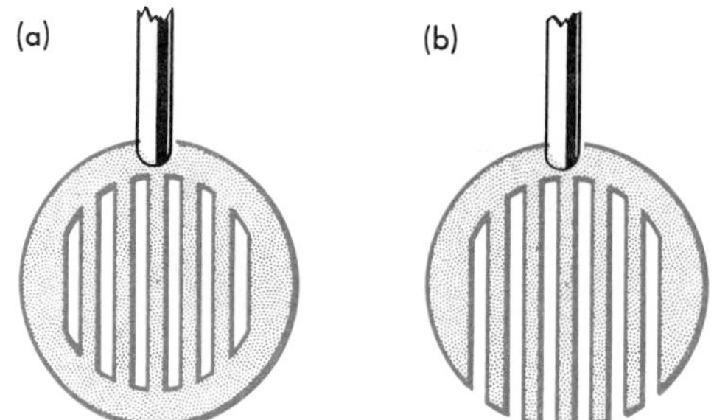

Fig. 29N. Slotted copper disks for the demonstration of induced eddy currents.

If the solid disk is replaced by a slotted disk, as shown in Fig. 29N(a), strong currents are induced in the vertical bars as they enter the field, and the disk stops quickly. If the slots are open at one end as in diagram (b), each bar is an open circuit and no large induced currents can be produced. Consequently, the disk is not strongly retarded but swings through the magnetic field rather freely.

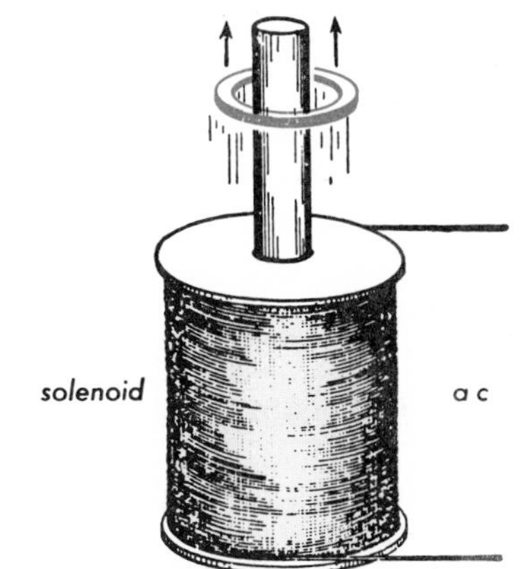

Fig. 29O. A metal ring is flipped up in the air by means of induced currents. A demonstration of Lenz's law.

Another interesting demonstration is illustrated in Fig. 29O. A coil of wire with an extra long iron core is set on end, and a solid metal ring or band slipped over the top as shown. At the instant an alternating emf is applied to the coil, the metal ring is thrown upward several feet into the air. The explanation is not difficult, since the arrangement is quite the same as a *step-down transformer*; the solenoid acts as a primary of many turns and the ring acts as a secondary of only one turn. As the current first starts to flow in one direction in the primary, the expanding magnetic field induces an oppositely directed current in the ring. The field set up by the ring current therefore opposes the field of the primary, and the repulsion of like poles pushes the ring upward.

It is to be noted that Lenz's law and Faraday's law are not enough to explain the ring's behavior. The strong repelling force depends also upon the difference in phase between the magnetic induction produced at the ring by the solenoid, and the current in the ring. Due to the impedance of the ring, the current I lags behind the magnetic induction B, and their interaction gives rise to an overall repulsion.

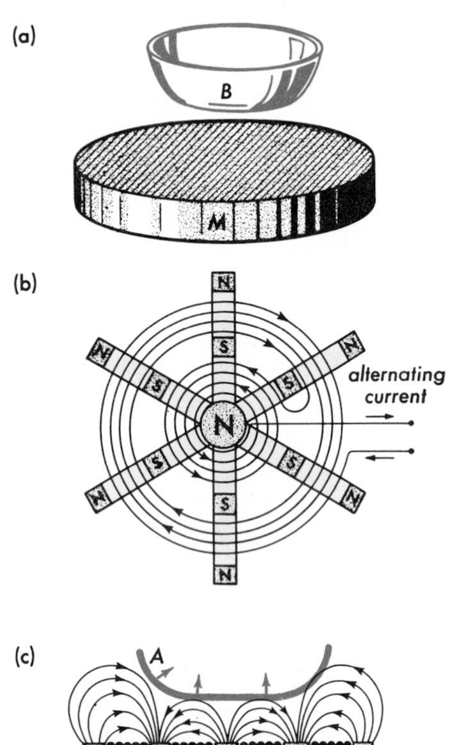

Fig. 29P. A metal bowl is suspended in mid-air. For details of the construction and dimensions of the levitator, see *Am. J. Phys.*, Vol. 31, No. 12, pp. 925-929, December, 1963.

29.11. Levitation

The phenomenon known as "levitation" is another illustration of Lenz's law. A metal bowl B, as in Fig. 29P(a), is supported in stable equilibrium in mid-air just above an electromagnet M of special design. Top and side views of the iron core and coil windings are shown in diagrams (b) and (c). Excited by an alternating current, the raised iron knobs, labeled N and S, reverse their polarity periodically with the current. As the electron current builds up in the direction indicated in diagram (b), the magnetic induction grows. With the aluminum bowl in place as in diagram (c), the growing field induces strong eddy currents in the aluminum conductor. These currents in turn give rise to opposing fields. Since the primary field being created by an alternating current increases and decreases rapidly, the bowl always experiences an upward force.

Should the bowl move to one side, as for example to the left in diagram (c), the changing field at A will induce stronger electron currents on that side of the bowl and give rise to an increased repulsion, pushing the bowl back toward the center as indicated. The strong induced currents give rise to so much heat that the bowl soon becomes hot.

Because the coil windings of a levitator have a relatively large inductive reactance, a fairly large capacitance must be inserted in the ac circuit to raise the power factor close to unity, and thereby keep the current in the levitator coils at a maximum and the current supplied by the source at a minimum.

29.12. Hysteresis

In Sec. 28.7, it was shown how a rising electron current in a coil containing iron gives rise to a magnetization curve as shown in Fig. 28I. When an alternating current is applied to such an inductance, thereby reversing the magnetizing field H with each half cycle, the magnetization B lags behind as shown in Fig. 29Q. As the elementary magnets within the iron try to line up with H, first one way and then the other, the tendency to turn around gives rise to mechanical stresses in the iron; these in turn produce heating. This wasted energy due to the cyclic magnetization is given by the area within the *hysteresis loop* in Fig. 29Q and is called *hysteresis loss.*

Hysteresis losses are not to be confused with other losses due to eddy currents set up in the iron core (see Fig. 29M). To reduce these eddy currents to a minimum, thereby reducing heat losses, the iron core is laminated, that is, built up of layers of thin iron sheets.

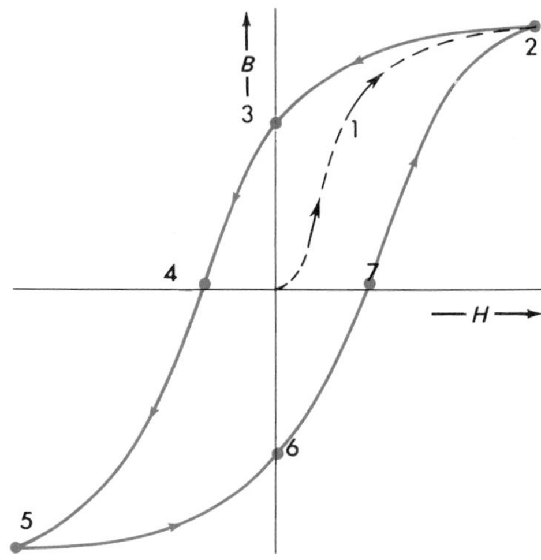

Fig. 29Q. Hysteresis loop.

problems

1. A capacitance of 65.0 μF is connected to a circuit carrying a current with a frequency of 2000 Hz. What is the capacitive reactance?

2. A capacitance of 50.0 μF is connected to a circuit containing a current with a frequency of 1000 Hz. Find the capacitive reactance.

3. What electron current will store up 5.5×10^{-2} joules of energy in an inductance of 35.5 mH? [Ans. 1.760 A.]

4. What resistance connected in series with a capacitance of 24.0 μF will give the circuit a time constant of 12.0 s?

5. A capacitor of 44.0 μF is connected to a resistor of 25,000 Ω. Calculate the time constant.

6. An iron bar 40.0 cm long and 2.0 cm in diameter is wound with copper wire to form a solenoid. If the iron has a permeability number of 796, and the inductance is 0.40 H, how many turns does it have? [Ans. 713 turns.]

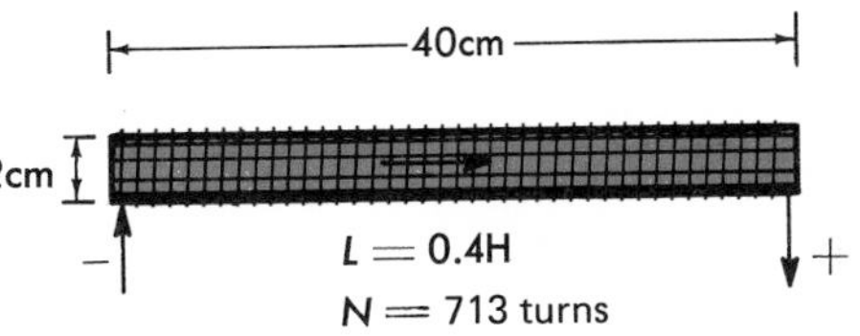

Prob. 6.

7. What resistance connected in series with an inductance of 2.50 mH will give the combination a time constant of 2.0×10^{-3} s.

8. A solenoid 40.0 cm long and 4.0 cm in diameter is uniformly wound with 500 turns of wire. Find its inductance when it has (a) an air core, and (b) an iron core with a permeability number of 2780.

9. A 45.0-Ω resistor is connected in series with a 0.150-H inductor, a 50.0-μF capacitor, and an ac generator delivering 208 V at a frequency of 60 Hz. Find

(a) the inductive reactance, (b) the capacitive reactance, (c) the overall reactance, (d) the impedance, and (e) the electron current. [Ans. (a) 56.5 Ω, (b) 53.0 Ω, (c) 3.50 Ω, (d) 45.1 Ω, (e) 4.61 A.]

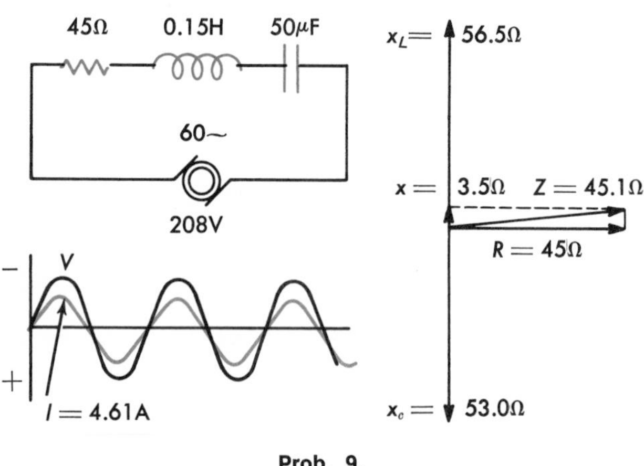

Prob. 9.

10. In the circuit of a radio receiver a 540-μF capacitor is connected in series with a 12.0-mH, a 2.60-Ω resistor, and an ac generator delivering 6.30 V at 60.0 Hz. Calculate (a) the inductive reactance, (b) the capacitive reactance, (c) the total reactance, (d) the impedance, and (e) the electron current.

11.* A capacitance of 28.0 μF is connected in series with an inductance of 240 mH, a resistance of 36.0 Ω, and an ac generator delivering 120.0 V at a frequency of 50 Hz. Find (a) the inductive reactance, (b) the capacitive reactance, (c) the combined reactance, (d) the impedance, (e) the rms electron current, (f) the phase angle between the voltage and current, (g) the power factor, and (h) the power.

12.* A capacitance of 30.0 μF is connected in series with a resistance of 18.0 Ω, an inductance of 150 mH, and an ac generator delivering 220.0 V at 60.0 Hz at its terminals. Find (a) the capacitive reactance, (b) the inductive reactance, (c) the total reactance, (d) the impedance, (e) the rms electron current, (f) the phase angle between V and I, (g) the power factor, and (h) the power. [Ans. (a) 88.4 Ω, (b) 56.5 Ω, (c) 31.86 Ω, (d) 36.59 Ω, (e) 6.01 A, (f) 60.5° lag, (g) 0.492, (h) 651 × 10^2 W.]

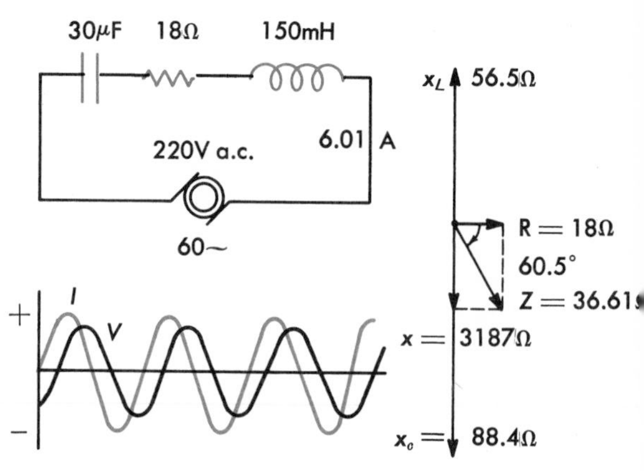

Prob. 12.

13.* An inductance of 85.0 mH, a capacitance of 0.32 μF, and a resistance of 550Ω are connected in series to each other and to a generator delivering 208 V (rms) at a frequency of 1000 Hz. Calculate (a) the inductive reactance, (b) the capacitive reactance, (c) the total reactance, (d) the impedance, (e) the rms electron current, (f) the phase angle between V and I, (g) the power factor, and (h) the power.

14.* A resistance of 210.0 Ω, a capacitance of 0.750 μF, and an inductance of 150.0 mH are connected in series to a generator delivering an rms voltage of 120.0 V at 500 Hz. Find (a) the capacitive reactance, (b) the inductive reactance, (c) the total reactance, (d) the impedance, (e) the rms electron current, (f) the phase angle between V and I, (g) the power factor, and (h) the power.

30 The atomic structure of matter

In dealing with the physical properties of matter it is convenient to divide substances into three forms or states: (1) *the solid state*, (2) *the liquid state*, and (3) *the gaseous state.* Most substances may be made to take on any of these three forms simply by altering the temperature.

The atomic theory of matter assumes that all matter in the universe is made up of ultramicroscopic bodies called atoms and that these are at all times in a rapid state of motion. The nature of this motion and its activity depends upon the temperature and the state of the matter in question, as well as upon the kinds of atoms of which it is composed.

30.1. Kinds of Atoms

Although there are thousands of different substances known to the scientific world, they are all, when broken down into small components, found to be composed of one or more kinds of atoms. A substance that contains atoms of one kind only is called an *element,* while those containing more than one kind are called *compounds* or *mixtures.* Iron, copper, aluminum, platinum, mercury, hydrogen, and helium are examples of elements; whereas water, salt, brass, wood, and air are examples of compounds and mixtures.

The technical names and chemical abbreviations of a few of the more commonly known elements are given in Table 30A. A complete table of the more than 100 known elements is given in Appendix IV.

With each element it is customary to associate two numbers: one is called the *atomic number*, the other the *atomic weight.* The atomic number, given at the left in the tables, specifies the position that element always occupies with respect to all the others, while the atomic weight on the right gives the average weight of

TABLE 30A
Some of the chemical elements atomic weights based on carbon-12 as 12 even

Atomic No.	*Element*	*Symbol*	*Atomic Weight*
1	hydrogen	H	1.0080
2	helium	He	4.0026
3	lithium	Li	6.9390
4	beryllium	Be	9.0122
6	carbon	C	12.0111
7	nitrogen	N	14.0067
8	oxygen	O	15.9994
10	neon	Ne	20.1830
13	aluminum	Al	26.9815
26	iron	Fe	55.847
29	copper	Cu	63.540
47	silver	Ag	107.870
50	tin	Sn	118.69
78	platinum	Pt	195.09
79	gold	Au	196.97
80	mercury	Hg	200.59
82	lead	Pb	207.19
88	radium	Ra	225.92
92	uranium	U	238.03
94	plutonium	Pu	239.16
103	lawrencium	Lw	257.00

one atom of that element relative to the carbon-12 isotope as having a weight of 12.000000 (see Appendix VI). On this basis, the lightest known element, hydrogen, has an average weight of approximately unity.

To illustrate the minuteness of individual atoms, the actual masses in kilograms and approximate diameters in meters of the lightest element, hydrogen, and the very heavy element, plutonium, are as follows:

$$1.\ \text{hydrogen}\quad \begin{cases} \text{mass} = 1.673 \times 10^{-27}\ \text{Kg} \\ \text{diameter} = 1.058 \times 10^{-10}\ \text{m} \end{cases}$$

$$94.\ \text{plutonium}\quad \begin{cases} \text{mass} = 4.02 \times 10^{-25}\ \text{Kg} \\ \text{diameter} = 6.27 \times 10^{-10}\ \text{m} \end{cases}$$

The actual mass of any atom in kilograms can be obtained by multiplying the atomic weight of that element by the unit atomic mass $1.6605311 \times 10^{-27}$ Kg.

A *compound* is a homogeneous pure substance composed of two or more different elements bonded together chemically, which are present in definite proportions; compounds usually possess properties differing from those of the constituent elements. A *mixture* is a substance composed of two or more elements or compounds in which the constituents are not chemically bonded.

Although the intricate structure of each atom plays an important part in its physical and chemical behavior, we will neglect this detailed structure for the time being and think only of each atom as being a tiny sphere-like particle with a very small mass. Later, in other chapters where it is pertinent to do so, the structure of individual atoms will be considered in detail.

30.2. Molecules

One of the most important properties of atoms is their ability to act upon one another at a distance. Some atoms when they come close together attract each other, while others exhibit a force of repulsion. When, at the close approach of two or more atoms, attraction occurs, the atoms may combine to form a molecule. Once a molecule has formed, it will move about and behave as a unit particle under various physical conditions.

Molecules in general may contain almost any number of atoms. Those having only one atom are called *monatomic molecules,* those with two are called *diatomic molecules,* and those with three, *triatomic molecules.* Examples of monatomic molecules are helium (He), neon (Ne), and krypton (Kr); of diatomic molecules are hydrogen (H_2), nitrogen (N_2), oxygen (O_2), and carbon monoxide (CO); and of triatomic molecules are ozone (O_3), carbon dioxide (CO_2), water (H_2O), and hydrocyanic acid (HCN) (see Fig. 30A). Besides these simplest atomic aggregates, there are molecules known to contain many atoms. Along with triatomic molecules they are called *polyatomic molecules.*

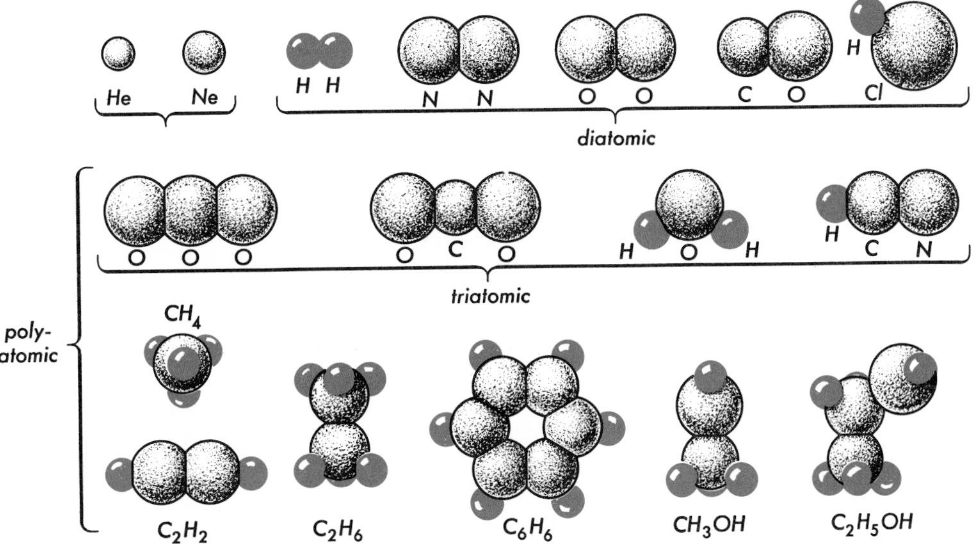

Fig. 30A. Schematic diagrams of a few common molecules. First row: Helium, neon, hydrogen, nitrogen, oxygen, carbon monoxide, hydrochloric acid. Second row: Ozone, carbon dioxide, water, hydrocyanic acid. Third row: Methane, acetylene, benzene, methyl alcohol, ethyl alcohol.

It is clear from the diagrams in Fig. 30A that the atoms of a molecule may be of the same kind or may be different. The question as to why some atoms cling together in pairs and others do not is a subject involving the structure of the atoms themselves. If the individual atoms of a molecule are brought much closer together than their normal separation, they repel each other and are pushed apart. If they are pulled farther apart, the forces become attractive, pulling them together. In other words, they act as though they were connected by springs as shown in Fig. 30B. Pushed closer together or pulled farther apart, they tend to move back to some equilibrium distance. In terms of energy they occupy a position of *minimum potential energy.* To push them closer together or to separate them requires work. At large distances, all atomic forces become very weak so that if by some means or other the atoms of a molecule are pulled far enough apart they become completely separated as free atoms.

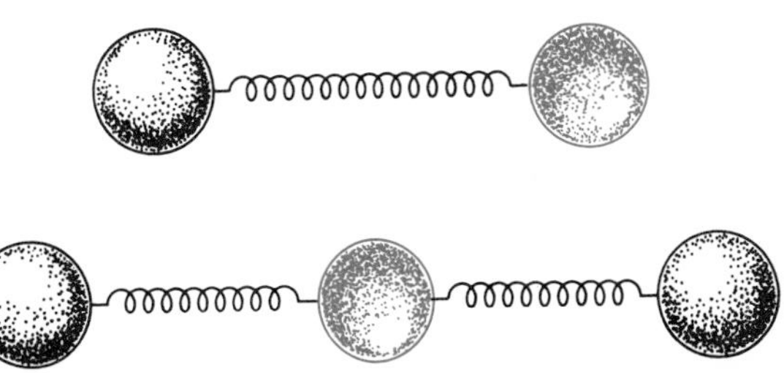

Fig. 30B. The forces between atoms in a molecule behave like springs.

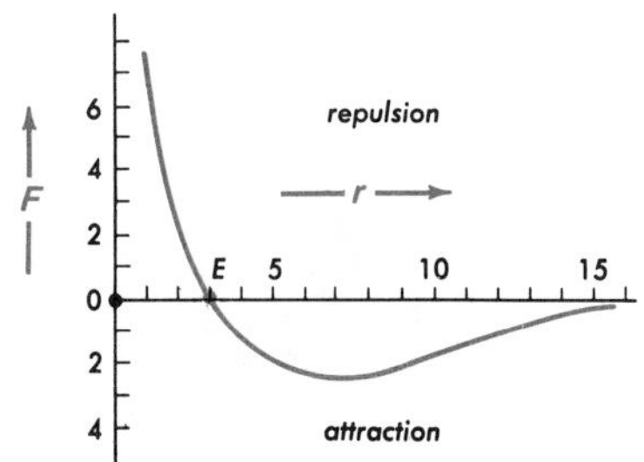

Fig. 30C. Typical graph of the force between two atoms of a diatomic molecule.

A graph of the forces between atoms is shown in Fig. 30C. The horizontal scale giving the distance r between atoms will be slightly different for different atoms, but the equilibrium position E is approximately 3×10^{-10} m.

30.3. Molecular Weight

The molecular weight of a substance is defined as the sum of the atomic weights of the atoms which make up one molecule of that substance. A carbon dioxide molecule, for example, has two oxygen atoms of weight 16 and one carbon atom of weight 12. The molecular weight of carbon dioxide is therefore $16 + 16 + 12 = 44$. Similarly, the molecular weight of nitrogen is 28, oxygen 32, and helium 4. To find the mass of a molecule in grams, its molecular weight should be multiplied by unit atomic mass 1.673×10^{-27} Kg.

30.4. Five States of Matter

As already stated, matter on this earth of ours may exist in three states: (1) the solid state, (2) the liquid state, and (3) the gaseous state. If a solid is heated sufficiently it can be made to melt or liquefy, and by continued heating it can be boiled or vaporized. As a vapor, it is in the gaseous state. If, on the other hand, a gas is cooled sufficiently, it will condense and become a liquid. The continued cooling of a liquid will cause it to solidify or freeze. In the case of water, nature performs all these changes of state: ice is melted to become water, and water is vaporized to become steam; water vapor or clouds condense to become rain, and rain freezes to become ice or hail. Although it may sometimes require extreme heat or extreme cold, all substances can be transformed from any one state to another.

In addition to these three states of matter, so well known here on the earth, there are at least two extraterrestrial states that are quite different (and will be treated in Secs. 30.9 and 30.10 and in later chapters): (4) *the plasma state*, and (5) *the nucleonic state.*

30.5. The Gaseous State

When a substance is in the gaseous state, it is in an extremely rarefied condition. Most of the atoms are grouped together into molecules which, on the average, are very far apart. These molecules are not at rest but are moving about with extremely high speeds, bumping into each other and into the walls of the container. It is the bumping of many millions of molecules against the walls of the containing vessel that gives rise to what is called gas pressure.

A good example of gas pressure is to be found where air has been pumped into an automobile tire or into a toy balloon. Since there are so many more air molecules bombarding the rubber walls inside than outside, the walls are held out by greater bombardment. In addition to moving linearly, a gas molecule, made up of two or more atoms, also vibrates and rotates about its center of mass. As the temperature of the gas is raised, all of these motions increase in speed, causing an increase in pressure. As the temperature is decreased, the atomic motions slow down, decreasing the pressure.

Molecular motion can be illustrated by means of a mechanical model as shown in Fig. 30D. Small steel marbles are placed between two parallel glass plates and set into motion by means of vibrating metal strips around the sides. Each strip V is mounted at the end of a short strip of spring steel and is set into vibration by means of small electromagnets S. As the steel balls bump into these strips, they are bounced off with high speed. On the average, the small steel marbles move considerably faster than the larger ones. This is characteristic of the different-sized molecules in a mixture of two different gases like helium and neon. By increasing the vibrations of the strips the steel marbles move faster. This is analogous to the heating of a gas to a higher temperature.

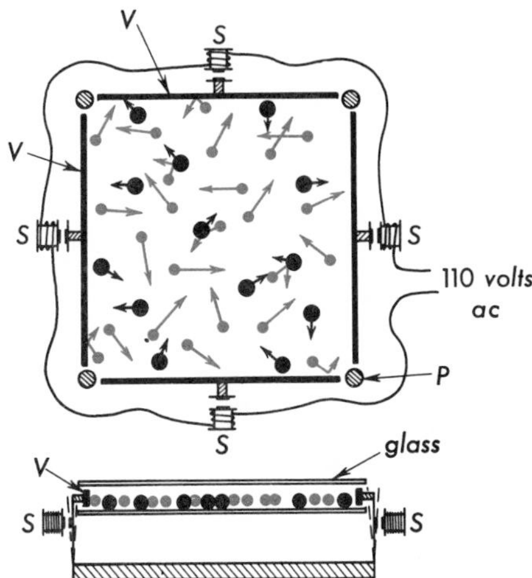

Fig. 30D. Mechanical model illustrating the random motion of molecules in a gas.

30.6. The Liquid State

When a gas is continually cooled, the molecular motion slows down until at a certain temperature the gas condenses into a much smaller volume and changes into a liquid. Although the molecules continue to move, they no longer move as rapidly as they did in the gaseous state. Being much closer together, however, they now attract each other with sufficiently strong forces to cause them to move in closely packed swarms.

The swarming of honeybees as they fly through the air is comparable to the molecules of a gas, while their subsequent collection on the branch of a tree corresponds to condensation into the liquid state.

30.7. Brownian Motion

Although no one has ever observed directly the random motions of molecules, it is possible to observe in a microscope the resultant recoils of larger particles under their continual bombardment. The effect was first discovered in 1827 by Robert Brown,* a British botanist, who observed the irregular but life-

*Robert Brown (1773–1858), noted British botanist, was born on December 21, 1773, at Montrose. After two years of college, he went to Australia where he spent four years collecting over 4,000 new plant specimens. In 1810, he published the first of his great four-volume work on plants and their classification. In 1827, he put forward his idea that the dancing motion of microscopic inanimate particles of matter in water or gas is due to molecular motion of the fluid molecules and not some biological organism. It is for this discovery that he is best known in the world of physics.

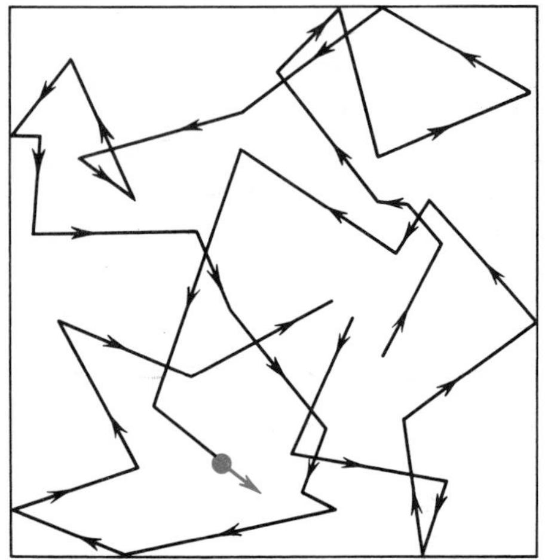
Fig. 30E. Diagram of the random path of a single molecule.

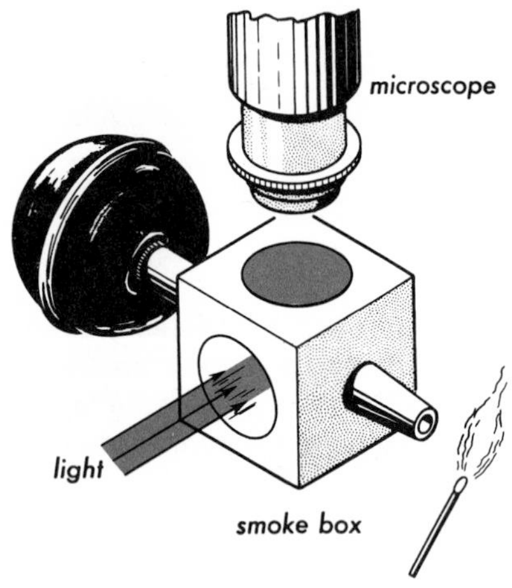

Fig. 30F. Experimental arrangement for observing the Brownian motion of smoke particles.

like motions of small particles suspended in a liquid. These microscopic particles appear to be continually agitated and make a succession of quick jumps first one way and then another. The path of a single particle is illustrated in Fig. 30E. Such motions are called Brownian movements, after their discoverer. These curious Brownian movements were first explained by Sir William Ramsey in 1879 and may be observed in either liquids or gases. The invisibly small molecules of air or water, as the case may be, move at relatively high speeds and, bombarding the larger visible particles vigorously from all sides, make them dart here and there. The larger the particles, the slower their Brownian movement.

One method of observing Brownian motion in a gas is illustrated in Fig. 30F. Smoke from the tip of a match, just extinguished, is drawn into a small box by squeezing and releasing the rubber bulb. A strong beam of light from a carbon arc, entering the box through a glass lens in the side, illuminates the smoke particles, enabling them to be seen from above with a high-power microscope. The tiny smoke particles appear as bright starlike points darting first one way and then another.

To observe Brownian movement in a liquid, a small amount of powdered gamboge (an orange-yellow gum resin) is first put into some distilled water, and one drop of this solution put on a microscope slide. By illuminating the slide with a strong light, the microscopic gamboge particles will be seen to dance about as they are continually being hit by water molecules. If one remembers that the gamboge particles are thousands of times heavier than the water molecules, it will be realized that the latter must be moving with very high speeds to cause such visible recoils.

30.8. The Solid State

As the temperature of a liquid is lowered, the molecular activity decreases. This permits the molecules to pack a little more closely together and accounts for the slight contraction of a liquid on cooling, and conversely for its expansion on heating. As the molecules come closer and closer together, the tendency of each molecule to wander through the liquid decreases. If the temperature is lowered still further a point is ultimately reached where the liquid freezes and becomes a solid.

In the solid state, each molecule is confined to a definite small space between neighboring molecules. This is illustrated in Figs. 30G, 30H, and 30I by atomic models of ultramicroscopic crystals. The model in Fig. 30G illustrates a cubic lattice, a simple type of structure in which the atoms take positions at the corners of cubes. Common table salt with its two kinds of atoms, sodium

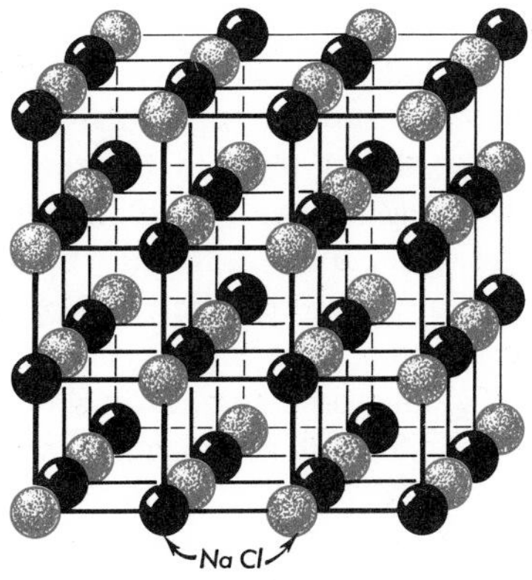

Fig. 30G. Atomic model for sodium chloride (NaCl is common table salt).

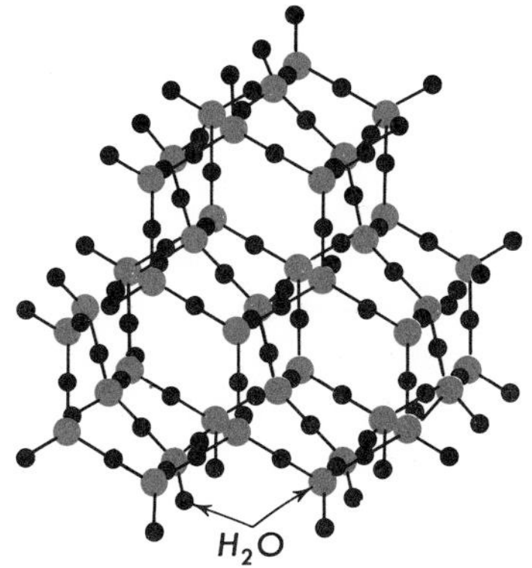

Fig. 30H. Atomic model for ice (H_2O).

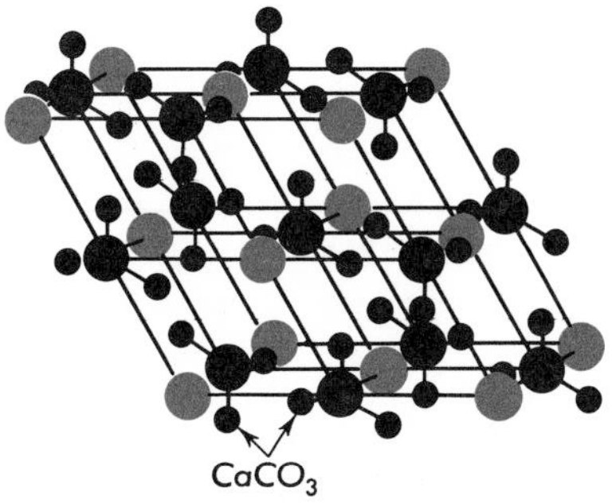

Fig. 30I. Atomic model for iceland spar, or calcite, $CaCO_3$.

Fig. 30J. Photographs of snow crystals exhibiting hexagonal structure.

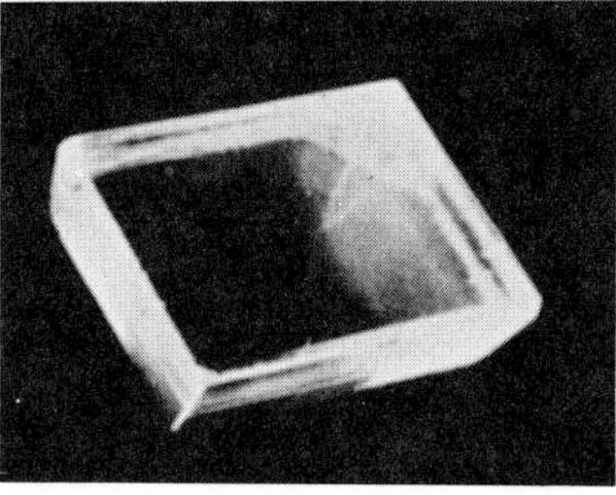

Fig. 30K. Natural crystals of quartz and calcite.

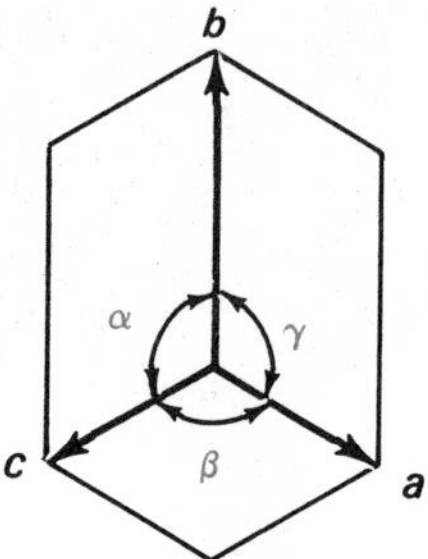

Fig. 30L. General diagram of a unit cell.

and chlorine, always forms such a cubic lattice, the individual atoms alternating in kind in each of the three directions, Na, Cl, Na, Cl, Na, etc.

The crystal model in Fig. 30H is of the hexagonal lattice form in which the principal structure presents parallel hexagonal "holes" through the crystal. Water, in freezing to form ice, or snowflakes, takes on this form (see Fig. 30J). Note that within the atomic lattice each oxygen atom is bound by connecting links between four hydrogen atoms, while each hydrogen atom is linked between two oxygen atoms. The silicon and oxygen atoms of *quartz*, chemically SiO_2, take on a somewhat similar structure, and in the natural state also exhibit a hexagonal structure (see Fig. 30K).

The third model, Fig. 30I, shows the atomic structure for a crystal of calcite. Calcite, which chemically is calcium carbonate ($CaCO_3$), is a clear transparent crystal found in nature. Because of its particular structure it has interesting optical properties, which will be discussed in a later chapter on polarized light. Note how the calcium and carbon atoms form the corners of parallelograms, with each carbon atom surrounded by three oxygen atoms.

X-Ray studies of crystalline forms of matter show that practically all solids belong to one of seven basic forms. Each of these seven fundamental geometrical patterns of the crystal lattice may be illustrated by the smallest section which contains a representative portion of the crystal structure. Such portions are called *unit cells.* The repetition of the unit cell structure in all directions will reproduce nearly all of the known solids. The subject dealing with the properties of these crystal forms is known as *solid state physics.*

While the dimensions of unit cells differ between substances, and depend directly upon the kinds of atoms that go to make up the structure, most of them are parallelepipeds, in which the sizes and shapes are defined by the lengths of the three axes *a, b,* and *c*, and the angles between them α, β, and γ (see Fig. 30L):

Cubic	$a = b = c$	$\alpha = \beta = \gamma = 90°$
Tetragonal	$a = b \neq c$	$\alpha = \beta = \gamma = 90°$
Orthorhombic	$a \neq b \neq c$	$\alpha = \beta = \gamma = 90°$
Monoclinic	$a \neq b \neq c$	$\alpha = \gamma = 90°$; $\beta \neq 90°$
Triclinic	$a \neq b \neq c$	$\alpha \neq \beta \neq \gamma \neq 90°$
Hexagonal	$a = b \neq c$	$\alpha = \beta = 90°$; $\gamma = 120°$
Rhombohedral	$a = b = c$	$\alpha = \beta = \gamma \neq 90°$

Variations of the seven types of unit cells give rise to thirty-two known crystal lattices. All thirty-two are based upon the fourteen unit cells shown in Fig. 30M. The atom sizes in this drawing have been scaled down with respect to the axis distances between them, in order to see the structure. Properly scaled models of three unit cells, made up of atoms of the same kind, are shown in Fig. 30N.

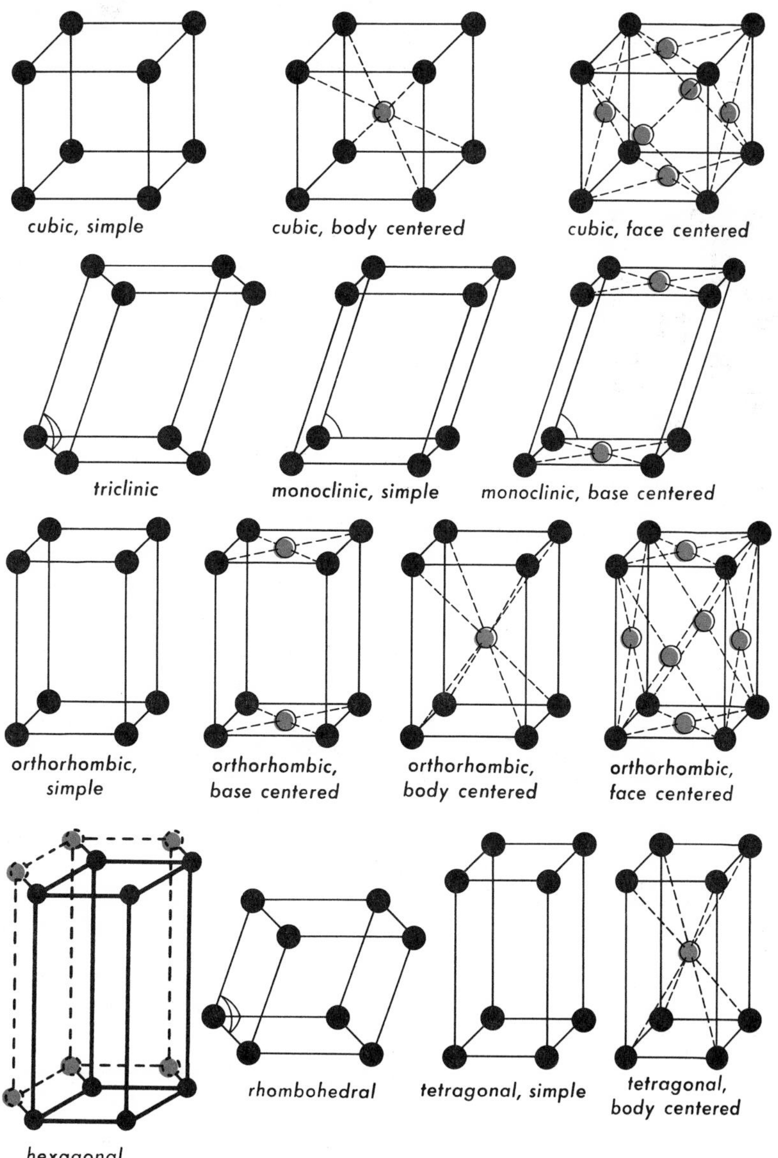

Fig. 30M. Fourteen variations of the seven types of unit cells which go to make up the crystal lattices of solids.

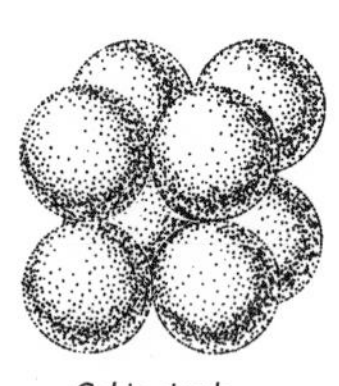

Cubic, simple

Cubic, body centered

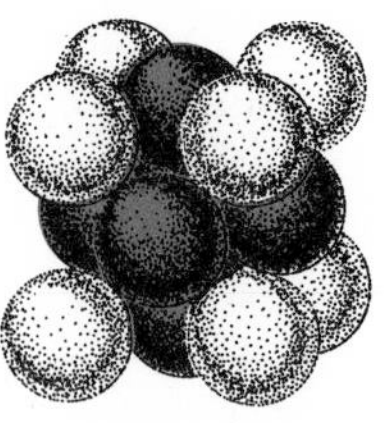

Cubic, face centered

Fig. 30N. Unit cells showing the close packing of atoms in three variations of the cubic crystal lattice.

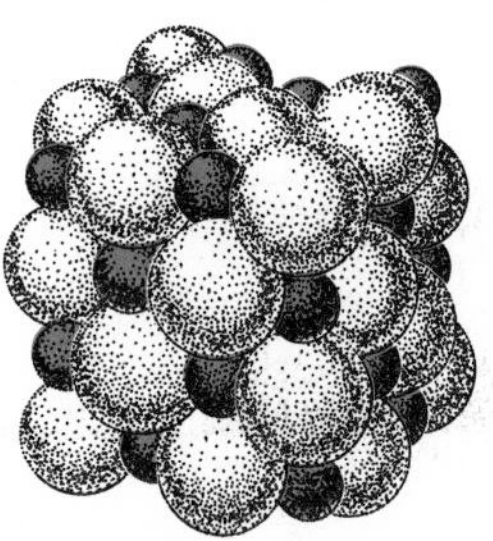

Fig. 30O. The face-centered cubic structure of sodium chloride, NaCl. Colored spheres represent Na^+ and gray spheres Cl^-.

TABLE 30B
Some elements and their cubic crystal structures

Face-centered		Body-centered	
Element	*a* *(Å)*	*Element*	*a* *(Å)*
Aluminum	4.0493	Barium	5.0250
Copper	3.6149	α Iron	2.8665
Gold	4.0786	Rubidium	5.6300
γ Iron	3.5910	Sodium	4.2906
Lead	4.9505	Strontium	4.8500
Lithium	4.404	Titanium	3.3060
Nickel	3.5239	Tungsten	3.1147
Platinum	4.0862	Uranium	3.4740
Silver	4.0862	Zirconium	3.6200

A crystal lattice containing several unit cells of the compound NaCl, sodium chloride, is shown in Fig. 30O. This simple cubic structure is a more exact representation of the solid state lattice in general than is the open type of drawing in Fig. 30G.

These fourteen unit cells are called Bravais lattices, and represent skeletal structures where all atoms shown are of the same kind. Additions of other atoms in different ways in different substances make up the complete structures. For example, calcite is a rombohedral structure with $a = b = c$, and $\alpha = \beta = \gamma \neq 90°$, where the atoms shown are calcium (see Fig. 30I). Carbon atoms, each with three oxygen atoms, are placed along the three axes, halfway between the calcium atoms.

It should be noted that in representing the solid state of matter by unit cells the number of atoms per unit cell in the extended crystal lattice is not the same as shown in Fig. 30M. Some of the atoms of a single unit cell are shared by neighboring unit cells. A little study of the extended crystal lattice shows that the following rules can be applied to find the relative numbers of atoms that go to make up a solid.

1. *An atom lying completely within a unit cell belongs wholly to that cell.*
2. *An atom lying in the face of a unit cell belongs equally to two unit cells and, therefore, counts as one-half an atom for that particular cell.*
3. *An atom lying on one edge of a unit cell is shared equally by four unit cells, and therefore counts as one-quarter of an atom per unit cell.*
4. *An atom lying at a corner of a unit cell is shared equally by eight unit cells, and therefore counts for one-eighth of an atom.*

A number of chemical elements that form face-centered or body-centered cubic structures are listed in Table 30B. The size of the structure is specified in each case by the dimension *a* between cube corners, and is given in angstroms: 1 angstrom = 1×10^{-10} m.

While some elements or compounds always seem to form the same crystal pattern on solidifying, others are known to take on any one of a number of different forms. For example, two of the forms of iron are given in Table 30B. While most of the different forms of crystals known today have been found in nature, there are some that have been produced in the laboratory only. Diamond, one of several known crystal forms of carbon atoms, is a closely packed crystal that has, until recently, defied laboratory reproduction. Small diamonds for use in the manufacturing of high-speed cutting tools are now produced in quantities by the General Electric Company. It was in the company's laboratories that the production of real diamonds was accomplished by applying extremely high temperatures and pressures to small graphite slugs.

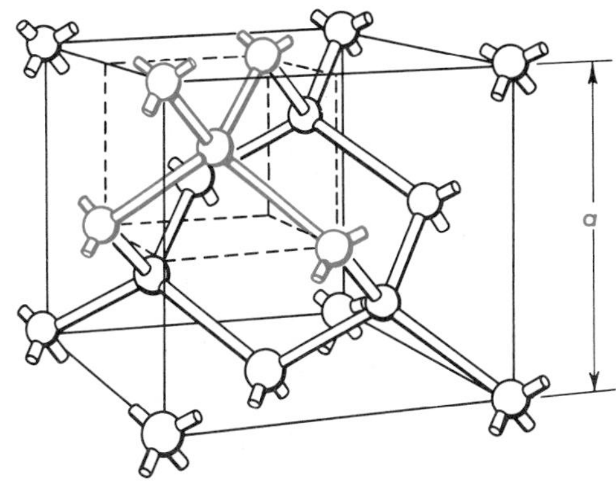

Fig. 30P. Diamond crystal structure. For carbon, silicon, and germanium $a = 3.56$, 5.43, and 5.66 Å, respectively. Nearest-neighbor spacing is $a\sqrt{3}/4$, and maintains tetragonal symmetry. (After Shockley.)

The important features of the diamond structure are shown in Fig. 30P, and this is the characteristic structure for the elements C, Si, Ge, Sn, and Pb in column IV-A of the Periodic Table (see Appendix IV). Note that while the outermost atoms form a large cube, all atoms are bound by chemical bonds to their four nearest neighbors. Furthermore, each set of four nearest neighbors lies at corners of a cube, with atoms diagonally opposite each other on the square sides. For C, Si, and Ge, $a = 3.56$, 5.43, and 5.66 Å, respectively, while the nearest-neighbor spacing is $a\sqrt{3}/4$.

While some crystal types present a more open structure than others, the actual size of each atom in the models shown above has been reduced in order to reveal the positions of others behind.

Actually, the atoms in most liquids begin to form localized crystal arrays before solidification takes place but, due to the rapid state of atomic vibration, each localized crystal region can move with respect to another. A liquid may therefore be looked upon as a transition state between the gas where individual molecules exist and the solid where individual atoms become part of a crystal structure and can no longer be associated with any particular molecule.

Metals, in general, when they cool down from the molten state, solidify into thousands of ultramicroscopic crystals that pack closely together to form a three-dimensional mosaic. This is well illustrated by the electron-microscope photographs reproduced in Fig. 30Q. Note the clearcut cubic structure of pure aluminum.

While each atom or molecule in a solid is confined to a definite space within the body lattice, it is in a state of vibration within that space. As the temperature decreases, this motion becomes slower and slower until at absolute zero, $-273°C$, all molecular motion ceases. By molecular motion is meant the motion of the molecule as a whole. At absolute zero, however, the atoms of certain solids are still vibrating. This residual energy of vibration is known to be an inherent property of some solids, which cannot be utilized or taken away.*

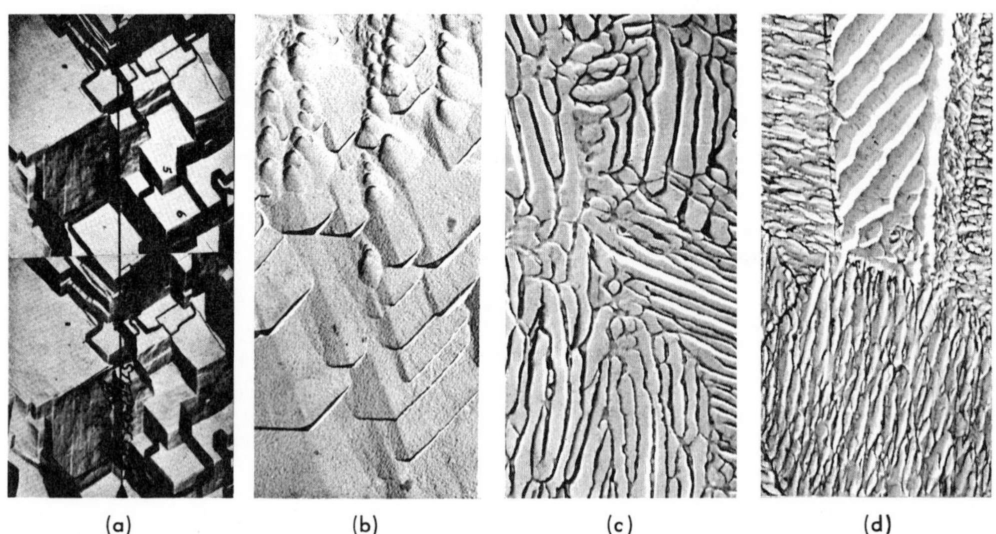

Fig. 30Q. Electron microscope photographs showing the crystalline-like structure of metals: (a) pure aluminum 5600 X, (b) magnesium-aluminum alloy 13,000 X, (c) polished steel 14,000 X, and (d) polished copper 14,000 X. (Courtesy of R. D. Heidenreich, Dow Chemical Co.)

30.9. The Plasma State

There are numerous stars in the universe, including our own sun, which exhibit a state of matter quite different from anything we find in nature here on the earth. This state, the plasma state, consists of a low or high density gas in which a very high percent of the atoms are highly ionized. With essentially equal numbers of positive and negative ions moving about at extremely high speeds, the effective temperature of the medium ranges in the thousands and millions of degrees. Extensive plasma studies are being conducted today in many science laboratories by sending high voltage electrical discharges through different gases. For laboratory and natural examples, see Secs. 41.1, 56.10, and 63.11.

*An introductory book on crystal structure is Alan Holden and Phylis Singer, *Crystals and Crystal Growing* (Doubleday & Co., Garden City, New York).

30.10. The Nucleonic State

It has long been known that certain stars in the heavens have densities thousands of times greater than anything found on the earth. Present day knowledge of atomic structure has led to the postulate that such densities are to be attributed to a special state in which atomic nuclei are stripped of nearly all of their extranuclear electrons, and under strong binding forces packed closely together.

This is a reasonable assumption since the density of matter within the average nucleus in the nucleonic state is approximately 2.290×10^{17} Kg/m^3. This is twenty million million times greater than the density of terrestrial lead. (*Note:* The hydrogen nucleus has a mass of 1.672×10^{-27} Kg, and a radius of 1.20×10^{-15} m, and the density of common lead is 1.14×10^4 Kg/m^3.) See Sec. 62.8 for further examples of the nucleonic state.

questions

1. What are the three states of matter? How do these states differ from each other? Which, in general, is the most compact?

2. How many known elements are there? What constitutes an element?

3. What is meant by (a) atomic number and (b) atomic weight?

4. Give an example of (a) a monatomic molecule, (b) a diatomic molecule, (c) a triatomic molecule, and (d) a polyatomic molecule.

5. What general treatment of most solids will change their state to the liquid or gas?

6. What is Brownian motion? How is it observed?

7. What can you say about the arrangement of atoms in a solid, like iron? In a solid like common table salt?

8. How could you set up an experiment to demonstrate the forces between the atoms of a linear triatomic molecule? If you were to push the outer atoms of a molecule toward each other and suddenly release them, what kind of motion do you think would ensue?

9. Describe general characteristics of the plasma and nucleonic states. Where do these states occur naturally?

Properties  of light

Light and its various phenomena present some of the most interesting studies in the whole realm of physics. They are interesting because the results of many experiments are revealed through the sense of vision as color phenomena. Equally important and every bit as interesting is the historical development and discovery of the various principles, concepts, and properties of light which give rise to these phenomena.

All of the various known properties of light are conveniently described in terms of the experiments by which they were discovered and the many and varied experiments by which they are now continually demonstrated. Numerous as they are, these experiments may be grouped together and classified under one of the three following heads: (1) *geometrical optics*, (2) *physical optics*, and (3) *quantum optics.* Each of these may be subdivided as follows:

Geometrical Optics
- rectilinear propagation
- finite velocity
- reflection
- refraction

Physical Optics
- diffraction
- interference
- polarization
- double refraction

Quantum Optics
- photoelectric effect
- Compton effect
- atomic excitation
- pair production

The first group, geometrical optics, treated in this chapter and the following chapter, deals with those optical phenomena that are most easily described with straight lines and plane geometry. The second group, physical optics, dealing with the wave nature of light, is treated in Chaps. 35, 36, 37, and 40, whereas the third group, dealing with the quantum aspects of light, is treated in Chaps. 37, 43, and 51 to 59.

31.1. The Rectilinear Propagation of Light

The rectilinear propagation of light is another way of saying that "light travels in straight lines." The fact that objects may be made to cast fairly sharp shadows is an experimental demonstration of this principle. Another illustration is the image formation of an object produced by light passing through a small opening, as diagrammed in Fig. 31A. In this figure, the object is an ordinary incandescent light bulb. In order to see how an image is formed, consider the rays of light emanating from a single point **a** near the top of the bulb. Of the many rays of light radiating in all directions, the ray that travels in the direction of the hole passes through to the point **a′** near the bottom of the image screen. Similarly, a ray leaving **b** near the bottom of the bulb and passing through the hole will arrive at **b′** near the top of the image screen. Thus it may be seen that an inverted image is formed.

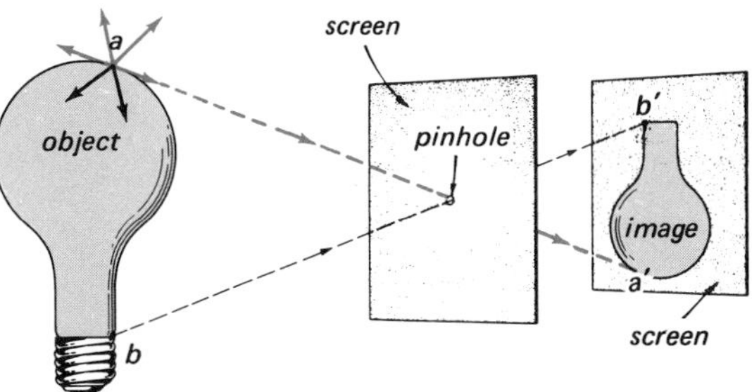

Fig. 31A. An illustration of the principle that light travels in straight lines.

If the image screen is moved closer to the pinhole screen, the image will be proportionately smaller, whereas if it is moved farther away the image will be proportionately larger. The same thing happens when either the object or the pinhole is moved. Excellent photographs can be made with this arrangement by making a pinhole in one end of a small box and placing a photographic film or plate at the other. Such an arrangement is called a pinhole camera. For good, sharp photographs the hole must be very small, because its size determines the amount of blurring produced. The photograph shown in Fig. 31B was taken with such a camera. Note the undistorted perspective lines of the building and depth of focus.

Fig. 31B. Photograph taken with a pinhole camera.

31.2. The Speed of Light

For two thousand years it was believed that light traveled with an infinite speed. It was assumed that when any major event happened among the distant stars, the event could be seen instantly at all other points in the universe.

Galileo once tried to measure the speed of light, but without success. Galileo stationed himself on one hilltop with one lamp and an assistant on another hilltop with a similar lamp. Galileo would first uncover his lamp for an instant, sending a short flash of light to the assistant. As soon as the assistant saw this light he uncovered his own lamp, sending a flash back to Galileo, who noted the total time elapsed. After numerous repetitions of this experiment at greater and greater distances between observers, Galileo came to the conclusion that they could not uncover their lamps fast enough and that light probably travels with an infinite

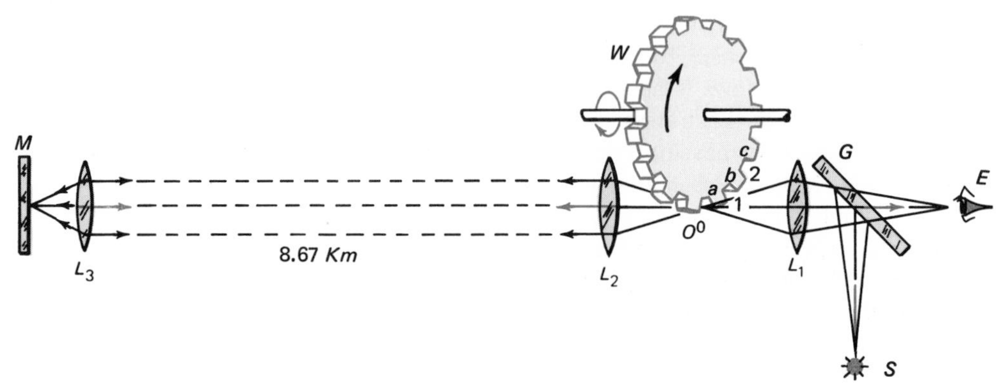

Fig. 31C. Experimental arrangement used by Fizeau in determining the speed of light.

speed. Knowing as we do now that light travels with the amazing speed of 300,000 Km/s, it is easy to see why Galileo's experiment failed.

The first terrestrial method of measuring the speed of light was devised by Fizeau in 1849.* His experimental arrangement is shown in Fig. 31C. Light from an intense source S was reflected from a semitransparent mirror G and then brought to a focus at the point O by means of a lens L_1. After being made into a parallel beam by a second lens L_2, the light traveled a distance of 8.67 Km to a hilltop, where a mirror M and lens L_3 reflected the light back again. Returning by the same path, some of the light passed through the mirror G and entered the eye of the observer at E.

The purpose of the rotating toothed wheel was to chop the light beam into short flashes and to measure the time it takes each of these signals to travel over to the far mirror and back. With the wheel at rest and in such a position that the light passes through an opening between two teeth at O, the observer at E will see an image of the light source S. If the wheel is now set rotating with slowly increasing speed, a condition will soon be reached in which the light passing through 0 will return just in

*Armand Fizeau (1819–1896), French physicist, was born of a wealthy French family that enabled him to be financially independent. Rather than shun work, however, he devoted his life to diligent experimental work in science. His most important achievement was the measurement of the speed of light in 1849, carried on in Paris between Montmartre and Suresnes. Prior to this work, it was believed that light had an infinite speed. He also gave the correct explanation of the Doppler principle as applied to light coming from the stars and showed how the effect could be used to measure stellar velocities. He carried out his experiments on the velocity of light in a moving medium in 1851, and showed that light is dragged along by a moving stream of water.

time to be stopped by a, that passing through opening 1 will return just in time to be stopped by b, etc. Under these conditions the image will be completely eclipsed from the observer. By further increasing the speed, the light will reappear, increasing in intensity until a maximum is reached. This will occur when the flashes sent out through the openings 0, 1, 2, 3, etc., return just in time to get through the openings 1, 2, 3, 4, etc., respectively. With a wheel containing 720 teeth, Fizeau observed this maximum at a speed of 25 rps. The time required for the light to travel over and back can therefore be calculated as 1/25 times 1/720, or 1/18,000th of a second. This, from the measured distance over and back of 17.34 Km, gave a speed of 313,000 Km/s.

31.3. Michelson's Measurements of the Speed of Light

In the years that followed these earliest experiments, several investigators improved upon Fizeau's apparatus and methods of observation, and obtained more accurate values for the speed of light. Of these, Michelson's* contributions and improvements stand out above the rest. Replacing the toothed wheel by a small eight-sided mirror and increasing the light path to about 70 Km, Michelson in 1926 obtained a value of 299,796 Km/s.

An extensive and critical study of the values of the speed of light measured by all observers has been made over the last forty years and to this date the most probable value is

$$c = 299{,}792.5 \text{ Km/s} \qquad (31a)$$

For practical purposes where calculations are to be made to four significant figures, the speed of light in air or in a vacuum may be assumed to be

$$c = 3.0 \times 10^8 \text{ m/s}$$

One is justified in using this round-number value since it differs from the more accurate value in Eq.(31a) by less than $\frac{1}{10}$th of 1%.

Example 1. A toothed wheel of the kind used by Fizeau, containing 720 teeth, is used to measure the speed of light in air. If the distant mirror is located 37.50 Km away, how fast will the wheel be turning when the first eclipse occurs? Assume the speed of light to be 3.0×10^8 m/s.

***Albert A. Michelson (1852–1931), distinguished American physicist, was celebrated for the invention and development of the interferometer, an optical instrument, now named the Michelson stellar interferometer in his honor. This instrument is used to establish the length of the standard meter in terms of the wavelength of light, to make ether drift experiments (see Chap. 48 on Relativity), to determine the rigidity of the earth, to measure the distances and the diameters of giant stars, and to measure the speed of light. He was the first American scientist to be awarded the Nobel Prize in physics (1907).**

Solution. Since the distance each light pulse travels is twice the distance to the mirror, or 75,000 m, the time t taken to cover this distance is x/v:

$$t = \frac{x}{v} = \frac{7.50 \times 10^4 \text{ m}}{3.0 \times 10^8 \text{ m/s}}$$

$$t = 2.50 \times 10^{-4} \text{ s}$$

In this short time the wheel rotates from the center of one opening to the center of the adjacent tooth. With 720 teeth there will be 1440 such intervals around the wheel. The time it takes the wheel to make one revolution will just be the product of these two numbers:

$$T = 2.50 \times 10^{-4} \times 1440$$

$$T = 0.360 \text{ s}$$

Since the frequency of revolution is $1/T$,

$$\nu = 2.778 \text{ rev/s}$$

31.4. The Speed of Light in Stationary Matter

In 1850, Foucault completed and published the results of an experiment in which he had measured the speed of light in water. This was a crucial experiment, for it settled a long existing controversy concerning the nature of light. According to Newton and his followers, light was believed to be made up of small particles or corpuscles emanating from a source. Huygens, on the other hand, regarded light as being composed of waves, similar in nature perhaps to water waves or sound waves. Now, Newton's corpuscular theory required light to travel faster in a dense medium like water than it did in a less-dense medium like air, whereas Huygens' wave theory required it to travel slower. By sending light back and forth through a long tube of water, Foucault found its speed to be less than that in air. This was a strong confirmation of Huygens' wave theory.

Years later, Michelson also measured the speed of light in water and found a value of 225,000 Km/s. This is just $\frac{3}{4}$ the speed in a vacuum. In common glass, the speed is still lower, being about $\frac{2}{3}$ the speed in vacuo, or 200,000 Km/s. In air, the speed is very little less than the speed in a vacuum, differing only by about 70 Km/s at sea level and less at higher altitudes where the air is less dense. For most practical cases this difference can be neglected, and the speed in air can be said to be the same as in a vacuum.

31.5. The Refractive Index

The ratio between the speed of light in a vacuum and the speed in a medium is called the *refractive index,* or the *index of refraction* of the medium:

$$\frac{\text{Speed in vacuo}}{\text{Speed in a medium}} = \text{refractive index}$$

Symbolically, we write

$$\frac{c}{v} = \mu \tag{31b}$$

The Greek letter μ (mu) is frequently used to represent this ratio. Substituting the velocities given in the preceding section, we may calculate the following refractive indices:

$$\begin{aligned} &\text{for water,} && \mu = 1.333 \\ &\text{for glass,} && \mu = 1.520 \\ &\text{for air,} && \mu = 1.000 \end{aligned} \tag{31c}$$

Very exact measurements of the refractive index of air give a value 1.00029.

Various kinds of glass have different refractive indices. For most common glasses they range from 1.50 to 1.70. See Table 32A in the next chapter.

31.6. Optical Path

In order to derive one of the basic principles in geometrical optics, it is convenient to define a quantity called the *optical path.* The distance light travels in any medium is given by the product $v \times t$:

$$d = vt$$

Since by definition $\mu = c/v$, solving for v gives $v = c/\mu$, and we can write

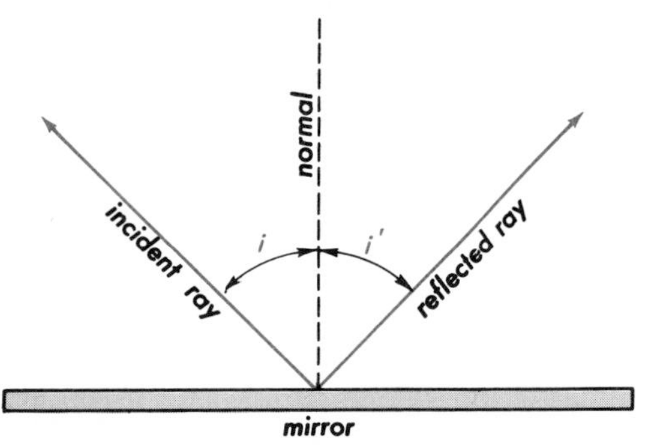

Fig. 31D. Diagram illustrating the law of reflection from a plane surface.

$$d = \frac{c}{\mu} t$$

which becomes

$$\mu d = ct$$

The product μd is called the *optical path* and represents the distance light travels in a vacuum in the same time that light travels a distance d in the medium:

$$\text{Optical Path} = \mu d \tag{31d}$$

When a light ray has different segments d_1, d_2, d_3, etc., of its path in substances having different indices μ_1, μ_2, μ_3, etc., the total optical path is

$$[\text{OP}] = \mu_1 d_1 + \mu_2 d_2 + \mu_3 d_3 + \cdots \tag{31e}$$

The refractive index of a transparent medium is a measure of what is called its "optical density." A high refractive index signifies a medium of high optical density, and a low refractive index signifies a medium of low optical density.

31.7. The Law of Reflection

Experiment shows that, whenever a ray of light is reflected from a plane surface, the nature of the reflected light can be described in terms of a number of simple and well-defined laws. The simplest of these is the one known as the law of reflection. According to this law, the angle at which a ray of light strikes the reflecting surface is exactly equal to the angle the reflected ray makes with the same surface. Instead of measuring the angle of incidence and the angle of reflection from the mirror surface, however, it is customary to measure both from a line perpendicular to the plane of the mirror. This line as shown in Fig. 31D is called the *normal.* As the angle i increases, the angle i' increases by exactly the same amount so that, for all angles of incidence,

$$\text{angle } i = \text{angle } i' \tag{31f}$$

A second part of this law stipulates that the reflected ray lies in the plane of incidence, the plane of incidence being defined as the plane containing the incident ray and the normal. In other words, *the incident ray, the normal, and the reflected ray all lie in the same plane.*

In speaking of a mirror surface, one does not necessarily mean a silvered plate of glass; a mirror is any surface smooth enough to produce regular reflection as it has just been described.

31.8. Image in a Plane Mirror

The image of one's self seen in a mirror is formed by rays of light traveling in straight lines which are reflected according to the law of reflection. All objects seen in a plane mirror are images formed by reflection. This can be demonstrated by the experiment shown in Fig. 31E. A lighted candle O is placed on the table near a plate of glass MN. With the candle itself hidden in the box H, the observer at E sees only the reflected image at I. If a glass of water is placed at B, this image appears as a real candle burning under water.

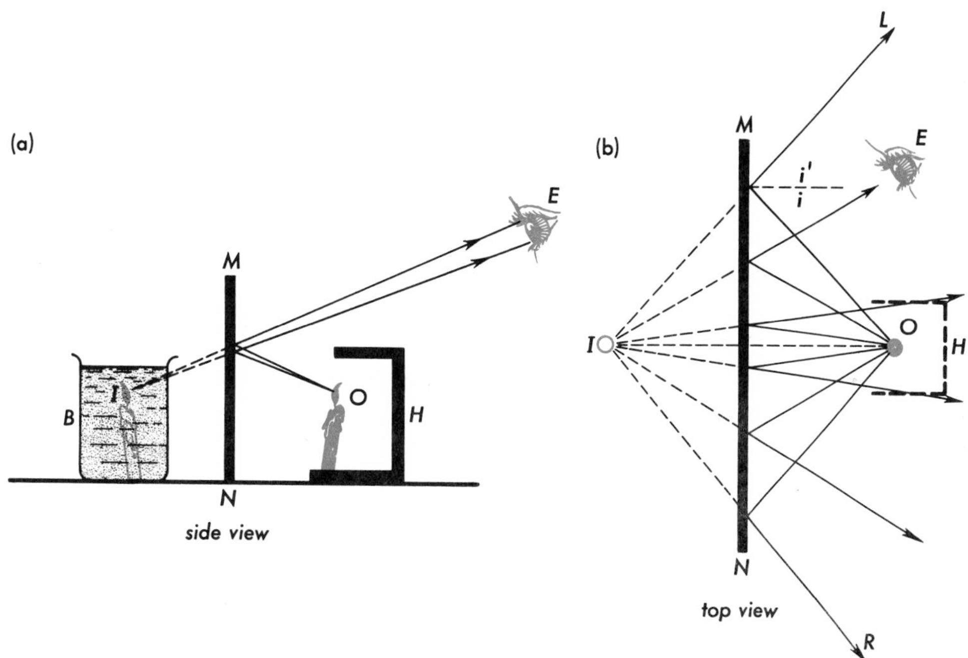

Fig. 31E. An experiment illustrating reflection from a mirror or plate of glass. Light from the candle flame at *O* appears to come from *I*.

As shown in the top view, all rays of light leaving the source O are reflected according to the law of reflection. To an observer anywhere between L and R on the right side of the mirror, all

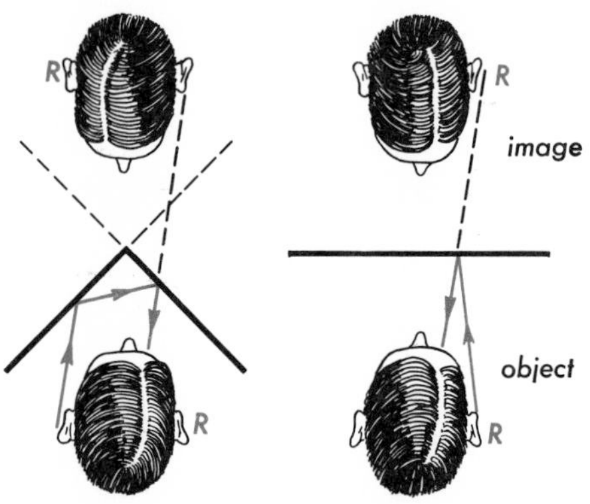

Fig. 31F. One's own image seen in 90° mirrors is normal, that seen in a plane mirror is perverted.

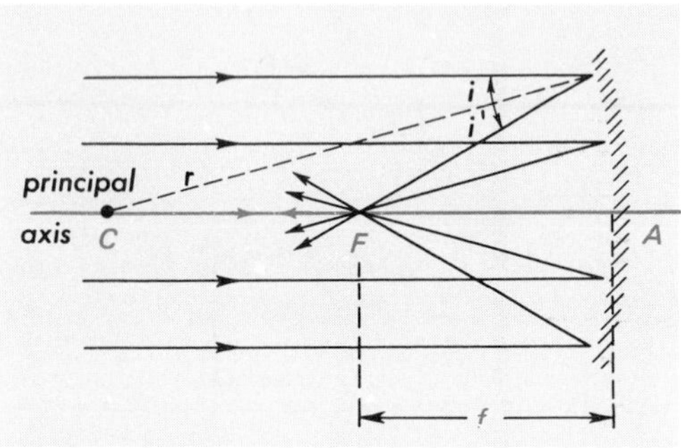

Fig. 31G. The focal point *F* and focal length *f* of a concave mirror.

light appears to come from the same point I. This image point is just as far behind the mirror as the object O is in front of it, and the two lie on the same perpendicular to the mirror.

The image one sees in a plane mirror is not a real image but a virtual image. A virtual image is one from which rays seem to radiate but actually do not. In the figure the rays do not come from I, they come from O and by reflection reach the observer.

This experiment illustrates a trick commonly used to make ghostlike figures appear to move about a room or stage. Light from real persons or objects, located below or above the stage, is reflected from a large sheet of plate glass at the front of the stage. With proper drapes and a darkened room, the illusion is very effective.

If one looks at his own face in a plane mirror, the image observed is technically described as *perverted.* The image is the same as though the face were reproduced as a rubber mask and the mask turned inside out and viewed from the new front. The right ear of the subject becomes the left ear of the image, and vice versa.

To see one's face as others see it, two front silvered mirrors should be placed 90° apart and touching each other along one edge as shown in Fig. 31F. The observer's right ear will then be seen, because of two reflections, as the right ear of his image, etc. This experiment must be performed to be appreciated, since many people's faces are, unknowingly, slightly unsymmetrical. Seen in 90° mirrors, all such irregularities are reversed; they therefore appear double in magnitude and are very noticeable.

31.9. Concave Mirrors

The concave mirror is an optical device which may by pure reflection form images on a screen. Such mirrors are often used in optical instruments in place of a lens. There are several very good reasons for this, one of them being that the concave mirror does not exhibit chromatic aberration, and another that there is only one curved surface to prepare and polish instead of two or more.

A spherical mirror has the form of a circular section of a hollow sphere as shown in cross section in Fig. 31G. The center point A of the section is called the *vertex,* and a line from the center of curvature of the sphere through the vertex is called the *principal axis.* The radius of the sphere *r* is called the *radius of the mirror.*

Because spherical mirrors are symmetrical about their axes, cross-sectional diagrams are sufficient to show their optical properties. If the mirror is polished and silvered on the inner surface, it is called a *concave mirror*, while if silvered on the outer surface, it is a *convex mirror.*

The cross-sectional diagram of Fig. 31G shows how a beam of parallel light is reflected by a concave mirror. Each ray striking the mirror obeys the law of reflection, namely, that the angle of incidence i equals the angle of reflection i'. The point F where the rays cross the principal axis is called the *principal focus,* and the distance A to F is called the *focal length f.*

If the mirror is silvered on the outer surface as in Fig. 31H, it becomes a convex mirror, and parallel incident light rays are reflected as if they came from a point F on the axis. The different rays, each obeying the law of reflection, diverge after reflection and never come to a focus. Nevertheless, the distance A to F is called the *focal length* of the convex mirror.

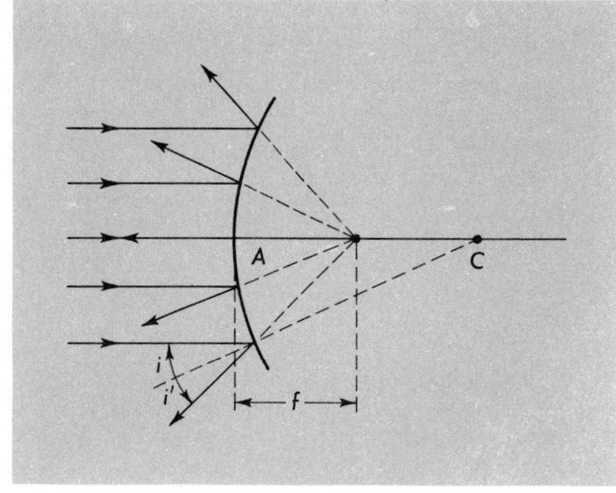

Fig. 31H. The focal point F and focal length f of a convex mirror.

31.10. Image Formation

If an illuminated object O is located in front of a concave mirror as shown in Fig. 31I, a real image I can be formed nearby. All rays emitted by the object point Q and reflected by the mirror come to a focus at Q′. All rays emitted by the object point M would upon reflection come to a focus at M′. For every object point in QM emitting rays, there will be a corresponding image point in Q′M′ where focus is produced.

If the eye is located at E, the illuminated object will appear at Q′M′, but inverted. If a screen is located at Q′M′, a sharply defined image will be observed there. Because the image can be formed on a screen, it is called a *real image.*

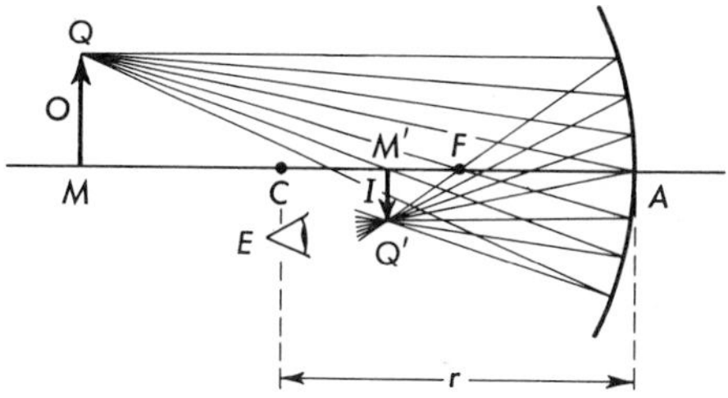

Fig. 31I. A concave mirror forms a real image.

The geometry of the reflection from a concave or convex mirror is such that the focal length AF is always equal to $\frac{1}{2}$ the radius of curvature r, where r = AC, and C is the center of curvature. As an equation,

$$AF = \tfrac{1}{2}AC$$

$$f = \frac{r}{2} \qquad (31g)$$

It is common practice in optical diagrams involving a concave or convex mirror to show incident light rays moving from left to right.

(1) When an incident ray encounters a convex surface the radius r is positive.

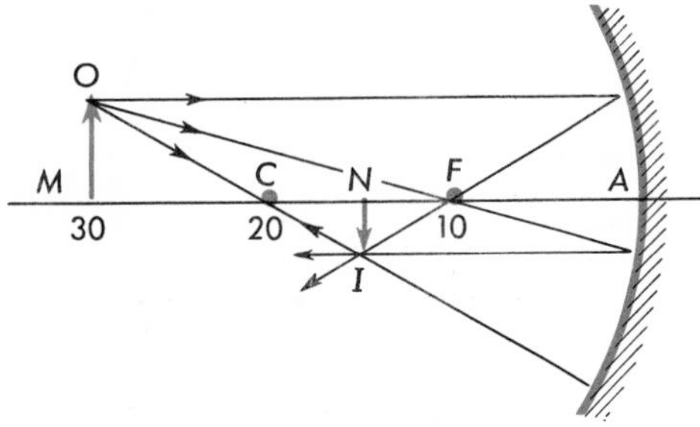

Fig. 31J. Graphical construction for locating the image formed by a concave mirror.

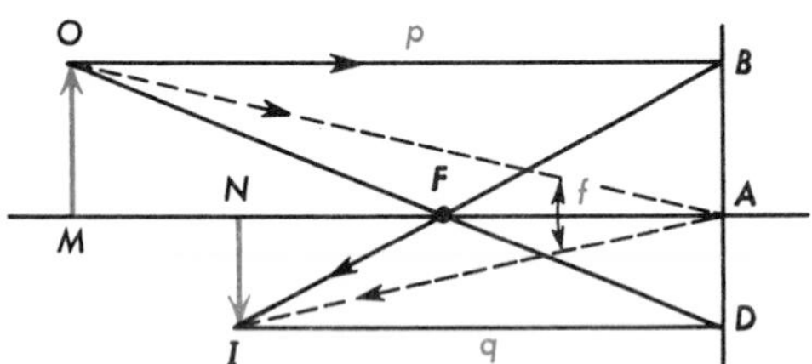

Fig. 31K. Geometrical diagram for the derivation of the object–image distance formula: Eq.(31h).

(2) When an incident ray encounters a concave surface the radius r is negative.

As an illustration of the image-forming properties of a concave spherical mirror, consider the graphical construction in Fig. 31J. An object O is located 30 cm from a concave mirror of radius $r = -20$ cm, center at C. By Eq.(31g) F must be halfway between A and C, giving $f = +10$ cm.

A light ray from O parallel to the principal axis is reflected, by definition of the focal point, through F. By the reversibility of light rays, another ray from O passing through F is reflected parallel to the principal axis. Where these two rays cross at I, the image is formed. A third ray from O through the center of curvature C strikes the mirror normally and is reflected back on itself where it passes through I. Any two of these three rays are sufficient to locate the image. The third ray is then a check upon the other two.

We can derive a simple relation between *object distance, image distance,* and *focal length* of a spherical mirror by redrawing the rays in Fig. 31J to form the simplified diagram shown in Fig. 31K, and then applying the principles of elementary geometry. From similar BID and BFA, we can write proportionalities for corresponding sides as follows:

$$\frac{BD}{q} = \frac{BA}{f}$$

From similar triangles DOB and DFA, we can also write

$$\frac{BD}{p} = \frac{AD}{f}$$

Adding equals to equals, we obtain

$$\frac{BD}{p} + \frac{BD}{q} = \frac{BA}{f} + \frac{AD}{f}$$

or

$$\frac{BD}{p} + \frac{BD}{q} = \frac{BD}{f}$$

$$\frac{1}{p} + \frac{1}{q} = \frac{1}{f} \qquad (31h)$$

To find the image distance for the illustration in Fig. 31J, Eq. (31h) can be applied directly. Given are the quantities $p = 30$

cm and $f = +10$ cm. By substitution

$$\frac{1}{30} + \frac{1}{q} = \frac{1}{10}$$

$$\frac{1}{q} = \frac{1}{10} - \frac{1}{30}$$

$$\frac{1}{q} = \frac{3}{30} - \frac{1}{30}$$

from which

$$\frac{1}{q} = \frac{2}{30}$$

and $$q = \frac{30}{2} = 15 \text{ cm}$$

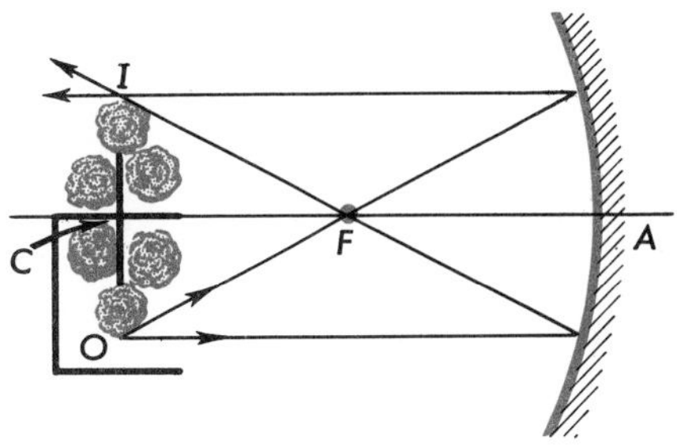

Fig. 31L. Diagram for the phantom bouquet.

An interesting experiment can be performed with a large concave mirror under the conditions illustrated in Fig. 31L. A flower hanging upside down in a box and placed just below the center of curvature will form a real and erect image at I directly above. An observer to the left cannot see the flower directly but can see the real image. So real is this image that it cannot be distinguished from a real object; the rays of light as shown in the diagram diverge from I, the same as they would if the object were located there.

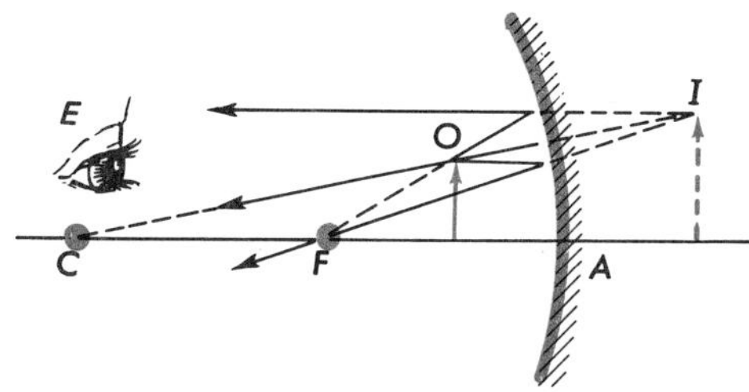

Fig. 31M. Diagram showing the formation of a virtual image.

In Fig. 31M an object is placed inside the focal point; the rays after reflection diverge as if they had come from the point I. To the eye of an observer at E, a virtual image is seen magnified and right side up at I. As a problem, let the object distance $p = 10$ cm and the focal length $f = +20$ cm. Substitution of these in Eq.(31h) gives

$$\frac{1}{10} + \frac{1}{q} = \frac{1}{20}$$

$$\frac{1}{q} = \frac{1}{20} - \frac{1}{10}$$

$$\frac{1}{q} = \frac{1}{20} - \frac{2}{20}$$

from which

$$\frac{1}{q} = -\frac{1}{20}$$

or $$q = -20 \text{ cm}$$

The image is located 20 cm from the mirror, the minus sign indicating that it is virtual and on the opposite side of the mirror from the object.

No matter where a real object is located in front of a convex mirror, the image is virtual and cannot be formed on a screen. When in using Eq.(31h) the focal length of a convex mirror is known, its value is substituted with a minus sign.

Convenient sign conventions for all spherical mirror problems, solved by the use of Eq.(31h), are the following:

(1) Numerical values of real object distances are positive.
(2) Numerical values of real image distances are positive.
(3) Numerical values of focal lengths of concave mirrors are positive, while those of convex mirrors are negative.

A formula for the size of the image formed by spherical mirrors may be derived from the geometry shown in Fig. 31K. The dashed line representing a ray from O to A is shown reflected at an equal angle to pass through the image point I. These lines form similar triangles OAM and IAN. Since corresponding sides are proportional, we may write

$$\frac{-\mathrm{IN}}{\mathrm{OM}} = \frac{q}{p}$$

Calling OM the object height O, and IN the image height I, we may write

$$\frac{I}{O} = -\frac{q}{p} \qquad (31i)$$

The minus sign has been inserted to account for the image inversion. The sign convention to be used here is that erect objects and images are positive, while inverted objects and images are negative. The ratio I/O is commonly called the *magnification,* and may be written

$$M = -\frac{q}{p} \qquad (31j)$$

In actual practice spherical mirrors are capable of forming reasonably sharp images if their apertures are small compared with their focal lengths. If the mirror sizes are large, however, the rays reflected from the outer edges cross the axis at different distances as shown at the left in Fig. 31N. This focusing defect gives rise to what is called *spherical aberration.*

A parabolic mirror on the other hand brings all rays to a focus at one point, as shown at the right. A small source of light located at the focal point of a parabolic reflector becomes a parallel beam after reflection, a principle used in spotlights, searchlights, and automobile headlights.

In all optical problems the + signs are always written into the answers as well as the − signs.

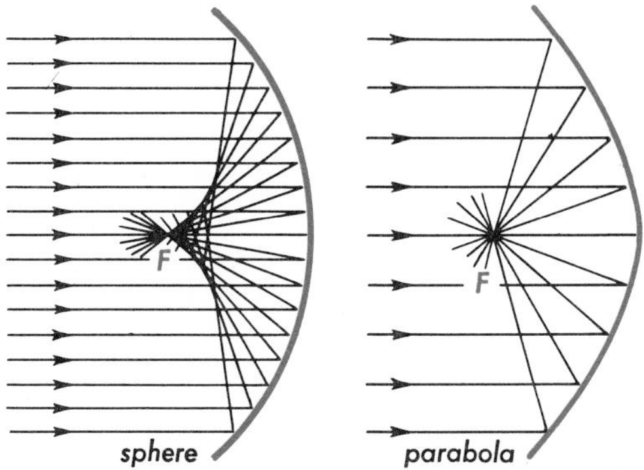

Fig. 31N. Diagrams showing the caustic curve obtained with a spherical mirror and the point focus with a parabolic mirror.

Example 2. An object 3.0 cm high is located 10.0 cm in front of a converging mirror with a focal length of +8.0 cm. Find (a) the image distance, (b) the image size, and (c) the magnification.

Solution. The given quantities are $p = +10.0$ cm, $f = +8.0$ cm, and $O = +3.0$ cm. For part (a) we can use Eq.(31h), solve for the image distance q, and substitute the given quantities:

$$q = \frac{p \times f}{p - f} = \frac{10 \times 8}{10 - 8}$$

$$q = +40.0 \text{ cm}$$

For part (b) use Eq.(31i), solve for the image size I, and substitute the appropriate known quantities, and obtain

$$I = -O\frac{q}{p} = -3\,\frac{40}{10}$$

$$I = -12.0 \text{ cm}$$

The minus sign signifies an inverted image 12.0 cm long. See the diagram in Fig. 31O. For part (c) we use Eq.(31j) and substitute known quantities:

$$M = -\frac{q}{p} = -\frac{12}{3}$$

$$M = -4.0$$

The image is inverted, and 4 times the size of the object.

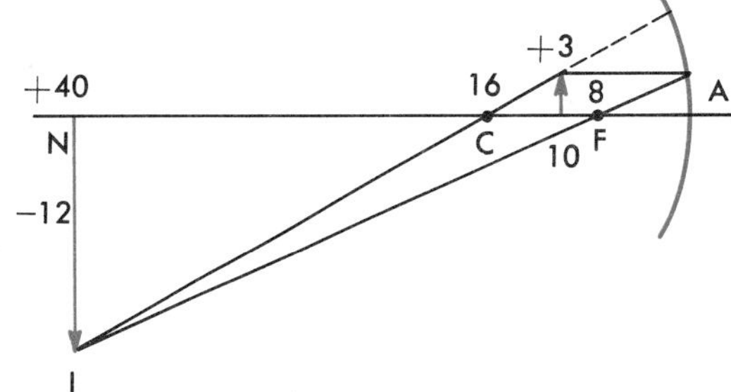

Fig. 31O. Diagram for Example 2.

---

problems

Unless otherwise instructed, use $c = 2.998 \times 10^8$ m/s.

1. If Fizeau's speed of light experiment is performed with the distant mirror 32.0 Km from the toothed wheel containing 360 teeth, how fast would the wheel have to turn for each light pulse to return through the center of the first succeeding opening?

2. One of the brightest stars in the sky is approximately 7.25 light years away. Calculate its distance from the earth in meters. One light year is the distance light travels in one year.

3. Find the speed of light in a titanium oxide crystal if the refractive index is 3.3408. [Ans. 0.897×10^8 m/s.]

4. Find the speed of light in a strontium titanate crystal if the refractive index is 2.4360.

5. The average distance to the moon is 384,000 Km from the earth. How long does it take light from the moon to reach the earth?

6. A ray of light is incident on a block of dense flint glass for which the refractive index is 2.168. Find the speed of light in the glass. [Ans. 1.383×10^8 m/s.]

7. Two mirrors are standing in a vertical position with two edges touching each other, and making an angle of 90° with each other. A point of light is located 3.0 cm from one mirror and 4.0 cm from the other. Using the law of refraction, (a) find all three images graphically, and (b) find the radius of the circle that can be drawn through all four points.

8. A concave mirror has a radius of −18.0 cm. If an object 3.0 cm high is located on the axis and 15.0 cm in front of the mirror, find (a) the image distance, (b) the image size, and (c) the magnification.

9. An object 2.50 cm high is located 15.0 cm in front of a concave mirror with a radius of −20 cm. Find (a) the image distance, (b) the image size, and (c) the magnification. [Ans. (a) +30.0 cm, (b) −5.0 cm, (c) −2.0 cm.]

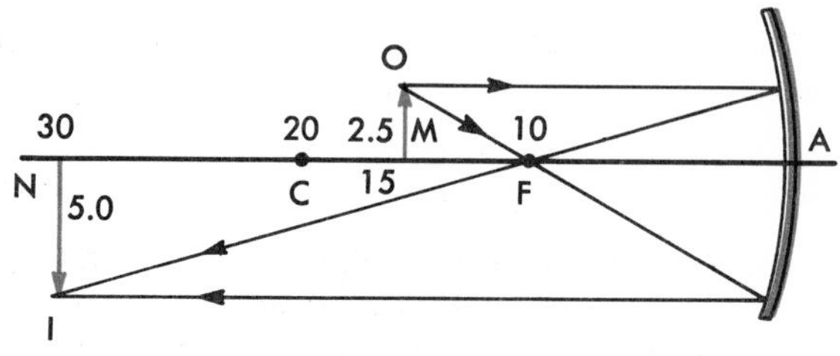

Prob. 9.

10. A concave mirror has a radius of −24.0 cm. If an object 3.0 cm high is located 30.0 cm in front of the mirror, find (a) the image position, (b) the size of the image, and (c) the magnification.

11. If an object 2.80 cm high is located 25.0 cm in front of a concave mirror with a radius of −20.0 cm, find (a) the image distance, (b) the image size, and (c) the magnification.

12. An object 2.0 cm high is located 8.0 cm in front of a concave mirror with a focal length of +10.0 cm. Find (a) the image position, (b) the image size, and (c) the magnification. [Ans. (a) −40.0 cm, (b) +10.0 cm, (c) +5.0.]

13. A concave mirror has a focal length of +8.0 cm. If an object 3.2 cm high is located on the axis 6.0 cm

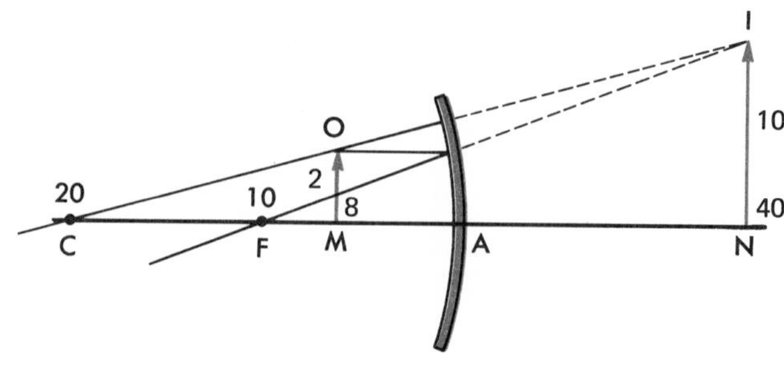

Prob. 12.

in front of the mirror, find (a) the image distance, (b) the image size, and (c) the magnification.

14. A convex mirror has a radius of +16.0 cm. An object 6.0 cm high is located 12.0 cm in front of the mirror. Find (a) the image distance, (b) the image size, and (c) the magnification.

15. An object 5.0 cm high is located 25.0 cm in front of a convex spherical mirror having a radius of +30.0 cm. Find (a) the image distance, (b) the image size, and (c) the magnification. [Ans. (a) +9.38 cm, (b) +1 875 cm, (c) +0.3752.]

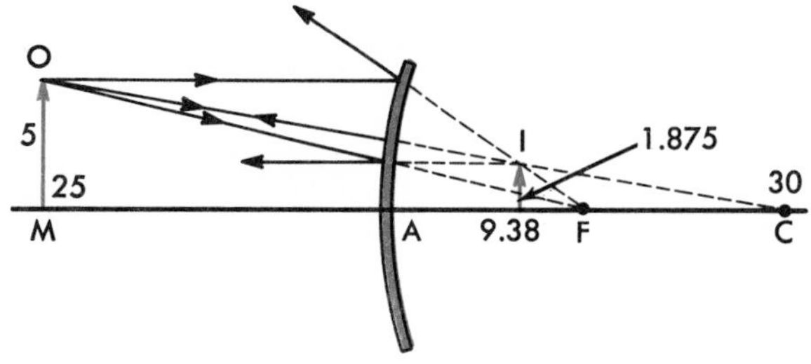

Prob. 15.

32 Refraction and dispersion

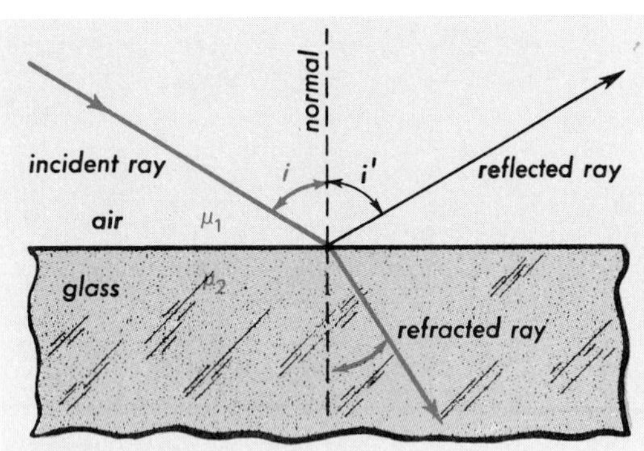

Fig. 32A. Reflection and refraction of light at the boundary of a glass surface.

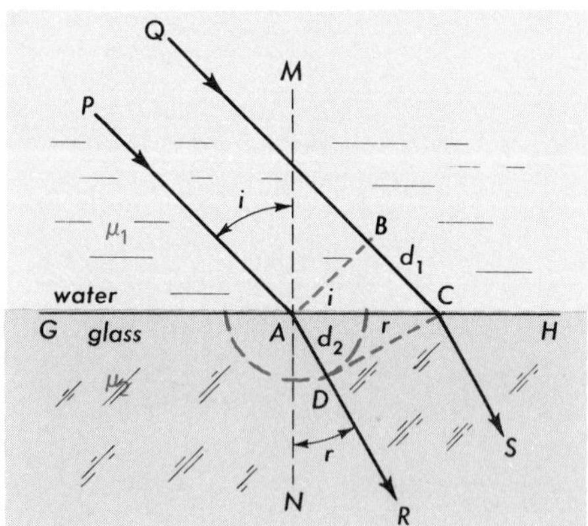

Fig. 32B. Graphical construction for refraction at a boundary separating two optical media.

Light is one of the many forms of energy, and as such, the rate at which light flows through a transparent medium is always less than the rate of flow through free space. In the previous chapter the ratio of c, the speed of light in a vacuum, to v the speed of light in any given medium, is defined as the *refractive index,* or *index of refraction:*

$$\frac{c}{v} = \mu \qquad (32a)$$

In other words, each transparent substance has its own specific refractive index.

32.1. Refraction at a Boundary

When light traveling in one medium of index μ_1 falls on the smooth boundary surface of a second medium of index μ_2, part of it is reflected according to the law of reflection and the remainder is refracted (or bent) into the medium (see Fig. 32A). The change in direction is due to the change in speed of the light as it crosses the boundary. The direction of the refracted ray, like the incident and reflected rays, is always measured by the angle it makes with the normal.

The angle of refraction, r, is found by experiment to depend upon two factors: (1) *the angle of incidence i* and (2) *the refractive indices of the two media.*

To determine the angle of refraction from these two factors, we perform the following graphical construction (see Fig. 32B). A parallel beam of light of width PQ in water is incident at an angle i on the surface of glass. From the point A where the beam first strikes the surface, a line is drawn perpendicular to the beam intersecting QC at B. Now let the distance BC $= d_1$, and with a proper radius d_2, and a center at A, describe the arc of a circle as shown. From the point C a tangent is drawn intersecting the arc at D. The refracted ray ADR is then drawn in and the other edge of the ray CS drawn parallel to it.

The magnitude of the radius d_2 is determined by noting that while the upper edge of the ray in the upper medium travels the distance d_1 with a velocity v_1, the lower edge of the ray travels in the lower medium the distance d_2 with a velocity v_2. Since these optical paths must be equal in time, we must write

$$\mu_1 d_1 = \mu_2 d_2 \qquad (32b)$$

Solving for d_2, we obtain

$$d_2 = \frac{\mu_1}{\mu_2} d_1$$

For the two right triangles ABC and ACD, we can write

$$\frac{d_1}{AC} = \sin i \qquad \frac{d_2}{AC} = \sin r$$

from which

$$d_1 = AC \sin i$$

and

$$d_2 = AC \sin r$$

Direct substitution of these values of d in Eq. (32b) gives

$$\mu_1 AC \sin i = \mu_2 AC \sin r$$

or

$$\mu_1 \sin i = \mu_2 \sin r \qquad (32c)$$

It was the Dutch astronomer and mathematician Willebrord Snell* who first discovered by experiment that this relation holds for all angles of incidence. This equation is therefore called Snell's law, and is sometimes written in the form

$$\frac{\sin i}{\sin r} = \frac{\mu_2}{\mu_1} \qquad (32d)$$

or

$$\frac{\sin i}{\sin r} = \mu \qquad (32e)$$

***Willebrord Snell (1591–1626), Dutch astronomer and mathematician, was born at Leyden in 1591. At the age of twenty-one he succeeded his father as professor of mathematics at the University of Leyden. In 1617, he determined the size of the earth from measurements of its curvature between Alkmaar and Bergen-op-Zoom. In 1621, he discovered the law of refraction which now carries his name.**

where μ is called the *relative index* between the two media, i.e., the second medium index divided by the first. Since $\mu_1 = c/v_1$ and $\mu_2 = c/v_2$, Eq.(32d) can also be written

$$\frac{\sin i}{\sin r} = \frac{v_1}{v_2} \tag{32f}$$

Example 1. Light, in air, is incident at an angle of 45° on the surface of a glass plate for which the refractive index is 1.5260. Through what angle is the light deviated upon refraction at the top surface?

Solution. The given quantities are $i = 45.0°$, $\mu_1 = 1.0$, and $\mu_2 = 1.5260$. First we find the angle of refraction r by the use of Eq.(32d). Solving for $\sin r$, and substituting given values, we obtain

$$\sin r = \frac{\mu_1}{\mu_2} \sin i = \frac{1.0}{1.5260} 0.70711$$

$$\sin r = 0.4634$$

$$r = 27.61°$$

Since the deviation of the light is given by the difference between the angle i and the angle r, we obtain

$$i - r = 45.0° - 27.61° = 17.39°$$

32.2. Displacement in a Parallel Plate

One very useful principle concerning the behavior of light is *the reversibility of light rays. If, in any of the experiments or illustrations already described, the light rays could be reversed in direction, they would be found to retrace their paths exactly.*

If a beam of light, on being refracted into a denser medium like glass, is bent toward the normal, the light passing through and out of this denser medium into the air should be bent away from the normal. This can be demonstrated by sending light through a plane-parallel plate of glass as illustrated in Fig. 32C. In (c) the light is incident on the first surface at an angle i and is refracted at an angle r. This internal ray is now incident on the second surface at the same angle r and is refracted into the air at the same angle i. The light thus emerges in a direction parallel to the original beam, but laterally displaced from it.

This lateral displacement is zero for normal incidence as in diagram (a) and increases with the angle i as shown in diagrams (b), (c), and (d), respectively. If the parallel plate is very thin, as in the case of an ordinary windowpane, the displacement is quite small and for most practical purposes can be neglected.

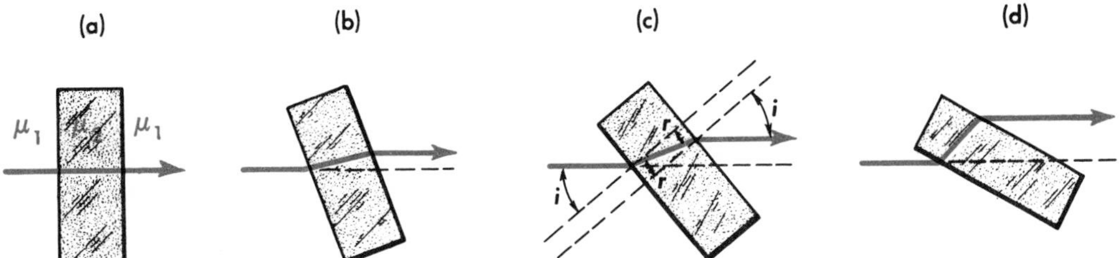

Fig. 32C. Illustration of the lateral displacement of a beam of light as it passes through a parallel plate of glass.

A detailed drawing showing the geometry of the refraction of light at both boundaries of a thick parallel plate will enable the reader to apply Snell's law, and the simple elements of trigonometry to derive the following equation:

$$x = t \sin i \left(1 - \frac{\mu_1 \cos i}{\mu_2 \cos r}\right) \quad (32g)$$

where x is the lateral displacement between the incident and transmitted rays, t is the plate thickness, i is the angle of incidence, r is the angle of refraction, and μ_1 and μ_2 are the refractive indices of the air and the plate, respectively.

32.3. Refraction by a Prism

When light passes through a prism, it is refracted at two surfaces, once on the way in and once on the way out. If the two sides involved are parellel, as they are in Fig. 32D, diagram (a), the emergent ray is always parallel to the incident ray. If the sides are not parallel, as in diagrams (b), (c), and (d), the emergent ray has a different direction. The larger the angle A between the two refracting surfaces, the larger is the angle of deviation D. Upon entering the prism at the first surface [see diagram (d)], the light is bent toward the normal. Emerging into the air from the second surface, the light is bent away from the normal. Note in Fig. 32D that neither the apex nor the base of the prism has any effect on the deviation of the light.

In verifying these results by experiment, light of only one color should be used, because white light will spread out into a spectrum of colors. Light of one color only is readily obtained by inserting a piece of red or green colored glass into a beam of white light.

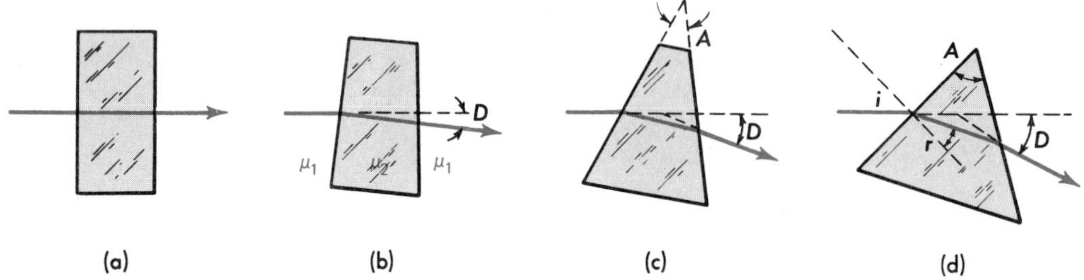

Fig. 32D. Illustration of the bending of a beam of light by prisms made of the same glass.

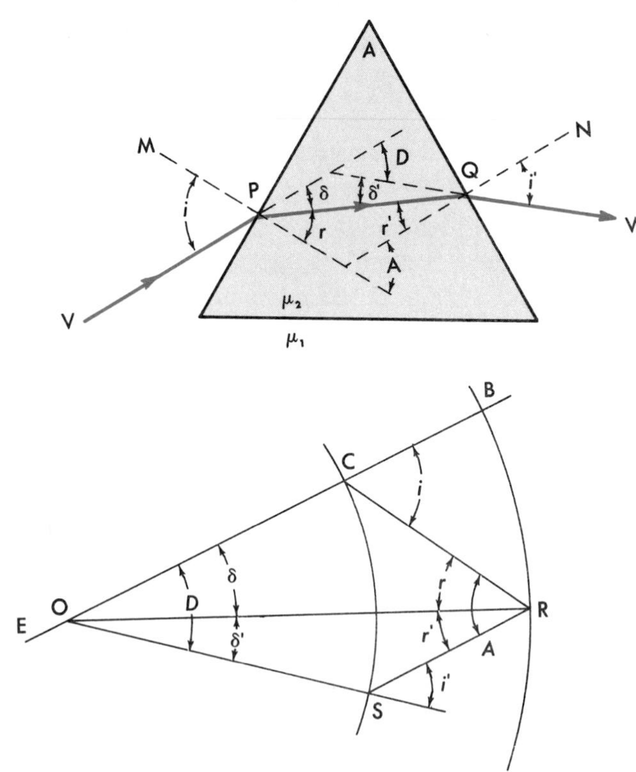

Fig. 32E. Graphical construction for refraction by a prism.

A relatively simple graphical method of tracing a given ray of light through a prism is shown in Fig. 32E. Here we have a ray of light VP in air incident at an angle i on the first face of a prism of angle A and refractive index μ_2. In this diagram $A = 60°$, $\mu_2 = 1.5$, and $i = 60°$.

Starting at one side, a line EF is first drawn parallel to the incident ray VP. With a center at any point O, and with radii, in this particular case, of 1.0 unit and 1.5 units, arcs CS and BR are drawn of indefinite length. From the intersection C a line is now drawn parallel to the normal M, intersecting the second arc at R. The line OR is drawn next, and from the point P of the prism a parallel line is drawn intersecting the second face at Q. Starting at R, a line is next drawn parallel to the normal N, intersecting the first arc at S. Finally the line OS is drawn in, and from the point Q on the second prism face a parallel line QW is drawn as the emergent ray.

In triangle OCR the length of side OC is 1.00 for air, the length of side OR is 1.50 for μ_2, and the angle opposite side OR is $180° - i$. If we now apply the laws of sines to this triangle, we can write

$$\frac{\sin\,(180° - i)}{\mu_2} = \frac{\sin r}{\mu_1}$$

The sine of any angle i is always equal to the sine of 180° minus that same angle. Therefore,

$$\frac{\sin i}{\mu_2} = \frac{\sin r}{\mu_1}$$

from which we obtain

$$\frac{\sin i}{\sin r} = \frac{\mu_1}{\mu_2}$$

The same derivation can be applied to the triangle ORS.

Since the above construction obeys Snell's law, the accuracy of the graphical results depends upon the sharpness of the pencil used and the care with which the diagram is made. Furthermore, the lower diagram as well as the prism diagram contains all of the angles involved in the prism, including the angle of deviation D.

Example 2. A ray of light incident at an angle of 56° on one surface of a glass prism is refracted into the prism, and out into the air through the second surface. If the angle between these two surfaces is 60°, and the refractive index is 1.6250, find the total deviation of the light ray.

Solution. The given quantities are $i = 56°$, $A = 60°$, and $\mu = 1.6250$. Using both diagrams in Fig. 32E, we first find the refractive angle r at the first surface by applying Eq.(32e). Solving for sin r, and substituting known quantities, we find

$$\sin r = \frac{\sin i}{\mu} = \frac{0.8290}{1.6250} = 0.5102$$

which gives

$$r = 30.68°$$

Subtracting r from A gives

$$r' = 29.32°$$

Solving Eq. (32e) for sin i, and changing unprimed terms by primed terms, and substituting known quantities, we find

$$\sin i' = \mu \sin r' = 1.6250 \times 0.4897$$

$$\sin i' = 0.7958$$

which gives $$i' = 52.73°$$

Since $i = \delta + r$, and $i' = \delta' + r'$, subtraction of known angles gives

$$\delta = 25.32° \qquad \text{and} \qquad \delta' = 23.41°$$

And since $D = \delta + \delta'$, we find

$$D = 48.73°$$

The light ray has been deviated through an angle of 48.73°.

32.4. Critical Angle

When light passes from a less dense medium, such as air, into a more dense medium, like glass or water, the angle of refraction is always less than the angle of incidence. As a result of this decrease in angle, there exists a range of angles for which there is no refracted light. To see what this range of angles is, consider the diagram in Fig 32F, where for several angles of incidence the corresponding angles of refraction are shown. It is to be noted that, in the limiting case where the incident rays approach the angle of 90°, i.e., where they graze along the surface, the refracted rays approach a certain angle C, beyond which no refracted light is possible. For a boundary separating any two media this limiting angle, called *the critical angle,* depends for its value upon the indices of refraction.

To calculate the critical angle of refraction, one takes the angle of incidence $i = 90°$ and angle r = angle C. Since $\sin 90° = 1$, Snell's law becomes

$$\frac{\mu_2}{\mu_1} = \frac{1}{\sin C}$$

or

$$\sin C = \frac{\mu_1}{\mu_2} \tag{32h}$$

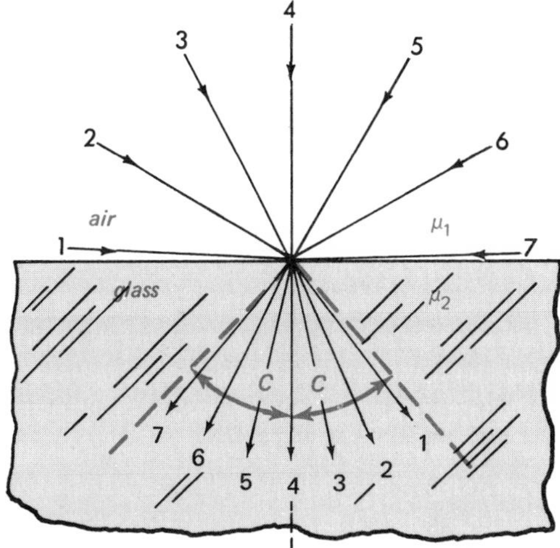

Fig. 32F. Diagram illustrating the critical angle.

For the most common of crown glass $\mu_2 = 1.515$, and with $\mu_2 = 1.000$ for air substitution in this formula gives $C = 41.3°$. For water of index $\mu_2 = 1.33$, it gives $C = 49°$. It should be noted in particular that the critical angle is measured from the normal, and not from the refracting surface.

Example 3. Calculate the critical angle for a crystal of rutile, TiO_2, for which the refractive index for violet light is 3.3408.
Solution. The known quantity is $\mu = 3.3408$. By direct substitution in Eq.(32h), we obtain

$$\sin C = \frac{1}{\mu} = \frac{1}{3.3408} = 0.29933$$

which, from a table of sines, gives

$$C = 17.42°$$

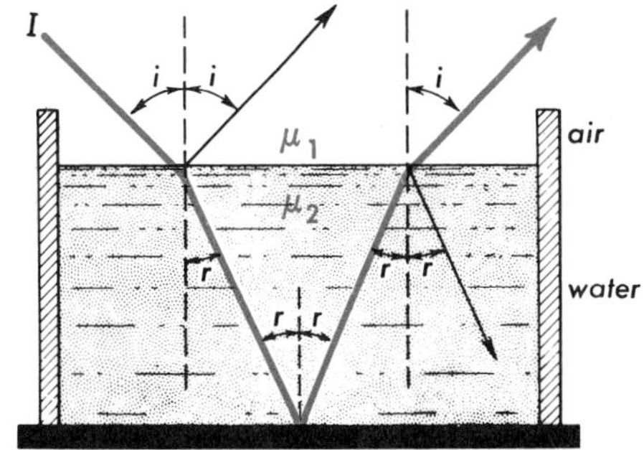

Fig. 32G. Illustration of reflection and refraction.

32.5. Total Reflection

Another experiment illustrating the reversibility of light rays is shown in the diagram of Fig. 32G. A beam of light is refracted

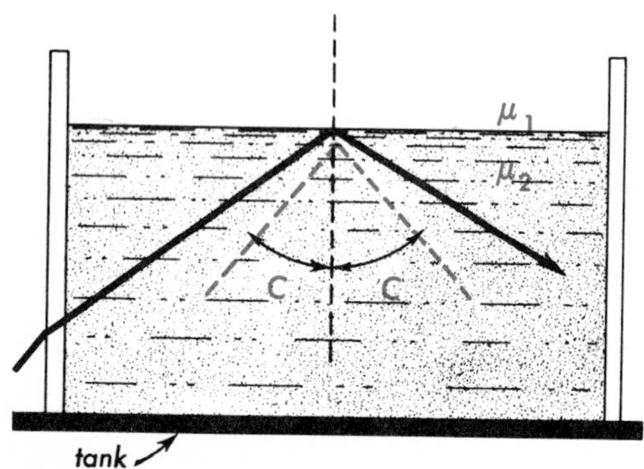

Fig. 32H. Illustration of total reflection and the critical angle *C*.

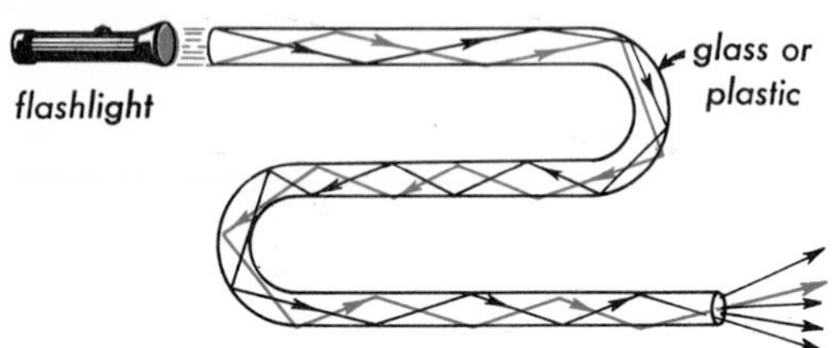

Fig. 31I. Light follows a bent rod by total reflection.

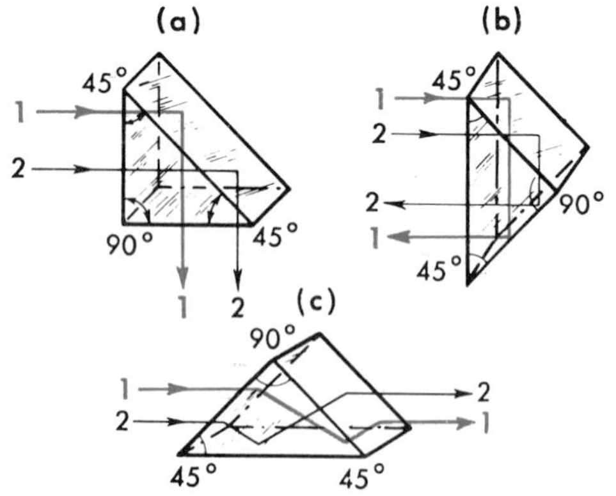

Fig. 32J. Total-reflection prisms.

at an angle *r* into a tank of water. From there it is reflected from a silvered mirror at the bottom of the tank, illustrating the law of reflection in a medium other than air. The reflected ray arriving at the upper surface at the same angle *r* is refracted into the air at the incident angle *i*. At each refraction at the air-water boundary, a small amount of the incident light is reflected, as indicated by the fine-lined arrows.

When a beam of light within a medium like water or glass approaches the surface at an angle greater than the critical angle, all of the light is reflected back into the medium. In other words, a water-to-air or glass-to-air surface acts under these conditions like a perfect reflector. This phenomenon is called *total internal reflection.* Since no light can be refracted into the water at such an angle (see Fig. 32F), none inside the water at large angles of incidence can be refracted out. The experiment is illustrated with a tank of water as shown in Fig. 32H. If light is sent into the water through a glass plate in one end, the light approaches the upper surface at an angle greater than *C*, and is totally reflected back into the water as shown.

An interesting demonstration can be performed with a clear glass or plastic rod bent into almost any form as shown in Fig. 32I. Light, on entering one end, reflects from wall to wall by total reflection, causing it to follow the rod to the end and emerge as a divergent beam. Various instruments used by physicians and surgeons employ this principle for internal body observations.

A whole new field of optics known as *fiber optics* has developed out of this principle in the last few years. Thousands of long thin glass fibers are bundled together to form a stranded cable. Each end of this cable is securely clamped in a ring and the two ends are ground and polished flat. A lens is then used to focus a sharply defined image on one end. The light entering each fiber then travels along to the other end, where the same orderly array of fiber ends reproduces the image.

Another demonstration consists of placing a lighted tungsten lamp in the bottom of a pitcher of water and pouring the water slowly into a larger vessel. The light follows the stream of water and produces an interesting display of light where it splashes into the other vessel. (Care should be taken to avoid electrical shock from this experiment.)

Total reflection is also employed in optical instruments such as telescopes, microscopes, prism binoculars, spectroscopes, etc. The optical parts employing this principle are known as *total reflection prisms.* Such prisms are usually made of common glass with one angle a right angle and the other two 45° angles. As illustrated in Fig. 32J, there are three ways in which these prisms may be used. Incident normally upon the first surface, as in (a), the light enters the prism without deviation. Arriving at the second surface at an angle of 45°, just 3° greater than the critical angle, the light is totally reflected according to the law of reflection. Having thus been deviated through 90°, the light passes normally through the third surface without further deviation. The prism has therefore acted like a plane mirror with its reflecting surface at 45°.

In diagram (b), the light enters normally near one end of the long diagonal face of the prism. When it arrives at the second surface at 45°, total reflection takes place exactly as in diagram (a). A second reflection occurs at the third surface, sending the light out near the bottom of, and normal to, the first surface. The light has thus been reversed in direction. Used in this way, the prism performs the function of two prisms, each used as in diagram (a).

In diagram (c) the light enters the first prism face at an angle. After refraction, the light is totally reflected from the second face and then refracted out of the third surface to be parallel to the original beam. Used in this way the prism is called an *erecting prism.* The incident ray, 1, which is on top, reverses its position and emerges from the prism at the bottom.

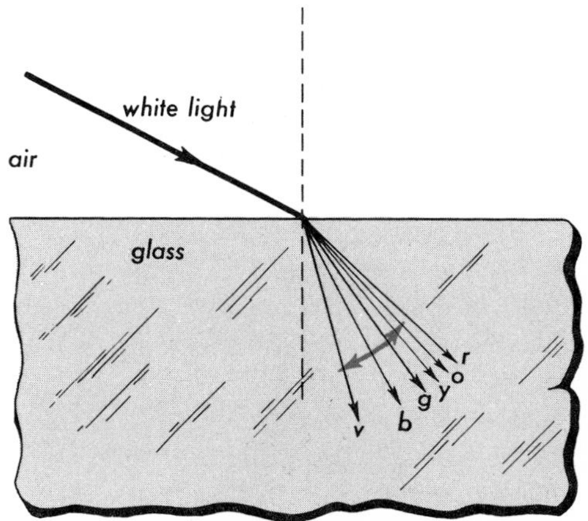

Fig. 32K. Refraction of white sunlight into its spectrum colors.

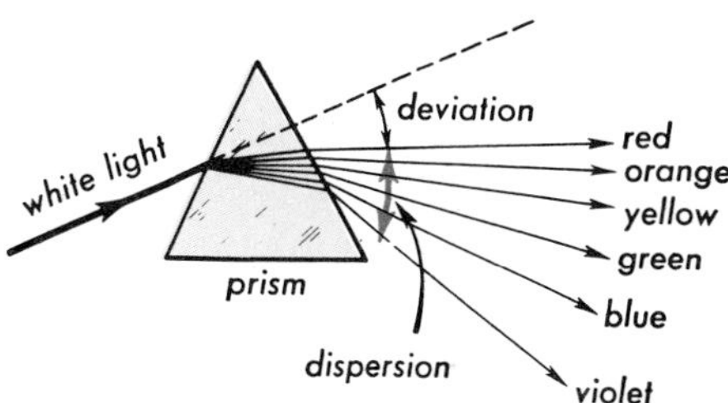

Fig. 32L. Refraction at both surfaces of a prism produces dispersion.

32.6. Dispersion

The passage of sunlight through many precious and semi-precious stones, and through transparent crystals and prisms of glass, produces colors of great brilliance. Observing that emeralds are always green and rubys are always red, it was believed by the early philosophers that the spectral colors exhibited by diamonds must somehow come from within the crystal itself.

The first demonstration that the spectrum colors, seen when sunlight passes through a glass prism, are already present in the white sunlight was put forward by Newton. He clearly demonstrated that the function of the prism was simply to separate the different colors already present. It may be seen in Fig 32K how, *with white light, incident at an angle on the smooth surface of a piece of glass, each color is refracted by a different amount* to produce its own angle of deviation. *Red light is refracted least and violet light is refracted most.* The angular spread of all the colors produced by sending white light through a prism is called the *dispersion* and the band of color so produced is called *a spectrum* (see Fig. 32L).

If white light is sent through a group of similar prisms made of different substances, each prism will be found to have a

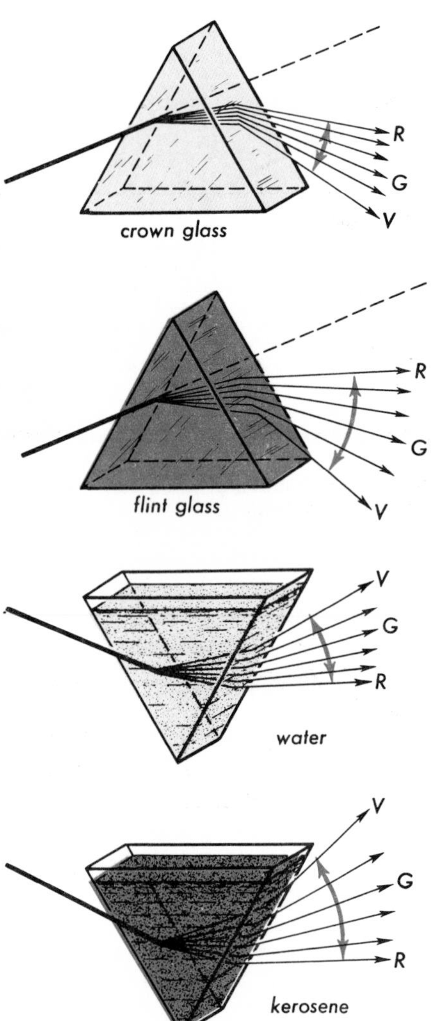

Fig. 32M. Illustration of the relative dispersions of solid as well as liquid prisms.

different dispersion. This can be demonstrated for solids by *flint* and *crown-glass prisms,* and for liquids by *kerosene, carbon bisulfide,* and *water.* It will be noted that the two glass prisms in Fig. 32M, one of flint glass and the other of crown glass, produce quite different dispersions. The liquid prisms, produced by filling thin-walled glass troughs with liquid, also disperse light by different amounts.

Since different colors are refracted by different amounts, the index of refraction is different for each color. In a vacuum all colors travel with the same speed, 3.0×10^8 m/s, but in a transparent medium, like glass or water, they travel considerably slower and at different speeds. Among the spectrum colors, red travels the fastest and violet the slowest, with the speeds of all other colors somewhere in between. In air there is very little dispersion and in a vacuum there is absolutely none. This latter statement is proved by the fact that, when the dark star of an eclipsing binary passes in front of its brighter companion, all colors disappear and reappear simultaneously. If one color were to travel slightly faster than another, the dip in stellar intensity for that color would have plenty of time in its many years of travel to the earth to get ahead.

The refractive indices for a number of transparent solids are given in Table 32A. It will be noted that, although the values for any one substance do not vary greatly between colors, the values for blue and violet are the largest and those for orange and red are the smallest. Note the relatively high values for diamond and strontium titanate and the relatively low values for ice.

The wavelengths of the different colors of light are given in angstrom units, where

$$1 \text{ angstrom} = 1 \text{ Å} = 10^{-10} \text{ m} \qquad (32i)$$

or

$$10^{10} \text{ Å} = 1 \text{ m}$$

(For a discussion of the angstrom unit, see Sec. 35.5.)

In the physics laboratory the index of refraction is determined with a prism, usually one having an angle of 60°. The prism is placed on a spectrometer where the spectrum of white light is observed in a small telescope, and the angles of refraction are measured separately for each color.

A quantitative measure of the *dispersion* of transparent materials is obtained by the following relation:

$$\text{dispersion constant} = \frac{\mu_V - \mu_R}{\mu_Y - 1} \qquad (32j)$$

where μ_R, μ_Y, and μ_V are the refractive indices for *red, yellow,* and *violet* light, respectively. The numerator is a direct measure of *angular spread* ϕ between the two ends of the spectrum, and the denominator is a direct measure of θ, the *deviation* of light (see Fig. 32L). The angle θ represents the *average deviation* of the spectrum.

TABLE 32A
Refractive index for several transparent solids

Substance	Violet 4100 Å	Blue 4700 Å	Green 5500 Å	Yellow 5800 Å	Orange 6100 Å	Red 6600 Å
	Color wavelength λ in angstroms					
Crown glass	1.5380	1.5310	1.5260	1.5225	1.5216	1.5200
Light flint	1.6040	1.5960	1.5910	1.5875	1.5867	1.5850
Dense flint	1.6980	1.6836	1.6738	1.6670	1.6650	1.6620
Quartz	1.5570	1.5510	1.5468	1.5438	1.5432	1.5420
Diamond	2.4580	2.4439	2.4260	2.4172	2.4150	2.4100
Ice	1.3170	1.3136	1.3110	1.3087	1.3080	1.3060
Strontium titanate, $SrTiO_3$	2.6310	2.5106	2.4360	2.4170	2.3977	2.3740
Rutile, TiO_2	3.3408	3.1031	2.9460	2.9072	2.8894	2.3742

Example 4. Find the value of the dispersion constant for diamond.
Solution. Using the refractive indices for diamond given in Table 32A, and substituting directly in Eq.(32j), we obtain

$$\text{disp. const.} = \frac{2.4580 - 2.4100}{2.4172 - 1.0000}$$

$$= \frac{0.0480}{1.4172} = 0.03387$$

32.7. Prism Combinations

While substances that produce large deviations also produce large dispersions, the two properties are by no means proportional to each other. If a flint-glass prism, for example, produces twice the dispersion of a crown-glass prism, it is not true that the deviation of each color by the flint prism is twice that of the crown-glass prism. Useful devices illustrating this fact can be demonstrated by combining two prisms in opposition as shown in Fig. 32N.

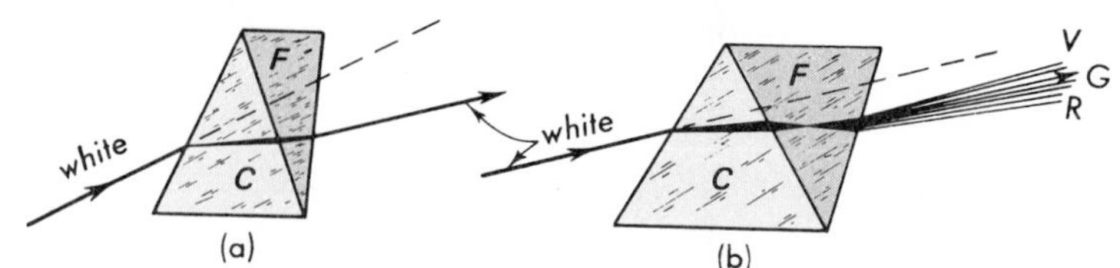

Fig. 32N. Prism combinations: (a) achromatic prism giving deviation without dispersion, (b) direct-vision prism giving dispersion without deviation.

For the achromatic combination in (a), the angles of both prisms are so selected that each prism alone will produce the same total dispersion. Since flint glass has the higher dispersive power, the flint prism will have a smaller angle as shown. Placed in opposition, the crown glass spreads the colors out and the flint prism bends them back parallel to each other again. Since the deviation produced by the two prisms is not the same, light will emerge as white light but in a different direction from that in which it first entered.

For the direct-vision combination in (b), the angles of the prisms are so selected that each prism alone will produce the same deviation for green light. For two such matched prisms the flint prism will produce the greater dispersion. Combined in opposition, the green light comes out on the far side, parallel to the incident white light on the left and the other spectrum colors on either side as shown.

32.8. The Rainbow

The rainbow is nature's most spectacular display of the spectrum of white light. The required conditions for the appearance of the phenomenon are that the sun be shining in one part of the sky and the rain be falling in the opposite part of the sky. Turning one's back to the sun, the bright primary bow and sometimes the fainter secondary bow, with colors reversed, are seen as the arcs of circles. From a high vantage point or an airplane, these bows may form complete circles whose common center lies in the direction of the observer's shadow.

The elementary theory of the rainbow was first given by Antonius de Demini in the year 1611 and later developed more exactly by Descartes. The general characteristics of the *primary* and *secondary bows* are satisfactorily accounted for by considering only the reflection and refraction of light by spherical raindrops. To understand how the phenomenon arises, we first confine our attention to an individual raindrop as shown in Fig. 32O. A ray of sunlight is shown entering a single raindrop at a point A near the top. At this point some of the light is reflected (not shown), and the remainder refracted into the liquid sphere. At this first refraction the light is dispersed into its spectrum colors, violet being deviated the most and red the least.

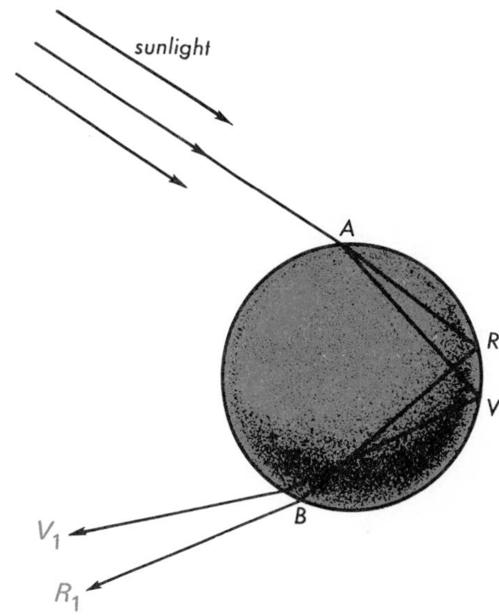

Fig. 32O. Dispersion of sunlight by a single raindrop. (Primary rainbow.)

Arriving at the opposite side of the drop, each color is partly refracted out into the air (not shown) and partly reflected back into the liquid. Reaching the surface at the lower boundary, each color is again reflected (not shown) and refracted. This second refraction is quite similar to that of a prism shown in Fig. 32L, where refraction at the second surface increases the dispersion already produced at the first. This is the path of the light in thousands of drops giving rise to the bright primary rainbow.

In Fig. 32P, a ray of sunlight, coming from the same direction as in Fig. 32P, is shown entering a single raindrop at a point C near the bottom. After one refraction and two internal reflections the light is again refracted and dispersed, this time in a direction not greatly different from that in Fig. 32P. This is the path of the light in thousands of drops giving rise to the fainter secondary rainbow with its colors reversed.

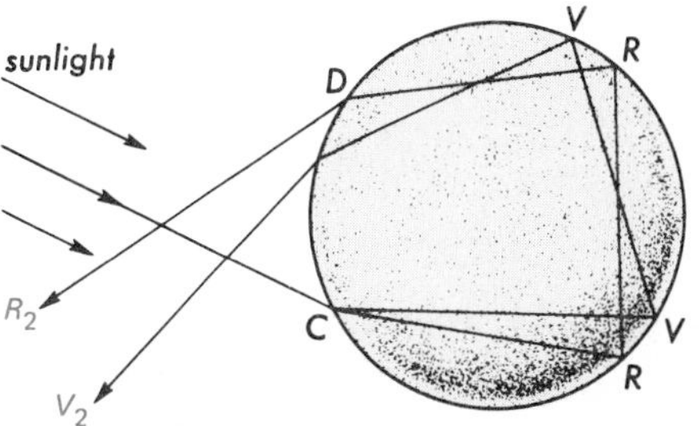

Fig. 32P. Dispersion of sunlight by a single raindrop. (Secondary rainbow.)

Of all the sun's rays falling on one face of each individual drop, only a small part of them are responsible for the main features of both rainbows. The reason for excluding the others will be explained in later paragraphs. Assuming for the present that the two rays shown are the only rays to be considered, let us see why the bows appear as they do in the sky.

As shown in Fig. 32Q, the primary bow appears inside the secondary bow and arises from sunlight entering the tops of drops properly located. Those in a region R_1 refract red light toward the observer's eye at O, and the violet and other colors over his head. Drops in the region of V_1 refract violet light to the observer's eye at O, and the red and other colors toward his feet. In other words, the light seen from any one drop is only one color, all drops giving this color lying on the arc of a circle. The reason they lie on the arc of a circle is that the angle between the incident sunlight and the refracted light of any one color is of necessity the same for each drop. In the primary bow, this angle is 42° for the red light and 40° for the violet.

The secondary bow is formed by similar reasoning and appears at higher angles of elevation, and with the colors reversed. The angles subtended by the secondary bow are 50° for the red and 54° for the violet.

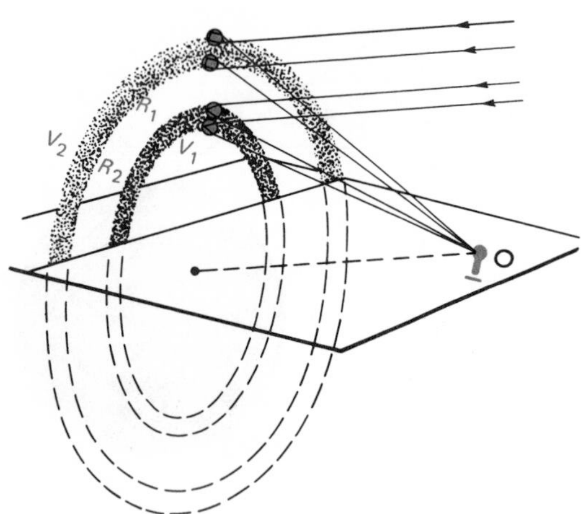

Fig. 32Q. The primary and secondary rainbows as seen by an observer at *O*.

32.9. The Theory of the Rainbow

The complete theory of the rainbow was first proposed by Thomas Young, and later worked out in detail by Potter and Airy. To understand why the particular rays shown in Fig. 32P are responsible for the rainbow, and that other rays which certainly enter the drop can be neglected, see Fig. 32R. Here, in the parallel beam of sunlight entering a single drop, our attention is confined to the rays of only one color. By this simplification, the phenomenon of dispersion is dispensed with and we consider only the reflection and refraction of red light. As each of the parallel red rays A, B, C, etc., from the sun enter the drop, they are deviated according to the law of refraction. At the opposite side of the drop, in the region d to u″, these rays are partly reflected to the lower left boundary at a′, b′, c′, etc., where, by refraction, they pass out into the air in the directions of A′, B′, C′, etc., respectively, and are partly refracted in the direction of a″, b″, c″, etc., respectively.

From the diagram it will be noted that a ray like A, entering at the very edge of the drop, is deviated through an angle close to 180°, that is, it emerges in almost the opposite direction to that in which it entered. The same is true of a ray like Q nearer the center of the drop. Ray U is exactly reversed in direction and therefore deviated exactly 180°. Ray D, on the other hand, is seen to be deviated least of all and is therefore referred to as the ray at minimum deviation. In going from A to U with the incident light, the emergent light is deviated less and less until it reaches a minimum for D′ and then increases again, reaching 180° with the axial ray UU′. The net result of this behavior is seen to be a slight crowding together of a considerable number of nearly parallel rays at minimum deviation where the light emerges as an intense and nearly parallel beam B′ to G′.

It should be noted that raindrops are spheres and not circles, as represented in the figures, and that the refracted rays emerge as cones of light. If Fig. 32R is rotated about the axial ray UU′, the emerging rays A′, B′, C′, etc., are confined to a cone bounded at the edges by the rays that have suffered the least deviation. In the direction of D′, the edge of the cone, the radiation is very intense, and inside the cone the rays are divergent and the radiation feeble. Outside the cone there is no light. Thus the selected ray A of the incident light in Fig. 32P is the ray D in Fig. 32R.

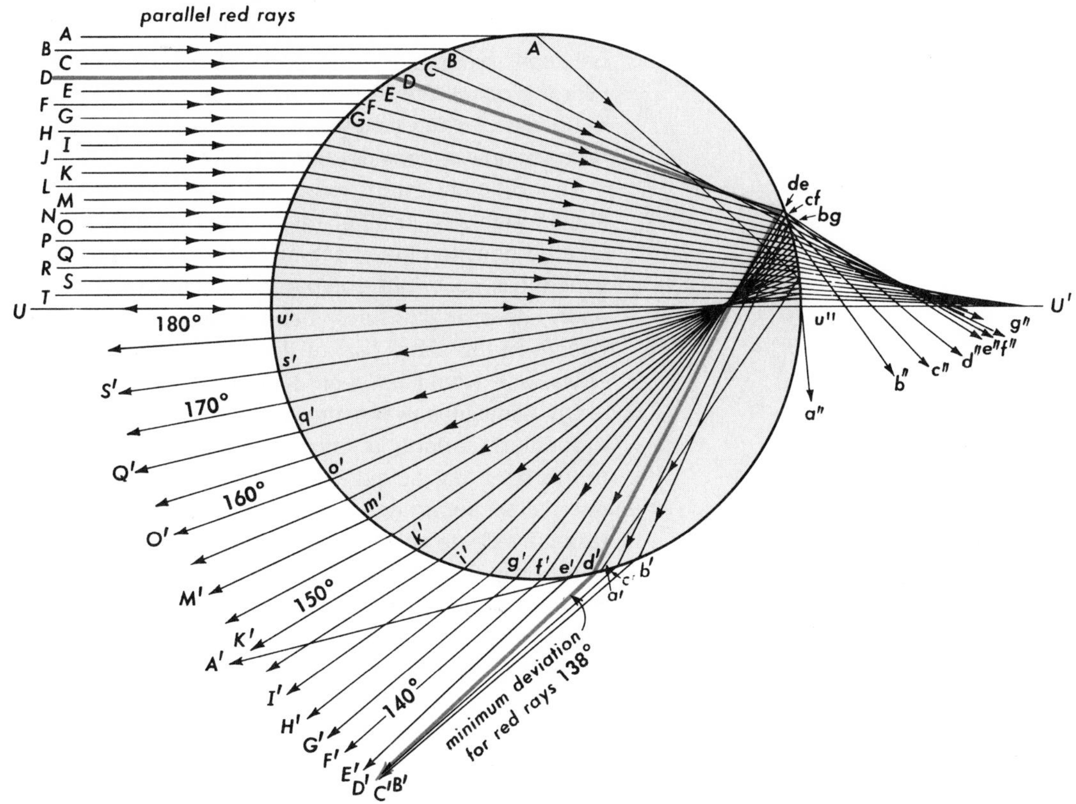

Fig. 32R. Illustration of the refraction and reflection of light by a single raindrop and the minimum deviation of certain rays that produce the primary rainbow.

Similar diagrams for other colors lead to angles of minimum deviation and cones of light whose angles decrease in the order of the spectral colors: red, orange, yellow, green, blue, and violet. An experimental demonstration of this can be made by sending a beam of parallel light from a carbon arc through a round glass bulb filled with water. The refracted cones of light falling on a screen in back of the arc source form a complete primary rainbow. Outside this primary bow, and with colors reversed, is the fainter secondary bow.

To understand the secondary rainbow, additional rays must be added to Fig. 32R. Internally reflected rays from the points a′, b′, c′, etc., are drawn up to where they again strike the surface of the drop and are there refracted out into the air. Out of these rays, a given set of rays, like those for the primary bow, will have a preferred direction in which the light is most intense. When the figure is rotated about the axial line UU′, the rays form a secondary cone of light, the inner edge of which is sharply defined.

It is interesting to point out that no light emerges in the region between the primary and secondary cones of light. This agrees with the observations that the region between the two rainbows is quite dark, whereas outside the secondary bow and inside the primary bow a considerable amount of light is visible.

Theoretically three, four, and five reflections within raindrops should give rise to other rainbows. The third and fourth bows are located between the observer and the sun and, because the direct sunlight is so bright compared with the faint bows, the phenomenon has probably never been observed. The fifth bow, however, occurs in the same part of the sky as the primary and secondary bows, and would be seen except for the faintness of the light.

On occasions when the primary and secondary rainbows are particularly bright, a third bow just inside the primary, and a fourth bow just outside the secondary bow, may be seen. These are called supernumerary bows, and are due to peculiar interference effects of light (see Chap. 35). This interference occurs between pairs of rays that are parallel to each other on emergence, but which have traveled different paths within the drop. Such pairs of rays, for example, are D′ and E′, C′ and F′, B′ and G′, and A′ and Q′. The two rays in each of these pairs are just those that cross each other at the reflecting surface d to u″; they are therefore symmetrical with the corresponding incident pairs of rays.

problems

Note: Use five-place trigonometry tables for problems in this chapter.

1. Blue light is incident at an angle of 42° on the smooth surface of a diamond. Find the angle of refraction (a) graphically, and (b) by calculation. See Table 32A for the refractive index.

2. A ray of green light is incident at an angle of 75° on a block of dense flint glass. Find the angle of refraction (a) graphically, and (b) by calculation.

3. Red light is incident at an angle of 65° on a block of plastic for which the refractive index is 1.5290. Find the angle of refraction (a) graphically, and (b) by calculation. [Ans. 36.35°.]

4. A plate of glass with parallel sides is 18.0 cm thick and has a refractive index for yellow light of 1.5225. If a ray of yellow light enters one side at an angle of 68.5°, find the lateral displacement of the emergent ray (a) graphically, and (b) by calculation.

5. A clear block of ice with parallel sides is 41.2 cm thick. Ice has a refractive index for green light of 1.3110. If a ray of green light enters one side of the block at an incident angle of 70.0°, find the lateral displacement of the light emerging from the other side (a) graphically, and (b) by calculation.

6. A rectangular aquarium with thin plate glass walls and filled with water is 22.5 cm thick. Calculate (a) the lateral displacement of a beam of green light incident

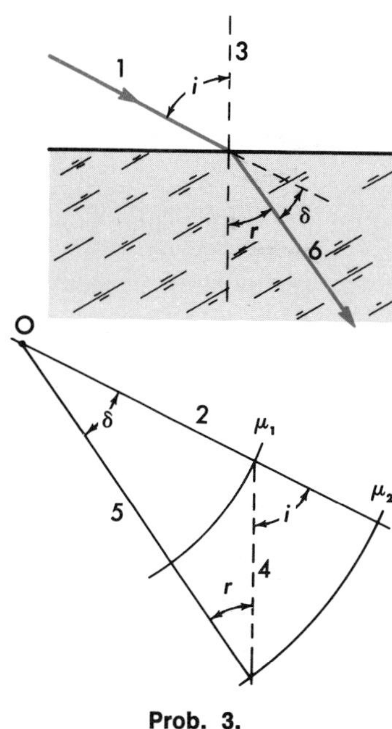

Prob. 3.

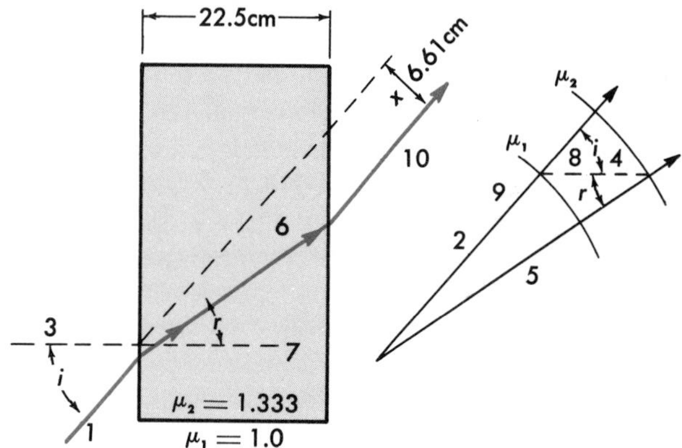

Prob. 6.

on one side at an angle of incidence of 48°. Assume the refractive index of water to be 1.3330. (b) Solve graphically as a check on your answer. Neglect the glass. [Ans. 6.610 cm.]

7.* A flint glass prism with a refractive index of 1.7300 for orange light has a refracting angle of 56°. If a ray of orange is incident on one surface at 60°, find the deviation of the emergent ray (a) graphically, and (b) by calculation.

8.* A crown glass prism has a refracting angle of 55°. Find the angle of deviation for a ray of yellow light, incident on one surface at an angle of 50°. Use the refractive index given in Table 32A. Solve (a) graphically, and (b) by calculation.

9. Find the critical angle for a piece of optical glass having a refractive index of 1.4550. [Ans. 43.42°.]

10. If the critical angle for a piece of crown glass is 42.0°, find the refractive index.

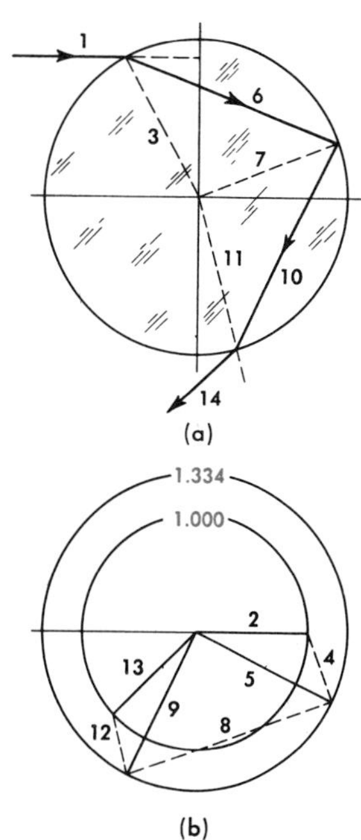

Prob. 15.
Graphical solution for Problem 15. (a) Ray diagram. (b) Construction diagram following method described in Sec. 32.8.

11. Calculate the value of the dispersion constant for dense flint glass of the kind given in Table 32A.

12. Find the dispersion constant for a rutile crystal. See Table 32A. [Ans. 0.5068.]

13. Determine the value of the dispersion constant for strontium titanate. See Table 32A.

14.* A ray of red light is incident on a spherical drop of water as shown in Fig. 32R. Find the angle of deviation for a ray like I, at a distance $\frac{3}{5}$ the way up from the center. Assume a refractive index of 1.3320.

15.* Violet light is incident on a spherical drop of water as shown in Fig. 32R. Find the angle of deviation (a) graphically, and (b) by calculation, for a ray 9/10 the way up from the center toward the top. Assume a refractive index of 1.3340 and one internal reflection. [Ans. 138.6°.]

33 Lenses

History tells us that the lens is a very old optical instrument dating back at least 500 years B.C. One historical account states that a converging lens of rock crystal is known to have been found in the ruins of Nineveh, and another that "burning glasses" were manufactured by the Greeks in large quantities several centuries B.C.

Today lenses are used in thousands of optical devices and instruments, of which some of the most common are: *cameras, picture projectors, microscopes, telescopes, binoculars, periscopes, range finders, transits, magnifiers, and lasers.*

The primary function of a lens is to form images of real objects. Although most lenses are made of common glass, a few special lenses are made of other transparent materials like fused and crystal *quartz,* plastics, and crystal *fluorite.* To understand the principles upon which a lens functions, imagine a set of several matched prisms and blocks of glass arranged in the order shown in Fig. 33A. In the first arrangement, the prisms are made so as to refract the incoming parallel light rays and to converge them to a point at F. In the second arrangement, the parallel rays are made to diverge as if they had come from a common point F′. In each system the greatest deviation occurs at the outermost prisms, for they have the greatest angle between the two refracting surfaces. No deviation occurs for the central rays, for at that point the glass faces are parallel to each other.

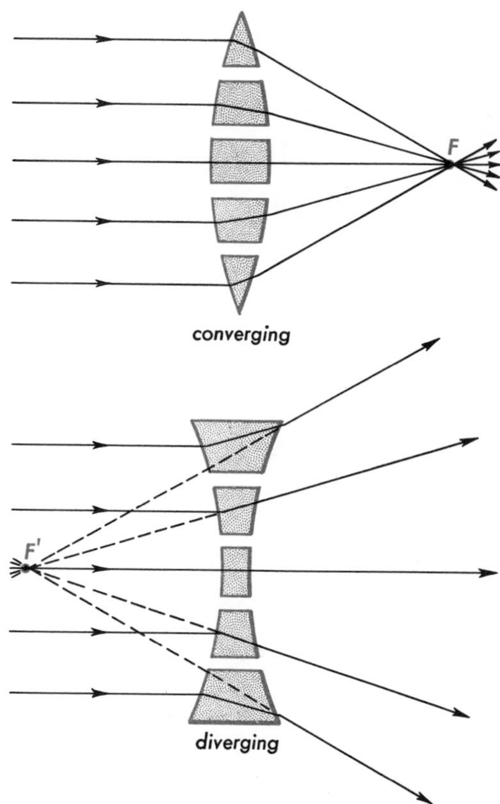

Fig. 33A. Matched sets of prisms illustrating lens-like action.

A real lens is not made of prisms, as indicated in Fig. 33A, but of a solid piece of glass with surfaces ground to the form of a sphere. Cross sections of several standard forms are shown in Fig. 33B. The first three lenses, which are thicker in the center, are called *converging* or *positive lenses,* while the last three, which are thinner in the center, are called *diverging* or *negative lenses.* Special names attached to each of the six lens types shown are: (1) *double convex,* (2) *plano–convex,* (3) *convex miniscus,* (4) *double concave,* (5) *plano–concave,* and (6) *concave miniscus.*

There are two good reasons why lenses have spherical sur-

Fig. 33B. Cross sections of standard forms of common lenses.

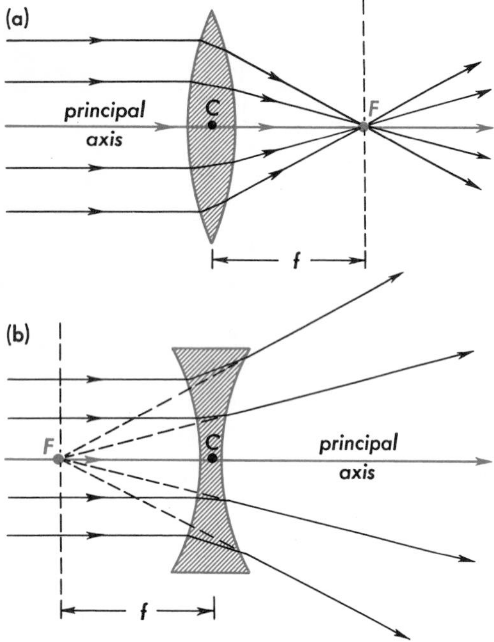

Fig. 33C. Converging and diverging lenses.

faces: first, with this shape they form reasonably good images; and second, a spherical form is by far the most practical shape to which smooth polished surfaces can be ground.

Diagrams showing the refraction of light by converging and diverging lenses are given in Fig. 33C. The principal axis in each case is a straight line passing through the center of a lens perpendicular to the two faces at the points of intersection. The principal focus F lies on the principal axis; it is defined for a converging lens as the point where light rays parallel to the principal axis are made to cross, and for a negative lens as a point from which light rays parallel to the principal axis appear to originate. *By symmetry every lens has two principal foci, one on each side of the lens and at the same distance from the center of the lens.* The distance from the focal point to the center of the lens is called the focal length:

$$CF = \text{focal length} = f$$

A plane perpendicular to the principal axis which passes through either principal focus is called the *focal plane.* Parallel light rays entering the lens from any other direction than shown in the diagrams will come to a focus at some point on the focal plane. This point is readily located by remembering that a ray through the center of the lens does not change in direction.

The greater the curvature of the two surfaces of a lens, the shorter is its focal length. The reason for this, as can be seen from the diagrams, is that the greater the curvature the greater is the deviation of the light rays passing through, near the edges of the lens.

One important principle concerning lenses is the reversibility of light rays. If a point source of light is placed at F in Fig. 33C(a), the rays of light that strike the lens will be refracted into a parallel beam of light moving to the left. Similarly, in Fig. 33C(b), if light rays are converging toward the focal point F they will be refracted by the lens into a parallel beam.

33.1. Image Formation

When an object is placed on one side of a converging lens beyond the principal focus, a real image will be formed on the opposite side of the lens. This is illustrated in Fig. 33D. If the object is moved closer to the focal point, the image will be formed farther away from the lens and will be bigger, that is, magnified. As the object is moved farther away from the lens, the image is formed closer to the focal point and is smaller in size.

In general, there are two ways of accurately determining the position of an image: one is by graphical construction and the other is by use of the lens formula:

$$\frac{1}{p} + \frac{1}{q} = \frac{1}{f} \qquad (33a)$$

where *p is the object distance, q the image distance,* and *f the focal length.*

The graphical method is illustrated in Fig. 33E. Consider the light emitted by some one particular point like O in the object. Of the rays going out from this point in all directions, the ray OA traveling parallel to the principal axis will be refracted to pass through the focal point F [see Fig. 33C(a)]. The ray OC arriving

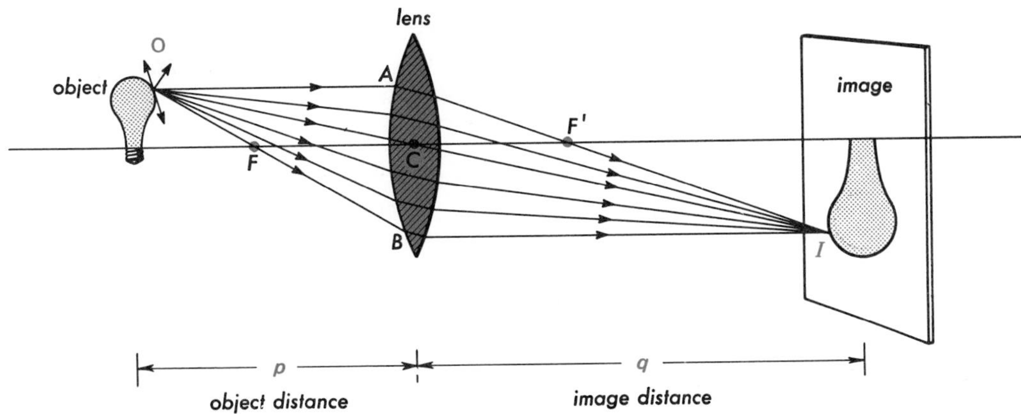

Fig. 33D. Ray diagram illustrating the formation of a real image by means of a single converging lens.

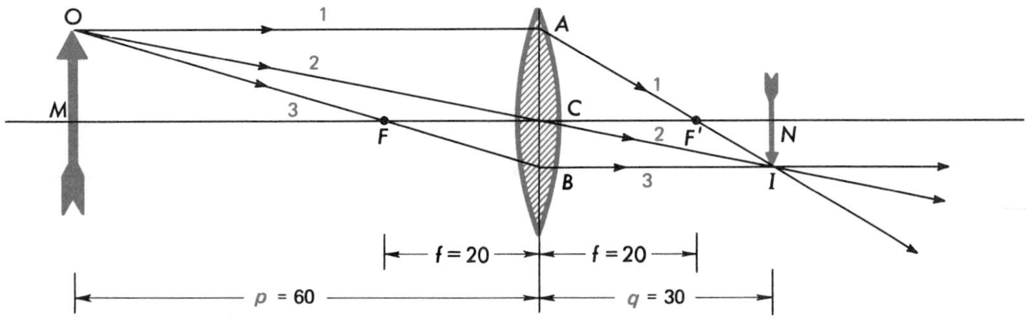

Fig. 33E. Graphical determination of image position and size.

at the center of the lens where the faces are parallel will pass straight through, meeting the other ray at some point I. These two rays locate the tip of the image at I. All other rays from the point O which strike the lens will be brought to a focus at this same point. To check this, note that the ray OF, which passes from O through the left-hand focal point, by the principle of the reversibility of light rays, will be refracted parallel to the principal axis, crossing the other ray at I, as shown.

In many practical cases the focal length of a lens is known, and it is common practice to determine the image distance when an object is placed at a fixed distance in front of the lens. In such cases Eq.(32a) is first solved for the unknown before substitutions are made in the formula. Solving for q, we obtain

$$q = \frac{p \times f}{p - f} \tag{33b}$$

The size of the image can be calculated from the following simple relation:

$$\frac{\text{size of image}}{\text{size of object}} = \frac{\text{image distance}}{\text{object distance}}$$

This is the image formula,

$$\frac{I}{O} = -\frac{q}{p} \tag{33c}$$

in which the ratio I/O is called the *magnification:*

$$M = \frac{I}{O} \tag{33d}$$

Example 1. An object 3.0 cm high is located 60.0 cm in front of a converging lens having a focal length of +20.0 cm. Find (a) the position of the image, (b) the image size, and (c) the magnification.

Solution. The given quantities are $p = 60.0$ cm, $O = 3.0$ cm, and $f = +20.0$ cm. (a) By direct substitution of these quantities in Eq.(33b), we obtain as the object distance

$$q = \frac{p \times f}{p - f} = \frac{60 \text{ cm} \times 20 \text{ cm}}{60 \text{ cm} - 20 \text{ cm}}$$

$$q = +30.0 \text{ cm}$$

(b) To find the size of the image we use Eq.(33c) by first solving for I, and then substituting known quantities:

$$I = -\frac{O\,q}{p} = -\frac{3.0 \text{ cm} \times 30.0 \text{ cm}}{60.0 \text{ cm}}$$

$$I = -1.50 \text{ cm}$$

(c) For the magnification we substitute directly in Eq.(33d) and find

$$M = \frac{I}{O} = \frac{-1.50 \text{ cm}}{3.0 \text{ cm}}$$

$$M = -0.50$$

The image is 30.0 cm to the right of the lens, is inverted, is 1.50 cm high, and is half the size of the object. If a centimeter rule is used to solve this problem graphically, the resultant diagram will look like the one shown in Fig. 33E. Each line is drawn in its proper position, length, and direction, and when the image is located by rays (1), (2), and (3) the position and size of the image can be measured to scale. Drawn carefully, the graphical results will agree in every detail with those calculated.

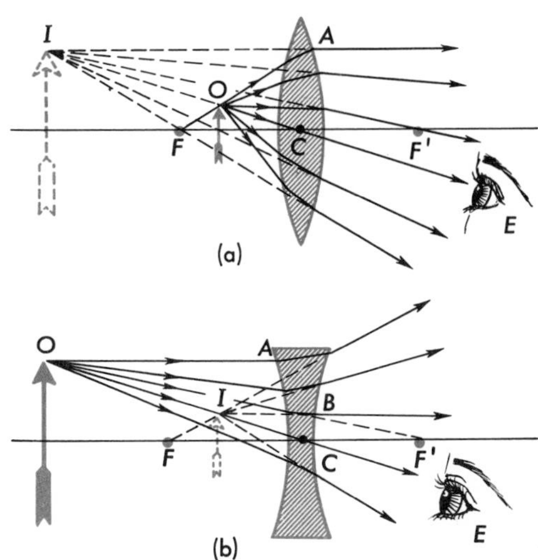

Fig. 33F. The formation of virtual images.

33.2. Virtual Images

The images formed by the lenses in Figs. 33D and 33E are *real. Real images* are defined as those that can be formed on a screen and are characterized by the fact that rays of light are actually brought together to a focus there. *Virtual images* are not real, they cannot be formed on a screen, and the rays from different points on the object do not pass through corresponding points in the image. Virtual images may be observed with a converging lens by placing an object close to the lens and inside the focal point, or by a diverging lens with the object at any point. These two examples are illustrated in Fig. 33F.

In the first case the lens is used as a magnifier, or reading glass. Rays of light radiating from the point of the object at O are refracted in the proper direction, but are not sufficiently deviated to come to a focus. To the observer's eye at E, these rays appear to be coming from a point I back of the lens. This is a *virtual image, right side up and magnified.* To find this image graphically, we observe that the ray FOA must be refracted parallel to the principal axis. The ray OC through the center of the lens goes on undeviated. These two refracted rays extended backward intersect at I. If the lens formula, Eq.(33b), is used to find the image in such a case, the image distance q will come out as a negative quantity, showing it to be a virtual image on the same side of the lens as the object.

In the case of a negative lens the image is always virtual, closer to the lens, and smaller in size than the object. As shown in Fig. 33F(b), light rays diverging from the object point O are made more divergent by the lens. To the observer's eye at E, these rays appear to be coming from the point I back of, but close to, the lens. To find this image we observe that the ray OA parallel to the principal axis must be refracted in such a direction that it appears to come from F. The ray OC through the center goes on undeviated. Since these two directions intersect at I, the image is formed there.

In applying the lens formula to a diverging lens, the focal length f is always *negative* in sign. To illustrate this, consider the following example.

Example 2. An object 3.0 cm high is located 30.0 cm in front of a diverging lens having a focal length of −15.0 cm. Find (a) the image position, (b) the image size, and (c) the magnification.

Solution. The known quantities are $p = +30.0$ cm, $O = 3.0$ cm, and $f = -15.0$. (a) Direct substitution in Eq.(33b) gives for the image distance

$$q = \frac{p \times f}{p - f} = \frac{30 \times (-15)}{30 - (-15)}$$

$$q = -10.0 \text{ cm}$$

(b) Solving Eq.(33c) for I and substituting known quantities gives for the image size:

$$I = -\frac{Oq}{p} = -\frac{3.0 \text{ cm} \times (-10.0 \text{ cm})}{30.0 \text{ cm}}$$

$$I = +1.0 \text{ cm}$$

(c) Direct substitution in Eq.(33d) gives for the magnification

$$M = \frac{I}{O} = \frac{1.0 \text{ cm}}{3.0 \text{ cm}} = +0.333$$

The image is 10.0 cm in front of the lens, the minus sign signifying it is not real, but virtual. The image is also erect, and one-third the size of the object.

A convenient sign convention for all lens problems solved with Eq.(33b) is the following:

(1) Numerical values of real object distances are always positive.
(2) Numerical values of real image distances are positive; numerical values of virtual image distances are negative.
(3) Numerical values of focal lengths of convergent lenses are positive, of divergent lenses are negative.

It is customary in all lens diagrams to show objects on the left side of the lens, so that *all incident light rays travel from left to right.*

33.3. Conjugate Foci

Since the lens equation, Eq.(33a), is symmetrical in p and q, it follows that a real image and the object from which it was formed may be interchanged. For example, in Figs. 33D and 33E, if the object is located at I, the image would be located at O. The distances p and q are called *conjugate distances,* O and I *conjugate points,* and the intersections of the optic axis with the object and image planes *conjugate foci.*

In demonstrating conjugate distances with a lens and screen, the object and the image can be interchanged in position, or the

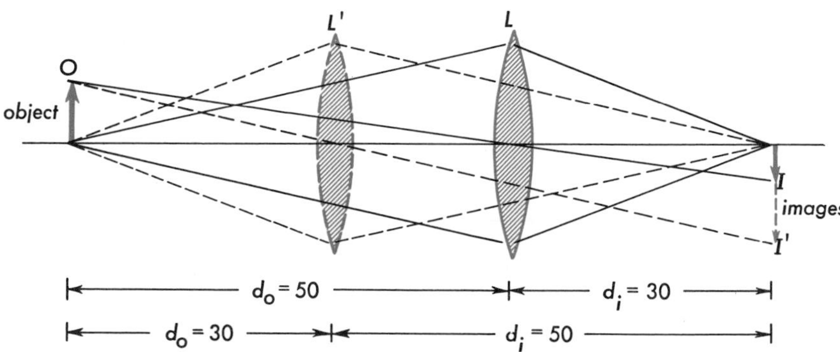

Fig. 33G. Conjugate foci for a single converging lens.

lens can be moved. If, for example, an object distance $p = 30$ cm and an image distance $q = 50$ cm, the lens may be moved to a new position $p = 50$ cm. The image will be formed at $q = 30$ cm. In other words, for a fixed distance between object and image screen, there are two lens positions of good image formation (see Fig. 33G). Because of the image–object relation, Eq.(33c), the two images will differ in size, the one being smaller than the object by the ratio 3:5 as shown by the solid arrow, and the other larger by the ratio 5:3 as shown by the dotted arrow.

33.4. The Lens Maker's Formula

To grind and polish a lens to some predetermined focal length, the refractive index of the glass should be known. Usually the refractive index is specified for the particular wavelength of yellow light emitted by a sodium lamp. With the index known, the radii of curvature of the two spherical surfaces can be calculated from the equation:

$$\frac{1}{f} = (\mu - 1)\left(\frac{1}{r_1} - \frac{1}{r_2}\right) \tag{33e}$$

The sign convention for r_1 and r_2 is based upon the following rules:

(1) Light rays entering and passing through a lens are always drawn from left to right.
(2) When such a ray encounters a convex surface, the radius r is positive.
(3) When a light ray encounters a concave surface, the radius r is negative.

To illustrate the use of the lens maker's formula, consider the following example.

Example 3. A plano–convex lens with a focal length of +50.0 cm is made of crown glass which for yellow light has a refractive index of 1.5200. Calculate the radius of curvature of the grinding and polishing tools that must be used to make this lens.
Solution. The given quantities are $\mu = 1.5200$, $f = +50.0$ cm, and $r_1 = \infty$. A flat surface has an infinite radius. Direct substitution of these quantities in Eq.(33e) gives

$$\frac{1}{50} = (1.52 - 1)\left(\frac{1}{\infty} - \frac{1}{r_2}\right)$$

$$\frac{1}{50} = 0.52\left(0 - \frac{1}{r_2}\right)$$

$$\frac{1}{50} = -\frac{0.52}{r_2}$$

$$r_2 = -50 \times 0.52 = -26.0 \text{ cm}$$

The second surface has a radius of −26.0 cm.

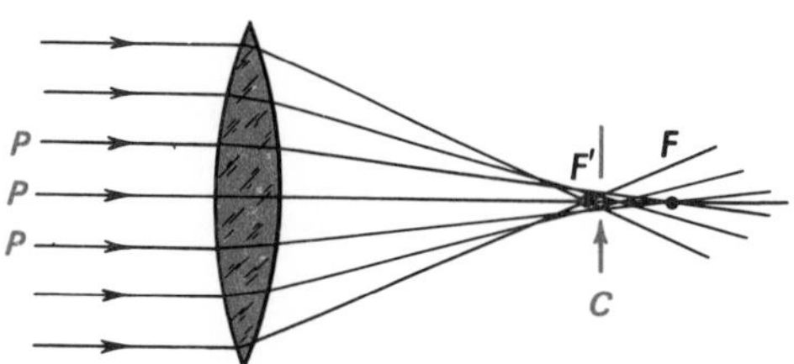

Fig. 33H. Spherical aberration of a lens. *P*, paraxial rays; *C*, circle of least confusion.

33.5. Defects of the Image

Although a simple converging lens may be made to form a relatively clear image of almost any object, there is present in every image a number of common defects tending to blur it. These defects are known as *spherical aberration, chromatic aberration, curvature of field, astigmatism, distortion,* and *coma.* Although some of these *aberrations,* as they are called, can be partly or almost entirely corrected by one means or another, they cannot all be eliminated entirely. These corrections are refinements that are usually considered in the design of lenses and are of some importance in the understanding of the principal action of a lens. We will be content to consider briefly the first two defects mentioned above—namely, spherical aberration and chromatic aberration.

33.6. Spherical Aberration

Spherical aberration is an undesirable defect in the focusing properties of single glass lenses and is attributed to the fact that spherical surfaces are not exactly the correct surfaces to which a lens should be ground and polished. The reason they are not correct is shown for a double convex lens in Fig. 33H. Rays of light parallel to the principal axis which pass through the outer parts of the lens are not brought to exactly the same focus as those rays passing through the central portion. The result is that nowhere can a sharply defined image of a distant object be formed on a screen.

When a screen is placed between F and F′ and a blurred image is obtained, it is not difficult to find a position where the least blurring occurs. This point, C in the diagram, is called the *circle of least confusion.*

There are various ways in which spherical aberration in a lens may be reduced. Some of these are easily carried out, while others require expert lens design.

(1) The easiest way to reduce spherical aberration is to place a circular diaphragm in front of the lens and allow only the central bundle of rays to pass through. Such a procedure reduces the size of the circle of least confusion and thereby produces sharper images. This is one of the functions of the *iris diaphragm* in the lens cell of a camera. The smaller the effective diameter of a lens, the more sharply defined are its image-focusing properties. Reduced aperture, however, reduces the light-gathering power and for some purposes is not desirable.

Rays passing through or near the center of a lens, and at the same time making relatively small angles with the principal axis, are called *paraxial rays.* It is for such rays only that reasonably sharp focus is obtained and the equations used in the preceding sections can be applied.

(2) Because peripheral rays are deviated through too great an angle (see Fig. 33H), any method that will bring about lesser deviation from the outer edges of a lens will result in better focusing. The principle of minimum deviation offers one such method, because by carefully selecting the radii of curvature for the two lens faces, the peripheral rays can be brought to much more nearly the same focal point as the paraxial rays (see Fig. 33I). In diagram (a), parallel rays entering normal to the flat surface of a plano–convex lens are refracted at the second surface only, the outer rays being deviated through too great an angle. In (b), the outer rays, because they enter one face and leave the other at nearly the same angle, are near minimum deviation and cross the axis farther out. If, for any given object distance and image distance, the radii of curvature r_1 and r_2 are so chosen that *the peripheral rays pass through the lens at minimum deviation,* the lens will have a minimum of spherical aberration.

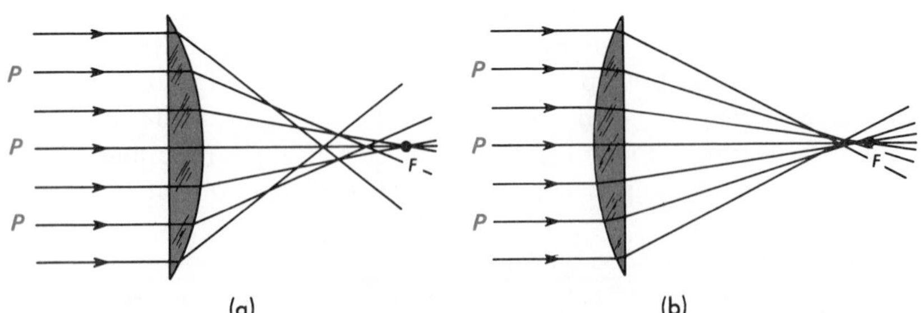

Fig. 33I. Spherical aberration for parallel rays is different on the two sides of a plano–convex lens. *P*, paraxial rays.

(3) To correct for spherical aberration, the two lens surfaces are sometimes ground and polished to other than a spherical form. Such a process, called *aspherizing,* is not only tedious and difficult, but any lens so made is good for only one pair of object and image distances.

(4) A fourth method of correcting spherical aberration is to combine a positive crown-glass lens with a negative flint-glass lens. Although both lenses have spherical surfaces, the curvatures of the two can be so chosen that the errors of one practically cancel those of the other.

33.7. Chromatic Aberration

When white light passes through a lens close to the edge, it is dispersed in much the same way that it is when passing through a large-angle prism (see Fig. 33J). The violet light, being deviated the most, comes to a focus nearer the lens than the red. The ray passing through the center of the lens and along the principal axis is not dispersed. For white light a single lens, therefore, cannot possibly form a sharply defined image.

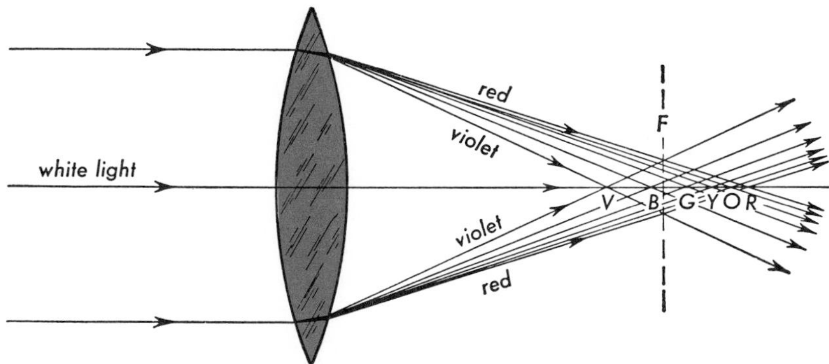

Fig. 33J. Ray diagram illustrating chromatic aberration with a single converging lens.

To correct a lens for chromatic aberration, use is made of the principle of the achromatic prism [see Fig. 32N]. Two prisms, one of crown glass, the other of flint glass, are so chosen that when placed in opposition they produce deviation without dispersion.

A similar combination can be constructed of flint- and crown-glass lenses, as illustrated in Fig. 33K, whereby the dispersion in one lens is compensated for by the opposite dispersion in the other, and yet the light is deviated to bring all colors to a common focus. Such a combination is called an *achromatic lens.* All first-

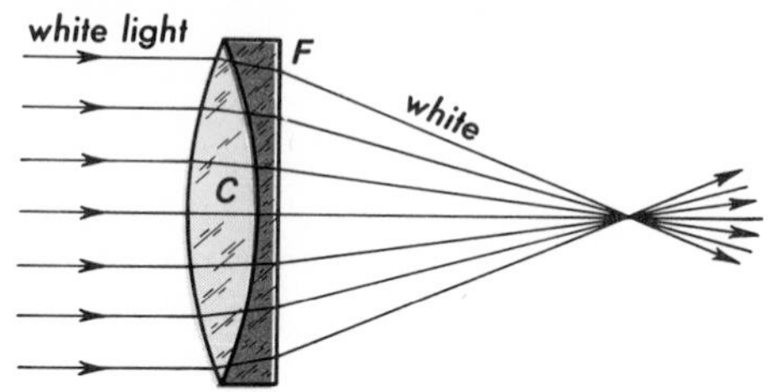

Fig. 33K. Achromatic lens combination.

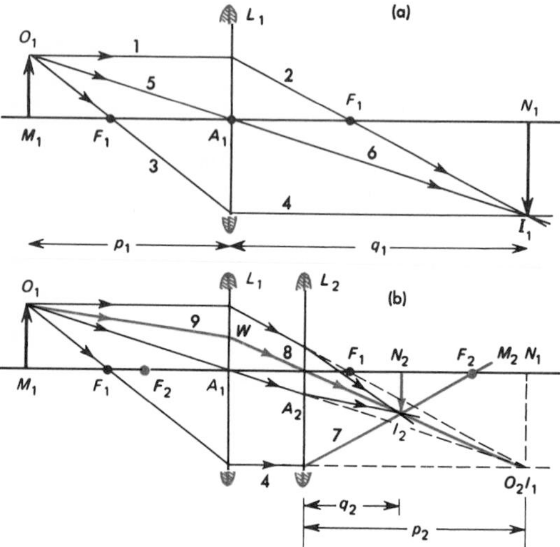

Fig. 33L. Illustration of the parallel-ray method for graphically locating the final image formed by two lenses.

class optical instruments use achromatic lenses. By the proper selection of surface curvatures, spherical aberration as well as chromatic aberration can be minimized with two lenses. The two exposed surfaces are chosen to give minimum deviation, and the two inner surfaces adjusted to correct chromatic aberration.

33.8. Two-Lens Combination

Optical instruments often employ more than one lens to form an image of an object. Consider, for example, two converging lenses spaced some distance apart as shown in Fig. 33L. In the lower diagram an object O_1M_1 is located at a given distance p_1 in front of the first lens, and an image I_2N_2 is formed a distance q_2 from the second lens. We will first apply graphical methods to find this image and then see how to apply the thin-lens formula to obtain the same result.

The first step is to disregard the second lens and find the image formed by the first lens as shown in diagram (a). In the diagram, the parallel-ray method is applied to the object O_1M_1, and the image I_1N_1 is obtained as a *real* and *inverted image.* Any two of the three incident rays 1, 3, and 5 are sufficient for the purpose.

We now insert the second lens in its proper position, as shown in diagram (b), and locate its focal points F_2, equal distance on each side of A_2. It will now be noted that ray 4 from the first lens is parallel to the axis and by the definition of focal length, must pass through F_2 as ray 7. To find the path of a second ray from L_2 we note that once we have found the image I_1N_1 in diagram (a), all the rays leaving O_1 would be refracted to intersect at I_1. Making use of this fact, we now construct a ray by drawing line 8 back from I_1 through A_2 to W at the first lens. Line 9 is then drawn in connecting W and O_1.

Since ray 9, as refracted by lens L_1, passes through the center of lens L_2, it goes on undeviated and crosses ray 7 at the point I_2. Once this point has been located we can draw in the image I_2N_2. All rays refracted by lens L_1 toward I_1 will upon passing through L_2 be refracted toward I_2.

As a check on the graphical solution, we can calculate the image position by using the single-lens formula.*

* For a more complete account of geometrical optics, see F. A. Jenkins and H. E. White, *Fundamentals of Optics* (McGraw-Hill, New York, 1957), 3rd ed.

Example 4. Two thin lenses with focal lengths of +12.0 cm and +16.0 cm, respectively, are located 8.0 cm apart. An object is located 20.0 cm in front of the first lens. Find (a) the image position for the first lens alone, and (b) the final image position using both lenses.

Solution. The given quantities are $p_1 = 20.0$ cm, $f_1 = +12.0$ cm, $f_2 = +16.0$ cm, and $d = 8.0$ cm. Substituting directly in Eq.(33b) for the first lens alone, we obtain

$$q_1 = \frac{p_1 \times f_1}{p_1 - f_1} = \frac{(+20) \times (+12)}{(+20) - (+12)}$$

$$q_1 = +30.0 \text{ cm}$$

This image formed by the first lens alone is therefore *real,* and 30 cm to the right of A_1. This image becomes the object for the second lens, and since it is 22.0 cm from A_2, the object distance becomes −22.0 cm. The minus sign is necessary and results from the fact that the object distance is measured to the right of the lens. Since the rays approaching the second lens are converging toward O_2, this object is *virtual* and its distance therefore has a negative sign.

Applying the lens formula Eq.(33b) to the second lens, we have $p_2 = -22.0$ cm and $f_2 = +16.0$ cm:

$$q_2 = \frac{p_2 \times f_2}{p_2 - f_2}$$

$$q_2 = \frac{(-22) \times (+16)}{(-22) - (+16)}$$

$$q_2 \doteq +9.26 \text{ cm}$$

The final image is 9.26 cm to the right of the second lens and is real.

The magnification of the system is the ratio of the final image size I_2 divided by the original object size O_1, and is given by the product of the magnification of the first lens and the magnification of the second:

$$M = M_1 \times M_2$$

$$M = \left(\frac{I_1}{O_1}\right) \times \left(\frac{I_2}{O_2}\right) \tag{33f}$$

When two *thin lenses* are placed in contact, the combination behaves as a single lens with a focal length of its own. If f_1 and

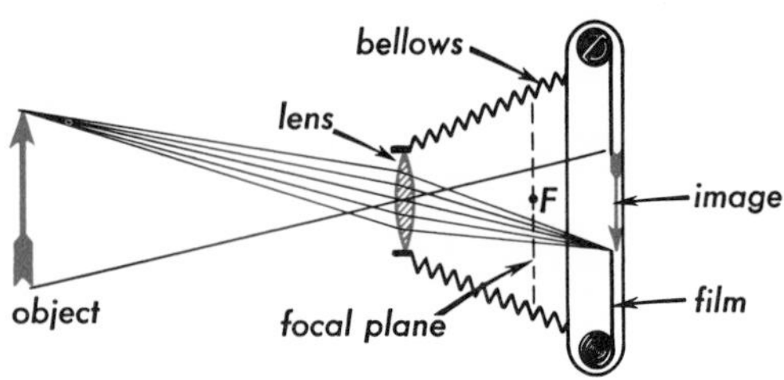

Fig. 33M. Diagram of the image formation by a camera.

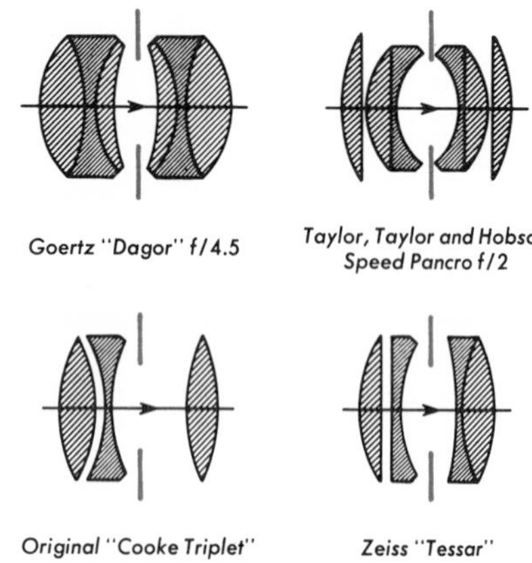

Fig. 33N. Symmetrical and unsymmetrical camera lenses.

f_2 represent the focal lengths of the two lenses, respectively, the equivalent focal length f of the combination is given by

$$\frac{1}{f} = \frac{1}{f_1} + \frac{1}{f_2} \tag{33g}$$

Example 5. An achromatic lens is composed of two thin lenses: a converging crown-glass lens with a focal length of +8.0 cm, and a diverging flint-glass lens with a focal length −12.0 cm. Find the equivalent focal length of the combination, when the two lenses are in contact.

Solution. The given quantities are $f_1 = 8.0$ cm and $f_2 = -12.0$ cm. Direct substitution in Eq.(33g) gives

$$\frac{1}{f} = \frac{1}{8} - \frac{1}{12} \qquad \frac{1}{f} = \frac{3}{24} - \frac{2}{24} \qquad \frac{1}{f} = \frac{1}{24}$$

or

$$f = +24.0 \text{ cm}$$

33.9. *The Camera*

Since the photographic camera employs only a single lens unit, it may be considered as one of the simplest of all optical instruments. As illustrated by the roll-film camera in Fig. 33M, a converging lens forms a *real* and *inverted image* on the film. If the object is far away, the light rays approaching the lens are nearly parallel and the image is formed at the focal plane. If the object is close up, the image will be formed beyond the focal plane as shown in the diagram. To permit distant landscapes or "close ups" to be taken with the same camera, a bellows is used, allowing the lens distance to be varied at will. Motion of the lens to the proper image distance is called *focusing.*

Only a simple converging lens is used in the cheapest of cameras, which means that all of the common defects of images are present to give rise to a slightly blurred or diffuse image. In more expensive cameras, however, the most objectionable defects are fairly well corrected by a compound lens made of several individual lenses. As a rule, a good camera lens will contain from three to five lens elements and will partially correct for *chromatic aberration, spherical aberration, astigmatism,* and *curvature of field.*

Four typical high-quality camera lenses containing several lens elements are shown in Fig. 33N. Each lens contains an adjustable diaphragm or stop, shown in color.

The purpose of an iris diaphragm is to decrease the effective aperture of a lens and hence increase its *f*-number. Such practice is desirable in photographing still objects because the smaller the lens opening, the sharper will be the focus of near and far as well as central and peripheral objects.

The f-number of a lens is equal to its focal length divided by its diameter:

$$f\text{-number} = \frac{F}{D} \qquad (33h)$$

33.10. The Eye

Some aspects of this most remarkable optical instrument, the human eye, have been presented in Introduction B. There it is pointed out that a single eye is in principle an exceptionally fine camera, with an elaborate lens system on one side and a sensitive screen or photographic film called the *retina* on the other.

When light from a distant object passes through the lens system of the eye, it is refracted and brought to a focus on the retina. There a real but inverted image of the object is formed. It is a most amazing fact that, while all retinal images are inverted, as shown in Fig. 33O, they are interpreted by the brain as being erect.

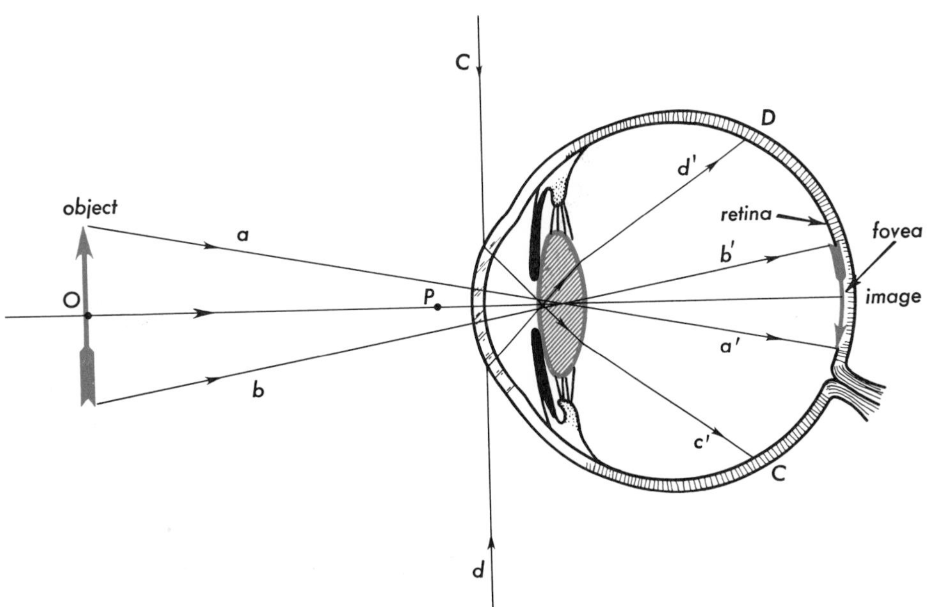

Fig. 33O. The human eye is similar to a camera. All retinal images are inverted.

Accommodation is the ability to focus the eyes on near and far objects. In a camera the focusing of a picture on the photographic film or plate is accomplished by moving the lens toward or away from the film. In the human eye, however, *focusing is brought about by changing the shape of the crystalline lens.* This is accomplished by a rather complicated system of ligaments and muscles. Due to a tension which exists in the lens capsule, the crystalline lens, if completely free, would tend to become spherical in shape (Introduction, Fig. B2).

The edge of the lens is surrounded by the *ciliary muscle* which, by contracting, causes the lens to bulge out. This reduces the focal length of the lens, bringing nearby objects to focus on the retina. When the ciliary muscle relaxes, the suspensory ligaments, being under tension, pull at the edges of the lens, thus tending to flatten it. Under these conditions the focal length increases, bringing distant objects to focus on the retina. This is the accommodation process.

The normal eye is most relaxed when it is focused for parallel light, i.e., for objects far away. To study the detail of an object, however, the object should be brought close to the eye. The reason for this is that the closer the object is to the eye, the larger is the image formed on the retina. A distance of about 25 cm (10 in.) is found to be the distance of most distinct vision. Prolonged observation at distances of 25 cm or less will result in a considerable amount of fatigue and eyestrain.

33.11. Eye Correction with Spectacle Lenses

As the average person grows older the crystalline lens of the eye tends to harden and the muscles that control it to grow weaker, thus making accommodation more and more difficult. The existence of these conditions is referred to as *presbyopia.* The speed of the hardening varies among individuals. If the length of the eyeball is such that parallel incident rays converge to a point in front of the retina, the person is nearsighted and is said by the eye specialist to have *myopia* [see Fig. 33P(a)]. If parallel incident rays converge to a point behind the retina, as in diagram (b), the person is farsighted and is said to have *hypermetropia.*

To correct these defects a diverging spectacle lens of the proper focal length is placed in front of the myopic eye and a converging lens of the proper focal length in front of the hypermetropic eye. The function of such lenses is shown in Fig. 33Q. For the nearsighted eye, rays from a nearby object at some point P will, in the absence of spectacles, come to focus on the fovea

F. Insertion of the proper diverging lens will now diverge parallel rays as if they came from P and thus bring a distant object to focus at F.

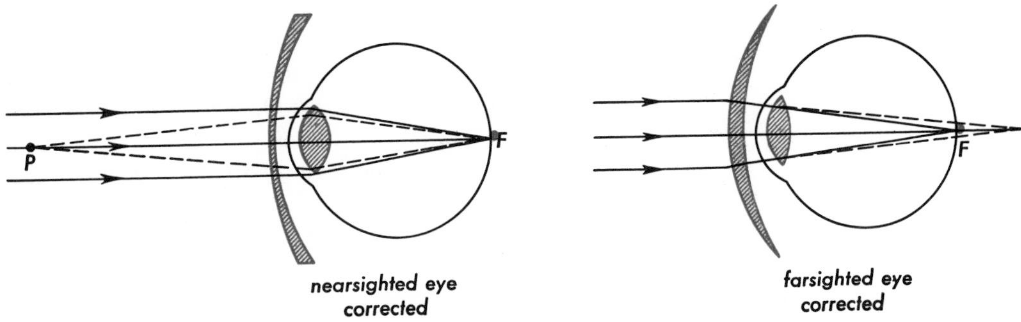

Fig. 33P. Typical eye difficulties of certain individuals.

For the farsighted eye, a converging lens adds some convergence to the incoming rays before they meet the eye lens and thus enables distant objects to be seen in good focus. To see close at hand, this same eye requires the use of a converging lens of still greater power. In other words, this person should wear bifocals, lenses whose upper and lower halves have different focal lengths.

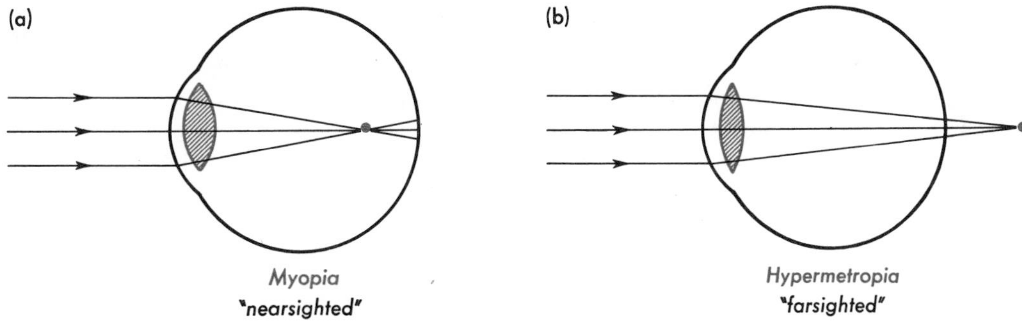

Fig. 33Q. Nearsighted and farsighted eyes can be corrected by the proper selection of spectacle lenses.

It is customary in optometry and ophthalmology to express the focal length of any lens in *diopters* and to speak of the power of a lens in such terms.

The power of a lens in diopters is given by the reciprocal of the focal length in meters:

$$\frac{1 \text{ meter}}{\text{focal length in meters}} = \text{diopters}$$

$$\frac{1}{f} = P \qquad (33i)$$

A lens with a focal length of +50 cm, for example, has a power of +2 diopters (D), $P = +2$ D, whereas one of +20 cm focal length has a power of +5 D, $P = +5$ D, etc. Converging lenses have a plus power while diverging lenses have a minus power.

problems

1. An object 2.50 cm high is located 6.0 cm in front of a converging lens with a focal length of +4.0 cm. Determine graphically, and by calculation, (a) the image distance, (b) the image size, and (c) the magnification.

2. A converging lens with a focal length of +6.0 cm is located 8.0 cm from an object 2.0 cm high. Find graphically, and by calculation, (a) the image distance, (b) the image size, and (c) the magnification.

3. A converging lens with a focal length of +9.0 cm is located 6.0 cm from an object 1.50 cm high. Find graphically, and by calculation, (a) the image distance, (b) the image size, and (c) the magnification. [Ans. (a) −18.0 cm, (b) +4.50 cm, (c) +3.0 cm.]

4. An object 1.50 cm high is located 5.0 cm in front of a converging lens with a focal length of +8.0 cm. Determine graphically, and by calculation, (a) the image distance, (b) the image size, and (c) the magnification.

5. A diverging lens with a focal length of −16.0 cm is located 24.0 cm in front of an object 4.0 cm high. Determine graphically, and by calculation, (a) the image distance, (b) the image height, and (c) the magnification.

6. An object 5.0 cm high is located 9.0 cm in front of a diverging lens with a focal length of −6.0 cm. Find graphically, and by calculation, (a) the image distance, (b) the image height, and (c) the magnification. [Ans. (a) −3.60 cm, (c) +2.0 cm, (c) 0.40.]

7. A lens made of crown glass has a refractive index of 1.520 for yellow light. If the two lens surfaces have radii of +8.0 cm and −12.0 cm, for r_1 and r_2, respectively, find its focal length.

8. A miniscus lens with radii $r_1 = +15.0$ cm and $r_2 = +25.0$ cm has a refractive index for yellow light of 1.6250. Calculate its focal length.

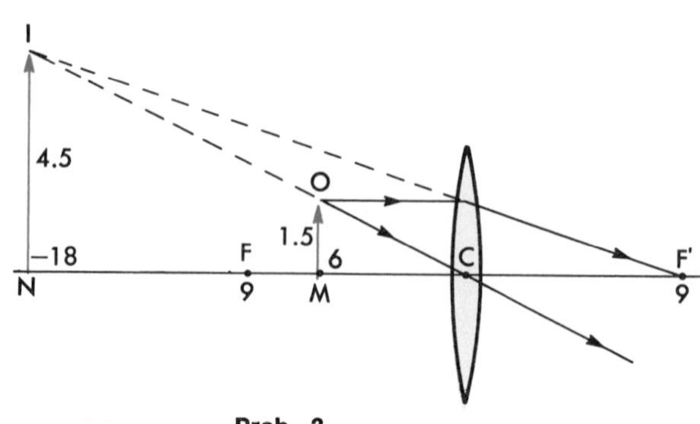

Prob. 3.

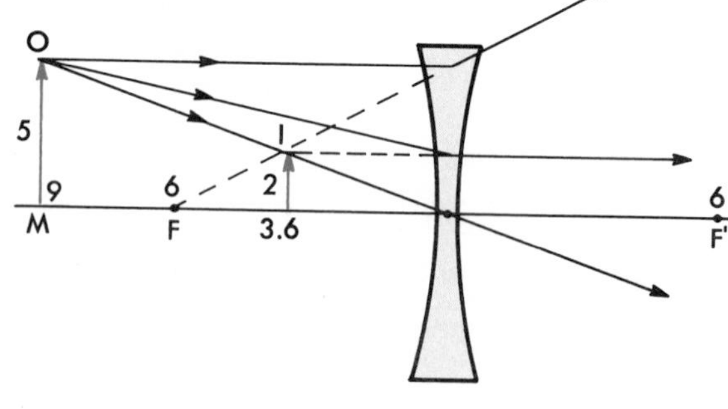

Prob. 6.

9. An equi–convex lens has a refractive index of 2.450, and radii of $r_1 = +30.0$ cm and $r_2 = -30.0$ cm. Calculate its focal length. [Ans. +10.34 cm.]

10. An equi–convex lens is made of dense flint glass with radii $r_1 = +30.0$ cm and $r_2 = -30.0$ cm. Using the refractive indices given in Table 32A, find the focal length for (a) violet light, and (b) for red light. Carry your answer to four significant figures.

11. A converging lens is made of crown glass and has radii $r_1 = +12.0$ cm and $r_2 = +24.0$ cm. Using the refractive indices given in Table 32A, find the focal length for (a) red light, and (b) violet light. Express your answers to four significant figures.

12.* An object 2.0 cm high is located 25.0 cm in front of a lens of focal length +10.0 cm. A second lens of focal length −30.0 cm is located 8.0 cm beyond the first lens. Find (a) the image distance for the first lens alone, (b) the final image distance from the second lens, and (c) the image size. [Ans. (a) +16.67 cm, (b) +12.19 cm, (c) −0.975.]

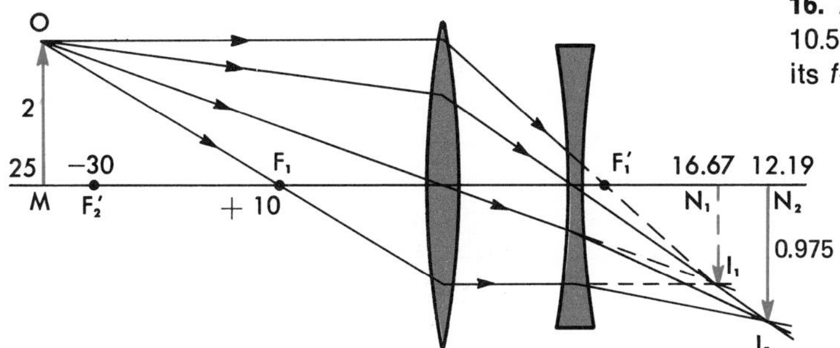

Prob. 12.

13.* An object 3.0 cm high is located 15.0 cm in front of a converging lens of focal length +10.0 cm. A second lens of focal length +24.0 cm is located 6.0 cm beyond the first lens. Find (a) the image distance for the first lens alone, (b) the position of the final image, and (c) the final image size.

14.* An equi–convex lens of crown glass with an index of 1.5200, and a plano–concave flint glass lens with an index of 1.6700, are placed in contact to form an achromatic lens. If all curved surfaces have radii of 10.0 cm, find (a) the focal length of each lens, (b) the power of each lens, (c) the focal length of the combination, and (d) the power of the combination.

15.* A flint glass lens with radii $r_1 = -5.0$ cm and $r_2 = -30.0$ cm and a refractive index of 1.6280 is combined with a crown glass lens with radii $r_1 = +6.0$ cm and $r_2 = -8.0$ cm and a refractive index of 1.5000 to form an achromatic lens. Find (a) the focal length of each lens, (b) the power of each lens, (c) the focal length of the combination, and (d) the power of the combination. [Ans. (a) −9.55 cm, +6.86 cm, (b) −10.47 D, +14.58 D, (c) +24.33 cm, (d) +4.11 D.]

16. A high speed camera lens has a focal length of 10.50 cm, and an aperture wide open of 4.25 cm. Find its *f*-number.

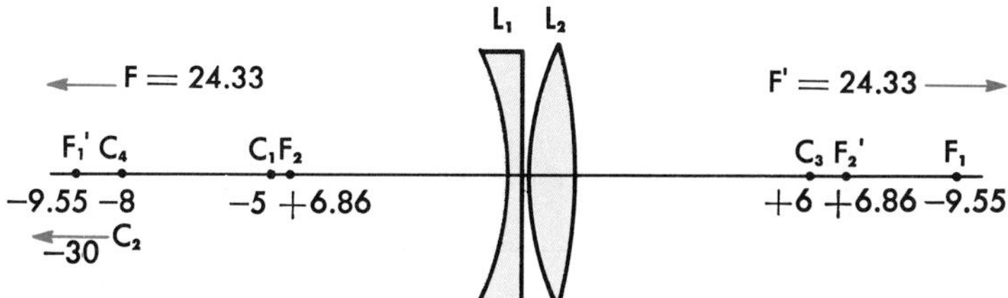

Prob. 15.

The science of color

The beautiful colors of precious stones adorned the crowns of the emperors and rulers of the world for centuries. Diamonds, emeralds, rubies, and sapphires derive their colors from well-known principles of optics. In the preceding chapter we have seen how prisms of diamonds, glass, and quartz, etc., disperse white light into spectral colors. In this chapter we will see how colored lights and pigments are mixed to produce many colors.

Color vision is perhaps man's most valued gift of nature. While color is for the most part a physiological phenomenon, its origin is considered by some to belong to the realm of physics. There is, on the one hand, the theory of *color mixing* and, on the other, the theory of *color vision.* The first of these theories deals with the action of matter on light before it reaches the eye, and the second with the visual functions of the eye. The science of color mixing has been made possible through the discovery that all colors can be completely analyzed by spreading them out into a prismatic spectrum. The science of color vision, on the other hand, involving the optics of the eye as well as the physiological functions of the entire vision mechanism, is not completely understood. Both of these subjects will be treated in this chapter on the science of color.

34.1. Effect of Illumination on Color

To see a body in its true color, that body must be illuminated by light of the same color. If a red rose, as an illustration, is placed in the different colors of a prismatic spectrum it will appear a brilliant red in red light and grey or black in all the others.

white red yellow green blue violet brown

colored yarns

sodium lamp or flame

Fig. 34A. Experiment with colored skeins of yarn showing that, to see an object in its true surface color, it must be illuminated by the proper light.

Another experiment is illustrated in Fig. 34A, where yellow light from a sodium arc lamp is shown illuminating a row of colored skeins of yarn. When the lamp is turned on, only the yellow yarn appears with its true color; the white yarn is yellow and the others are black or grey. If the same set of colored yarns is illuminated with red light, only the red yarn will appear in its true color; the white yarn will now be red, and the others will be grey or black. In other words, unless the source emits the proper colors, the body cannot be seen in its true color. Sunlight will show each yarn in its true color, for sunlight contains all colors of the spectrum.

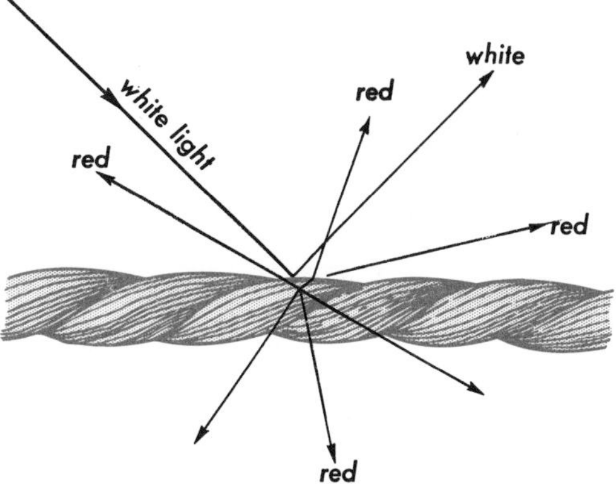

Fig. 34B. Illustration of color.

34.2. Surface Color

The above experiments demonstrate what is called *surface color.* When sunlight falls on a red rose, red yarn, red paint, or red glass, all of the colors except red are absorbed and do not get through or out again. The red, as it passes through, is reflected and refracted by the fine grains of pigment and comes out in all directions as shown in Fig. 34B.

Not all of the other colors are completely absorbed, for a small amount of each color is reflected from the first surface the white light strikes. This may be illustrated by a polished sheet of red glass. Although the glass appears red from both sides, a small amount of white light is reflected from the top surface, obeying the law of reflection. The red, on the other hand, is reflected and refracted in the usual way at each surface.

The three aspects of surface color are *hue, brightness*, and *saturation.* Hue refers to the *name* of a color, brightness to the relative *magnitude* of the sensory response, and saturation to the color *strength.* Hue is qualitative and is the most distinctive aspect of color, for without hue there is no color. Hue cannot be defined but only exemplified: red, yellow, green, blue, violet, purple, and various intermediaries between these are hues. *Brightness* is a subjective intensity and may exist alone, as in white light. White is devoid of hue and hence is devoid of color. Hue cannot exist alone, for if we have hue it has a certain brightness and saturation. Illustrations of these three concepts are shown in Fig. 34C.*

Colors that do not contain any trace of white light are said to be *saturated.* The more white they contain, the less saturated they become. Pink is not a saturated color since it is a mixture of red and white. This may be demonstrated by mixing a small amount of red pigment with white paint, or, what is still more striking, by pulverizing a piece of red glass. As the glass is ground finer and finer the amount of white light reflected is increased by the increasing surface area, until the powder becomes almost white. Although the red light is still present, the white light by comparison is much stronger. A similar effect is produced by trans-

*Figure 34C is a color photograph inserted after p. 532.

parent substances like crystals and window glass; when powdered they become white. *The smaller the amount of white light mixed in with a color, the greater is the saturation.*

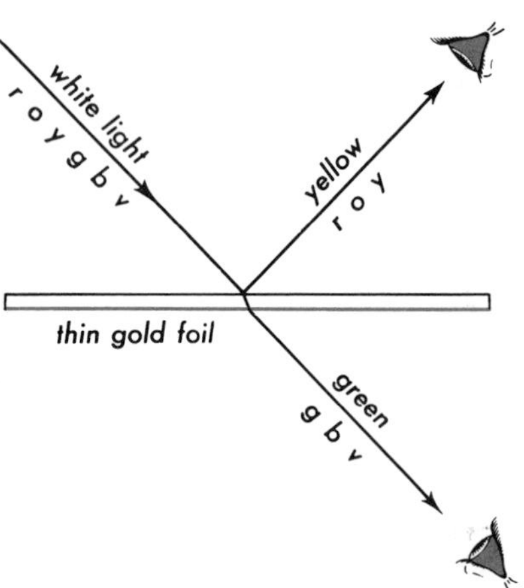

Fig. 34D. A thin gold foil appears yellow-orange by reflected light and blue-green by transmitted light.

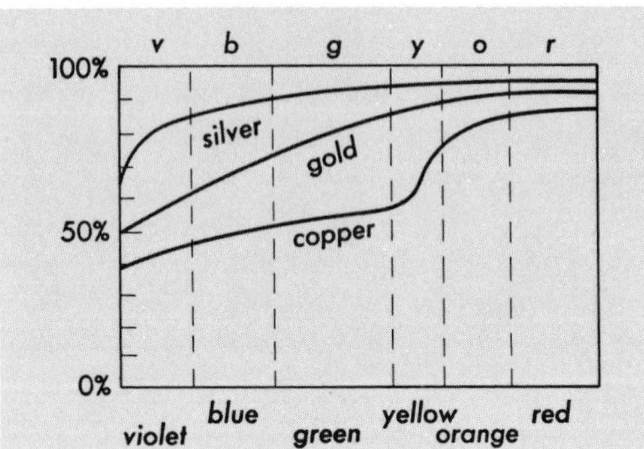

Fig. 34E. Graphs showing the reflecting power of metals for different colors of the spectrum.

34.3. Metallic Color

Some substances appear to be one color by reflected light and a different color by transmitted light. This is particularly true of metals and of certain aniline dyes. Gold, for example, is always yellow-orange by reflected light but, if thin enough, is blue-green by transmitted light (see Fig. 34D).

White light, composed of the spectrum colors, red, orange, yellow, green, blue, and violet, is incident on the thin film of gold. Although all of these colors are partially reflected and partially transmitted, the predominant colors in the transmitted light are green, blue, and violet, while those in the reflected light are red, orange, and yellow. To the eye the mixture of reflected colors appears yellow, and the mixture of transmitted colors appears green.

Graphs of the reflecting power of copper, silver, and gold are reproduced in Fig. 34E. Copper, it will be noted, reflects about 80% of all red light incident upon it and only 40% of the violet. Curiously enough, all metals are good absorbers of colors they best reflect, so that white light incident on a thin copper foil is partly robbed of red, orange, and yellow by having some of each of these colors reflected and some absorbed. Since smaller amounts of the green, blue, and violet are reflected and absorbed, these colors will predominate in the transmitted light, giving it, like gold, a blue-green or cyan appearance. If the metal is too thick, it becomes opaque to all colors. In a rough way the curves in Fig. 34E represent the absorption of light by metals as well as the reflecting power. Silver, like so many other metals, is a good reflector of all colors and therefore is nearly white.

34.4. Mixing Spectrum Colors

Over a period of many years, different color charts and color theories have been proposed, some of them good and some of them bad. Because the most successful theories have, of necessity, been detailed and complicated, some simplification of their concepts and an explanation of their common principles will be given here.

As a starting point, consider the experiment shown in Fig. 34F in which a narrow beam of white light from a carbon arc and lens falls on a glass prism and is spread out into a complete spectrum. With the prism located near the center of curvature of a large concave mirror, all colors after reflection are brought to a focus on a translucent glass rod where, combined again, they produce white. A large white card is next held in front of the mirror to act as a screen to control the colors that are permitted to mix at the rod. By screening off violet, blue, and green, for example, the remaining colors, red, orange, and yellow, come together and the rod appears orange.

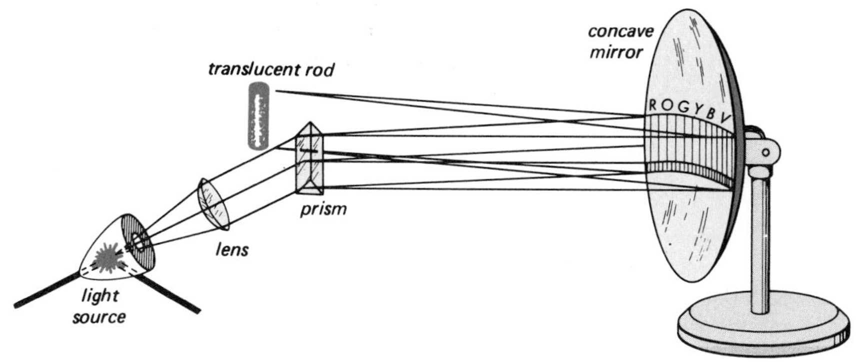

Fig. 34F. Experimental arrangement for mixing pure spectrum colors to form all primary colors.

We now proceed to divide the spectrum up into three equal parts, as shown at the lower left in Fig. 34G,* and to call these parts the *additive primaries.* When red and orange are allowed to mix, the rod appears a bright red; when yellow and green are mixed the rod appears bright green, and when blue and violet are mixed it appears blue-violet. As colors these additive primaries, red, green, and blue, appear like the three large circular areas at the upper left in Fig. 34G.

The next step is to mix the *primary colors* two at a time and to observe their resultant color mixture. When primary red and primary green mix at the glass rod, they produce yellow; red and blue produce magenta; and green and blue produce cyan, a light blue-green. These, the so-called *subtractive primaries,* are shown by the three large circles at the upper right in Fig. 34G, and the overlapping areas at the upper left. The pure spectrum colors that go to make up each subtractive primary are shown at the lower right.

34.5. The Color Triangle

The color triangle, as illustrated in Fig. 34H, is a triangular arrangement of the additive and subtractive primaries with white at the center. Red, green, and blue are located at the corners,

*Figure 34G is a color photograph inserted after p. 532.

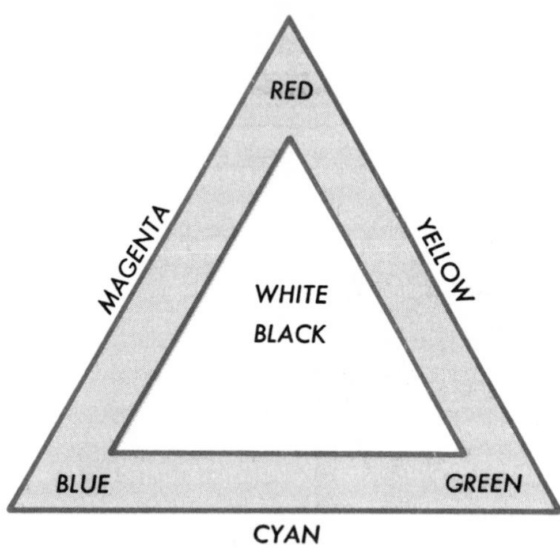

Fig. 34H. Diagram of the color triangle, with the additive primaries at the corners and the subtractive primaries at the sides.

while magenta, yellow, and cyan are located at the sides. The order of the colors is such that the sum of any two additive primaries at the corners gives the subtractive primary between them on the sides, and the sum of all three primaries gives white at the center.

Colors opposite each other on the color triangle are *complementary. Two colors are said to be complementary if when added together they produce white.* Magenta and green are complementary, for when added together, as can be seen from their spectral distributions in Fig. 34G, they contain all of the spectrum colors of white light. Similarly red and cyan, as well as yellow and blue, are complementary.

34.6. Additive Method of Color Mixing

The mixing of colored lights described in the two preceding sections is called the additive method of color mixing and differs greatly from the subtractive method to be described in the following section. An interesting experiment for demonstrating the additive method is shown in Fig. 34C. Three boxes containing white lights are arranged to illuminate separately the three sides of a white pyramid. A matched set of glass filters, one for each of the additive primary hues, red, green, and blue, respectively, is placed in front of each box opening, thereby illuminating the pyramid faces as shown in the left-hand diagram.

Upon rotating the pyramid slowly a point is reached, as shown in the right-hand diagram, where pairs of lights mix in equal amounts on each of the three faces. These mixtures are the subtractive primaries, magenta, yellow, and cyan. As the pyramid turns from position (a) to position (b), all variations of two colors are seen on the pyramid faces. Television in full color is produced by the additive method of color mixing.

34.7. Subtractive Method of Color Mixing

This is the method most familiar to everyone, the method used in the mixing of pigments to produce various colored paints. For this purpose the subtractive primaries, *magenta, yellow,* and *cyan,* often referred to by artists as *red, yellow,* and *blue,* are the most useful. The mixing in equal amounts of any two subtractive primaries will produce the additive primary lying between them on the color triangle. When cyan and yellow paints are mixed, the result is green.

At first it seems strange that yellow and cyan, neither one of which has the appearance of an additive primary, should produce green when mixed together. A spectrum analysis of these two colors, as shown at the lower right in Fig. 34G, shows that green and yellow are spectrum colors common to both.

Mixing by the subtractive method is demonstrated with prisms and filters in Fig. 34I.* To see what happens to each spectral hue in each filter, the white light is first spread out into its complete spectrum. To illustrate, the yellow filter alone in diagram (h) absorbs blue and violet, and the cyan filter alone in (f) absorbs red and orange. When both are inserted as in diagram (d), only green and yellow are transmitted. To the eye this mixture appears bright green. The other two pairs of filters in diagrams (e) and (i) give the other two primaries, red and blue.

To carry these experimental demonstrations to the mixing of paint, each little grain of pigment is like a piece of colored glass (see Fig. 34J). Assuming the oil in which the yellow pigment is imbedded to be transparent, white light entering the paint is reflected and refracted as shown. Wherever blue or violet rays pass through pigment grains, they are absorbed. After many reflections and refractions the red, orange, yellow, and green can still escape. Together these four colors (see Fig. 34I) appear as yellow.

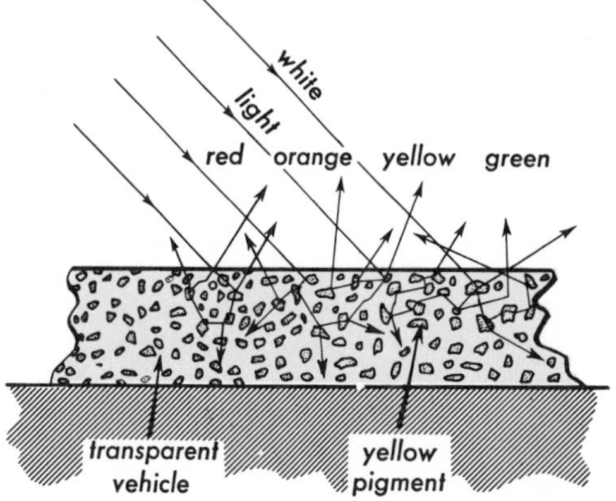

Fig. 34J. Illustration of the absorption of blue and violet light by yellow paint and the emission of red, orange, yellow, and green.

When yellow and cyan pigments are mixed together as illustrated by the detailed diagram in Fig. 34K, only green and yellow light is transmitted by both pigments.

The essential difference between the additive method and subtractive method of color mixing is just that suggested by the name; in the additive method the resultant color is just the *sum* of the two constituents used to produce it, and in the subtractive method it is just the *difference* between the two. Addition always produces a brighter color, and subtraction produces a darker color. Just as the additive mixing of red, green, and blue produces white, so the subtractive mixing of magenta, yellow, and cyan produces black. Similarly, two complementary colors, when mixed additively, produce white, and when mixed subtractively, produce black.

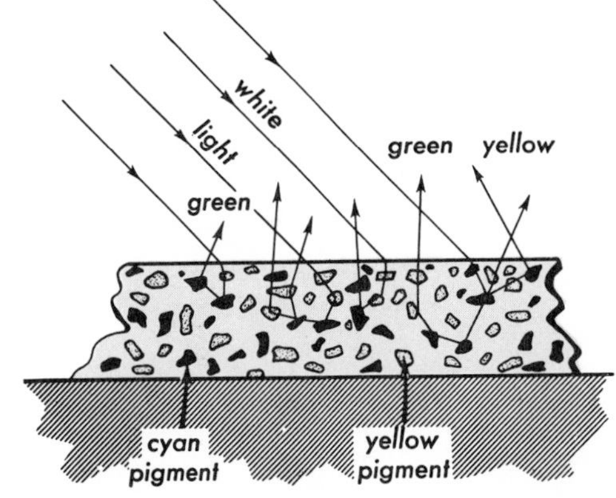

Fig. 34K. When blue and yellow paints are mixed together, green and yellow are the only pure spectral colors transmitted by both pigments.

34.8. Color Vision

When radiant energy at different wavelengths of the spectrum falls upon the retina of the normal human being, the visual sensations vary as shown at the top in Fig. 34L.† The maximum, which occurs in the green at $\lambda = 5550$ Å, is assigned the arbitrary value of 1000. On either side of this maximum the response falls off smoothly toward the violet at one end and the red at the other (for Å see p. 543).

The *standard luminosity curve* is experimentally determined by

*Figure 34I is a color photograph inserted after p. 532.

†Figure 34L is a color photograph inserted after p. 564.

matching the brightness of one color against that of another for each part of the spectrum and then measuring the relative amounts of energy in each of the two color fields. In comparing green and red, for example, much less intensity is required to give green light a brightness apparently equal to that of a red light. The solid curve is therefore a plot of *photometric energy magnitudes* and not relative brightness.

Brightness is a *sensory magnitude* in light just as loudness is a sensory magnitude in sound. Both vary over a wide range of values as the logarithm of the energy. To double the brightness of a surface, its emission must increase many fold. A plot of the logarithms of the luminosity gives the *relative brightness* curve for an equal-energy spectrum. In other words, the dotted curve represents the relative brightness of the colors of a constant-energy spectrum and clearly indicates the rather abrupt cutoff at either end.

During the past century, many attempts to formulate a scientific theory of color vision have been made. While some of these theories have met with considerable success, none of them has been able to explain every known phenomenon. The most successful theory was first advanced by the English scientist, Thomas Young, and later improved by the German scientist, von Helmholtz. According to the Young–Helmholtz theory, the tiny cones in the retina of the eye (see Fig. B2) are of three kinds.

One set of cones produces the visual sensation of red, the second set gives the sensation of green, and the third set the sensation of blue. A set of sensation graphs for each of these color-sensitive cones is given by the center curves in Fig. 34L. The R curve shows that to stimulate the red-response cones any wavelength from spectral violet to red is satisfactory, but wavelength 6000Å will produce the maximum response. Similarly the B and G cones are seen to be stimulated by a whole range of different wavelengths.

When pure spectrum yellow enters the eye, as represented by y in the diagram, both the R and G cones respond equally and the sensation is yellow. If pure spectral red and pure spectral green are permitted to enter the eye (like r and g in the diagram), both the R and G cones again respond equally and the sensation produced is yellow. Because of the stimulus equality, the brain is unable to tell the difference from the y stimulus, and the mixture has neither *redness* nor *greenness.* It is therefore possible to obtain a yellow hue with no spectral yellow present. A similar behavior occurs near wavelength 5000Å where the B and G cones are stimulated equally to produce a *cyan hue.*

If the eye is subjected to faint light of wavelength 4500Å, the

Fig. B23. Fatigue images enable the above objects to appear in their natural colors.

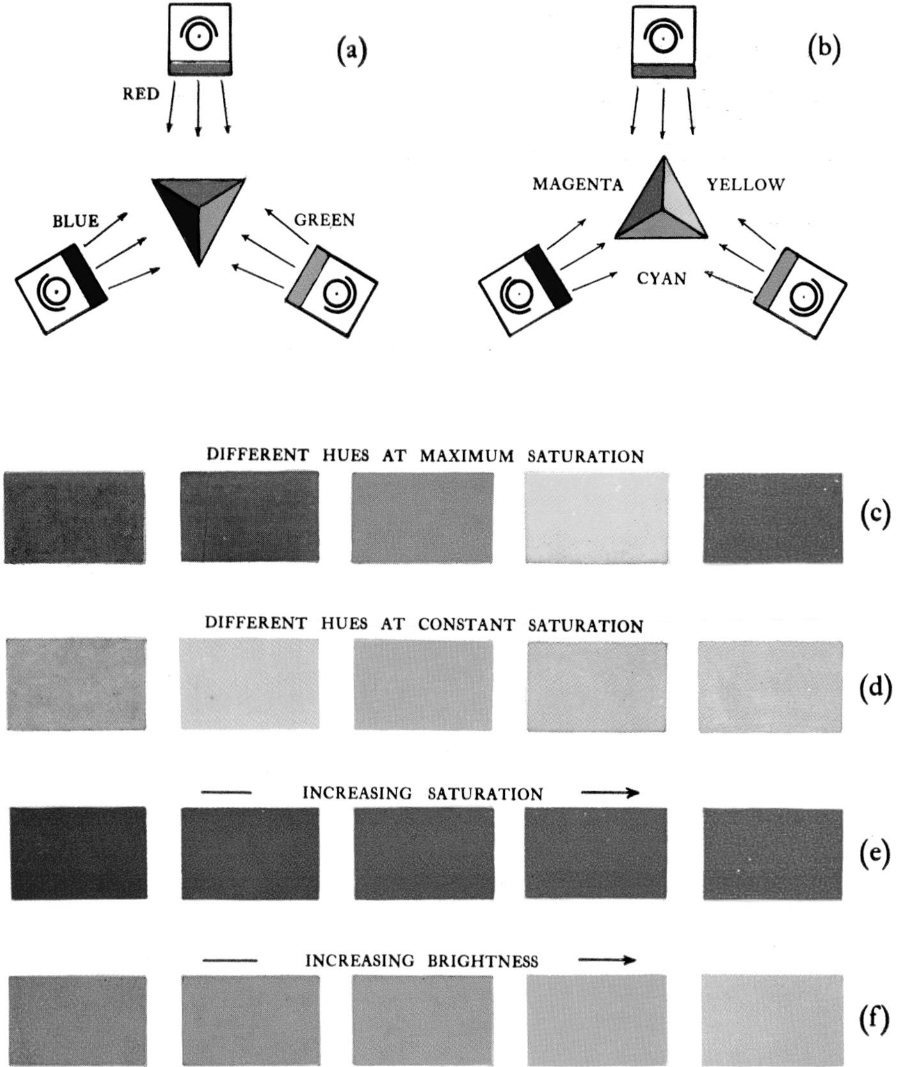

Fig. 34C. (a) Additive primaries. (b) Equal mixing of primary pairs. (c) Different hues at their maximum saturation values. (d) Different hues at constant saturation and equal brightness. (e) The same hue at constant brightness but increasing saturation. (f) The same hue at constant saturation but increasing brightness.

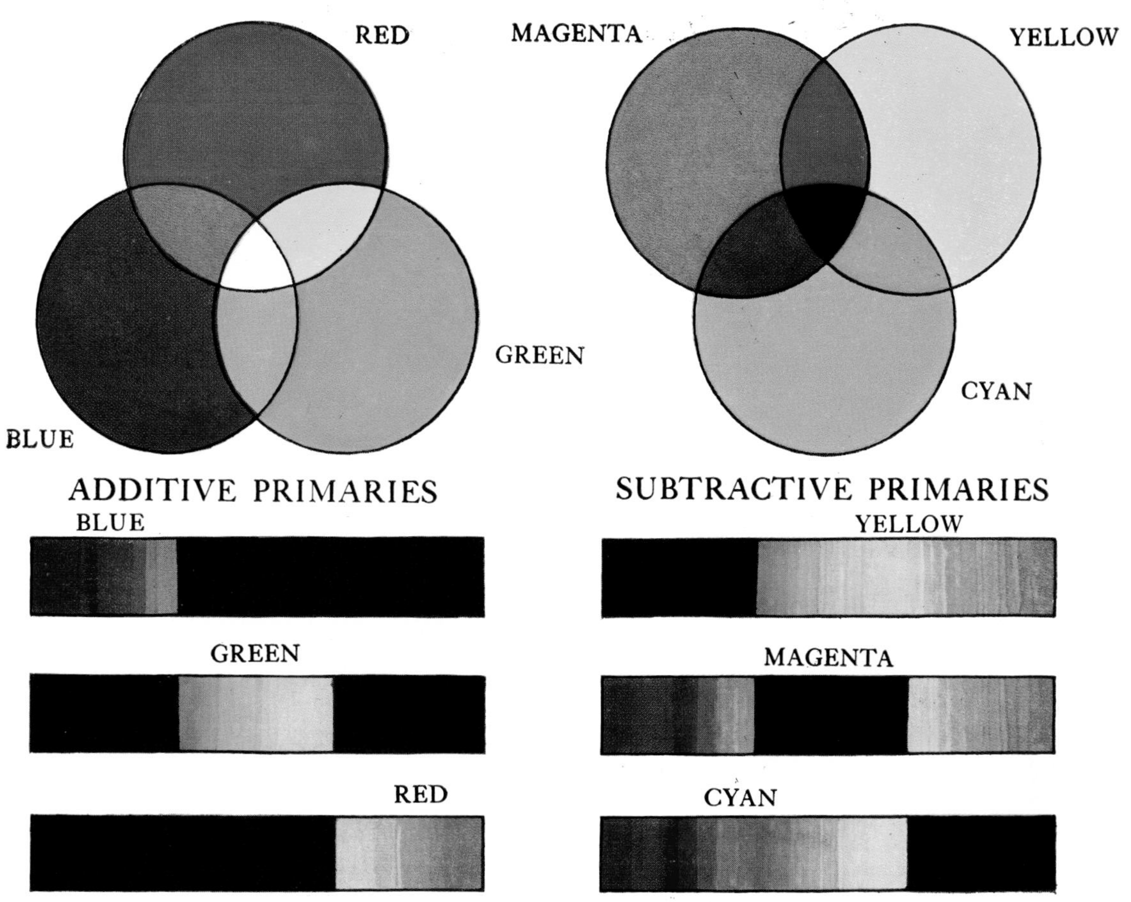

Fig. 34G. Primary colors showing their combinations and component spectral colors.

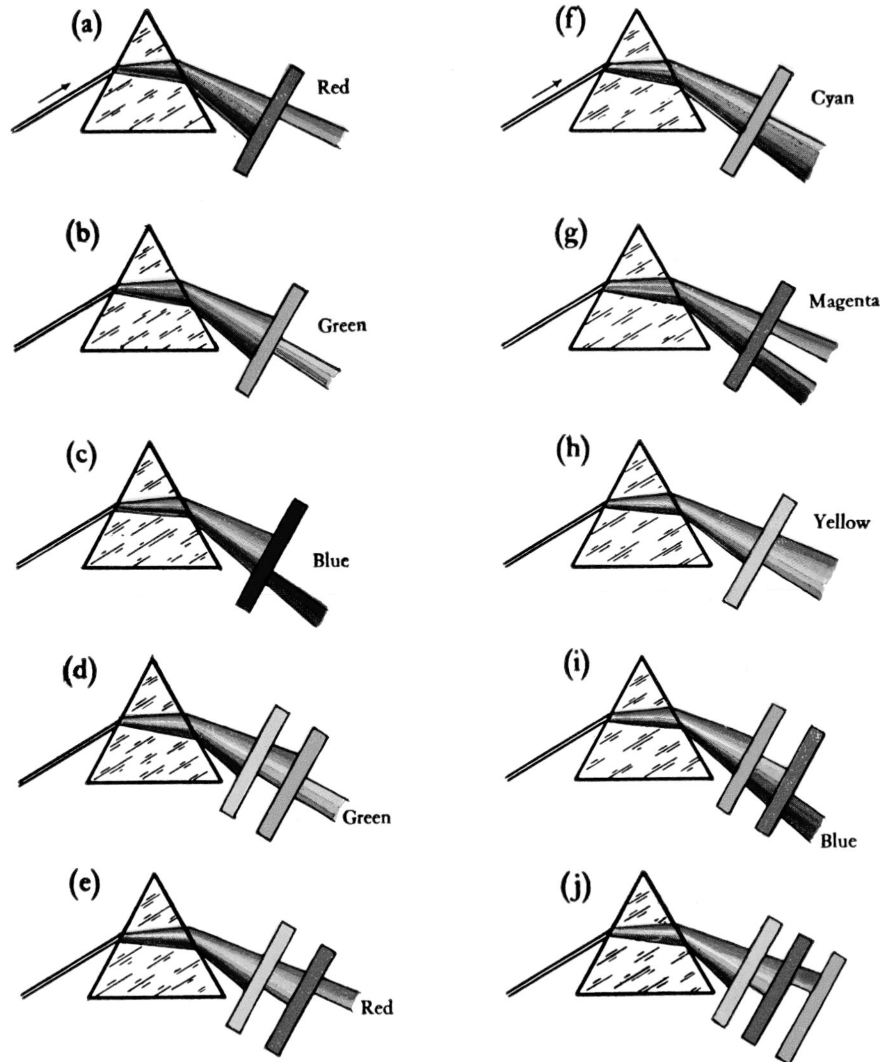

Fig. 34I. Diagram illustrating the absorption of spectral colors by colored filters and the subtractive method of color mixing.

visual sensation is *blue,* but when the intensity is raised the hue turns to violet or purple, indicating a noticeable stimulation of the R cones. This is the evidence for the small "bump" in the R curve in Fig. 34L. White is produced by the presence of all wavelengths in equal amounts, but it can also be produced by as few as three wavelengths.

By the additive process of three primary responses, red, green, and blue, all of the thousands of recognized hues can be produced. The power of the eye and the barin to synthesize colors is to be compared with the reverse process by which the ear and brain are able to analyze musical tones into components.

34.9. Color Deficiency and Color Blindness

About 8% of males and 1% of females are color deficient or color blind, that is, do not have normal color vision. Although there are many forms and degrees of this defect, the two most common types are called *protanopia* and *deuteranopia.** Numerous tests and experiments indicate that protanopia is due to the absence of R cones in the retina [see Fig. 34L(b)], whereas deuteranopia arises wherever the G cones have the same spectral response as the normal R cones.

The true *protanope* is characterized by his observation that the long-wavelength end of the spectrum is green and stops at about 6800Å, instead of the normal 7600Å. Although he is able to match colors reasonably well, the number of hues seen by this individual is only a small fraction of those seen by the normal person. With only two primary colors, blue and green, at his disposal, he sees only those hues produced by their mixture in all possible proportions.

To the *deuteranope,* the spectrum is not shortened at the ends, but, since the G and R cones are equally stimulated with all the longer wavelengths, he sees only yellow from about 5700Å on. With only red and blue primaries, only hues described by the normal as yellow, blue, or white are produced. Although various methods have been devised for detecting color deficiencies, the most sensitive and accurate determinations are made with an optical instrument known as the *anomaloscope.*

Color vision with only two primaries, as in protanopia and deuteranopia, is called *dichromacy,* whereas vision with only a partial

* Both of these forms of *dichromacy* are hereditary, recessive, and sex linked. Theoretically, one woman in seven is a genetic carrier who does not herself exhibit color deficiency but transmits it *through* half of her daughters and *to* half of her sons. If one of these dichromatic males marries a normal woman, all of their children will be normal but the daughters will all be carriers.

deficiency of one of the three cone types is called *anomalous trichromacy.* In the *anomalous trichromat,* there is a reduction in the brightness of either red, green, or less commonly blue, but the number of possible hues is greater than with the *dichromat* and, in many cases, approaches the *normal* individual who is a *trichromat.*

34.10. Photopic and Scotopic Vision

In a well-lighted room or in bright sunlight, the peak sensitivity of the eye is in the yellow-green part of the visible spectrum. When the light is extremely faint, however, the maximum shifts to the blue-green region and practically all color discrimination disappears. Two brightness sensitivity curves, one for high-level illumination and the other for very low illumination are shown in Fig. 34L. Although the peaks are drawn to the same height, the vertical scales for the two are different. The P curve is actually thousands of times higher than the S curve.

Under daytime illumination, normal vision is acquired by what is called *photopic vision,* a condition whereby the color-sensitive cones in the retina of the eye are responsible for visual sensations. On dark nights, however, when the illumination is very low, the highly sensitive rods account for what little vision is attained, and we have what is called *scotopic vision. Photopic vision is cone vision; scotopic vision is rod vision.* The normal eye contains about 7 million cones and 130 million rods.

An interesting demonstration may be performed with an ordinary projection lantern, a slide that is half red and half blue, and an iris diaphragm located in front of the projection lens. The red and blue glass of the slide should be matched for equal brightness under normal projection on a white screen. As the iris diaphragm is narrowed down, the red field will appear to fade more rapidly than the blue, and finally to disappear altogether. The persistence of the blue is more strikingly observed by directing the eyes to one side of the two-colored fields. If the original matching of red and blue corresponds to equal brightness points like (a) and (b) in Fig. 34L, the reduced illumination corresponds to the unequal brightness points (c) and (d). This observed phenomenon is called the *Purkinje effect.*

34.11. The ICI Chromaticity Diagram

Well-planned steps toward a quantitative measurement of color were taken by the International Commission on Illumination in 1931. At that time three additive primaries, red, green, and blue, were adopted, in which the visible spectrum was divided into three overlapping spectral-response curves somewhat similar to those in Fig. 34L. Although a treatment of this standard ICI system* must be left for more advanced studies, it should be mentioned here that any given color sample can be measured with a spectroscope in terms of the three adopted primaries, and the results of the measurements can be expressed by two numbers. These two numbers can then be plotted on a graph.

When the pure spectrum colors ROYGBV are matched against a mixture of the standard primaries, a smooth curve as shown in Fig. 34M is obtained. With white at the center, the complete gamut of all possible color mixtures lies within the enclosed area RGBVW, with the purples P and magentas M confined to the region RWV between the two ends of the spectrum.

* For a treatment of the ICI color system, see F. W. Sears, *Principles of Physics* (Addison-Wesley Publishing Co., Inc., Reading, Massachusetts), Chap. 13.

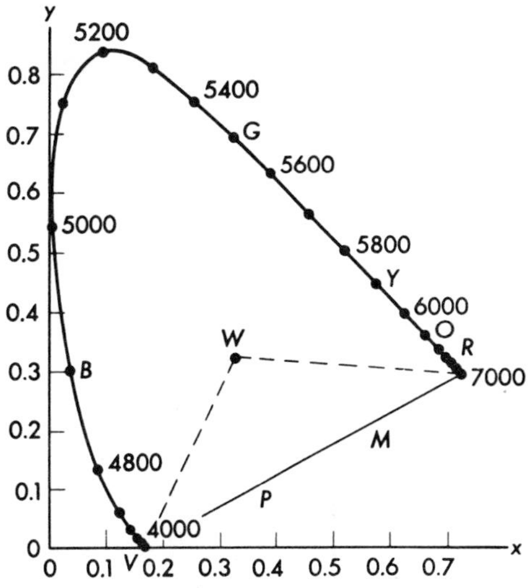

Fig. 34M. ICI chromaticity diagram.

questions

1. The following pairs of colors are mixed additively. What is their resultant color? (a) red and green, (b) red and blue, (c) blue and green, (d) blue and yellow, and (e) red and cyan.

2. The following pairs of colors are mixed subtractively. What is their resultant color? (a) yellow and cyan, (b) magenta and cyan, (c) magenta and yellow, (d) magenta and green, and (e) red and cyan.

3. Make charts showing the various parts of the pure spectrum colors belonging to each of the additive and subtractive primaries.

4. Diagram the color triangle from memory.

5. Draw scotopic and photopic curves for day and night vision, and briefly explain the Purkinje effect.

6. Yellow and magenta are mixed (a) additively, and (b) subtractively. What are the resultant colors in each case?

7. (a) What color added to red will give white? (b) What color subtracted from red will give black?

8. What colors are complementary to each of the following: (a) red, (b) yellow, (c) green, (d) cyan, (e) blue, (f) magenta, (g) white, and (h) black?

9. How can it be shown that the actual colors of the spectrum combine to form the colors shown on the color triangle? Describe the experiment.

10. What are complementary colors? When two complementary colors are added together, what spectrum colors would be present? If they are mixed subtractively, what spectrum colors would be present?

11. Which of the two methods of color mixing produces brighter colors as the result of mixing?

12. What color added to red will give (a) white, (b) magenta, and (c) yellow?

13. What color mixed subtractively with yellow will produce (a) green, (b) red, and (c) black?

14. Make a diagram and briefly explain (a) how yellow and cyan pigments when mixed as paints can produce green. (b) Do the pigment particles themselves become green?

35 Diffraction and interference of light

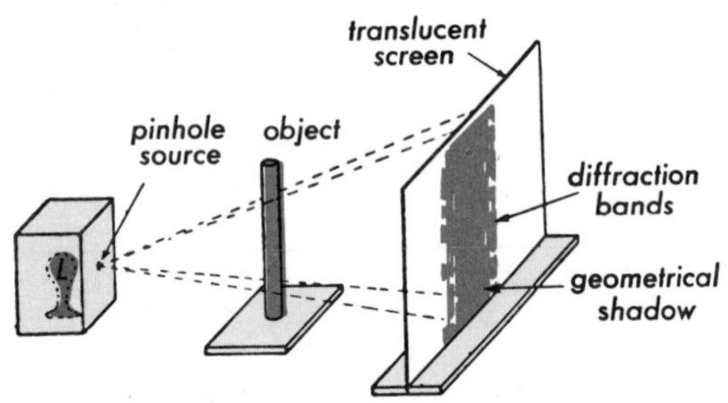

Fig. 35A. The shadow cast by the light from a small source is not sharp at the edges, but exhibits a banded structure.

When light passes close to the edge of any object, it is bent in its path and travels on in a new direction. This bending of light around corners is called *diffraction.*

To observe the phenomenon of diffraction, the following simple experiment may be performed in a darkened room. A box containing a light bulb and a pinhole is placed on one side of the room and a ground-glass observing screen or photographic film is placed on the other. Objects of various kinds are then placed about halfway between the source and the screen as shown in Fig. 35A. This is the arrangement used in obtaining the photograph reproduced in Fig. 35B. Notice that the edges of the shadows are not sharp but are bounded at the edges by narrow

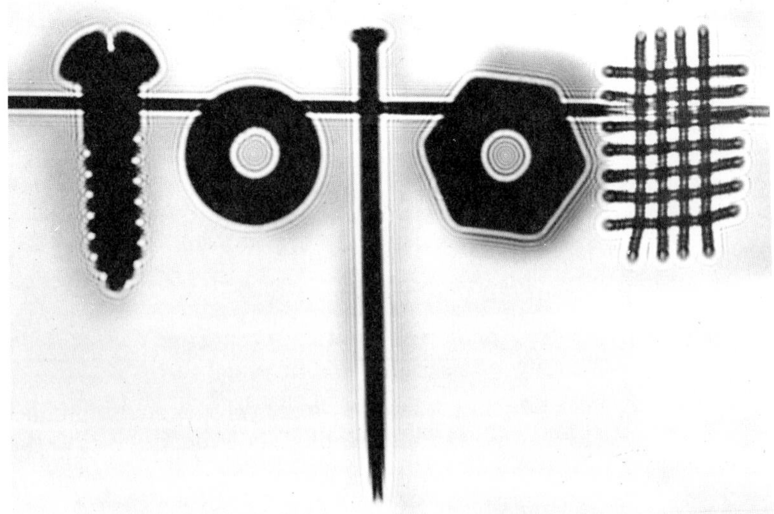

Fig. 35B. Photographs of the shadows cast by small objects. The narrow bands are due to the diffraction of light.

bands or fringes. At the center of two figures the fringes form sets of concentric rings.

35.1. Huygens' Principle

The phenomenon of diffraction was explained in the time of Newton by assuming that light is composed of small particles or corpuscles obeying the ordinary laws of mechanical motion. And so it was that Newton and his followers held for many years to the idea that a source of light is a source of high-speed particles radiated in all directions.

Although such a viewpoint was accepted for many years, it was later abandoned in favor of a wave theory of light, according to which a beam of light is made up of many waves of extremely short wavelengths. By adopting the wave hypothesis, a complete and adequate account of the phenomena of reflection, refraction, diffraction, interference, and polarization was finally formulated on a mathematical basis at the beginning of the nineteenth century by Augustin Fresnel, a French physicist. The wave theory of light was first proposed by the English physicist Robert Hooke in 1665 and improved 20 years later by the Dutch scientist and mathematician, Christian Huygens.*

Everyone has at some time or another dropped a stone in a still pond of water and watched the waves spread slowly outward in ever-widening concentric circles. In the analogous case of a point source of light, the spreading waves form concentric spheres moving outward with the extremely high speed of 3.0×10^8 m/s. This is represented diagrammatically in Fig 35C. Each circle represents the crest of a wave so that the distance between consecutive circles is one wavelength.

According to Huygens' principle, every point on any wave front may be regarded as a new point source of waves. Regarding each of any number of points like a, b, c, etc., as point sources like S, secondary wavelets spread out simultaneously as shown. The envelope of these an instant later is the new wave front A, B, C, etc., and still later the wave front L, M, N, etc. Although Huygens' principle at first glance might seem to be a useless play with circles, it has quite general application to many optical phenomena.

A direct experimental demonstration of Huygens' principle is illustrated in Fig. 35D. Plane waves approaching a barrier AB from the left are reflected or absorbed at every point except at S, where they are allowed to pass on through. When the experiment is carried out with water, one can see the waves spreading out in all directions as if S were a point source.

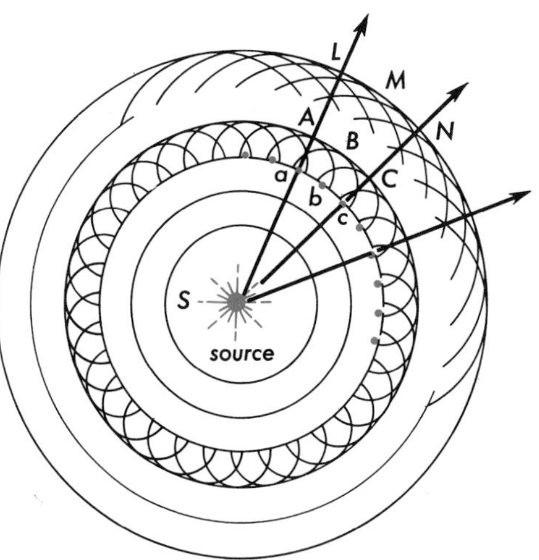

Fig. 35C. Diagram of waves spreading out from a point source. The secondary wavelets and new wave fronts illustrate Huygens' principle.

*Christian Huygens (1629–1695), famous Dutch physicist, was a contemporary of Isaac Newton. Born at The Hague in 1629, young Christian got his first ideas about waves and their propagation by watching the ripples on the canals about his home. Although his chief title-deed to immortality is his development of the wave theory of light, he made many and valuable contributions to mathematics and astronomy. He improved upon the method of grinding telescope lenses and discovered the Orion nebula, part of which is now known by his name. He was elected to the Royal Society of London in 1663, and delivered before that august body the first clear statement of the laws governing the collision of elastic bodies. He died a confirmed bachelor at The Hague in 1695.

If AB is an opaque screen and S is a pinhole small in comparison to the wavelength of light, the light waves will spread out in hemispheres with S at their center. If S is a long narrow slit (perpendicular to the page), the waves spread out with cylindrical wave fronts. Cross sections of all of these cases are represented by the semicircles, the light traveling in the direction of the arrows.

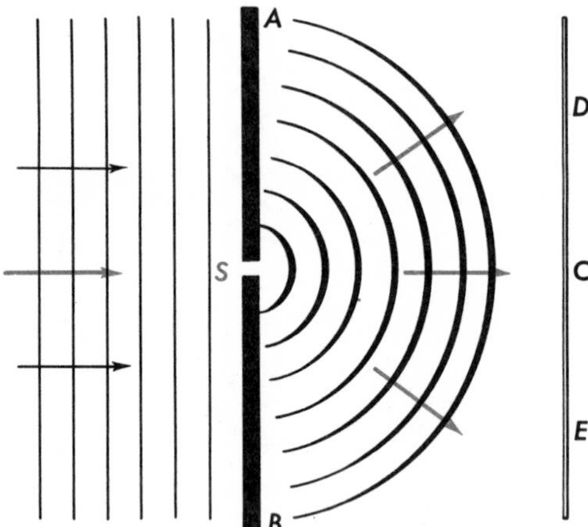

Fig. 35D. Diagram of the diffraction of waves at a small opening also illustrates Huygens' principle.

The action of a converging lens on light waves is illustrated in Fig. 35E. If a point source of light is placed at the focal point, as in diagram (a), the expanding waves pass through the lens and come out as plane waves, i.e., as parallel light. In diagram (b), incident plane waves are shown emerging from the lens as converging waves which come to a focus at F. The change brought about by the lens can be explained by the fact that light travels faster in air than it does in glass.

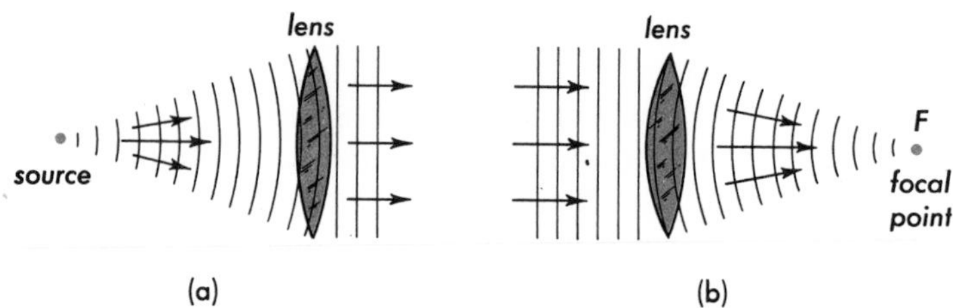

Fig. 35E. The behavior of light waves as they pass through a converging lens.

It is important to note that the time taken for light rays leaving the point source and arriving at the point image is the same for all paths.

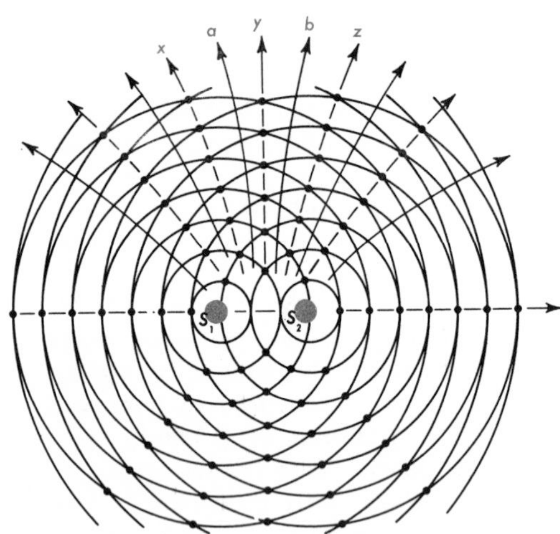

Fig. 35F. Concentric waves traveling outward from a double source, producing what is called an interference pattern.

35.2. Interference

When two stones are dropped simultaneously into a still pond of water, two sets of waves will spread outward as shown in Fig. 35F. As these waves cross each other, they act one upon the other, producing what is called an *interference pattern.* Where the crests of two waves come together at the dotted intersections, they are in step, or in phase, and the amplitude of the water surface is increased. Where the crest of one wave and the trough of another come together, they are out of step, or out of phase, and the amplitude of the water surface is reduced.

The in-phase regions of the waves move outward along the dotted lines, such as x, y, and z, and we have what is called *constructive interference.* The out-of-phase regions move outward along the solid lines, such as a and b, and we have what is called *destructive interference.*

An instantaneous photograph of such a wave pattern is shown in Fig. 35G. Note how clearly the interference regions of the waves stand out. Photographs of this kind, as well as direct observations of such wave patterns, are readily made as follows. A glass tray for maintaining a shallow water layer can be made from a piece of window glass and a wooden frame. A thin metal strip, clamped at one end and set vibrating up and down over the water, is used as a source. A piece of wire, fastened to the vibrating end of this strip, should have one wire end dipping into the water for a single-wave source, and both ends dipping into the water for a double source. Intermittent viewing of the waves through a slotted disk or illumination by means of a stroboscopic light source makes the wave pattern appear to stand still or to progress in slow motion.

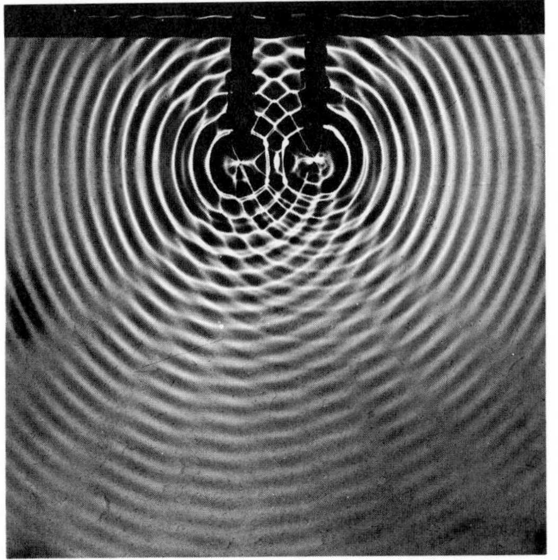

Fig. 35G. Ripple-tank photograph of the interference of water waves from two sources. (Courtesy, Physical Sciences Study Committee Project.)

35.3. Coherence

Coherence is a condition that must exist between two or more waves if a steady state of interference is to be observed, and is a condition involving the relative phases of waves wherever they are brought together.

If two wave sources are set up to emit identical frequencies, and the sources are made to vibrate in step, out of step, or to maintain a constant phase difference between them, the waves they emit are said to be *coherent.*

In the case of the water waves as demonstrated in Fig. 35G, the two sources are made to vibrate in phase with each other by mounting the two prongs on one vibrating metal strip. When two separately mounted metal strips are used, each with a single prong dipping in the water, each may be set vibrating with any random phase. As long as they have the same vibration frequency the sources will maintain the same phase difference, the waves will be coherent, and a steady interference pattern will be produced. With different phase angles between the sources, however, the direction lines, x, a, y, b, and z, as shown in Fig. 35F, will be different.

In order to obtain interference patterns with light waves, two or more coherent sets of waves are derived from the same light source. We find by experiment that it is impossible to obtain interference from two separate sources, such as two lamp filaments set side by side. This failure is caused by the fact that the light from any one source is not an infinite train of waves. On the

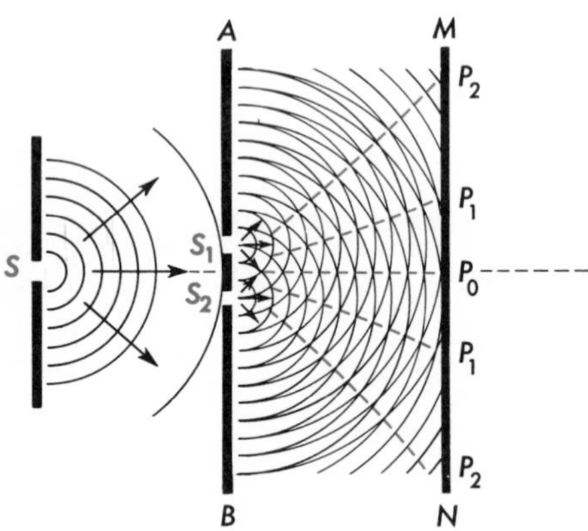

Fig. 35H. Diagram of Young's double-slit experiment illustrating the interference of light waves.

*Thomas Young (1773–1829), Englishman of science, was born June 13, 1773 of a Quaker family. At the age of 14, he knew Latin, Greek, French, Italian, Hebrew, Arabic, and Persian. He studied medicine at Edinburgh and Gottingen, became a practicing physician in 1799, and made professor of physics at the Royal Institution in 1801. Young is best known for his work in optics, particularly experiments demonstrating the wave properties of light. His work on the elastic properties of solids led to his name becoming attached to the stretch modulus of solids. In 1801, he described the vision defect known as astigmatism and put forward the hypothesis, later developed by H. von Helmholtz, that color perception depends on the presence in the retina of three kinds of nerve fibers which respond, respectively, to red, green, and violet light. He should certainly be classified as one of the great men of science.

contrary, emission is random and there are sudden changes in phase occurring in very short intervals of time (of the order of 10^{-8} s).

Thus, although interference patterns may exist for a short time interval, they will shift in position and shape each time there is a phase change, and no interference fringes will be seen. To produce a steady prolonged interference pattern, the difference in phase between any pair of points in the two sources must remain constant. It is characteristic of any interference experiment that the sources must have a point-to-point phase relation, and sources that have this relation are called coherent sources.

35.4. Young's Double-Slit Experiment

Young's* double-slit experiment, first performed with sunlight and pinholes in 1801, served as a crucial test deciding between Newton's corpuscular theory of light and Huygens' wave theory. This is represented schematically in Fig. 35H. Sunlight from a pinhole S was allowed to fall on a distance screen containing two pinholes, S_1 and S_2. The two sets of spherical waves emerging from the two holes interfered with each other in such a way as to form a symmetrical pattern of bands on another screen MN.

For convenience it is now customary to perform Young's experiment with narrow slits in place of pinholes. If S, S_1, and S_2 in Fig. 35H represent the cross sections of three narrow slits, the light falling on the farther screen MN has the appearance of equidistant bands or fringes, as shown by the photograph in Fig. 35I. The bright fringes correspond to the points P_o, P_1, P_2, etc., and the dark fringes to the points halfway between.

As the waves travel outward from each slit S_1 and S_2, they cross each other only at points that lie along the dotted lines shown in the diagram. These lines represent the areas where the crests of two waves come together and produce a maximum brightness. About halfway between these dotted lines lie other areas where the crest of one wave and the trough of another cancel each other and produce darkness. This is the same interference phenomenon as is illustrated by water waves in Fig. 35G. With light waves, where the bright fringes are formed there is constructive interference, and where the dark fringes appear there is destructive interference.

This experiment is frequently performed in the elementary physics laboratory, and from measurements of fringe and slit spacings, as well as double-slit to screen distance, the wavelengths of different colors of light are calculated.

A formula for the wavelength of light can be derived from the

the screen, and d the distance between slit centers. P_0 is located on the perpendicular bisector of the double slit S_1 and S_2. geometry of Fig. 35J. Let P be the position of any bright fringe on

The two rays emerging from S_1 and S_2 parallel to CP are brought to a focus at P. Line S_2A, drawn perpendicular to the two rays, forms a right triangle S_1AS_2. By this construction the short side S_1A becomes the extra distance that light must travel from the upper slit to arrive at the screen MN.

To produce a bright fringe at P, the interval S_1A must be equal to one whole wavelength, two whole wavelengths, three whole wavelengths, etc., for only then will waves from S_1 and S_2 arrive at P in phase. From the right triangle S_1AS_2 we can write

$$\frac{n\lambda}{d} = \sin\theta \tag{35a}$$

where

$$n = 1, 2, 3, 4, \ldots$$

Since line CP_0 is perpendicular to MN and S_2A is perpendicular to CP, angle S_1S_2A equals angle P_0CP, and we can write

$$\frac{x}{D} = \sin\theta \tag{35b}$$

Since the fringes are so close together, and the focal length f is long by comparison, D and f are so nearly equal we can write

$$\frac{x}{f} = \sin\theta \tag{35c}$$

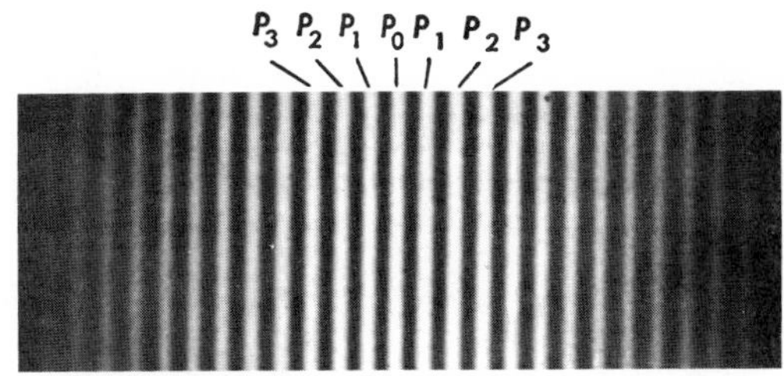

Fig. 35I. Interference fringes produced by a double slit as in Young's experiment.

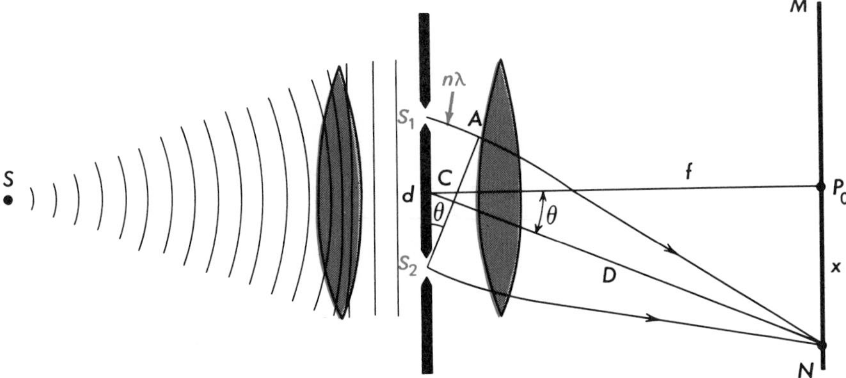

Fig. 35J. Geometrical relations for the double-slit experiment.

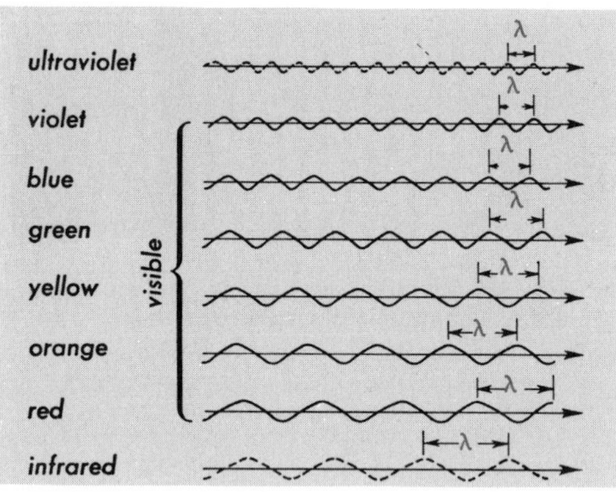

Fig. 35K. Diagram showing the relative wavelengths of light.

Combining left-hand sides of Eqs.(35a) and (35c), we obtain

$$\frac{n\lambda}{d} = \frac{x}{f} \tag{35d}$$

from which

$$x = \frac{n\lambda f}{d} \tag{35e}$$

This formula shows that on increasing the slit spacing d, the fringe spacing decreases. On increasing the wavelength λ, the bands are farther apart.

By measuring the fringe spacing x, the distance between slit centers, and f, the wavelength of different colors of light can be calculated. Repeated experiments, carefully performed, give the following results.

Violet, $\lambda = 4100 \times 10^{-10}$ m
Blue, $\lambda = 4700 \times 10^{-10}$ m
Green, $\lambda = 5500 \times 10^{-10}$ m
Yellow, $\lambda = 5800 \times 10^{-10}$ m
Orange, $\lambda = 6100 \times 10^{-10}$ m
Red, $\lambda = 6600 \times 10^{-10}$ m

As illustrated by the drawing of waves in Fig. 35K, red light has the longest waves.

These wavelengths, measured by the double-slit experiment, are therefore average values, since each color corresponds to a range of different wavelengths.

Example 1. Young's double-slit experiment is performed by a student in the laboratory, and the following measurements are recorded: the spacing between slit centers is 0.556 mm, the fringes are 0.985 mm apart, and the focal length of the lens is 82.6 cm. Find (a) the wavelength of the light, and (b) its color.

Solution. The given quantities are $d = 5.56 \times 10^{-4}$ m, $x = 9.85 \times 10^{-4}$ m, and $f = 0.826$ m . Since $n = 1$ in this example, we may solve Eq.(35d) for λ, and substitute known quantities directly, as follows:

$$\lambda = \frac{xd}{nf} = \frac{9.85 \times 10^{-4} \times 5.56 \times 10^{-4}}{1.0 \times 0.826}$$

$$\lambda = 6630 \times 10^{-10} \text{ m}$$

Comparison of this wavelength with the above table shows the light to be *red.*

35.5. The Angstrom as a Unit of Length

Because the wavelengths of light are so very short, the physicist has adopted a smaller unit of length than the meter, centimeter, or millimeter. This unit is called the *angstrom* (Å), after the Swedish scientist by that name. In 1868 Ångstrom published a map of the visible spectrum of the sun, and on this map he labeled the wavelengths in ten-millionths of a millimeter. Since that time, light waves have been specified in these units.

In one meter there are 10,000,000,000 angstroms:

$$1 \text{ m} = 10^{10} \text{ Å} \tag{35f}$$

For all electromagnetic waves, visible or invisible, the velocity c in a vacuum is 3×10^8 m/s, and the following wave equation holds true:

$$c = \nu\lambda \tag{35g}$$

where, for the *MKSA* system, ν is the frequency in Hz and λ is the wavelength in meters. From this we see that the longer the wavelength, the lower the frequency; and the shorter the wavelength, the higher the frequency.

Here is a list of wavelengths of the approximate center of each color band given in angstroms.

Violet	$\lambda = 4100$ Å
Blue	$\lambda = 4700$ Å
Green	$\lambda = 5500$ Å
Yellow	$\lambda = 5800$ Å
Orange	$\lambda = 6100$ Å
Red	$\lambda = 6600$ Å

In other units green light, for example, has a wavelength of 5.5×10^{-5} cm, 5.5×10^{-7} m, or 0.55 μ.

35.6. Phase Change on Reflection

When light waves are incident on a boundary separating two optically transparent media in which the velocity is different, the incident wave train is divided into reflected and refracted trains.

If the incident wave is in a medium of lower optical density than the second, the reflected wave changes phase by π radians, or 180°, while the refracted wave does not. If the incident wave is in a medium of higher optical density than the medium it is approaching, there is no phase change on either reflection or refraction. Just how this affects the interference of light waves will be explained in detail in the next section.

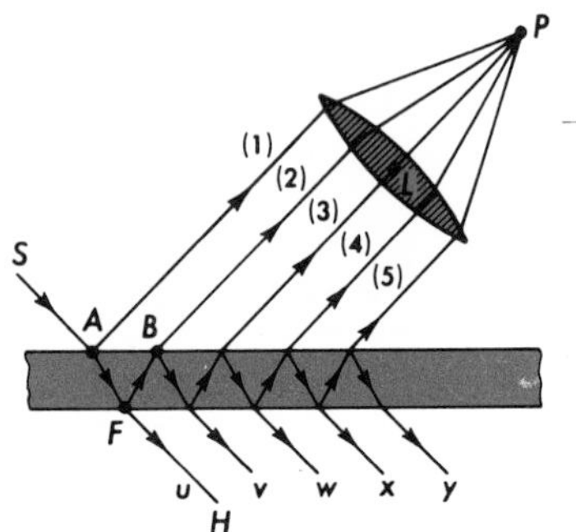

Fig. 35L. Multiple reflections in a plane-parallel film.

35.7. Interference by Multiple Reflections

Some of the most spectacular color phenomena in nature arise from the multiple reflections of light between the two surfaces of a thin transparent medium. These effects are familiar to everyone who has observed the colors displayed by sunlight falling on soap bubbles, or on thin oil films on the surface of water in a puddle. To investigate the origin of these color effects, we will consider an idealized case of reflection from a thin layer of transparent material with perfectly plane and parallel sides, as shown in Fig. 35L.

Let a ray of light from a source S be incident on the surface of the film at A. Part of this light will be reflected as ray (1) and part refracted in the direction AF. Upon arrival at F, part of the latter will be reflected to B and part refracted toward H. At B the ray FB will again be divided, etc.

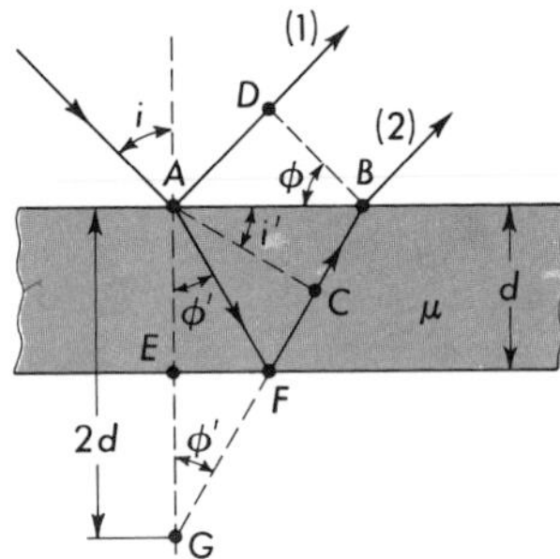

Fig. 35M. Optical path difference between two consecutive rays in multiple reflection (see Fig. 35L).

A continuation of this process produces two sets of parallel rays, one emerging from each side of the film. In each of these sets the amplitude and the intensity decrease from one ray to the next. If the set of parallel reflected rays is now collected by a lens and focused at the point P, each ray will have traveled a different distance, and the phase relations may be such as to produce destructive or constructive interference at that point. It is the interference of the many waves coming together that produces the colors of thin films when they are viewed by the naked eye. In such a case L becomes the lens of the eye, and P becomes the fovea at the center of the retina.

In order to find the phase difference between the rays, we must first evaluate the difference in the optical path traversed by a pair of successive rays, such as rays (1) and (2). During the time light travels a distance x in a medium of refractive index μ, light in air or a vacuum travels a greater distance equal to μx. The product μx for any medium is called the *optical path* [see Eq.(31d)]:

$$\text{optical path} = \mu x \tag{35h}$$

Let d in Fig. 35M be the thickness of the film, μ its index of refraction, λ the wavelength of the light, and i and i' the angles of incidence and refraction. If BD is perpendicular to ray (1), the optical paths from D to B to the focus of the lens will be equal. Starting at A, ray (2) has the path AFB in the film of index μ, and ray (1) the path AD in air of index $\mu = 1$.

The optical path difference between the two rays is, therefore,

$$\Delta x = \mu(\text{AFB}) - (\text{AD})$$

If BF is extended to intersect the perpendicular line AE at G, AF = GF because of the equality of the angles of incidence and reflection at the lower surface. Thus we have

$$\Delta x = \mu(\text{GC} + \text{CB}) - (\text{AD})$$

Now AC is drawn perpendicular to FB; so the broken lines AC and DB represent two successive positions of a wave front reflected from the lower surface. The optical paths must be the same by any ray drawn between two wave fronts; so we may write

$$\mu(\text{CB}) = (\text{AD})$$

The path difference then reduces to

$$\Delta x = \mu(\text{GC}) = \mu(2d \cos i')$$

If this path difference is a whole number of wavelengths, we might expect rays (1) and (2) to arrive at the focus of the lens in phase with each other and produce a maximum of intensity. However, we must take account of the fact that ray (1) undergoes a phase change of π at reflection, while ray (2) does not, since it is internally reflected (see Sec. 35.6). The condition, therefore, produces minima

$$2\mu d \cos i' = n\lambda \qquad (35i)$$

minima

where $n = 1, 2, 3, 4$, etc., and is called the *order number.*

Next we examine the phases of the remaining rays (3), (4), (5), etc. Since the geometry is the same, the optical path difference between rays (2) and (3) will also be given by Eq.(35i). But there are only internal reflections involved, so that if Eq.(35i) is satisfied, rays (2) and (3) will be in the same phase. The same holds for all succeeding pairs, and we conclude that under these conditions rays (1) and (2) will be 180° out of phase, and rays (2), (3), (4), etc., will be in phase with each other.

It can be shown that if the amplitudes of rays (2), (3), (4), . . . ∞, are added together, their sum is just equal to the amplitude of ray (1). This means that ray (1) exactly cancels all the others and that the interference is complete and the minima are actually zero.

Intensity maxima, on the other hand, will occur when the optical path difference between rays (1) and (2) is given by

$$2\mu d \cos i' = (n + \tfrac{1}{2})\lambda \qquad (35j)$$

maxima

where the order number $n = 1, 2, 3, 4, \ldots \infty$.

Under these conditions ray (2) will be in phase with ray (1), but rays (3), (5), (7), etc., will be out of phase with (2), (4), (6), etc. Since (2) has a greater amplitude than (3), and (4) a greater amplitude than (5), etc., these pairs will not cancel each other. Since the stronger series combines with (1), the greatest amplitude of all, there will be a maximum intensity. The transmitted rays emerging from the lower side of the film in Fig. 35L also produce interference bands when viewed from below.

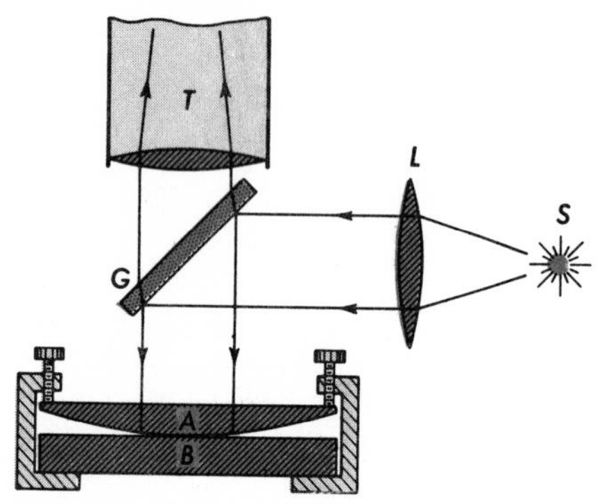

Fig. 35N. Experimental arrangement used in viewing and measuring Newton's rings.

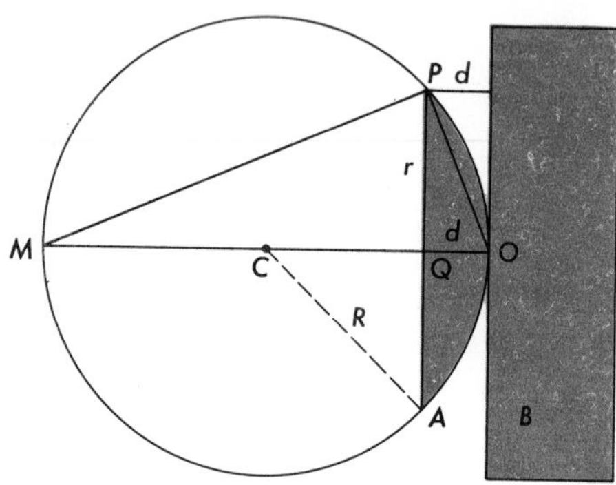

Fig. 35O. Geometry for deriving the wavelength of light from the measured diameters of interference rings.

35.8. Newton's Rings

If interference is produced in an air film between the convex surface of a long-focus plano–convex lens and a plane glass surface, the fringes will be concentric rings. Such fringes were first studied in detail by Newton, but were not correctly explained until years later.

As a laboratory experiment the observations are usually made at normal incidence as shown in Fig. 35N. A clear glass plate G reflects monochromatic light from an appropriate source down onto the lens and plate. After multiple reflections the light is transmitted by G and observed directly above in a low-power measuring microscope (see Fig. 35O).

Under these conditions the positions of the principal maxima are given by Eq.(35j), where d is the thickness of the air film at each successive ring. If we let R be the radius of the lens surface A, and assume A and B are just touching at the center, the value of d for any ring can be derived from Fig. 35O as follows: From a theorem in geometry △MPQ and △POQ are similar right triangles and corresponding sides are proportional. We can write, therefore,

$$\frac{d}{r} = \frac{r}{2R - d} \tag{35k}$$

If R is very large compared with d, as in the case of the Newton's rings experiment, we can drop the d in the denominator to obtain

$$\frac{d}{r} = \frac{r}{2R}$$

or

$$d = \frac{r^2}{2R} \tag{35ℓ}$$

This is the so-called *sagitta formula.*

An example of Newton's rings by reflection is shown in Fig. 35P. The central spot is where the two surfaces touch, causing darkness. There, light reflected from the flat surface changes phase by 180°, whereas light internally reflected from the curved surface does not.

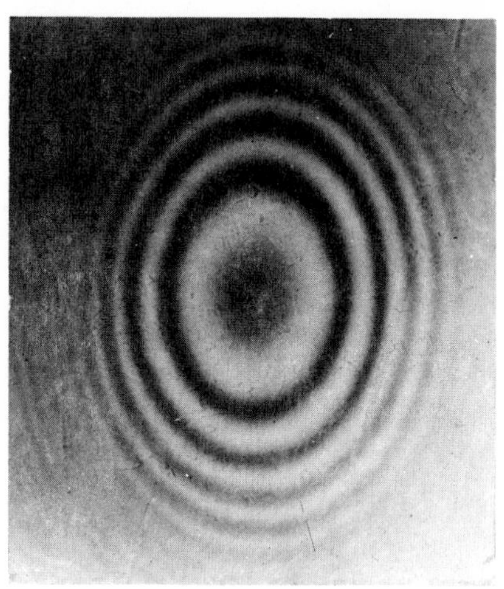

Fig. 35P. Newton's rings by reflection.

If we count the first dark ring out from the center as $n = 1$, the thickness $d = \frac{1}{2}\lambda$ will make the path difference 1λ, and the two rays will again destructively interfere. For the second dark ring out from the center, $n = 2$, the thickness $d = \frac{2}{2}\lambda$, the path difference is 2λ, and again the two waves will destructively interfere. In general, we can write

$$d = \frac{n}{2}\lambda$$

where

$$n = 0, 1, 2, 3, 4, \ldots .$$

Equating the two values for d, we obtain

$$\frac{r^2}{2R} = \frac{n}{2}\lambda$$

or

$$\lambda = \frac{r^2}{nR} \tag{35m}$$

Newton's dark rings

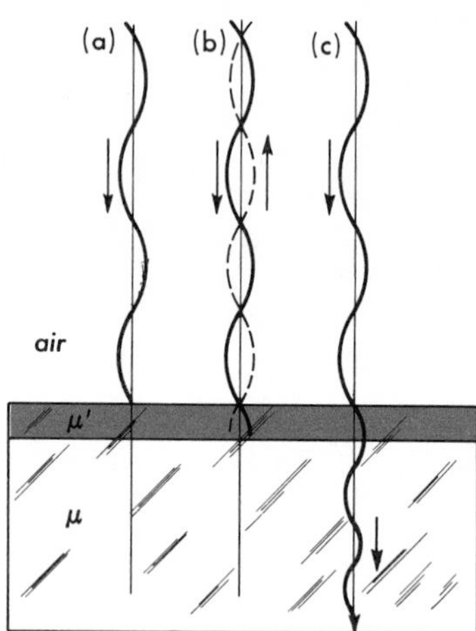

Fig. 35Q. Diagram showing the action on light waves produced by a nonreflecting film on a glass surface.

Example 2. A student observes Newton's rings in a laboratory experiment using a sodium lamp as a source of light. If several measurements of the diameter of the *25th* dark ring give an average value of 2.335 cm, and the lens surface radius is recorded as 9.25 m, find the wavelength of the light.

Solution. The given quantities are $r = 1.1675 \times 10^{-2}$ m, $R = 9.25$ m, and $n = 25$. By direct substitution in Eq.(35m), we obtain

$$\lambda = \frac{r^2}{nR} = \frac{(1.1675 \times 10^{-2})^2}{25.0 \times 9.25}$$

$$\lambda = 5894 \times 10^{-10} \text{ m}$$

$$\lambda = 5894 \text{ Å}$$

35.9. Nonreflecting Films

The pale purple coating on the surfaces of the lenses used in high-quality optical instruments like cameras, binoculars, microscopes, etc., is for the purpose of reducing light reflections. The surfaces are coated with a film of hard, transparent material of index μ' and one-quarter of a wavelength thick. The thickness d is given by

$$d = \tfrac{1}{4}\lambda' \tag{35n}$$

so that the light reflected at normal incidence is almost completely suppressed by interference. This corresponds to $n = 0$ in Eq.(35i), which here is a condition for a minimum. The incident light with wavelength λ falls on the upper surface as shown in Fig. 35Q(a). Upon entering the medium, its wavelength is reduced to

$$\lambda' = \lambda/\mu \tag{35o}$$

The waves reflected from the lower surface have an extra path of one-half wavelength λ' over those from the upper surface, and the two, combined with the weaker waves from multiple reflections, interfere destructively as shown in (b). Complete destruction will occur for a film in contact with a glass of higher index μ, if the film index μ' is given by

$$\mu' = \sqrt{\mu} \tag{35p}$$

With this condition satisfied, the incident light is not reflected but passes through the surface, diagram (c), as if by a kind of resonance effect. A similar coating on the other side of the glass lens, prism, or plate will act similarly and transmit all of the light.

The coating material of refractive index μ' is selected for green light $\lambda = 5500$ Å, and made $\frac{1}{4}\lambda'$ thick for this wavelength. The slightly different index for red and blue light means the film is not exactly $\frac{1}{4}\lambda'$ for them and a small amount of red and blue light is reflected, hence the purple hue.

Example 3. Find the thickness of the film to be deposited on a lens surface that will make it nonreflecting. Assume the refractive index of the glass to be 1.6900 for green light $\lambda = 5500$ Å

Solution. The given quantities are $\lambda = 5.50 \times 10^{-7}$ m and $\mu =$ 1.6900. We first find the refractive index of the film material to be used. By direct substitution in Eq.(35p), we find

$$\mu' = \sqrt{\mu} = \sqrt{1.6900} = 1.300$$

To find the wavelength of the light in this film we use Eq.(35o), which upon direct substitution gives

$$\lambda' = \frac{5.50 \times 10^{-7}\text{ m}}{1.30} = 4.23 \times 10^{-7}\text{ m}$$

Since by Eq.(35n) the thickness of the film must be exactly *one-quarter* of this wavelength, we find

$$d = \frac{4.23 \times 10^{-7}\text{ m}}{4.0} = 1.058 \times 10^{-7}\text{ m}$$

$$d = 1058\text{ Å}$$

---

problems

1. A double slit with a separation of 0.460 mm is illuminated by green light from an arc lamp. If the wavelength of the light is 5400 Å, how far behind the slits must one observe the fringes if they are to be 1.0 mm apart?

2. Red light of wavelength 6560 Å falls normally on a double slit. Interference fringes observed on a screen 1.50 m away are found to be 3.20 m apart. What is the double slit separation?

3. Young's double slit experiment is performed with red light of wavelength $\lambda = 6438$ Å. If the fringes are measured with a measuring microscope 80.0 cm behind the double slit, and 15 fringes are found to cover 8.62 mm, find the double slit spacing. *Note:* Assume $n = 15$. [Ans. 0.896 mm.]

4. Blue light of wavelength 4250 Å from a narrow slit falls on a double slit having a measured separation of 0.360 mm. If the interference fringes are observed on a screen 5.0 m away, what is the fringe spacing in millimeters?

5. Yellow light is incident normally on a double slit with a separation of 0.485 mm. If the fringes on a screen 2.50 m away are 1.80 mm apart, find the wavelength.

6. A double slit with a separation of 0.2460 mm is illuminated with blue light of wavelength $\lambda = 4300$ Å. If the fringes are observed on a screen 2.0 m away, what is the fringe spacing? [Ans. 3.496 mm.]

7. In a laboratory experiment in which Newton's rings are observed, the 20*th* dark ring has a diameter of 2.160 cm, and the lens surface a recorded radius of 12.40 m. Find (a) the wavelength of the light, and (b) its color.

8. Yellow light from a sodium arc lamp is used for observing Newton's rings in the laboratory. If the diameter of the 15*th* dark ring is 1.850 cm, and the wavelength of the light is 5893 Å, what is the radius of the lens surface?

9. Newton's rings are observed with red light of wavelength 6560 Å, and the 30*th* dark fringe has a diameter of 2.560 cm. Find the radius of the convex lens surface. [Ans. 8.33 m.]

10. A plano–convex lens in which the radius of the curved surface is 12.0 m is used in observing Newton's rings. If the 20*th* dark ring has a diameter of 2.186 cm, find (a) the wavelength of the light, and (b) its color.

11. A nonreflecting film is to be deposited on a dense flint-glass lens surface. If the light has a wavelength of 5.50×10^{-7} m, and the refractive index of the optical glass is 1.6641, find (a) the refractive index required of the film material, and (b) its thickness.

12. A double convex lens with a refractive index of 1.5625 is to be coated on both sides with a nonreflecting film. If the light has an average wavelength of 5.50×10^{-7} m, find (a) the refractive index of the film material to be used, and (b) the film thickness required. [Ans. (a) 1.250, (b) 1100 Å.]

36 Single and multiple aperture diffraction

In the preceding chapter, the interference effects produced by the light waves from two narrow identical slits are treated in detail. In the photograph of the interference fringes (Fig. 35I), it can be seen that the fringe intensity is a maximum at the center of the pattern, and falls off symmetrically to zero on either side. The envelope of these peak intensities is attributed to diffraction, and the spacing between fringes is attributed to interference.

Interference is the result of bringing together a finite number of waves to produce a resultant intensity (two in the case of the double slit), while diffraction is the result of bringing together an infinite number of infinitesimals over a given wave front. This is the subject of the present chapter, considering first how it applies to a single aperture.

36.1. Diffraction by a Single Slit

An experimental arrangement for observing diffraction is shown in Fig. 36A. A single slit is a rectangular aperture, long in comparison to its width. An adjustable slit S is set up with its long dimension horizontal, and illuminated by parallel light of one wavelength. This beam of monochromatic light is obtained by the use of a source of light with a filter, a very narrow slit S′, and two lenses L_1 and L_2.

An actual photograph of the light that falls on a screen such as the one at the right in the diagram is reproduced in Fig. 36B. The photograph shows a wide central band and narrow bands symmetrically located on either side. For this photograph the distance $S'L_1$ was 25 cm, and L_2P was 100 cm. The width of slit S′ was 0.10 mm and S was 0.090 mm. When S′ was widened to more than 0.33 mm, the details of the pattern began to disappear. On the original photograph the total width of the central band was 9.68 mm. The light source was a small mercury arc and a violet glass filter transmitting only the mercury violet light, $\lambda = 4358 \times 10^{-10}$ m.

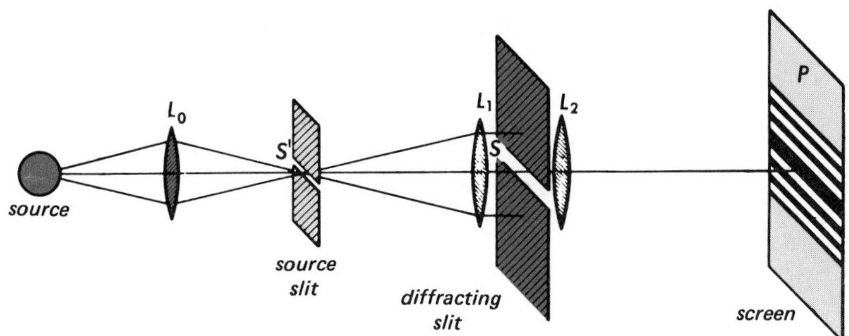

Fig. 36A. Fraunhofer diffraction: experimental arrangement for obtaining the diffraction pattern of a single slit.

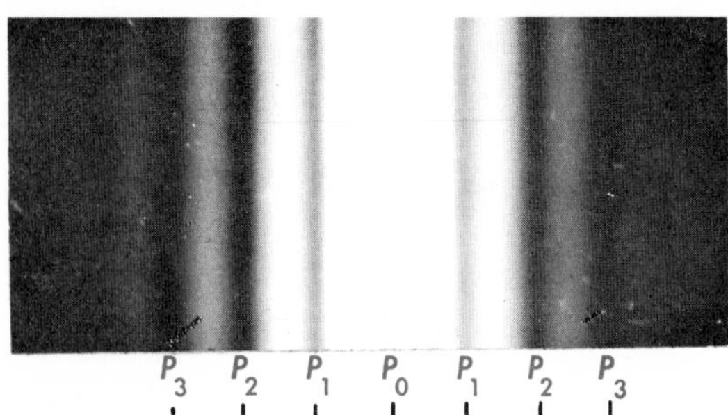

Fig. 36B. Photographs of the single-slit diffraction pattern.

This diffraction pattern can be observed directly by ruling a groove on an unused photographic plate with a penknife, holding it in front of the eye, and then looking directly at the light coming through another such slit several feet away.

The explanation of the single-slit pattern lies in the interference of many waves and is similar in principle to the interference of two waves described in Sec. 35.3. The many waves to be considered here can be thought of as being sent out from every point on a wave crest at the instant that it crosses the plane of the slit.

The cross-section diagram of Fig. 36C shows a slit AB, of width b, with parallel wave crests approaching from the left. The wave crest at the slit is shown divided into 12 imaginary segments of equal width. Each of these segments may be thought of as a new source for a secondary wavelet. Let us now choose a point P_1 on the distant screen where the light intensity is observed to be zero, corresponding to the point P_1 in Fig. 36B. This is a point in Fig. 36C where the length of the light path BCP_1 is one whole wavelength λ greater than the light path AP_1. In other words, the path $BC = 1\lambda$.

To see why this is just the right condition for no light on the screen, consider the wave diagram in Fig. 36D. The points marked a, b, c, etc., correspond to the relative phases of the wavelets arriving at P_1 at the same instant from all 12 of the slit elements. The heights of the vertical lines give the relative displacements of the instantaneous light contributions at P_1 due to the different slit elements. Note that the wavelet from (a) has a small upward displacement, while the wavelet from (u) has an equal downward displacement. One cancels the other to produce darkness. At this same instant the wavelet from (b) has a larger upward displacement, while the wavelet from (v) has an equal downward displacement; thus they cancel each other. Similarly, the elements (c) and (w) may be paired off with opposite displacements, and the process continued across the slit. Each pair of displacements is seen to cancel out and to produce destructive interference, or darkness, at P_1

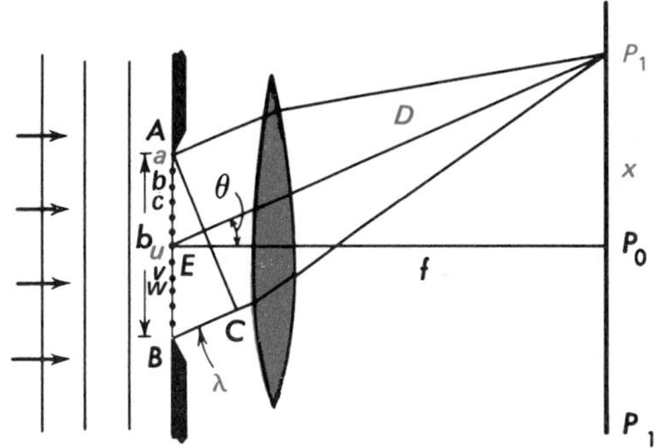

Fig. 36C. Geometry for the single-slit diffraction experiment.

Suppose we now consider a point higher up on the screen corresponding to the center of the next dark band, P_2 of Fig. 36B. For this point the light path BC in Fig. 36C will be two whole wavelengths. If the slit is again divided into an equal number of small segments, the phases of the light wavelets arriving at P_2 will again be found to cancel in pairs.

When this treatment is applied to the point P_0 at the center of the screen, all the paths are the same, all wavelets arrive in phase, and we obtain the bright center band.

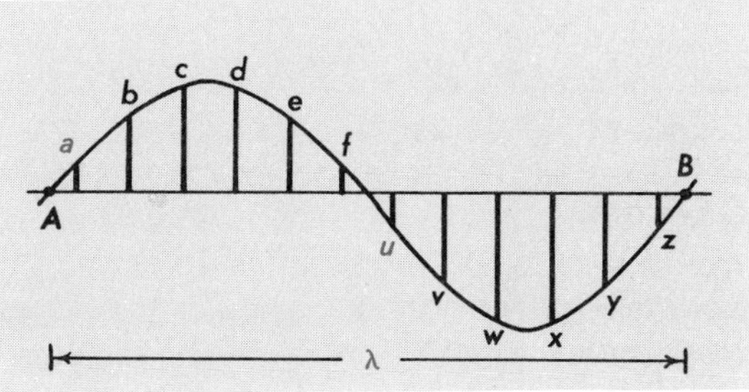

Fig. 36D. Graph of the single-slit wavelet contributions for the first dark band, point P_1 of Fig. 36C.

If the above treatment of pairing-off light contributions from small elements of a single aperture is carried out over all angles of θ, complete cancellations will be found to occur only when the path difference BC is exactly a whole-number multiple of one wavelength, i.e., BC $= 1\lambda, 2\lambda, 3\lambda, 4\lambda$, etc. For the dark bands, then, we can write BC $= n\lambda$, where $n = 0, 1, 2, 3$, etc. Since line AC is perpendicular to EP_1 and line AB is perpendicular to EP_0, the two triangles can be assumed to be similar, and the following proportions between corresponding sides can be written:

$$\frac{n\lambda}{b} = \frac{x}{D} \qquad (36a)$$

But $x/D = \sin\theta$, and we may write

$$\frac{n\lambda}{b} = \sin\theta \qquad (36b)$$

from which we can write

$$n\lambda = b\sin\theta \qquad (36c)$$

dark bands

This formula shows that by widening the slit the diffraction bands become narrower, and vice versa. By increasing the wavelength the bands become wider.

If the path difference BC in Fig. 36C is not equal to a whole number of wavelengths λ, the wavelet contributions to those points on the screen will not cancel out, and this accounts for the bright bands.

A more detailed theory shows that the light intensity on the screen has a distribution like that graphed in Fig. 36E. If we call the central intensity 100%, the maximum intensity of the side bands reaches the relatively low values of 4.7%, 1.6%, 0.83%, etc. Note carefully that the dark points P_0, P_1, P_2, etc., are equally spaced, but that the maxima do not come exactly halfway between.

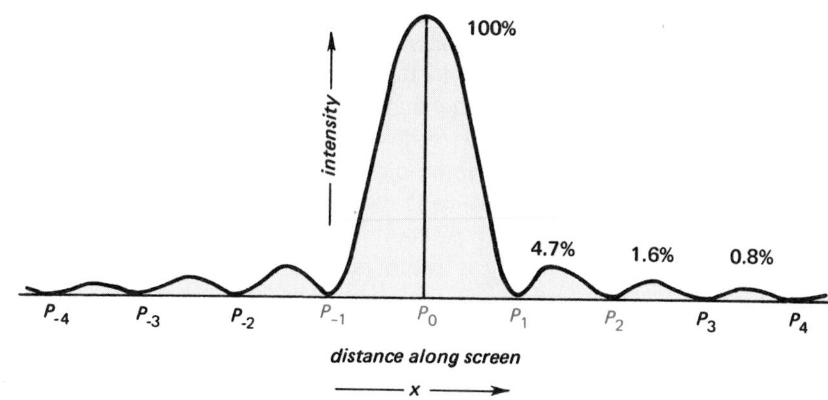

Fig. 36E. Single-aperture diffraction pattern.

To find the distance from the cènter point P_0 to the first dark band, we place $n = 1$ in Eq.(36a), and solve for x_1 to obtain

$$x_1 = \frac{\lambda D}{b} \tag{36d}$$

The value of x_1 also gives directly the width of all side bands, as well as the halfwidth of the central bright band.

Example 1. A parallel beam of monochromatic light falls on a single slit 1.0 mm wide. When the diffraction pattern is observed on a screen 2.0 m away, the central band is found to have a width of 2.50 mm. Find the wavelength of the light.

Solution. The given quantities in this problem are $D = 2.0$ m, $b = 1.0 \times 10^{-3}$ m, $n = 1$, and $x = 1.250 \times 10^{-3}$. Using Eq.(36a) we first solve for λ, then substitute the known quantities, and find

$$\lambda = \frac{xb}{nD} = \frac{1.25 \times 10^{-3} \times 1 \times 10^{-3}}{1 \times 2}$$

$$\lambda = 6.25 \times 10^{-7} \text{ m}$$

In angstrom units this wavelength is 6250 Å, meaning that the light is red in color.

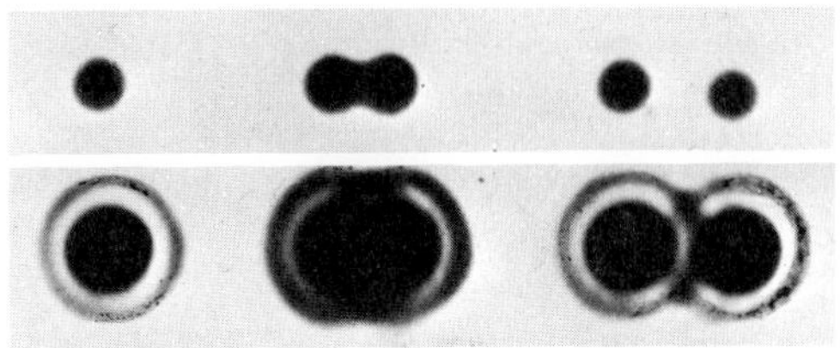

Fig. 36F. Photographs of diffraction images of one point source taken with a circular aperture, two points close together, and two point sources farther apart. Top: short exposure; bottom: longer exposure.

The graph of the intensity pattern shown in Fig. 36E is from the mathematical treatment of light called the Fraunhofer diffraction from a slit. The equation is

$$I = k \frac{\sin^2 \beta}{\beta^2}$$

where I is the intensity and β is given by

$$\beta = \frac{\pi}{\lambda} b \sin \theta$$

36.2. Diffraction by a Circular Aperture

The diffraction pattern formed by light passing through a circular aperture is of considerable importance, as it applies to the resolving power of telescopes and other optical instruments. The resolving power refers to the ability of an instrument to reveal fine detail in the object being viewed.

Owing to the diffraction of light waves as explained in the preceding section, light through a circular aperture produces a diffraction pattern having the same general intensity variations as given by Fig. 36E. Being circular, however, the parallel bands of light from a slit aperture are replaced by concentric circles with a bright disk at the center. It is as if the graph of Fig. 36E were rotated around the center line.

A lens acts as a circular aperture for light passing through it, and the image it forms for every bright spot in any object is a tiny diffraction pattern. The photograph in Fig. 36F shows that, with pinholes in a screen as objects, the images formed by a single lens are composed of tiny disks surrounded by faint concentric rings of light. The larger the lens aperture, the smaller the diffraction patterns. The distant stars act as point objects, and their images formed by a telescope objective are diffraction patterns of this kind.

We can see from this why the magnification by a telescope or microscope is limited, and cannot exceed certain values. If the eyepiece of an instrument has too high a magnifying power, each point in the object is observed as a disk, and the image appears blurred. The mathematical treatment of diffraction by a circular aperture requires Bessel functions and leads to the same formula as Eq.(36d) but with the factor 1.22 introduced in place of $n = 1$ in Eq. (36a):

$$x = 1.22 \frac{\lambda D}{b} \tag{36e}$$

where b is the diameter of the circular aperture and x is the radius of the disk of the diffraction pattern. Transposing D to the other side of the equation, and noting that D is usually hundreds of times greater than x, the quantity x/D can be replaced by θ, and we obtain

$$\theta_1 = \frac{1.22\lambda}{b} \tag{36f}$$

where the angle θ_1 is in radians. The circular disk at the center of the diffraction pattern is called the *Airy disk*.

Sound waves from the circular aperture of a radio loud-speaker will form diffraction patterns of the same kind. Such behavior gives rise to marked changes in sound quality at different points around a room. The microwaves from a radar reflector radiate outward as a single-aperture diffraction pattern, with a central maximum radiated straight forward.

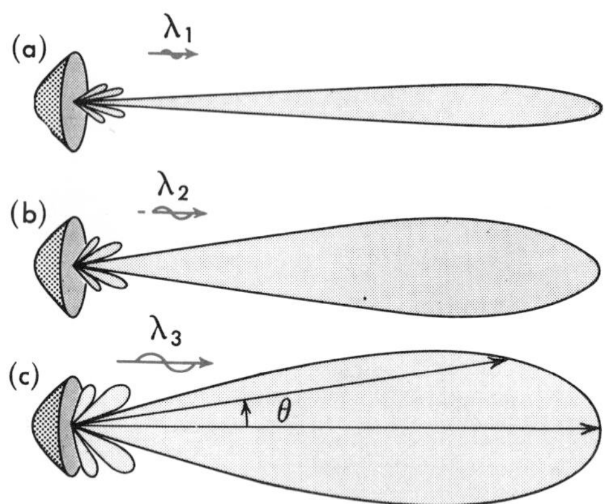

Fig. 36G. Polar diagrams of the diffraction patterns for waves of different wavelength from the same parabolic reflector.

The *lobe* patterns shown for three different wavelengths in Fig. 36G are polar graphs of the intensity contour shown in Fig. 36E. In such polar graphs the intensity in any direction making an angle θ with the central line is plotted from the center out. The length of any arrow drawn at any angle θ is therefore proportional to the intensity radiated in that direction.

The shorter the wavelength and the greater the diameter of the circular aperture emitting the waves, the narrower the lobe pattern. Light waves from a point source at the focus of a parabolic mirror will produce a very narrow beam as shown in diagram (a), while radar and microwaves, with their longer and longer wavelengths, will produce much wider beams as shown in diagrams (b) and (c).

Example 2. The parabolic reflector for a radar transmitter has a diameter of 2.50 m. If the emitted beam has a wavelength of 3.20 cm, find the angular width of the central lobe pattern (a) in radians, and (b) in degrees.
Solution. The given quantities are $b = 2.50$ m and $\lambda = 3.20 \times 10^{-2}$ m. Since θ_1 in Eq.(36f) is half the angular width of the central lobe pattern, in radians, its value must be doubled:

$$2\theta_1 = 2\,\frac{1.22\lambda}{b} = \frac{2.44 \times 3.2 \times 10^{-2}}{2.5 \text{ m}}$$

$$2\theta_1 = 0.03123 \text{ rad}$$

Since 1 radian = 57.3°, the angular width in degrees is

$$2\theta_1 = 57.3 \times 0.03123 = 1.789^\circ$$

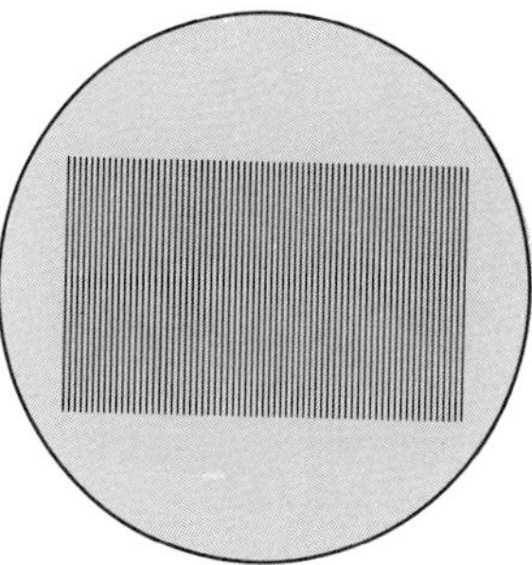

Fig. 36H. Schematic diagram of the grooves or rulings on a diffraction grating.

36.3. The Diffraction Grating

The diffraction grating is an optical device widely used in place of a prism for studying the spectrum of light sources and measuring the wavelengths they emit. Since the grating is a very powerful instrument for the study of spectra, we shall treat in considerable detail the intensity pattern it produces. We shall find that the pattern is quite complex in general, but that it has a number of features in common with that of the double slit treated in Chap. 35. In fact, the latter may be considered as an elementary grating of only two slits.

Gratings are made by ruling fine grooves with a diamond point either on a glass plate to produce a transmission grating or on a polished metal mirror to produce a reflection grating. As illustrated in Fig. 36H, rulings on a diffraction grating are all parallel and equally spaced. The very best gratings are several inches wide and contain up to 30,000 lines per inch.

The transmission grating and its effect on light is idealized by the cross-section diagrams in Fig. 36I. The heavy colored lines represent the rulings which permit no light to get through and the open intervals between them represent the undisturbed parts of the glass which transmit the light and act like the parallel slits in Young's double-slit experiment. In diagram (a) parallel light is shown arriving at the grating surface as a succession of plane waves. The light then passes through the openings, spreads out as Huygens' wavelets, and forms new wave fronts parallel to the grating face. These wave fronts, parallel to the original waves, constitute a beam of light W traveling on in the same direction as the original beam.

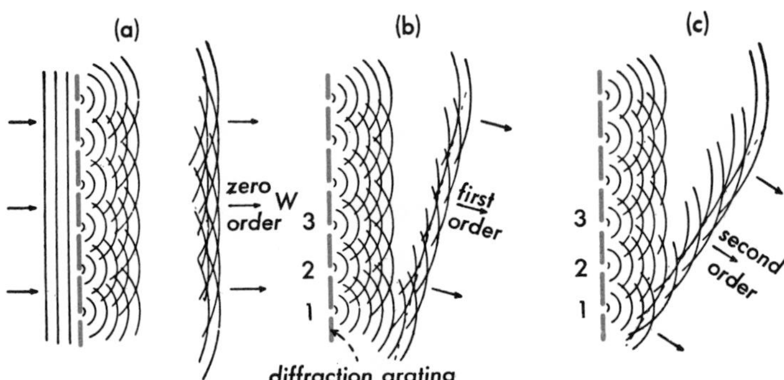

Fig. 36I. Diagrams showing the formation of wave fronts displaying the various orders of interference observed with a diffraction grating.

These are not the only wave fronts, however, for other beams of parallel light are to be found traveling away from the grating in other directions. Two other such wave fronts are illustrated in diagrams (b) and (c). In (b), a dotted line is drawn tangent to the seventh wave from opening 1, the eighth wave from opening 2, the ninth wave from opening 3, etc., to form what is called a wave front of the first order of interference. In (c), a line is drawn tangent to the fourth wave from opening 1, the sixth wave from opening 2, the eighth wave from opening 3, etc., to form what is called a wave front of the second order of interference. Similarly, by taking every third wave or every fourth wave from consecutive slits, other parallel wave fronts corresponding to the third or fourth orders are found moving off at greater angles. By symmetry, all of the orders found on one side of the zeroth order are also found at the same angle on the other side.

Experimentally, there are two methods of observing the various orders of interference from a small diffraction grating; one is to place the grating directly in front of the eye, and the other is to place it in the parallel beam of light between two lenses as shown in Fig. 36J. In the latter case the second lens is shown converging the various wave fronts of the different orders to a focus on a distant screen. If the source is a slit as shown at the left, and a colored glass filter is used to let through light of any one color, say violet, the light falling on the screen will appear as shown in the top photograph in Fig. 36K. Each vertical line is an image of the slit source and is violet in color.

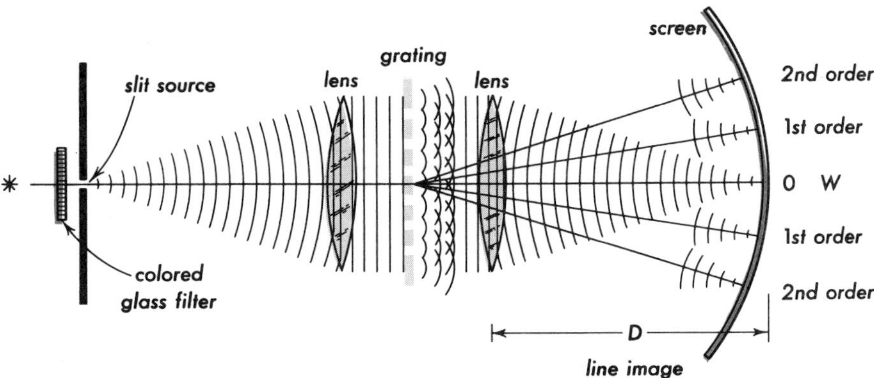

Fig. 36J. How the wave fronts of the various orders of interference from a diffraction grating are brought to a focus by the same lens.

If the three diagrams in Fig. 36I are redrawn for light of a longer wavelength, i.e., a greater distance between waves, the central beam of light W would travel on in the same direction as before, but the various *orders of interference* would be diffracted out at greater angles. Should green light of one wavelength be used, the slit images formed on the screen would be farther apart than for violet light, as illustrated by the images marked G in Fig. 36K. This lower photograph was taken with both violet and green light from a mercury arc passing through the grating. These line images are called spectrum lines.

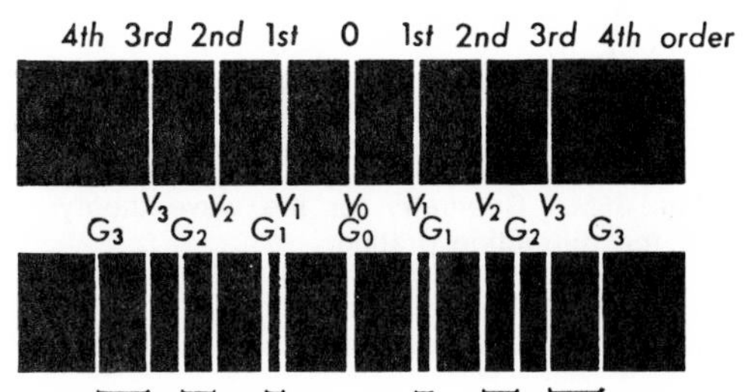

Fig. 36K. Photographs of the different orders of interference of violet and green light obtained with a diffraction grating as shown in Fig. 36J.

It will be noted that the separation of the spectrum lines V and G in the *third order* is three times as great as in the *first order*. In other words, any two spectrum lines are separated by an amount that is proportional to the order of interference.

If white light is sent through a grating, all of the different wavelengths, corresponding to the different colors, form their own characteristic wave fronts and produce a complete and continuous spectrum in each order of interference. This is illustrated by a diagram in Fig. 36L. Since the zeroth order for all colors comes to the same point, the central image is white. Because the width of each spectrum is proportional to the order, the higher orders overlap one another more and more. The violet of the third order, V_3 for example, falls on the red of second order, R_2.

The general appearance of a spectrum, produced by a diffraction-grating spectograph, can be seen in the photographs reproduced in Chap. 37.

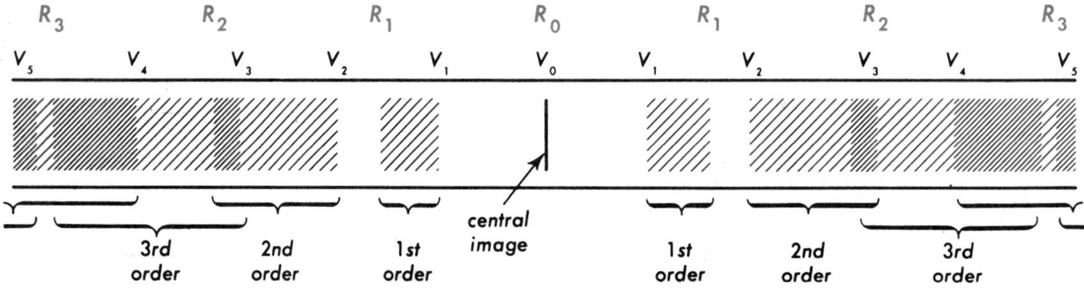

Fig. 36L. Diagram of the first several orders of the continuous spectrum as displayed by a diffraction grating.

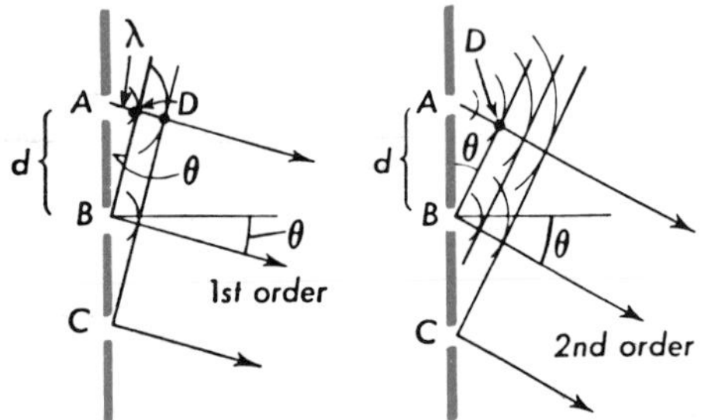

Fig. 36M. Geometry for the wave theory of the diffraction grating.

36.4. Simple Mathematical Theory of the Diffraction Grating

The theory of the diffraction grating is similar to that of the double slit and is shown in its simplest form in Fig. 36M. These diagrams derive their construction from Fig. 36I. The wave fronts for the first order emerge at such an angle θ that the difference in path between the rays from any two consecutive openings, like 1 and 2, is just one wavelength. Since any tangent drawn to any circle is always perpendicular to the radius drawn through the point of contact, triangle ABD is a right triangle, and $\sin\theta = \lambda/d$. Transposing, we obtain

$$\lambda = d \sin\theta \tag{36g}$$

where λ is the wavelength of the light, d is the grating spacing, and θ is the angle that the emergent light of the first order makes with the grating normal.

By similar reasoning, and by the use of diagrams like the one shown for the second order, it will be seen that spectra of the second, third, fourth, etc., order are formed at such angles θ that the difference in path between consecutive slits is 2λ, 3λ, 4λ, etc. In general, the side AD of the right triangle ABD must be equal to $n\lambda$, where $n = 1, 2, 3, 4$, etc., and $\sin\theta = n\lambda/d$. If we transpose as before, we obtain the general formula

$$n\lambda = d \sin\theta \tag{36h}$$

bright lines

In this general grating formula, n is the *spectrum order.*

Example 3. Red light of one particular wavelength falls normally on a grating having 4000 lines per cm. If the second-order spectrum makes an angle of 36° with the grating normal, what is the wavelength of the light?

Solution. Since the grating has 4000 lines per cm, the spacing between the lines is 1/4000, or $d = 0.000250$ cm. The other given quantities are $\theta = 36°$ and $n = 2$. Substituting in Eq.(36h) and solving for λ, we get

$$\lambda = \frac{d \sin \theta}{n} = \frac{2.5 \times 10^{-6}\text{ m} \times \sin 36°}{2}$$

$$\lambda = \frac{2.5 \times 10^{-6}\text{ m} \times 0.5878}{2} = 7.35 \times 10^{-7}\text{ m}$$

or $$\lambda = 7350\text{ Å}$$

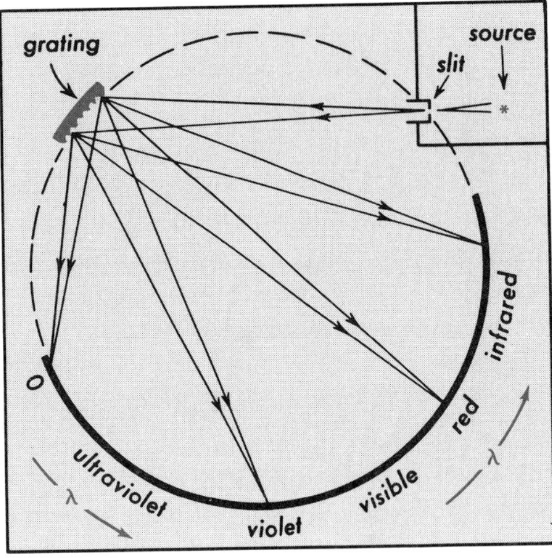

Fig. 36N. Diagram of a spectrograph employing a concave diffraction grating: the Paschen mounting.

If the incident parallel light makes an angle ϕ with the grating normal, Eq.(36h) takes the more general form

$$n\lambda = d(\sin \theta + \sin \phi)$$

the plus sign being used when θ and ϕ are on the same side of the grating normal.*

36.5. Concave Gratings

Transmission gratings were first made by Fraunhofer, a German physicist, in 1819, and the first reflection gratings were made by H. A. Rowland,† an American physicist, in 1882. Although Rowland's first gratings were ruled on flat surfaces, his best ones were ruled upon the polished surfaces of concave mirrors.

One of the most useful of all spectrographs to be found in the research laboratory today is one whose design was originally devised by F. Paschen. A concave reflection grating with a radius of curvature r is mounted in one corner of a dark room. The slit and light source are located in another corner and a long plateholder directly opposite (see Fig. 36N).

Light from the source to be studied passes through the narrow slit and then falls on the grating to be diffracted. Note that the grating performs the double function of dispersing the light into a spectrum and of focusing it as well.

* For a more detailed treatment of interference and diffraction phenomena, see F. W. Jenkins and H. E. White, *Fundamentals of Optics* (McGraw-Hill, New York, 1957).

†Henry A. Rowland (1848–1901), American physicist, is noted principally for his ruling of the first high-quality diffraction gratings and his publication of a large and detailed photograph of the sun's spectrum. He was the recipient of many honors, including the Rumford Medal and the Draper Medal.

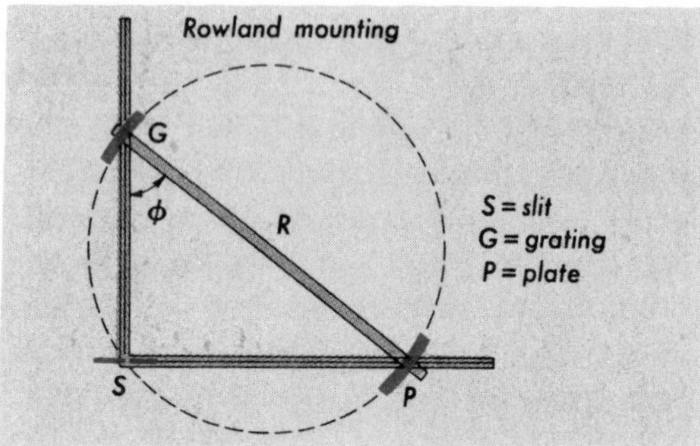

Fig. 36O. Diagram of the Rowland mounting for a concave reflection grating.

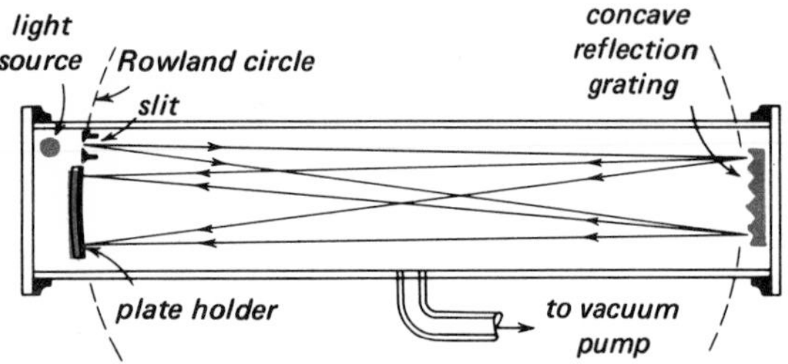

Fig. 36P. Diagram of an Eagle-mounting spectrograph employing a concave reflection grating.

The slit, grating, and photographic plateholder are all located with high precision on the periphery of a circle whose diameter is equal to the radius of curvature of the grating. Such an arrangement brings the different wavelengths to focus all along the plateholder. This circle is called the *Rowland circle* in honor of H. A. Rowland.

When a photograph of any part of the spectrum is desired, a strip of plate or film is placed in the proper place in the plateholder and exposed to the spectrum. The original photographs in Figs. 37O and 37Q were made with a 21-ft diameter Paschen spectograph.

36.6. The Rowland Spectrograph

Another useful type of mounting for a concave reflection grating was first developed by Rowland and is commonly referred to as the Rowland mounting.

As shown in Fig 36O, the grating G and plateholder P are fixed to opposite ends of a rigid beam of length R. The two ends of this beam rest on swivel trucks which are free to move along two tracks at right angles to each other. The slit S is mounted just above the intersection of the two tracks. With this arrangement, the portion of the spectrum reaching the plate may be varied by sliding the beam one way or the other, thus varying the angle of incidence ϕ. It will be seen that this effectively moves S around the Rowland circle. For any setting the spectrum will be in focus on P, and it will be nearly a normal spectrum because the angle of diffraction $\theta \simeq 0$. The track SP is usually graduated in wavelengths since, as may be easily shown from the grating equation, the wavelength in a given order arriving at P is proportional to the distance SP.

36.7. The Vacuum Spectrograph

Another useful type of mounting for a concave reflection grating, called the *Eagle mounting,* is shown in Fig. 36P. Different wavelength regions of the spectrum are brought to focus on the photographic plate by turning and moving the grating and plateholder by fine adjusting screws (not shown). Adjustments are made so that the slit, grating, and plateholder lie on the Rowland circle.

Since the light at no point, from source to photographic plate, traverses glass elements, such a spectograph can be mounted in a suitable housing and highly evacuated for the study of the ultraviolet and extreme ultraviolet spectrum of any source.

Oxygen and nitrogen gases absorb broad wavelength regions of the ultraviolet, from 1900 Å to approximately 50 Å. Spectrum lines throughout this entire region are therefore to be photographed only by highly evacuated instruments of this kind. While ordinary clear dry air at and near sea level is transparent to ultraviolet light down to 1900 Å, the ozone high in the stratosphere absorbs strongly in the region 1900 Å to 3000 Å, and sunlight in this band does not reach the earth's surface.

36.8. Prism Spectrographs

One of the most common forms of prism spectrographs is shown in Fig. 36Q. This *Littrow* type instrument, as it is called, employs a long-focus lens, a slit, a 30° glass prism silvered on the back surface, and a curved photographic plateholder.

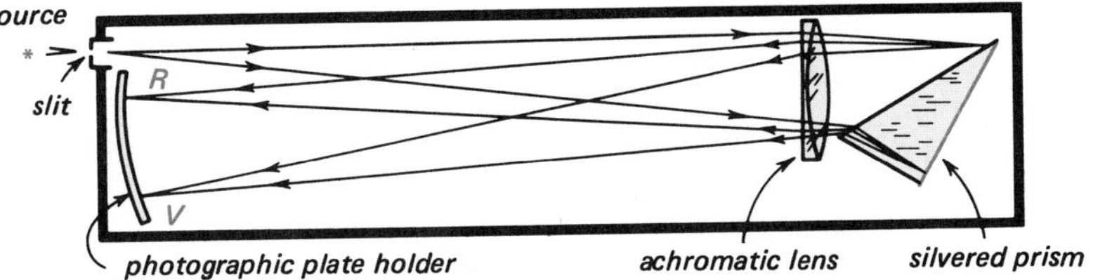

Fig. 36Q. Littrow type of prism spectrograph showing dual use of a lens and prism.

In this instrument a single lens serves a dual function; it provides a parallel beam of light incident upon the prism face, and it brings the emergent light of different wavelengths to a focus at different points on the photographic plateholder. Since the light crosses the glass–air boundary twice, the dispersion of the colors is the same as for an unsilvered 60° prism.

When a glass-prism spectograph is used to study a source of light, only a small part of the ultraviolet spectrum can be photographed. The reason for this is that glass absorbs ultraviolet light at wavelengths less than 3600 Å. To photograph the shorter waves, lenses and prisms made of quartz are frequently used. Quartz is transparent to ultraviolet light as far down in wavelength as 2000 Å. Beyond this point the waves are absorbed by air.

Glass-prism spectrographs are seldom used for the infrared spectrum, since the dispersion for these wavelengths is so small.

problems

1. Plane waves of light are incident normally on a narrow slit 0.356 mm wide. A lens with a focal length of 1.50 m, located directly behind the slit, forms a diffraction pattern in its focal plane. If the wavelength of the light is 6560 Å, find the total width in millimeters of the central bright band.

2. If light with a wavelength of 6000 Å falls on a slit 0.50 mm wide, and then on a screen 2.0 m behind the slit, find the width of the central bright band.

3. A single slit 0.20 mm wide is illuminated by a beam of light of wavelength 5.50×10^{-7} m. Find the width of the central diffraction band when viewed at a distance of 5.0 m from the slit. [Ans. 2.750 cm.]

4. A radio loud speaker has a circular aperture 30.0 cm in diameter. Find the angular width of the central lobe pattern (a) in radians, and (b) in degrees, for sound waves with a frequency of 10,000 Hz. Assume the speed of sound to be 350.0 m/s.

5. The pupil of a human eye has a diameter of 3.20 mm when situated in an average lighted house. Green light from a small point source, and with a wavelength of 5.50×10^{-7} m, is observed on the retina 2.750 cm beyond the optical center of the lens. Find the diameter of the Airy disk.

6. The largest telescope in the world at Mt. Palomar, California, has a reflecting objective mirror with a diameter of 5.08 m and a focal length of 16.87 m. What is the diameter of the Airy disk image of distant stars if the average wavelength of light is 5.50×10^{-7} m. [Ans. 0.00446 mm.]

7. A radio loud speaker consists of a vibrating circular cone with an aperture of 28.50 cm. Find the angular spread of the central lobe pattern in (a) radians, and (b) in degrees, for sounds with a frequency of 5000 Hz. Assume the speed of sound to be 350.0 m/s.

8. A telescope lens has a diameter of 8.0 cm and a focal length of 1.0 m. Find the diameter of the Airy disk image of a distant star if the average wavelength of light is 5500 Å.

9. In the equipment for an underwater sound system, a circular diaphragm 50.0 cm in diameter is used as a transmitter. Its frequency of oscillation of 30,000 Hz sends out high frequency sound waves like a searchlight. At some distance from the source the intensity will be that of the central Airy lobe pattern from an opening with the diameter of the diaphragm. Find the angular spread of the waves from this source if the velocity of sound in water is 1435 m/s. [Ans. 13.32°.]

10. A small source of radar waves, with a frequency of 2.0 GHz, is located at the focal point of a parabolic reflector having a diameter of 1.0 m. If the speed of the waves emitted is 3.0×10^8 m/s, what is the angular diameter in degrees of the central lobe pattern?

11. A parallel beam of blue light of wavelength 4500 Å falls normally on a plane diffraction grating having 9000 lines per centimeter. At what angle with the grating will the second order spectrum be diffracted?

12. Light of two wavelengths, 5200 Å and 5500 Å, falls normally on a plane of diffraction grating having 3500 lines per centimeter. The emergent light is focused on a screen by a lens with a focal length of 1.50 m. Assuming a curved screen find the distance in centimeters between the two spectrum lines (a) in the first order, and (b) in the second order. [Ans. (a) 1.575 cm, and (b) 3.150 cm.]

13. A diffraction grating with 5000 lines per centimeter is used as shown in Fig. 36J. If each of the two lenses has a focal length of 1.50 m, find the width of the first order spectrum of white light as it is formed on the screen. Assume $\lambda = 4.0 \times 10^{-7}$ m and 7.0×10^{-7} m for the shortest and longest wavelengths, and a curved screen of radius 1.50 m.

14. Yellow light from a sodium lamp falls normally on a diffraction grating. Because this is a course grating a large number of orders are observed. If the angle between the central image and the 20*th* order is 32.50°, find the number of grating lines per centimeter on the grating. Assume $\lambda = 5893$ Å.

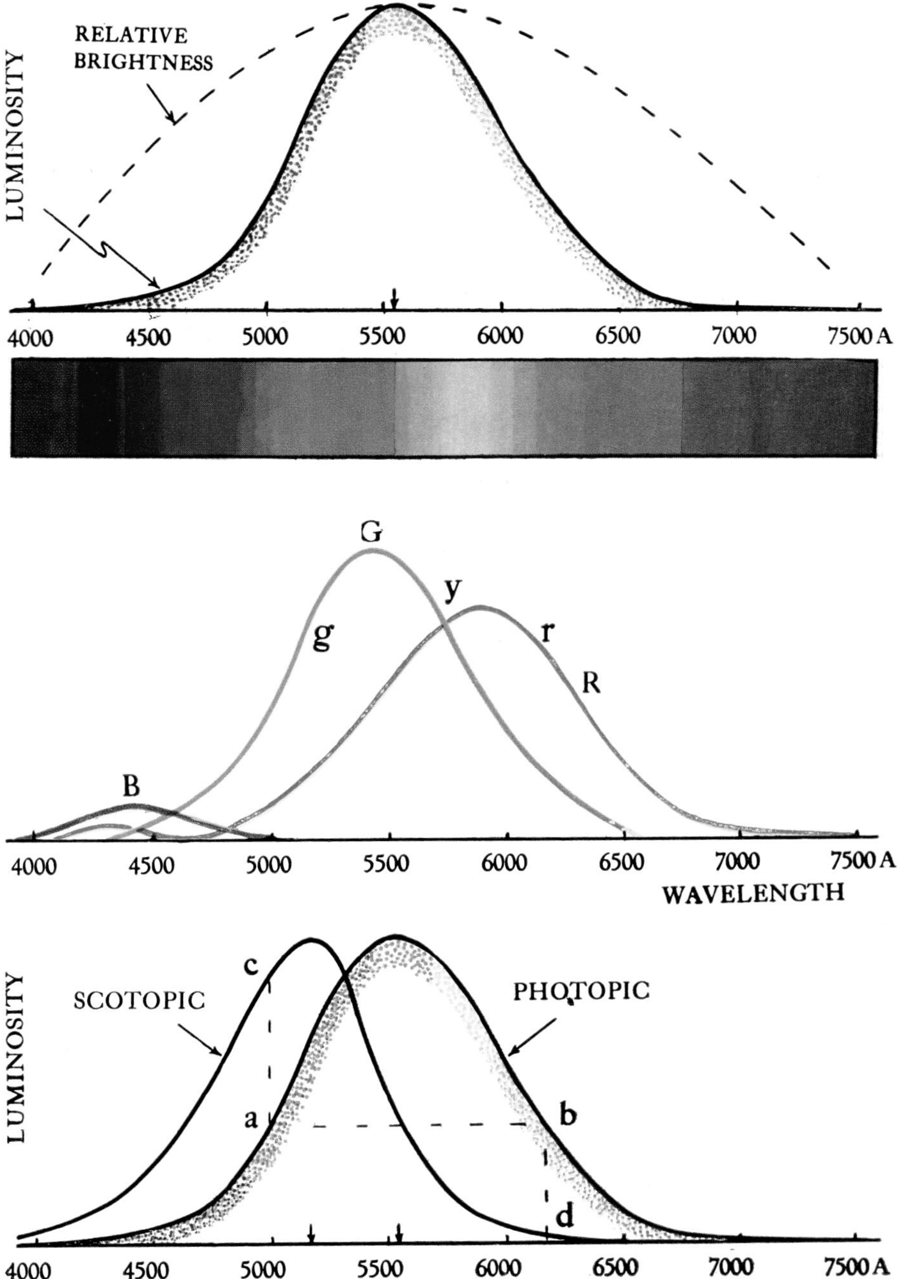

Fig. 34L. (a) Standard luminosity and relative brightness curves for the visible spectrum. (b) Tri-stimulus curves for the red, green, and blue sensitive cones of the retina. (c) Photopic and scotopic curves comparing cone vision by day with rod vision by night.

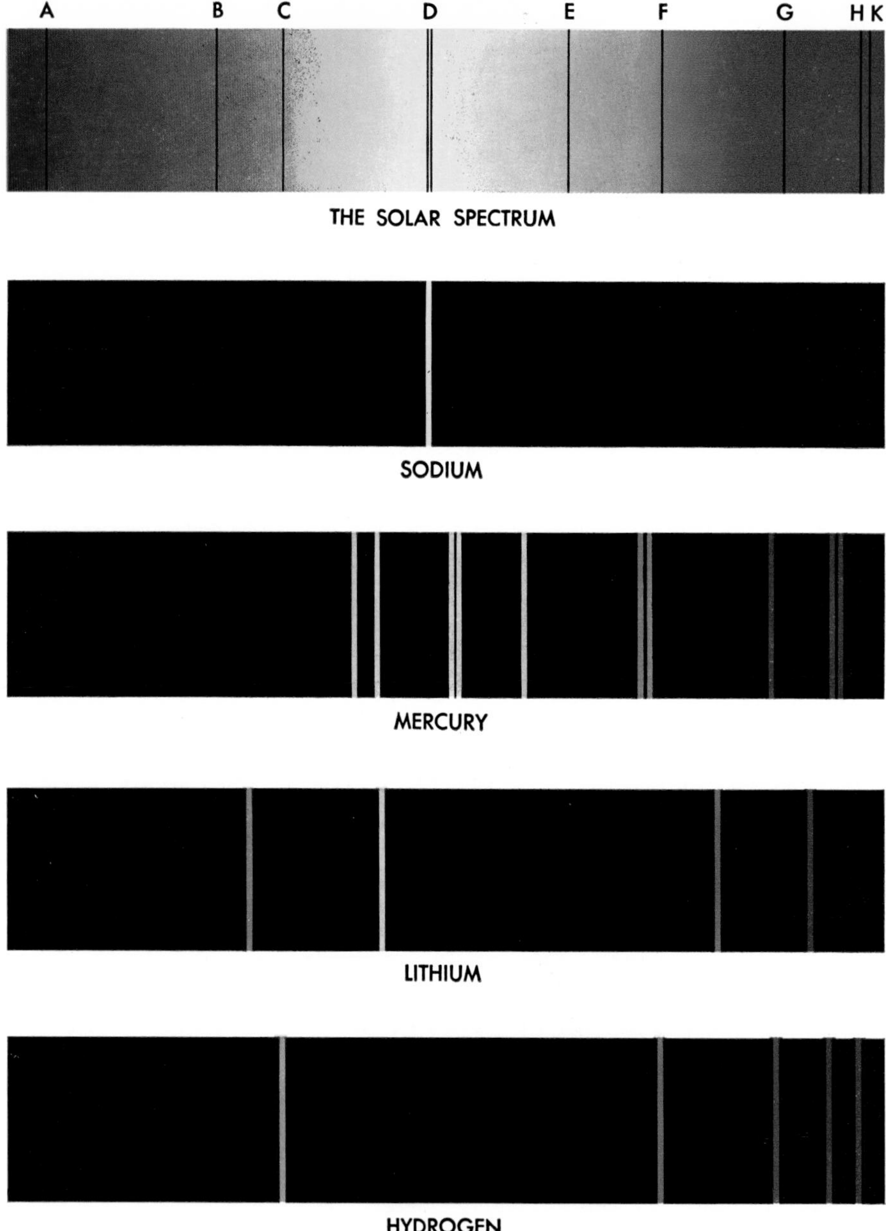

Fig. 37D. The solar spectrum and a few bright-line spectra.

15.* A diffraction grating containing 15,000 lines per centimeter is used in a Rowland mounting of 6.0 m diameter (see Fig. 36O). (a) Find the angle between the slit and the grating when the mercury line $\lambda = 5461$ Å falls in the first order at the center of the photographic plate. (b) Find the linear dispersion on the photographic plate in Å/cm. [Ans. (a) 55.0°, (b) 6.37 Å/cm.]

37 Light sources and their spectra

We have seen in the preceding chapter how prisms and diffraction gratings are used to spread the light from any source into a spectral array. Such a wavelength-ordered array, whether observed directly by eye in a spectroscope, or photographed in black and white or in color with a spectrograph, is called a spectrum.

The wavelengths of light emitted by hot solids, such as the tungsten wire in an incandescent lamp, or by hot gases, such as the mercury atoms in a fluorescent lamp, depend upon the nature of the emitting substance, as well as its temperature. While the distribution of wavelengths for a hot gas differs widely among chemical elements, the radiation from different hot solids like the metals, raised to the same high temperature, is nearly the same. All spectra, regardless of the source, may be classified under one of the following headings:

Continuous emission spectra
Line emission spectra
Continuous absorption spectra
Line absorption spectra
Band spectra

37.1. Continuous Emission Spectra

When a block of metal like iron or copper is heated slowly to incandescence, the first noticeable change in its appearance occurs at a temperature of about 1000°K. At this temperature, the metal has a dull red glow. As the temperature continues to rise, the color changes slowly to orange, then to yellow, and finally to white.

If the metal, as it is slowly being heated, is observed through a spectroscope, the first appearance of visible light will be found at the extreme red end of the spectrum. As the temperature rises, the light spreads slowly out across the spectrum until, at white heat, the entire band of visible colors from red to violet is seen. At the orange stage where the temperature is about 1500°K, the pure spectrum colors contain red, orange, and yellow; when the yellow stage is reached where the temperature is about 2000°K, the spectral green is included. When the white stage is reached at about 3000°K, and the spectrum is complete, a further rise in temperature continues to increase the intensity of each color without a noticeable change in color.

What the spectroscope has done in such an experiment is to separate all of the light waves according to their wavelengths, the longest waves of red light at the one side, the shortest waves of violet light at the other, and the intermediate waves at their proper places in between. The fact that the color is continuous from red through violet is characteristic of the spectrum of all solids and liquids; this means that there is a continuous set of different wavelengths present.

37.2. The Spectrum

To demonstrate the existence of an ultraviolet and infrared spectrum, an experiment of the type illustrated in Fig. 37A may be performed. The visible light from a carbon-arc lamp is made to pass through a quartz lens and prism to be focused on a nearby screen.

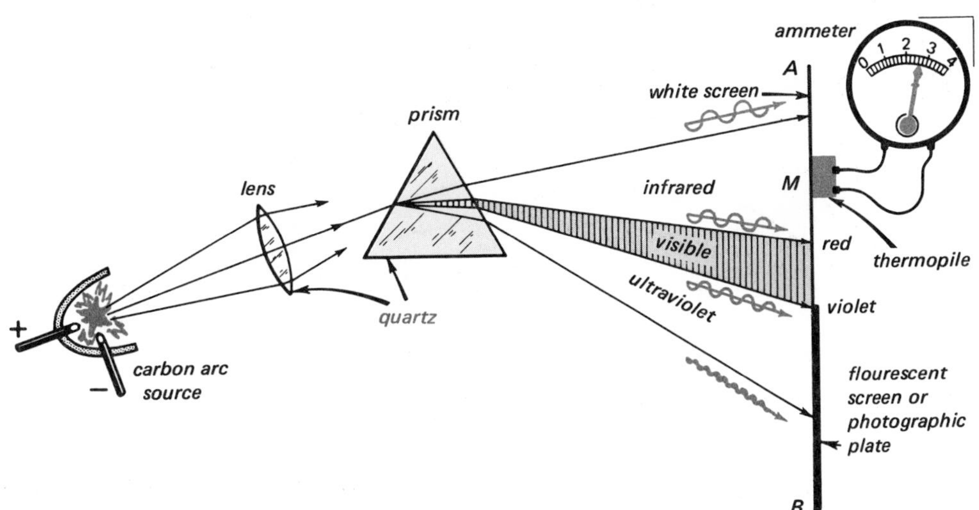

Fig. 37A. Experiment demonstrating the existence of the ultraviolet and infrared rays beyond the visible spectrum.

If at the violet end of the spectrum the screen is painted with luminous paint, a bright fluorescence will be observed for a short distance beyond the visible violet. When the screen is replaced by a photographic plate, the exposed and developed picture will again show the extension of the spectrum into the ultraviolet.

To detect the presence of the infrared radiations, a thermopile is conveniently used, as shown at the top of the screen. Connected to an ammeter, a thermopile measures the amount of light energy falling upon its front face. If the thermopile is first placed to receive violet light, and then slowly moved across the visible spectrum out into the infrared region beyond, the ammeter will show a steady rise in current. The current will continue to rise until a maximum is reached at a point in the region of M, and then it will drop off slowly as the thermopile approaches the end of the screen at A. A graph of the energy from the carbon arc source, for the different parts along the screen, is shown by the 3000°K curve in Fig. 37B.

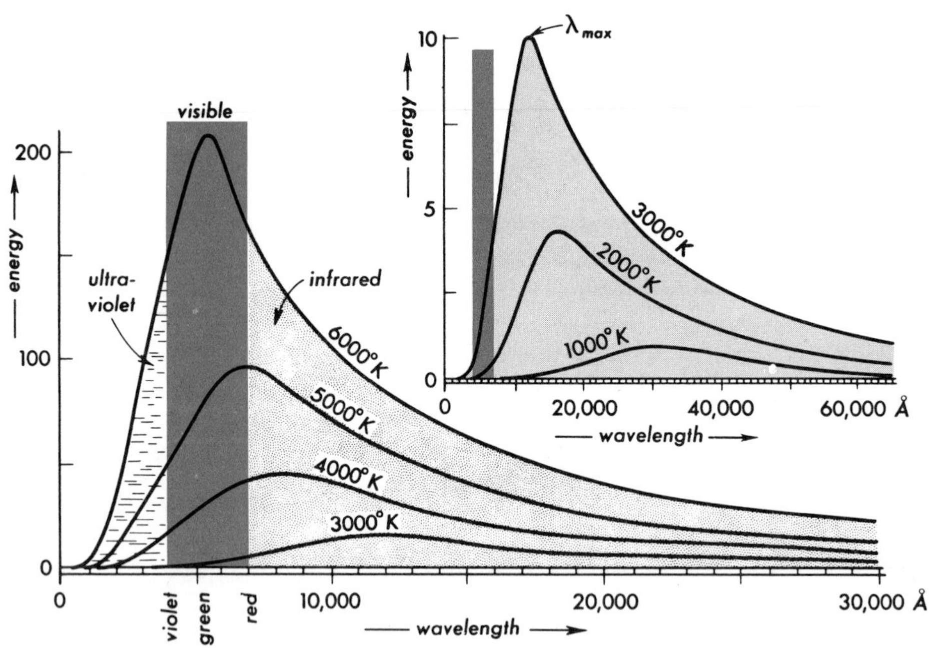

Fig. 37B. Distribution of the energy emitted by a hot solid at different temperatures.

Each curve represents the amount of energy given out over the entire spectrum by a solid at different temperatures. Studying these curves, one will observe that at low temperatures very little light is emitted in the visible spectrum. At 1000°K, only the visible red is seen and even that is very faint. At 2000°K, not only does the brightness of the red increase, but the other colors, orange, yellow, and green, appear. At 3000°K, the temperature of a low-current carbon arc or tungsten-filament light, all of the visible spectrum is emitted, but the maximum radiation is in the infrared. At 6000°K, the temperature of the surface of the sun, the maximum energy is radiated in the green of the visible spectrum, with an appreciable amount of ultraviolet light on the one side and the infrared on the other. Thus the visible spectrum, as seen by the human eye, is but a small band out of all the waves emitted by a body as hot as the sun.

37.3. Wien's Displacement Law

It is an interesting fact that the maximum energy radiated by a hot body shifts to shorter and shorter waves as the temperature rises (see Fig. 37B). To be more exact, if the temperature of a body is doubled, the radiated energy maximum, λ_{max}, shifts to $\frac{1}{2}$ the wavelength. If the temperature is tripled, the energy maximum shifts to $\frac{1}{3}$ the wavelength, etc. This is known as Wien's* displacement law, and is written as an algebraic equation:

$$\lambda_{max} T = C \qquad (37a)$$

where C is a constant, found by experiment to have a value

$$C = 2.8970 \times 10^{-3} \text{ mK}^\circ$$

T is the absolute temperature, and λ_{max} the wavelength in meters at which the maximum energy is radiated. By substituting the value of the constant C in Eq.(37a), the wavelength maximum radiated by a hot body can be calculated for any temperature.

Example 1. A hot body is raised to a temperature of 6000°K. Find the wavelength maximum at which energy is radiated.
Solution. The known quantities are $T = 6000°\text{K}$ and $C = 2.897 \times 10^{-3}$ m°K. Solving Eq.(37a) for the wavelength λ, and substituting the known quantities, we find

$$\lambda_{max} = \frac{C}{T} = \frac{2.897 \times 10^{-3} \text{ m°K}}{6 \times 10^3 \text{ °K}}$$

$$\lambda_{max} = 4.83 \times 10^{-7} \text{ m}$$

$$\lambda_{max} = 4830 \text{ Å}$$

*Wilhelm Wien (1864–1928), German physicist, is chiefly known for important discoveries with cathode rays, canal rays, and the radiation of light. He was awarded the Nobel Prize in physics in 1911 for his discovery of the displacement law of heat radiation named in his honor.

Wien's displacement law is related to *black body radiation,* and the Stefan-Boltzmann law presented in Sec. 15.5.

37.4. Emission and Absorption

The rate at which a body radiates or absorbs heat depends not only upon the absolute temperature, but upon the nature of the exposed surfaces as well. Objects that are good emitters of heat are also good absorbers of the same kind of radiation. This is known as *Kirchhoff's law of radiation.* A body whose surface is blackened is an excellent emitter as well as an excellent absorber. If the same body is chromium plated, it becomes a poor emitter and a poor absorber.

If the outside surface of a hot coffee cup were painted a dull black, the rate of cooling would be more rapid than if it were chromium plated. A highly polished surface, as in the Dewar flask, would help by reflection to keep radiant heat from crossing the boundary.

Black clothes should not be worn on a hot day, since black is a good absorber of the sun's radiant heat. While black is also a good emitter, the external temperature is higher than the body temperature and the exchange rate is therefore such as to heat the body. White clothes are worn in hot climates because white is a good reflector and therefore a poor absorber.

The best laboratory approximation of a black body is a hole in a blackened box. Practically all heat entering such a hole would be absorbed inside. Black velvet cloth or a surface painted dull with lampblack will absorb about 97% of the radiant heat falling on it, and may for many purposes be considered a black body. Polished metal surfaces, however, are far from black bodies; they absorb only about 6% of the incident energy and reflect the remainder. Most other substances have absorption ratios between these two extremes.

37.5. The Quantum Theory

The first successful attempt to explain the shape of the black-body radiation curves as shown in Fig. 37B was made by Max Planck* in 1900. Planck's theoretical considerations led him to the conclusion that matter is composed of a large number of oscillating particles and that all conceivable vibration frequencies of these particles are possible. Although the frequency of any one particle according to classical theory could have any value, he assumed that the vibration energy must be given by

***Max Planck (1858–1947), German theoretical physicist, was born in Kiel, on April 23, 1858. He studied in Munich and Berlin and devoted much of his life to theoretical physics, particularly to thermodynamics. He published several books on this subject and is called the father of the quantum theory of radiation. For his contributions to the theory of black-body radiation, he was awarded the Nobel Prize in physics for the year 1918.**

$$E = nh\nu \tag{37b}$$

where ν is the frequency of vibration, h is a constant, and n is a whole number,

$$n = 1, 2, 3, 4, 5, \ldots \tag{37c}$$

When an oscillator emits radiant energy, it does so in the form of electromagnetic waves and only in "chunks" given by Eq.(37b).

The whole number n is called a *quantum number,* h is called *Planck's constant,* and hv is called a *quantum* of energy, or a photon. Today we know that all quanta of radiation have an energy hv and all quanta of the same frequency have the same energy. Quanta of high frequency, such as gamma rays, have a large amount of energy, while those of low frequency, such as radio waves, have a small amount of energy.

From his theory Planck derived a radiant-energy formula for which the rate of emission of a black body is a maximum at the value given by Wien's displacement law, Eq.(37a), and falls off at higher and lower wavelengths as shown in Fig. 37B. Planck's formula for the radiated energy E is

$$E_\lambda\,\Delta\lambda = \frac{hc^3\,\Delta\lambda}{\lambda^5(e^{hc/\lambda kT} - 1)} \tag{37d}$$

where E_λ = joules per second per square meter of surface in the wavelength band between λ and $\lambda + \Delta\lambda$, c is the velocity of light, λ is the wavelength, T is the absolute temperature, e is the base of the Naperian logarithms, k is the so-called *Boltzmann constant* determined from the general gas laws, and h is Planck's constant:

$$h = 6.6262 \times 10^{-34}\ \text{J s}$$

$$k = 1.3805 \times 10^{-23}\ \text{J/°K}$$

$$c = 2.9979 \times 10^{8}\ \text{m/s}$$

$$e = 2.7183$$

37.6. The Complete Spectrum

Visible, ultraviolet, and *infrared* light waves do not represent all of the known kinds of electromagnetic radiation. A complete chart of the known spectrum is shown in Fig. 37C. Beyond the visible and infrared toward longer wavelengths, we find the *heat waves* and the *wireless waves,* while beyond the ultraviolet toward shorter wavelengths we find the *X rays* and the *gamma rays.*

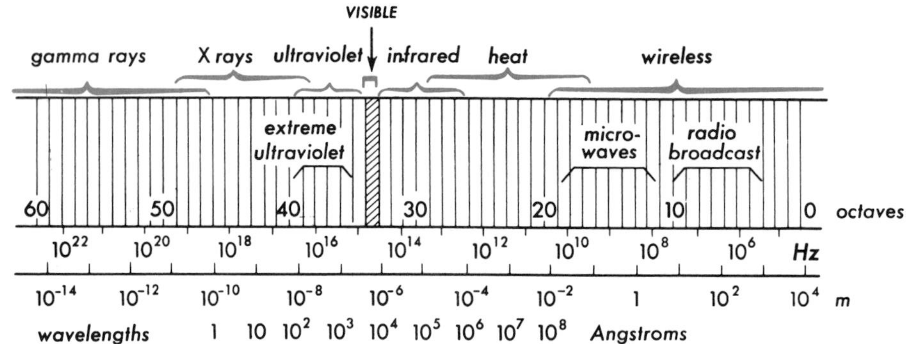

Fig. 37C. Complete wavelength and frequency chart of the electromagnetic spectrum as it is now known.

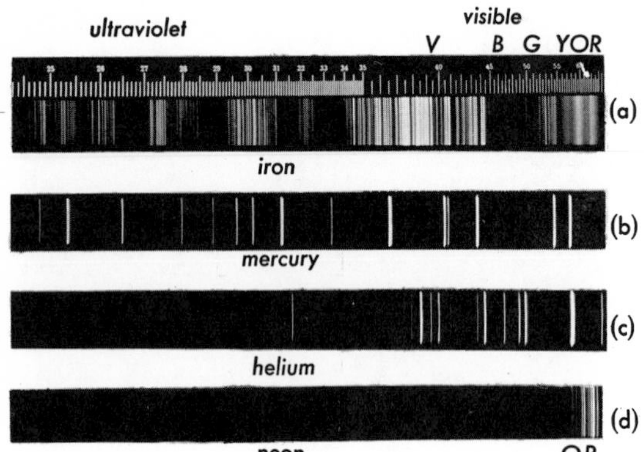

Fig. 37E. Photographs of the line emission spectrum from four different elements in the gaseous state.

In spite of the tremendous expanse of wavelengths ranging all the way from the longest wireless waves several miles in length to γ-ray waves one-million-millionth of a centimeter in length, all electromagnetic waves travel with the same velocity in vacuum: 3×10^8 m/s.

Although their velocities in a vacuum are all the same, the properties of the various waves differ considerably. One striking illustration of these differences is found in the response of the human eye. Of the entire spectrum, only one very narrow band of waves can be seen, all the rest being invisible. Another illustration is the passage of light waves through the atmosphere. With the exception of the band of waves known as the extreme ultraviolet, the air is fairly transparent to all electromagnetic waves. To waves of the extreme ultraviolet, the air is quite opaque. *Fog is opaque to all but the wireless waves.*

37.7. Line Emission Spectra

When the slit of a spectrograph is illuminated by the light from a mercury arc, a sodium lamp, a helium or a neon discharge tube, a number of bright lines appear on the photographic plate in place of a continuous spectrum (see Figs. 37D*and 37E).

It is important to realize that line spectra derive their name from the fact that a slit is used whose image constitutes a line. If a small circular opening were used in place of a slit, a disk image would appear in the place of each line.

The ability to discharge between two or more wavelengths, dif-

*Figure 37D is a color photograph inserted after p. 564.

fering only slightly from one another, is therefore increased by the use of a slit.

The most intense spectrum lines are obtained from metallic arcs and sparks. The flame of a carbon arc may be used for demonstration purposes by previously soaking the *positive carbon rod* in various chemicals. An experimental arrangement for projecting the spectrum on a large screen is shown in Fig. 37F. Common salt water (sodium chloride in solution) gives a brilliant yellow line characteristic of sodium. Solutions of strontium or calcium chloride will show other strong spectrum lines in the red, green, and blue.

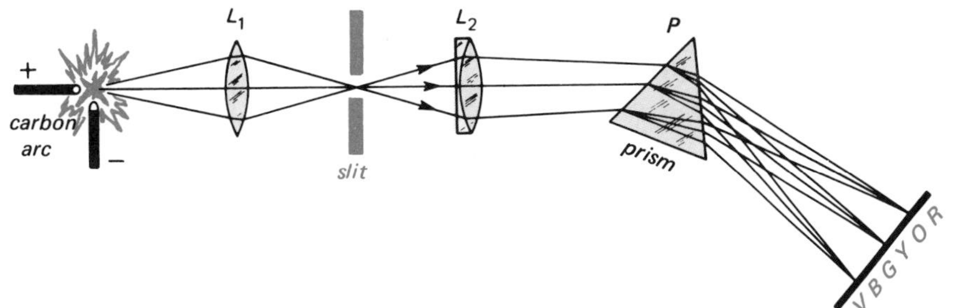

Fig. 37F. Experimental arrangement used in demonstrating spectrum lines in emission.

While a continuous emission spectrum arises from hot solids, a *line spectrum always arises from a gas at high temperatures and low pressures.* It is the gas flame of the carbon arc that gives rise to the line emission spectrum in Fig. 37F.

37.8. Continuous Absorption Spectra

Continuous absorption spectra are usually produced by passing the light of a continuous emission spectrum through matter in the solid or liquid state. Good demonstrations can be performed by allowing white light to pass through colored glass. When the light is later dispersed by a prism, the missing colors will in general cover a wide band of wavelengths. A red piece of glass, for example, will absorb all visible light but the red. A magenta-colored piece of glass will absorb the whole central part of the visible spectrum.

37.9. Line Absorption Spectra

Line spectra in absorption are produced by sending continuous white light through a gas. Experimentally, the gas or vapor is inserted in the path of the light as shown in Fig. 37G. Light from a carbon arc, after passing as a parallel beam through a glass tube containing sodium vapor, is brought to a focus at the slit C. From there the light passes through a lens L_3 and a prism P to form a spectrum on the observing screen.

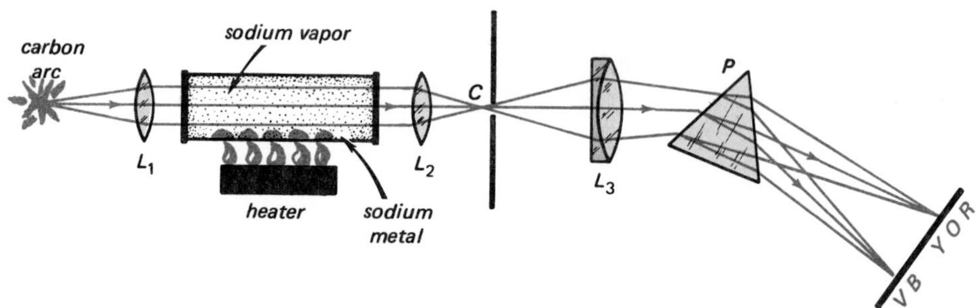

Fig. 37G. Experimental arrangement for demonstrating the line absorption spectrum of sodium vapor.

Sodium is chosen as an example for demonstration purposes because of its convenience. The vapor is produced by inserting a small amount of metallic sodium in a partially evacuated glass tube and heating it with a small gas burner. As the metal vaporizes, filling the tube with sodium vapor, a dark line will appear in the yellow region of the spectrum.

If a photograph is taken of this absorption, and the photographic plate is long enough to extend into the ultraviolet, many absorption lines as shown in Fig. 37H are detected. A systematic array of absorption lines like this occurs with only a few elements, principally with the alkali metals, lithium, sodium, potassium, rubidium, and cesium. All elements in the gaseous state, however, give rise to a number of absorption lines, usually in the ultraviolet region of the spectrum. The absorption of yellow light by normal

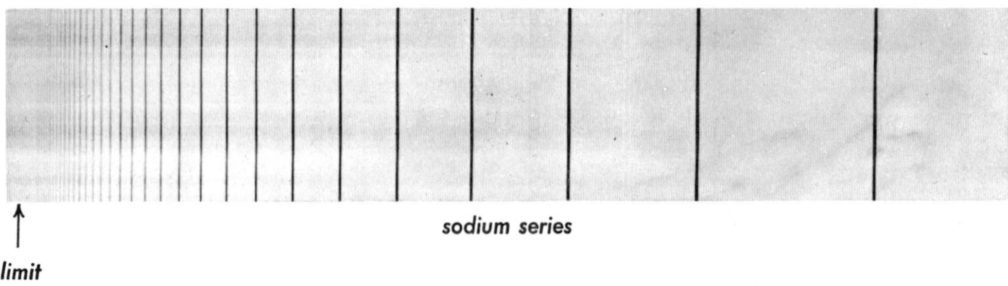

Fig. 37H. Absorption spectrum of sodium vapor. The principal series of sodium. (After F. A. Jenkins.)

sodium atoms, for example, is a kind of resonance phenomenon. By virtue of their electronic structure, atoms have definite and discrete natural frequencies to which they will vibrate in resonance. When light of one of these frequencies passes by, they respond to vibration and in so doing absorb the light energy.

37.10. The Sun's Spectrum

The solor spectrum (see color plate, Fig. 37D), consisting of a bright colored continuous spectrum interspersed by thousands of dark lines, was first observed by Wollaston in 1802, and independently discovered and studied by Fraunhofer in 1817. Fraunhofer mapped out several hundred of these lines and labeled eight of the most prominent lines by the first letters of the alphabet. The strongest of these lines, now called *Fraunhofer lines,* are illustrated in Fig. 37I.

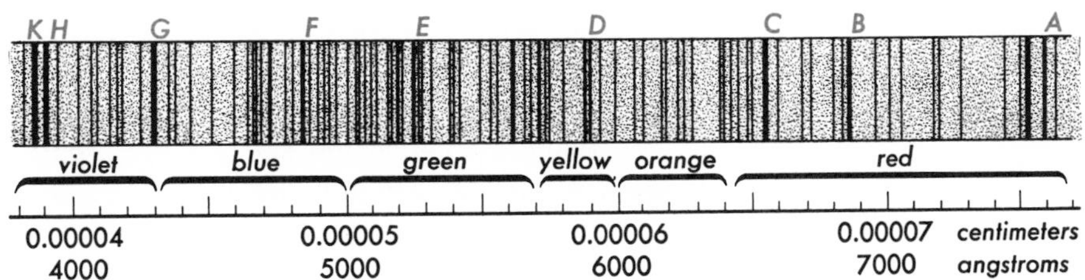

Fig. 37I. Diagram of the solar spectrum indicating the most prominent lines labeled with the first letters of the alphabet as they first were by Fraunhofer.

In 1882, the American physicist H. A. Rowland photographed and published a 40-ft-long map of the sun's spectrum. Two small sections of Rowland's map are reproduced in Fig. 37J. These lines

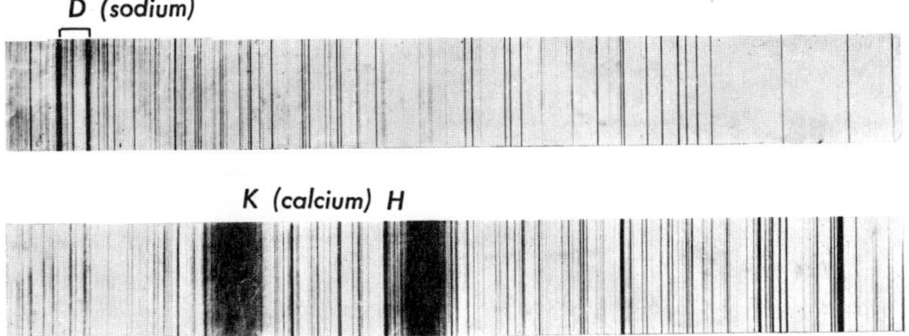

Fig. 37J. Photographic reproductions of the solar spectrum taken from Rowland's original map.

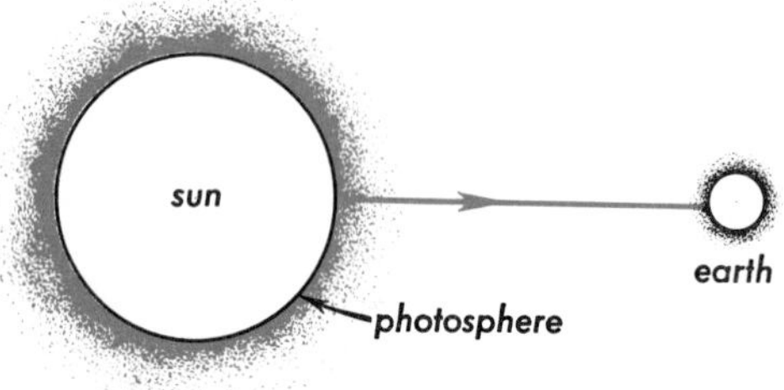

Fig. 37K. Light from the sun must pass through the solar atmosphere and the earth's atmosphere before reaching an observer on the earth's surface.

are explained as being due to the absorption of light by the solar atmosphere.

The surface of the sun at a temperature of 6000°K emits light of all wavelengths, i.e., a continuous emission spectrum. As this light passes out through the cooler gas layers of the solar atmosphere (see Fig. 37K), certain wavelengths are absorbed. Because the absorbing medium is in the gaseous state, the atoms and molecules there do not absorb all wavelengths equally, but rather they absorb principally those wavelengths they would emit if heated to a high temperature. Thus the atoms of one chemical element with their own characteristic frequencies absorb certain wavelengths, whereas the atoms of other elements absorb certain other wavelengths.

Before the sunlight reaches the earth's surface where it can be examined by an observer with a spectrograph, it must again pass through absorbing gases, this time the earth's atmosphere. Here, too, certain wavelengths are partially absorbed, producing other dark lines.

That the missing wavelengths correspond to definite chemical elements is illustrated by the diagram in Fig. 37L. The center strip (b) represents a small section of the visible spectrum as obtained with sunlight entering the slit of a spectrograph. The upper and lower strips, (a) and (c), represent the line spectrum observed when an iron arc and a calcium arc are successively placed in front of the same slit. Where each calcium line occurs in the laboratory source, an absorption line is found in the sun's spectrum. The same is true for each iron line. The remaining lines, not matched by an iron or calcium line, are due to other elements.

It has been possible by spectrum photographs of this kind to identify about two-thirds of the known chemical elements as existing on the sun. The reason why not all 90 or more elements are found is that some are too rare to produce absorption, whereas

Fig. 37L. Schematic diagram illustrating the comparison of laboratory spectra from different elements with the many-line spectrum of the sun.

for other elements existing within the sun in large enough quantities the temperature is either too high or too low to bring out their lines.

Nine prominent Fraunhofer lines labeled in Fig. 37I have been identified as follows:

A, oxygen.................. $\lambda = 7594$ Å
B, oxygen.................. $\lambda = 6870$ Å
C, hydrogen............. $\lambda = 6562$ Å
D, sodium................. $\lambda = 5893$ Å
E, iron........................ $\lambda = 5270$ Å
F, hydrogen............. $\lambda = 4861$ Å
G, iron........................ $\lambda = 4308$ Å
H, calcium................ $\lambda = 3969$ Å
K, calcium................ $\lambda = 3935$ Å

37.11. The Doppler Effect and the Sun's Rotation

It is not difficult to determine which of the Fraunhofer lines are due to absorption by the sun's atmosphere and which are due to the earth's atmosphere. The sun, like the earth, is rotating about an axis, and this motion produces for an observer on the earth a slight change of wavelength of light. This change in wavelength is due to the well-known Doppler effect so often observed with sound.

On one side of the sun, the east limb, the surface emitting light and the absorbing gases are approaching the earth at a high speed, while on the other side, the west limb, the emitting surface and gases are receding from the earth.

According to the Doppler principle, the light waves emitted by the approaching side are crowded together to give a higher frequency, while those emitted by the receding side are lengthened out to give a lower frequency. Since the absorbing gases are also moving, the absorption lines due to these gases should be shifted in the solar spectrum.

The lines marked by arrows in Fig. 37M(a) show the Doppler shift. The lines marked by brackets, on the other hand, are produced by the earth's atmosphere which, because it is stationary with respect to an observer on the earth's surface, gives rise to unshifted lines. Remaining fixed, the unshifted lines serve as fiducial marks from which to observe and measure the shift in the solar lines.

The lower photograph (b) in Fig. 37M shows that at the solar poles, where there is relatively no motion toward or away from the earth, no Doppler shift is observed in the solar lines.

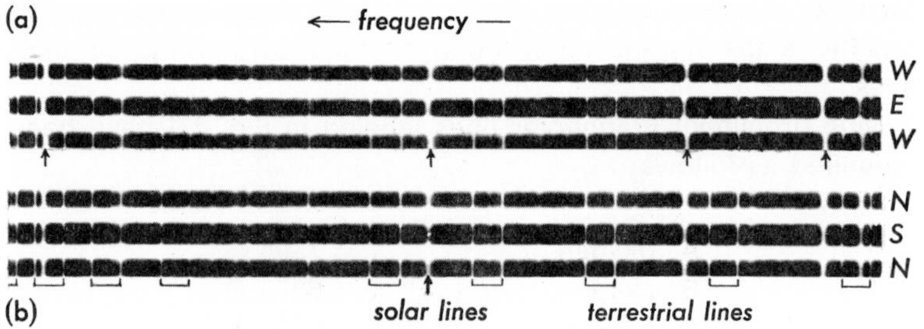

Fig. 37M. Photographs of the spectrum of different regions of the sun's disk. *E* and *W* were taken with the light from the east and west limbs of the sun. The lines marked by an arrow show a Doppler shift as evidence of the sun's rotation.

37.12. The Flash Spectrum

The Fraunhofer lines of the solar spectrum are not absolutely black, that is, devoid of all light; they are dark only in contrast with the far brighter colored background. Actually the sun's atmosphere is not cold but, as seen at the time of a total eclipse, is quite hot and emits light of its own. When this light is observed in a spectroscope, or photographed with a spectrograph, it consists of a bright-line spectrum called a *flash spectrum.*

The photograph of a flash spectrum reproduced in Fig. 37N was made in the following way. During a solar eclipse, at just the instant before the moon's disk blanks out all of the sun's disk, leaving only a narrow bright crescent of the sun to be seen on one side, the light is allowed to enter a spectrograph.

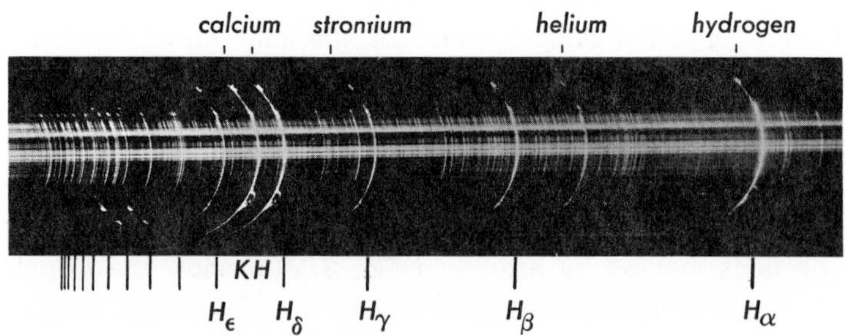

Fig. 37N. Photograph of the flash spectrum of the sun taken at the time of a total eclipse. Note the prominences, called Baily's beads. (Courtesy of the Lick Observatory.)

With the customary slit and collimator lens removed from the instrument, each spectral line becomes a crescent-shaped image of the sun as cast by light of that wavelength. Note the high intensity of the H and K lines due to ionized calcium, and the solar prominences that appear at the same points on each image. Note also the high intensity of the lines marked H_α, H_β, H_γ, H_δ, and H_ϵ, as well as the succeeding lines, indicating a long series of spectral wavelengths. These lines are due to hydrogen and are known as the *Balmer series.*

The spectra of many of the distant stars are composed almost exclusively of the lines of the Balmer series, while others like our own sun exhibit more complex arrays.

37.13. The Balmer Series of Hydrogen

The first successful attempt to obtain a formula that represents the hydrogen series was made by Balmer in 1885. Since that time, these lines have become known as the Balmer series of hydrogen. Balmer's formula is written

$$\lambda = B\left[\frac{n_2^2 \times n_1^2}{n_2^2 - n_1^2}\right] \tag{37e}$$

where λ = wavelength in angstroms, and

$$B = 911.267 \text{ Å}$$

$$n_1 = 2$$

$$n_2 = 3, 4, 5, 6, 7, \ldots$$

If the number 3 is substituted for n_2 in the above formula, the wavelength λ of the first line of the series is calculated. Likewise, if the number 4 is substituted in its place, the wavelength of the second line can be calculated, etc. When these calculations are carried out, the following wavelengths are obtained for the first four lines:

Calculated	*Measured*
$H_\alpha = B\frac{36}{5} = 6561.1$ Å	6562.1 Å
$H_\beta = B\frac{64}{12} = 4860.8$ Å	4860.7 Å
$H_\gamma = B\frac{100}{21} = 4339.4$ Å	4340.1 Å
$H_\delta = B\frac{144}{32} = 4100.7$ Å	4101.3 Å

These wavelengths, as well as those calculated for other lines of the series, agree remarkably well with the measured values.

Balmer did not derive his formula from any theory, but simply formulated it from the measured wavelength for each series line. The meaning of whole numbers n_1 and n_2 is given in Sec. 44.2.

Example 2. Calculate the wavelength of the fifth line of the Balmer series of hydrogen, using the empirical formula, Eq.(37e). **Solution.** The known quantities are $n_1 = 2$ and $n_2 = 7$. Direct substitution in Balmer's formula gives

$$\lambda = B\left[\frac{n_2^2 \times n_1^2}{n_2^2 - n_1^2}\right] = 911.267\left[\frac{49 \times 4}{49 - 4}\right]$$

$$\lambda = 3969.07 \text{ Å}$$

37.14. The Temperature Effect

Raising the temperature of a source of light brings out new spectrum lines and causes others to disappear. This is illustrated by a small section of the spectrum of vanadium, element number 23, in Fig. 370. The first three photographs were taken by heating small bits of vanadium metal in an electric furnace and photographing the light coming from the vapor just above the hot metal. The fourth photograph was made by placing a small piece of vanadium metal in the tip of the positive carbon of an arc, and the fifth by a high-voltage electric spark jumping between two vanadium metal rods.

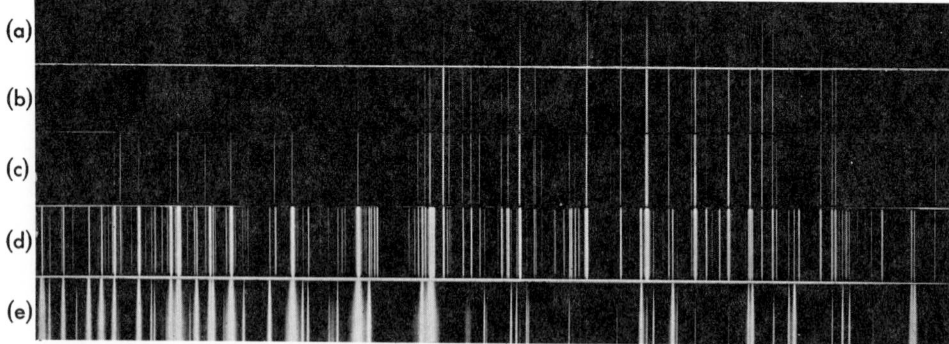

Fig. 370. Ultraviolet spectrum of vanadium, element 23: (a) 2000° K; (b) 2300° K; (c) 2600° K; (d) from a direct-current arc between vanadium metal electrodes. (e) High-voltage electric spark between vanadium metal electrodes. (After A. S. King.)

Though the top spectrum taken at a temperature of 200°K appears to be quite different from the lower one taken at a temperature at least twice as high, all of the lines arise from vanadium atoms and are characteristic of that element alone.

It is a well-founded and general rule that as the temperature of a gas is increased, the maximum intensity shifts toward shorter wavelengths. At a low temperature, for example, the lines in the visible part of the spectrum of an element may be brighest, while at a higher temperature those in the ultraviolet become most intense.

37.15. Relation between Emission and Absorption Spectra

When the line emission spectrum of an element is compared with the line absorption spectrum of the same element, the lines are found to coincide exactly. This is illustrated by a small section of the complex spectrum of iron in Fig. 37P. The strips (a) and (c), above and below, show the emission lines from the hot flame of an iron arc, while the middle strip (b) shows the absorption lines resulting from the passage of a continuous emission spectrum through cooler iron vapor.

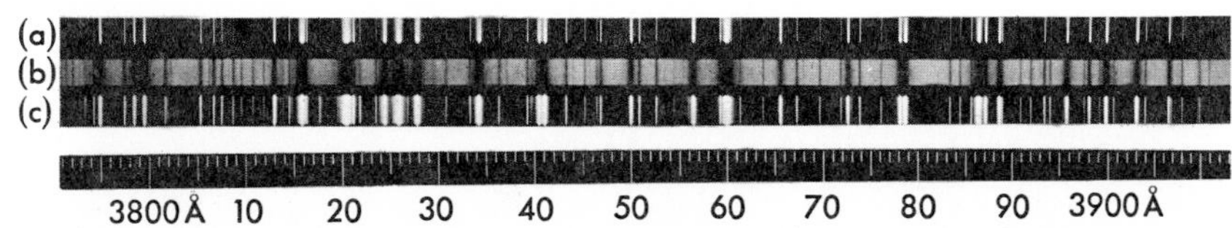

Fig. 37P. Emission and absorption spectrum of iron. (After Anderson and Smith.)

To give a simple explanation which is not exactly correct, we may picture the emission of light as due to the motions or vibrations of the electrons in the atoms of the source. These moving electric charges give rise to electromagnetic waves having the same frequencies as the electrons themselves. In any source of light only a small percent of the atoms have their electrons vibrating at any given time. These few, which we refer to as vibrating atoms, are called *excited atoms,* while those not vibrating are called *unexcited atoms.*

When yellow light from a sodium arc passes through sodium vapor, as in Fig. 37G, many individual atoms respond and become excited. In becoming excited the atoms have absorbed the incident light waves from the beam. This is like the resonance of two tuning forks that may be demonstrated for sound. Only when the sound waves from the first fork have exactly the same frequency as the second fork does the second fork pick up the motions and vibrate.

In the event that white light is sent through sodium vapor, only those light waves having frequencies equal to the natural frequencies of the atoms are absorbed. This is the explanation of the series of absorption lines in Fig. 37H. Again, when white light passes through iron vapor, only those light waves having frequencies equal to the natural frequencies of iron atoms are absorbed.

Although the atoms which are set into vibration by absorbing light from the beam emit the light again a small fraction of a second later, their chance of emitting it in some one direction is equally probable for all directions. Very little of this re-radiated light is therefore given out in the forward direction, parallel with the incident light.

37.16. Band Spectra

All of the line spectra described thus far are known to arise from single free atoms in a heated gas. Molecules of two or more atoms also give rise to spectrum lines grouped together into what are called bands. As shown by the reproductions in Fig. 37Q, these bands have the appearance of flutings.

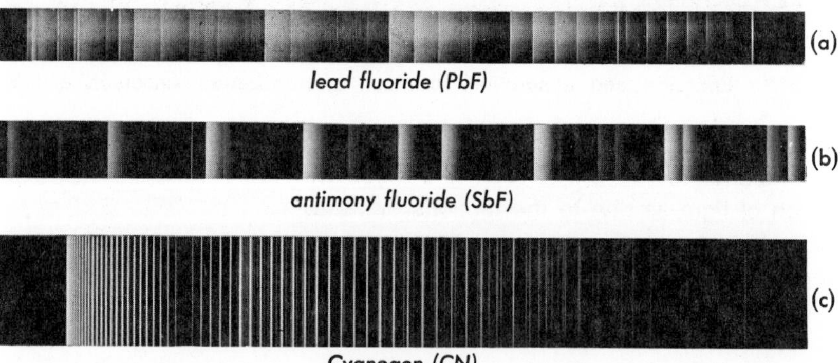

Fig. 37Q. Band spectra taken with a large spectograph. (After Jenkins.)

Each fluting in the spectrum of a diatomic molecule is not a continuous band but a set of regularly spaced lines. The third photograph in Fig. 37Q is a very greatly enlarged picture of a single band taken in the second order of a 21-ft grating spectrograph of the type shown in Fig. 36N.

The left-hand edge of the band is called the band head and the right-hand side the tail of the band. Note that one line near the band head is missing. The mystery of this missing line is now well understood, for it is the starting point of the band in place of the band head, and is called the band origin. The theory of band spectra and the present-day knowledge of how diatomic molecules emit so many frequencies will be taken up in another chapter.

problems

1. (a) At what wavelength will the maximum energy be radiated from a black body if its temperature is 3000°C? (b) In what region of the spectrum is this radiation located?

2. If the wavelength at which the maximum energy is radiated from a black body is 3650 Å, what is its temperature (a) on the centigrade scale, and (b) on the absolute scale? In what region of the spectrum is this radiation?

3. Find the wavelength at which maximum energy will be radiated from a black body if its temperature is 2027°C. To what region of the spectrum does this radiation belong? [Ans. (a) 1.260×10^{-6} m, (b) infrared.]

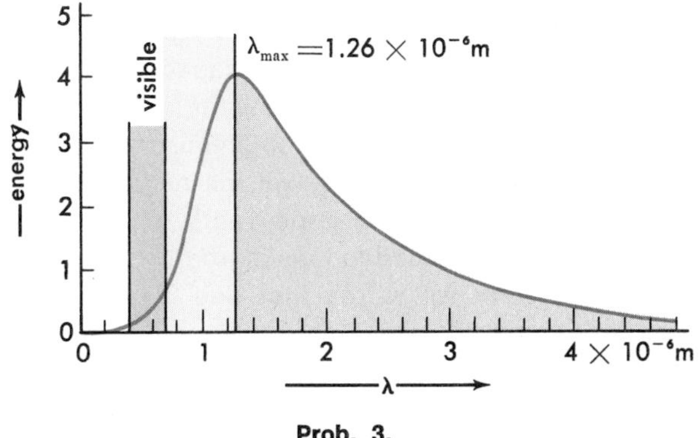

Prob. 3.

4. The maximum energy radiated by a given black body has a wavelength of 2.580×10^{-6} m. Find its temperature (a) on the absolute scale, and (b) on the centigrade scale. (c) To what region of the spectrum does this radiation belong?

5. The maximum energy radiated from a certain star is found to be at 2550 Å. What is its surface temperature (a) on the absolute scale, (b) on the centigrade scale, and (c) to what region of the spectrum does this radiation belong?

6. A photon, or quantum of radiation, given off by a black body has a wavelength of 5400 Å. What is its energy in joules? Assume $n = 1$. [Ans. 3.679×10^{-19} J.]

7. A quantum, or photon, has a wavelength of 2.45 Å. Find its energy.

8. Find the wavelength of the sixth line of the Balmer series of hydrogen.

9. What is the wavelength of the tenth line of the Balmer series of hydrogen? [Ans. 3749.2 Å.]

10. Calculate the wavelength of the 100*th* line of the Balmer series of hydrogen.

11. Determine the wavelength of the series limit of the Balmer series of hydrogen.

12. (a) Calculate the wavelength maximum for radiation from a star whose temperature is 20,000°K. (b) To what region of the spectrum does this radiation belong? [Ans. (a) 1448 Å, (b) extreme ultraviolet.]

38 Electromagnetic waves and vacuum tubes

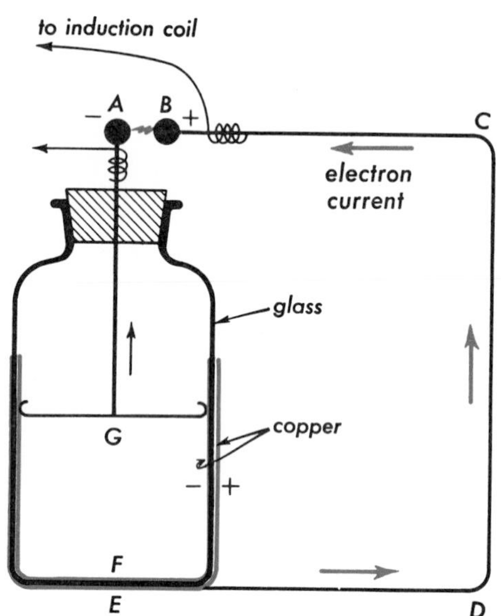

Fig. 38A. The discharge of a Leyden jar is oscillatory.

The transmission of code signals by wireless, of voice and music by radio, and of voice, music, and moving pictures by television, are some of the most remarkable achievements of civilized man. The electromagnetic waves carrying these signals through the air, and across the great reaches of interplanetary space with the speed of light, 300,000,000 m/s, are nothing less than miraculous.

It is the purpose of this chapter to introduce some of the early discoveries leading to wireless telegraphy. This will be followed by the basic principles of an oscillating circuit, and a treatment of the fundamental principles of vacuum tubes and transistors as they are used in hundreds of modern electronic circuits.

38.1. The Leyden Jar

A cross section of a "Leyden jar" of the type invented by the Dutch scientist Musschenbroek in 1746 is shown in Fig. 38A. Two metallic conductors forming the plates of a capacitor are separated by a glass bottle as a dielectric insulator. When such a capacitor is connected to a source of high potential, one plate will become positively charged and the other will be negative. If the source voltage is high enough, an electric spark will jump between the terminals indicating a sudden discharge of the capacitor, and an electron current will surge first one way and then the other around the circuit.

This oscillatory current was first postulated by Joseph Henry, then derived from theory by Lord Kelvin, and later proven experimentally by Fedderson. Fedderson, looking at a capacitor discharge with a rotating mirror, observed that each initial breakdown spark was followed by a succession of fainter sparks. The initial spark ionizes the air, making of it a good conductor and, of the entire system ABCDEFGA, a complete electrical circuit.

38.2. The Oscillatory Circuit

The Leyden jar circuit in Fig. 38A contains, in addition to the *capacitance,* an *inductance* as well. The single loop FGABCD and E forms practically one turn of a coil. An inductance and capacitance, connected as shown in simplest schematic form in Fig. 38B, form the necessary elements of all oscillating circuits.

If, initially, the capacitance is charged as indicated, the surplus electrons on the plate below cause a surge of negative charge counterclockwise around the circuit to neutralize the positives and, in so doing, set up a magnetic field in and around the inductance. When the positives become neutralized and the electron current tends to cease, the magnetic flux linking the circuit decreases and keeps the electron current flowing in the same direction. Once this field has vanished and the current has ceased, the capacitance is found to be in a charged condition, the upper plate negative and the lower plate positive.

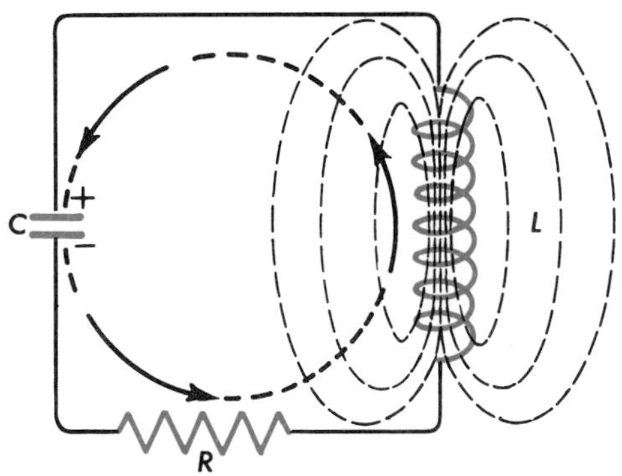

Fig. 38B. Schematic diagram of an oscillating circuit.

Having reversed the charge on the capacitance, the above process will repeat itself, this time the electron current surging clockwise around the circuit. Thus the current rushes first in one direction, then the other, oscillating back and forth in an electrical way just as any spring pulled to one side and released vibrates in a mechanical way (see Fig. 38C).

When a straight leaf spring is pulled to one side and released, the kinetic energy it gains upon straightening keeps the spring moving, and it bends to the other side. Just as the vibration amplitude of the spring slowly decreases because of *friction,* so also does the current in the electrical circuit decrease because of *electrical resistance.* A graph showing how current slowly dies out in an electric circuit is given in Fig. 38D. These are called *damped vibrations,* or *damped oscillations.* If the resistance of the circuit is high, the damping is high and the current quickly dies out after only a few oscillations. If the resistance is low, however, the damping is small, the amplitude decreases slowly, and there are many oscillations.

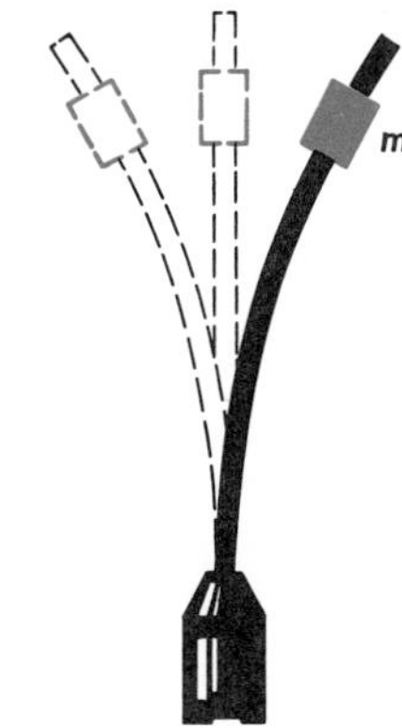

Fig. 38C. A vibrating spring is like an electrical oscillating circuit.

To calculate the frequency of an oscillating circuit, either of the following formulas may be used:

$$T = 2\pi\sqrt{LC}$$

$$\nu = \frac{1}{2\pi\sqrt{LC}} \qquad (38a)$$

where L is the inductance in henries, C is the capacitance in farads, T is the time for one complete oscillation in seconds, and ν is the number of oscillations per second. T is the period and ν the frequency. The formula above is to be compared with the analogous formula for the period of a vibrating spring:

$$T = 2\pi\sqrt{m/k} \tag{38b}$$

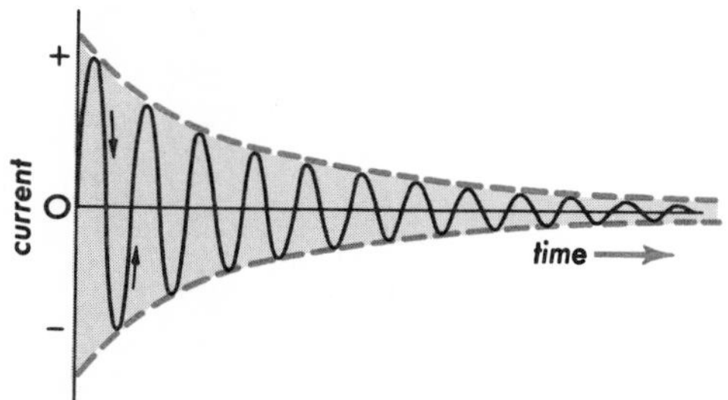

Fig. 38D. Graph of the damped oscillations of an electrical circuit.

The mass m for the spring is analogous to the inductance L for the circuit, and the stiffness $1/k$ is analogous to the capacitance C. An increase of the inductance L, or capacitance C, or both, increases the period and decreases the frequency of the oscillating circuit.

Example 1. A Leyden jar with a small capacitance of 0.01 μF is connected to a single turn of wire (about 15 cm in diameter) having an inductance of 1.0 μH. Calculate the natural frequency of the circuit.

Solution. Since 1 henry = 10^6 microhenries and 1 farad = 10^6 microfarads, direct substitution for L and C in Eq.(38a) gives

$$\nu = \frac{1}{2\pi\sqrt{LC}} = \frac{1}{2\pi\sqrt{1 \times 10^{-6}\,\text{H} \times 1 \times 10^{-8}\,\text{F}}}$$

$$\nu = 1{,}592{,}000 \text{ Hz}$$

or

$$\nu = 1.592 \text{ MHz}$$

38.3. Maxwell's Electromagnetic Wave Theory

In 1856 James Clerk Maxwell wrote his now famous theoretical paper on electromagnetic waves. In this scientific publication, he proposed the possible existence of electromagnetic waves and at the same time postulated that if such waves could ever be produced, they would travel through free space with the speed of light.

Light itself, said Maxwell, is propagated as an electromagnetic wave, and electrically produced waves should differ from light only in their wavelength and frequency. Because Maxwell gave no clues as to how such waves might be generated or detected, their real existence was not discovered until 32 years later when Heinrich Hertz made his important discovery.

38.4. Hertzian Waves

In 1888, a young German scientist, Heinrich Hertz,* began a series of experiments in which he not only produced and detected electromagnetic waves, but also demonstrated their properties of reflection, refraction, and interference. One of his experimental arrangements is diagrammed in Fig. 38E.

The transmitter consists of two spheres QQ′ located near the ends of two straight rods MN separated by a spark gap S. With the two rods connected to an induction coil I, sparks jump across the gap S, giving rise to oscillating currents in MN. That such a generator is an oscillating circuit can be seen from the fact that the spheres QQ′ form the plates of a capacitor and the rods form the inductance.

The receiver, or detector, consists of a single loop of wire with a tiny spark gap at R. This circuit, too, is an oscillating circuit with the spark gap as a capacitance and the loop as an inductance. Tuning the transmitter frequency to that of the receiver is accomplished by sliding the spheres QQ′ along the rods MN, resonance being indicated by the appearance of sparks at R.

With apparatus of this general type, Hertz was able to transmit signals a distance of several hundred feet. He found that large metal plates would reflect the radiation, and that at normal incidence the reflected waves would interfere with those coming up to set up standing waves with nodes and loops. As the receiver was moved slowly away from the reflector, nodes and loops were located by the appearance of sparks only at equally spaced intervals.

With a large prism of paraffin he demonstrated refraction, and with a lens made of pitch he focused the waves as a glass lens focuses visible light.

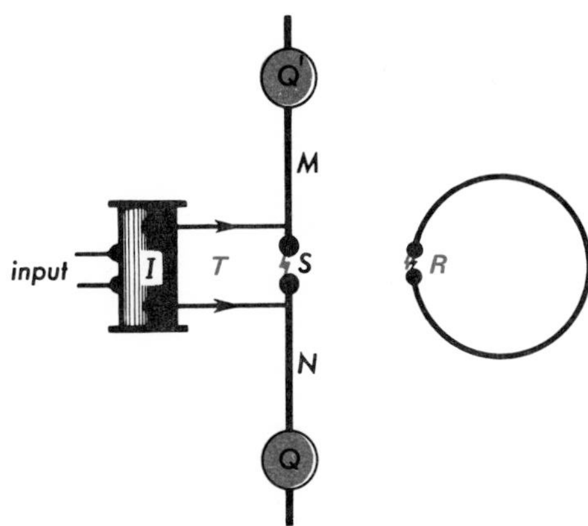

Fig. 38E. Schematic diagram of the apparatus with which Hertz produced and detected the first radio waves.

*Heinrich Rudolf Hertz (1857–1894), German physicist, was born at Hamburg, February 22, 1857. He studied physics under Helmholtz in Berlin, at whose suggestion he first became interested in Maxwell's electromagnetic theory. His researches with electromagnetic waves which made his name famous were carried out at Karlsruhe Polytechnic between 1885 and 1889. As professor of physics at the University of Bonn, after 1889, he experimented with electrical discharges through gases and narrowly missed the discovery of X rays described by Röntgen a few years later. By his premature death, science lost one of its most promising disciples.

38.5. Electromagnetic Waves

To visualize the production of waves by a Hertzian oscillator, consider the schematic diagram in Fig. 38F. Let the rods MN and spheres Q and Q′ be charged initially as indicated, and consider the electrostatic action of the charges on a small charge C located some distance away. The negative charge Q_1 attracts C with a force *a* and the positive charge Q_2 repels it with a force *b*. Since by symmetry these two forces are of equal magnitude, their resultant $C\mathcal{E}$ is parallel to MN. If the isolated charge is farther away as at D, the resultant force is also parallel to MN, but weaker. In other words, the electric field $\mathcal{E}$ at points C and D is up and par-

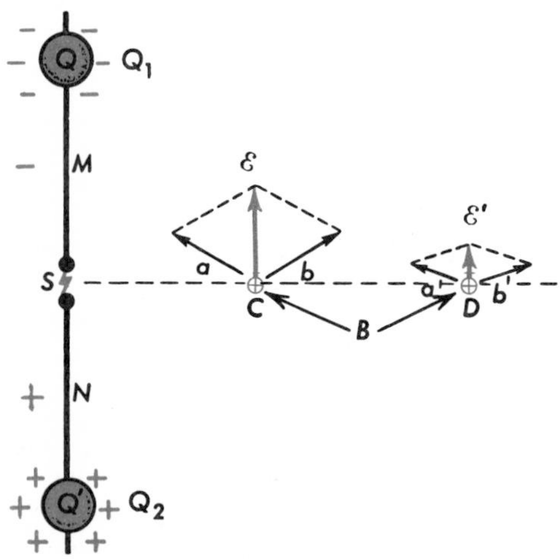

Fig. 38F. A Hertzian dipole.

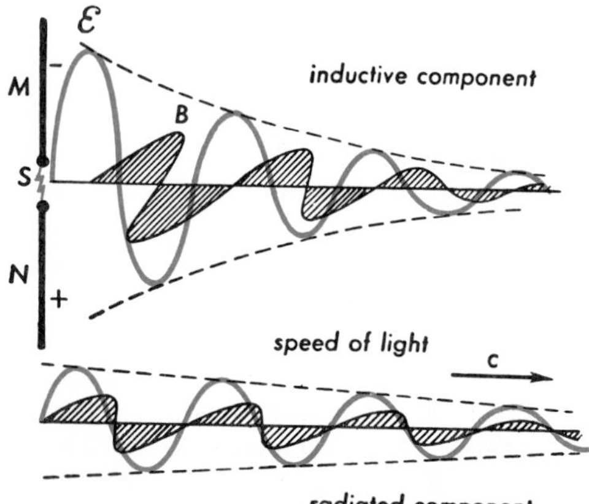

Fig. 38G. Graph of the electromagnetic waves emitted by a Hertzian dipole.

allel to MN, decreasing in intensity as the distance from the transmitter increases.

Suppose that a spark jumps the gap S and oscillation sets in. One-half cycle after the condition shown in Fig. 38F, electrons have surged across the gap, charging Q positively and Q′ negatively. With reversed charges the resultant force on C and D will be down instead of up. Thus it is seen how oscillations in the transmitter, which constitute a surging of electrons back and forth between M and N, give rise to a periodically reversing electric field at distance points.

In addition to an electric field at C and D, the surging electrons in MN give rise to a magnetic field as well. When the electron current is down (using the conventional left-hand rule), the magnetic induction B at C or D is perpendicular to and into the plane of the page, and when the electron current is up, the magnetic induction is out from the page. The surging of the charges therefore gives rise to a periodically reversing magnetic induction, the direction of which is at right angles to the electric intensity at the same points.

According to Maxwell's theory, the $\mathcal{E}$ and B fields do not appear instantly at distance points; time is required for their propagation. The speed of propagation, according to Maxwell (and this has been confirmed by numerous experiments), is the same as the speed of light. The changing $\mathcal{E}$ and B fields at C therefore lag behind the oscillating charges in MN, and those at D lag behind still farther.

Figure 38G is a graph of the instantaneous values of the electric and magnetic fields as they vary with distance from the transmitter. At certain points the fields are a maximum and at other points they are zero. As time goes on, these electric and magnetic waves move away from the transmitter with a speed of 2.9979×10^8 m/s.

The mathematical theory of electromagnetic radiation shows that, close to the transmitter, the $\mathcal{E}$ and B fields, called the *inductive components,* are 90° out of phase and that their magnitudes fall off very rapidly with distance. Farther out, however, the two get in step with each other and their amplitudes fall off more slowly, as shown in the diagram. The latter are called the *radiated components* and are the ones detected at great distances.

Suppose now that a series of sparks is made to occur in the gap S of a transmitter as in Fig. 38H. Each spark will give rise to a damped oscillation in MN, which in turn sends out a damped electromagnetic wave. The succession of sparks sends out a train of such waves which, as they leave the antenna, decrease rapidly in magnitude at first, then more slowly as they get farther away. Only the electric component of such waves is shown in the diagram.

If an electrical conductor is located at some distant point, the + and − charges within it will, as such waves go by, experience up and down forces tending to oscillate them. If the conductor is an oscillating circuit whose natural frequency is that of the passing waves, resonance will occur and currents of electrons will surge up and down.

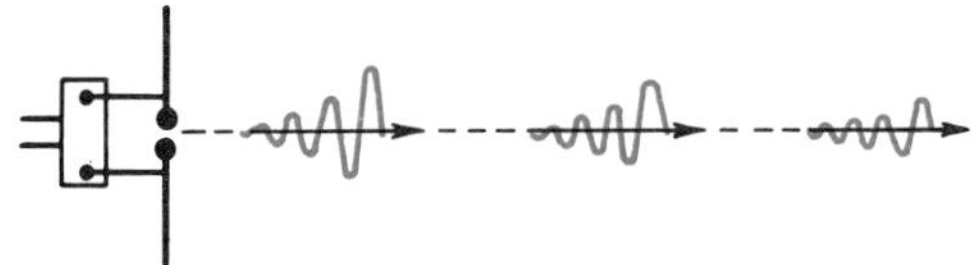

Fig. 38H. Damped electromagnetic waves from a Hertzian oscillator.

38.6. Air-Core Inductances and Transformers

When a high-frequency alternating current is sent through a solenoid with an iron core or the primary of an iron-core transformer, the back emf is so large that the current as well as the magnetic induction cannot build up to any appreciable value before it reverses in direction. The result is that the current hardly gets started in one direction before it stops and reverses.

In an iron-core transformer the back emf in the primary winding so retards the building up of strong fields that little or no induced currents can be "drawn" from the secondary. To overcome this difficulty, the iron core is done away with, so that we have what is called an *air-core transformer.* In the absence of any iron, the current in the coil may rise to an appreciable value each time it changes in direction. The rapidly increasing and diminishing flux that links both circuits induces a current in the secondary of exactly the same frequency.

Air-core transformers, consisting of nothing more than two coils of a few turns each, a primary winding and a seconary winding, are used extensively in radio, microwave, and television transmitters and receivers. In these instances the alternating currents with frequencies of thousands and even millions of hertz are usually referred to as *radiofrequencies,* and the transformers are referred to as *radiofrequency transformers.*

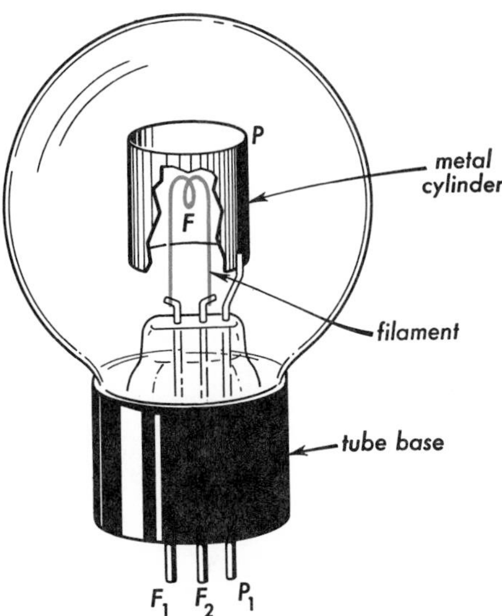

Fig. 38I. Diagram of a Fleming valve, or rectifier tube. Such tubes are now called diodes.

38.7. The Vacuum-Tube Rectifier

While the great American inventor Thomas A. Edison was striving by a process of trial and error to produce a satisfactory electric light bulb, he made an accidental discovery, the importance of which was first recognized and used successfully by Sir John Fleming. Now called a vacuum-tube rectifier or diode, the Fleming valve is used in some radio and television transmitters and receivers to change alternating current into direct current.

The Fleming valve, as shown in Fig. 38I, consists of a highly evacuated glass bulb containing a wire filament that is heated

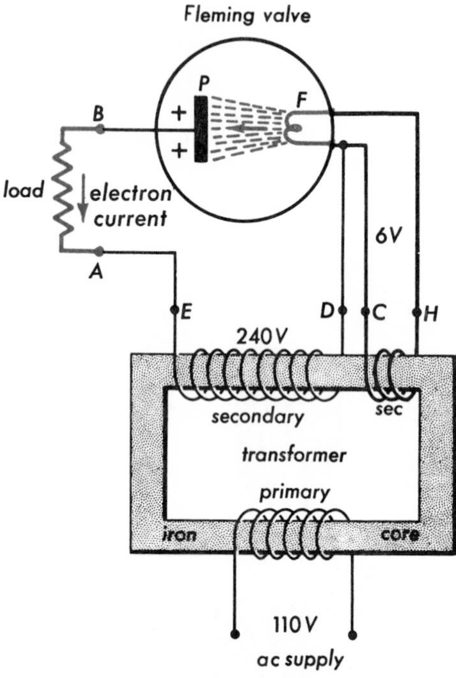

Fig. 38J. Circuit diagram of a Fleming valve rectifier.

electrically to incandescence. Surrounding the filament and connected to the outside through the tube base and a prong P_1 is a cylindrical metal plate P. When the filament is heated to incandescence, it gives off large quantities of electrons in much the same way that water, when heated to the boiling point, gives off steam. The emission of electrons by a hot body is called *thermionic emission* and is due to the high temperature and not to the electric current. Heating a metal by any other means will produce the same effect. Electrons emitted from hot metal surfaces are called *thermoelectrons.*

The principal action of the *filament* F and *plate* P is explained by means of a typical electric circuit shown schematically in Fig. 38J. The circuit consists of a *transformer* having *two secondary windings,* a *Fleming valve,* and a *load.* The latter, shown as a resistance, represents any electrical device requiring unidirectional current for its operation. With an alternating current of 110 V supplied to the primary, a high voltage, 240 V for example, is delivered by one secondary to the terminals ED and a low voltage of 6 V alternating current is delivered by the other secondary to the terminals CH. The latter, called the *filament winding,* is for the purpose of heating the filament.

When for a fraction of a second the plate P of the tube is positively charged and the filament F is negatively charged, the electrons from F are attracted to the plate P and constitute an electron current flowing across the vacuum space PF and through the load from B to A. One-half cycle later, when the potential is reversed and P becomes negatively charged and F positively charged, the electrons from F are repelled by P and very little current flows.

The emf's in each part of the rectifier circuit are shown by graphs in Fig. 38K. The primary emf of 110 V is shown in (a), the secondary emf of 240 V in diagram (b), and the *rectified* or *pulsating emf* through the load AB in diagram (c).

38.8. Full-Wave Rectifier

A full-wave rectifier tube, sometimes called a *duo-diode,* is essentially a double Fleming valve with two plates and two filaments (see Fig. 38L). The two prongs F_1 and F_2 in the base are connected to both filaments in series, while the prongs P_1 and P_2 are connected one to each plate.

A schematic diagram of a rectifier circuit employing such a tube is shown in Fig. 38M. Here an iron-core transformer with one primary and two secondary windings is used, differing from the single-phase rectifier in Fig 38J in that the center of each secondary winding is now connected to the load. CHJ is the filament winding and supplies current to both filaments (shown as one bent wire) while GED is the high-voltage winding. The latter supplies an alternating potential to the plates so that, when P_1 is + and P_2 is −, electrons from the filament are attracted to P_1, and, when a moment later P_1 is − and P_2 is +, electrons from the filament are attracted to P_2.

In the first instance an electron current flows around the circuit $F_1P_1GEABHJF_1$, and in the second it flows around the circuit $F_2P_2DEABHCF_2$. In each case the current has gone through the load AB in the same direction and has pulsating characteristics as shown in Fig. 38N.

If such a pulsating current were used to supply the direct current needed in every radio receiver, a loud objectionable hum with a frequency of 120 cycles would be heard. To make this current a steady smooth direct current, as illustrated by the straight line in the same graph, and thus eliminate the hum, a *filter circuit* as shown in Fig. 38O is used. The terminals A and B are connected to, and replace, the load A and B in Fig. 38M. K is an iron-core inductance and C_1 and C are capacitors of large capacity.

As the current through AabB starts to flow, the capacitors become charged, as shown, and a magnetic field is created around K. This has a retarding action which prevents the current from reaching its otherwise peak value. When a moment later the filament-to-plate current drops to near zero, the capacitors discharge and the field around K collapses, thus sending a current through AB. This process is repeated with each pulse of electrons from either plate of the tube, and the current through ab remains steady. Large capacities and large self-inductances deliver more constant voltage.

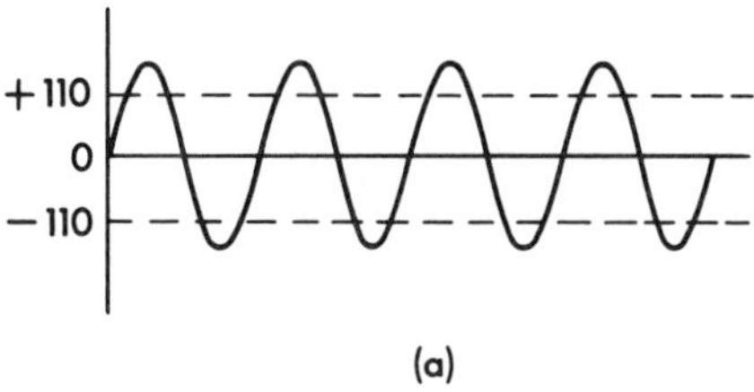

(a)

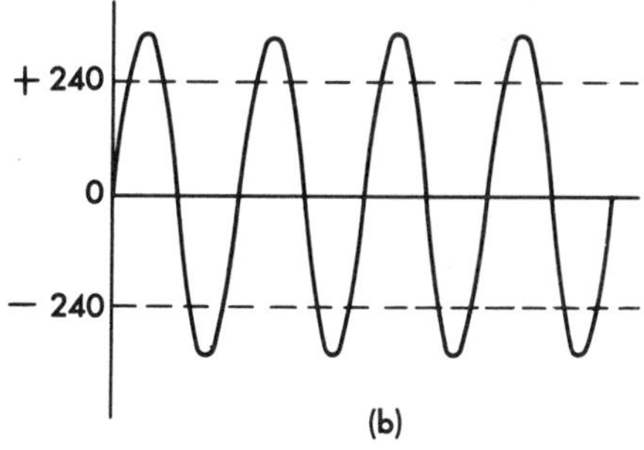

(b)

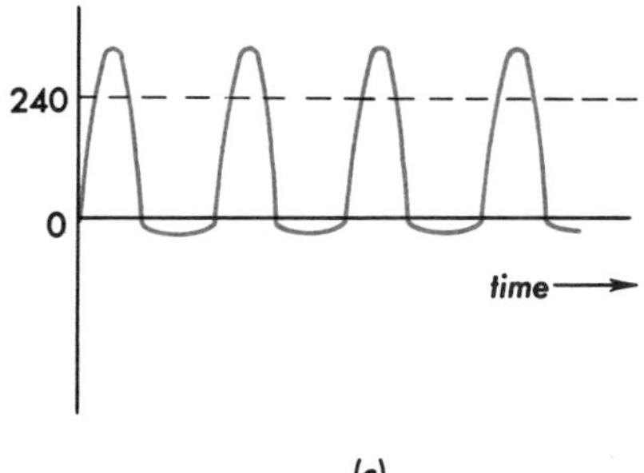

(c)

Fig. 38K. Alternating current as rectified by a Fleming valve or diode.

38.9. Modern Vacuum Tubes

Every electronics enthusiast today knows that there are hundreds of different kinds of tubes. Some contain two filaments and two plates, while others contain as many as three or four separate grids. Although a treatment of such complex tubes is out of place here, the fundamental principles of all of them are little different from De Forest's audion. One important difference, however, is illustrated in Fig. 38P, and that is the employment in most tubes of a *cathode* in place of a filament as a source of thermal electrons.

A fine tungsten-wire filament is threaded through two small holes running lengthwise through a porcelain-like insulating rod.

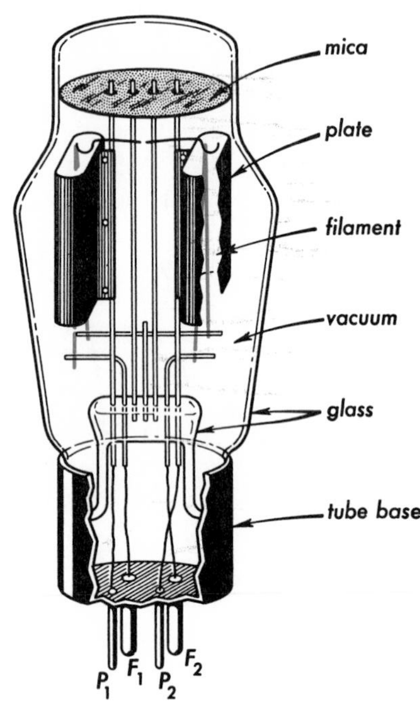

Fig. 38L. Drawing of a full-wave rectifier tube.

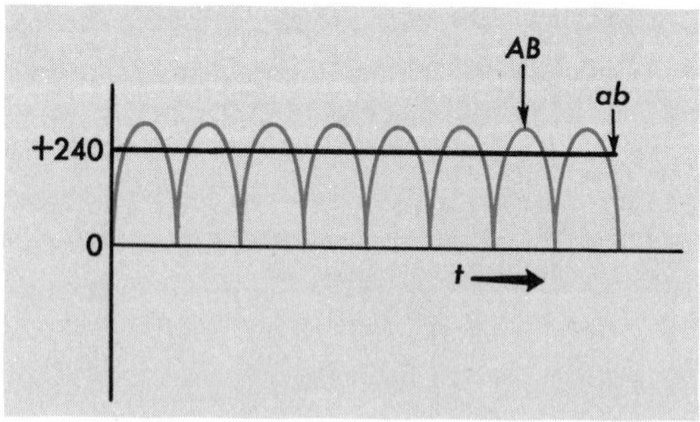

Fig. 38N. Rectified voltage from a full-wave rectifier circuit.

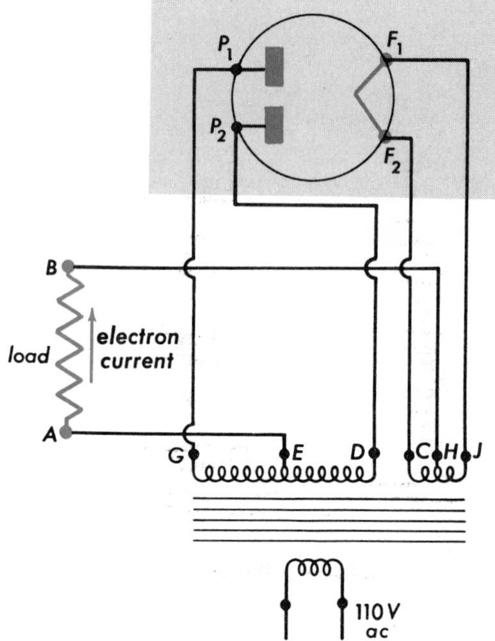

Fig. 38M. Diagram for a full-wave rectifier circuit.

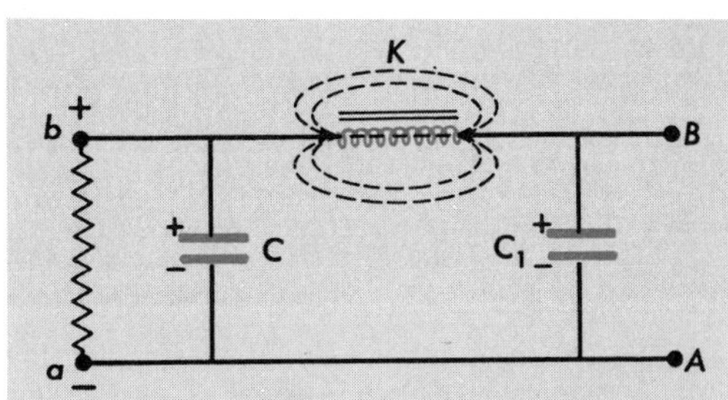

Fig. 38O. Electrical filter circuit for "smoothing out" pulsating direct current.

Fitting snugly around this rod is the *cathode,* a metal cylinder coated on the outside with a thin layer of thorium, strontium, or cesium oxide. These particular oxides are copious emitters of electrons when heated to a dull-red heat. Insulated from the cathode, the filament as a source of heat can be, and generally is, connected directly to an appropriate transformer winding.

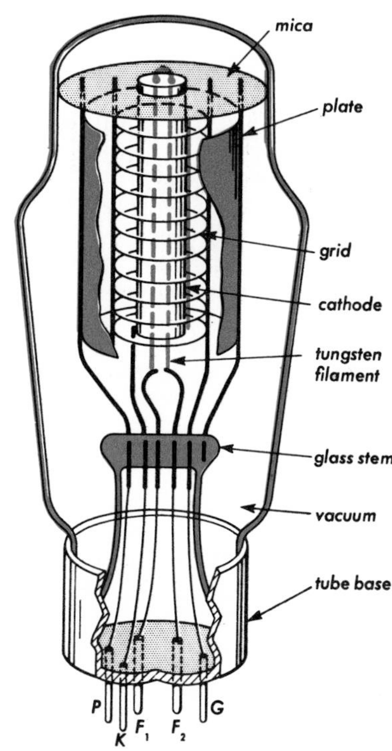

Fig. 38P. A modern radio tube with a cesium-coated cathode as a source of thermal electrons. The filament serves only to heat the cathode.

38.10. Vacuum-Tube Oscillator

To broadcast the human voice by radio, a generator of alternating current of extremely high frequency and constant amplitude is required. In commercial broadcasting stations and amateur transmitters, this function is performed by a vacuum tube and circuit of relatively simple design.

One type of oscillator circuit is shown in Fig. 38Q. In the type of vacuum tube shown schematically here, a cylinder or plate K, called the *cathode,* is coated with a thin layer of *thorium, strontium,* or *cesium oxide.* These oxides are copious emitters of electrons when heated to a dull red heat by the filament F. When the switch S is closed, connecting the B battery to the plate of the tube, an electron current from the cathode K to the plate P starts a current in the circuit PRVL_3K. This growing current in L_3 creates an expanding magnetic field, which, cutting across L_2, induces a current in the grid circuit in such a direction that the grid becomes negative. A negative charge on the grid causes the plate current to decrease. This decreasing current causes the field about L_3 to collapse, thus inducing a reversed current in the grid circuit and therefore a positive charge on the grid. Such a charge increases the plate current, and the above process is repeated.

If the two circuits, L_2C_2 and PRVL_3, are properly tuned by adjusting C_2, resonance will occur and energy from the B battery will be continuously supplied to keep the oscillations going with constant amplitude. The graph of the continuous oscillations shown in Fig. 38R represents the voltage across L_3 as it varies in time. The L_2C_2 circuit controls the frequency by controlling the grid potential while the large voltage and current fluctuations take place in the L_3 circuit.

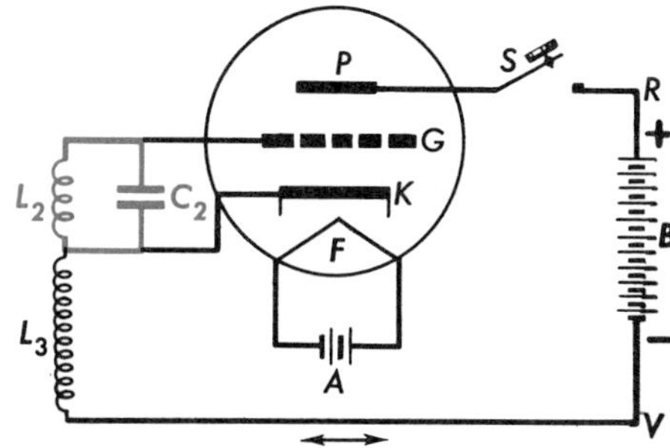

Fig. 38Q. Vacuum-tube oscillator circuit for generating radio waves of constant amplitude.

38.11. Vacuum-Tube Amplifier

One of the most important functions of the vacuum tube is its use as an *amplifier* of radiofrequency or audiofrequency currents, as shown in Fig. 38S. The *input* resistor represents some part of any circuit in which a weak but varying current is flowing; the

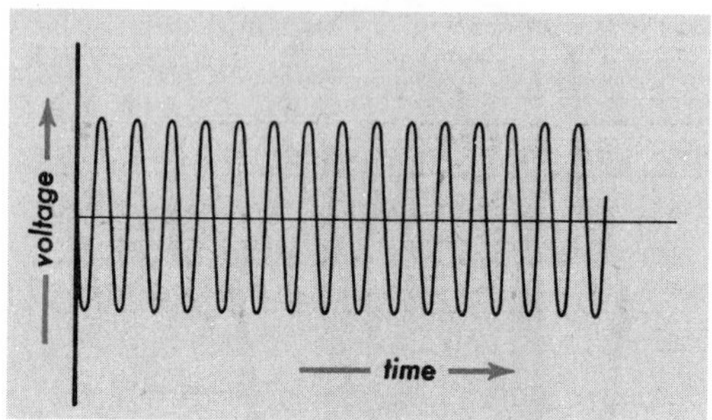

Fig. 38R. Continuous oscillations in a vacuum-tube oscillator circuit like that in Fig. 38Q.

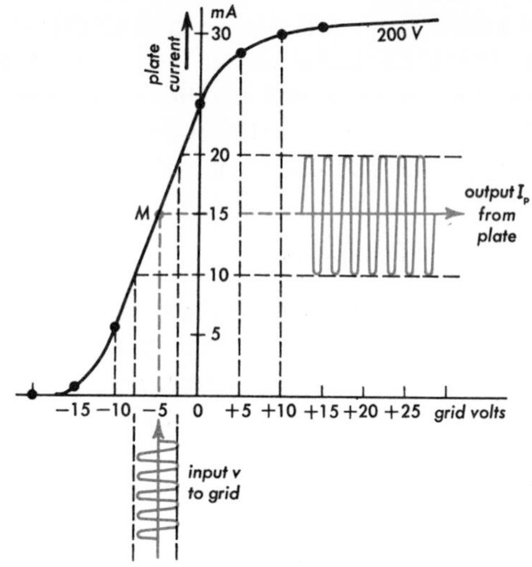

Fig. 38T. Graph showing amplifier operation.

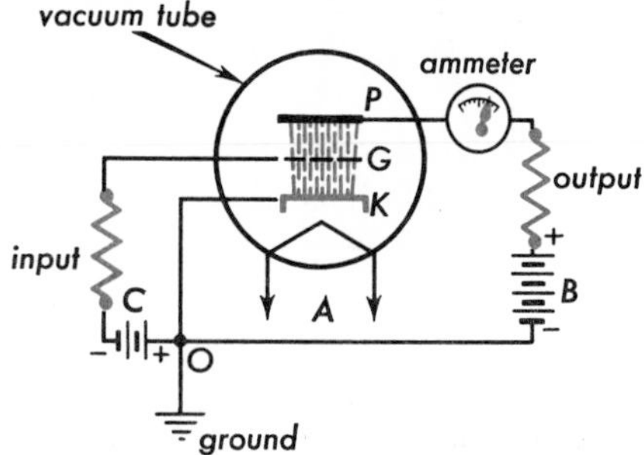

Fig. 38S. Amplifier circuit with one vacuum tube.

output resistor represents another circuit to which a stronger current of the same form is delivered. In some cases these are resistors as shown, but in others they are the primary and secondary windings of separate transformers. The source of the additional energy is the B battery plate supply.

In amplifying any given signal current, a faithful reproduction of the *wave form* must be carried out, otherwise *distortion* will result; musical sounds from a radio will be harsh or pictures from a television receiver will be blurred. To amplify without distortion, a tube that has a long straight section in its *characteristic curve* must be used, and it should be operated at the center of this straight portion. Such an operation is shown by the graph in Fig. 38T.

To make the tube operate at M, a small battery, called a C battery or C bias, is inserted in the grid circuit to maintain the grid at a negative potential. For the curve and tube shown, this requires −5 V, while for other types of tubes it might well require greater or smaller potentials.

When no input signal potentials are imposed, the grid is held at −5 V and a steady current of 150 mA flows through the plate and output circuit. If now an alternating current like a radio frequency of constant amplitude is impressed across the input terminals, the grid potential will rise and fall in the same way, and an undistorted but amplified current will flow in the plate and output circuit. The time variations in grid potential are shown at the bottom in Fig. 38T, and the corresponding plate current oscillations at the right. If the input radio frequency is voice-modulated, the amplified current will also be voice-modulated without distortion. It should be noted that if the impressed grid voltage variations are too large, say −20 to +10 V, the amplified currents will reach the curved portions of the curve above and below, and *distortion* of the *wave form* will result. As long as the tube is operated on the straight portion of the curve, the plate current is directly proportional to the impressed grid potential, and faithful amplification takes place.

questions

1. What is an oscillatory circuit? What are its three principal elements?

2. Upon what does the natural frequency of a circuit depend? What is the formula for the frequency?

3. What is electrical resonance? Under what conditions does it arise?

4. What are Hertzian waves? What is a Hertzian dipole?

5. What are electromagnetic waves? What is their nature? With what speed do they travel?

6. What are damped oscillations? How can damping be reduced?

7. Draw from memory a schematic wiring diagram of a full-wave rectifier showing the vacuum tube, transformer, and load.

8. Make a schematic diagram of a full-wave rectifier and filter circuit consisting of a transformer, vacuum tube, inductance, two capacitors, and a load.

9. Diagram the circuit of a vacuum-tube oscillator for generating high radio frequencies of constant amplitude.

10. Draw from memory an amplifier circuit with one vacuum tube.

problems

1. Determine the frequency of an oscillation circuit containing a 6.0 μF capacitor and a 6.0 μH inductor, if they are connected in parallel.

2. What capacitance connected in parallel to an inductance of 4.50 μH will produce an oscillating circuit with a frequency of 5.0×10^4 Hz?

3. What inductance connected to a capacitance of 0.250 μF will produce a circuit with a natural frequency of 1.0 megahertz? [Ans. 0.1013 μH.]

4. Calculate the frequency of an oscillating circuit containing an inductance of 2.50 μH and a capacitance of 2.50 μF, if they are connected in parallel.

5. Calculate all of the possible frequencies that can be obtained by combining two or three of the following elements to form an oscillation circuit: $C_1 = 3.0\ \mu F$, $C_2 = 6.0\ \mu$F, and $L = 4.0\ \mu$H.

6. A 20.0-μF capacitor is connected across a 50.0-μH inductor. What is the frequency of the third harmonic of the oscillating circuit? [Ans. 1.510×10^6 Hz.]

7. A 25.0-μH inductor is connected across a 16.0-μF capacitor. Calculate the frequency of the fourth harmonic of this circuit.

8. What capacitance connected in parallel to an inductance of $2.50 \times 10^{-2}\ \mu$H will produce an oscillating circuit with a frequency of 5.0 MHz?

9. A 5.0-mH inductor is connected across a 50.0-μF capacitor. Find its frequency as an oscillation circuit. [Ans. 318.3 Hz.]

10. A 30.0-μF capacitor is connected in parallel to a 5.0-μH inductor. Calculate the frequency of the circuit.

39 The solid state and semiconductors

One of the most active and important branches of science and technology today is called *solid state physics.* This is a field of research concerned with the study of the physical properties of solids and includes such subjects as the detailed configurations of atoms in solids, the behavior of free and bound electrons in a crystal lattice, the electrical conductivity of pure substances and those containing impurities, and the magnetic and mechanical properties of solids at low and high temperatures. Since solid state physics has grown to such huge proportions (and so has the number of people active in the field), only a small part of the subject will be given in this chapter.

39.1. Conductors and Nonconductors

The crystal structure of the common highly conducting metals, like copper, silver, gold, and platinum, is such that the outermost electrons are shared by all the atoms. The complete inner shells of electrons are bound to their individual nucleus, but the outermost electrons in uncompleted shells, the so-called *valence electrons,* are free to wander throughout the substance. This diffusion of electrons is similar to the random motion of molecules in a gas.

In contrast with *good conductors* there are *good insulators,* called *nonconductors,* which have practically no free electrons. In substances like quartz, mica, and sulfur, all of the electrons remain bound to their respective atoms. The resistivity of a good conductor is as low as 10^{-7} or 10^{-8} ohm-meters, compared to values as high as 10^{16} ohm-meters for an insulator like quartz.

39.2. Semiconductors

There are a large number of solids that are neither good conductors of electricity nor good insulators. Since the resistance range between these two groups of materials is about 10^{23}, a majority of known substances lie in between. These substances are called *semiconductors.* In them, electrons are capable of being moved only by the application of relatively strong electric fields of hundreds of thousands of volts per meter.

Of the large number of semiconductors known to science, certain ones are of considerable importance. Typical examples are the crystalline forms of the elements listed in column IV-A of the periodic table (see Appendix IV). Two important ones are *silicon* and *germanium.*

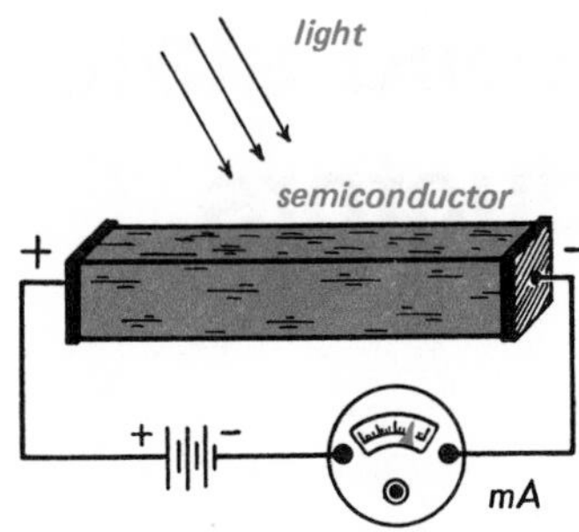

Fig. 39A. Circuit diagram for demonstrating the photoconductivity of a semiconductor like germanium or silicon.

Figure 39A is a diagram of a small germanium crystal about 5 mm square and 2 cm long, connected to a battery and a milliammeter by wires, and completing an electric circuit. When light is allowed to fall on the crystal, its electrical resistance decreases and the current rises. This response to light is instantaneous and is called *photoconductivity.*

If the germanium crystal is heated, the current again rises, indicating a decrease in electrical resistance. This *heating effect* is not instantaneous, however, since it takes a long time for the current to return to its original value, that is, for the temperature of the crystal to return to room temperature. The resistance of metallic conductors behaves in just the opposite way; their resistance increases with a rise in temperature.

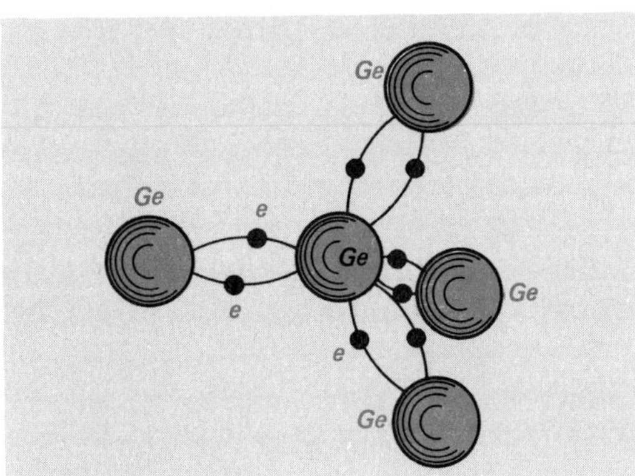

Fig. 39B. Each atom in a germanium crystal is bound at the center of a tetrahedron formed by its four nearest neighbors.

In order to explain the light and heat effects described above, we must refer to the crystal lattice of semiconductors. Silicon and germanium atoms each have what the chemists call four *valence electrons,* that is, four electrons that enter into the chemical binding in solids. The atomic pattern of atoms in both crystals is a tetrahedral structure, as shown in Fig. 30P. In Fig. 39B it will be seen that each atom shares one of its electrons with each neighbor, and the neighbor in turn shares one of its four with it. Such a sharing of electrons between two atoms is called a *covalent bond.*

Because of the difficulty of drawing a three-dimensional tetrahedral lattice structure, it is convenient to flatten the diagram out and represent the bonding as a square lattice, as shown in Fig. 39C.

At temperatures close to absolute zero, all electrons in a crystal are tied up strongly by these chemical bonds. When the crystal is raised to room temperature, however, the thermal vibrations of the atoms are sufficient to break some of the bonds and free some of the electrons to wander throughout the crystal. Where an electron has broken free, as shown at the upper right and lower left in Fig. 39C, a hole has been created and the process is referred to as *dissociation.* Since that part of the crystal was neutral beforehand, it now lacks an electron, and the vacant hole is equivalent to a net positive charge.

Owing also to thermal agitation, a *bound* electron next to a hole can move across to fill the gap, the net motion of the negative charge from one bonded position to another being in effect equivalent to the motion of a hole in the opposite direction. The motion of a hole is, therefore, equivalent to the motion of a positive charge. This action is shown at the lower center in Fig. 39C.

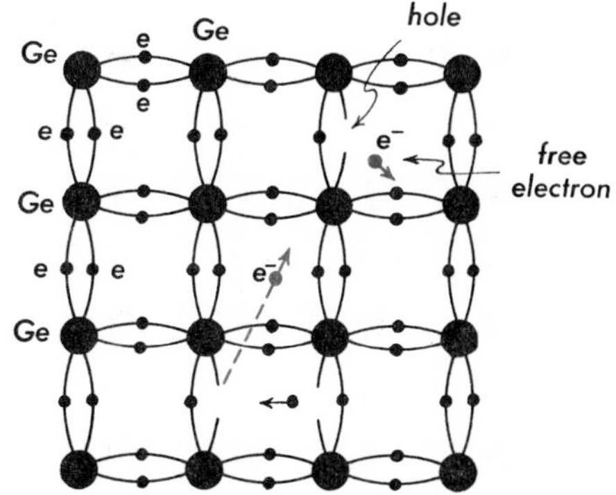

Fig. 39C. Schematic diagram of the covalent bonding of atoms in a germanium crystal. Thermal agitation breaks some bonds and liberates electrons.

39.3. N-Type and P-Type Crystals

The widespread use of semiconductors in such devices as solar cells and transistors has resulted from the technical development of pure semiconductor crystals impregnated with minute quantities of certain impurities. The crystals most commonly used for these purposes are those mentioned in the preceding section, *silicon* and *germanium.*

If crystals are formed with *arsenic* as an impurity, the arsenic atoms, with five valence electrons each, provide a crystal lattice with extra electrons. Such a crystal as shown in Fig. 39D is therefore one in which each arsenic atom donates one free electron to the system. With arsenic present in quantities of one to a million, *donor atoms* are on the average about 100 atoms apart, or there are about 10^{17} arsenic atoms and 10^{17} free electrons per cubic centimeter. In a good conductor like copper there are approximately 10^{23} free electrons per cm^3.

By thermal agitation a few bound electrons are also "shaken loose" and an equal number of holes thereby created. The ratio of the number of *donor electrons* to the number of unbound electrons or *holes* is approximately 10,000 to 1. Since by far the majority of free-to-move charge carriers are electrons, the lattice is called an *N-type crystal.*

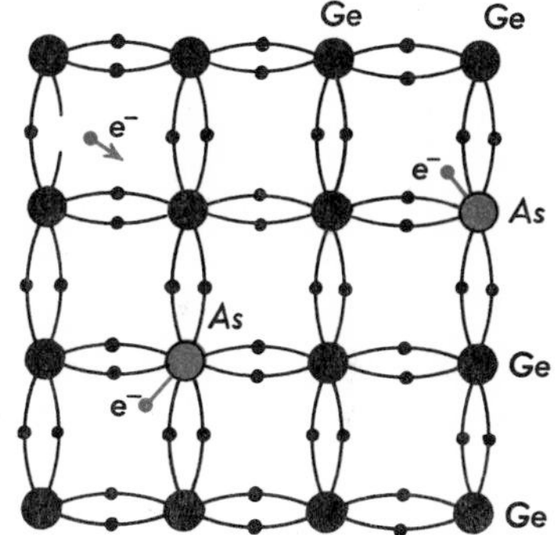

Fig. 39D. N-type crystal lattice with arsenic atoms as an impurity.

If crystals are grown with *aluminum* as an impurity, the aluminum atoms, with only three valence electrons each, form a crystal lattice with an electron deficiency, that is, with holes (see Fig. 39E). Such a crystal is therefore one in which each aluminum atom provides one hole to the system that is free to accept an electron.

By thermal agitation a few bound electrons are also shaken loose and an equal number of holes are produced. Since by far the majority of the charge carriers are holes, and these act like positive charges, this type of lattice is called a *P-type crystal.*

Since the donor electrons in an N-type crystal, and the holes in a P-type crystal, far outnumber the electrons or holes contributed by thermal agitation, the donor charges are called *majority carriers,* and those caused by dissociation are called *minority carriers.*

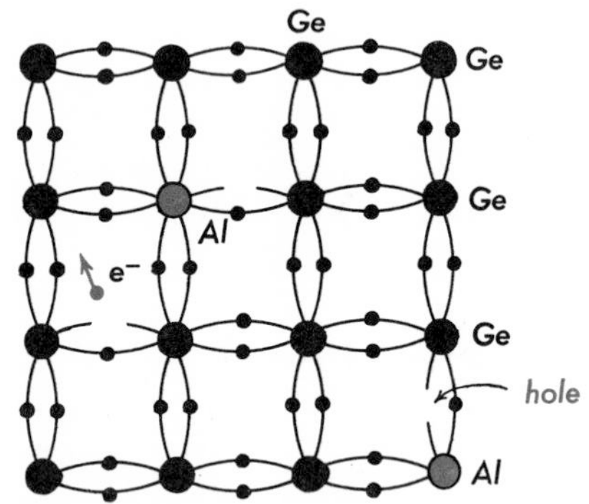

Fig. 39E. P-type crystal lattice with aluminum atoms as an impurity.

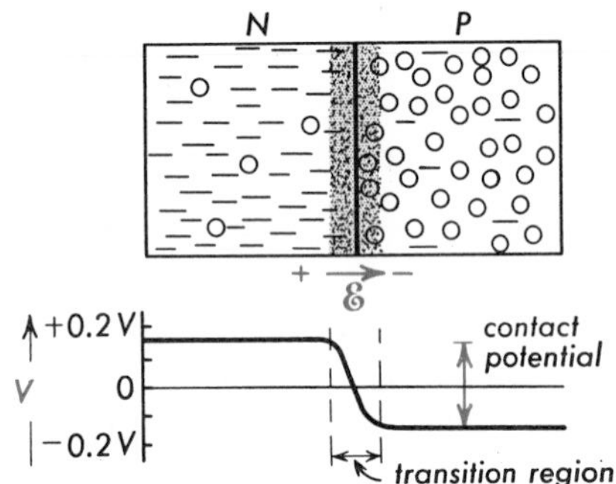

Fig. 39F. When P and N crystals are brought into contact, a difference of potential is set up between them.

Neither of these crystals, by itself, has a net charge. The surplus of free negatives in an N-type crystal is compensated for by the positive charges on the arsenic nuclei, while the surplus of holes in the P-type crystal is compensated for by the deficiency in positive nuclear charge of the aluminum nuclei.

When light falls on a crystal as in Fig. 39A, the light is absorbed within a few atomic layers. The absorbed energy breaks some of the electron bonds and creates holes. This process is called *photoionization.* The potentials applied at the ends of the crystal cause the electrons to move to the left, and the holes to the right. This flow of charge constitutes a current.

When the light is shut off, free electrons fall at random into holes as the crystal cools. The falling of an electron into a hole is called *recombination.*

39.4. The PN Junction, or Diode

When two semiconductors of the P and N types are brought into contact, as shown in Fig. 39F, they form what is called a *PN junction* or *diode.* In the region of contact, a cloud of free electrons in the N crystal diffuses across the boundary to the right, much the same as gas atoms diffuse through a porous ceramic material.

Since electrons leave the N crystal, that side of the junction acquires a positive potential, while the P crystal gains electrons and acquires a negative potential. As this diffusion of electrons continues, the potential difference between the two sides rises. The filling of holes in the P crystal gives rise to more holes developing in the N crystal, and this action is the same as though holes had diffused across the boundary to the left.

As the N crystal becomes more positive, and the P crystal more negative, electrons will be attracted back toward the left, and an equilibrium condition will develop in which equal numbers of electrons will be crossing the boundary in opposite directions.

The electrostatic potential of different points across the crystal boundary under equilibrium conditions, as just outlined, is shown graphically below the PN junction in Fig. 39F. Notice that the sudden drop of the potential in the region of the junction gives rise to a large electric field $\mathcal{E}$.

Although various methods for producing diodes have been developed commercially, some mixing of the two semiconductor materials is purposely brought about at the junction. This area of mixing, called the *transition region,* accounts for the smooth way in which the potential curve changes from point to point through this region.

For a typical PN junction the transition region is about 6×10^{-5} mm thick, and the potential difference, called the *contact potential,* may have any value from a small fraction of a volt to 1 or 2 V depending on the two materials in contact. These values indicate an electric field $\mathcal{E}$ of several million volts per meter. This is called the *diffusion field* $\mathcal{E}$, shown in green at the center of the diagram.

If we now fuse metal plates to the ends of a PN junction and connect them to a milliammeter, the device becomes effective as a solar battery or cell (see Fig. 39G). When the entire crystal is maintained at a constant temperature in a darkened room, no current will be observed through the milliammeter. The reason for this is that *reverse contact potentials,* due to electron diffusion, are set up between the crystal ends and the metallic electrodes, so that no potential difference exists between E and C [see diagram (b)].

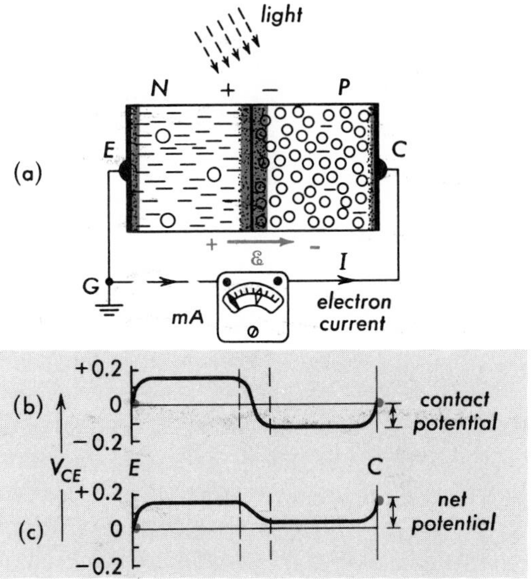

Fig. 39G. (a) PN junction used as a solar battery cell. (b) Potential graph when cell is in the dark, and (c) when it is in light.

If we now shine light on the PN junction, the light is absorbed, freeing additional electrons and creating holes. By virtue of the strong electric field $\mathcal{E}$ in the transition region, electrons now move to the left and holes to the right, and we have a current. Such a current is readily measured by a milliammeter.

The drift of electrons to the left lowers its potential while available free holes move to the right and raise its potential. The lead connections have not changed their contact potentials; so we now have a net useful potential difference as shown in diagram (c). Acting as the terminals of a battery cell the end plates send an electron current I through the external circuit.

Since the useful ionization process arising from the absorption of light occurs only in the surface layers of atoms, solar batteries are made with very thin crystals deposited on some insulating material which serves as a rigid backing.

The electrostatic potential graphs in diagrams (b) and (c) are drawn assuming 0.15-V contact potentials at the ends. These are typical but their values will depend upon what metals are used.

39.5. PN-Junction, or Diode, Rectifier

When a PN junction is connected to a battery for the purpose of sending a current through it, there are two ways in which the voltage can be applied. If the P crystal is connected to the positive terminal of the battery as shown in Fig. 39H, electrons will be pulled to the right and holes to the left. Both of these constitute a current. Note carefully that holes are being pulled from where there are lots of holes and electrons from where there are lots of electrons, and we obtain a large current.

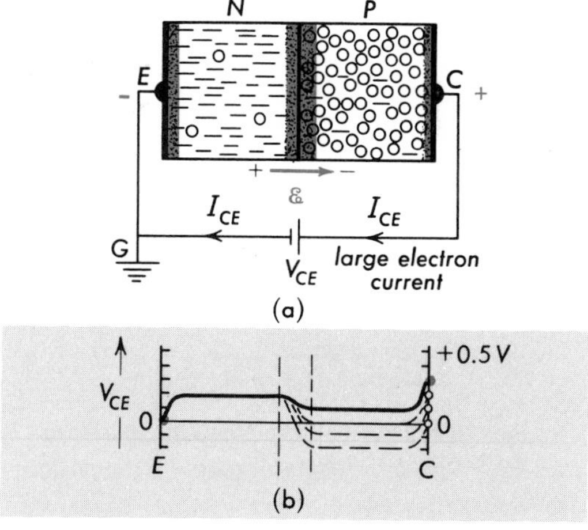

Fig. 39H. Schematic diagram of a PN junction, or diode, with an applied voltage (forward bias). Graphs showing potentials across the junction at different voltages V_{CE}.

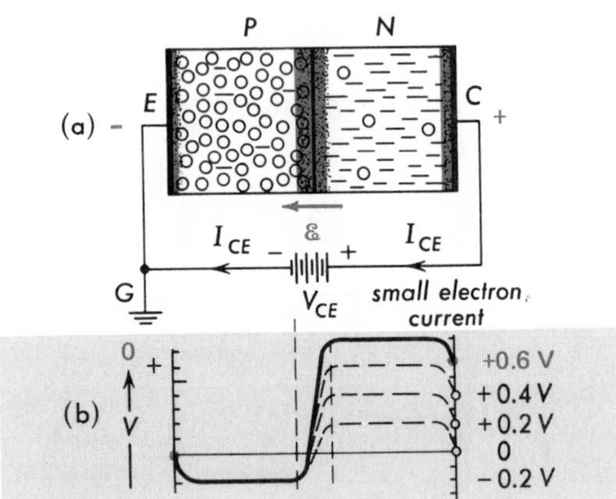

Fig. 39I. Schematic diagram of a PN junction, or diode, with an applied voltage (reverse bias). Graphs show potentials across the function at different voltage *V*.

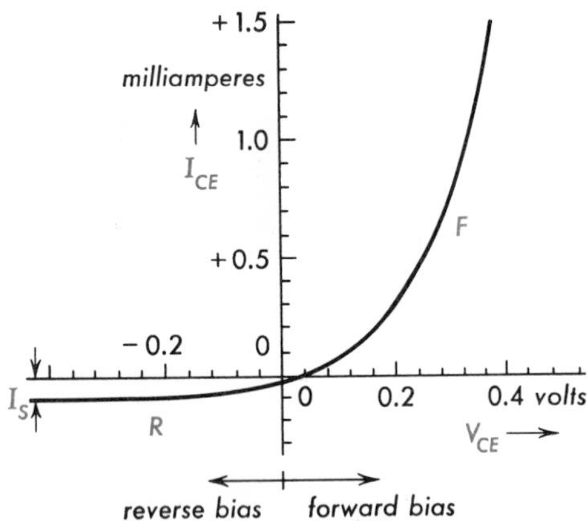

Fig. 39J. Typical characteristic curve for a PN-junction diode.

If we reverse the PN junction as in Fig. 39I, we will be trying to pull holes from where there are only a few holes, and electrons from where there are only a few electrons, and experimentally we obtain a relatively small current.

If we now apply different voltages, in turn, across a PN junction and measure the current for each value, we obtain a graph of the type shown in Fig. 39J. This so-called *characteristic curve* shows that in one direction the current increases rapidly with small increases in voltage, whereas in the opposite direction the current is small and remains small even for relatively large values.

This is why a PN junction acts like a *rectifier* of alternating currents. When P is positive with respect to N, a large current flows and the junction has what is called a *forward bias.* When P is negative with respect to N, there is a small current and the junction is said to have a *reverse bias.*

With a small forward bias V_{CE} on the PN junction we are operating in the F region of the characteristic curve. Since this applied potential difference is in opposition to the diffusion field potential, the resultant drop in potential across the transition region is flattened out as shown in Fig. 39H(b). As the forward bias is increased, the current rises and the resultant potential curve flattens still more.

With a reverse bias V_{CE} on the PN junction, we are operating in the R region of the characteristic curve and there is a small current through the transition region. Even though there is a high positive charge on the N-crystal side of the junction, there are so few electrons to pull across the boundary from the P crystal that saturation is produced by a relatively small reverse bias. Reverse-bias potentials of many volts cannot increase this current and it will remain constant.

39.6. Transistor Triode

A transistor is composed of three semiconductor elements, two of the N-type crystals and one of the P-type crystals (see Fig. 39K). This combination is referred to as an *NPN-type transistor.* We can also have a *PNP-type transistor.*

Suppose we now apply a potential difference V_{BE} across the first junction of the NPN transistor and a potential difference V_{CB} across the second junction as shown in the diagram. Because of the reduced electric field across the first junction, electrons from the emitter E move to the right, and the positive holes from the base B move to the left. Operating in the F region of Fig. 39J, a small voltage V_{BE} will give rise to a relatively large current across this junction. With a reverse bias on the second junction, electrons from the P crystal try to move to the right, and holes from the collector C to the left. Operating in the R region of the characteristic curve, little or no transport of charge takes place. Since there are few holes in the collector and few electrons in the base, then an increase of V_{CB} even to a large value will not produce an appreciable current. Because of this blocking action of the second junction a large current will flow between the emitter E and the base B.

By making the center element of the transistor very thin, as shown in Fig. 39L, an important change takes place. The electrons diffusing across the first junction have little time to find a hole and be neutralized. Most of them are quickly attracted into the collector crystal by the high positive potential.

Because of the high resistance vertically along the thin P crystal, few electrons will get through to the base B. Hence the current across the two junctions is approximately the same.

Since a few electrons do recombine with holes in the center element, however, the current I_C is not quite as large as the current I_E, so that the ratio is slightly less than unity:

$$\frac{I_C}{I_E} = \alpha \tag{39a}$$

A typical value of α, for a well-designed transistor, would be 0.98, or 98%.

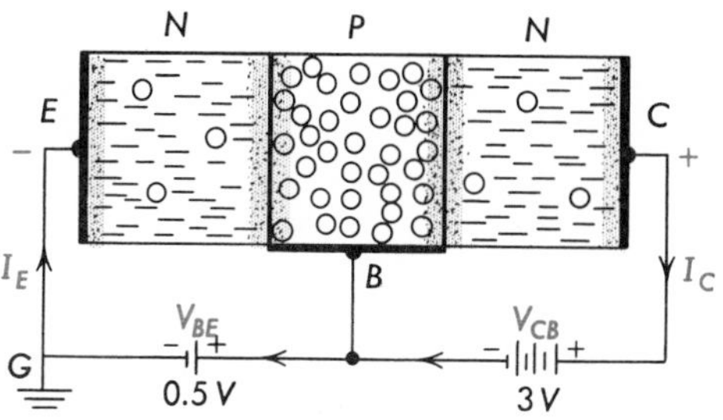

Fig. 39K. Schematic diagram of an NPN transistor, or triode, showing typical forward and reverse bias voltages.

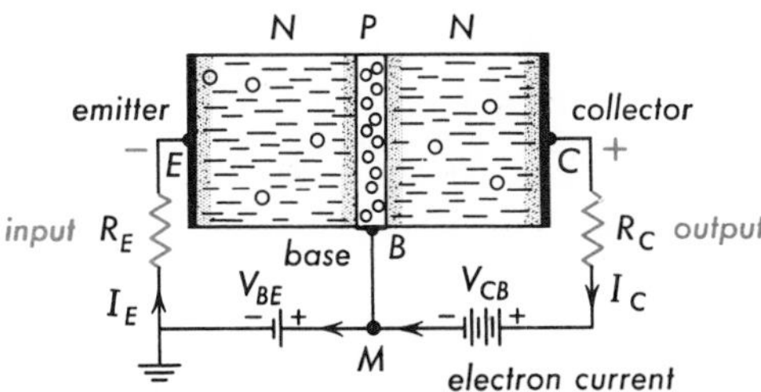

Fig. 39L. Circuit diagram showing how a transistor or triode is used as a voltage amplifier.

39.7. Transistor Structure

Junction diodes and triodes consist of semiconductors having relatively thin regions of change from N-type material to P-type material. There is a deliberate attempt in the manufacturing process to produce nonuniform distributions of impurities.

The physical structure of one type of NPN transistor is shown in Fig. 39M. From the dimensions given it will first be observed how very small it is. Note secondly how very thin the base region is. In some transistors the base is no more than 10,000 Å thick while the transition region is not over 500 Å. Thin as transition regions are, there are many atomic layers, since interatomic distances are from 2 to 4 Å.

In some manufacturing processes the end crystals, with their metal electrodes already soldered or welded on, are heated and fused into the base wafer by pressure.

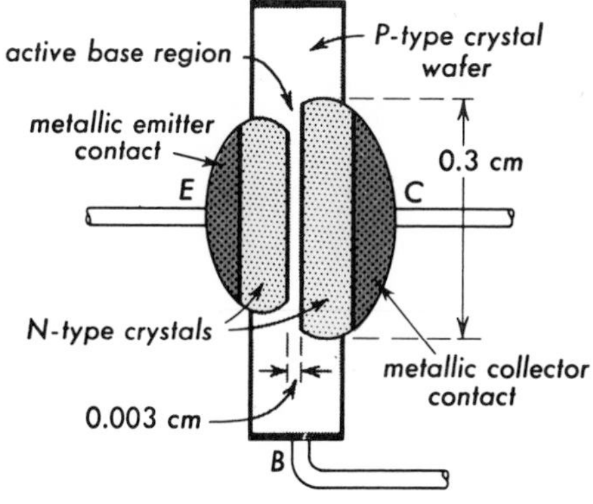

Fig. 39M. Cross-sectional diagram of an NPN transistor, or triode. The N crystals under pressure and temperature are fused into the P-type crystal wafer.

39.8. Single-Stage Transistor Amplifier

An amplifier circuit using a transistor in place of a vacuum tube is shown in Fig. 39L. Since the current I_C is very nearly equal to

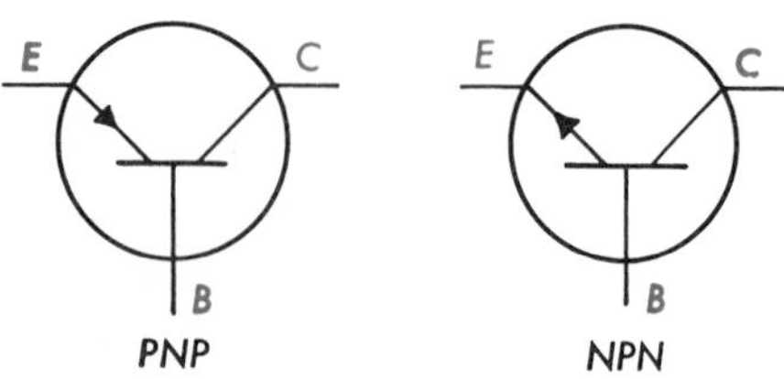

Fig. 39N. Schematic diagrams of transistors. Arrows are opposite to electron flow.

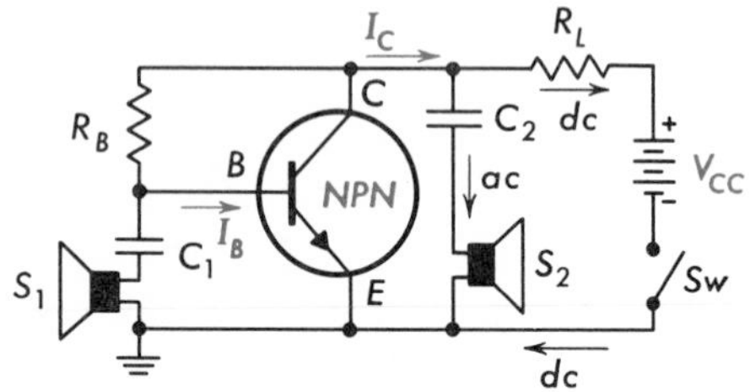

Fig. 39O. Circuit diagram of a one-way call system employing one transistor.

the current I_E, little electron current flows through BM. With the input resistance R_E small, and the output resistance R_C large, the nearly equal currents through them signify a small $I_E R_E$ drop across the input and a large $I_C R_C$ drop across the output. Hence, there is a voltage gain and a power gain.

The ratio of the output power $I_C{}^2 R_C$ to the input power $I_E{}^2 R_E$ is called the power gain:

$$A = \frac{I_C{}^2 R_C}{I_E{}^2 R_E} \tag{39b}$$

A typical power gain would be $A = 40$. If we now apply a weak alternating current as an input power, the ac output power in the collector circuit could be 40 times larger.

Simple schematic diagrams of transistors, as used in circuit diagrams, are shown in Fig. 39N.

The arrow is always shown on the emitter lead and its direction indicates the flow of positive current through the emitter material. The arrow therefore distinguishes between NPN and PNP transistors.

The basic principles of a transistor triode are analogous to those of a vacuum-tube triode, the base functioning very much as a control grid. A small alternating voltage is applied between B and E, and an amplified current I_C flows from the collector C.

As an example of the application of a single transistor as a voltage amplifier, consider the circuit diagram in Fig. 39O. This is a diagram of a *call system* in which by speaking into the first loud-speaker S_1 the amplified voice can be heard emerging from a distant loud-speaker S_2.

When the switch Sw is closed, an electron current flows from the battery (−), through the switch, up through the NPN transistor, and through R_L to the battery (+). The function of R_B is to adjust the voltage across CE so that most of the potential difference is across CB, the collector, and a relatively small voltage is across BE, the emitter (see Fig. 39L). R_B is called the *biasing resistor* and is carefully selected so as to adjust the transistor for maximum amplification.

When the sound vibrations of the voice enter S_1, they set the cone vibrating. In some types of speakers a small coil is mounted on the apex of the cone, and as the coil vibrates back and forth in the strong magnetic field of an alnico permanent magnet, a minute "voice current" is generated. The speaker functions in this way as a microphone.

Since the generated voice current is an alternating current of varying amplitude and frequency, some of its passes through C_1

and is superimposed upon the input direct current to the emitter. Together these two currents constitute a varying dc as an input load.

The amplified signal from the collector circuit is also a varying dc. The dc portion of this current returns through R_L to the battery, while the ac portion passes through C_2 and the speaker where it is converted into sound. Notice that C_1 and C_2 prevent dc battery current from flowing through S_1 and S_2, respectively. R_L limits the amount of direct current through the transistor and is called the *load resistor.*

To understand the basic principles involved in transistor operation, typical characteristic curves for a transistor triode are given in Fig. 39P. The upper set of curves (A) applies to the *output* and show how the collector current I_C varies with different voltages across CE The lower curve (B) applies to the *input* and shows how the current I_B into the base varies with different emitter voltages across BE.

As a sample operation we select an NPN triode with the characteristics shown in Fig. 39P, and we choose a battery voltage $V_{CC} = 10$ V. To obtain good amplification it is then good practice to provide the appropriate load resistor R_L so that the voltage across CE is about $\frac{1}{2}V_{CC}$. In this example, therefore, we select $V_{CE} = 5$ V. These two points for V_{CC} and V_{CE} are shown on the horizontal voltage scale in diagram (A).

Upon drawing a vertical line at 5 V, an appropriate base current curve is selected, and the one chosen is $I_B = 0.20$ mA. A straight line is then drawn through P and V_{CC}, as the output current–voltage operating path, and a horizontal line extended from P to establish the corresponding collector current $I_C = 25$ mA.

We can now determine the value of the appropriate load resistor R_L, since the *IR* drop across it should be approximately 5 V. This leaves the other 5 V for the transistor. Applying Ohm's law, $V = IR$, we can write

$$5 \text{ V} = 25 \text{ mA} \times R_L$$

from which we obtain

$$R_L = 200\ \Omega$$

A normal biasing resistor R_B of 50 KΩ to 100 KΩ will alter this so little its effect is negligible (see R_2, R_4, and R_8 in Table 39A).

With the selection of $I_B = 0.2$ mA for the input to the base, a horizontal line can be drawn through this point, as shown in diagram (B) of Fig. 39P. Where this line intersects the curve at Q a vertical line is drawn to find $V_{BE} = 0.25$ V.

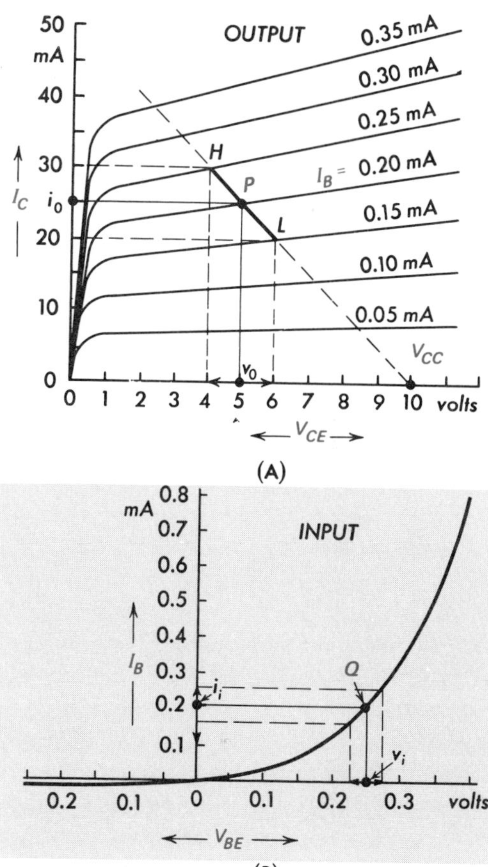

Fig. 39P. Characteristic curves for the operation of a typical transistor triode.

The values thus far determined are the dc operating voltages and current, and we now apply an alternating potential difference to BE through the capacitor C_1. Suppose this alternating potential has a maximum amplitude of 0.025 V as shown by the double arrow at the bottom in diagram (B). This produces a current swing of I_B from approximately 0.15 mA to 0.25 mA.

Referring these values to the output operating path PV_{CC} on the upper graphs, the output current I_C swings from 20 mA to 30 mA while V_{CE} swings from 4 V to 6 V.

The reason the output operates along the slanted line PV_{CC} may be explained as follows. As an input voltage V_{BE} rises, diagram (B), the base current I_B rises. A rise in I_B, diagram (A), causes a rise in collector current I_C. This increased current through the load resistor R_L produces a bigger IR drop across R_L leaving less of the battery voltage V_{CC} across the resistor V_{CE}.

The voltage amplification of a transistor triode can be defined in several ways, but if we take as a definition *the ratio of the output voltage to the input voltage,* we obtain from Fig. 39P

$$A_V = \frac{v_o}{v_i} = \frac{1.0 \text{ V}}{0.025 \text{ V}} = 40$$

The current amplification may be defined as *the ratio of the output current to the input current.* Using the values from Fig. 39P as an example,

$$A_I = \frac{i_o}{i_i} = \frac{5 \text{ mA}}{0.05 \text{ mA}} = 100$$

The transistor is not a source of energy; it simply converts dc energy obtained from the battery to ac energy by the control signal applied at the base. These amplification values just illustrated are theoretical only and are not actually realized in practice. For one thing, the input capacitor C_1 and the output capacitor C_2 limit markedly the input and output frequencies. These and internal power losses limit the *power amplification* to approximately 40, as stated by Eq.(39b).

39.9. Three-Stage Transistor Amplifier

A circuit diagram for a three-stage amplifier is shown in Fig. 39Q. This application is called an *intercommunication system,* in which each of two identical speakers is used as a microphone or as a loud-speaker. When the reversing switch Sw_2 is in the *UP* position, speaker S_1 is used as a microphone and S_2 as a loud-speaker, whereas with the switch in the *DOWN* position their functions are reversed.

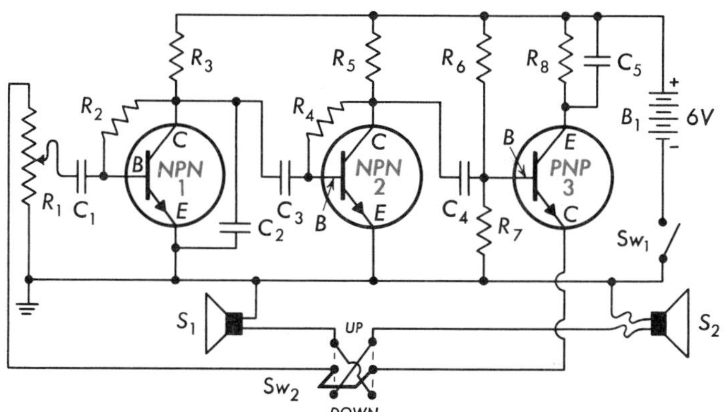

Fig. 39Q. Complete circuit diagram of a two-way intercommunication circuit employing three transistors. (Courtesy, General Electric Co.)

The first transistor circuit forms the *input stage* in which the voice current is received from the speaker acting as a microphone. The second transistor circuit forms the *driver stage* because it receives the amplified signal current from the first stage. It is called the driver stage because it "drives" the third stage. This final transistor circuit is the *output stage* which powers the speaker acting now as a speaker.

Capacitor C_2 has a relatively small capacitance and shunts part of the ac away from the second stage. This is done in order to prevent the high-frequency portion of the sound signal from reaching the final stage of amplification and the loud-speaker. There are limits to the frequencies that a loud-speaker can handle without distortion. The lower ac signals with frequencies in the middle of the audible range are passed by the larger capacitance C_3 to EB, the input of the second stage.

The output of the second stage passes the amplified ac signal through C_4 to the final stage. Since the emitter of the PNP transistor is at the top, the amplified voice signal emerges via the collector C and passes through the switch Sw_2 to the remote speaker S_2. This speaker ignores the dc portion of the current and reacts to the variations as if they were ac.

Resistor R_8 limits the amount of dc current through PNP 3, while C_5 carries the ac output signal from the second stage to the emitter of the third stage. If C_5 were not provided, part of the

TABLE 39A
Resistance and capacitance values for a three-stage amplifier circuit

R_2	100 KΩ	C_1	0.22 μF
R_3	3.3 KΩ	C_2	0.05 μF
R_4	47 KΩ	C_3	0.22 μF
R_5	1.5 KΩ	C_4	6 μF (electrolytic)
R_6	470 Ω	C_5	50 μF (electrolytic)
R_7	1.5 KΩ	S_1	20 Ω
R_8	47 Ω	S_2	20 Ω

K = 1000

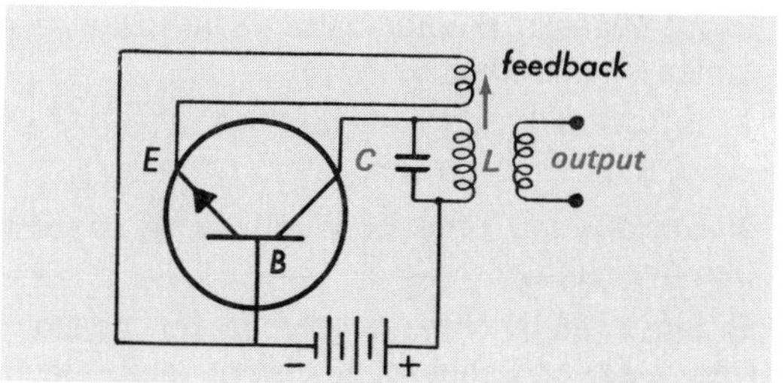

Fig. 39R. Oscillator circuit using an NPN transistor.

power needed for driving the remote speaker would be lost in R_8. Table 39A gives a list of appropriate resistor and capacitor values.

Figure 39R shows a simple oscillator circuit employing an NPN transistor. The oscillation frequency is determined by L and C in the collector circuit, and feedback of a weak oscillating signal to the emitter is accomplished by the small coil F which picks up induced voltages from L.

questions

1. (a) What is a semiconductor? (b) What is a P-type crystal? (c) What is a PN junction?

2. (a) What is a solar battery? (b) What are the principles of the solar battery?

3. (a) What is a transistor? (b) What is a PNP transistor?

4. Explain the photoconductivity of a semiconductor like germanium.

5. Since an N-type semiconductor crystal has more free electrons than holes, why is it electrically uncharged?

6. Since a P-type semiconductor crystal has more holes than free electrons, why is it electrically uncharged?

7. Make a circuit diagram of a transistor amplifier using a PNP transistor. Show the (+) and (−) terminals of any batteries.

8. Make a diagram showing what instruments you would connect to a PNP transistor to obtain readings for plotting curves like those in Fig. 39P. How would you obtain different voltages and read the currents?

9. If each of the three stages of the circuit diagram in Fig. 39Q has an amplification factor of 12, what is the over-all amplification?

10. Make a circuit diagram of a two-stage intercommunication system using an NPN transistor for the first stage and a PNP transistor for the second.

11. Make a circuit diagram of a three-stage intercommunication system using three NPN transistors.

12. If a 12-V battery is used for a transistor circuit of the kind shown in Fig. 39O, and a base current $I_B = 0.25$ mA is selected for its operation, find (a) the desirable voltage across CE, (b) the corresponding collector current I_C, (c) the load resistance to be used, (d) the base voltage V_{BE}, (e) the theoretical voltage amplification, and (f) the theoretical current amplication. Use the graphs in Fig. 39P. [Ans. (a) 6.0 V, (b) 32.0 mA, (c) 187.5 V, (d) 0.275 V, (e) 42, (f) 106.]

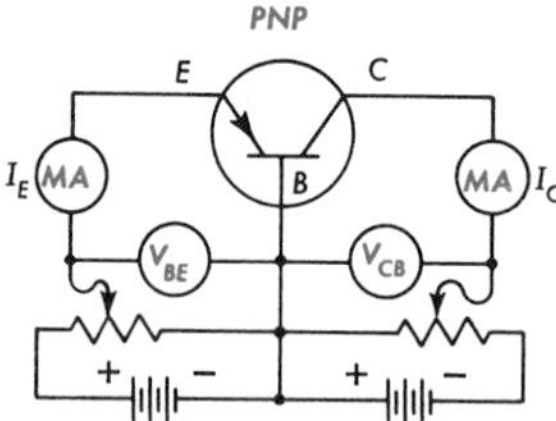

Prob. 8.

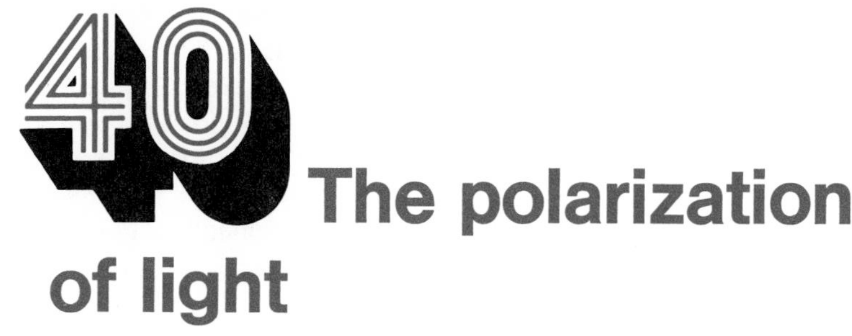

40 The polarization of light

The experiments described in Chaps. 35 and 36 illustrating the *diffraction* and *interference* of light are generally regarded as proof that *light is a wave motion.* Although such experiments enable the experimentalist to measure accurately the wavelengths of light, they give no information of the kinds of waves involved. The reason for this is that all types of waves, under the proper conditions, will exhibit diffraction and interference.

The desired information in the case of light waves is found in another group of phenomena known as *polarized light.* Some of the phenomena, which will be described in this chapter, are considered to be a proof that *light is a transverse wave motion* in contrast with the longitudinal wave motion in sound.

In the case of longitudinal waves the vibrations are always parallel to the direction of propagation, so that in a plane at right angles to the direction of travel there is no motion and hence there is perfect symmetry. If light is a transverse wave motion, the vibrations of a beam of light are all at right angles to the direction of propagation and there may or may not be perfect symmetry around the direction of travel. If perfect symmetry does not exist for a beam of light, the beam is said to be *polarized.*

The experimental methods by which light may be polarized are classified under one of the following heads:

reflection
double refraction
selective absorption
scattering

40.1. Plane-Polarized Light

A better understanding of the experiments to be described in this chapter can best be attained by first presenting the graphical methods of representing transverse waves. We assume at the outset that each light wave is a transverse wave whose vibrations are along straight lines at right angles to the direction of propagation. Furthermore, we assume that a beam of ordinary light consists of millions of such waves, each with its own plane of vibration, and that there are waves vibrating in all planes with equal probability. Looking at such a beam end-on as in Fig. 40A, there should be just as many waves vibrating in one plane as there are vibrating in any other. This then can be referred to as perfect symmetry.

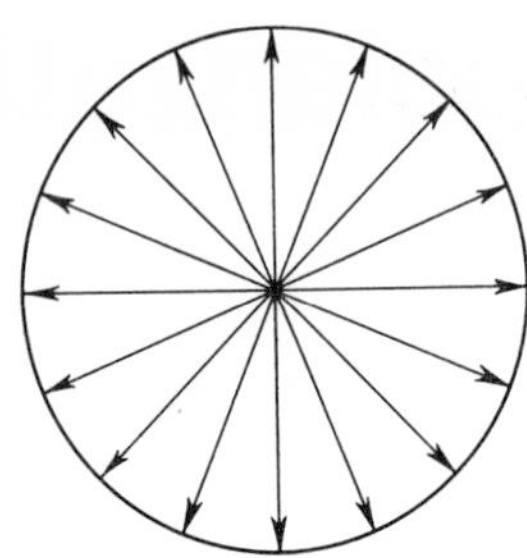

Fig. 40A. End-on view of a beam of unpolarized light illustrating schematically the equal probability of all planes of vibration.

If, by some means or other, all the waves in a beam of light are made to vibrate in planes parallel to each other, the light is said to be *plane polarized.* Diagrams illustrating each light are shown in Fig. 40B. The top diagram (a) represents plane-polarized light waves traveling to the right and vibrating in a vertical plane, while the second diagram (b) represents a ray of plane-polarized light vibrating in a horizontal plane. The dotted line indicating waves in diagram (a) is usually omitted.

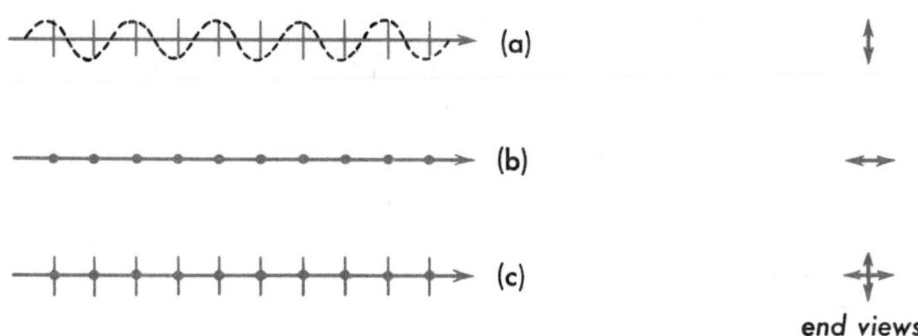

Fig. 40B. Diagrams illustrating plane-polarized rays of light.

It can be shown that a beam of ordinary unpolarized light, vibrating in all planes, may be regarded as being made up of two kinds of vibrations only, half of the waves vibrating in a vertical plane as in diagram (a) and the other half vibrating perpendicular to it as in diagram (b). The reason for this is that waves not vibrating in either of these two planes can be resolved into two components, one component vibrating in a vertical plane and the other vibrating in a horizontal plane. Although these two components may not be equal to each other, the similarly resolved components from all waves will average out to be equal. Diagram (c) is regarded therefore as being equivalent to ordinary unpolarized light.

40.2. Polarization by Reflection

When ordinary unpolarized light is incident at an angle of about 57° on the polished surface of a plate of glass, the reflected light is plane polarized. This fact was first discovered by Etienne Malus, a French physicist, in 1808. The experiment usually performed to demonstrate his discovery is illustrated in Fig. 40C.

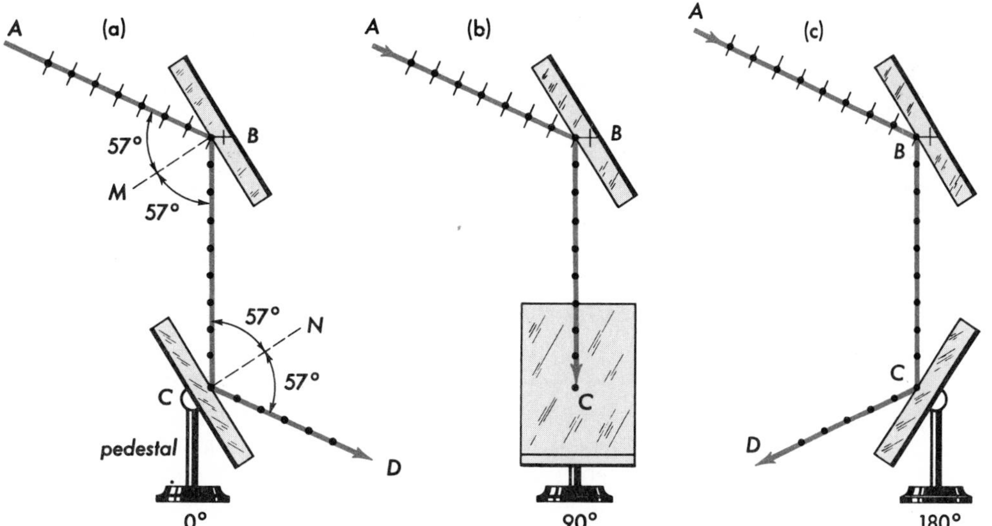

Fig. 40C. Common experiment performed to demonstrate the polarization of light by reflection from a smooth glass surface.

A beam of unpolarized light AB is incident at an angle of 57° on the first glass surface at B. This light is again reflected at the same angle by a second glass plate C placed parallel to the first, as in diagram (a). If now the lower plate is rotated about the line BC by slowly turning the pedestal on which it is mounted, the intensity of the reflected beam CD is found to decrease slowly and vanish completely at an angle of 90°. With further rotation the reflected beam CD appears again, reaching a maximum at an angle of 180° as shown in diagram (c). Continued rotation causes the intensity to decrease to zero again at 270°, and to reappear and reach a maximum at 360°, the starting point as in diagram (a). During this one complete rotation the angle of incidence on the lower plate, as well as the upper, has remained at 57°.

If the angle of incidence on either the upper or lower plate is

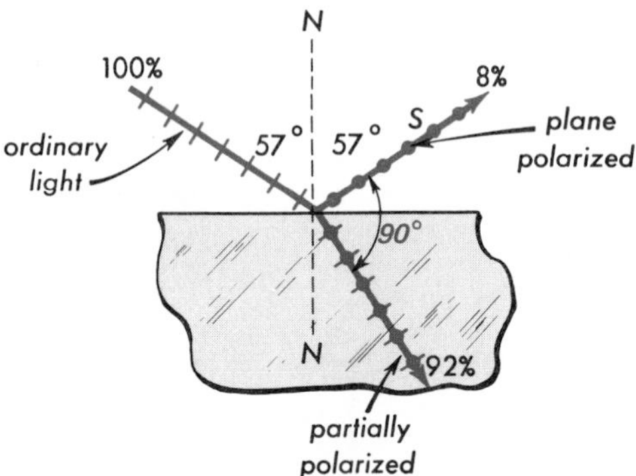

Fig. 40D. Light reflected from glass at an angle of 57° is plane polarized, while the refracted light is only partially plane polarized.

not 57°, the beam CD will go through maxima and minima every 90° as before, but the minima will not go to zero. In other words, there will always be a reflected beam CD.

A complete mathematical theory of the polarization of light by reflection was first given by Fresnel in 1820. The remarkable confirmation of this theory, in every detail, by experimental observations on the behavior of light and measurements, establishes Fresnel as the greatest contributor to the whole field of optics.

The expansion of the above experiment is made clearer by a detailed study of what happens to ordinary light when it is reflected at the polarizing angle of 57° from glass. As illustrated in Fig. 40D, 8% of the light is reflected as plane-polarized light vibrating in the plane at right angles to the plane of incidence, and the other 92% is refracted as partially plane-polarized light, 42% vibrating perpendicular to the plane of incidence and 50% vibrating parallel to the plane of incidence. The plane of incidence is defined as the plane passing through the incident ray and the ray normal NN. In nearly all diagrams the plane of the page is the plane of incidence.

If in Fig. 40D the angle of incidence is changed to some other value than 57°, the refracted beam will not be plane polarized but will contain a certain amount of light vibrating parallel to the plane of incidence. In general, the light reflected from a transparent medium like glass or water is only partially plane polarized; only at a certain angle, called the *polarizing angle,* is it plane polarized. It was Sir David Brewster, a Scottish physicist, who first discovered that *at the polarizing angle the reflected and refracted rays are 90° apart.* This is now known as *Brewster's law.* The polarizing angle for water is 53°, for at this angle the reflected and refracted rays make an angle of 90° with each other.

Because these two rays make 90° with each other, the angle of incidence i and the angle of refraction r are complements of each other and $\sin r$ in *Snell's law* ($\sin i/\sin r = \mu$) can be replaced by $\cos i$, giving

$$\frac{\sin i}{\cos i} = \mu \qquad \text{or}$$

$$\tan i = \mu \qquad (40a)$$

This formula is useful in calculating the angle of polarization. For example, with water, $\mu = 1.33$, angle $i = 53°$; whereas for glass with $\mu = 1.54$, angle $i = 57°$.

Returning to the experiment demonstrated in Fig. 40C, we

observe that the reflected light from the first mirror is plane polarized as shown, and that the refracted light goes into the glass plate where it is absorbed by the black paint on the back face. The second mirror acts as a testing device or analyzer for polarized light. A certain fraction of the incident waves is reflected when the vibrations are perpendicular to the plane of incidence, and all are refracted (to be absorbed) when the vibrations are parallel to the plane of incidence.

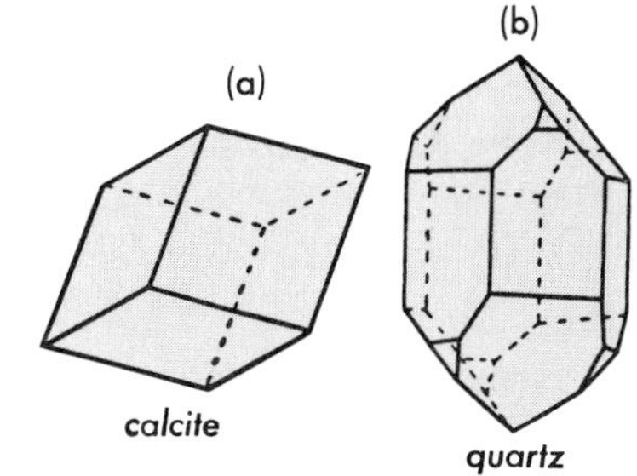

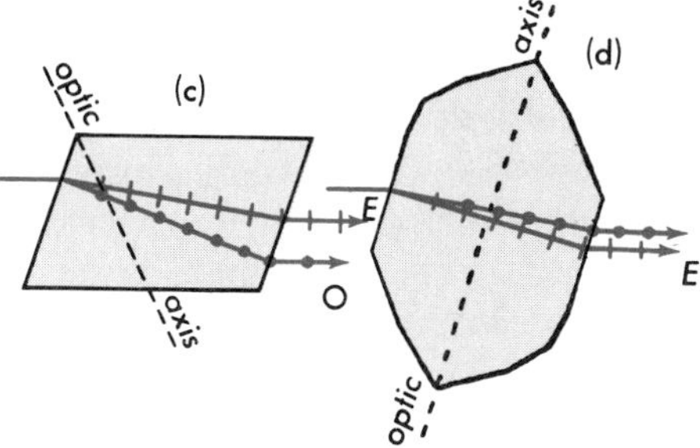

Fig. 40E. Diagrams and cross sections of calcite and quartz crystals showing double refraction and polarization.

Example 1. Yellow light is incident on the smooth surface of a block of dense flint glass for which the refractive index is 1.6640. Find the polarizing angle.
Solution. The only known quantity is the refractive index, $\mu = 1.6640$. To find the polarizing angle we substitute directly in Eq. (40a), and obtain

$$\tan i = 1.6640$$

Looking up the angle in the trigonometry table on the inside back cover, we find

$$i = 59.0°$$

40.3. Polarization by Double Refraction

The double refraction of light by Iceland spar (calcite) was first observed by a Swedish physician, Erasmus Bartholinus, in 1669, and later studied in detail by Huygens and Newton. Nearly all crystalline substances are now known to exhibit the phenomenon. The following are but a few samples of crystals that show this effect: *calcite, quartz, mica, sugar, topaz, selenite, aragonite,* and *ice.* Calcite and quartz are of particular importance because they are used extensively in the manufacture of special optical instruments.

Calcite, as found in nature, always has the characteristic shape shown in Fig. 40E(a), whereas quartz has many different forms, the most complicated of which is illustrated in diagram (b). Each face of every calcite crystal is a parallelogram whose angles are 78° and 102°. Chemically, calcite is a hydrated calcium carbonate, $CaCO_3$; and quartz is silicon dioxide, SiO_2.

Not only is light doubly refracted by calcite and quartz, but both rays are found to be plane polarized. One ray, called the *ordinary ray,* is polarized with its vibrations in one plane, and the other ray, called the *extraordinary ray,* is polarized with its vibrations in a plane at right angles to the first. This polarization is illustrated in diagrams (c) and (d) by *dots* and *lines* and can be proved by a glass plate rotated as plate C in Fig. 40C, or with some other analyzing device like a *Nicol prism* or a *polarizing film.* These devices will be described in the next two sections.

Since the two opposite faces of a calcite crystal are always parallel to each other, the two refracted rays always emerge parallel to the incident light and are therefore parallel to each other. If the incident light falls perpendicularly upon the surface of the crystal, as in Fig. 40F, the extraordinary ray will be refracted away from the normal and will come out parallel to, but displaced from, the incident beam. The ordinary ray will pass straight through without deviation.

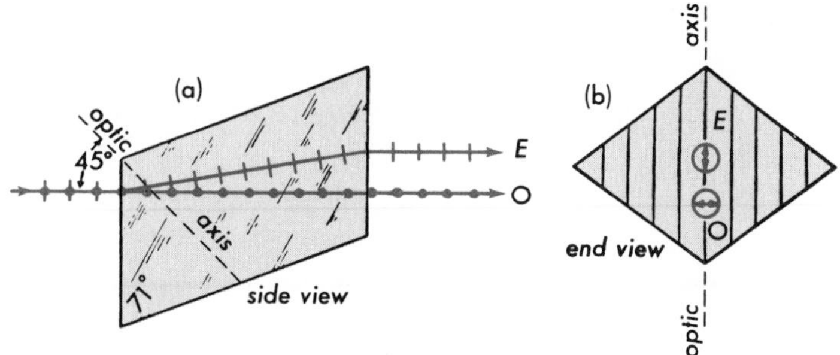

Fig. 40F. Double refraction in calcite. At normal incidence the *O* ray travels straight through and the *E* ray is refracted to one side.

In general, the O ray obeys the ordinary laws of refraction, and in this way the crystal acts like glass or water, whereas the E ray obeys no such simple law and behaves quite abnormally. In other words, the O ray travels with the same velocity regardless of its direction through the crystal, whereas the velocity of the E ray is different in different regions. This is the origin of the designation "ordinary" and "extraordinary."

One important property of calcite and quartz is that there is one and only one direction through either crystal in which there is no double refraction. This particular direction, called the *optic axis,* is shown by the dashed lines in Fig. 40E. The optic axis, it should be noted, is not a single line through a crystal, but a direction.

A plane passing through the crystal parallel to the optic axis and perpendicular to one face of the crystal is called a *principal section.* The plane of the page in Fig. 40F(a) is but one of any number of principal sections which, from the end view in diagram (b), appears as a vertical line. A useful rule always to be remembered is that the vibrations of the O ray are always perpendicular to the optic axis.

40.4. The Nicol Prism

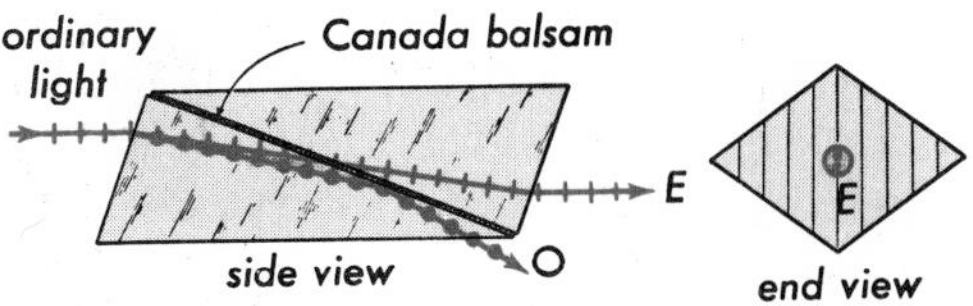

Fig. 40G. Cross section and end view of a Nicol prism showing the elimination of the *O* ray by total reflection.

The Nicol prism is an optical device made from a calcite crystal and used in many optical instruments for producing and analyzing polarized light. Such a prism, as illustrated in Fig. 40G, is made by cutting a crystal along a diagonal and cementing it back together again with a special cement called *Canada balsam.* Canada balsam is used because it is a clear transparent substance whose reflective index is midway between that of the calcite for the O and E *rays.*

Optically the Canada balsam is more dense than calcite for the E ray and less dense for the O ray. There exists, therefore, a critical angle of refraction for the one O ray but not for the E ray. After both rays are refracted as the first crystal surface, the O ray is *totally reflected* by the first Canada balsam surface, as illustrated in the diagram, while the E ray passes on through to emerge parallel to the incident light. Starting with ordinary unpolarized light, a Nicol prism thus transmits plane-polarized light only.

If two Nicols are lined up one behind the other as in Fig. 40H, they form an optical system frequency used in specially constructed microscopes for studying the optical properties of other crystals. The first Nicol which is used to produce plane-polarized light is called the *polarizer,* and the second which is used to test the light is called the *analyzer.*

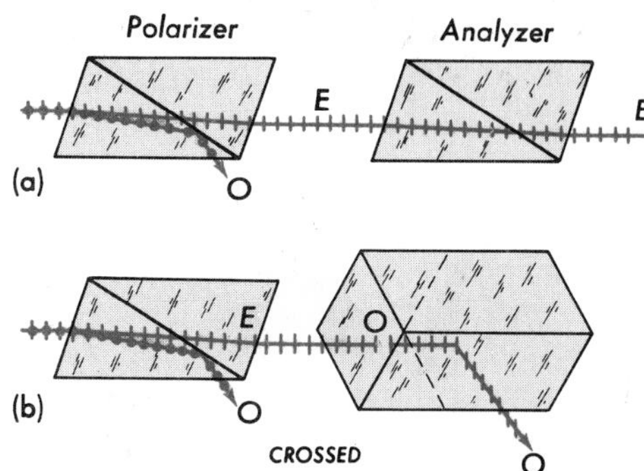

Fig. 40H. Two Nicol prisms mounted as polarizer and analyzer: (a) parallel Nicols; (b) crossed Nicols.

In the parallel position, diagram (a), the polarized light from the polarizer passes on through the analyzer. Upon rotating the analyzer through 90°, as in diagram (b), no light is transmitted. For the same reason that the O vibrations in the original beam were totally reflected in the polarizer, the E vibrations are totally reflected as O vibrations in the analyzer.

Rotated another 90°, the light again gets through the analyzer just as in the parallel position in diagram (a). Still another 90° finds the Nicols crossed again, with no light passing through.

40.5. Polarization by Selective Absorption

When ordinary light enters a crystal of tourmaline, double refraction takes place in much the same way that it does in calcite, but with this difference: one ray, the so-called O ray, is entirely absorbed by the crystal, while the other ray, the E ray, passes on

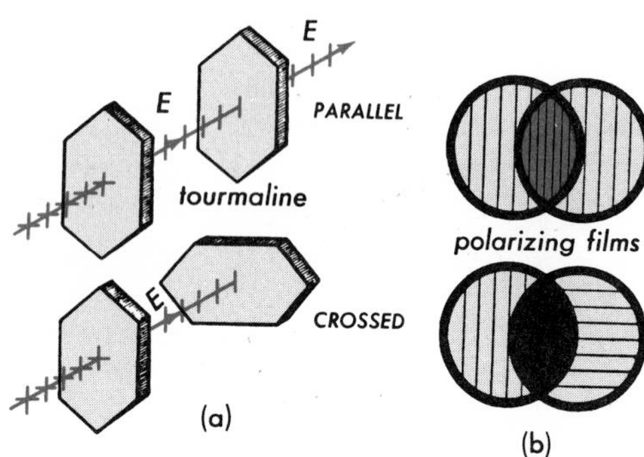

Fig. 40I. Diagrams illustrating the polarization of light by (a) tourmaline crystals, and (b) polarizing films.

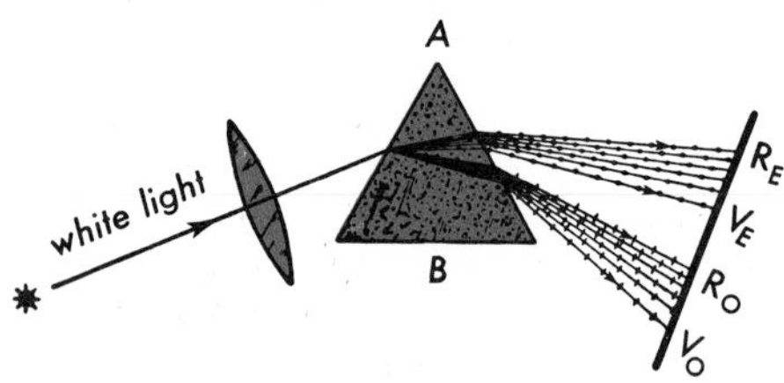

Fig. 40J. Refraction of white light by a prism cut from a calcite crystal.

through. This phenomenon is called "selective absorption" because the crystal absorbs light waves vibrating in one plane and not those vibrating in the other.

Tourmaline crystals are therefore like Nicol prisms, for they take in ordinary light, dispose of the O vibrations, and transmit plane-polarized light as illustrated in Fig. 40I(a). When two such crystals are lined up parallel, with one behind the other, the plane-polarized light from the first crystal passes through the second with little loss in intensity. If either crystal is turned at 90° to the other, i.e., in the *cross position,* the light is completely absorbed and none passes through.

The behavior of tourmaline and similar optical substances is due to the molecular structure of the crystal. To draw an analogy, the regularly spaced molecules of a single crystal are like the regularly spaced trees in an orchard or grove. If one tries to run between the rows of trees carrying a very long pole held at right angles to the direction of motion, the pole must be held in a vertical position. If it is held in the horizontal plane, the runner will be stopped.

The reason tourmaline is not used in optical instruments in place of Nicol prisms is that the crystals are yellow in color and do not transmit white light.

A more satisfactory substance for this purpose, which does transmit white light, is the specially manufactured material known as "Polaroid." This material is made in the form of very thin films, which have the general appearance of the more common substance "Cellophane," and is made from small needle-shaped crystals of an organic compound *iodosulfate of quinine.* Lined up parallel to each other and embedded in a *nitrocellulose mastic,* these crystals act like tourmaline by absorbing one component of polarization and transmitting the other. Two such films mounted separately in rings between thin glass plates are shown schematically in Fig. 40I(b). In the crossed position no light can pass through both films, whereas in the parallel position white light vibrating in the plane indicated by the parallel lines is transmitted. Many practical applications are being found for polarizing films of this kind, particularly wherever glaring light is not desired. The glaring light reflected at an angle from a table top, a book, a window pane, the water, or the road ahead when one is driving a car is polarized and can be partly eliminated by polarizing films.

40.6. Dispersion by a Calcite Prism

In Fig. 40J a prism is shown cut from a calcite crystal with the optic axis parallel to the refracting edge A. The optic axis, being perpendicular to the page, is represented by dots. (For the direction of the optic axis in calcite, see Fig. 40E.)

When white light is incident on one side of this prism, two completely separated spectra emerge from the other side. Not only is each spectrum complete in all its colors from red to violet but the light in each is plane polarized. This can be demonstrated with an analyzing device like a Nicol prism, or polarizing film. By inserting the analyzer anywhere in the light beam and rotating it, one spectrum disappears first; then, 90° from it, the other fades and disappears while the first returns to full intensity.

The vibrations of all colors in the lower spectrum in Fig. 40J are perpendicular to the optic axis and are O vibrations. The upper spectrum with all vibrations parallel to the optic axis consists of E vibrations. If a prism is cut so that the refracted light as it travels through the crystal is parallel to the optic axis, only one spectrum is produced.

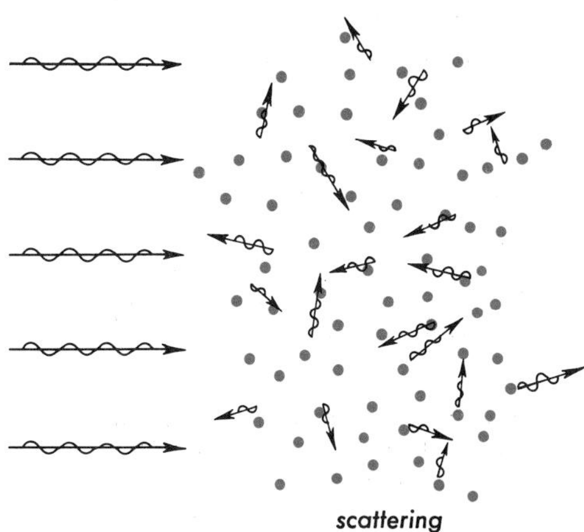

Fig. 40K. Light waves are scattered by air molecules.

40.7. Scattering and the Blue Sky

The blue of the sky and the red of the sunset are due to a phenomenon called "scattering." When sunlight passes through the earth's atmosphere, much of the light is picked up by the air molecules and given out again in some other direction. The effect is quite similar to the action of water waves on floating objects. If, for example, the ripples from a stone dropped in a still pond of water encounter a small cork floating on the surface, the cork is set bobbing up and down with the frequency of the passing waves.

Light is pictured as acting in the same way on air molecules and fine dust particles. Once set into vibration by a light wave, a molecule or particle can send out the absorbed light again, sometimes in the same direction but generally in almost any other direction. This is illustrated schematically in Fig. 40K. Waves of light are shown being scattered at random in all directions.

Experiments show, in agreement with the theory of scattering, that the shortest waves are scattered more readily than longer waves. To be more specific, the scattering is inversely proportional to the fourth power of the wavelength:

$$\text{scattering} \propto \frac{1}{\lambda^4} \tag{40b}$$

According to this law the short waves of violet light are scattered

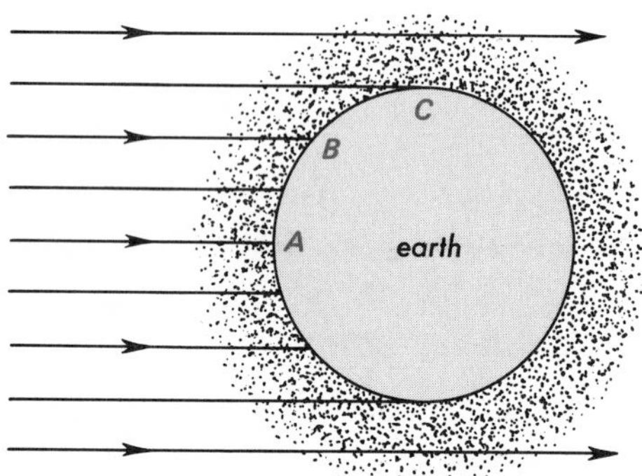

Fig. 40L. Schematic diagram showing the scattering of light by the air molecules of the earth's atmosphere.

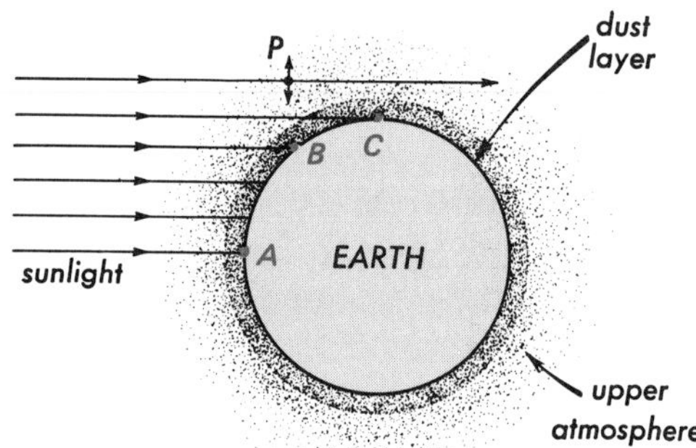

Fig. 40M. The scattering of light by a layer of dust near the earth's surface causes the sun to turn yellow, then orange, and finally red at sunset.

about ten times as readily as the longer waves of red light. The other colors are scattered by intermediate amounts. Thus when sunlight enters the earth's atmosphere, *violet* and *blue light* are scattered the most, follower by *green, yellow, orange,* and *red,* in the order named. For every ten violet waves ($\lambda = 4 \times 10^{-7}$ m) scattered from a beam, there is only one red wave ($\lambda = 7 \times 10^{-7}$ m):

violet	blue	green	yellow	orange	red
10	6	3	2.5	2	1

At noon on a clear day when the sun is directly overhead, as illustrated by an observer at A in Fig. 40L, the whole sky appears *light blue.* This is the composite color of the mixture of colors scattered most effectively by the air molecules. It can be demonstrated that light blue is obtained by the added mixture of *violet, blue, green,* and *yellow.*

40.8. The Red Sunset

The occasional observation of an orange-red sunset is attributed to the *scattering of light* by fine dust and smoke particles near the earth's surface. This is illustrated in Fig. 40M. To an observer at A, it is noonday and the direct sunlight from overhead, seen only by looking directly at the sun itself, travels through a relatively short dust path. As a result, very little violet and blue are scattered away and the sun appears white.

As sunset approaches, however, the direct sunlight has to travel through an ever-increasing dust path. The result is that an hour or so before sundown, when the observer is at B, practically all of the blue and violet have been scattered out and, owing to the remaining colors, red, orange, yellow, and a little green, the sun appears yellow. At sunset, when the observer is at C, the direct rays must travel through so many miles of dust particles that all but red are completely scattered out and the sun appears red. At this same time the sky overhead is still light blue. If the dust blanket is too dense, even the red will be scattered appreciably from the direct sunlight and the deepening red sun will become lost from view before it reaches the horizon.

An excellent demonstration of scattering by fine particles is illustrated in Fig. 40N. A parallel beam of white light from a carbon arc and lens L_1 is sent through a water trough with glass sides. After passing through an iris diaphragm at the other end, a second lens L_2 forms an image of the circular opening on the screen. To produce the fine particles for scattering, about 40 g of photographic fixing powder (hyposulfite of soda) are first dissolved in about 7.5 l. (2 gal) of water. Next, about 1 to 2 cm^3 of concentrated sulfuric acid is added and the contents thoroughly mixed in the trough.*

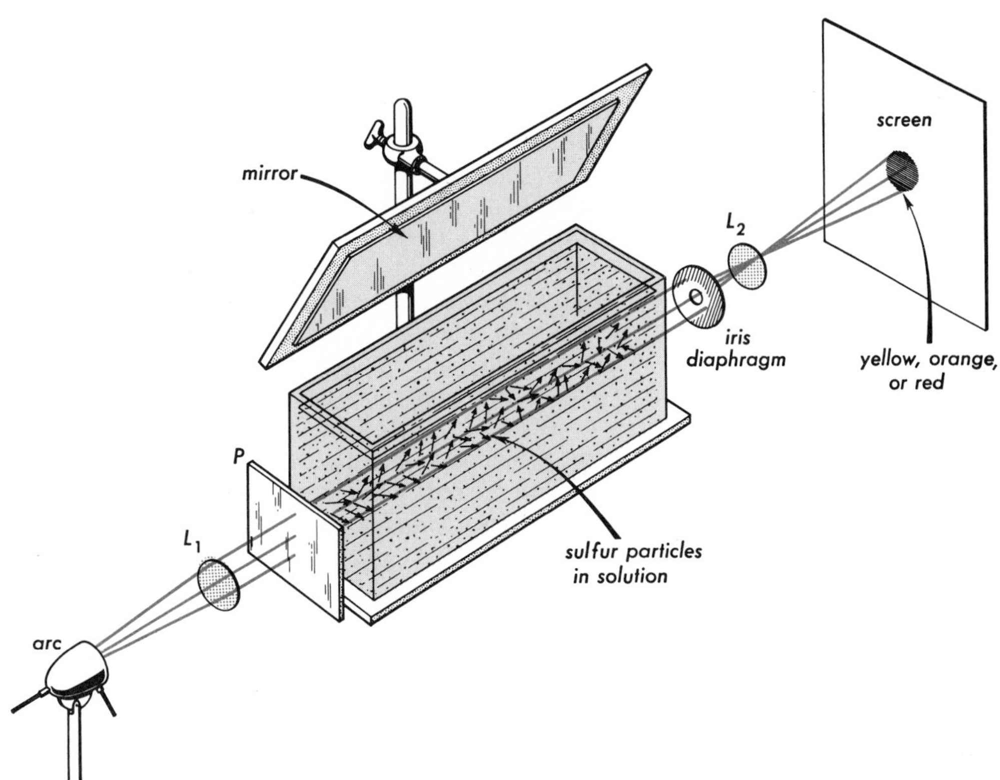

Fig. 40N. The sunset experiment: demonstration of the scattering and polarization of light by small particles.

As the microscopic sulfur particles begin to form, scattered blue light will outline the parallel beam through the trough. A little later, when more particles have formed, the entire body of water will appear light blue, due principally to multiple scattering. Light scattered out of the central beam of light is scattered again and again before emerging from the trough. At first the transmitted light which falls on the screen appears white. Later, as more scattering takes out the shorter wavelengths, this image representing the sun turns yellow, then orange, and finally red.

* The correct amount of acid to produce the best results is determined by trial. The first visible precipitate should appear after 2 or 3 min.

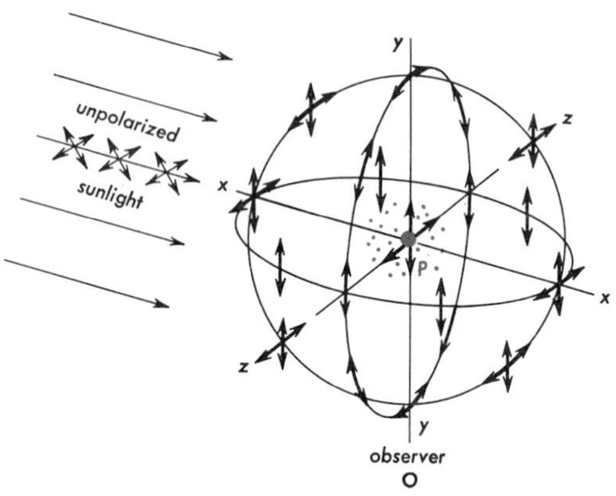

Fig. 40O. Diagram showing the polarization of light by scattering from fine particles.

40.9. Polarization by Scattering

If the blue of the sky is observed through a piece of polaroid, the light is found to be partially plane polarized. This polarization can also be seen in the scattering experiment described above. Observed through a polaroid film, the beam in the tank appears bright at one orientation of the polaroid and disappears with a 90° rotation.

Scattering is not a practical means of polarizing light because the polarization is usually incomplete and the intensity is quite low. The polarization of the blue light of the sky, however, is direct evidence of the transverse character of light waves.

In Fig. 40O, let P represent any of the millions of air molecules or tiny dust particles high overhead on a clear sunny day. Unpolarized sunlight is incident from just above the horizon on the left. Suppose an incident wave, vibrating in the *xy* plane, is absorbed and sets a particle at P vibrating in the *y* direction. Upon giving up this light the wave can be emitted in almost any direction except along the *y* axis. To emit a wave in the *y* direction the wave would have to be longitudinal. Since light waves are not longitudinal, but are transverse, the *y* direction is forbidden.

If the incident wave is vibrating in the *xz* plane, the particle at P will be set vibrating along the *z* axis. Emission by this particle is now allowed in all directions except along the *z* axis. Hence an observer looking at the blue sky, in a direction at right angles to the incident sunlight, will find the light plane polarized with its vibrations perpendicular to the *xy* plane. Note that no particles at P can be set vibrating along the *x* axis, since this would require an incident light wave to be longitudinal.

It is well known that light is composed of electromagnetic waves, and that such waves have two vibration components. Each wave has an *electric* component vibrating in one plane and a *magnetic* component vibrating in a plane at right angles (see Fig. 38G). Numerous experiments show, however, that the electric vibrations are the only ones responsible for all the known optical effects.

40.10. Optical Properties of Gems

From the earliest times, gemstones have held a particular fascination for mankind. Diamonds, emeralds, rubies, and sapphires are but a few that have been used as a medium of exchange and as a means of stabilizing fortunes during periods of social and political stress.

For centuries numerous attempts have been made to produce

gemstones synthetically, but it is only during recent years that the true synthetic gems have been manufactured. These have exactly the same chemical and physical properties, and in most cases are far more perfect in their crystal formation than their natural counterparts.

The first and most important gemstone materials to be synthesized were from the corundum family: *ruby* and *sapphire.* Corundum is the hexagonal crystal form of α alumina, Al_2O_3. Pure corundum crystals are transparent and water-white, and are called *white sapphire.* A few percent of chromic oxide, Cr_2O_3, as an impurity in the corundum crystal produces the ruby, while small amounts of titania, iron, and other metal oxides produce sapphires of other colors.

The natural "star ruby" and "star sapphire" are some of the rarest and most treasured of the gems. These natural or genuine stones have the same composition as ordinary rubies, but, in addition, they contain numerous microscopic needles of titania (TiO_2) scattered through the body of the crystal in a symmetrical, three-dimensional pattern. Such stones are usually cut *en cabochon* (dome-shaped, with a flat base). Incident light from a point source is scattered by the needles and gives rise to a six-rayed star.

American industry has succeeded in duplicating nature's feat, and has synthesized star rubies and star sapphires of different colors. These crystals have the same fine needle-like inclusions that produce the six-rayed star effect, and therefore have the same optical properties. The so-called "cat's eye" and "tiger's eye" stones are similar but with all the tiny needles or hollow tubes, as the case may be, lined up in one direction only.

Since 1930, emeralds have been synthesized in small sizes and quantities, and since 1961 diamonds have been synthesized in small sizes and used for highly specialized machine tools of various kinds.

The optical properties of the *asteriated* or star ruby can be demonstrated by cutting a small piece of clear plastic sheet in a hexagon, or square, and winding fine wire around it as shown in Fig. 40P. Looking through this wire mesh at a point source 2 or 3 m away will reveal the star or single-line light pattern. Overlapping of wires has little effect on the pattern you observe.

Large gemstones 10 cm to 20 cm in diameter, and over 4000 carats (1 carat = 200 mg) in size, are synthesized by American and foreign industry today. Large quantities of these stones are used as jewel bearings in high quality instruments.

The beautiful spectrum colors (the fire) of the diamond are surpassed today by several synthetic gems, namely strontium

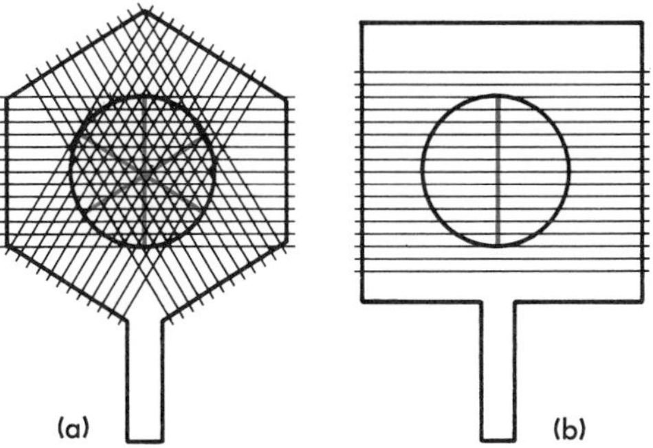

Fig. 40P. Wire wound frames for the observation of the star and line diffraction patterns seen in star and ruby sapphire, and in cat's eye and tiger's eye gems.

titanate and rutile. A table of the refractive indices of these two crystals, along with diamond, are given in Table 32A. The refractive indices of calcite, quartz, and fused quartz are given in Table 40A.

TABLE 40A
The refractive indices* of several crystals

Wave-length (Å)	*Calcite*		*Quartz*		*Fused Quartz*
	μ_O	μ_E	μ_O	μ_E	μ
4046 (V)	1.6813	1.4969	1.5572	1.5667	1.4697
4861 (B)	1.6678	1.4908	1.5497	1.5590	1.4632
5893 (Y)	1.6584	1.4864	1.5442	1.5534	1.4584
6563 (R)	1.6544	1.4846	1.5419	1.5509	1.4564

*Indices are for the O ray (μ_O) and the E ray (μ_E).

problems

1. Find the polarizing angle for green light $\lambda = 5300$ Å reflected from a crystal of titania, TiO_2. See Table 32A.

2. Find the polarizing angle for red light incident on a diamond crystal. See Table 32A.

3. The polarizing angle for blue light incident on the surface of a piece of dense flint glass is 59.3°. Find the refractive index. [Ans. 1.6842.]

4. If the polarizing angle for yellow light reflected from the polished surface of fused quartz is 55.57°, what is the refractive index?

5. If the critical angle for a piece of glass is 45.0°, what is (a) the refractive index, and (b) the polarizing angle?

6. The critical angle for the ordinary ray of yellow light on the surface of calcite is 37.1°. Find (a) the refractive index, and (b) the polarizing angle. [Ans. (a) 1.6578, (b) 58.90°.]

7.* Blue light is incident at an angle of 55° on the first surface of a calcite prism which is cut with the optic axis parallel to the refracting edge. If the prism angle is 60°, find (a) the deviation of the O ray, and (b) the deviation of E ray. See Table 40A for the refractive indices.

8.* A prism is cut from a quartz crystal with the optic axis parallel to the refracting edge, and the two faces making an angle of 60° with each other. If light is incident on one face at an angle of 50°, find the angle at which (a) the O ray, and (b) E ray, is refracted. Assume the light is red, and the indices are those given in Table 32A.

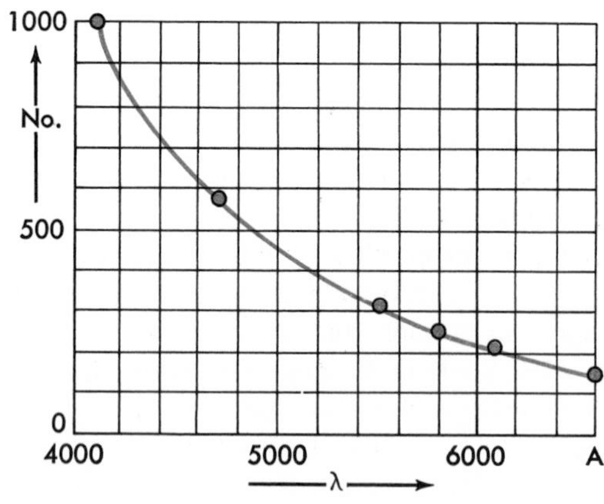

Prob. 9.

9. If 1000 waves of violet light are scattered from air molecules of the atmosphere, (a) find the number of blue, green, yellow, orange, and red waves scattered. Assume the wavelengths to be those given in Table 32A. (b) Plot a graph of wavelengths vs. number of waves scattered. [Ans. (a) 1000, 579, 309, 250, 204, 149, (b) graph.]

10. Find the ratio of light waves scattered by fine particles with two different wavelengths of light: blue light $\lambda = 4300$ Å, and orange light $\lambda = 6200$ Å.

11. Calculate the ratio of the numbers of light rays scattered by the air for ultraviolet light $\lambda = 3600$ Å, and infrared light $\lambda = 8600$ Å.

41 The discovery of the electron

Modern physics, dealing principally with atoms, molecules, and the structure of matter, has developed at such a tremendous rate within the past three-score years that it now occupies the center of attention of many leading scientists the world over. Recent discoveries in atomic physics have had, and will continue to have, a tremendous influence on the development of civilization. Because the subject of atomic physics is relatively new, it is logical to treat the subject matter associated with each major discovery in roughly chronological order.

41.1. Electrical Discharge through a Gas

In 1853 an obscure French scientist by the name of Masson sent the first electric spark from a high-voltage induction coil through a partially evacuated glass vessel and discovered that, instead of the typical spark observed in air, the tube was filled with a bright glow. Several years later, Heinrich Geissler,* a German glass blower in Tübingen, developed and began to manufacture gaseous discharge tubes. These tubes, made in diverse sizes, shapes, and colors of glass, and resembling the modern neon and argon signs used in advertising, attracted the attention of physicists in the leading scientific institutions and universities of the world. They purchased many of these "Geissler tubes" and used them for study and lecture demonstrations.

In 1869, W. Hittorf of Munster,† with improved vacuum pumps, observed a dark region near one electrode of the electrical discharge that grew in size as the exhaustion was continued. This is but one of a number of phases of the study of electrical discharges through gases that were observed and studied a few years later by Sir William Crookes.‡

In Fig. 41A, a long glass tube about 4 cm in diameter and 150 cm long is shown connected to a mercury diffusion pump and a mechanical vacuum pump. The purpose of the pumps is to enable

***Heinrich Geissler (1814–1879), German physicist, was born in Igelshieb, Saxe-Meiningen, Germany, May 24, 1814. He was educated as a glass blower and received an honorary Ph.D. from the University of Bonn in 1868. His scientific work includes the discovery of the density of water, and the invention of a mercury pump for producing a high vacuum. He also invented glass tubes of elaborate shapes in which electrical discharges in rarified gases produced different colors. These "Geissler" tubes were the forerunners of today's advertising neon signs.**

†Johann Wilhelm Hittorf (1824–1914), German physicist, was born at Bonn on March 27, 1824. He served most of his long and fruitful life as professor of physics and chemistry at the University of Münster. His most important work was on the motion of ions during electrolysis and the study of the spectra of gases and vapors. He studied electrical discharges in gases and discovered a number of properties of cathode rays.

one to observe continuously the changes in the electrical discharge as the air is slowly removed from the tube. The purpose of the *trap* is to freeze out any mercury vapor and to prevent it from reaching the discharge. High voltage from an induction coil is shown connected to the two electrodes, one at either end of the tube.

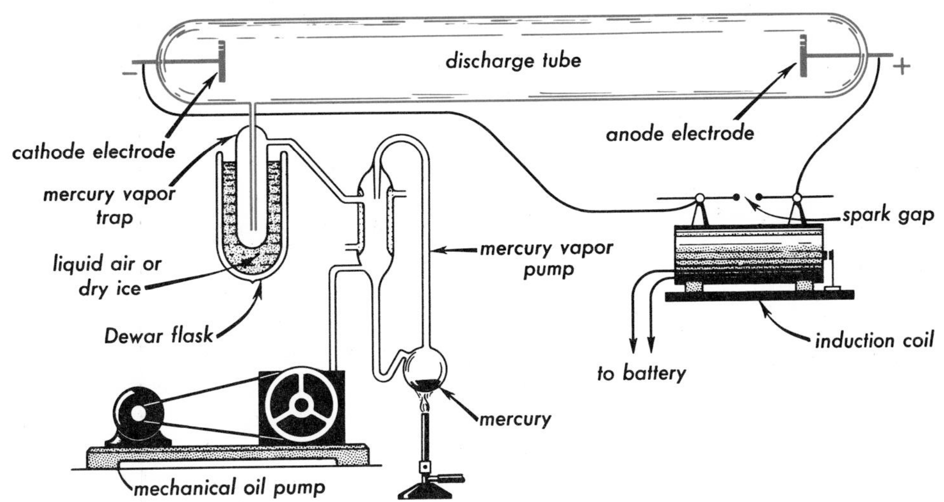

Fig. 41A. Diagram of a gaseous discharge tube, showing the electrical connections as well as the vacuum pumps and accessories.

Although an induction coil does not deliver direct current, its characteristics are such that the potentials are higher on half of the alternations than they are on the other, and the two electrodes act nearly the same as if a high-voltage direct current were used. The negative electrode under these circumstances is called the *cathode,* and the positive electrode the *anode.*

As the long tube is slowly pumped out, an emf of 10,000 to 15,000 V will produce the first discharge when the pressure has dropped to about $\frac{1}{100}$ of an atmosphere, i.e., at a barometric pressure of about 8 mm of mercury. This first discharge, as illustrated in diagram (a) of Fig. 41B, consists of long, thin streamers. As the gas pressure drops to about 5 mm of mercury, sometimes called a Geissler-tube vacuum, the discharge widens until it fills the whole tube as shown in diagram (b). At a still lower pressure of about 2 mm, a dark region called the *Faraday dark space* appears in the region of the cathode, which divides the bright discharge into two parts, a long pinkish section called

‡Sir William Crookes (1832–1919), English physicist and chemist, became at the age of 22 an assistant at the Radcliffe Observatory in Oxford. He was knighted in 1897, received the Order of Merit in 1910, and was president of the Royal Society from 1913 to 1915. He invented and made the first focusing type of X-ray tube. His experiments with electrical discharges through rarefied gases led to his discovery of the dark space that now bears his name.

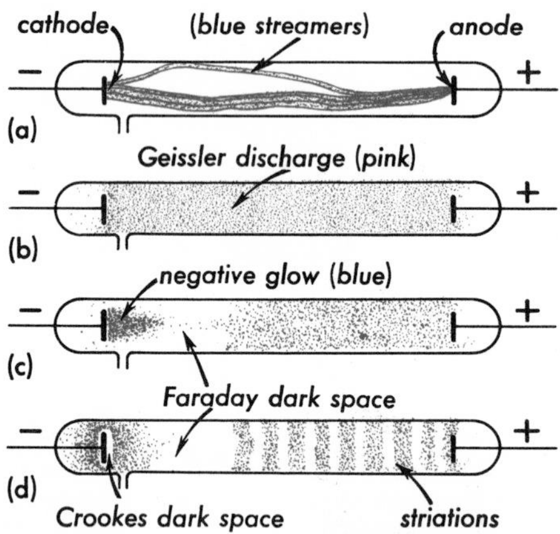

Fig. 41B. Sketches of the general appearance of a high-voltage electric discharge through rarefied air of various stages of evacuation.

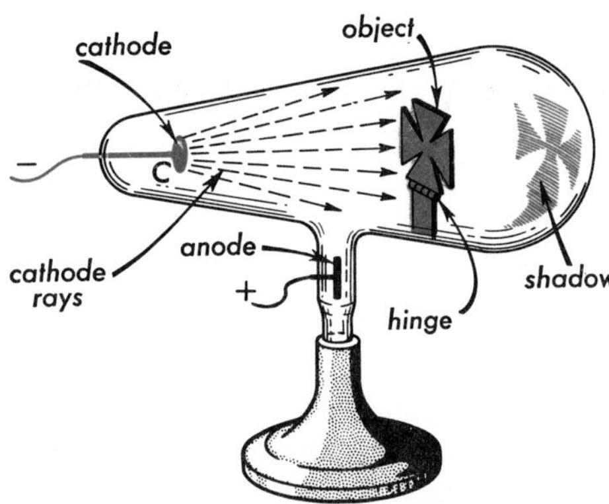

Fig. 41C. A Crookes discharge tube for demonstrating that cathode rays travel in straight lines.

the *positive column* and a short bluish section called the *negative glow.* As the pressure drops still further, the Faraday dark space grows in size and the negative glow moves away from the cathode, producing another dark space between it and the cathode. With the appearance of the second dark region, called the *Crookes dark space,* the positive column divides into a number of equally spaced layers, called "striations."

As the pumping proceeds, the striations and the negative glow grow fainter, and the Crookes dark space widens, until finally, at a pressure of about 0.01 mm, it fills the whole tube. At this point a new feature appears: the whole glass tube itself glows with a faint greenish light.

41.2. Cathode Rays

The green glow in the final stage of the gaseous discharge just described was soon found to be a *fluorescence of the glass produced by invisible rays emanating from the cathode itself.* These *cathode rays,* as they are called, believed by Crookes to be an "ultra gaseous state" and by Hittorf to be a "fourth state" of matter, were discovered to be tiny corpuscles which we now call *electrons.* In the relatively free space of a highly evacuated tube, cathode particles, torn loose from the atoms of the cathode, stream down the length of the tube and seldom collide with a gas molecule until they hit the glass walls.

The first important discovery concerning the nature of cathode rays was that they travel in straight lines. This was first revealed by Hittorf, in 1869, by casting shadows of objects placed inside the discharge tube. Hittorf's discovery is usually demonstrated by a tube of special design, as shown in Fig. 41C.

Where the rays strike walls of the tube, the glass fluoresces green, while in the shadow it remains dark. Under continuous bombardment of the walls by cathode rays, the fluorescence grows fainter because of a fatigue effect of the glass. This effect is demonstrated by tipping the object down on its hinge, thus permitting the rays to strike the fresh glass surface. Where the shadow appeared previously, a bright green image of the object is clearly visible.

That *cathode rays have momentum and energy* was first demonstrated in 1870, by Crookes, who used a tube of special design as illustrated in Fig. 41D. Leaving the cathode and acquiring a high speed on their way toward the anode, the rays strike the mica vanes of a small pinwheel and exert a force, causing it to turn and thus roll along a double track toward the anode. When it reaches the end of the track, a reversal of the potential, making the right-hand electrode the cathode, will send it rolling back toward the anode, now at the left. From this experiment Crookes concluded that cathode particles have *momentum,* and that they therefore have *mass, velocity,* and *kinetic energy* $\frac{1}{2}mv^2$.

That *cathode rays are negatively charged particles* was first discovered in Paris in 1895 by Jean Perrin. A discharge tube of special design usually used to demonstrate this property is illustrated in Fig. 41E. A beam of cathode rays is narrowed down to a thin pencil or ribbon of rays by a narrow slit near the cathode. The path of the rays is made visible by allowing them to strike a long strip of metal painted with zinc sulfide, a fluorescent paint. By placing a horseshoe magnet over the outside of the tube, as illustrated, the path of the cathode rays is bent down. If the polarity of the magnet is reversed, the path is bent up. The bending shows that they are charged, and the direction of bending shows the kind of charge. Being charged, a stream of particles is like an electron current. From the direction of the magnetic field and the current, and by application of the left-hand rule (see Sec. 25.5), the charge is found to be *negative.* [Remember that the left-hand rule applies to a current from (−) to (+).]

The penetrating power of cathode rays was first demonstrated by Heinrich Hertz and his assistant, P. Lenard, by passing cathode rays through thin aluminum foils. Out in the air, the rays were found to retain sufficient power to cause fluorescence and phosphorescence.

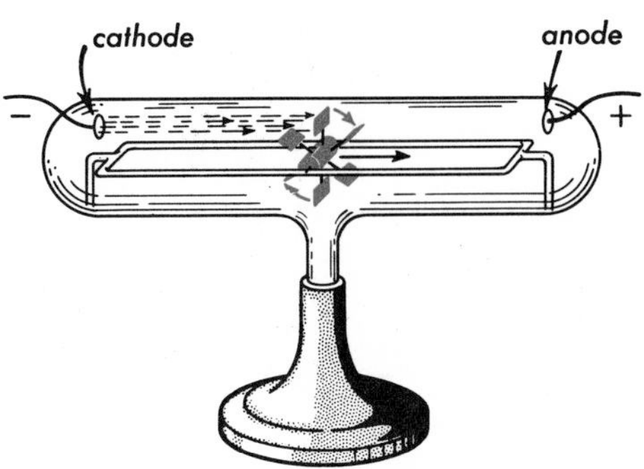

Fig. 41D. Experiment showing that cathode rays have momentum and energy. Cathode rays striking the vanes of a small pinwheel cause it to roll from one end of the tube to the other.

41.3. J. J. Thomson's Experiments

When, in 1895, it was discovered that cathode rays were negatively charged particles, the question immediately arose whether they were all alike. It was clear from the beginning that two things would have to be done: (1) measure the amount of charge on the particles and (2) measure the mass of the particles.

Although the first attempts to measure the electronic charge and mass were not entirely successful, J. J. Thompson* did succeed, in 1897, in determining the velocity of the rays and in measuring the ratio between their charge and mass.

The discharge tube designed for these experiments is shown in Fig. 41F. Cathode rays, originating at the left-hand electrode and limited to a thin pencil of rays by pinholes in diaphragms DD, are made to pass between two parallel metal plates and the magnetic field of two external solenoids to a fluorescent screen at the far end.

When the two metal plates P are connected to a source of

***Sir Joseph John Thomson (1856–1940), English physicist, was educated at Owens College, Manchester, and at Trinity College, Cambridge. He was appointed Cavendish professor at Cambridge in 1884, and professor of physics at the Royal Institution, London, in 1905. He was awarded the Nobel Prize in physics in 1906, was knighted in 1908, and elected to the presidency of the Royal Society in 1915. He became master of Trinity College in 1918 and helped to develop at Cambridge a great research laboratory attracting scientific workers from all over the world.**

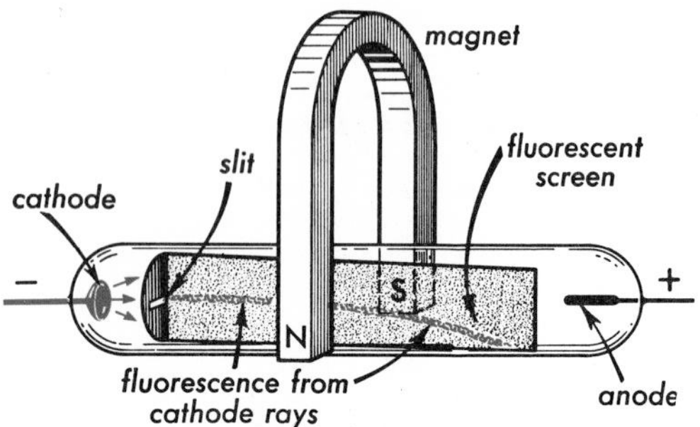

Fig. 41E. The bending of a beam of cathode rays in the field of a magnet demonstrates that cathode rays are negatively charged particles.

high voltage, the particles experience a downward force, and their path curves to strike the screen at N. Without a charge on the plates, the beam passes straight through undeviated and strikes the screen at S.

When the magnetic field alone is applied, so that the magnetic lines are perpendicular to the plane of the page, the path of the rays curves upward to strike the fluorescent screen at some point M. If both the electric field and the magnetic field are applied simultaneously, a proper adjustment of the strength of either field can be made, so that the deflection downward by the one is exactly counteracted by the deflection upward of the other. When this condition is attained, a measurement of the magnetic induction B and the electric intensity $\mathcal{E}$ permits a calculation of the velocity of cathode rays.

41.4. Deflection in an Electric Field

In Chap. 23, on the theory of electricity, it is shown that if e is the charge on a body located in an electric field of strength $\mathcal{E}$, the force exerted on the body is given by [see Eq.(23f)]

$$F_E = e\mathcal{E} \tag{41a}$$

where $\mathcal{E}$ is in newtons per coulomb, or in volts per meter. See Eqs.(23n) and (23o):

$$\mathcal{E} = \frac{V}{d} \tag{41b}$$

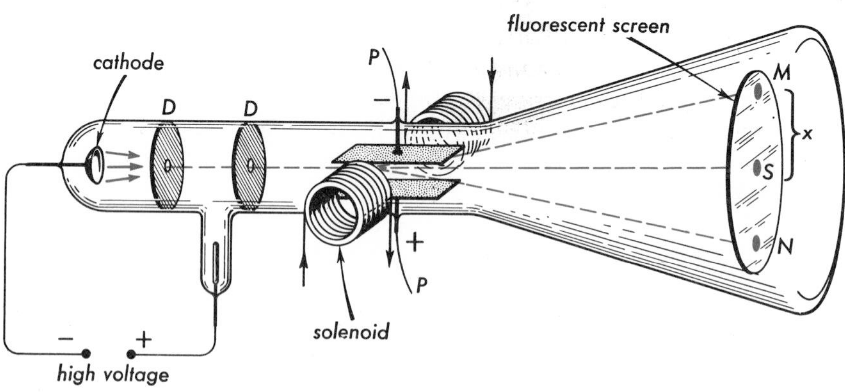

Fig. 41F. Diagram of cathode ray tube used by J. J. Thomson to measure the velocity of cathode rays.

As a charged particle like an electron enters the electric field between two charged plates (shown in Fig. 41G), this force acts straight downward, parallel to the field lines at all points. The net result is that the particle traverses a parabolic path in much the same way that a projectile follows a parabolic path in the earth's gravitational field.

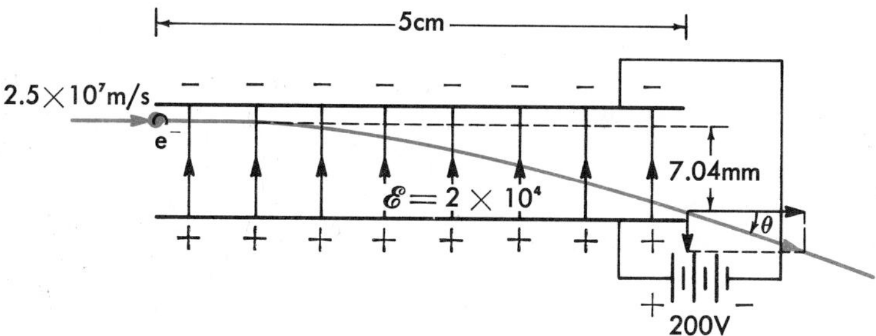

Fig. 41G. Electrons in a uniform electric field $\mathcal{E}$ follow a parabolic path.

To find the distance and direction an electron beam is deflected in a given field, we first apply Eq.(41a) and Newton's second law of motion:

$$F = ma \qquad (41c)$$

Since the two forces are one and the same, we can equate them, and find for the acceleration

$$a = \frac{e\mathcal{E}}{m} \qquad (41d)$$

To find the vertical distance h, we use Eq.(2q) from mechanics, and write

$$h = \tfrac{1}{2} at^2 \qquad (41e)$$

where t is the time the electrons are in the field $\mathcal{E}$. This time is given by the kinematic equation from mechanics, *distance divided by the velocity:*

$$t = \frac{\ell}{v} \qquad (41f)$$

If the new direction of the velocity is required, we can apply Eq.(2o), and find for the velocity u,

$$u = at \qquad (41g)$$

Combining the two velocity components u and v, as shown in Fig. 41G, we obtain

$$v_r = \sqrt{u^2 + v^2} \tag{41h}$$

and

$$\frac{u}{v} = \tan\theta \tag{41i}$$

Example 1. A beam of electrons with a velocity of 3.0×10^7 m/s enters a uniform electric field at right angles to the lines of force. If the field is produced by applying 500 V to two parallel plates 6.0 cm in diameter and 2.0 cm apart, find (a) the field intensity $\mathcal{E}$, (b) the downward acceleration, (c) the time the force acts, (d) the distance h deflected, (e) the electrons' downward velocity u, (f) the electrons' final velocity, and (g) the beam's direction angle θ. Give values to five significant figures.

Solution. The given quantities are $v = 3.0 \times 10^7$ m/s, $V = 500$ V, $\ell = 0.060$ m, $d = 0.020$ m, $e = -1.60219 \times 10^{-19}$ C, $c = 2.99793$, and $m = 9.1096 \times 10^{-31}$ Kg. To find the field intensity we use Eq.(23n), and substitute known values:

$$\mathcal{E} = \frac{V}{d} = \frac{500 \text{ V}}{0.02 \text{ m}} = 2.50 \times 10^4 \frac{\text{V}}{\text{m}}$$

or

$$\mathcal{E} = 2.50 \times 10^4 \frac{\text{N}}{\text{C}}$$

The acceleration is obtained by using Eq. (41d):

$$a = \frac{e\mathcal{E}}{m} = \frac{1.60219 \times 10^{-19} \times 2.50 \times 10^4}{9.1096 \times 10^{-31}}$$

$$a = 4.3970 \times 10^{15} \text{ m/s}^2$$

The time the electrons take to cross the field is given by Eq. (41f):

$$t = \frac{\ell}{v} = \frac{0.060 \text{ m}}{2.99793 \times 10^7 \text{ m/s}} = 2.00138 \times 10^{-9} \text{ s}$$

The distance the beam is deflected is given by Eq.(41e):

$$h = \tfrac{1}{2}at^2 = \frac{4.3970 \times 10^{15} \times 4.00552 \times 10^{-18}}{2}$$

$$h = 8.8061 \times 10^{-3} \text{ m} = 8.8061 \text{ mm}$$

The electrons' downward velocity is given by Eq.(41g):

$$u = at = 4.3970 \times 10^{15} \times 2.00138 \times 10^{-9}$$

$$u = 8.8001 \times 10^{6} \text{ m/s}$$

The resultant electron velocity is given by Eq. (41h):

$$v_r = \sqrt{u^2 + v^2} = \sqrt{(8.8001 \times 10^6)^2 + (3.0 \times 10^7)^2}$$

$$v_r = 3.12641 \times 10^7 \text{ m/s}$$

and the angle θ is given by Eq. (41i):

$$\tan \theta = \frac{u}{v} = \frac{8.7940 \times 10^6}{3.0 \times 10^7} = 0.293337$$

$$\theta = 16.348°$$

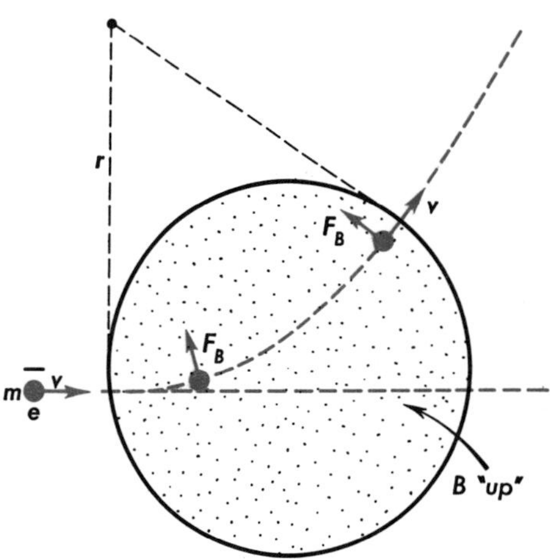

Fig. 41H. Electrons in a uniform magnetic field B follow a circular path.

41.5. Deflection in a Magnetic Field

In Sec. 27.1 it is shown that if e is the charge on a body moving through a magnetic field B with a velocity v, the force acting upon it is given by

$$F_B = Bev \tag{41j}$$

Since this force is always at right angles to both the magnetic induction and the direction of motion, the particle will traverse a circular path (see Fig. 41H). By counterbalancing the two forces F_E and F_B, i.e., by making them equal in magnitude and opposite in direction, the two relations can be set equal to each other:

$$e\mathcal{E} = Bev \tag{41k}$$

By canceling the charge e on both sides of this equation, we obtain

$$\mathcal{E} = vB$$

from which

$$v = \frac{\mathcal{E}}{B} \tag{41ℓ}$$

where $\mathcal{E}$ is in volts per meter, B is in teslas, and v is in meters per second. If we insert the known values of $\mathcal{E}$ and B, the *velecity* v

can be calculated. The results show that cathode rays generally travel with a speed of sevaral thousand miles per second, about $\frac{1}{5}$ *the speed of light.* Furthermore, the velocity is not always the same but depends upon the voltage applied between the anode and cathode. By increasing this voltage, the velocity of the rays is increased.

Tubes used for scanning and observing moving pictures by modern television receivers are quite similar in shape and principle to J. J. Thomson's cathode-ray tube of Fig. 41F.

41.6. The Ratio of Charge to Mass, e/m

The next step taken by Thomson was to measure the deflection of the cathode beam produced by a magnetic field alone and, from this, to calculate the ratio between the charge e and the mass m of the electron. To do this, he reasoned that, if a charged particle moving through a uniform magnetic field has a force exerted on it at right angles to its direction of motion, causing it to move in the arc of a circle, the force is of the nature of a centripetal force. Calling F_B a centripetal force,

$$F_B = m\frac{v^2}{r}$$

and from Eq. (41j), we obtain

$$Bev = m\frac{v^2}{r} \tag{41m}$$

Solving for e/m, we obtain

$$\frac{e}{m} = \frac{v}{Br} \tag{41n}$$

where r is the radius of the circular arc in meters through which the particles are deviated; v is the velocity of the particles in meters per second, as measured in the last section; m is the particle mass in kilograms; and B is the magnetic induction in teslas. With all of these known, the value of e/m can be calculated. It is found to be

$$e/m = 1.7588028 \times 10^{11}\ \frac{\text{C}}{\text{Kg}} \tag{41o}$$

Such a large number means that the mass of a cathode ray

particle in Kg is extremely small, compared with the charge it carries in coulombs. If now it were possible by some experiment to measure the charge *e* alone, the value could be substituted in Eq.(41f) and the mass *m* calculated.

Example 2. A beam of electrons with a velocity of 2.0×10^7 m/s enters a uniform magnetic field at right angles to the lines of force. If the magnetic induction is 5.0×10^{-4} T, find the radius of curvature of their path. Use atomic constants to five significant figures.
Solution. The known quantities are $v = 2.0 \times 10^7$ m/s, $B = 5.0 \times 10^{-4}$ T, $e = 1.60219 \times 10^{-19}$ C, and $m = 9.1096 \times 10^{-31}$ Kg. Solving Eq.(41m) for *r*, and substituting known quantities directly, we find

$$r = \frac{mv}{eB} = \frac{9.1096 \times 10^{-31} \times 2.0 \times 10^7}{1.60219 \times 10^{-19} \times 5.0 \times 10^{-4}}$$

$$r = 0.227429 \text{ m} = 22.74 \text{ cm}$$

41.7. Millikan's Oil-Drop Experiment

Millikan* began his experiments on the electronic charge *e* in 1906. His apparatus is illustrated by the simple diagram in Fig. 41I. Minute oil drops from an atomizer are sprayed into the region just over the top of one of two circular metal plates, V+ and V−. Shown in cross section, the upper plate is pierced with a tiny pinhole P through which an occasional oil drop from the cloud will fall. Once between the plates, such a drop, illuminated by an arc light from the side, is observed by means of a low-powered microscope.

With the switch S in the "up" position, the capacitor plates are grounded so that they are not charged. Under these conditions, the oil drop falling under the pull of gravity has a constant velocity. This *terminal velocity,* as it is called, is reached by the drop before it enters the field of view and is of such a value that the downward pull of gravity, F_g, in Fig. 41J(a), is exactly equalized by the upward resisting force of the air. By measuring this velocity of fall, the force F_g can be calculated and from it the mass of the oil drop determined. The velocity of the drop can be determined by using a stop watch to measure the time required for the drop to fall the distance between the two cross hairs illustrated in Fig. 41K.

***Robert Andrews Millikan (1868–1953), American physicist, was educated at Oberlin College and Columbia University, and became for 25 years professor of physics at the University of Chicago and for 30 years president of the Norman Bridge Laboratory at the California Institute of Technology in Pasadena. He served during World War I in the research division of the Signal Corps with the rank of lieutenant colonel. His principal contributions to science were his measurement of the charge on the electron, his photoelectric determination of the energy in a light quantum, and his precision study of cosmic rays. He was the second American to be awarded the Nobel Prize in physics (1923). He was also awarded the Edison Medal, the Hughes Medal of the Royal Society, the Faraday Medal, and the Mattenci Medal.**

As the drop nears the bottom plate, the switch S is thrown "down," charging the two parallel plates positive and negative. If now the drop has a negative charge, as illustrated in diagram (b), there will be an upward electrostatic force F_E, acting to propel the drop up across the field of view. The drop will move upward with a constant velocity if F_E is greater than the gravitational force F_g. Again using the stop watch, this time to measure the velocity of rise, we can calculate the upward force F_E. Knowing the force, and the voltage on the capacitor plates, we can compute the charge on the drop.

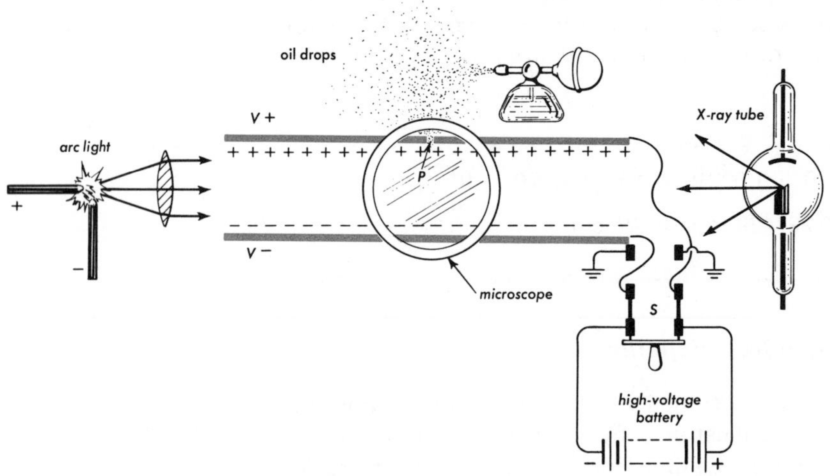

Fig. 41I. Schematic diagram of Millikan's oil-drop experiment. With this experiment the charge on the electron was determined.

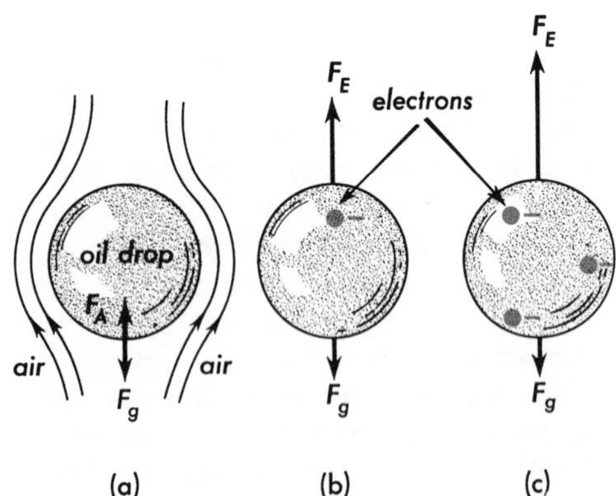

Fig. 41J. Diagrams of oil drop with extra electronic charges.

As the drop nears the top plate, the switch S is thrown "up" and the plates are again grounded. Under these conditions the drop falls again, under the pull of gravity alone. Upon nearing the bottom plate, the switch is again thrown "down" and the drop rises once more. When this process is repeated, a single drop may be made to move up and down many times across the field of view. Each time it falls, the velocity is measured and the mass computed, while each time it rises the velocity is measured and the charge computed.

Millikan found that, if X rays were allowed to pass through the apparatus while an oil drop was being observed, the charge on the drop could be increased or decreased almost at will. One time, on rising, the velocity would be low due to a small charge [see diagram (b) in Fig. 41J], while the next time the velocity would be high due to a larger charge, as in diagram (c). Regardless of the amount of charge, the rate of fall for a given drop will always be the same, because the total mass of a number of electrons is so small compared with the mass of the oil drop that their added mass is not perceptible.

Millikan, and numerous other experimenters who have repeated these experiments, have found that the charge on a drop is never less than a certain minimum value, and is always some integral multiple of this value. In other words, any one electron is like every other electron, each carrying this minimum charge called e:

$$e = -1.6021917 \times 10^{-19}\ \text{C} \tag{41p}$$

This is the most recent and probable value of the electronic charge.

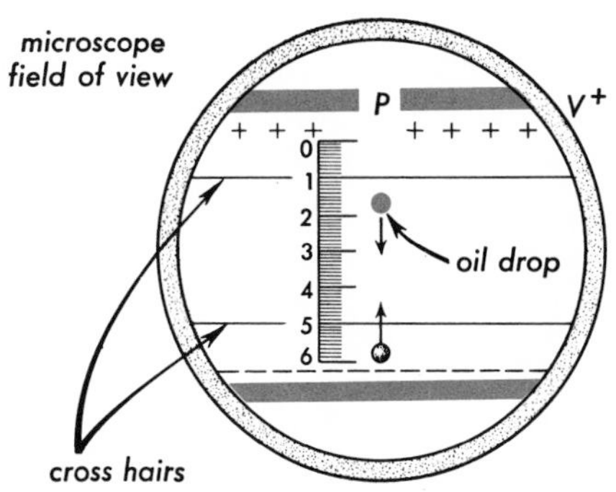

Fig. 41K. Microscope field of view showing oil drop.

41.8. The Mass of the Electron

From Millikan's determination of the charge on the electron and Thomson's measurement of e/m, the mass of the electron can be calculated by dividing one value by the other. Using the most accurately known values for both e and e/m, we obtain

$$m = \frac{e}{e/m} = \frac{1.6021917 \times 10^{-19}\ \text{C}}{1.7588028 \times 10^{11}\ \text{C/Kg}}$$

which gives

$$m = 9.1095585 \times 10^{-31}\ \text{Kg} \tag{41q}$$

This mass is unbelievably small; its value has been determined many times and by many experimenters, and yet it is always the same.*

* For a more complete and elementary treatment of these early experiments, see R. A. Millikan, *Electrons + and −* (University of Chicago Press, Chicago).

problems

1. A beam of electrons enters a uniform magnetic field where $B = 6.50 \times 10^{-3}$ T, and in a direction at right angles to the lines of induction. If the electrons have a velocity of 5.85×10^{7} m/s, find the radius of their path.

2. A stream of electrons with one-tenth the speed of

light enters a uniform magnetic field at right angles to the lines of magnetic induction. What will be the radius of their circular path if $B = 4.82 \times 10^{-3}$ T?

3. A magnetic field of 3.20×10^{-3} T is used in J. J. Thomson's experiment shown in Fig. 41F. What potential difference applied to the parallel plates will keep their paths straight? Assume the plates are 8.0 mm apart, and the velocity of the stream of electrons is 2.80×10^7 m/s. See Eq. (23n). [Ans. 717 V.]

4. An electron beam enters a uniform magnetic field where $B = 8.40 \times 10^{-4}$ T. If they follow a circular path with a radius of 12.50 cm, find their velocity.

5. A beam of electrons enters a uniform magnetic field where $B = 2.40 \times 10^{-4}$ T. If they are bent into a circular path of radius 8.20 cm, what is their velocity?

6. A beam of electrons is injected into a uniform magnetic field where $B = 1.840 \times 10^{-3}$ T. If they have a velocity of 2.650×10^7 m/s, find the diameter of their circular path. [Ans. 16.38 cm.]

7.* Two flat parallel metal plates 10.0 cm in diameter and 2.0 cm apart are connected to a 500-V battery. A beam of electrons enters the electric field between the plates with a velocity of 4.50×10^7 m/s. How far will they be deviated from their original path by the time they reach the other side? First find (a) the electric field intensity, (b) the time the electrons are in the field, (c) the deviation h, and finally (d) the deflection angle θ.

8.* Two parallel plates 8.0 cm in diameter and 1.250 cm apart are connected to a 50.0-V battery. A stream of electrons with a velocity of 2.0×10^7 m/s is sent through between the plates. Find (a) the electric field intensity, (b) the time the electrons are in the field, (c) the beam's deflection h, and (d) the angle of deflection θ.

9.* A battery of 200 V is applied to two parallel plates 5.0 cm in diameter, and 1.00 cm apart. An electron beam with a velocity of 2.50×10^7 m/s is sent through between the plates as shown in Fig. 41G. Find (a) the electric field intensity, (b) the time the electrons are in the field, (c) the deflection h, and (d) the angle through which the beam has been deflected. [Ans. (a) 2.0×10^4 N/C, (b) 2.0×10^{-9} s, (c) 7.04 mm, (d) 15.72°.]

10.* A cathode ray tube of the kind developed by J. J. Thompson has a pair of deflection plates 0.80 cm apart and 5.0 cm long (see Fig. 41F). A 400-V battery is connected to these plates, and a beam of electrons with a velocity of 4.0×10^7 m/s is sent through between them. If the observing screen is 20.0 cm beyond the plates, find (a) the field intensity, (b) the time the electron beam is between the plates, (c) the deflection h, (d) the angle of deflection h, and (e) the displacement on the screen.

11. In J. J. Thomson's experiment a magnetic field of 5.80×10^{-3} T is applied to deflect the electron beam. From the applied voltage it is known that the beam velocity is 2.50×10^7 m/s. If the two parallel plates used to produce the electric deflection are 6.0 mm apart, what voltage should be applied to make the beam go straight through without deviation?

12. A cathode ray tube is used to measure the velocity of an electron beam. If a 600-V battery is applied to the two plates that are 5.0 mm apart, and the magnetic induction needed to make the beam go straight through without deviation is 7.56×10^{-3} T, find the beam velocity. Use nonrelativistic equations. [Ans. 1.587×10^7 m/s.]

42 Isotopes and the periodic table

Although no one has ever seen individual atoms, there is no doubt that such particles really exist. To the physicist and chemists who have built up and established the present-day theories of the structure of matter, atoms are as real as any material objects large enough to be seen with the eyes or to be felt with the hands. Their reality is evidenced by hundreds of experiments that can be planned and executed in the research laboratory.

As the subject of atomic physics is developed in this and the following chapters, it will become more and more apparent that, although a physicist requires an extremely imaginative mind, the accumulated knowledge of atoms, their structure, and their behavior under a multitude of conditions is based upon exact results of experiments performed with the greatest of accuracy and precision.

42.1. The Discovery of Positive Rays

During the latter part of the nineteenth century, when many physicists were investigating the properties of cathode rays, Goldstein* designed a special discharge tube; with it he discovered new rays called *canal rays.* The name "canal rays" is derived from the fact that the rays, traveling in straight lines through a vacuum tube in the opposite direction to cathode rays, pass through and energe from a canal or hole in the cathode. A tube designed to illustrate this is shown in Fig. 42A.

Shortly after the measurement of the ratio of the electronic charge of the electron to its mass by J. J. Thomson in 1896, W.

***Eugen Goldstein (1850–1930), German physicist, was born in Gleiwitz, Germany, and educated at the University of Berlin. He remained at that institution as a research assistant until 1878 when he was transferred to the Berlin Observatory. From 1890–96, he did research at the Physikalische Technische Institute, and from 1896–1927, did independent research at Berlin-Schöneberg. His principal contributions to knowledge were in the field of electrical discharges in rarified gases, and through these studies he discovered canal rays, the electrical deflection of cathode rays, the spectra of a number of ionized atoms, and the band spectrum of the helium molecule**

Wien* deflected a beam of canal rays in a magnetic field and came to the conclusion that the rays consisted of positively charged particles. Owing to this and other experiments, canal rays have become more commonly known as *positive rays.*

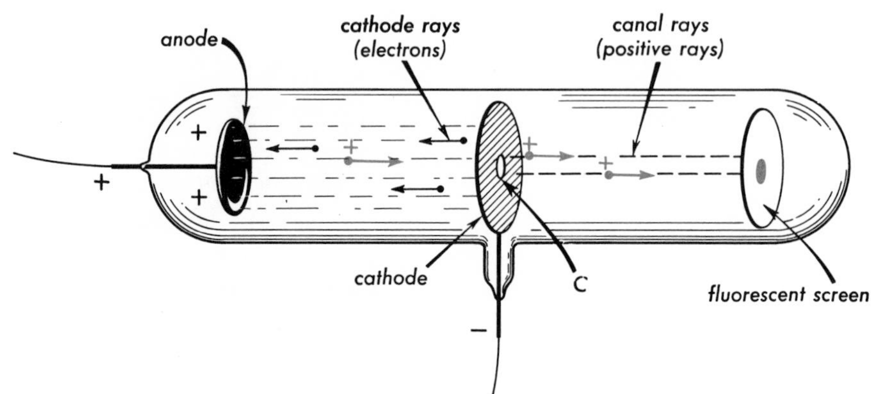

Fig. 42A. Experiment illustrating canal rays discovered by Goldstein.

Since the time of Goldstein's discovery, positive rays have been found to be charged atoms of different weights. The origin of the charge carried by such atoms is explained briefly as follows. As the electrons from the cathode stream down the tube toward the anode, they occasionally collide with the atoms and molecules of the small quantity of remaining gas, knocking electrons from them. This process, called *ionization,* is illustrated by a schematic diagram of a single oxygen atom in Fig. 42B. Before the collision, the atom as a whole, with its eight electrons and eight equal positive charges on the nucleus, has no net charge. After one of the electrons is removed by collision, it has only seven electrons and therefore a net positive charge equivalent in amount to the charge of one electron.

Since the atom is now positively charged, the anode repels and the cathode attracts such atoms, accelerating them toward the cathode. There exist, therefore, between the anode and cathode, two streams of particles: electrons moving toward the anode, and positively charged atoms or molecules moving toward the cathode.

Of the many particles striking the cathode in Fig. 42A, the ones moving toward the small opening C, constituting the observed canal rays, pass straight through to the fluorescent screen. As each atom or molecule strikes the screen, a tiny flash of light is produced. These tiny flashes, which can be seen individually in the field of view of a microscope, are called *scintillations.*

*Wilhelm Wien (1864–1928), German physicist, was born in Goffken, East Prussia. He studied at the Universities of Göttingen, Heidelberg, and Berlin, and then served as assistant to Helmholtz. He wrote on optics and especially on black-body radiation for which in 1911, he was awarded the Nobel Prize. He also wrote on discharges through gases, cathode rays, X rays, and positive rays. Wein's most important contributions to black-body radiation are contained in two laws named after him. He developed a formula for the energy density at different wavelengths radiated by a hot body, and the wavelength displacement of the maximum with a change in temperature. He showed that positive rays undergo electric and magnetic deflection and showed a keen interest in modern theoretical physics. In 1913, he lectured at Columbia University in New York.

Any process by which an electron is removed from an atom or molecule is called *ionization*, and the resulting charged particle is called a *positive ion*. The amount of charge carried by an electron is a unit called *the electronic charge*.

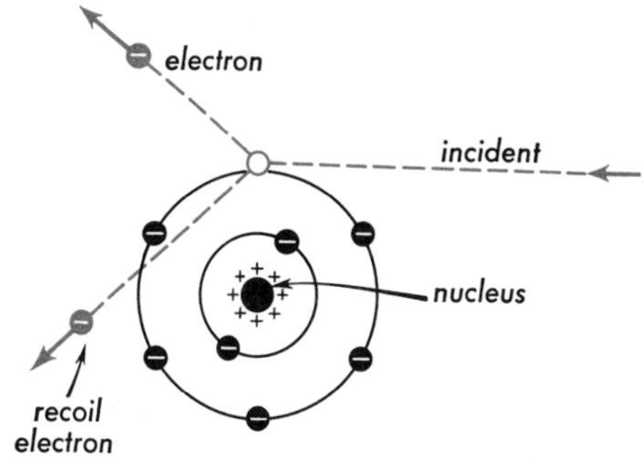

Fig. 42B. Schematic diagram of an oxygen atom in the process of becoming ionized by a collision with a high-speed electron.

42.2. The Thomson Mass Spectrograph

Ever since the time canal rays were shown to be positively charged atoms or molecules of the gas contained within the discharged tube, physicists have tried to determine with ever-increasing accuracy the mass and charge of the individual ray particles. Although the charge and mass of every electron were known from Thomson's and Millikan's experiments to be the same as those for every other electron, it could be postulated that the mass of the positive rays should be different for the atoms of different chemical elements. The further postulation could be made that if each positive ion were produced by the removal of one electron from a neutral atom, all positive ions should have the same net charge. This, in part, is anticipating what is now known.

In 1911, J. J. Thomson developed a method of measuring the relative masses of different atoms and molecules by deflecting positive rays in a magnetic and an electric field. The apparatus he developed for doing this is shown schematically in Fig. 42C; it is called *Thomson's mass spectrograph*.

The entire spectograph, enclosed in an airtight glass chamber, is first thoroughly evacuated; then a small quantity of the gas, the

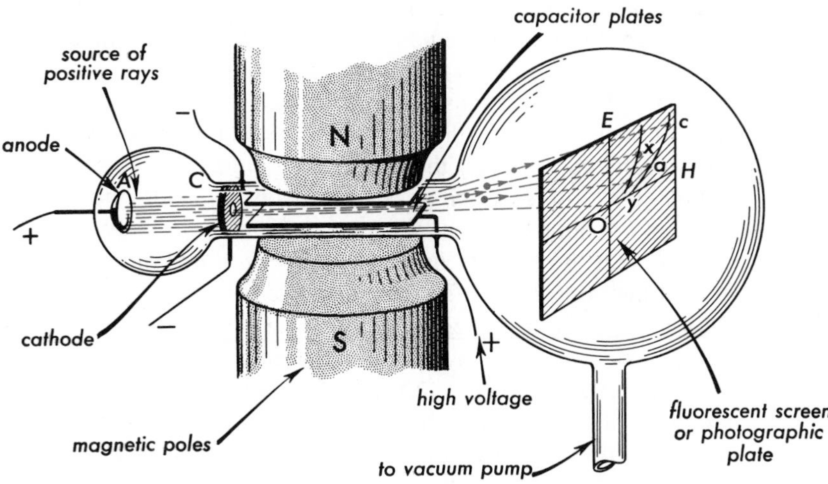

Fig. 42C. Diagram of J. J. Thomson's mass spectrograph.

masses of whose atoms are to be measured, is admitted to the bulb at the left. When a high voltage is applied to this chamber, electrons from the cathode ionize the atoms and molecules in the region between the anode A and the cathode C. Traveling to the right, many of these positively charged particles pass through the narrow hole in the cathode, thus forming a very narrow pencil of rays. Leaving the cathode with a constant velocity, they then pass between the poles of an electromagnet and the parallel plates of a capacitor, and thence to a fluorescent screen at the far end of the chamber.

The two parallel plates, when charged, exert an upward force on the particles, deflecting them from the point O toward E. The magnetic field, on the other hand, with its magnetic lines vertically downward and in the plane of the page, exerts a force at right angles to this, deflecting the particles "into" the page from the point O toward H.

Suppose now that the apparatus contains a pure gas like helium, all of the atoms of which have exactly the same mass. Of these atoms, the ones that are ionized in a region near the cathode C cannot attain a very high speed before reaching the cathode. Since these atoms remain longer in the deflecting fields, their paths are bent considerably up and back to a point such as *c* on the screen. Particles ionized near the anode A, on the other hand, attain a high speed upon reaching the cathode and, being under the influence of the deflecting fields for a shorter time, have their paths bent only a little, to a point like *a* on the screen. Since the velocities of the particles vary considerably, a bright streak or line of fluorescence will appear on the screen. From a calculation of the forces exerted by both fields, it is found that the line on the screen should have the shape of a parabola.

If the gas in the apparatus is not pure but contains two kinds of atoms, the positive ions passing through the cathode will have two different masses. Although each ion will contain the same positive charge, and will therefore experience the same electric and magnetic forces when passing through the fields, the heavier particles will not be deflected as much as the lighter ones. The net result is that the heavier particles form one parabolic curve like *xy*, and the lighter particles another curve like *ac*.

By substituting a photographic plate for the fluorescent screen and exposing it to the rays for several minutes, photographs like those reproduced in Fig. 42D are obtained. The continual bombardment of the photographic plate by atoms and molecules has the same effect as does light, and images are produced upon development. The upper half of each picture is taken with the connections as shown in Fig. 42C, and the lower half by reversing the polarity of the electromagnet and exposing for an equal length of time.

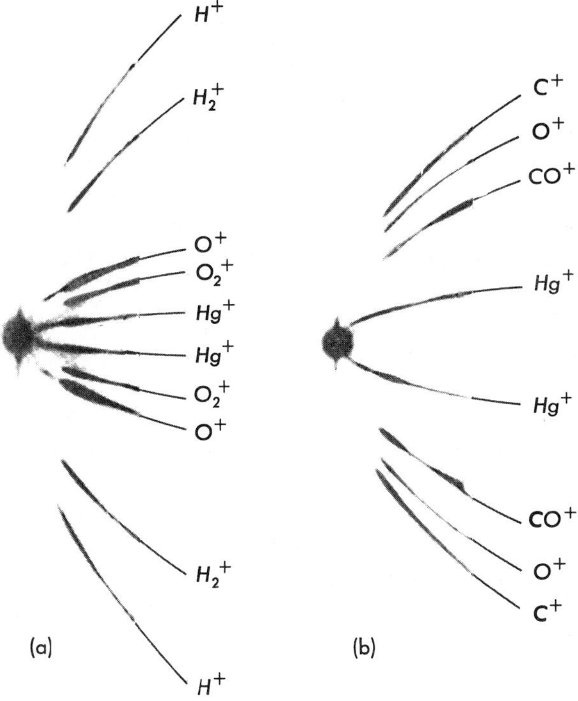

Fig. 42D. Reproductions of the photographs of parabolas made with Thomson's mass spectrograph.

When photograph (a) was taken, the spectrograph contained *hydrogen, oxygen,* and *mercury,* and the magnetic field was relatively weak. From the known strengths of both the electric and magnetic fields, and the assumption that each atom carries a unit positive charge, the mass of the atoms producing each parabola can be calculated. The results of these calculations show that the two largest parabolas are due to ionized hydrogen atoms (H^+) of mass 1, and ionized hydrogen molecules ($H_2{}^+$) of mass 2. The next three are due to ionized oxygen atoms (O^+) of mass 16, ionized oxygen molecules ($O_2{}^+$) of mass 32, and ionized mercury atoms (Hg^+) with a mass of approximately 200.

When photograph (b) was taken, the mass spectrograph contained carbon monoxide gas and mercury vapor, and the magnetic field was relatively strong. Upon calculating the masses of the particles producing the different parabolas, the four intense lines were identified as due to ionized carbon atoms (C^+) of mass 12, ionized oxygen atoms (O^+) of mass 16, ionized carbon monoxide molecules (CO^+) of mass 28, and ionized mercury atoms (Hg^+) of mass about 200. The three faint parabolas which show in the original photograph but probably not in the reproduction are due to doubly ionized atoms of *carbon, oxygen,* and *mercury.*

A doubly ionized atom or molecule is one that has lost two electrons rather than only one and, having a net positive charge of two units, is designated by two (+) signs as superscripts. Since the particles have double charges, the electric and magnetic forces exerted on them are double those for singly ionized atoms and they produce larger parabolas, because they undergo greater deflections.

The principal conclusion to be drawn from Thomson's experiments is: *Positive rays or canal rays are charged atoms or molecules of whatever gas is present in the apparatus.*

It is significant to point out that, while Thomson found many atoms could be doubly and some even triply ionized, hydrogen could never be found more than singly ionized or helium more than doubly ionized. The reason for this, as will be seen later, is that neutral hydrogen atoms have only one electron and neutral helium atoms only two. All other elements have more than two electrons.

42.3. The Periodic Table of Elements

From present-day knowledge of physics, chemistry, and astronomy, it is quite certain that the entire universe is made up of 80 to 90 stable elements. By an element we mean a substance composed of atoms having identical chemical properties. All but two or three of these elements have been found in the earth's crust, some of them in much greater abundance than others. Silicon and iron are examples of abundant elements, whereas platinum is an example of a rare element.

Long before the Thomson mass spectrograph had been devised and used to measure the relative masses of atoms, the chemist had arranged all of the elements in a table according to their atomic weights. The most common form of this arrangement is given in Appendix IV. Divided as they are into eighteen separate groups, all elements in the same column have similar chemical properties. In Group I-A, for example, the elements Li, Na, K, Rb, Cs, and Fr, known as the *alkali metals,* have one set of chemical properties, whereas the elements Be, Mg, Ca, Sr, Ba, and Ra in Group II-A, known as the *alkaline earths,* have another set of chemical properties. The largest group of elements having similar chemical properties is the fourteen rare earth elements listed by themselves starting with Ce, element 58, in the next to the last row at the bottom of the table.

The names of the elements are all indicated by one-letter and two-letter symbols. The full names are given in the second column of Appendix VI. The number in the first column before each abbreviation is the order number of that element and is called *the atomic number.* The average weight of atoms of that element, called *the atomic weight,* is given in the last column (see Table 30A).

The atomic weights of all elements are based upon the weight of carbon 12. This is purely an arbitrary selection of a unit of weight but one which has considerable significance when it is noted that the weights of the first 25 elements, with the exception of chlorine ($C\ell$), atomic number 17, are very close to whole numbers. This suggests the possibility that the weights of all atoms are really whole number units of the unit of weight, the hydrogen atom, and that those weights of an element which differ considerably from whole numbers are incorrectly determined values. On the strength of this, Prout was the first to propose the hypothesis that all elements are made of hydrogen atoms as building stones. These suppositions, as will be seen later, are partly true.

42.4. Thomson's Discovery of Isotopes

In 1912, Thomson, in comparing the mass of the neon atom with the known masses of other elements, discovered two parabolas for neon in place of one. Upon computing the masses of the particles involved, the stronger of two parabolas was found to be due to particles of mass 20 and the other, a fainter parabola, to particles of mass 22.

Since the atomic weight of neon was then known to be 20.2, Thomson expressed the belief that neon is composed of two kinds of atoms, 90% of which have a mass of 20 and the other 10% a mass of 22. Because these two kinds of atoms exist as a mixture and cannot be separated chemically, their atomic weight, when measured by chemical methods, is found to be their average value, 20.2.

The discovery of two kinds of neon atoms, identical chemically but differing in atomic weight, suggested the possibility that all other elements whose atomic weights were not whole numbers might also be mixtures of atoms that do have whole number weights. Not only has this been confirmed by experiment, but a large majority of the elements have been found to be mixtures of from two to ten different kinds of atoms.

To all atoms of different weight belonging to the same element, Soddy gave the name *isotopes.* The external structures of all isotopes of a given element are identical. The three atoms, Ne-20, Ne-21, and Ne-22, shown in Fig. 42E, are stable neon isotopes. Each of these neutral atoms, before it is ionized to become a positive ray, has ten external electrons and ten positive charges on the nucleus. They differ only in the weight of the nucleus.

Atoms having different weights but belonging to the same chemical element have the same atomic number and are called isotopes.

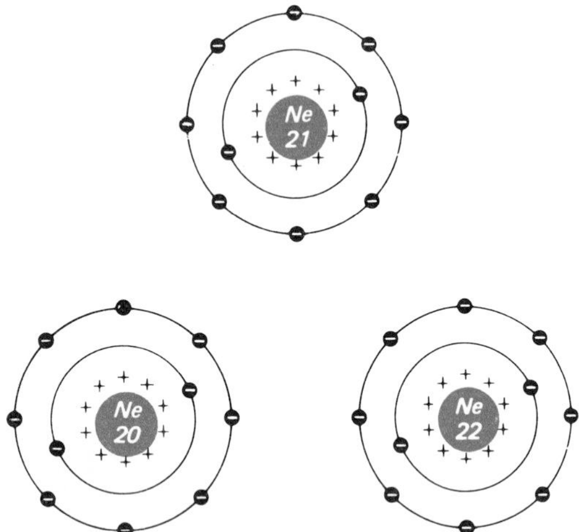

Fig. 42E. Schematic diagrams of three kinds of neon atoms, one of mass 20 and the others of masses 21 and 22. The external electron structures of the three isotopes are identical.

42.5. Aston's Mass Measurements

Immediately following World War I, in 1919, F. W. Aston* developed a new and improved type of mass spectrograph, employing both the electric and magnetic fields. The chief improvement of this device over Thomson's mass spectrograph was the "focusing" of the rays of different velocities to the same point on the screen or photographic plate. This had two important effects: (1) it made it possible to observe rare isotopes which might otherwise escape detection, and (2) it produced sharper images of the different masses on the photographic plate, so that their masses could be more accurately measured.

An Aston mass spectrogram is reproduced in Fig. 42F(a). In taking this particular photograph, Aston had introduced into his apparatus, among other things, a little *hydrochloric acid* (HCl), *carbon monoxide* (CO), and *sulfur dioxide* (SO_2). Being close together in the periodic table, these elements furnish an excellent demonstration of the linear shift of atoms and molecules, differing in mass by one unit. It is found from this, and other photographs, that sulfur has three isotopes with masses 32, 33, and 34, and that chlorine has two isotopes of mass 35 and 37.

Since the atomic weight of chloride is 35.453, then for every atom of mass 37 in a given quantity of chlorine gas there are four of mass 35. Mixed together in these proportions, they give an average mass of 35.4.

The photographic lines corresponding to masses 28, 36, and 38 are due to diatomic molecules CO and HCl, each molecule having the combined weight of its constituent atoms. Since there are two relatively abundant chlorine isotopes, there are two kinds of HCl molecules. One type, H^1Cl^{35}, has a mass of 36; and the other type, H^1Cl^{37}, a mass of 38.

A CO molecule of the type producing the strong line at mass 28 in Fig. 42F(a) is shown schematically in Fig. 42G. Since the

***Francis William Aston (1877–1945), British scientist, was born in Birmingham and educated at Malvern College and Cambridge University. He became assistant lecturer in physics at the Birmingham University in 1909, and received the Mackenzie Davidson Medal of the Röntgen Society in 1920. In 1922, he was awarded the Hughes Medal of the Royal Society and the coveted Nobel Prize in chemistry for his work on atomic mass measurements. He wrote an authoritative book entitled *Isotopes,* in which a full account of his work is given.**

molecule is neutral, there are just as many electrons surrounding the two bound atoms as there are positive charges on the nuclei (six on the carbon nucleus and eight on the oxygen nucleus). When the molecule becomes ionized and is moving through the apparatus as a positive ray, it contains one less electron than the number shown. Since the mass of the electrons is negligibly small, the mass of the molecule is 12 + 16 or 28 mass units.

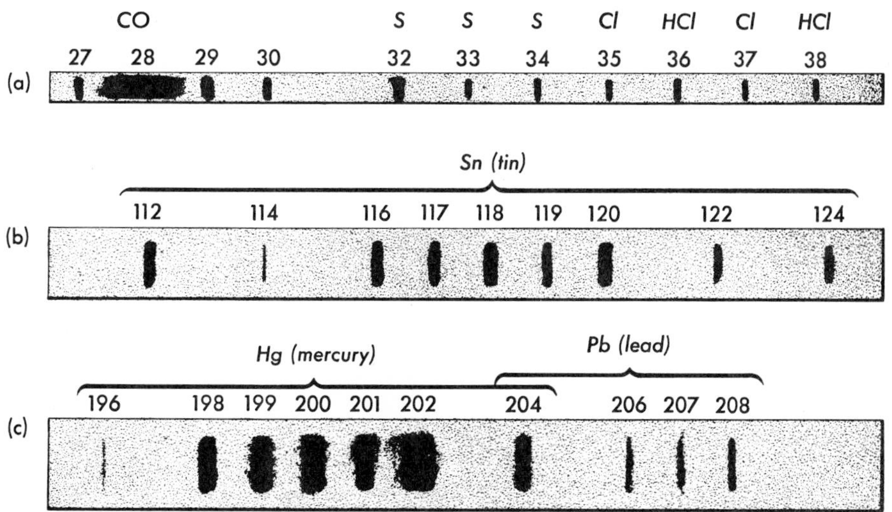

Fig. 42F. Reproductions of photographs taken with a mass spectrograph illustrating the linear shift of atoms differing by one unit of mass: (a) carbon monoxide, sulfur, chlorine, and HCl lines; (b) isotopes of tin; (c) isotopes of mercury and lead.

So successful was Aston with his mass measurements and his determination of isotopes of different elements that he attempted an investigation of the entire periodic table. All of the known elements are listed in Appendix VI, with all of their observed stable isotopes. In each case, the most abundant isotope is indicated in heavy type, while the very rare isotopes, i.e., those present to less than 1%, are listed in parentheses. Where more than one isotope is set in heavy type, the isotopes occur with almost equal abundance. The masses printed in italics represent unstable atoms which are responsible for *radioactivity,* the subject of Chap. 52. Recent developments in mass spectroscopy have made it possible to detect exceptionally rare isotopes. In neon, for example, an isotope of mass number 21 has been found, making three in all, with relative abundances as follows:

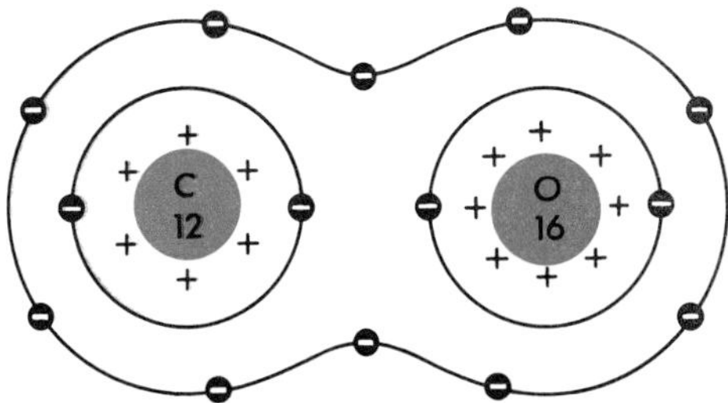

Fig. 42G. Schematic diagram of a diatomic molecule, carbon monoxide (CO).

Isotope	Ne-20	Ne-21	Ne-22
Abundance, %	90.92	0.26	8.82

In a pure carbon monoxide gas, all of the molecules are diatomic and alike in every respect except for mass. Since there are two carbon isotopes, 12 and 13, and three oxygen isotopes, 16, 17, and 18 (see Appendix VI), there are six different combinations of atoms to form molecules. These are $C^{12}O^{16}$, $C^{12}O^{17}$, $C^{12}O^{18}$, $C^{13}O^{16}$, $C^{13}O^{17}$, and $C^{13}O^{18}$. The relative abundances of all but the C^{12} and O^{16} isotopes are so small, however, that more than 90% of the molecules in a given quantity of gas are of the type $C^{12}O^{16}$, with a mass of 28.

42.6. Isobars

Another mass spectrograph of remarkably high precision was devised in 1933 by an American physicist, K. T. Bainbridge.

Two photographs taken with this instrument are shown in Fig. 42F. The middle picture (b) shows the many isotopes of tin, and the lower plate (c) the isotopes of mercury and lead. The rare lead isotope 204 falls on top of the strong mercury isotope 204. Such coincidences are called *isobars: Atoms having the same mass but belonging to different chemical elements are called isobars.*

The first pair of isobars (see Appendix VI) occurs in argon and calcium. The principal isotope of argon, atomic number 18, has a mass of 40, as does also the principal isotope of calcium, atomic number 20. Other examples are Cr^{54} and Fe^{54}, Ge^{76} and Se^{76}, Rb^{87} and Sr^{87}, Zn^{92} and Mo^{92}. The isobars Hg^{204} and Pb^{204} are illustrated in Fig. 42F(c).

All isotopes and isobars of all elements are called *nuclides.* In other words, every different kind of nucleus is a different *nuclide.*

42.7. Unit Atomic Mass and the Hydrogen Atom

Until 1927, all oxygen atoms were thought to have the same mass and were arbitrarily chosen to be the standard by which all atomic masses were measured. At this time Giauque and Johnson discovered the existence of two rare oxygen isotopes with masses 17 and 18. So rare are these heavier particles that in every ten thousand oxygen atoms twenty of them have a mass of 18, and only four a mass of 17.

Retaining natural oxygen with its mixture of three isotopes as a standard, the chemists continued to use $\frac{1}{16}$ the weight of this mixture as *unit atomic weight.* The physicist, on the other hand, found it most convenient for their purposes to adopt a mass scale based upon the mass of the most abundant oxygen atom as exactly 16, and $\frac{1}{16}$ of this as *unit atomic mass.*

As isotope mass determinations (measured largely by research physicists) became more and more accurate, and mass differences became more important, the slight differences between the two scales more and more of a problem.

In 1960 the International Union of Pure and Applied Physics (IUPAP) met in Ottawa and adopted the atomic mass scale based upon the carbon-12 isotope as having a mass of exactly 12. The same scale was adopted by the International Union of Pure and Applied Chemistry (IUPAC) at their Montreal meeting in 1961. While this atomic weight scale differs ever so slightly from the older O = 16 scale, the accurate masses of isotopes show greater differences, as can be seen in Appendix VII.

Standard unit atomic mass is now generally accepted to be $\frac{1}{12}$ of the mass of the carbon-12 isotope. On this basis very accurate measurements give for the mass of the hydrogen atom 1.0081456 atomic mass units (amu), a value nearly 1% higher than unity.

For many practical purposes it is convenient to know the masses of atoms in kilograms. For easy calculations the following value may be used:

$$M = 1.6605311 \times 10^{-27}\ \text{Kg} \qquad (42a)$$

unit atomic mass

This number multiplied by the atomic mass of any atom will give its mass in kilograms.

Compared with the mass of the electron, namely,

$$m = 9.1095585 \times 10^{-31}\ \text{Kg} \qquad (42b)$$

electron mass

an atom of unit mass would be 1823 times as heavy. The hydrogen atom is slightly heavier than one unit mass and is 1836.1091 times as heavy as the electron. This latter number is convenient to know, for it is often quoted to illustrate the enormous difference between the mass of the nucleus of a hydrogen atom and the mass of its one and only electron.

Atomic number is defined as the number ascribed to an element specifying its position in the periodic table of elements (see column 1, Appendix VI).

Mass number is defined as the whole number nearest the actual mass of an isotope measured in atomic mass units (see column 4. Appendix VI).

Atomic weight is defined as the average weight of all the isotopes of an element, weighted according to relative abundance and expressed in atomic mass units (see column 5, Appendix VI).

Example 1. If the atomic weight of platinum is 195.09 amu, how many atoms are there in 1.0 Kg of platinum metal?
Solution. The known quantities are $M_{\text{P}} = 1.0$ Kg, $M = 1.6605 \times 10^{-27}$ Kg/amu, and At.wt = 195.09 amu. The average mass of one platinum atom, in Kg, is the product of the At.wt and M:

$$m = 195.09 \times 1.6605 \times 10^{-27} \text{ Kg}$$

$$m = 3.239 \times 10^{-25} \text{ Kg}$$

The number of these atoms in 1.0 Kg is given by

$$n = \frac{1.0 \text{ Kg}}{3.239 \times 10^{-25} \text{ Kg}}$$

$$n = 3.087 \times 10^{24} \text{ atoms}$$

Example 2. The two stable isotopes of boron have atomic numbers of 10 and 11, respectively. Their accurate masses are given in Appendix VIII as 10.012939 amu and 11.009305 amu, respectively. Find their relative abundance in a normal mixture if the atomic weight is 10.8240 amu.
Solution. The given quantities are B-10.012939 amu, B-11.009305 amu, and their mixture B-10.811 amu. Calling x the percent of isotope 11, and $(100 - x)$ the percent of isotope 10, we can write

$$11.009305\,x + 10.012939\,(100 - x) = 10.824 \times 100$$

Multiplying, we have

$$11.009305\,x + 1001.2939 - 10.012939\,x = 1082.40$$

And solving for x, we find

$$x = \frac{81.106}{0.99637} = 81.4\% \text{ boron-11}$$

The other 18.6% is boron-10.

---

problems

1. If the atomic weight of silver is 107.80 amu, how many atoms are there in one kilogram of metallic silver?

2. The atomic weight of calcium is 40.08 amu. How many atoms are there in one kilogram of calcium?

3. Lead has an atomic weight of 207.19 amu. Find the number of atoms in 50.0 g of lead. [Ans. 1.453×10^{23} atoms.]

4. Barium has an atomic weight of 137.34 amu. How many atoms are there in 100 g of barium?

5. The atomic weights of hydrogen and oxygen are 1.00797 amu and 15.9994 amu, respectively. Find the number of water molecules, H_2O, in one kilogram of water.

6. Name the six (a) alkali metals, and (b) alkaline earths (see Appendix IV). [Ans. (a) Li, Na, K, Rb, Cs, and Fr, (b) Be, Mg, Ca, Sr, Ba, and Ra.]

7. Define or briefly explain in your own words the meaning of (a) atomic mass unit, (b) isotopes, (c) isobars, (d) molecular weight, and (e) positive rays.

8. An examination of Appendix VI shows that hydrogen and chlorine each have two stable isotopes: 1 and 2 for H; and 35 and 37 for Cl. Find to four significant figures the mass in kilograms of each of the four kinds of hydrochloric acid molecules.

9.* Chlorine has two stable isotopes, 35 amu and 37 amu. The normal mixture of these atoms has an atomic weight of 35.460 amu. What percent of the normal mixture is composed of (a) Cl^{35}, and (b) Cl^{37} atoms? Use the isotope masses listed in Appendix VIII. [Ans. (a) 75.4%, (b) 24.6%.]

10.* The two stable isotopes of copper have atomic weights of 62.93 amu and 64.93 amu, respectively. The normal mixture of these atoms has the atomic weight of 63.54 amu. What percentage of the normal mixture is composed of (a) Cu^{63}, and (b) Cu^{65}?

11.* Magnesium has three stable isotopes: 24, 25, and 26 amu, respectively. If 10.11% of the normal mixture is composed of Mg^{25} atoms, what percentage of the normal mixture is composed of (a) Mg^{24}, and (b) Mg^{26} atoms? The atomic weight of magnesium is 24.312 amu. See Appendix VIII.

12.* Potassium has three stable isotopes: 39, 40, and 41, respectively. If in the normal mixture the rare isotope K^{40} has a relative abundance of only 0.0119%, find the relative abundance of (a) K^{39}, and (b) K^{41} atoms. The atomic weight of potassium is 39.102 amu. [Ans. (a) $K^{39} = 93.07\%$, (b) $K^{41} = 6.92\%$.]

The photoelectric 43 effect

The photoelectric effect was discovered by Heinrich Hertz in 1887 when he observed that ultraviolet light, falling on the electrodes of a spark gap, caused a high-voltage discharge to jump greater distances than when it was left in the dark. One year later, Hallwachs made the important observation that ultraviolet light falling on a negatively charged body caused it to lose its charge, whereas a positively charged body was not affected. Ten years later J. J. Thomson and P. Lenard showed independently that the action of the light was to cause the emission of free negative charges from the metal surface. Although these negative charges are no different from all other electrons, it is customary to refer to them as "photoelectrons."

43.1. Photoelectrons

The photoelectric effect, in its simplest form, is demonstrated in Fig. 43A. Light from a carbon arc is focused by means of a

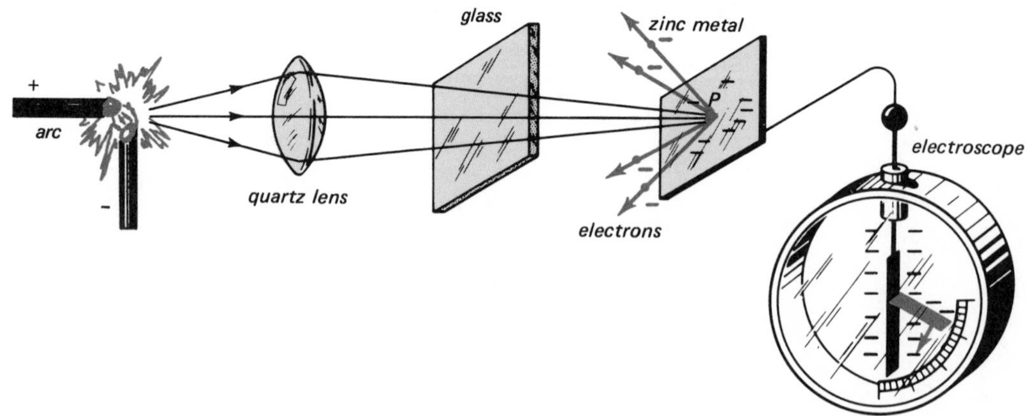

Fig. 43A. Experimental arrangement for demonstrating the photoelectric effect. When the glass plate is inserted, the effect stops.

quartz lens onto a freshly polished plate of zinc metal. When the plate is charged negatively and the light is turned on, the gold leaf of the attached electroscope slowly falls. It falls because the electrons, under the action of the light, leave the zinc plate at the illuminated spot P. When the plate is positively charged, the gold leaf does not fall, showing that the plate retains its charge. The same result of no discharge is observed if the zinc plate is negatively charged and a sheet of glass is inserted, as shown in the figure. When the glass is removed, the gold leaf again falls. Since common glass transmits visible and infrared light, but not ultraviolet, we conclude from the latter result that electrons are liberated only by ultraviolet light. This is also generally true for nearly all of the known metals.

A few elements—the alkali metals, *lithium, sodium, potassium, rubidium,* and *cesium*—are exceptions to this, for they will eject photoelectrons when visible light falls on them. For this reason the *alkali metals* are often used in the manufacture of photoelectric cells.

43.2. The Photoelectric Cell

Photoelectric cells are usually made by depositing a thin layer of an alkali metal on the inner surface of a small vacuum tube (see Fig. 43B). If the cell is to operate in ultraviolet light, it is

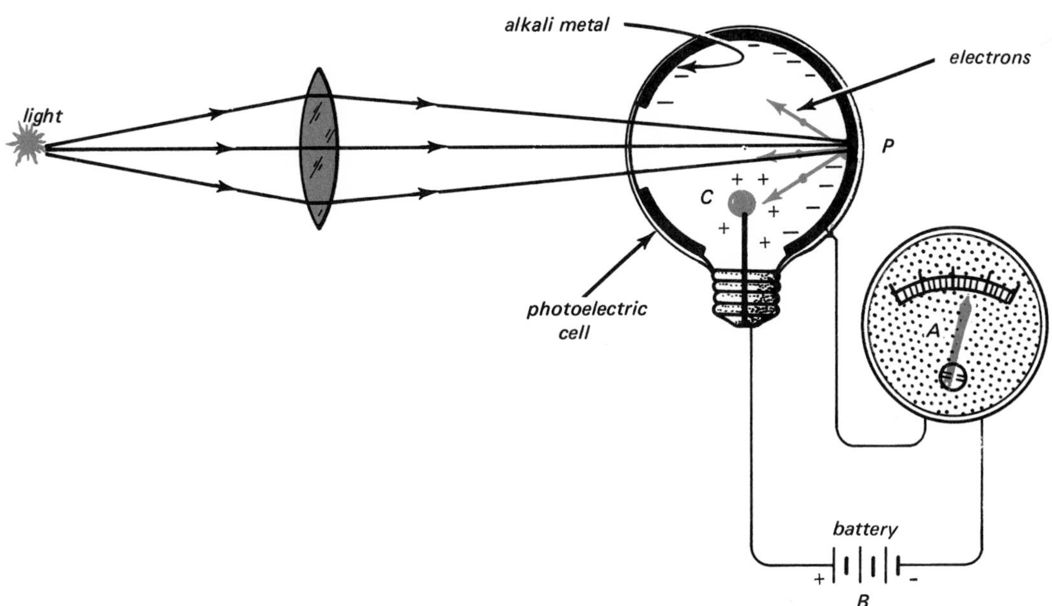

Fig. 43B. Diagram of a photoelectric cell, showing the light beam and electrical connections necessary for its operation.

made of quartz, whereas if it is to be used in visible light it is made of common glass. The cell must be thoroughly evacuated, as the oxygen content of the air will combine chemically with the active metal layer, contaminating its surface and making it insensitive to visible light. A small section of the cell is always left clear to serve as a window for the incoming light. Photoelectrons. upon leaving the metal surface, are attracted and collected by the positively charged electrode C. The photosensitive surface, the cathode, and the collector, the anode, are maintained at a constant potential difference by the battery B.

A beam of light shining through the window of a photoelectric cell acts like a switch that completes an electric circuit. When the light strikes the metal P, there is a flow of electrons to the collector C, thus causing a current to flow around the circuit. This current can be measured by means of an ammeter at A. If the intensity of the light increases, the number of photoelectrons increases and the current therefore rises. When the light is shut off, the photoelectric action ceases and the current stops. If the metal film is positively charged, the cell becomes nonreactive to light, since electrons released from the plate are held back by electrostatic attraction. All of these factors are readily demonstrated by a simple electrical circuit arranged as shown in Fig. 43B.

43.3. Practical Applications

Talking motion pictures, television, and burglar alarms are but three of the hundreds of practical applications of the photoelectric cell. The simplest of these is the burglar alarm, in which a beam of infrared light (invisible to the eye) is projected across the room into a photoelectric cell connected as shown in Fig. 43B. When an intruder walks through the beam, thus interrupting the beam for an instant, the photoelectric current ceases momentarily. An electric relay in place of the ammeter at A in the circuit moves, causing another electric circuit to be completed and thereby ringing an electric bell.

During the filming of talking motion pictures, a sound track is produced photographically on the side of the master motion-picture film. Such sound tracks are shown in Fig. 43C. In strip (a), which is just a sample of one of the several kinds of sound tracks, the sound vibrations on the stage are converted into electrical vibrations by the stage microphone and then carried over wires to the camera taking the pictures. There the electrical impulses are made to move one of the jaws of a narrow slit through which a beam of light passes to the edge of the film.

Loud sounds open the slit wide with each vibration, allowing a large amount of light through.

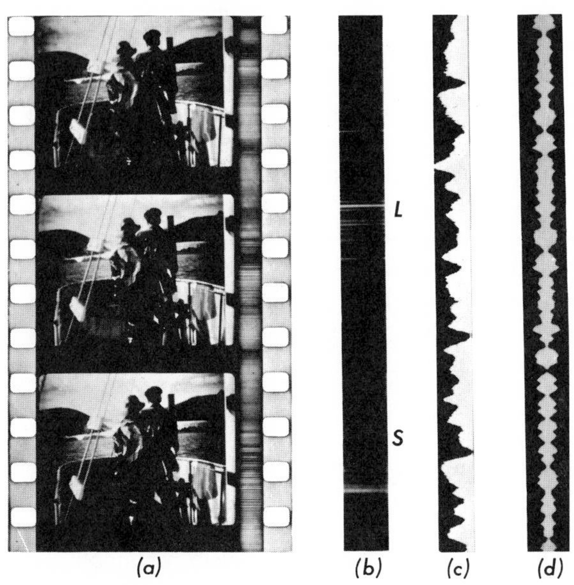

Fig. 43C. (a) Section of a moving-picture film showing the single variable-density sound track. (b) Enlarged section of sound track from (a). (c) Section of a unilateral variable area sound track. (d) Section of a bilateral variable area sound track.

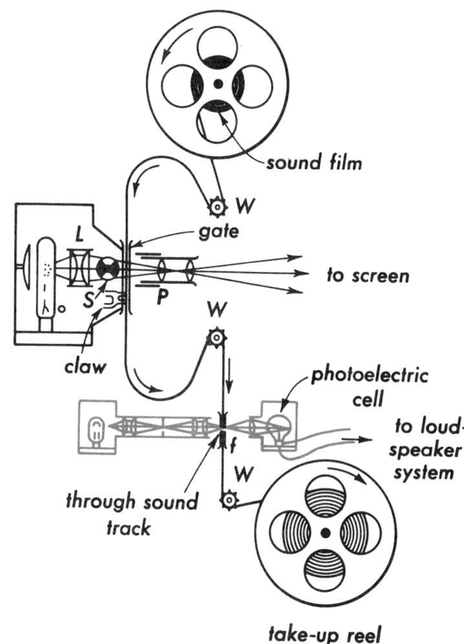

Fig. 43D. Cross section of a motion-picture projector with sound attachment.

When the film is developed and positives are made for distribution, the loud sounds show up as periodic bands with considerable contrast as at L in strip (b). The latter strip is an enlarged section of the *single variable-density* sound track seen on the right in photograph (a). Weaker sounds produce bands with less contrast as at S. Strips (c) and (d) are enlarged sections of two other types of sound track used in other patented recording systems.

When a sound film is projected on the screen in the theater (see Fig. 43D), the film for the pictures themselves must of necessity move intermittently through the projection system P of the projection machine. As the film moves downward, each picture (frame) stops momentarily in front of the condensing lenses L and then moves on for the next frame. While the film is moving, the light is cut off by a rotating shutter S, and while it is at rest the light passes through to the screen. Thus the continuous motion seen on the screen is the result of a number of still pictures projected one after the other in rapid succession. To make this motion seem smooth and not jumpy, it is standard practice to project 24 frames each second.

To produce the sound, a small subsidiary beam of light, shown in detail in Fig. 43E, shines through the sound track at a point 25 frames farther along on the film where the motion is no longer intermittent, but smooth. As the sound track moves through the focus line f of the subsidiary light at constant speed, the transmitted light falling on the photoelectric cell fluctuates exactly as the sound track interrupts it. The photoelectric cell then changes the fluctuating light beam into a fluctuating electric current with the same variations. When transmitted to the radio amplifier and loud-speaker, the fluctuating current is changed into sound vibrations. Thus, sound vibrations have been carried over a light beam from the photographic film to the photoelectric cell and then by means of a loudspeaker system reproduced as sound.

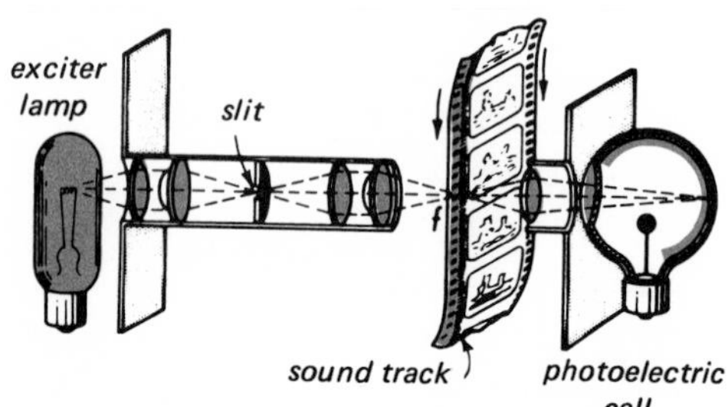

Fig. 43E. Detail of sound pickup system of a moving-picture projector showing the exciter lamp, sound track, and photoelectric cell.

43.4. Sound over a Light Beam

The sending of voice and musical sounds for several miles over a light beam is readily accomplished with a suitable light source as transmitter and a photoelectric cell as a receiver. A convenient laboratory demonstration can be made by using a small $\frac{1}{4}$-W neon glow lamp as a source of light, as shown in Fig. 43F.

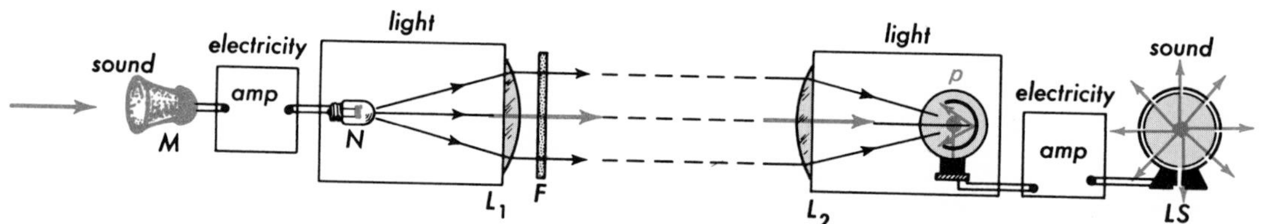

Fig. 43F. Voice and musical sounds can be sent long distances over a beam of light.

Sound waves entering the microphone M produce electric-current fluctuations which, after being strengthened by a two-stage amplifier, cause the intensity of the neon glow lamp N to fluctuate accordingly. Made into a parallel beam by a lens L_1, the light travels across the room to a second lens L_2 and a photoelectric cell, where the light is changed back into a varying electric current. This faint signal is then amplified by a two-stage amplifier before it is delivered to the loud-speaker.

If the microphone is replaced by a phonograph pickup, records can be played at the transmitter end, and excellent reproduction can be obtained from the loud-speaker. The light beam can be made completely invisible by placing an infrared filter in the light beam at F. Talking several miles over a beam of invisible light was developed to quite a high state of perfection during World War II. One system employs the infrared light from a glow discharge tube containing cesium, while several others, modulated by mechanically vibrating mirrors, employ the infrared from a tungsten-filament lamp. Another system employs the invisible ultraviolet light from a glow discharge tube containing gallium.

43.5. Velocity of Photoelectrons

The first measurements of the velocity of photoelectrons led to the very startling discovery that the velocity does not increase as the intensity of the light increases. Increasing the intensity of the light increases the number of photoelectrons, but not their velocity. This discovery, as we shall see later, has had far-reaching implications in its result, for it has played an important role in the development of the quantum theory and our modern concepts of light and atomic structure.

Lenard's experiments, performed as far back as 1902, showed that to increase the velocity of photoelectrons one must increase the frequency of the light, i.e., use shorter wavelengths. The shorter the wavelength of the light used, the higher the velocities of the electrons.

43.6. Einstein's Photoelectric Equation

Following an earlier idea of Planck's that light waves consist of tiny bundles of energy called *photons* or *quanta,* Einstein proposed an explanation of the photoelectric effect as early as 1905. His ideas were expressed in one simple relation, an algebraic equation destined to become famous in the annals of physics. Two Nobel Prizes, one to Einstein in 1921 and one to Millikan in 1923, have been granted on this, the photoelectric equation:

$$h\nu = W + \tfrac{1}{2}mv^2 \tag{43a}$$

The first term, $h\nu$, represents the total energy content of a single quantum of light incident on a metal surface, as shown in Fig. 43G. The letter h is a constant, called *Planck's constant of*

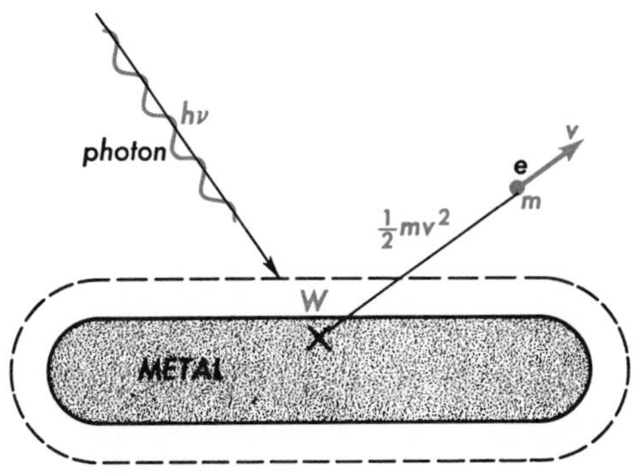

Fig. 43G. A light quantum (photon) of energy $h\nu$, incident on a metal surface, ejects an electron with a velocity v given by Einstein's equation.

action, which has the same value for all light waves regardless of the frequency ν. At or beneath the surface of the metal, this *light quantum,* better known as a *photon,* is completely absorbed and, in disappearing, imparts its total energy to a single electron. Part of this energy W is consumed in getting the electron free from the atoms and away from the metal surface; the remainder is used in giving the electron a kinetic energy $\frac{1}{2}mv^2$, and therefore a velocity. For some metals like platinum, the energy required to pull an electron away from the surface is large, whereas for other metals like the alkalies it is quite small. W is called the *work function* of the metal.

43.7. Millikan's Measurements of h

The letter h in Einstein's photoelectric equation is important because it is fundamental to the structure of all matter and is therefore *a universal constant.* Having first been introduced by Planck in 1901, the name *Planck's constant* has become firmly attached to this symbol h. The first experimental confirmation of Einstein's photoelectric equation came in 1912 when A. L. Hughes, and independently O. W. Richardson and K. T. Compton, observed that the energy of photoelectrons increased proportionately with the frequency. The constant of proportionality they found to be approximately equal to a constant, Planck's constant h.

Subsequently, Millikan carried out extensive experiments which established the photoelectric equation so accurately that his work is now regarded as giving one of the most trustworthy values for h.

To determine the value of h, it was necessary to measure the three factors, ν, W, and $\frac{1}{2}mv^2$, and calculate h as the unknown quantity in Eq.(43a). A schematic diagram of part of Millikan's apparatus is shown in Fig. 43H. Light from a source S through a

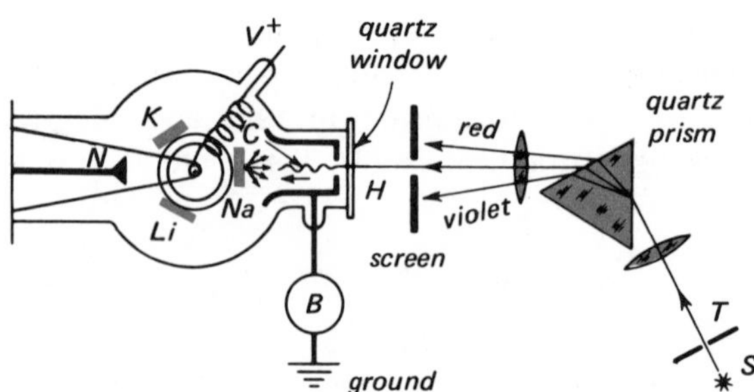

Fig. 43H. Diagram of apparatus used by Millikan in confirming Einstein's photoelectric equation.

slit T is dispersed by means of a prism, and the spectrum is focused on a screen as shown. With a small aperture in this screen any desired frequency of light ν could be admitted to the vacuum chamber through the window H.

Photoelectrons from any one of the three alkali metals, Na, K, or Li, could be obtained at will by turning the wheel R into the required position.

Previous experiments on the photoelectric effect had shown that good results could be obtained only when the metal surfaces were clean. By ingenious magnetic devices, operated from outside the vacuum chamber, Millikan was able to prepare uncontaminated metal surfaces just prior to each set of measurements.

By rotating R, one of the metal blocks could be brought opposite the knife N and a thin shaving of metal removed from the alkali metal. The fresh surface was then rotated 180° into a position directly in line with the light entering the window.

For each different frequency of light admitted to the chamber the velocity or energy of the photoelectrons had to be measured. This was accomplished by collecting the electrons in the cylinder C and measuring the accumulated charge by means of a sensitive electroscope or electrometer B.

By applying a positive potential to the metal block at V+ the electrons would arrive at C with lower speeds owing to the retarding action of the charges. The positive charge on the Na block, for example, attracts the fast ejected electrons, slowing them down.

The velocity with which the electrons leave the metal can therefore be determined by measuring the potential difference V which is just great enough to prevent the electrons from reaching C. This stopping potential, applied between V+ and the ground, can be equated to the photoelectron's ejected energy, by use of Eq.(23j). Replacing q by the electronic charge e, and the energy W by $\frac{1}{2}mv^2$, we obtain

$$Ve = \tfrac{1}{2}mv^2 \tag{43b}$$

In the *MKSA* system, V is in volts, e is in coulombs, m is in kilograms, and v is in meters/second. As we shall see in succeeding chapters this is a very useful and important equation.

43.8. The Photoelectric Threshold

Having made the measurements described in the preceding section, Millikan calculated the photoelectron energies for differ-

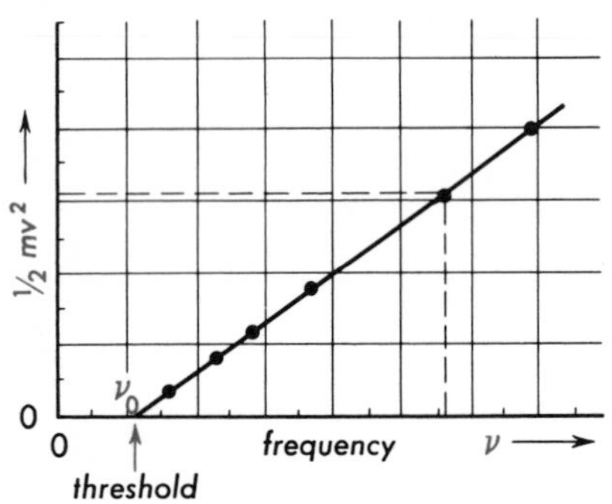

Fig. 43I. Graph showing the energy of photoelectrons ejected by light of different frequencies.

ent frequencies of light, and plotted the results on a graph as shown in Fig. 43I. The point at which the straight line intersects the bottom line determines the threshold frequency ν_0. The photoelectric threshold ν_0 is defined as the frequency of light which, falling on a surface, is just able to liberate electrons without giving the many additional kinetic energy. For such a frequency, the kinetic energy $\frac{1}{2}mv^2$ in Einstein's equation is zero and the energy of the photon is given by

$$W = h\nu_0 \tag{43c}$$

Equation (43a) can therefore be written in the form

$$h\nu = h\nu_0 + \tfrac{1}{2}mv^2 \tag{43d}$$

The meaning of ν_0 in this new equation is quite clear: For frequencies lower than ν_0 electrons are not liberated, whereas for frequencies greater than ν_0 they are ejected with a determined velocity.

The photoelectric threshold for most metals lies in the ultraviolet where the frequencies are relatively high. For the alkali metals the threshold lies in the visible and near-infrared spectrum. In other words, it takes photons of less energy to free electrons from the alkali metals than it does to free them from most other metals.

Since every quantity in Eq.(43d), except h, is a measured quantity, the equation can be solved for h:

$$h = \frac{\frac{1}{2}mv^2}{\nu - \nu_0} \tag{43e}$$

Upon substitution of all measured quantities Millikan obtained the value $h = 6.56 \times 10^{-34}$ joule second. The most recent value accepted for this universal constant is

$$h = 6.6261965 \times 10^{-34} \text{ joule second}$$

Since the frequency of visible green light is about 5.45×10^{14} Hz, the energy in a single photon or quantum of visible light is the product of these two numbers, or 3.611×10^{-19} J. In other words, it would take about 2.769×10^{18} photons to do one joule of work.

It was primarily for his outstanding experimental work in the determination of the value of Planck's constant *h,* and secondarily for his determination of the value of the electronic charge *e,* that Millikan was awarded the Nobel Prize in physics in 1923.

The photon, in ejecting an electron from a metal surface as in the photoelectric effect, disappears completely, i.e., it is annihilated. It has become common practice to specify the *work function* of a metal in volts. Since W in Eq.(43a) is in joules, and the kinetic energy of the photoelectrons is given by Eq.(43b), we write

$$V_0 e = h\nu_0 \tag{43f}$$

where e is the electronic charge in coulombs, ν_0 is the frequency of light at the photoelectric threshold in Hz, and V_0 is in volts.

Example 1. Ultraviolet light with a wavelength of 3650 Å falls on a metal plate, causing the emission of photoelectrons with a velocity of 5.440×10^5 m/s. Calculate (a) the frequency of the photoelectric threshold, (b) the corresponding wavelength, and (c) the work function of the metal in volts. Use atomic constants to four significant figures.

Solution. The given quantities are $\lambda = 3.650 \times 10^{-7}$ m, $v = 5.440 \times 10^5$ m/s, $h = 6.626 \times 10^{-34}$ Js, $e = 1.6022 \times 10^{-19}$ C, $c = 2.9979 \times 10^8$ m/s, and $m = 9.110 \times 10^{-31}$ Kg. We first find the frequency of the incident light by using the wave equation, $c = \nu\lambda$:

$$\nu = \frac{c}{\lambda} = \frac{2.9979 \times 10^8 \text{ m/s}}{3.650 \times 10^{-7}}$$

$$\nu = 8.213 \times 10^{14} \text{ Hz}$$

We next use the photoelectric Eq.(43d), which, solving for ν_0 and substituting known quantities, gives

$$\nu_0 = \nu - \frac{mv^2}{2h}$$

$$\nu_0 = 8.213 \times 10^{14} - \frac{9.110 \times 10^{-31} \times (5.440 \times 10^5)^2}{2 \times 6.626 \times 10^{-34}}$$

$$\nu_0 = 8.213 \times 10^{14} - 2.0344 \times 10^{14}$$

$$\nu_0 = 6.179 \times 10^{14} \text{ Hz}$$

Using the wave equation we find for the wavelength

$$\lambda_0 = \frac{c}{\nu_0} = \frac{2.9979 \times 10^8}{6.179 \times 10^{14}}$$

$$\lambda_0 = 4.852 \times 10^{-7} \text{ m} = 4852 \text{ Å} \quad \text{(green)}$$

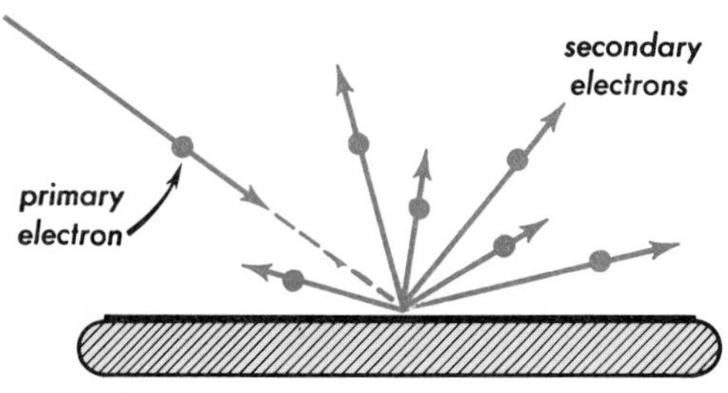

Fig. 43J. The impact of a single electron liberates additional electrons from a metal surface.

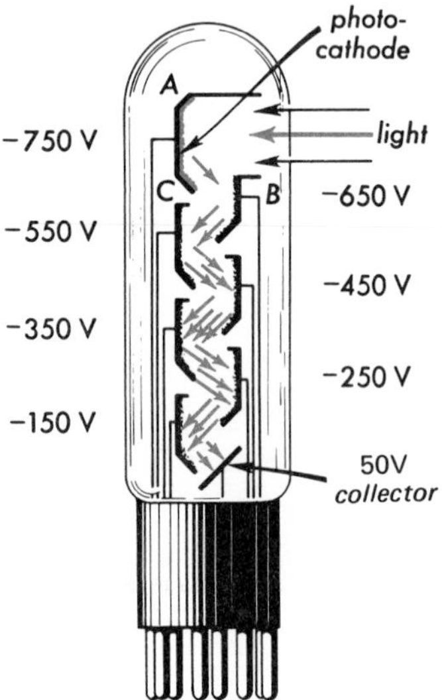

Fig. 43K. Photomultiplier tube with six stages. Cesium oxide, silver-coated photocathode.

To find the work function in volts, use Eq.(43f). Solving for V_0, and substituting, we find

$$V_0 = \frac{h\nu_0}{e} = \frac{6.626 \times 10^{-34} \times 6.179 \times 10^{14}}{1.6022 \times 10^{-19}}$$

$$V_0 = 2.5554 \text{ V}$$

43.9. Secondary Electrons

When electrons strike the surface of a metal plate, they knock additional electrons free from the surface. These are called *secondary electrons* and the process is called *secondary emission* (see Fig. 43J). As the speed of a primary or incident electron increases from zero to a few hundred volts, the number of secondaries increases toward a definite maximum. For most metal surfaces, this maximum is in the neighborhood of two, while for certain alkali metal films it may be as great as eight or ten. In general, it is greatest for surfaces having a *low work function.*

43.10. Photomultiplier Tubes

The process of secondary electron emission is widely used in a special type of photoelectric cell used most effectively in detecting faint light. A cross-sectional diagram of such a photomultiplier tube is given in Fig. 43K.

The number of photoelectrons from the photocathode A is proportional to the intensity of the incident light. These are attracted toward the next plate B, more positive by 100 V, where upon impact additional electrons are liberated. Attracted to the next more-positive plate C, still more electrons are liberated. By the time the collector plate has been reached, a small avalanche of electrons has developed, and a correspondingly large charge and current are led off through that electrode to a suitable recording device.

If each electron on impact releases n secondaries, then, in a tube with k stages, the number arriving at the collector would be n^k:

$$N = n^k \qquad (43g)$$

Example 2. A photomultiplier tube has one cathode, seven dynodes, and one collector electrode. If the multiplication factor for each dynode and the collector averages 4.50 electrons find the overall amplification of the device.

Solution. The given quantities are $n = 8.0$, and $k = 4.50$ electrons. By direct substitution in Eq.(43g), we find

$$N = n^k = 8.0^{4.50}$$

To find the answer we may use a log-log slide rule, and upon multiplying obtain

$$N = 11{,}585 \text{ electrons}$$

or we may take the logarithm of both sides of the equation, a calculator and write

$$\log N = \log 8.0^{4.50}$$

$$\log N = 4.50 \times \log 8.0$$

Looking up the log 8.0 in Appendix IX, we find 0.90309:

$$\log N = 4.50 \times 0.90309 = 4.0639$$

From Appendix IX, the number whose logarithm is 0.0639 is 1.1585, and with the whole number 4, we move the decimal point four places to the right:

$$N = 11{,}585 \text{ electrons}$$

This is an enormous gain over the signal obtained from a standard phototube. Photomultiplier tubes have been used most successfully with faint light, not only visible but infrared and ultraviolet as well.

problems

1. Find the energy (a) in joules and (b) in volts of a photon of green light if its wavelength is 5500 Å.

2. A photon of ultraviolet light has a wavelength of 2.640×10^{-7} m. Find its energy in (a) joules and (b) volts.

3. Ultraviolet light of wavelength 3500 Å falls on a

metal plate, which releases photoelectrons with a velocity of 6.75×10^5 m/s. Find the photoelectric threshold (a) frequency, and (b) wavelength. (c) Find the work function in volts. [Ans. (a) 5.43×10^{14} Hz, (b) 5517 Å, (c) 2.247 V.]

4. Visible violet light of wavelength 4150 Å falls on a metal plate, which then emits photoelectrons with a velocity of 2.750×10^5 m/s. Find (a) the frequency of the photoelectric threshold, and (b) its corresponding wavelength. (c) Find the work function in volts.

5. Light falls on a metal plate, emitting photoelectrons with a velocity of 6.25×10^5 m/s. If the photoelectric threshold is at $\lambda = 4250$ Å, find (a) the frequency and (b) the wavelength of the incident light, and (c) the work function in volts.

6.* Extreme ultraviolet radiation of short wavelength falls on a metal plate emitting electrons with a velocity of 2.55×10^6 m/s. If the work function is 2.680 V, what is (a) the frequency and (b) the wavelength of the incident radiation? Find (c) the frequency and (d) the wavelength of the photoelectric threshold. [Ans. (a) 5.12×10^{15} Hz, (b) 586 Å, (c) 6.48×10^{14} Hz, (d) 4630 Å.]

7.* If ultraviolet light of wavelength 3650 Å falls on a metal plate, whose work function is 2.450 V, find the velocity of the photoelectrons emitted.

8.* Photoelectrons with a velocity of 5.76×10^5 m/s are emitted by a metal surface whose work function is 3.620 V. Find (a) the frequency and (b) the wavelength of the photoelectric threshold. Find also (c) the frequency and (d) the wavelength of the incident radiation.

9. An eight-stage photomultiplier tube has an overall amplification factor of 14,500. Find the amplification factor per stage. [Ans. 4.61.]

10. A photomultiplier has ten dynodes and a collector. Each stage has a multiplication factor of 5.20 electrons. Find the overall multiplication of the tube.

11. A nine stage photomultiplier tube with a collector has an overall amplification factor of 18,700. Find the multiplication factor per stage.

12. If the overall amplification factor of a photomultiplier tube is 25,000, and it has eight dynodes and one collector, what is the average magnification factor per dynode? [Ans. 3.55.]

44 The structure of atoms

Early in the twentieth century, while Einstein was working out his special theory of relativity, J. J. Thomson proposed a type of electron shell structure for all atoms. His model structures were worked out by mathematics from Coulomb's law for charged particles and soon became known as the *"plumb-pudding atom."*

44.1. The Thomson Atom

Thomson visualized all of the positive charge of an atom as being spread out uniformly throughout a sphere about 10^{-10} m in diameter, with the electrons as smaller particles distributed in shells somewhat as shown in Fig. 44A. While the net force exerted by the positively charged sphere on each electron is toward the center of the sphere, the electrons mutually repel each other and form shells.

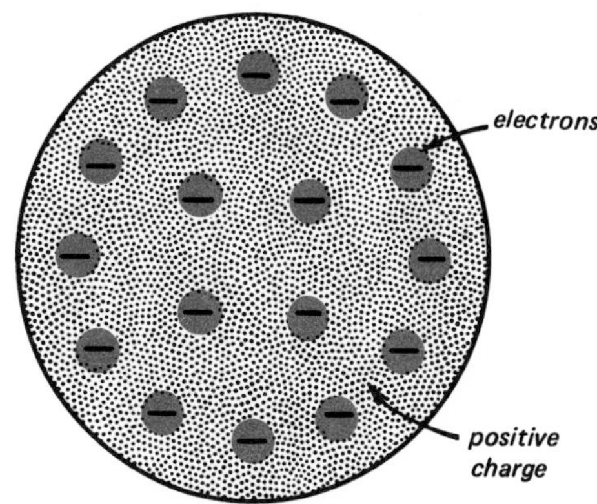

Fig. 44A. Diagram of the Thomson atom model.

An excellent demonstration of the tendency to form rings for a two-dimensional model is shown in Fig. 44B. A glass dish 15 to 25 cm in diameter is wound with about 30 turns of No. 14 insulated copper wire. The most common steel sewing needles are then mounted in small corks (8 mm diameter and 8 mm long) as shown at the left, and magnetized by stroking from top to bottom with the N pole of a strong alnico magnet.

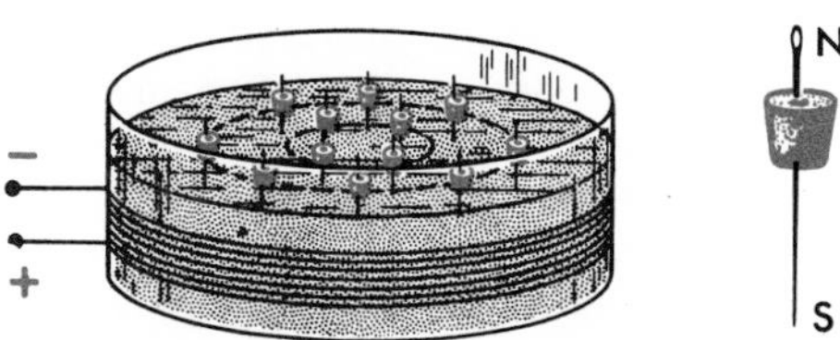

Fig. 44B. Floating needles in a magnetic field demonstrating the electron shell structure of the Thomson atom.

With water in the dish, and a current of 1 to 2 A through the coil, a single needle is placed upright in the water. Released, it will migrate to the center where the magnetic field is strongest. The addition of needles, one after another, near the edge of the dish, will result in the formation of geometrically symmetrical patterns and rings.

An increase or decrease in current will cause any given pattern to shrink or expand, corresponding to a greater or lesser positive charge. The stability of such ring patterns undoubtedly influenced the later extension by Bohr and Stoner of the quantized orbit model of the hydrogen atom to all atoms.

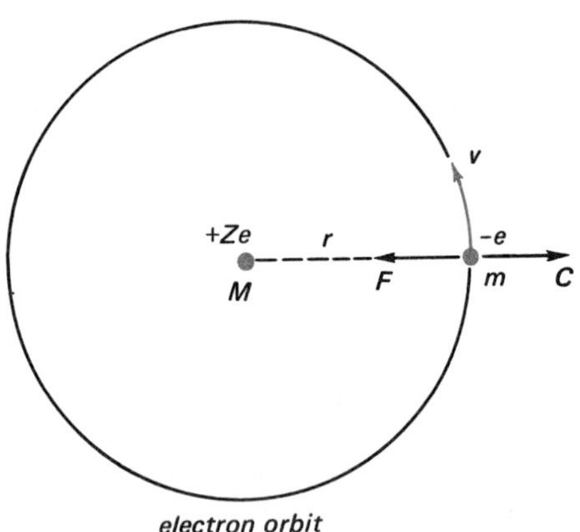

Fig. 44C. Orbital diagram of the hydrogen atom according to the Bohr theory.

44.2. Bohr's Theory of the Hydrogen Atom

In 1913 Niels Bohr* proposed a theory of the hydrogen atom that marked the beginning of a new era in the history of physics. With his theory, Bohr gave not only a satisfactory explanation of the Balmer series of hydrogen but a model for the structure of all other atoms as well.

Starting with what should be the simplest of all atoms, Bohr assumed that a hydrogen atom, atomic number $Z = 1$, consists of a nucleus with one positive charge $+e$ and a single electron of charge $-e$ revolving around it in a circular orbit of radius r (see Fig. 44C). Because it is 1836 times heavier that the electron, the nucleus could be assumed at rest.

To keep the electron in its orbit and prevent it from spiraling in toward the nucleus, or away from it to escape, Bohr next assumed that the inward centripetal force is due to, and therefore is, the inward electrostatic force F. From dynamics we know that the centripetal force is mv^2/r, and from Coulomb's law, Eq.(21a), the electrostatic force is $kZee/r^2$. Equating these two, we obtain

$$m\frac{v^2}{r} = k\frac{Zee}{r^2} \qquad (44a)$$

In the *MKSA* system of units,

m is in kilograms
v is in meters/second
e is in coulombs
r is in meters
Z is the atomic number
$k = 9 \times 10^9$ newton meter^2/coulomb^2

At this point Bohr introduced his second assumption, *the quantum hypothesis.* The electron, he assumed, cannot move in any sized orbit, stable under the conditions of the equation above, but in just certain *definite and discrete orbits.* The sizes of these orbits are governed by Eq.(44a) and the rule that the *angular momentum of the electron in its orbit is equal to an integer n times a constant h divided by 2π:*

$$mvr = n\frac{h}{2\pi} \qquad (44b)$$

$$n = 1, 2, 3, 4, 5, \ldots$$

*Niels Bohr (1885–1962), Danish physicist, was born at Copenhagen, the son of Christian Bohr, professor of physiology at the University of Copenhagen. After taking his Ph.D. degree at Copenhagen in 1911, he studied for one year under J. J. Thomson at Cambridge, and one year under Ernest Rutherford at Manchester. Returning to Copenhagen in 1913, with the results of the Rutherford scattering experiments fresh in his mind, he worked out and published his now famous theory of the hydrogen atom. In 1920 Bohr was appointed head of the Institute for Theoretical Physics at the University of Copenhagen. In 1921 he was awarded the Hughes Medal of the Royal Society, and in 1922 the Nobel Prize in physics.

In this equation, n is called the principal *quantum number* and, because it can take whole number values only, it fixes the sizes of the allowed orbits. To find the radii of these "Bohr circular orbits," Eq.(44b) is solved for v, then squared and substituted in Eq.(44a) to give

$$r = \frac{n^2h^2}{4\pi^2me^2Zk} \tag{44c}$$

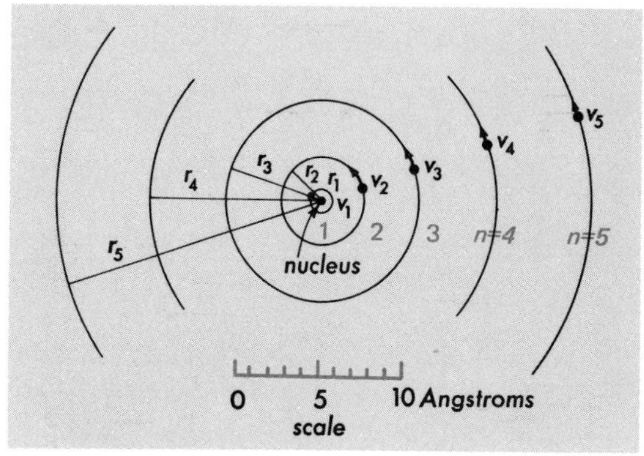

Fig. 44D. Scale diagram of the Bohr circular orbit of hydrogen.

If we put into this equation the known values of the constants e, m, h, Z, and k,

$$e = -1.602192 \times 10^{-19}\ \text{C}$$

$$m = 9.10956 \times 10^{-31}\ \text{Kg}$$

$$h = 6.62620 \times 10^{-34}\ \text{Js}$$

$$Z = 1.0$$

$$k = 8.98755 \times 10^{9}\ \text{Nm}^2/\text{C}^2$$

the orbits shown in Fig. 44D are calculated. The innermost orbit, with $n = 1$, $Z = 1$, has a radius $r = 0.529 \times 10^{-10}$ m, or 0.529 Å, and a diameter of 1.058 Å. More accurately,

$$r_1 = 0.529177 \times 10^{-10}\ \text{m} \tag{44d}$$

The second orbit is four times larger, and the third is nine times, etc. The constant h is *Planck's constant.*

The speed of the electron, when it is in any one orbit, can be determined from Eqs.(44b) and (44c). By substituting the value of r from Eq.(44c) in Eq.(44b) and solving for the speed v, we obtain

$$v = k\frac{2\pi e^2Z}{nh} \tag{44e}$$

In the innermost orbit, $n = 1$, $Z = 1$, the speed v is $\frac{1}{137}$ the speed of light. In the second orbit the speed is only $\frac{1}{2}$ as great, and in the third only $\frac{1}{3}$ as great, etc. With such small orbits and such high speeds, the number of revolutions per second becomes very high.

Since the circumference of any circular orbit is $2\pi r$, the frequency with which an electron goes around each orbit is given by

$$f = \frac{v}{2\pi r} \tag{44f}$$

In the second Bohr circular orbit, the frequency is calculated to be 10^{15} rps. This, by comparison with the frequency of visible light waves, is of the same order of magnitude.

It should be noted that the one and only electron in each hydrogen atom can occupy only one orbit at any one time. If the electron changes its orbit, it must move to one of the allowed orbits and never stop in between.

Since all the factors in Eq.(44c) are atomic constants, the equation for the radius of any orbit can be written in the simple form

$$r = r_1 \frac{n^2}{Z} \tag{44g}$$

and the velocity by the equally simple form

$$v = \frac{v_1 Z}{n} \tag{44h}$$

where $$v_1 = 2.18768 \times 10^6 \text{ m/s}$$

Example 1. A number of hydrogen atoms in a rarified gas may have their electrons excited to orbits of high quantum number n. Find (a) the radius, and (b) the speed of the electron in an atom where n is equal to 95. Use three significant figures.

Solution. The given quantities are $n = 95$, $r_1 = 0.529 \times 10^{-10}$ m, $Z = 1$, and $v_1 = 2.188 \times 10^6$ m/s. By direct substitution in Eq. (44g), we find

$$r = 0.529 \times 10^{-10} \text{ m} \times (95)^2$$

$$r = 4.77 \times 10^{-7} \text{ m}$$

and by direct substitution in Eq.(44h), we find

$$v = \frac{2.188 \times 10^6 \text{ m/s}}{95}$$

$$v = 2.303 \times 10^4 \text{ m/s}$$

44.3. Electron Jumps

Bohr's third and final assumption regarding the hydrogen atom concerns the emission of light. Bohr postulated that light is not emitted by an electron when it is moving in one of its fixed orbits, but only when the electron jumps from one orbit to another, as illustrated in Fig. 44E. Bohr said that the frequency of this light is not determined by the frequency of revolution but by the difference in energy between the initial and final orbit,

$$E_2 - E_1 = h\nu \tag{44i}$$

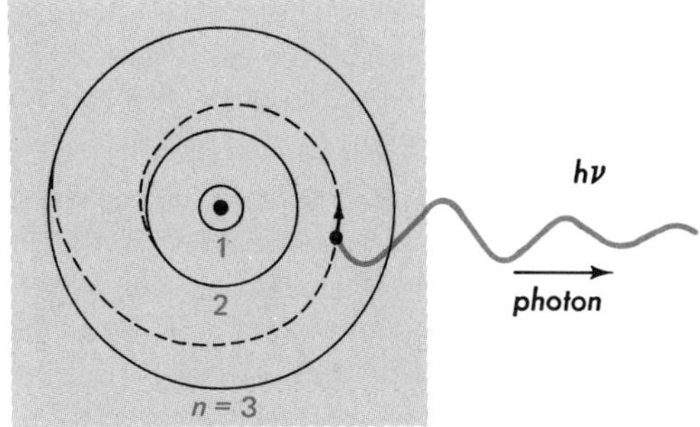

Fig. 44E. Schematic diagram of Bohr's quantum hypothesis of the radiation of light from a hydrogen atom.

where E_2 is the energy of the *initial orbit,* E_1 the energy of the *final orbit,* h is Planck's constant, and ν is the frequency of the light.

To illustrate this, let E_1, E_2, E_3, E_4, etc., represent the total energy of the electron when it is in the orbits $n = 1, 2, 3, 4$, etc., respectively. When, for example, the electron is in orbit $n = 3$ where its energy is E_3, and it jumps to orbit $n = 2$ where the energy is E_2 (see Fig. 44E), the energy difference $E_3 - E_2$ is ejected from the atom in the form of a light wave of energy $h\nu$ called a *photon.* Here, then, is the origin of light waves from within the atom.

44.4. Bohr's Success

The success of Bohr's theory is not to be attributed so much to the mechanical picture or model of the atom just proposed, but rather to the development of an equation that agrees exactly with experimental observations.

By combining the equations presented in the preceding section, Bohr derived an equation for the frequency ν of the light waves emitted by hydrogen atoms. This equation is

$$\nu = 3.28984 \times 10^{15}\ \text{Hz}\left(\frac{1}{n_1^2} - \frac{1}{n_2^2}\right) \tag{44j}$$

where n_1 and n_2 represent the *principal quantum numbers* of two orbits.

If we introduce the wave equation, valid for all waves,

$$c = \nu\lambda \tag{44k}$$

and replace ν by c/λ in Eq.(44j) it can be written

$$\lambda = 911.267\ \text{Å}\left(\frac{n_2^2 \times n_1^2}{n_2^2 - n_1^2}\right) \tag{44ℓ}$$

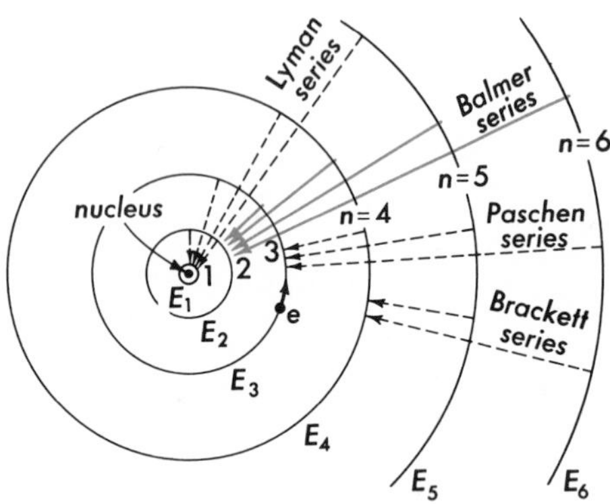

Fig. 44F. Diagram of the Bohr circular orbits of hydrogen showing the various electron jumps that give rise to the emission of light waves of different frequency.

where λ is the wavelength of the light in angstroms, n_2 is the quantum number of any orbit of the hydrogen atom in which an electron is confined, and n_1 is the quantum number of the orbit to which the electron jumps to emit light of wavelength λ.

Bohr found that, if in Eq.(44ℓ) he placed $n_1 = 2$ and $n_2 = 3$, the calculated wavelength $\lambda = 6564.7$ Å is obtained, which is extremely close to the measured wavelength of the red spectrum line of hydrogen. If he placed $n_1 = 2$ and $n_2 = 4$, the calculated wavelength agreed exactly with the measured wavelength of the blue-green spectrum line of hydrogen.

In fact, the entire series of lines in the hydrogen spectrum are exactly represented by Eq.(44ℓ), by setting $n_1 = 2$ and $n_2 = 3$, 4, 5, 6, etc. This series of lines, so prominently displayed by the sun and stars, as well as by any hydrogen discharge tube in the laboratory, is known as the *Balmer series* (see Sec. 37.14).

These quantum-number changes correspond, as shown in Fig. 44F, to an electron jumping from any outer orbit n to the next to the smallest orbit $n = 2$. In any high-voltage electrical discharge in a glass tube containing hydrogen gas, many thousands of atoms may each have their one and only electron jumping from orbit 3 to 2, while in many atoms the electron may be jumping from other orbits to $n = 2$. Hence, upon observing the light through a spectroscope, one may observe the entire Balmer series of lines.

44.5. Bohr's Predicted Series

Bohr's orbital model of the hydrogen atom not only accounts for the Balmer series of hydrogen, but also for many other observed lines as well.

By substituting $n_1 = 1$ and $n_2 = 2$, 3, 4, etc., in Eq.(44ℓ), one obtains a series of spectrum lines in the ultraviolet region of the spectrum. These lines were first photographed by T. Lyman of Harvard University, and the wavelengths are found to check exactly with calculations. This series, now called the Lyman series, which can only be photographed in a vacuum spectrograph, is reproduced in Fig. 44G. On the orbital picture of Fig. 44F, the Lyman series of lines arises from electron jumps from any outer orbit directly to the innermost orbit, the *normal state.*

If, in Eq.(44l), n_1 is set equal to 3 and n_2 to 4, 5, 6, etc., the calculated frequencies predict spectrum lines in the infrared spectrum. These lines were first looked for and observed, exactly as predicted, by F. Paschen; the series is now known by his name. Another series of lines arising from electron jumps, ending on orbit $n = 4$, was predicted and observed in the far infrared by

Brackett, and a fifth series still farther out in the infrared, ending on orbit $n = 5$, was first observed by Pfund.

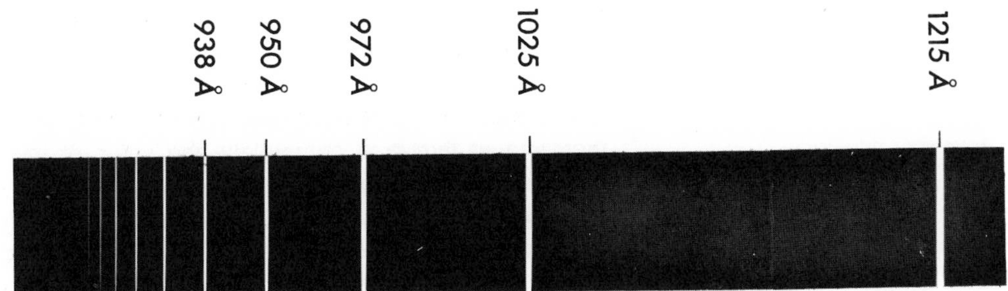

Lyman series of hydrogen

Fig. 44G. Photograph of the extreme ultraviolet series of hydrogen, predicted by Bohr's theory and first observed by Lyman.

Example 2. The wavelengths of all the known series of spectrum lines in hydrogen are given by Eq.(44ℓ), Calculate the wavelengths of the first line of (a) the Lyman series, (b) the Balmer series, (c) the Paschen series, (d) the Brackett series, and (e) the Pfund series.

Solution. The given quantities are for the electron jump from (a) $n = 2$ to $n = 1$, (b) $n = 3$ to $n = 2$, (c) $n = 4$ to $n = 3$, (d) $n = 5$ to $n = 4$, and (e) $n = 6$ to $n = 5$. By direct substitutions in Eq.(44ℓ), we obtain

$$\lambda = 911.267 \text{ Å} \left(\frac{4 \times 1}{4 - 1}\right) = 1215.0 \text{ Å}$$

$$\lambda = 911.267 \text{ Å} \left(\frac{9 \times 4}{9 - 4}\right) = 6561.1 \text{ Å}$$

$$\lambda = 911.267 \text{ Å} \left(\frac{16 \times 9}{16 - 9}\right) = 18{,}746.1 \text{ Å}$$

$$\lambda = 911.267 \text{ Å} \left(\frac{25 \times 16}{25 - 16}\right) = 40{,}500.8 \text{ Å}$$

$$\lambda = 911.267 \text{ Å} \left(\frac{36 \times 25}{36 - 25}\right) = 74{,}558.2 \text{ Å}$$

44.6. Normal and Excited Atoms

When the single electron of a hydrogen atom is in the innermost orbit, $n = 1$, the atom is said to be in its normal state or ground level. As the name implies, this is the condition of most free hydrogen atoms in a gas under normal room temperature and pressure. If an electrical discharge is sent through a vessel containing hydrogen gas, cathode rays (electrons) moving at high speed make frequent collisions with electrons, knocking some of them out of the atom completely and some of them into one of the outer allowed orbits, $n = 2, 3, 4$, etc.

When the electron is completely removed from the atom, the atom is said to be *ionized;* whereas when it is forced into an outer orbit, the atom is said to be *excited.* Once in an excited state, an atom will not remain that way long, for the electron under the attraction by the nucleus will jump to an inner orbit. By jumping to an inner orbit, the electron loses all or part of the energy it had gained.

When an electron is in an excited state, it does not necessarily return to the innermost orbit by a single jump, but may return by several jumps, thereby emitting several different light waves, or quanta.

44.7. Energy Levels

By combining Bohr's equations, Eqs.(44a) and (44b), the energy of an electron in a circular orbit of the hydrogen atom can be calculated. The total energy is just the sum of the kinetic energy $\frac{1}{2}mv^2$, and the potential energy (see Sec. 23.5):

$$E_t = E_k + E_p \tag{44m}$$

To find the potential energy of the electron in its orbit we use Eq.(23p). By this equation we see that the potential V, at any point at a distance r from the nuclear charge Ze is given by

$$V = k\,\frac{Ze}{r}$$

Since V is the work done per unit charge in carrying any charge from a distance r out to infinity, one must multiply by the electron's charge $-e$ to obtain as the stored potential energy, $-Ve$:

$$E_p = -k\,\frac{Ze^2}{r}$$

Using Eq.(44a) we can show the kinetic energy to be expressed as follows:

$$E_k = \tfrac{1}{2}mv^2 = k\,\frac{Ze^2}{2r}$$

We thus have the two forms of stored energy. Substituting these values of E_k and E_p in Eq.(44m) and the value of r from Eq.(44c), we obtain, as Bohr did,

$$E_t = -\frac{2\pi^2 me^4 Z^2 k^2}{n^2 h^2} \tag{44n}$$

The minus sign signifies that one must do work on the electron to remove it from the atom.

With the exception of the principal quantum number n, all quantities in this equation are the same for all orbits. We can therefore write

$$E_t = -R\,\frac{Z^2}{n^2} \tag{44o}$$

where R is constant and equal to

$$R = \frac{2\pi^2 me^4 k^2}{h^2}$$

which, upon substitution of the known values of all the constants, gives

$$R = 2.179914 \times 10^{-18} \text{ joules} \tag{44p}$$

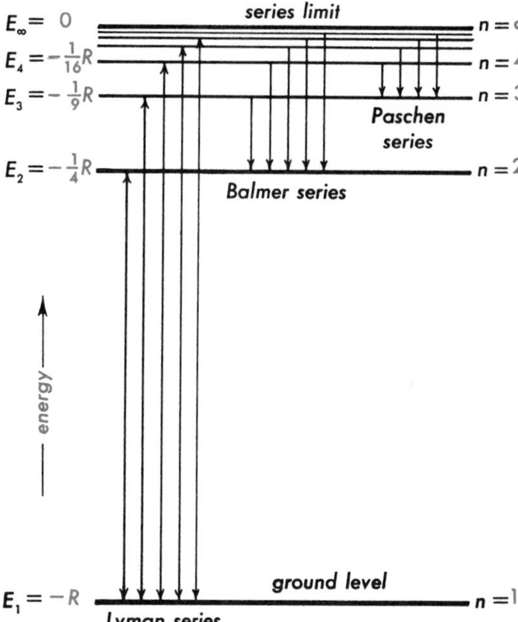

Fig. 44H. Energy-level diagram for the hydrogen atom. Vertical arrows represent electron jumps.

Equation (44o) is an important equation in atomic structure, for it gives the energy of the electron when it occupies any one of the different orbits of the hydrogen atom. Instead of drawing orbits to the scale of their radius as in Fig. 44D, it is customary to draw horizontal lines to an energy scale, as shown in Fig. 44H. This is called an *energy-level diagram.* The various electron jumps between the allowed orbits of Fig. 44F now become vertical arrows between the energy levels.

The importance of this kind of diagram is to be attributed to Bohr's third relation, Eq.(44i), where the energy $h\nu$ of each radiated light wave is just equal to the difference between two energies. The energy of each radiated photon is, therefore, proportional to the length of its corresponding arrow.

The first line of the Balmer series $\lambda = 6561$ Å, the red line in Figs. 37D and 37N, corresponds to the short arrow, $n = 3$ to $n = 2$. The second line of the same series is the blue-green line $\lambda = 4861$ Å, and corresponds to the slightly longer arrow, $n = 4$ to $n = 2$, etc.:

$$E_2 - E_1 = -R\left(\frac{1}{n_2^2} - \frac{1}{n_1^2}\right) = h\nu \tag{44q}$$

When an electrical discharge is sent through hydrogen gas, each atom, by collision with other atoms, has its only electron excited to an upper level, and then that electron jumps down again from one level to another, giving rise to the emission of light waves. If, as another experiment, a whole continuous spectrum of light waves is sent through a tube containing hydrogen gas, the hydrogen atoms will be in the ground level, $n = 1$, and by *resonance* may absorb frequencies corresponding to any one of the Lyman series. In absorbing one of these frequencies, the electron of that atom will jump to an upper energy level. The arrowheads at the top of these vertical lines, correspond, therefore, to resonance absorption. Those same excited electrons can then return by downward jumps, emitting light, and stopping finally on the ground level.

Resonance absorption is the explanation of the dark lines of the sodium spectrum shown in Fig. 37H and the solar spectrum in Fig. 37J.

Example 3. Calculate (a) the frequency, and (b) the wavelength of the second line of the Balmer series of hydrogen using Eq. (44q). Use constants with five significant figures.

Solution. The known quantities are $R = 2.17991 \times 10^{-18}$ J, $h = 6.6262 \times 10^{-34}$ Js, $n_2 = 4$, and $n_1 = 2$. Solving Eq.(44q) for the frequency ν and substituting known quantities, we obtain

$$\nu = -\frac{R}{h}\left(\frac{1}{n_2^2} - \frac{1}{n_1^2}\right) = -\frac{2.17991 \times 10^{-18}}{6.6262 \times 10^{-34}}\left(\frac{1}{16} - \frac{1}{4}\right)$$

$$\nu = 6.1684 \times 10^{14} \text{ Hz}$$

and by use of the wave equation, $c = \nu\lambda$, we obtain

$$\lambda = \frac{c}{\nu} = \frac{2.99793 \times 10^{8}}{6.1684 \times 10^{14}} = 4.8601 \times 10^{-7} \text{ m}$$

$$\lambda = 4860.1 \text{ Å}$$

44.8. Bohr-Stoner Scheme of the Building-Up of Atoms

Bohr and Stoner proposed an extension of the orbital model of hydrogen to include all of the chemical elements. As shown by the examples in Fig. 44l, each atom is composed of a positively charged nucleus with a number of electrons around it.

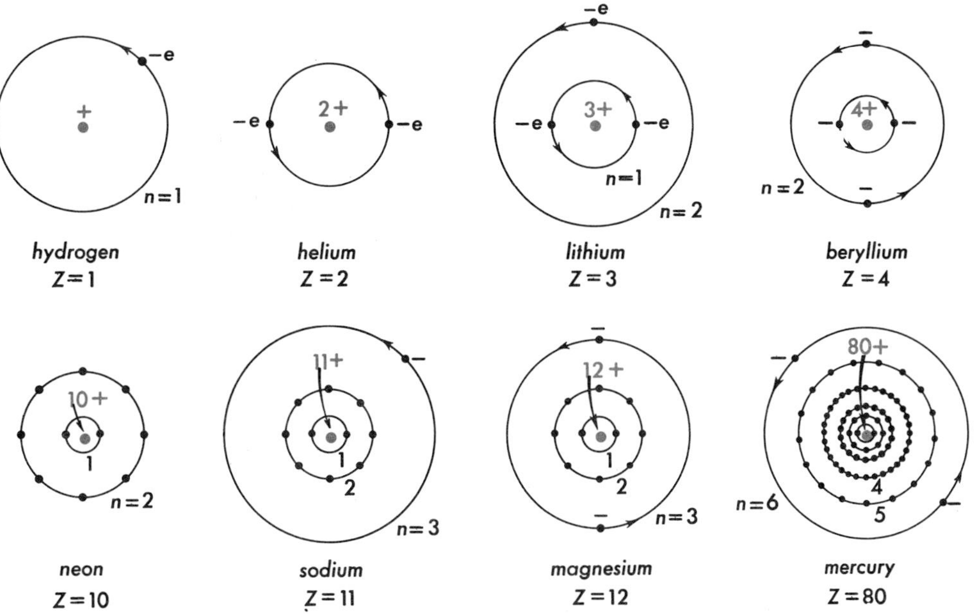

Fig. 44l. Bohr–Stoner orbital models for the light and heavy atoms of the periodic table.

Although the nucleus is a relatively small particle less than 10^{-14} m in diameter, it contains almost the entire mass of the atom, a mass equal in *atomic mass units* to the *atomic weight.*

The positive charge carried by the nucleus is equal numerically to the atomic number, and it determines the number of electrons located in orbits outside.

A helium atom, atomic number $Z = 2$, has two positive charges on the nucleus and two electrons outside. A lithium atom, atomic number $Z = 3$, contains three positive charges on the nucleus and three electrons outside. A mercury atom, atomic number 80, contains 80 positive charges on the nucleus and 80 electrons outside.

The orbits to which the electrons are confined are the Bohr orbits of hydrogen with $n = 1, 2, 3$, etc., and are called electron shells. Going from element to element in the atomic table, starting with hydrogen, electrons are added one after the other, filling one shell and then another. A shell is filled only when it contains a number of electrons given by $2n^2$. To illustrate this, the first shell $n =$ is filled when it has 2 electrons, the second shell $n = 2$ when it has 8 electrons, the third shell $n = 3$ when it has 18 electrons, etc. $2 \times 1^2 = 2$, $2 \times 2^2 = 8$, $2 \times 3^2 = 18$, etc.:

quantum number}	$n = 1$	$n = 2$	$n = 3$	$n = 4$
number of electrons}	2	8	18	32

Among the heavier elements there are several departures from the order in which the shells are filled. Although these departures are not important from the present standpoint, their nature is illustrated by the mercury atom (Fig. 44I). The four inner shells, $n = 1$, 2, 3, and 4, are entirely filled with 2, 8, 18, and 32 electrons, respectively, while the fifth shell contains only 18 electrons and the sixth shell 2 electrons. The reasons for such departures are well understood and are now known to follow another rule and will be shown in the next section.

It is important to note that, as the nuclear charge increases and additional electrons are added in outer shells, the inner shells, under the stronger attraction of the nucleus, shrink in size. The net result of this shrinkage is that the heaviest elements in the periodic table are not much larger in diameter than the lighter elements. The schematic diagrams in Fig. 44I are drawn approximately to the same scale.

The experimental confirmation of these upper limits to the allowed number of electrons in each shell is now considered one of the most fundamental principles of nature. A sound theoretical explanation of this principle of atomic structure was first given by W. Pauli, in 1925, and is commonly referred to as the *Pauli* exclusion principle.*

***Wolfgang Pauli (1900–1958), Austrian physicist, was born in Vienna, April 25, 1900, and awarded the Nobel Prize in physics for the discovery of the exclusion principle, which carries his name. He received his early education in Vienna, took his Ph.D. degree under Arnold Sommerfeld at Munich in 1921, and served as assistant to Max Born at the University of Göttingen. He served as professor of theoretical physics at the Federal Institute of Technology in Zurich, Switzerland, and visiting professor at the Institute for Advanced Study at Princeton, N.J., in 1931, University of Michigan in 1931 and 1941, and Purdue University in 1942. In 1946, he became a naturalized U.S. citizen. Pauli was the first to propose the existence of the neutrino, a small weightless, chargeless atomic particle that travels with the speed of light. The author is privileged to have met and heard W. Pauli speak on several occasions.**

44.9. Elliptical Orbits

Within only a few months after Bohr (in Denmark) published a report telling of his phenomenal success in explaining the hydrogen spectrum with circular orbits, Sommerfeld (in Germany) extended the theory to include elliptical orbits as well. Because these orbits played such an important role in later developments in atomic structure, they deserve some attention here.

The net result of Sommerfeld's theory showed that the electron in any one of the allowed energy levels of a hydrogen atom may move in any one of a number of orbits. For each energy level

$n = 1$, $n = 2$, $n = 3$, etc., as shown in Fig. 44H, there are n possible orbits.

Diagrams of the allowed orbits for the first three energy levels are shown in Fig. 44J. For $n = 3$, for example, there are three orbits, with designations $\ell = 2$, $\ell = 1$, and $\ell = 0$. The diameter of the circular orbit is given by Bohr's theory, and this is just equal to the major axes of the two elliptical orbits. The minor axes are $\frac{2}{3}$ and $\frac{1}{3}$ of the major axis.

It is common practice to assign letters to the ℓ values as follows:

$\ell = 0$	$\ell = 1$	$\ell = 2$	$\ell = 3$	$\ell = 4$
s	p	d	f	g

According to this system, the circular orbit with $n = 3$ and $\ell = 2$ is designated $3d$, while the elliptical orbit $n = 2$ and $\ell = 0$ is designated $2s$, etc. n is the *principal quantum number* and ℓ is the *orbital quantum number.* All orbits having the same value of n have the same total energy, the energy given by Bohr's equation for circular orbits, Eq.(44o).

Each of the allowed orbits of the Bohr–Sommerfeld model of the hydrogen atom becomes a subshell into which electrons are added to build up the elements of the periodic table in the Bohr–Stoner scheme. These subshells are tabulated as follows:

	n \ ℓ	subshells 0	1	2	3	4
	1	$1s$				
	2	$2s$	$2p$			
shells	3	$3s$	$3p$	$3d$		
	4	$4s$	$4p$	$4d$	$4f$	
	5	$5s$	$5p$	$5d$	$5f$	$5g$

The maximum number of electrons allowed in any one subshell is given by the relation

$$2(2\ell + 1)$$

This is called the *Pauli exclusion principle,* each subshell being filled when it contains the following number of electrons:

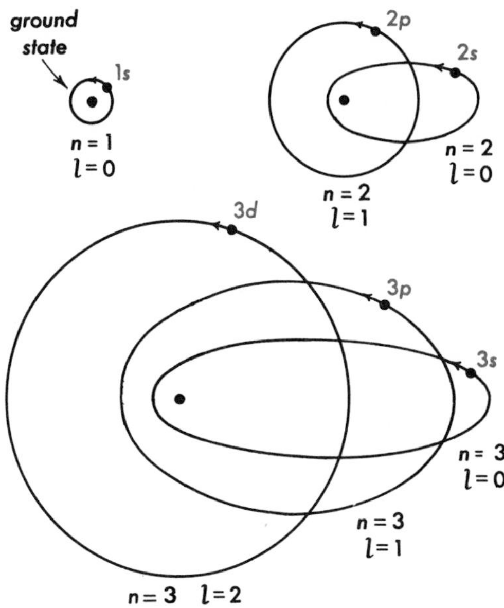

Fig. 44J. Electron orbitals for the hydrogen atom according to the Bohr–Sommerfeld theory.

$\ell = 0$	1	2	3	4
Subshell s	p	d	f	g
Number of electrons 2	6	10	14	18

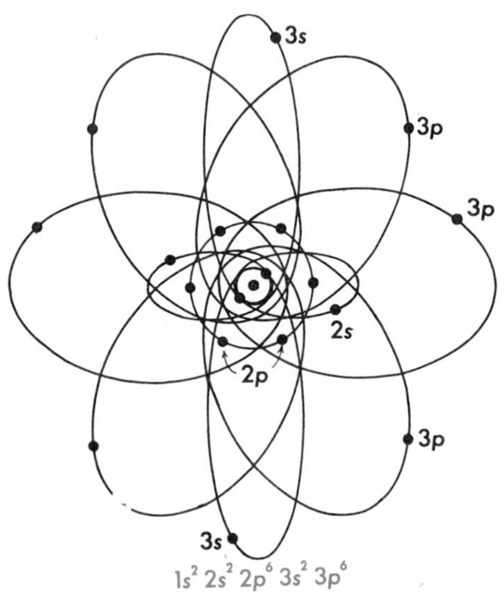

Fig. 44K. Electron configuration for an argon atom: $Z = 18$.

An orbital diagram of an argon atom is given in Fig. 44K. The electron configuration is given below, the exponents specifying the total number of electrons in that subshell. Because such elliptical orbits are not easily drawn, it is customary to group all subshells of the same n value together and show them in rings as in Fig. 44I.

A complete table of subshell buildup of all the known elements is given in Appendix V. The rules for the filling of subshells, and ones that hold throughout the periodic table are the following:

1. *Subshells are grouped under like values of* $n + \ell$.
2. *Groups are filled in the order of increasing* $n + \ell$.
3. *Within each* $n + \ell$ *group, subshells are filled in the order of decreasing* ℓ *values.*

problems

1. Calculate the diameters of the (a) 10*th*, (b) 30*th*, and (c) 100*th* orbit of the hydrogen atom according to Bohr's theory.

2. Calculate the wavelengths of the (a) seventh and (b) the eighth lines of the Balmer series of hydrogen.

3. Find the wavelengths of (a) the second and (b) the third lines of the Lyman series of hydrogen. [Ans. (a) 1025.2 Å, (b) 972.0 Å.]

4. Find the wavelengths of (a) the second and (b) the third lines of the Paschen series of hydrogen.

5. Determine (a) the diameter of the 15*th* circular orbit of hydrogen according to the Bohr theory. (b) Find the orbital speed of the electron.

6. Calculate (a) the diameter of the ninth circular orbit of hydrogen according to the Bohr theory. (b) Find the orbital speed of the electron. [Ans. (a) 8.57×10^{-9} m, (b) 2.431×10^5 m/s.]

7. Find the wavelength of the second line of the Brackett series in the hydrogen spectrum.

8. Make a diagram of (a) a germanium atom, atomic number 32, according to the Bohr-Stoner scheme. (b) Write down the complete electron configuration.

9. Make a diagram of (a) a cesium atom, atomic number 55, according to the Bohr-Stoner scheme. (b) Write down the complete electron configuration. See Appendix V. [Ans. (a) diagram, (b) $1s^2$, $2s^2$, $2p^6$, $3s^2$, $3p^6$, $3d^{10}$, $4s^2$, $4p^6$, $4d^{10}$, $5s^2$, $5p^6$, 6s.]

10. Make a diagram of (a) a rubidium atom, atomic number 37, according to the Bohr-Stoner scheme. (b) Write down the complete electron configuration. See Appendix V.

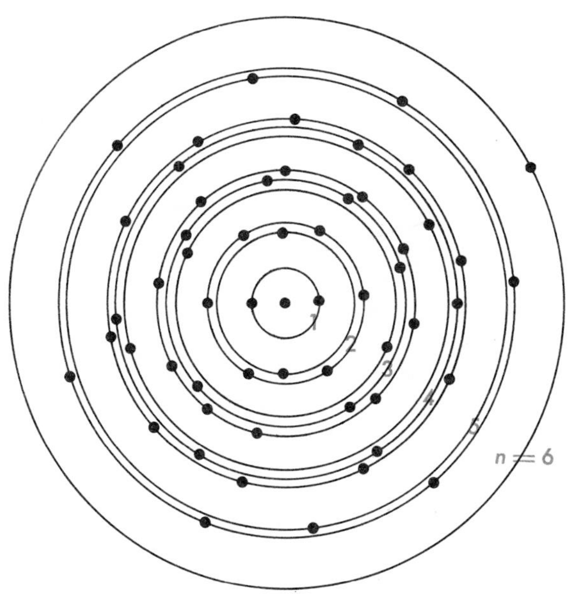

Prob. 9. Electron shells and subshells in the atom of cesium-55.

11. What would be the approximate quantum number for a circular orbit of hydrogen 0.50 mm in diameter?

12. Apply the Bohr theory of the hydrogen atom to ionized helium. Assume that a single electron moves around a nucleus with a charge of $+2e$. Write down the equations corresponding to Eqs. (44a), (44b), (44c), (44d), and (44n). [Ans. (a) $m\frac{v^2}{r} = k\frac{2e^2}{r^2}$, (b) $mvr = n\frac{h}{2\pi}$, (c) $r = \frac{n^2h^2}{8\pi^2me^2k}$, (d) $r_1 = 0.264589 \times 10^{-10}$ m, (e) $E_t = -\frac{8\pi^2me^4k^2}{n^2h^2}$.]

13. Apply the Bohr theory of the hydrogen atom to doubly ionized lithium atoms. Assume a single electron moving in the field of a nucleus with a charge of +3e. Write down the equations corresponding to Eqs. (44a), (44b), (44c), (44d), and (44n).

Spinning  electrons

With the development of the Bohr–Sommerfeld theory of the hydrogen atom in 1913, and its extension to the building-up of the electron structure of all atoms of the periodic table within only a few years, three new but important discoveries followed: (1) the discovery of electron spin, (2) the quantization of orbital electrons in a magnetic field, and (3) the direct experimental evidence for the existence of electron shells.

45.1. Orbital Mechanical Moment

The foundations of our present-day concepts of atomic structure were introduced into modern science when Bohr first proposed his theory of the hydrogen atom (see Chap. 44). According to Bohr's theory, the hydrogen atom is composed of a proton as a nucleus with a single electron revolving around it in a circular orbit. The quantum theory was introduced when Bohr assumed, through Eq.(44o), that the total energy of a hydrogen atom is given by

$$E_t = -\frac{Z}{n^2}R \qquad n = 1, 2, 3, 4, \ldots$$

where n is the *principal quantum number* and R is a constant:

$$R = \frac{2\pi^2 me^4k^2}{h^2}$$

$$R = 2.179914 \times 10^{-18}\ \text{J}$$

With the introduction of elliptical orbits as allowed states for the electron, a new quantum number ℓ was introduced. This new quantum number, too, has integral values only, and is assigned letters as follows:

$\ell = 0 \quad 1 \quad 2 \quad 3 \quad 4 \quad 5 \quad 6 \quad 7 \quad \ldots$
$\quad\ \ s \quad p \quad d \quad f \quad g \quad h \quad i \quad j \quad \ldots$

In this newer notation, the orbital angular momentum is given by

$$p_l = \ell \frac{h}{2\pi} \tag{45a}$$

The angular momentum p_l is frequently called the *mechanical moment,* and unit angular momentum $h/2\pi$ is frequently abbreviated $\hbar$:

$$\hbar = \frac{h}{2\pi} \tag{45b}$$

where $\hbar = 1.0545915 \times 10^{-34}$ Js.

The mechanical moment of an *s*-electron orbit is 0; of a *p*-electron orbit, $1\hbar$; of a *d*-electron orbit, $2\hbar$; of an *f*-electron orbit, $3\hbar$, etc.

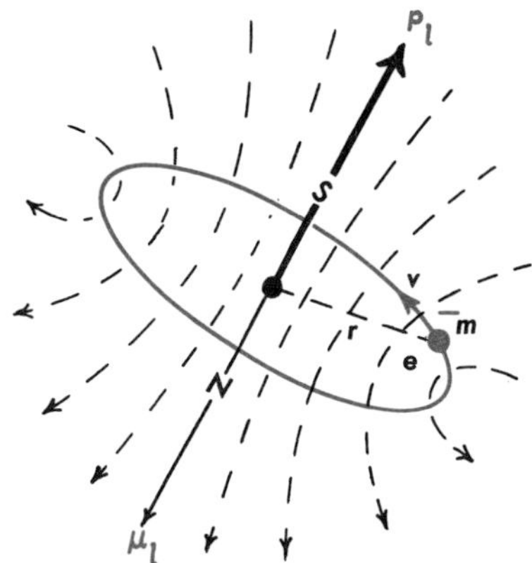

Fig. 45A. An orbital electron produces a magnetic field.

45.2. Orbital Magnetic Moment

Since an electron has a negative charge, its orbital motion, like that of electron current in a loop of wire, sets up a magnetic field. The direction of this field, as shown in Fig. 45A, is given by the *left-hand rule.* Since angular momentum is a vector quantity, p_l is shown pointing up along its axis of rotation. The direction of this mechanical moment is given by the *right-hand rule.* The mechanical moment of a rotating body is another term for its angular momentum (Sec. 13.7.).

The magnetic field produced by the orbital electron is quite similar to the field around a bar magnet, and is therefore specified as a magnetic dipole moment. This magnetic moment μ_l is related to the mechanical moment as follows:

$$\frac{\mu_l}{p_l} = \frac{e}{2m} \tag{45c}$$

where e and m are the charge and mass of the electron. The left-hand term μ_l/p_l is called the *gyromagnetic ratio.* It is the ratio between the magnetic moment and the mechanical moment. By substituting p_l from Eq.(45a), we obtain

$$\mu_l = \ell\hbar \frac{e}{2m} \tag{45d}$$

All symbols on the right, except ℓ, are fixed atomic constants, and together they form a unit of magnetic moment called the *Bohr magneton.* The Bohr magneton is given by

$$\mu_{\mathrm{B}} = \hbar \frac{e}{2m} \tag{45e}$$

which evaluated is equal to

$$\mu_{\mathrm{B}} = 9.2740966 \times 10^{-24}\ \mathrm{Am}^2 \tag{45f}$$

The magnetic moment for a *p*-electron orbit is one Bohr magneton, for a *d*-electron orbit is two Bohr magnetons, etc. An *s*-electron orbit with $\ell = 0$ has no mechanical moment and no magnetic moment.

45.3. Spectral Series

When the spectra of most of the elements in the periodic table are examined, they are found to be complex arrays of hundreds of lines spaced in what appear to be random patterns [see Fig. 45B(a)]. A few of the elements, however, give rise to a much simpler looking spectrum, with the lines arranged in series like those in Figs. 45B(b), 37D, and 37N. In addition to hydrogen, the elements revealing such simple spectral series are the elements n the first column of the periodic table (Appendix IV):

	Li	Na	K	Rb	Cs	Fr
$Z =$	3	11	19	37	55	87

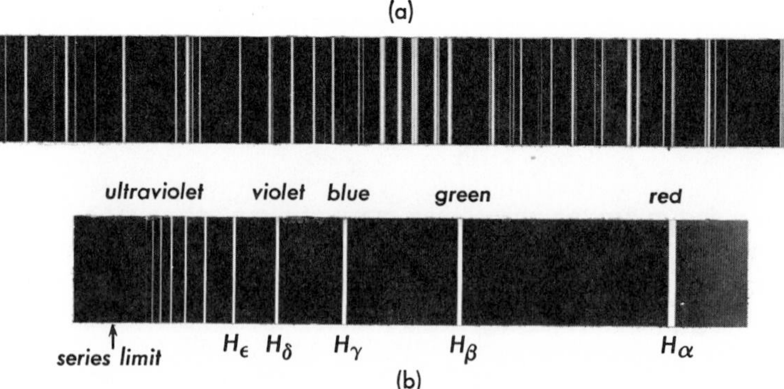

Fig. 45B. (a) Small section of the spectrum of titanium, $Z = 22$. (b) Photograph of the Balmer series of hydrogen, $Z = 1$.

The spectrum arising from each of these, the alkali metals, is composed of several spectral series in different wavelength regions, but having the same general appearance as shown in Fig. 37D. If the wavelengths of any one of these series are measured, and the frequencies are calculated and plotted, one obtains a graph of the kind shown in Fig. 45C.

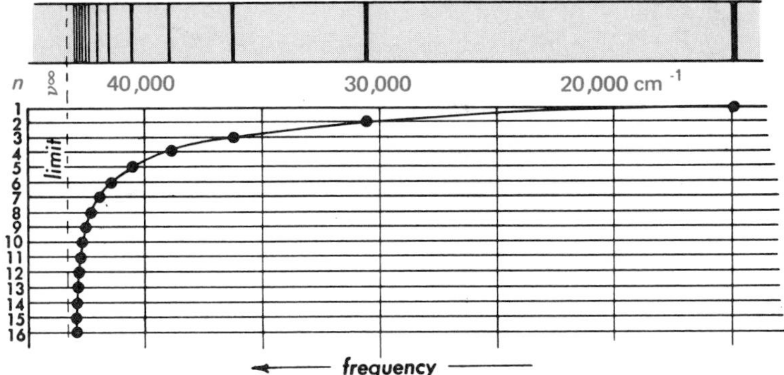

Fig. 45C. Frequency plot of the principal series in the spectrum of lithium, $Z = 3$.

The first successful attempt to fit all such lines of a series into one general formula was made by Rydberg* in 1896. His formula is

$$\nu_n = \nu_\infty - \frac{\mathcal{R}}{(n + \mu)^2} \tag{45g}$$

where ν_n is the frequency of the different lines n, and ν_∞ is the frequency of the series limit. For example, for the *principal series of lithium,* shown in Fig. 45C,

$$\mathcal{R} = 109{,}722 \text{ cm}^{-1}$$

$$\nu_\infty = 43{,}488 \text{ cm}^{-1}$$

$$\mu = 0.9596$$

$$n = 1, 2, 3, 4, \ldots$$

* The Rydberg constant $\mathcal{R}$ used here can be obtained by dividing the value of R given in Eq.(44p) by Planck's constant h and the speed of light c.

By substituting $n = 1$ in Eq.(45g), one obtains the frequency of the first line of the lithium series, $\nu_n = 14{,}915$ cm^{-1}, corresponding to $\lambda = 6705$ Å. By substituting $n = 2$, one obtains the frequency of the second line of the series, etc.

The success of the Rydberg formula is remarkable because by changing the constants ν_∞ and μ it fits all series in all spectra. $\mathcal{R}$ remains the same for all series in all elements. Because the actual frequencies of visible light waves are so extremely high, it is customary to divide them all by the speed of light ($c = 2.997925 \times 10^{10}$ cm/s). Such frequencies are then called *wave numbers.* The frequency of a spectrum line in wave numbers is therefore just equal to the number of wavelengths in a distance of 1 cm, instead of the number in 2.997925×10^{10} cm. Frequencies, in wave numbers, have the units of cm^{-1}.

45.4. The Spinning Electron

If the spectrum lines of hydrogen, lithium, sodium, and potassium are observed under high magnification, each series member is found to be a double line (see Fig. 45D). These closely spaced doublets arise from the fact that *all electrons are spinning.* The single electron in the hydrogen atom, which is responsible for the observed spectrum, is spinning around its own axis as it moves in an orbit around the nucleus. Similarly, the single-valence electron in all sodium atoms is spinning as shown in Fig. 45E.

Electrons in any completed (closed) subshell pair off with axes parallel but with opposite spin and orbit directions. Hence, in sodium, with $Z = 11$, the one outermost electron 3s is unpaired, and its spin constitutes the resultant spin of the entire electronic system. Furthermore, it is the jumping of this valence electron from one orbit to another that is responsible for the observed spectrum.

The outermost electrons in any atom are largely responsible for its ability to combine chemically with other atoms to form molecules and are called *valence* electrons.

The spinning of electrons in atoms was first proposed by Goudsmit* and Uhlenbeck,† in 1925, to explain the double-line structure in the spectra of the alkali metals. Each electron, whether it is bound to an atom or a crystal, or is alone in free space, has an angular momentum. The spin angular momentum is given by

$$p_s = s\hbar \qquad (45h)$$

where s is the spin quantum number and has the value $\frac{1}{2}$:

$$s = \tfrac{1}{2} \text{ only} \qquad (45i)$$

***Samuel A. Goudsmit (1902–), American physicist, was born in The Hague, Holland, July 11, 1902. He obtained his Ph.D. in physics at Leiden in 1927, and was married the same year. He became an instructor in physics at the University of Michigan in 1927, and a United States citizen not long afterward. He served as professor from 1932–1946, and joined the Brookhaven National Laboratory in 1948. He has received the Max Planck Award and is best known for his prediction of electron spin and his work on atomic spectra.**

†George E. Uhlenbeck (1900–), American physicist, was born in Batavia, Java, December 6, 1900 and received his PhD. at Leiden, Holland, in 1927. He became professor of physics at the University of Michigan in 1930, and gained the Henry S. Carhart Professorship from 1939 to 1960. He has received many honorary awards and is best known for his work with S. A. Goudsmit on the spinning electron.

Since an electron always has a negative charge, its spinning around its own mechanical axis generates a magnetic field like that shown in Fig. 45F. This field is similar to the field around a bar magnet and may be specified by its equivalent *magnetic moment.* The magnetic moment μ_s of a spinning electron is given by

$$\frac{\mu_s}{p_s} = 2\,\frac{e}{2m} \tag{45j}$$

and is oppositely directed to its mechanical moment. Note that the *gyromagnetic ratio* is twice that for an electron orbit [Eq.(45c)].

By substituting the value of p_s from Eq.(45h) in this formula, we obtain

$$\mu_s = \hbar\,\frac{e}{2m} \tag{45k}$$

Since this is the same as Eq.(45e), we see that while *a spinning electron has a mechanical moment of* $\frac{1}{2}\hbar$, *it has a magnetic moment of one Bohr magneton.*

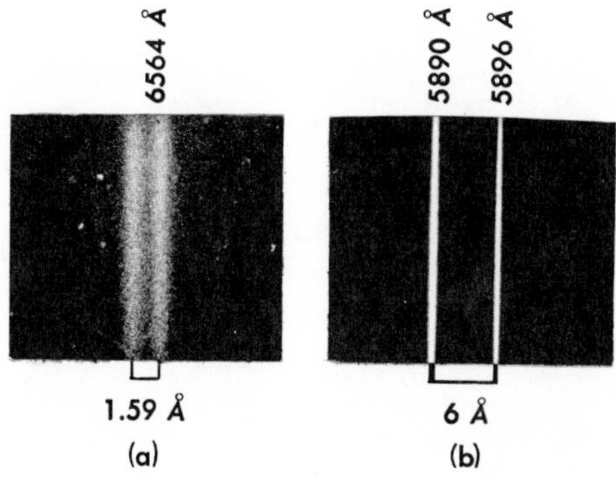

Fig. 45D. Highly magnified photographs showing the doublet structure of (a) the first member of the Balmer series of hydrogen (the red line), and (b) the first member of the principal series of sodium (the yellow line).

45.5. Electron Spin–Orbit Interaction

The fact that the spectrum lines in the Balmer series of hydrogen, and those in the series of the alkali metals, are doublets, is interpreted to mean that each of the energy levels of these atoms is double. (See Fig. 45G for the energy-level diagram of sodium.)

The doubling of energy levels in atoms having one valence electron is due to the interaction between the magnetic field of the electron orbit and the magnetic field of the electron spin. We have seen in Sec. 28.2 that a bar magnet located in a magnetic field has a torque exerted on it which tends to line it up parallel to the field. A spinning electron in a magnetic field behaves in exactly the same way; there is a torque acting upon it, trying to turn its axis parallel to the field. Owing to the mechanical properties of a revolving mass, the electron precesses around B in much the same way that a mechanical top precesses in a gravitational field.

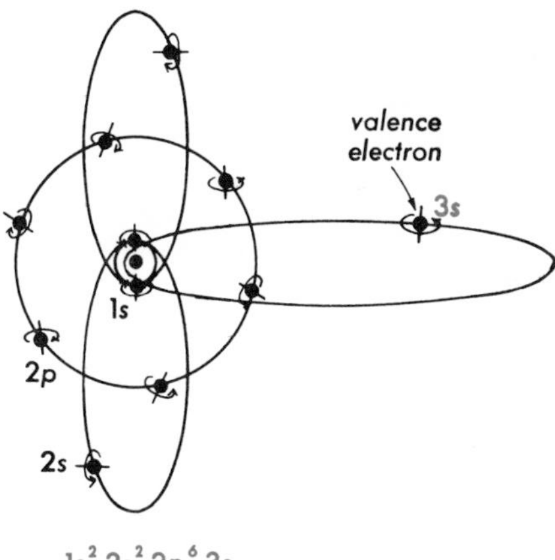

Fig. 45E. Atomic model of sodium showing the spinning of all electrons: $Z = 11$.

A schematic diagram of the precession of a spinning electron is given in Fig. 45H. Such a motion is called a *Larmor precession,* and its frequency f is given by

$$f = \frac{e}{4\pi m}\,B \tag{45ℓ}$$

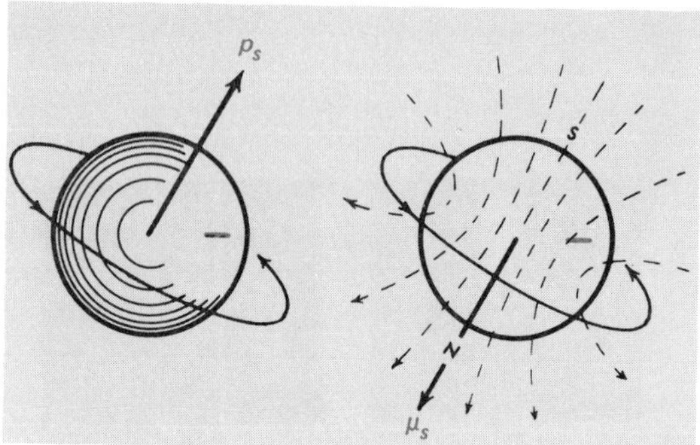

Fig. 45F. A spinning electron has a mechanical moment p_s and a magnetic moment μ_s.

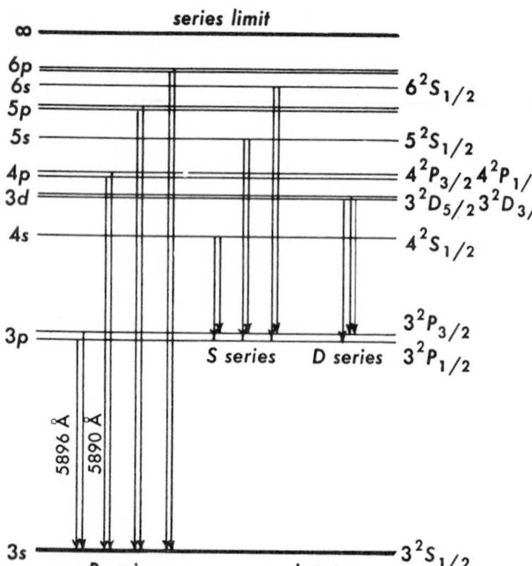

Fig. 45G. Energy-level diagram for the sodium atom, $Z = 11$.

Example 1. Sodium atoms are located in a magnetic field where $B = 1.50$ T. Find the Larmor precession frequency of the valence electron in its normal, or ground state, $^2S_{1/2}$. Use constants to five significant figures.

Solution. The given quantities are $B = 1.50$ T, $e = 1.60219 \times 10^{-19}$ C, and $m = 9.1096 \times 10^{-31}$ Kg. By direct substitution of these quantities in Eq.(45ℓ), we obtain

$$f = \frac{e}{4\pi m}B = \frac{1.60219 \times 10^{-19} \times 1.50}{4 \times 3.14159 \times 9.1096 \times 10^{-31}}$$

$$f = 2.09941 \times 10^{10} \text{ Hz}$$

A good demonstration of this precession can be made by a gyroscope of the kind shown in Fig. 45I. A nonconducting sphere, mounted free to turn in ball-bearings, is mounted in double gimbal rings and placed directly over the center of an electromagnet as shown. When the ball is set spinning in the position shown, and the magnetic field is turned on, the ball will retain its inclination angle as it precesses around the vertical axis. By reversing the magnetic field the precession will reverse direction.

Owing to orbital motion, as well as the positive charge on the nucleus, every electron in an atom is subjected to a magnetic field. To see how this field comes about, consider the simple case of a hydrogen atom with its one electron in an orbit around a positive charge. If we imagine ourselves riding around with the electron, looking out at the nucleus, we see this positive charge as though it were moving in an orbit around us. This moving charge gives rise to a magnetic field at the electron of the form shown in Fig. 45J. In this field the electron carries out a Larmor precession.

Since an electron has a spin angular momentum $s\hbar$, as well as an orbital angular momentum $\ell\hbar$, the total angular momentum of the atom will be the vector sum of the two, and its magnitude will depend upon their relative orientations. If we represent $\ell\hbar$ and $s\hbar$ by vectors as shown in Fig. 45K, their vector sum $j\hbar$ will represent the total angular momentum. j is called the *total quantum number.*

The quantum theory requires that all possible vector sums for these two quantities differ from each other by $\hbar$. For each value of the orbital quantum number ℓ, there are two possibilities,

either $$j\hbar = \ell\hbar + s\hbar$$

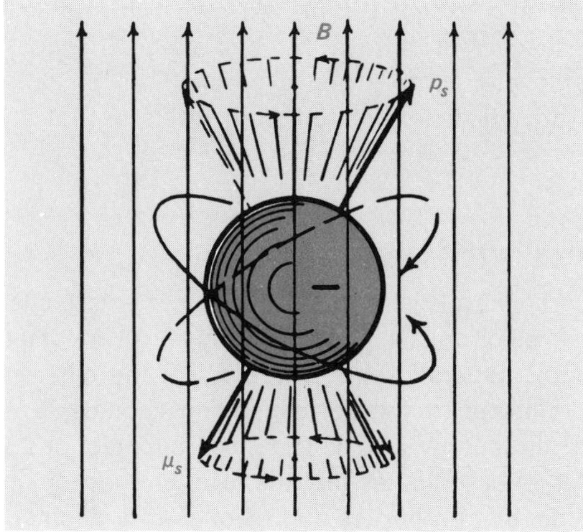

Fig. 45H. A spinning electron in a magnetic field precesses around an axis, parallel to the magnetic induction B.

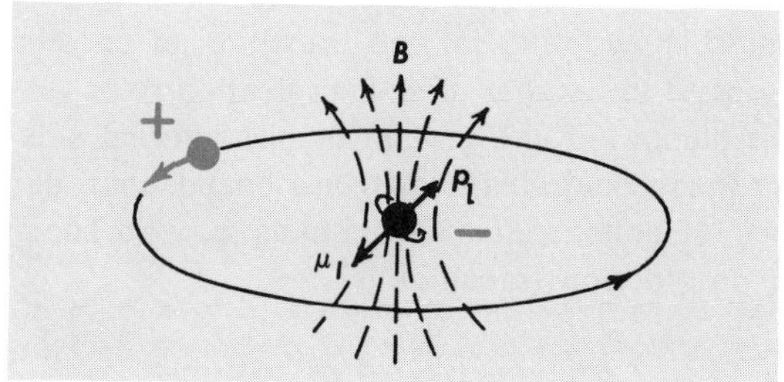

Fig. 45J. The magnetic field at an electron in an atom is due to the positively charged nucleus that appears to be going around it in an orbit.

Fig. 45I. A spinning ball gyroscope will precess in a magnetic field. (Note: A small permanent bar magnet is mounted inside and on the axis of the ball.)

or

$$j\hbar = \ell\hbar - s\hbar \qquad (45m)$$

Since all angular momenta have the common factor $\hbar$, the quantum numbers ℓ, s, and j may be used as vectors, and we can write

$$j = \ell + s \qquad \text{and} \qquad j = \ell - s \qquad (45n)$$

For a d electron, for example, $\ell = 2$ and $s = \frac{1}{2}$:

$$j = 2 + \tfrac{1}{2} = \tfrac{5}{2} \qquad \text{and} \qquad j = 2 - \tfrac{1}{2} = \tfrac{3}{2}$$

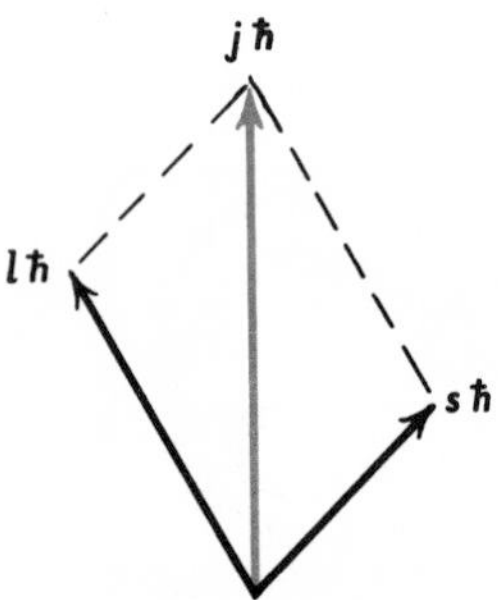

Fig. 45K. Angular momentum vectors for electron spin and orbital motions.

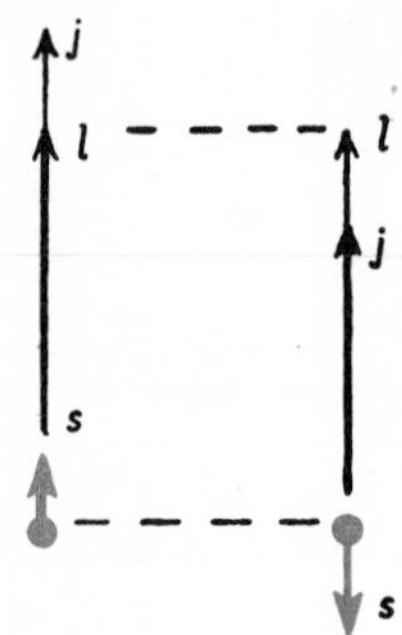

Fig. 45L. Angular momentum vectors for the two allowed states of an orbital electron.

All values of ℓ, except $\ell = 0$, will give two j values (see Fig. 45L), and these will always be half-integral. Since the total energy of the atom with ℓ and s parallel will be different from when they are oppositely directed, all levels except s levels will be double.

45.6. Selection Rules

In double spectra arising from atomic systems containing only one valence electron, i.e., one electron in an incompleted subshell, the small letters *s*, *p*, *d*, *f*, *g*, etc., for the different electron orbits are replaced by the corresponding capitals ^2S, ^2P, ^2D, ^2F, ^2G, etc., for the energy levels. The small superscript 2 in front of each capital letter indicates that the level in question, including *S* levels, has doublet properties and belongs to a doublet system.

Although all *S* levels are single, their doublet nature will later be seen to reveal itself when the atom is placed in a magnetic field. In order to distinguish between two fine-structure levels having the same n and ℓ values, the cumbersome but theoretically important half-integral subscripts are used.

Observation shows that, for the transition of an electron from one energy state to another, definite selection rules are in operation. This is illustrated in Fig. 45M by six different sets of transitions. From these diagrams, which are based upon experimental observations, selection rules for doublets may be summarized as follows: In an electron transition

ℓ changes by + 1 or − 1 only

and is written $$\Delta\ell = \pm 1$$

j changes by 0, +1 or − 1 only

and is written $$\Delta j = 0, \pm 1$$

with $0 \rightarrow 0$ forbidden.

The total quantum number n has no restrictions and may change by any integral amount. Note that transitions involving a change of ℓ by 2, e.g., $^2D \rightarrow {}^2S$, are forbidden.

Note how the energy-level differences ΔP, ΔD, and ΔF show up as frequency differences between pairs of spectrum lines. This follows from the fact that energies of all emitted photons are given by $h\nu$.

The relative intensities of the observed spectrum lines are

illustrated by the widths of the lines directly below each transition arrow at the bottom of the figure. Combinations between ^2P and ^2S always give rise to a doublet, whereas all other combinations give rise to two strong lines and one fainter line.

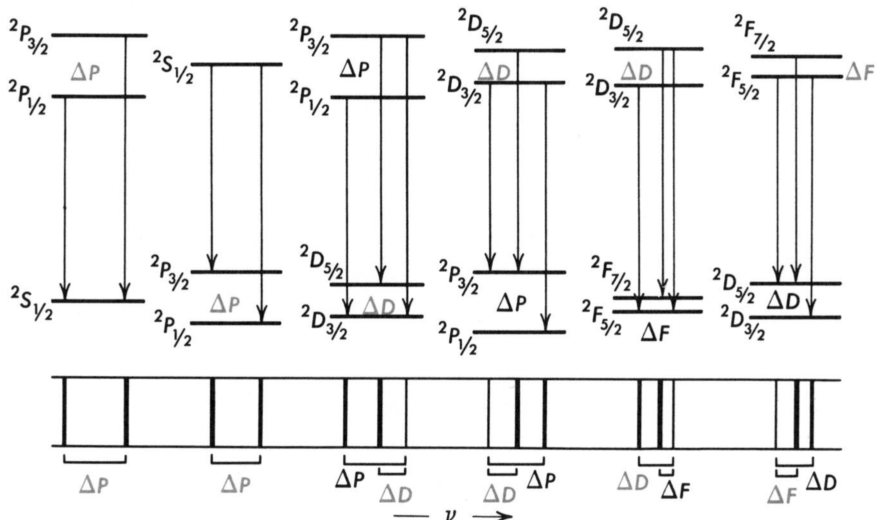

Fig. 45M. Diagrams of selection rules for transitions between doublet energy levels, and the appearance of the corresponding spectrum lines.

In designating any spectrum line like one of the yellow doublet in sodium, $\lambda = 5890$ Å, the lower state is written first, followed by the upper state: thus, $3^2S_{1/2} - 3^2P_{3/2}$. The other line of the sodium doublet, $\lambda = 5896$ Å, is written $3^2S_{1/2} - 3^2P_{1/2}$. Spectrum lines in absorption are written the same way, the lowest level first.

45.7. The Normal Order of Doublet Energy Levels

In the doublet energy levels of atomic systems containing one valence electron it is generally, but not always, observed that the energy level with $j = \ell - \frac{1}{2}$ lies lower than the corresponding level $j = \ell + \frac{1}{2}$. For example, in the case of p and d electrons, $^2P_{1/2}$ lies lower than $^2P_{3/2}$ and $^2D_{3/2}$ lies lower than $^2D_{5/2}$.

As explained in Sec. 45.5 and shown in Fig 45J, the orbital electron is subjected to a magnetic field arising from the positively charged nucleus. In this field the most stable state of a given doublet will be the one in which the spinning electron, thought of as a small magnet of moment μ_s, is parallel to the magnetic field. This is the state in which $j = \ell - \frac{1}{2}$. In the state $j = \ell + \frac{1}{2}$, the spin magnetic moment μ_s is opposite in direction to the field (see Fig. 45N).

Of the two possible orientations of the electron, the one $j = \ell - \frac{1}{2}$ is classically the more stable and lies lower on an energy-level diagram. To turn any magnet from a position where it lines up parallel to the field in which it is located to any position where it makes an angle with the field requires that work be done.

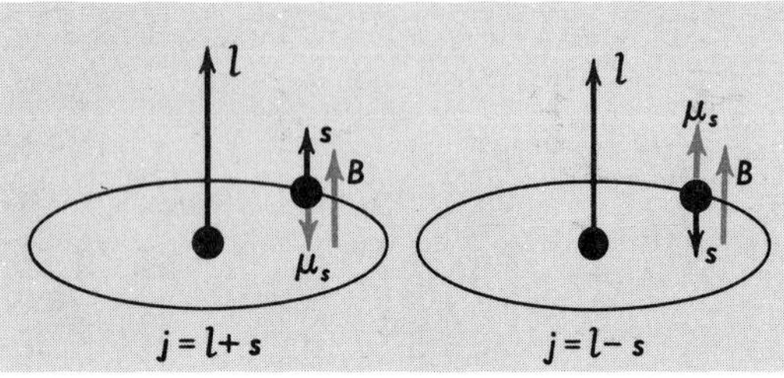

Fig. 45N. Illustrating the mechanical and magnetic moments of the spinning electron for doublet energy levels $j = \ell + s$ and $j = \ell - s$.

Example 2. The following table represents a list of the energy levels of the alkali metal cesium, Cs^{55}. The energies are given in wave numbers (cm^{-1}). (a) Plot an energy level diagram and label each level with its appropriate designation. Calculate (b) the frequencies in wave numbers, and (c) the wavelengths in angstroms, for the first three members of the principal series.

TABLE 45A
Energy levels for cesium atoms

Term Designations	Term Values (cm^{-1})	Term Designations	Term Values (Å)
6s, $^2S_{1/2}$	31404.6	6d, $^2D_{3/2}$	8815.6
6p, $^2P_{1/2}$	20226.3	6d, $^2D_{5/2}$	8772.8
6p, $^2P_{3/2}$	19672.3	8s, $^2S_{1/2}$	7087.8
5d, $^2D_{3/2}$	16905.0	4f, $^2F_{5/2,\ 7/2}$	6932.8
5d, $^2D_{5/2}$	16807.1	8p, $^2P_{1/2}$	5695.3
7s, $^2S_{1/2}$	12868.9	8p, $^2P_{3/2}$	5614.7
7p, $^2P_{1/2}$	9639.2	7d, $^2D_{3/2}$	5356.5
7p, $^2P_{3/2}$	9458.1	7d, $^2D_{5/2}$	5335.6

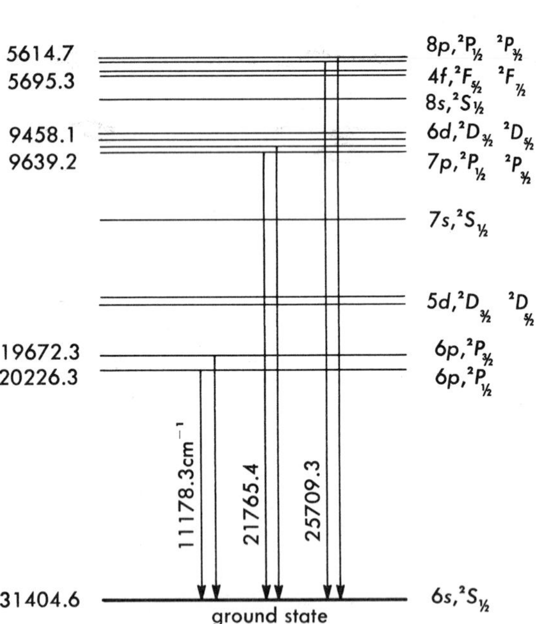

Fig. 45O. Energy level diagram for the cesium atom: answer to part (a), Example 2.

TABLE 45B
Frequencies and wavelengths for the principal series of cesium, Cs^{55}

	Transition Designations	ν (cm^{-1})	λ (Å)
1st	$6^2S_{1/2} - 6^2P_{1/2}$	11178.3	8945.9
	$6^2S_{1/2} - 6^2P_{3/2}$	11732.3	8523.5
2nd	$6^2S_{1/2} - 7^2P_{1/2}$	21765.4	4594.4
	$6^2S_{1/2} - 7^2P_{3/2}$	21946.5	4556.5
3rd	$6^2S_{1/2} - 8^2P_{1/2}$	25709.3	3889.6
	$6^2S_{1/2} - 8^2P_{3/2}$	25789.9	3877.5

Solution. A plot of the energies is given in Fig. 45O. Note how similar this diagram is to the one for sodium in Fig. 45G. Since the principal series arises from transitions from the P levels to the ground state, $6s$, $^2S_{1/2}$, the frequencies in wave numbers are given by the differences in term values. The wavelengths λ are given in angstroms, and are reciprocals of the frequencies in wave numbers, but with the decimal point properly located.

45.8. Space Quantization and the Zeeman Effect

When hydrogen atoms are located in a magnetic field B, the quantum theory requires that their electrons take on certain specified directions. These directions are determined as follows: The projection of the total angular momentum $j\hbar$ on the field direction B (see Fig. 45P) must take on half-integral values of $\hbar$, from the largest to the smallest possible, and all half-integral values in between. As an equation

$$j\hbar \cos\theta \quad m\hbar \tag{45o}$$

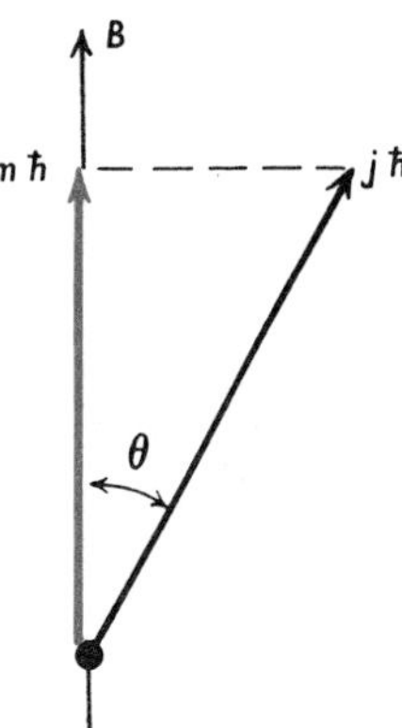

Fig. 45P. Orientation diagram of an atom in an external magnetic field B.

where m is the *magnetic quantum number,* and is given by

$$m = \pm\tfrac{1}{2}, \pm\tfrac{3}{2}, \pm\tfrac{5}{2}, \ldots \pm j \tag{45p}$$

If, for example, the total quantum number $j = \frac{5}{2}$, the allowed orientations of j are six in number, and are specified by

$$m = +\tfrac{5}{2}, +\tfrac{3}{2}, +\tfrac{1}{2}, -\tfrac{1}{2}, -\tfrac{3}{2}, -\tfrac{5}{2} \tag{45q}$$

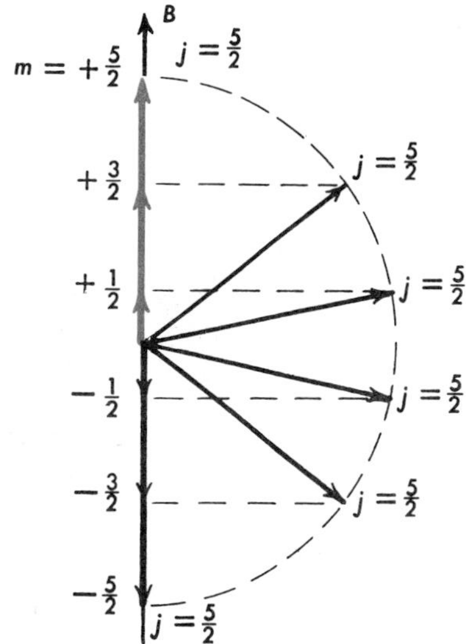

Fig. 45Q. Vector diagram representing space quantization of an atom in a magnetic field B.

These six orientations are shown in Fig. 45Q, and the process is referred to as *space quantization.* The minus values indicate only that the component of $j\hbar$ is opposite in direction to the field B.

A diagram of the precession of an atom in a magnetic field, when the electron is in a state $\ell = 2$, $s = \frac{1}{2}$, $j = \frac{5}{2}$, and $m = \frac{3}{2}$, is shown in Fig. 45R. Because the energy of the atom differs slightly between the different orientations of the electron, energy levels as well as spectrum lines will be split into a number of equally spaced components. To observe this phenomenon, the light source must be placed in a strong and uniform magnetic field, and the light observed with a spectrograph. The phenomenon, called the *Zeeman effect,* is observed in the spectra of all elements. Some line patterns contain only a few lines, while others contain many. Typical Zeeman patterns, as seen under high magnification, are reproduced in Fig. 45S.

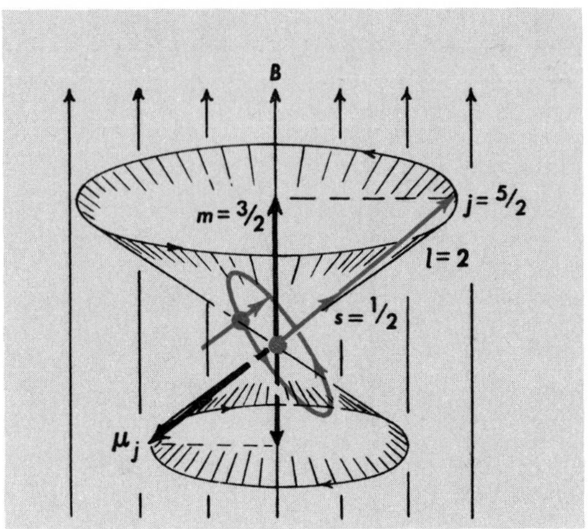

Fig. 45R. An electron spin and orbit precess together as a unit around the magnetic field direction *B*.

45.9. Pauli Exclusion Principle

We have now seen that four quantum numbers are required to specify the state of an electron in an atom. These are

$$\begin{aligned} n &= \text{principal quantum number} \\ \ell &= \text{orbital quantum number} \\ j &= \text{total quantum number} \\ m &= \text{magnetic quantum number} \end{aligned} \tag{45r}$$

According to the Pauli exclusion principle, no two electrons in the same atom can have all four quantum numbers alike. They may have three alike—but at least one must be different.

Consider, for example, the number of electrons that can have $n = 3$ and $\ell = 2$. Such electrons are designated 3*d*. The two *j* values possible are $j = \ell + s$ and $j = \ell - s$, i.e., $j = \frac{5}{2}$ and $j = \frac{3}{2}$ [see Eq.(45n)]. For $j = \frac{5}{2}$ there are six possible values of *m*, and for $j = \frac{3}{2}$ there are four possible values of *m*. Together, these are

$$\begin{aligned} j &= \tfrac{5}{2}, \; m = +\tfrac{5}{2}, +\tfrac{3}{2}, +\tfrac{1}{2}, -\tfrac{1}{2}, -\tfrac{3}{2}, -\tfrac{5}{2} \\ j &= \tfrac{3}{2}, \; m = \quad\;\; +\tfrac{3}{2}, +\tfrac{1}{2}, -\tfrac{1}{2}, -\tfrac{3}{2} \end{aligned} \tag{45s}$$

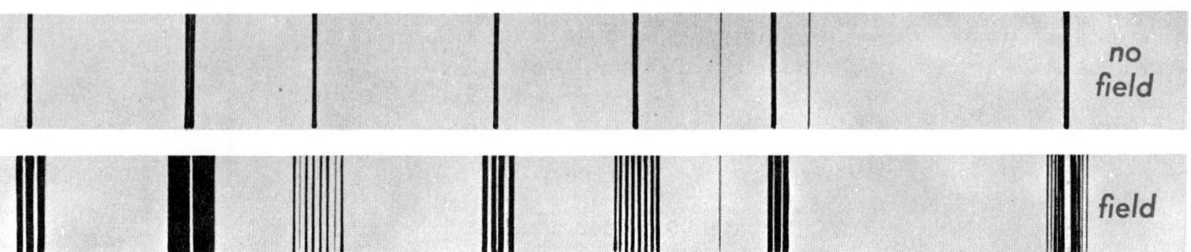

Fig. 45S. Small section of the spectrum of rhodium, $Z = 45$.(Upper) Ordinary lines with no magnetic field. (Lower) Zeeman patterns when light source is in strong magnetic field of 7.0 Wb/m^2. (After Harrison and Bitter.)

or ten possibilities in all. Note that this is just the number of electrons that fills an $\ell = 2$ subshell in the building up of elements in the periodic table. In a similar way, an *s* subshell can have two electrons, a *p* subshell 6, and an *f* subshell 14.

45.10. Elastic and Inelastic Impacts

When an electron collides with a neutral atom in a rarefied gas, the collision is either *elastic* or *inelastic.* An elastic collision is one in which the laws of conservation of momentum and conservation of mechanical energy are both upheld. In other words, the atomic particles behave as though they were perfectly elastic spheres; the total energy and total momentum before impact are equal to the total energy and total momentum after impact (see Fig. 45T).

An inelastic collision is one in which the impinging electron, in striking a neutral atom, hits one of the electrons and either knocks it into one of the outer orbits (energy levels), or knocks it completely out of the atom. In the first instance, we say the atom has been *excited,* and in the second case it has been *ionized.* In either case it is usually a valence electron that is involved.

To raise an electron from its normal state to an excited state, or to remove it from the atom, requires the expenditure of energy; this is supplied by the impinging electron. As a consequence, some of the total energy before collision is used for excitation or ionization, and what is left is divided between the two particles. Because the masses of atoms are thousands of times that of the electron, nearly all kinetic energy before impact, and after, is confined to the electron. The recoil velocity and kinetic energy of an atom that has been hit by a moving electron are relatively small.

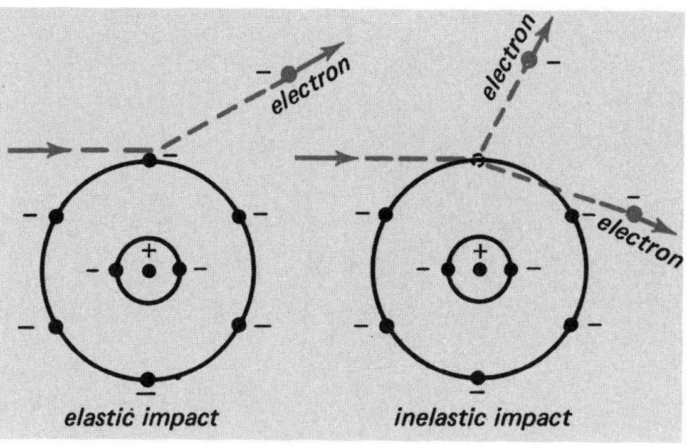

Fig. 45T. Schematic diagrams showing elastic and inelastic impacts.

45.11. Ionization Potentials

The ionization potential of an element is defined as the energy in electron volts required to remove the most loosely bound electron from the normal atom. The *electron volt* is defined as the energy equivalent to the kinetic energy of an electron accelerated through a potential difference of 1 V. In other words, an energy of 1 eV is 1.60219×10^{-19} J.

A graph of the ionization potentials of the elements of the periodic table is given in Fig. 45U. It is clearly seen that the alkali metals, Li, Na, K, Rb, Cs, and Fa, have low values, about 5 V, while the inert gases, He, Ne, A, Kr, Xe, and Rn, have the highest values. The inert gases represent those atoms in which all the electron subshells are complete. The adding of one more proton to the nucleus, and the addition of one more electron to the outer structure to make the next atom, an alkali metal, requires that electron to go into a new subshell, an outer orbit. Such an electron, being on the average farther away from the nucleus, requires less energy to remove it from the atom. As protons are added to the nucleus, and electrons are added in this same subshell, the binding of the electrons grows stronger and stronger.

A direct correlation between the low ionization potentials of the alkali metals and the beginning of new subshells, as shown by the arrows at the bottom of Fig. 45U, leads to the building-up of the periodic table as given in Appendix IV.

For a more complete account of atomic structure, see H. E. White, *Introduction to Atomic Spectra* (McGraw-Hill, New York).

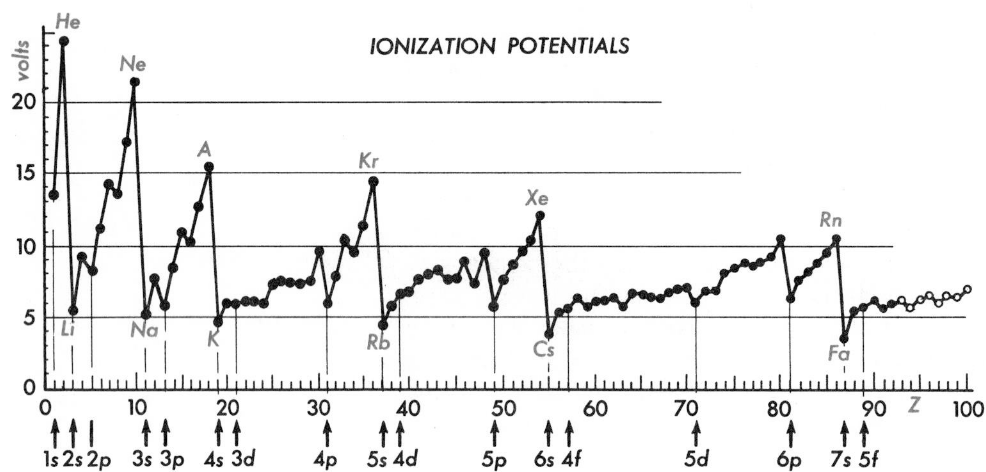

Fig. 45U. Ionization potentials of the elements.

questions and problems

1. (a) What is the atomic unit of angular momentum? (b) What is the atomic unit of magnetic moment?

2. What are the four quantum numbers that describe an atomic state of an electron that is bound to an atom?

3. What is the Pauli exclusion principle?

4. (a) What is meant by the excitation potential? (b) What is meant by the ionization potential?

5. Make a space quantization diagram for the following electronic state of an atom in a magnetic field: $\ell = 3$, $s = +\frac{1}{2}$, $j = \frac{7}{2}$.

6. Calculate (a) the lowest excitation potential, and (b) the ionization potential for cesium. See Fig. 45O, and Table 45A. [Ans. (a) 1.386 V, (b) 3.894 V.]

7. Using the table of term values for thallium in Prob. 9, calculate (a) the lowest excitation potential, and (b) the ionization potential for thallium.

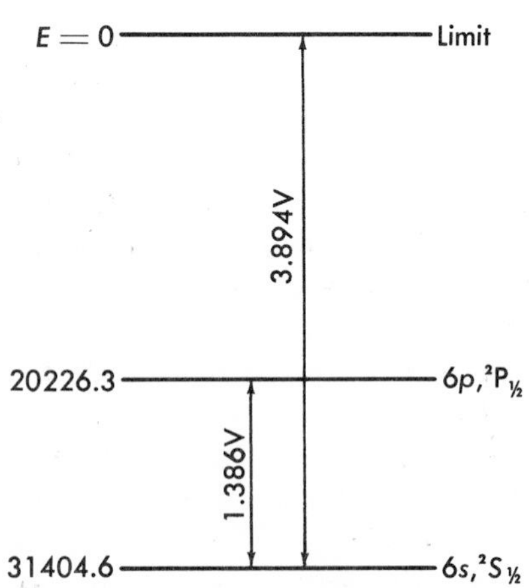

Prob. 6. Energy levels and excitation, and ionization potentials of cesium.

8. Calculate (a) the frequency in wave numbers, and (b) the wavelength in angstroms for the second member of the diffuse series in cesium. See Table 45A and Fig. 45O for energy levels.

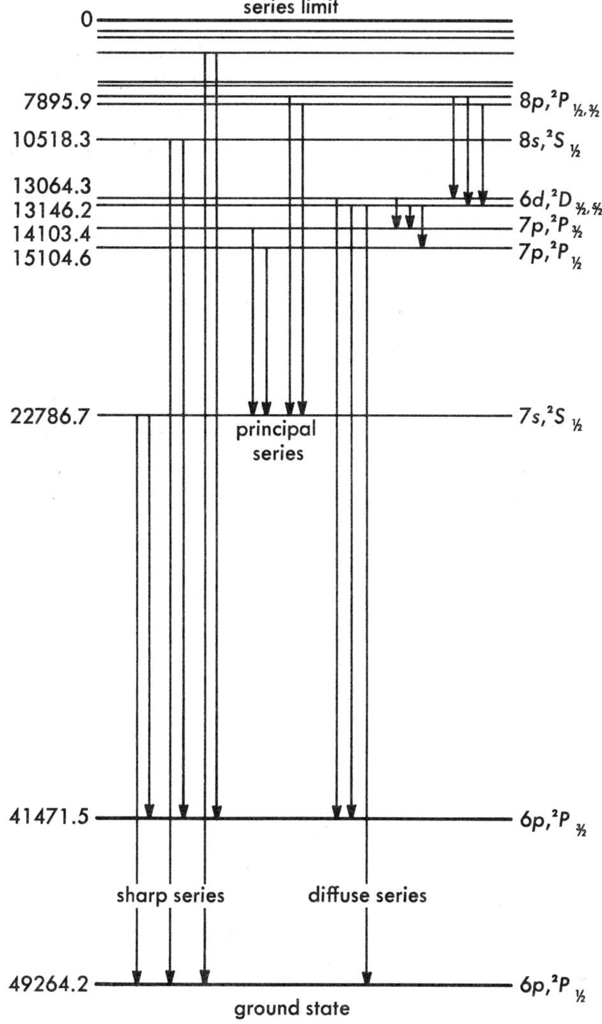

Prob. 9. Energy level diagram for the element thallium showing transitions giving rise to photons.

9. The following table lists the energy levels of the element thallium, in wave numbers, beginning with the ground state, $6^2P_{1/2}$. Make an energy level diagram and label each level with its *term value* and *term designation.*

TABLE 45C
Energy levels for thallium atoms

Term Designations	*Term Values (cm^{-1})*	*Term Designations*	*Term Values (cm^{-1})*
$6p,\ ^2P_{1/2}$	49264.2	$8s,\ ^2S_{1/2}$	10518.3
$6p,\ ^2P_{3/2}$	41471.5	$8p,\ ^2P_{1/2}$	7895.9
$7s,\ ^2S_{1/2}$	22786.7	$8p,\ ^2P_{3/2}$	7523.2
$7p,\ ^2P_{1/2}$	15104.6	$7d,\ ^2D_{3/2}$	7252.8
$7p,\ ^2P_{3/2}$	14103.4	$7d,\ ^2D_{5/2}$	7215.2
$6d,\ ^2D_{3/2}$	13146.2	$5f,\ ^2F_{5/2,\ 7/2}$	6945.8
$6d,\ ^2D_{5/2}$	13064.3	$9s,\ ^2S_{1/2}$	6098.2

Draw in a number of allowed transitions between levels and put arrows on their lower ends to represent emission of light.

10. Calculate (a) the frequency in wave numbers, and (b) the wavelength in angstroms for the second member of the sharp series in cesium. See Table 45A and Fig. 45O.

11. Determine (a) the frequencies in wave numbers, and (b) the wavelengths in angstroms for the first member of the sharp series in thallium. See Table 45C and the figure for Prob. 9.

12. Calculate (a) the frequencies in wave numbers, and (b) the wavelengths in angstroms for the second member of the sharp series in thallium. See Table 45C and the figure for Prob. 9. [Ans. (a) 38745.9 cm^{-1}, 30953.2 cm^{-1}, (b) 2580.9 Å, 3230.7 Å.]

13. Find (a) the frequency in wave numbers and, (b) the wavelengths in angstroms for the first member of the diffuse series of thallium. See Table 45C and the figure for Prob. 9.

Moving frames of reference

As an introduction to Einstein's theory of relatively let us consider the relative motions of bodies as seen from different frames of reference. We begin with the motion of a body in a medium which is itself moving. The drift of an airplane in a wind or the drift of a boat on a moving body of water is a good example.

46.1. The Airplane Problem

The pilot of a plane wishes to fly to a city directly to the north. If the plane has a cruising speed of 100 mi/h and a steady wind is blowing from the west with a velocity of 50 mi/h, at what angle should the pilot head his plane into the wind [see Fig. 46A(a)]? Because this type of problem is often solved incorrectly, its correct solution should be noted with care. The procedure to be followed is appropriately called the *domino method of vector addition.*

With both the direction and magnitude of the wind velocity

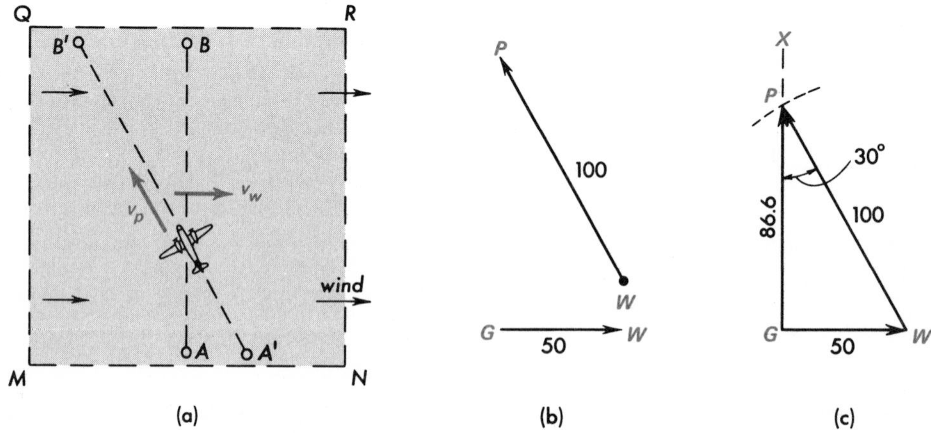

Fig. 46A. To fly a desired course, the wind velocity must be taken into account.

known, draw the first vector toward the east, 50 units long [see diagram (b)]. Label it with the moving body, the wind W at the head, and the ground G to which the velocity is referred, at the tail. Since only the magnitude of the airplane velocity is known, draw a temporary arrow 100 units long, at an arbitrary angle, and label it with the moving body, the plane P, at the head, and the air or wind W, to which the velocity is referred, at the tail.

The next step is to combine the two vectors with their like labels W together, as follows. After drawing the vector GW, draw a perpendicular line GX upward. With a compass of radius 100 units and the center at W, draw a short arc intersecting the vertical line at P.

The vector WP is then completed, and the length of the side GP measured. The vector GP of 86.6 pointing north represents the velocity of the plane P with respect to the ground G, while the angle 30°, measured from the triangle, gives the direction in which the plane must be headed.

Diagram (a) in Fig. 46A shows how the plane, heading in a direction 30° west of north, and flying through the air with a velocity of 100 mi/h, follows the northward land course from A to B with a *ground speed* of 86.6 mi/h. In the air mass (MNRQ), which is a moving frame of reference, the plane flies from A′ to B′.

Example 1. A ship is heading due west at a cruising speed of 45.0 Km/h. The third mate notes that the smoke trail from the funnel has a speed of 60.0 Km/h in a direction 30° south of east with respect to the ship's heading. Make vector diagrams and find graphically the true wind velocity.

Solution. The given quantities are the two velocities, 45.0 Km/h and 60.0 Km/h, and the angle, 30°. We first draw vectors to scale and in the proper direction as shown in Diagram A. Each end of both vectors is then labeled properly.

Combining these two vectors, with like labels together, we find graphically the following in Diagram B.

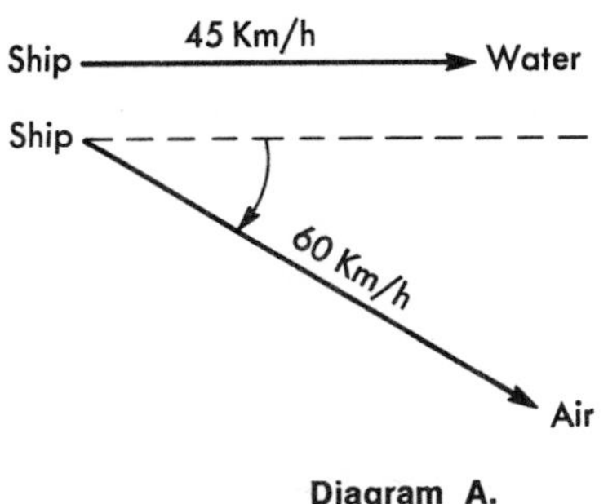

Diagram A.

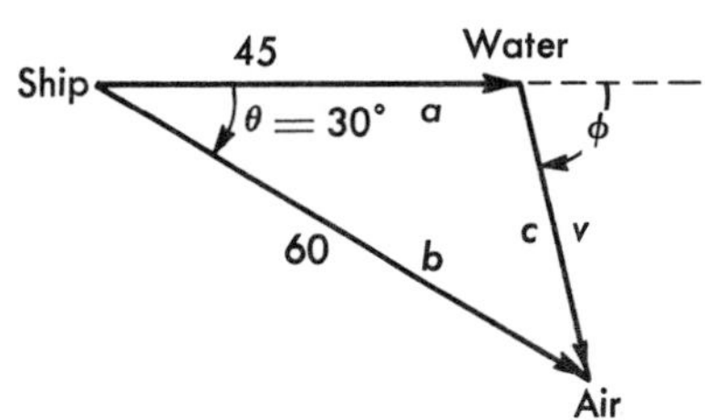

Diagram B.

To calculate the magnitude of the wind velocity with respect to the water, we can use the law of cosines, and to find its direction we can use the law of sines (see Appendix II). For the magnitude we write

$$c^2 = a^2 + b^2 - 2ab \cos \theta$$

$$v^2 = 45^2 + 60^2 - 2 \times 45 \times 60 \times 0.866$$

$$v = 30.80 \text{ Km/h}$$

And for the direction we can write

$$\frac{c}{\sin \theta} = \frac{b}{\sin (\pi - \phi)} = \frac{b}{\sin \phi}$$

Solving for ϕ,

$$\sin \phi = \frac{b \sin \theta}{c} = \frac{60 \times 0.500}{30.80}$$

from which $$\sin \phi = 0.9740$$

and $$\phi = 76.91°$$

$$v = 30.80 \text{ Km/h}$$

46.2. Relative Times for Two Planes

Because of its direct bearing upon Einstein's theory of relativity, the following problem should be of primary interest to every student. Suppose two pilots with identical planes are to fly to different cities equally far away. As shown in Fig. 46B one pilot flies north to city Y, at right angles to the wind, and returns, while the other flies east to city X, parallel to the wind, and returns. We now wish to find whether the two total flight times are different.

Let c represent the cruising speed of both planes, and v the velocity of the wind. Starting out for city Y, the first pilot, cruising at velocity c, sets his course west of north so that his flight path, with respect to the ground, is due north, as shown by the left-hand vector diagram. To return to home base H, he sets his course west of south so that his flight path is due south, as shown by the upper velocity triangle. Since his ground speed GP is the same each way, by the Pythagorean theorem for a right triangle, we find that

$$GP = \sqrt{c^2 - v^2}$$

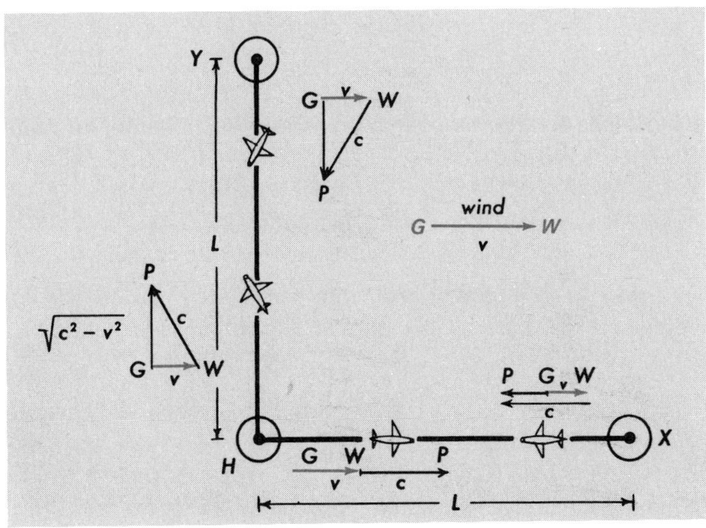

Fig. 46B. Comparisons of flight time for a plane flying downwind, upwind, and crosswind.

Starting out for city X, the second pilot, with the same air cruising velocity c, sets his course due east. Since his plane is flying *with* the wind, the ground speed GP is just the arithmetic sum of the two speeds:

$$GP = c + v$$

To return to home base H, the pilot sets his course due west. Flying against the wind, the plane has a reduced ground speed equal to the arithmetic difference between the two speeds:

$$GP = c - v$$

To find the total flight time $t_\perp$ of the first plane, we divide the total distance $2L$ by the velocity $\sqrt{c^2 - v^2}$:

$$t_\perp = \frac{2L}{\sqrt{c^2 - v^2}} \tag{46a}$$

To find the total flight time t of the second plane, the two different velocities, $c + v$ going and $c - v$ returning, must be used. Therefore, we have

$$t_{\parallel} = \frac{L}{c+v} + \frac{L}{c-v}$$

Placing these two terms over a common denominator, we obtain

$$t_{\parallel} = \frac{2Lc}{c^2 - v^2} \tag{46b}$$

One way to compare these flight times is to divide the perpendicular flight time by the parallel flight time and obtain

$$\frac{t_{\perp}}{t_{\parallel}} = \frac{2L}{\sqrt{c^2 - v^2}} \div \frac{2Lc}{c^2 - v^2}$$

Inverting the divisior and multiplying, we find

$$\frac{t_{\perp}}{t_{\parallel}} = \frac{2L}{\sqrt{c^2 - v^2}} \times \frac{c^2 - v^2}{2Lc} = \frac{\sqrt{c^2 - v^2}}{c}$$

from which we obtain the simplified result

$$\frac{t_{\perp}}{t_{\parallel}} = \sqrt{1 - \frac{v^2}{c^2}} \tag{46c}$$

This equation shows that flying with no wind blowing $v = 0$, the ratio of the two flight times is unity, which means that they are equal, as one would expect. When the wind is blowing, however, the ratio is less than unity, and the plane flying parallel to the wind requires the greater time. If the wind velocity increases to nearly that of the cruising speed of the planes, the ratio tends toward zero. If the wind velocity exceeds the cruising speed of the planes, the ratio becomes imaginary: the first plane is blown off its course and the second plane cannot get back to home base.

If will be left as a problem for the student to show that the time of flight over both of these two courses is greater when the wind is blowing than when it is calm.

Example 2. Two identical airplanes take off from the same airport, and with identical air speeds of 100.0 m/s fly to equally distant cities. They immediately turn around and return. City A lies 250 Km directly north, and city B lies 250 Km directly east. A wind is blowing from the west at 25.0 m/s. Find (a) the time of flight to each city, (b) the time to return, (c) each plane's total flight time, (d) the difference in total flight times, and (e) the ratio of total flight times.

Solution. The given quantities are $L = 2.50 \times 10^5$ m, $c = 100.0$ m/s, and $v = 25.0$ m/s. To find the answer to (a) we use one-half of Eq.(46a), and the first half of Eq.(46b). By direct substitution, we find

(a)

$$t_\perp = \frac{L}{\sqrt{c^2 - v^2}} = \frac{2.50 \times 10^5}{\sqrt{100^2 - 25^2}} = 2582 \text{ s}$$

$$t_{\parallel} = \frac{L}{c + v} = \frac{2.50 \times 10^5}{100 + 25} = 2000 \text{ s}$$

To return to home base, we use the second half of each equation. By direct substitution, we find

(b)

$$t_\perp = \frac{L}{\sqrt{c^2 - v^2}} = \frac{2.50 \times 10^5}{\sqrt{100^2 - 25^2}} = 2582 \text{ s}$$

$$t_{\parallel} = \frac{L}{c - v} = \frac{2.50 \times 10^5}{100 - 25} = 3333 \text{ s}$$

Total flight times are just the arithmetic sum of the two:

(c)

$$t_\perp = 2582 + 2582 = 5164 \text{ s}$$

$$t = 2000 + 3333 = 5333 \text{ s}$$

The difference in total flight times is

(d)

$$5333 - 5164 = 169 \text{ s}$$

And the ratio of the total flight times is

(e)

$$\frac{t_\perp}{t_{\parallel}} = \frac{5164 \text{ s}}{5333 \text{ s}} = 0.968$$

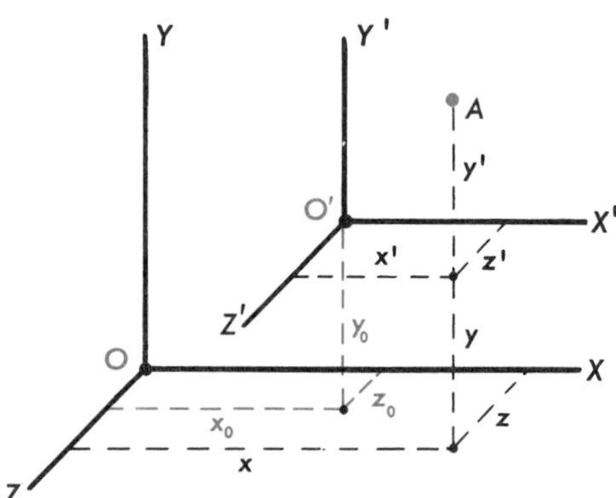

Fig. 46C. The coordinate distances of a point *A* measured in two different frames of reference (Cartesian coordinates).

As a check on this answer we may use **Eq. (46c)**, and find

$$\frac{t_\perp}{t_{||}} = \sqrt{1 - \frac{v^2}{c^2}} = \sqrt{1 - \frac{25^2}{100^2}}$$

$$\frac{t_\perp}{t_{||}} = 0.968$$

46.3. Frames of Reference

If two observers are moving with respect to one another, and both observers make measurements of any event, they could both be expected to come to the same conclusions as to what took place. In Fig. 46C we see two sets of rectangular, or *Cartesian*, coordinates called *frames of reference*. In the space common to these two frames is a single point marked A, and it is to this point that measurements are to be made. The first observer O′ in the upper right-hand frame measures the distance to A and finds the coordinates of this distance to be x', y', and z'. The second observer O in the lower left-hand frame measures the distance to A and finds coordinate distances x, y, and z.

Suppose that observer O′ now wishes to make measurements from which he can determine x, y, and z as observed by O. To do this, he measures the distance from O′ to O and finds the coordinates to be x_0, y_0, and z_0. He can now write down the following equalities:

$$\left.\begin{aligned} x &= x' + x_0 \\ y &= y' + y_0 \\ z &= z' + z_0 \end{aligned}\right\} \qquad (46d)$$

Suppose observer O wishes to make his own determination of x', y', and z' as observed by O′. To do this, he measures his distance from O to O′ and finds the coordinates to be x_0, y_0, and z_0. He then writes down the equations

$$\left.\begin{aligned} x' &= x - x_0 \\ y' &= y - y_0 \\ z' &= z - z_0 \end{aligned}\right\} \qquad (46e)$$

Note that the two sets of equations are the same and that they permit either observer to transform measurements made in his frame of reference to those made in the other. It is for this reason that such equations are called *transformation equations.*

46.4 Distance Measurements in Moving Frames of Reference

To transform measurements from one moving frame of reference to another, we will confine the motion to the line joining the two origins. It is along this straight line that x axes are set up for two frames, as shown in Fig. 46D. Here one observer O is located on a stationary platform C and the other observer O′ on a flat car C′ capable of moving freely along a track. Observer O and reference frame C will be assumed at rest, while observer O′ and car C′ will be assumed moving along together with constant velocity v.

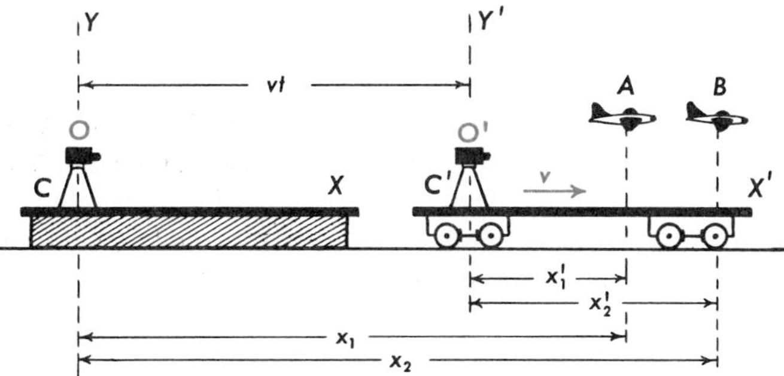

Fig. 46D. Distance measurements of two airplanes, *A* and *B*, from two frames of reference.

Both observers start their stop clocks at the instant O′ is opposite O. At some later time, both observers simultaneously note the time and snap pictures of two airplanes, A and B, directly over the track. From their stereophotographs, observer O finds the distances to be x_1 and x_2, while observer O′ finds the distances to be x'_1 *and* x'_2. Each observer now decides to use the transformation equations to find the other observer's distance measurements. Observer O uses Eq.(46e) and writes

$$x'_1 = x_1 - vt \qquad \text{and} \qquad x'_2 = x_2 - vt \tag{46f}$$

and observer O′ uses Eq.(46d) and writes

$$x_1 = x'_1 + vt \qquad \text{and} \qquad x_2 = x'_2 + vt$$

In each case they arrive at the same equations. Each observer finds that upon taking the difference between his own measured distances,

$$x_2 - x_1 = x'_2 - x'_1$$

Each observer concludes, therefore, that the distance between A and B is the same whether viewed from one frame or the other. The transformation of measurements from one moving frame of reference to another by means of the above equations is referred to as a *Galilean-Newtonian transformation.* Under such transformations, distances are said to be *invariant,* that is, they are the same.

We say, therefore, that in any Galilean-Newtonian system an object measured and found to have a length ℓ in one reference frame will be found to have the same length ℓ' when measured in any other reference frame:

$$\ell' = \ell \tag{46g}$$

Note that this equality of results does not depend upon the value of v or of t, but does depend upon all observations being made at the same instant, that is, *simultaneously.* In other words, anything happening in one frame at an instant t' is observed from the other frame as occurring at the same instant t:

$$t' = t \tag{46h}$$

46.5. Velocity Measurements in Moving Frames of Reference

We have seen in the preceding section that, under a Galilean–Newtonian transformation, the straight-line distance between two points is invariant. The question next arises whether the *velocity* of a moving body should be invariant, i.e., should the velocity be the same when observed from different frames which are themselves moving with different velocities? To find the answer to this question, we again make use of two observers, one stationary and the other on a flatcar as shown in Fig. 46E.

Both observers start their stopclocks at the instant the moving observer O′ is opposite the stationary observer O. At some later time, both observers simultaneously note the time t_1 as they snap stereo pictures of an airplane A_1 flying along and over the track. A short time later, both observers again note the time t_2 as they simultaneously snap pictures of the same plane at A_2. From their respective photographs each observer determines the plane's distance for each of the two times. Applying the transformation equations, Eq.(46f), they can write

$$x'_1 = x_1 - vt_1 \quad \text{and} \quad x'_2 = x_2 - vt_2$$

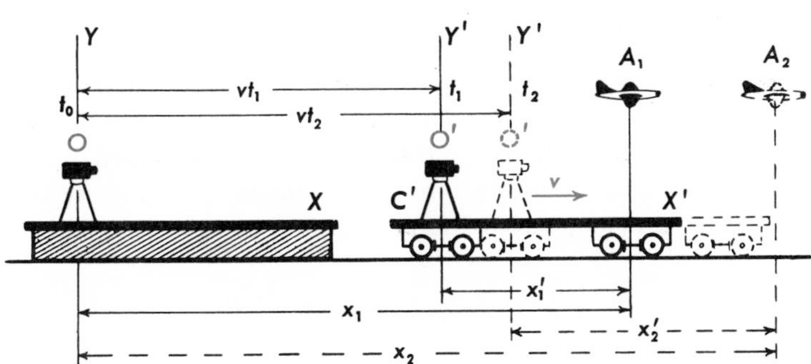

Fig. 46E. Velocity measurements of an airplane as observed from two frames of reference.

To find the average velocity of the plane, observer O′ takes his measured distance it has traveled, $x'_2 - x'_1$, and divides by the elapsed time $t'_2 - t'_1$. Taking the difference, he obtains

$$x'_2 - x'_1 = (x_2 - x_1) - (vt_2 - vt_1)$$

and dividing each term by either of the two equal time differences, he finds

$$\frac{x'_2 - x'_1}{t'_2 - t'_1} = \frac{x_2 - x_1}{t_2 - t_1} - \frac{v(t_2 - t_1)}{t_2 - t_1}$$

The term on the left represents the average velocity u' of the plane as observed by O′, while the middle term represents the average velocity u observed by O:

$$u' = \frac{x'_2 - x'_1}{t'_2 - t'_1} \quad \text{and} \quad u = \frac{x_2 - x_1}{t_2 - t_1}$$

Observer O′ can therefore write

$$u' = u - v \tag{46i}$$

Exactly the same equations can be written by observer O. Thus the two velocities measured by the two observers are not the same; they differ by the relative velocity of the two observers. We say that, *under a Galilean–Newtonian transformation, velocities are not invariant.*

46.6 An Accelerated Body Viewed from a Frame Moving with Constant Velocity

Suppose that the plane in Fig. 46E is increasing its speed, and by appropriate means of observation observers O and O′ determine its velocity when it passes point A_1, and again when it passes A_2. Using the transformation equation just derived for velocities, Eq.(46i), both observers can write down

$$u'_1 = u_1 - v \qquad \text{and} \qquad u'_2 = u_2 - v$$

Taking the difference between the two velocities u'_2 and u'_1, each would obtain

$$u'_2 - u'_1 = u_2 - u_1 \tag{46j}$$

Since each observer measured the time t between positions A_1 and A_2, each can divide his velocity difference by t to obtain the acceleration

$$\frac{u'_2 - u'_1}{t} = \frac{u_2 - u_1}{t}$$

or

$$a' = a \tag{46k}$$

In other words, the acceleration seen by both observers is exactly the same.

The conclusion to be drawn from this result is that *acceleration is invariant.* If we now assume the mass of a body is invariant, we can assume that the two observers could apply Newton's second law of motion, $F = ma$, and find the same force exerted by the plane's jet engines.

46.7. Falling Body Observed from a Constant-Velocity Frame

Suppose you as an observer O′, riding in a train, plane, bus, or ship with constant velocity, hold out a coin in front of you and drop it. The coin will appear to fall straight downward with the acceleration $g = 9.8\ \text{m/s}^2$.

If an observer outside on the ground were to observe the coin's motion, he would find it traverses a parabolic path. While the two observed paths would appear to be different, both observers would measure the same time of fall, and each could apply the transformation equations to determine what the other observer saw.

A simple demonstration of such an experiment is shown in Fig. 46F. A small car with a vertical stand is pulled along the table top at constant speed by means of an electric motor and drum. While the car is moving, an electric switch is opened; this deactivates an electromagnet and releases a steel marble for free fall. The ball falls in a small cup at the base of the stand, thus illustrating that to an observer O′ on the car the trajectory is straight downward.

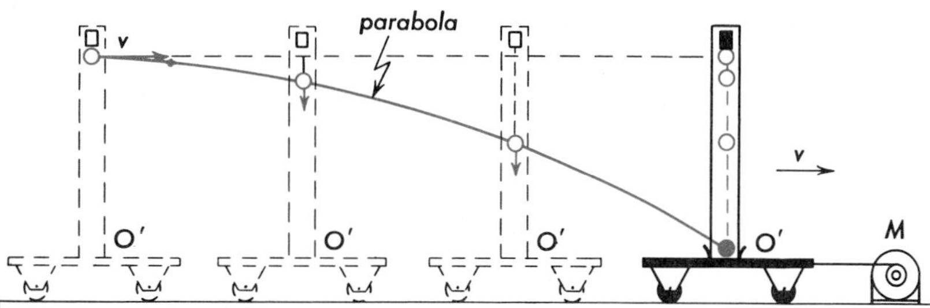

Fig. 46F. A falling-body experiment, showing the trajectory as viewed from a stationary frame and from a moving frame.

To a stationary observer O the released ball has an initial horizontal velocity v, and traverses the parabolic path as a projectile. If we apply the transformation Eq.(46i) to this example, the horizontal velocity u of the ball, as seen by observer O, is equal to the velocity v of the car, so that $u = v$. This gives $u' = 0$ as observed by O′, and the ball falls vertically downward.

46.8. Falling Bodies Observed from an Accelerated Frame

Suppose you, as an observer O′ riding in an accelerated vehicle, drop an object and observe its free fall. To an observer on the ground outside the object will appear to follow a parabolic path, but to you it will appear to fall in a straight-line path making an angle with the vertical. It will behave as though in addition to a downward acceleration g it also has a backward horizontal acceleration a.

An informative experiment demonstrating these observations is shown in Fig. 46G. A small car with a vertical stand attached is accelerated along the table top by a cord passing over two pulleys to a large mass *M*. Shortly after the car starts, an electric switch is opened, deactivating an electromagnet, releasing a steel marble for free fall. The marble falls in a small cup at one side of the base of the stand.

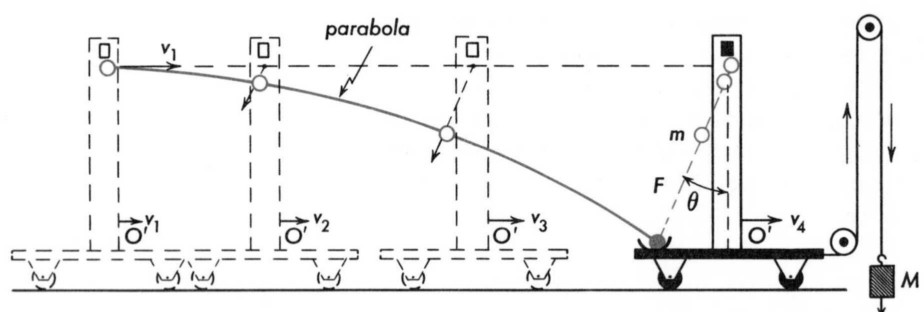

Fig. 46G. A falling-body experiment, showing the trajectory as viewed from a stationary frame and from an accelerated frame.

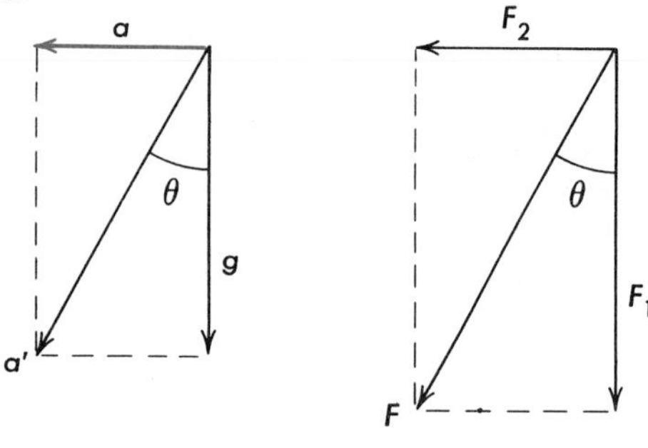

Fig. 46H. A falling body in an accelerated frame of reference appears to have two simultaneous accelerations, one an acceleration *g* vertically downward due to gravity, and the other an acceleration *a* opposite in direction to that in which the frame is accelerated.

To a stationary observer O, the released marble has an initial horizontal velocity v_1 (the velocity of the car at the instant of release), and it traverses the parabolic path as shown. To the accelerated observer O′ there appears to be a force *F* giving the marble an acceleration *a′* along a straight-line path making an angle θ with the vertical. This force is the vector resultant of the downward force of gravity F_1 and a horizontal force F_2. These forces, as well as their corresponding accelerations, *g*, *a*, and *a′*, are shown in Fig. 46H:

$$F_1 = mg, \qquad F_2 = ma, \qquad \text{and} \qquad F = ma'$$

Since there is no apparent reason for the horizontal force F_2 it is called a *fictitious force.* To the observer O this force does not exist and the marble obeys Newton's laws of motion.

46.9. Motion in a Rotating Frame

Imagine that you, as an observer O′, are on a merry-go-round and while it is turning with constant speed you place a marble on the floor at your feet. Since it is free to move, the marble will roll away from your feet and out along a curved path along the floor.

If a stone is fastened to a string and you hold the other end in your hand, it will not hang vertically but with the string making an angle with the vertical. At the center of rotation it will hang straight down, but at points away from the center the centrifugal component of force will increase the radius of its circular path.

If a large gun, fixed in position on the earth's surface, fires a shell at a distant ground target, the projectile deflects to the right in the northern hemisphere and to the left in the southern. The explanation of this phenomenon, that it is due to the earth's rotation, was first given by the French scientist Coriolis about the middle of the last century.

The clockwise rotation of winds and weather fronts in the southern hemisphere, and the counterclockwise rotation in the northern hemisphere, are due to the Coriolis forces on the moving air masses confined to the rotating earth.

To you as an observer on any rotating frame there is an apparent force F acting on every mass m. This force shown in Fig. 46I is not radially outward but makes an angle θ with the radius vector r. The radial component of this force is called the *centrifugal force* F_r, and the right-angled component is called the *Coriolis force* F_C.

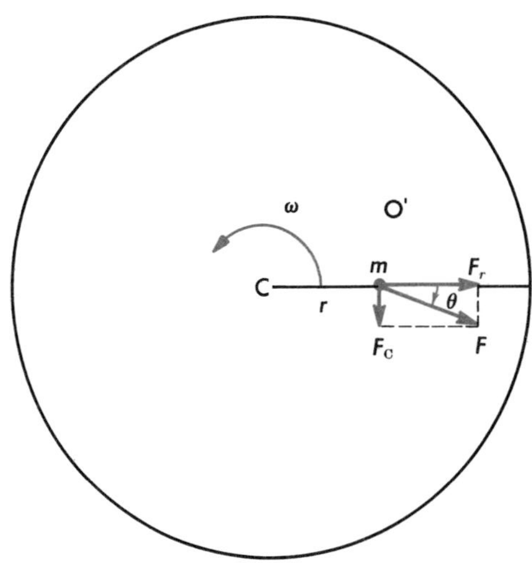

Fig. 46I. The centrifugal force F_r and the Coriolis force F_C are fictitious forces apparent to an observer O' on the rotating table.

By Newton's third law of motion the centrifugal force is equal and opposite to the centripetal force, and is given by Eq.(14k):

$$F_r = mr\omega^2 \tag{46\ell}$$

$$F_C = 2mv\omega \tag{46m}$$

Consider a demonstration in which a stream of water from a nozzle N, mounted on a turntable as shown in Fig. 46J, can be directed out across and a little above the surface. If the table is at rest and the stream of water is aimed at points A, B, C, or D, a stationary observer looking down from directly overhead will observe the water forming straight line paths NA, NB, NC, and ND, respectively.

If the table is set rotating at constant angular velocity ω, and the nozzle is pointed at the same points A, B, C, or D, one observes the water stream forming curved paths NA′, NB′, NC′, or ND′, respectively. Furthermore, if the velocity of projection v and the angular velocity ω remain constant, the curvature of all paths is approximately the same.

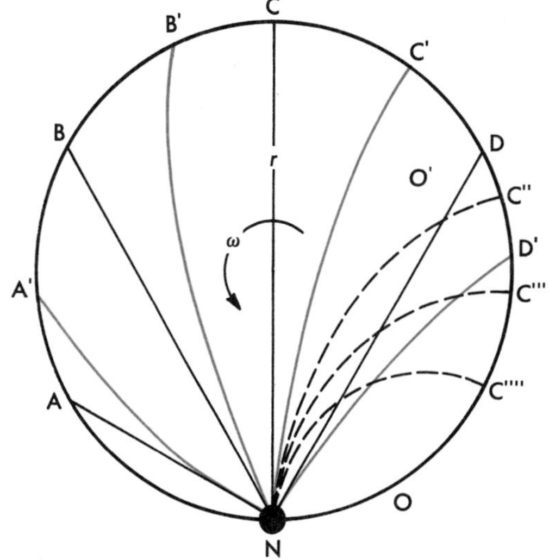

Fig. 46J. Paths of projectiles as seen from a stationary observer O, and a rotating observer O'.

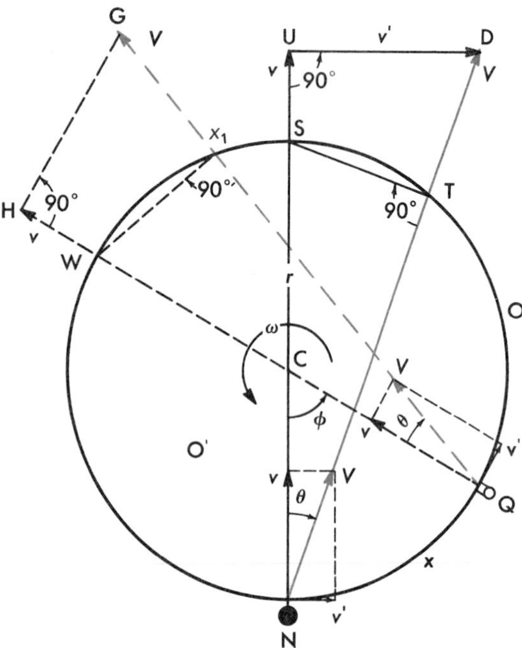

Fig. 46K. Geometrical relations for a rotating table and the Coriolis equations.

If the nozzle is directed toward a point like C, and the table is speeded up, the stream curvature increases. Such paths are shown as NC′, NC″, and NC‴. To see how such curved paths may be developed from a knowledge of classical mechanics, consider the illustration shown in Fig. 46K.

Consider a turntable of radius r rotating with an angular velocity ω (see Fig. 46K). A small toy machine gun is clamped on the periphery at N, and it is aimed in a direction that passes through the center C. The toy gun fires projectiles at regular intervals, and with a muzzle velocity v. Since the gun at N is moving at right angles to v, each bullet is also given a lateral velocity v'. This additional velocity component is given by Eq.(11f) as

$$v' = \omega r \tag{46n}$$

Each bullet fired from the gun has a velocity which is the vector sum of v and v'. As seen from the diagram, the resultant velocity V is given by

$$V = \sqrt{v^2 + v'^2} \tag{46o}$$

and its direction by

$$\tan \theta = \frac{v'}{v} \tag{46p}$$

To an observer in a stationary frame of reference O, the page of the book, the bullet traverses the straight line path ND. At some later time t, when the gun passes the point Q, another bullet is fired with the same speed, and it traverses the path QG. We now wish to calculate the time it takes each bullet to cross the table from N to T, or Q to X. Let the lines NU, UD, and ND represent the velocities v, v', and V, respectively, NS the diameter of the table $2r$, and NT the projectile's path above the table. Since the two right triangles NUD and NTS have equal angles, they are similar, and we can write corresponding sides proportional to each other:

$$\frac{\text{NT}}{\text{NS}} = \frac{\text{NU}}{\text{ND}} \qquad \text{or} \qquad \frac{\text{NT}}{2r} = \frac{v}{V}$$

which gives

$$\text{NT} = \frac{2rv}{V}$$

From mechanics we have *distance equals velocity multiplied by time*, from which the time t is given by distance divided by velocity:

$$t = \frac{2rv}{V^2} \tag{46q}$$

In this time t the table rotates through the angle ϕ, which is given by

$$\phi = \omega t \tag{46r}$$

where ϕ is in radians.

The distance the gun has moved is given by x, where

$$x = r\phi \tag{46s}$$

Example 3. A toy machine gun is clamped to the periphery of a turntable 3.0 m in diameter. The table rotates with a speed of 1.0 rad/s, and the gun fires bullets every ¼ second, with a muzzle velocity of 4.0 m/s. Find (a) the velocity component v', (b) the bullet's velocity V, (c) the angle θ, (d) the time it takes each bullet to cross the table, (e) the angle through which the table has turned in this time, and (f) the distance the gun has moved during this time. (g) Make a diagram.

Solution. The given quantities are $v = 4.0$ m/s, $r = 1.50$ m, and $\omega = 1.0$ rad/s. By direct substitution in Eq.(46n), we obtain

$$v' = r\omega = 1.50 \times 1.0 = 1.50 \text{ m/s}$$

Combining this velocity with the gun's muzzle velocity v, we use Eq.(46o) and obtain

$$V = \sqrt{v^2 + v'^2} = \sqrt{4^2 + 1.5^2} = 4.272 \text{ m/s}$$

To find the angle θ, we use Eq.(46p) as follows:

$$\tan\theta = \frac{v'}{v} = \frac{1.50}{4.00} = 0.3750$$

from which

$$\theta = 20°33' = 20.56°$$

We now construct the additional graph shown in Fig. 46L, drawing the table dimensions to scale, as well as the angles and velocities. The diagram is constructed to show each bullet's instantaneous position and direction as seen by observer O, at the time of 1.0 s. A smooth curve has been drawn through each bullet's position to show the path of the projectiles as seen by a rotating observer O′.

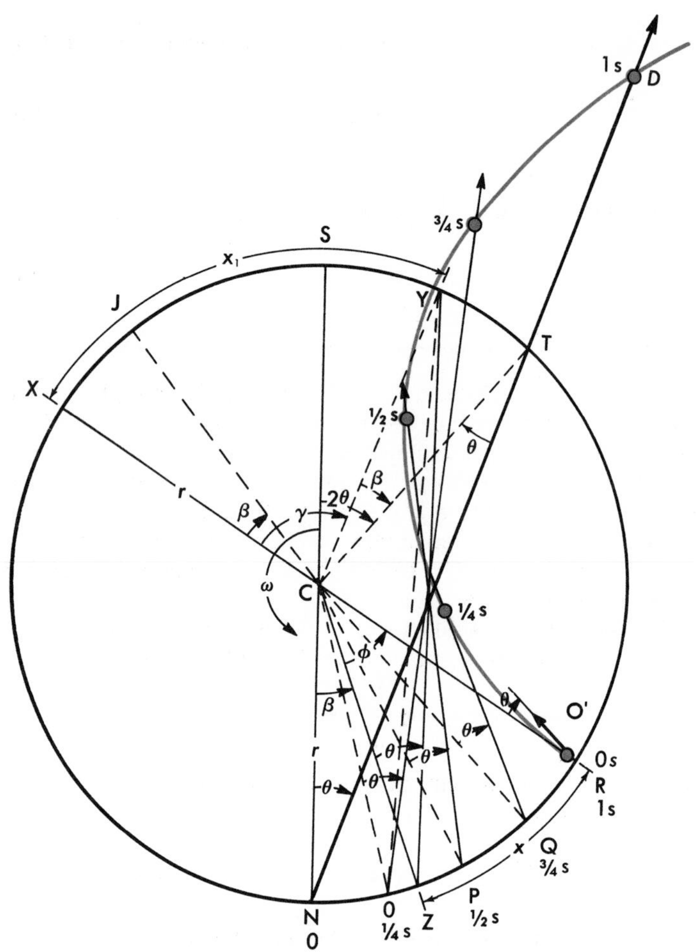

Fig. 46L. Geometrical relations for the rotating table described in Example 3.

We calculate the time required for a projectile to cross the table. By use of Eq.(46q), we find

$$t = \frac{2rv}{V^2} = \frac{2 \times 1.50 \times 4.0}{(4.272)^2} = \frac{12.0}{18.25}$$

$$t = 0.6575 \text{ s}$$

and for the angle ϕ, we obtain

$$\phi = \omega t = 1.0 \times 0.6575$$

$$\phi = 0.6575 \text{ rad} = 37.67°$$

With a protractor we now measure off the angle 37.67° backward from the line RC, and draw the lines ZC and ZY. The line ZY represents the path of a bullet that would be crossing the table boundary on the far side when another is just leaving the gun at point R. Using Eq.(46s), we obtain

$$x = r\phi = 1.50 \times 0.6575$$

$$x = 0.9863 \text{ m}$$

As viewed from the rotating table the bullets are following each other along the curved path with a speed that varies with their position. As the table rotates with constant velocity, observer O′ sees the curved path of the projectiles, unchanged and stationary.

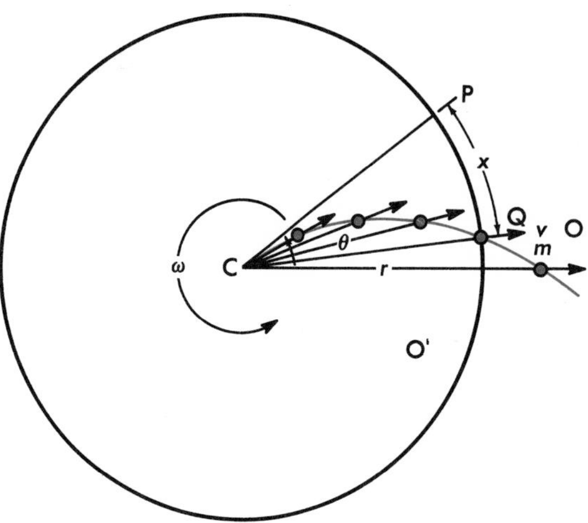

Fig. 46M. Diagram for the derivation of the formula for the Coriolis acceleration and the Coriolis force.

A derivation of a formula for the Coriolis acceleration and Coriolis force follows from Fig. 46M. A mass m is given a velocity v in a direction which is radially outward from C toward the stationary observer O. When it passes the point Q the table has turned through an angle θ. to the rotating observer O′, the projectile has moved away from the point P a distance x. From classical mechanics

$$x = \tfrac{1}{2}\, a_C t^2 \tag{46t}$$

Since $x = r\theta$ and $\theta = \omega t$, we can substitute and find

$$r\omega t = \tfrac{1}{2}\, a_C t^2 \tag{46u}$$

from which

$$a_C = \frac{2r\omega}{t}$$

Since the velocity v is just r/t, we obtain

$$a_C = 2v\omega \tag{46v}$$

as the Coriolis acceleration. By Newton's second law of motion, $F = ma$, the Coriolis force becomes

$$F_C = 2mv\omega \tag{46w}$$

These two equations are first approximations only, and hold for cases where angle θ is small, and not much greater than 2 or 3 degrees (see Fig. 46K). For larger angles the following equations are valid.

In Fig. 46L the length of the arc XY represents the distance the projectiles miss their target. This arc is given by

$$x_1 = r\gamma \tag{46x}$$

where

$$\gamma = \phi + \beta + 2\theta - \beta$$

or

$$\gamma = \phi + 2\theta \tag{46y}$$

Note from geometry that the arc ST subtends twice the angle θ at the center C that it does at N, and that the angle γ = XCY, rotated clockwise through the angle β, falls directly on angle JCT. In Example 3,

$$\gamma = 37.67° + 41.11° = 78.78°$$
$$\gamma = 1.375 \text{ rad}$$

and the distance x_1 is given by

$$x_1 = 1.50 \times 1.375 = 2.063 \text{ m}$$

46.10. Classical Relativity; Newtonian Mechanics

From the treatment of the kinematics of motion in this chapter, we have seen how an observer in one reference frame can make measurements of something happening in another reference frame and, by applying simple transformation equations, find the measurements that apply to the second frame.

We have seen that if the relative velocity of the two frames is constant, the distance between two points, or the length of an object measured from either frame, is found to be the same. If the *acceleration* of an object is measured from both frames, the two results again come out the same, but if the *velocity* is measured, the two values are different. In other words:

Distances and accelerations are invariant and do not depend upon any relative velocity of an observer, while velocities are variant.

Even though velecities may be different for two observers, the transformation equations make the two velocities compatible. If measurements of the motion of a body in one frame of reference are transformed to find the measurements that would apply in another frame, we say that we are applying the Newtonian transformation equations. These transformation equations are

$$\begin{aligned} x' &= x - vt \\ u' &= u - v \\ \ell' &= \ell \\ a' &= a \\ t' &= t \end{aligned} \tag{46z}$$

A set of coordinates that is fixed relative to an observer is called the observer's *frame of reference.* If a frame of reference is accelerated, a body initially at rest or moving in that frame appears to have a fictitious force acting upon it. Since, therefore, Newton's laws of motion do not apply in an accelerated frame of reference, a frame that is not accelerated is called a *Galilean–Newtonian* or *inertial frame of reference.*

In setting up the Galilean–Newton transformation equations, it was assumed that all measurements were simultaneous, i.e., that the light with which one sees an object travels with an infinite speed. If the relative velocities of moving frames are small compared with the speed of light (3.0×10^8 m/s), the speed of light can be assumed to be infinite, and the principles developed in this and the preceding chapters are valid. Newtonian mechanics applies, therefore, to velocities that are low compared with the speed of light, while a modified system called *relativistic mechanics* will apply to velocities comparable to the speed of light (see Chap. 48).

problems

1. A motor boat cruising through the water at 3.0 m/s is headed east straight across a river. If the water flows at the rate of 0.5 m/s to the south, find the velocity of the boat with respect to the bank.

2. To an observer on a ship sailing due north at 45 Km/h, it appears that a 30.0 Km/h wind is blowing from the southeast. Find the true wind velocity.

3. A pilot with a plane having a cruising speed of 65.0 m/s leaves an airport and sets his course at 30° south of east. After flying for 1.0 h, he discovers he is 160.0 Km directly east of his starting point. What is the average wind velocity that blew him off his course? [Ans. 34.59 m/s at 20.03° west of north.]

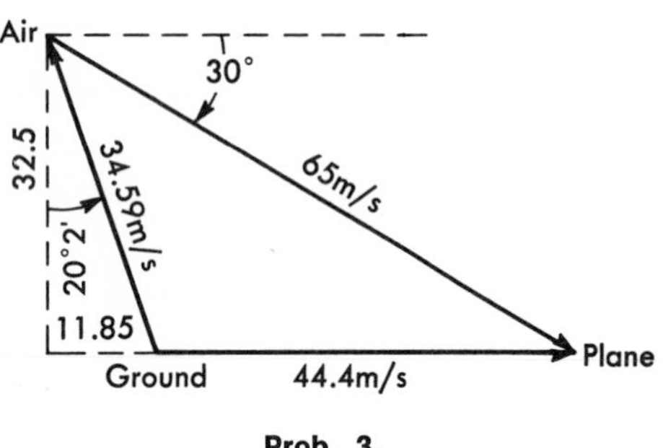

Prob. 3.

4. Two pilots flying identical aircraft with cruising speeds of 400 Km/h fly to distant cities 500 Km away, and return to home base. City X lies to the west, and city Y lies to the south. Aloft there is a 200-Km/h wind blowing from the east. Find (a) the time of flight to each city, (b) the time of flight returning, (c) the difference in total flight times, and (d) the ratio of the total flight times.

5.* Two swimmers starting simultaneously from the same anchored marker in a river swim to distant anchored markers, and return. One marker Y is directly across the stream 200 m, and the other marker X is up stream 200 m. If both swimmers have a water speed of 1.40 m/s, and the river flows at 0.250 m/s, (a) how long will it take each swimmer to reach his distant marker, (b) what is each swimmer's time to return, (c) what is the difference in the swimmers' total time, and (d) what is the ratio of their total times?

6.* Two identical airplanes take off from the same airport and fly to different cities 1000 Km away. They immediately turn around and return to home base. Their air speeds are both 600 Km/h. City X lies to the east and city Y lies to the north. Aloft a wind of 100 Km/h is blowing from the west. Find the time for each plane (a) to reach their distant cities, (b) to return to home base. Find (c) the difference in total flight times, and (d) the ratio of the total flight times. [Ans. (a) 1.429 h, 1.690 h, (b) 2.0 h, 1.690 h, (c) 0.0480 h, or 2.88 min, (d) 0.986.]

7. A freight train on a straight and level track is traveling at 25.0 m/s. A boy standing on the rear end of a 20.0-m flat car fires a small rocket in the forward direction with an acceleration of 3.0 m/s². Neglecting gravity, find the velocity of the rocket as it passes the far end of the flat car, (a) as seen by the boy, and (b) as seen by a ground observer. Find the acceleration of the rocket as seen by (c) the boy, and (d) a ground observer.

8. Solve Prob. 7 if the flat car is 28.0 m long, and is traveling 35.0 m/s on the tracks. Assume the small rocket has an acceleration of 3.20 m/s².

9. A railroad flat car, like the one shown in Fig. 46G, has an acceleration of 1.750 m/s². If a man standing on the car drops a stone from a height of 1.0 m above the floor, find (a) the angle of descent, and (b) the horizontal lag of the ball when it strikes the floor.

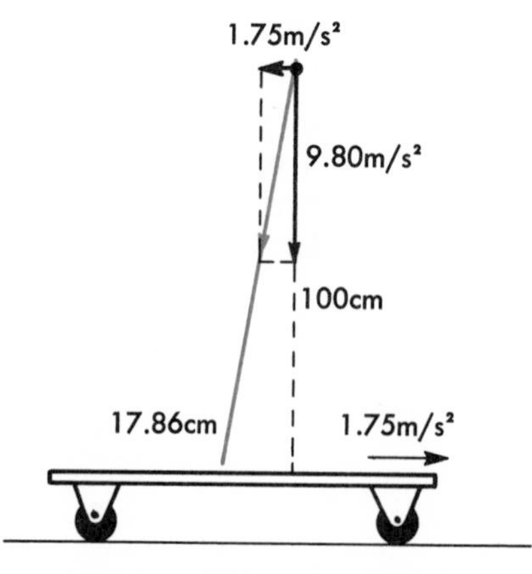

Prob. 9.

[Ans. (a) 10.12°, (b) 17.86 cm behind its point of release.]

10. A car like the one shown in Fig. 46G has an acceleration of 2.250 m/s². If a brass ball is dropped from a height of 1.50 m, find (a) the angle of descent, and (b) the horizontal lag of the ball as seen by an observer on the car.

11. A 50.0-g projectile is fired with a velocity of 25.0 m/s from a spring gun, as shown in Fig. 46J. If the table rotates at 6.0 rpm, find (a) the Coriolis acceleration, and (b) the Coriolis force.

12.* A stream of water from a nozzle clamped on the edge of a circular turntable 3.0 m in diameter shoots straight across the diameter and hits the center of a target with a velocity of 4.0 m/s. If the table is now set into rotation at 0.50 rad/s, find (a) the velocity increment v', (b) the velocity V, (c) the angle θ, (d) the time it takes each drop to cross the table, (e) the angle ϕ through which the table turns in this time, (f) the distance x the gun has moved in this time, (g) the distance x_1 the stream misses its target, (h) the Coriolis acceleration, and (i) the distance the stream would miss its target according to the Coriolis acceleration formula. (j) Make a diagram. [Ans. (a) 0.750 m/s, (b) 4.07 m/s, (c) 10.61°, (d) 0.724 s, (e) 20.75°, (f) 0.543 m, (g) 1.099 m, (h) 4.0 m/s², (i) 1.050 m, (j) diagram.]

13.* Solve Prob. 12 if the angular velocity of the table is 1.250 rad/s.

14.* Solve Prob. 12 if the angular velocity of the table is 2.0 rad/s.

15.* A merry-go-round with a diameter of 15.0 m is rotating at 0.250 rad/s. A boy on the outer edge aims an arrow at a target diametrically opposite on the merry-go-round. He fires the arrow with a velocity of $v = 60.0$ m/s. Find (a) the velocity component v', (b) the

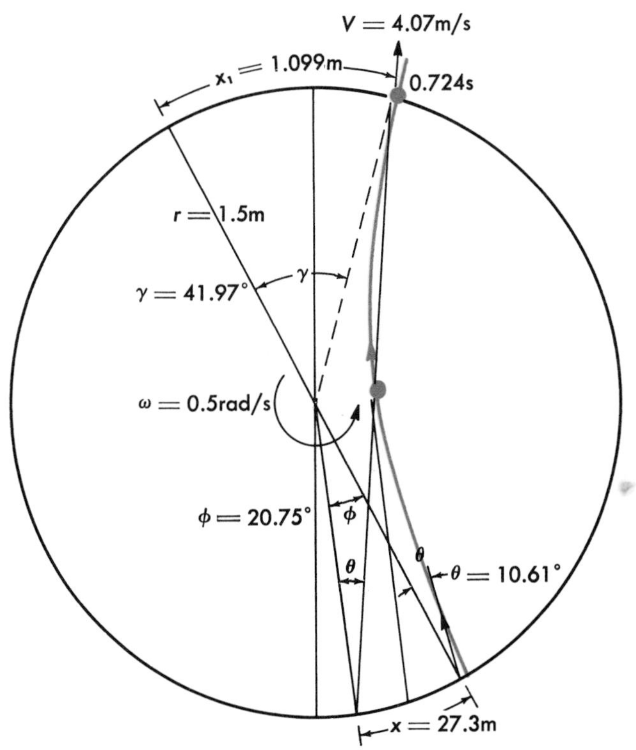

Prob. 12.

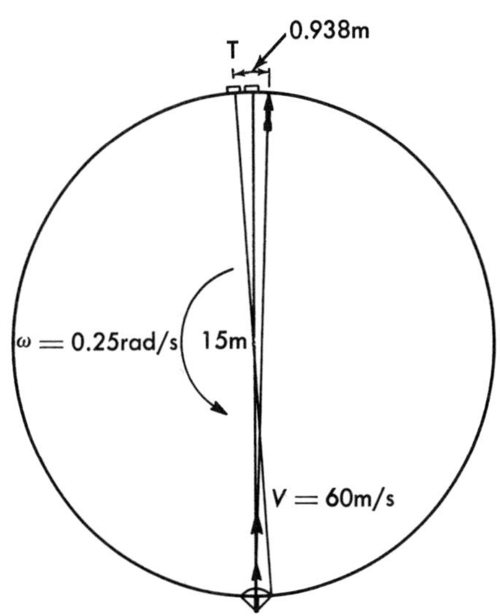

Prob. 15.

velocity V, (c) the angle θ, (d) the time it reaches the other side of the merry-go-round, (e) the angle ϕ, (f) the angle γ, (g) the distance the arrow misses the target, (h) the Coriolis acceleration, and (i) the distance the arrow would miss its target according to the Coriolis acceleration. (j) Make a diagram. [Ans. (a) 1.875 m/s, (b) 60.0 m/s, (c) 1.790°, (d) 0.250 s, (e) 3.581°, (f) 7.16°, (g) 0.938 m, (h) 30.0 m/s^2, (i) 0.938 m, (j) diagram.]

16.* Solve Prob. 15 if the merry-go-round is 12.0 m in diameter, rotating with an angular velocity of 0.280 rad/s, and the arrow is shot with a velocity of 50.0 m/s.

47 Interferometers and lasers

In this chapter we will study the *Michelson* interferometer,* and then Fizeau's experiment by which the speed of light is found to be altered by a moving stream of water. The latter leads directly to the principles of the famous *Michelson–Morley experiment* on ether drift, which in turn leads to Einstein's theory of relativity.

We will then consider the *Fabry–Perot interferometer* as it applies to the hyperfine structure of spectrum lines, and finally to the principles of the recently developed instruments called *lasers.*

*Albert Abraham Michelson (1852–1931), American physicist, was born of Jewish parents in Strelno, Germany, in December 19, 1852. His parents moved to San Francisco where he studied in the public schools; in 1873 he graduated from the U.S. Naval Academy and was physics and chemistry instructor for four years thereafter. In 1883, he became professor of physics at Case School of Applied Science, and while there, developed the interferometer known by his name. In 1892, he became Chairman of the Physics Department, University of Chicago, where he directed his attention to measuring the speed of light. He received many national and international awards for his research and was the first American to receive the Nobel Prize in physics (1907). He published several books on optics and is most famous for the Michelson interferometer, as well as its application to the famous Michelson-Morley experiment on ether drift. As a college student the author had the good fortune to meet Michelson and see him making measurements on the speed of light at the Mt. Wilson Observatory during the summer of 1926.

47.1. The Michelson Interferometer

The form of the Michelson interferometer generally found in the science laboratory is that shown in Fig. 47A. The optical parts consist of two mirrors, M_1 and M_2, and two parallel plates of glass, G_1 and G_2. Oftentimes the rear side of plate G_1 is lightly silvered (shown heavy in the figure) so that light coming from the source S is divided into (1) a reflected and (2) a transmitted beam of equal intensity. The light returning from M_1 passes through G_1 a third time before reaching the eye. The light returning from M_2 is reflected from G_1 and into the eye. The purpose of plate G_2 is to render the total path in glass equal for the two rays.

The mirror M_1 is mounted on a well-machined guide and can be moved along slowly by means of a screw V. When mirror M_2 is made exactly perpendicular to M_1 by screws on its back face, interference fringes similar to those found with a double slit may be seen, or photographed, at E. Photographs of typical fringes when mirror M_1 is at different distances are shown in Fig. 47B.

When monochromatic light is used as a source and the mirrors are in exact adjustment, circular fringes are observed as shown in photographs (a) and (b). If the mirrors are not exactly at right angles to each other, fringes like those in photographs (c) and (d) are obtained. If circular fringes are observed, and mirror M_1 is

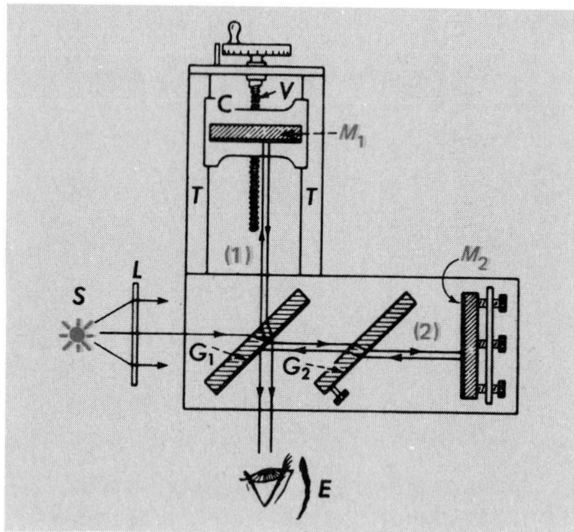

Fig. 47A. Diagram of the Michelson interferometer.

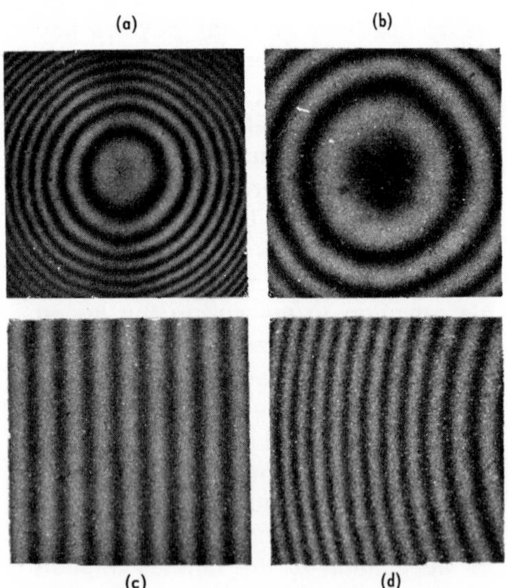

Fig. 47B. Interference fringe patterns as photographed with a Michelson interferometer.

slowly moved along by the turn of the screw V, the circular fringe pattern will expand or contract; if it expands, new fringes will appear as a dot at the center, widen, and expand into a circle; and if it contracts, fringes grow smaller, become a dot, and vanish at the center. If straight or curved fringes are observed, the motion of M_1 causes the fringes to drift across the field at right angles to the fringe lines.

The expansion, contraction, or drift in the pattern for a distance of one fringe corresponds to M_1 moving a distance of exactly $\frac{1}{2}$ wavelength of light. When M_1 moves back a distance of $\frac{1}{2}\lambda$, the total light path (1) increases a whole wavelength. If M_1 moves 1λ, the pattern will move two fringes because the total light path (1) has changed by 2λ. Any bright fringe that one observes is caused by both beams coming together in phase. When the one path is changed by $\frac{1}{2}\lambda$, 1λ, $\frac{3}{2}\lambda$, etc., the two beams arriving at the same field points will again be in phase.

By counting the number of fringes required to move the mirror M_1 a given distance, the wavelength of light can be calculated. This would appear to be the most direct and accurate method for the wavelength measurements of different light sources. Knowing the accurate wavelength of any light source, one can then use the interferometer to accurately measure distances.

It was by means of the Michelson interferometer that the standard meter was determined in terms of the wavelength of orange light $\lambda = 6057.80$ Å of krypton, element 36:*

$$1 \text{ meter} = 1{,}650{,}763.73 \text{ wavelengths}$$
(for orange light of krypton)

47.2. Velocity of Light in Moving Matter

In 1859, the French physicist Armand Fizeau measured the velocity of light in a moving stream of water and found that the light was carried along by the stream. A schematic diagram of his apparatus is shown in Fig. 47C.

Light from a monochromatic source S is separated into two beams by means of a lens L_1. These two beams pass through tubes A and B which contain water flowing rapidly in opposite directions. After reflection from M the beams traverse opposite tubes, so that upon arrival at L_1 one has traversed streams A and B in the direction of flow, while the other has traversed both

* Adopted as the international legal standard of length on October 14, 1960, by the General Conference on Weights and Measures in Paris, France. See Introduction C.

tubes but always against the flow. Part of each beam is reflected by the half-silvered plate G and the two brought together at S′ where interference fringes are produced.

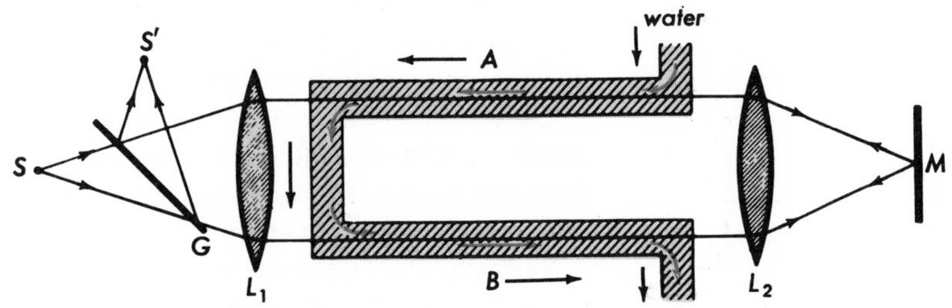

Fig. 47C. Fizeau's experiment for measuring the velocity of light in a moving medium.

If the light travels faster by one path than the other, the time will be different and the fringes formed at S′ will have shifted. Using tubes 1.5 m long and a water speed of 7.0 m/s, Fizeau found a shift of 0.46 of a fringe upon a reversal of the water stream. This shift corresponds to a decrease in the speed of light in one direction, and an increase in the other, of about half the speed of the water. In other words, the moving water has a dragging effect upon the light waves.

In 1818, the French physicist Augustin Fresnel derived a formula for this dragging effect, based upon the existence of what was then called the *ether.* His formula gives

$$v = v_0 + u\left(1 - \frac{1}{\mu^2}\right) \tag{47a}$$

where v is the velocity of light in water when the water is moving at a velocity u, v_0 is the velocity of light in stationary water, and μ is the index of refraction. For water, with an index of 1.33, $v' = 0.43v$ in reasonably good agreement with Fizeau's observations.

47.3. The Michelson–Morley Experiment

This, the most famous experiment in optics, was first performed by Michelson and Morley in 1881, in an effort to detect the motion of the earth through space. If the transmission of light through space requires an ether, that is, a medium for it to move in, then light should be dragged along by this ether as the earth moves

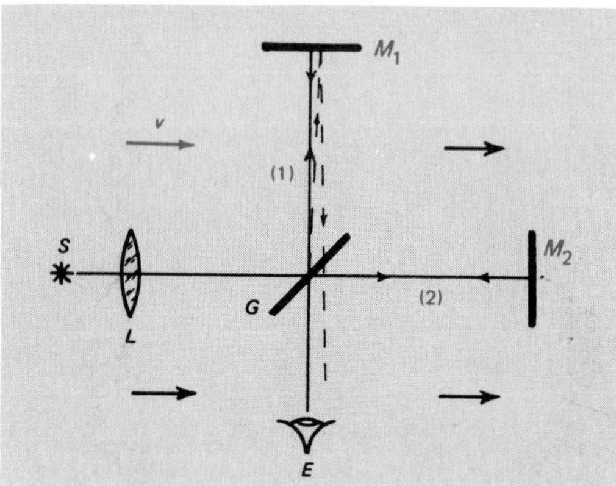

Fig. 47D. The Michelson interferometer arrangement for detecting an ether drift.

along through space. In order to detect such a drift, the Michelson interferometer appeared to be the most sensitive instrument to use.

In principle the ether drift test consists simply of observing whether there is any shift of the interference fringes of light in the Michelson interferometer when the entire instrument is turned through an angle of 90°. Let us assume that the interferometer and the earth are at rest and that the ether is moving by with a velocity v as shown in Fig. 47D. If no ether drag is effective, light paths (1) and (2) will be out and back, as shown by the solid lines and arrows, and a set of interference bands like those shown in Fig. 47B will be observed.

Normally, the mirrors of the interferometer are adjusted so the fringes are practically straight and parallel as shown in photograph (c), and quite wide so that any shift can be readily observed and measured. As a rule the light used with the Michelson interferometer is as nearly monochromatic as possible to make the intensity contour come down to zero between fringes.

If we now suppose the light to be dragged along by an ether, the time it takes for light to traverse path (1) at right angles to the ether stream, and the time it takes to traverse path (2), first with and then against the stream, will both be increased.

The times to traverse paths (1) and (2) are given in Eqs.(46a) and (46b) as

$$t_{\perp} = \frac{2L}{\sqrt{c^2 - v^2}} \qquad t_{\parallel} = \frac{2Lc}{c^2 - v^2} \tag{47b}$$

where c is the velocity of light *in vacuo,* and v is the very much slower drift velocity.

A little study of these equations will show that, while both times have been increased a slight amount, the increase is twice as large in the direction of motion. Furthermore, the ratio of the two times is given by

$$\frac{t_{\perp}}{t_{\parallel}} = \sqrt{1 - \frac{v^2}{c^2}} \tag{47c}$$

An ether drift should, therefore, cause a shift in the fringes observed in the interferometer. Since neither the earth's motion, nor the ether, can be stopped, in an effort to observe this shift, a rotation of the interferometer through 90° should have a similar effect. By interchanging paths (1) and (2), the time difference $t \; - t_{\perp}$ is reversed, and any fringe shift should be doubled.

Michelson and Morley made the light paths as much as 11 m long by reflecting the light back and forth between 16 mirrors, as shown in Fig. 47E. To prevent distortion by the turning of the instrument, the entire apparatus was mounted on a concrete block floating in mercury, and observations of the fringes were made as it rotated slowly and continuously about a vertical axis.

If we assume the ether velocity *v* to be 29.9 Km/s (the speed of the earth on its orbit around the sun), and the speed of light *c* to be 3×10^5 Km/s, a shift of $\frac{1}{2}$ a fringe should have been observed. No shift as great as $\frac{1}{10}$ of this was observed. Such a negative result was so surprising and so disappointing that others have repeated the experiment.

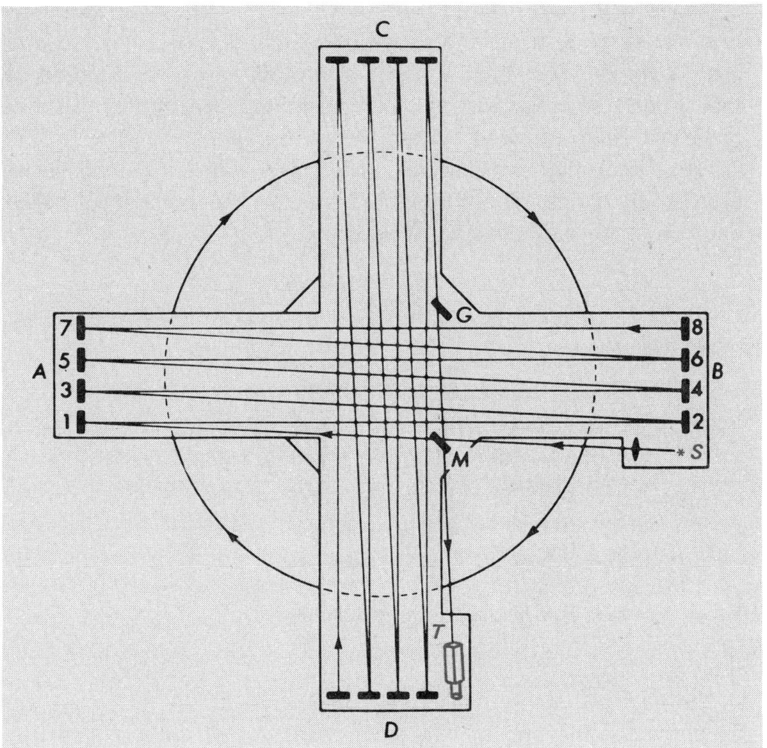

Fig. 47E. Miller's elaborate arrangement of the Michelson–Morley experiment to detect ether drift.

The most exacting work was done by D. C. Miller who used Michelson and Morley's arrangement, but with optical paths of 64 m in place of 11 m. While Miller thought he found evidence for a shift of $\frac{1}{30}$ of a fringe, the latest analysis of Miller's data makes it probable that no shift exists.

47.4 The Fabry–Perot Interferometer

Unlike the Michelson interferometer that produces interference fringe patterns with two coherent beams of light, the Fabry–Perot interferometer produces interference with a large number of coherent beams. The principles of this device are shown in Fig. 47F.

Two optically flat glass or quartz plates, each partially silvered on one face only, are mounted in rigid frames. By means of the fine screws the plates are adjusted until their two silvered surfaces are parallel to a high degree of precision. Light from an extended source S, upon passing through the interferometer, undergoes reflection back and forth, and the emerging parallel rays are brought together to interfere in the focal plane of a lens.

In Fig. 47F a ray of light from the point P is shown incident on the first surface at an angle θ. Part of this light is reflected and part is transmitted. Part of the transmitted ray 1 is reflected at the second surface and part is transmitted. Repeating this behavior at each mirrored surface it can be seen that rays 1, 3, 5, 7, etc., emerging as parallel rays have traveled successively greater distances. These numbers specify the number of times each ray traverses the gap of width d.

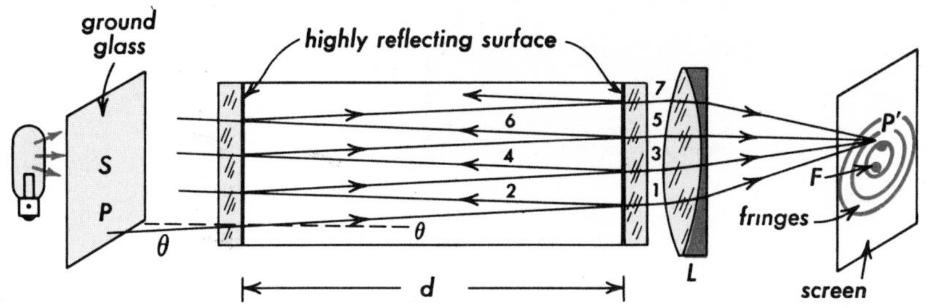

Fig. 47F. Diagram of the paths of light rays in a Fabry–Perot interferometer.

The *path difference* between successive rays 1, 3, 5, 7, etc., will be shown at the end of this section to be just $2d \cos \theta$. If this distance is exactly equal to a whole number of wavelengths, the emergent rays when brought together at the point P′ will all be in phase and produce a bright spot. For such a bright spot we can write

$$2d \cos \theta = n\lambda \tag{47d}$$

where n is a whole number and λ is the wavelength.

For all rays from all points of the source incident at the same angle θ, identical phase relations will exist, and the lens will bring all sets of parallel rays to a focus at points lying on a circle in the focal plane of the lens. For those rays in which the angle θ is such that the path difference between successively reflected rays is $(n + \frac{1}{2})\lambda$, the waves in alternate rays will be out of step and destructively interfere to produce darkness. Hence the existence of bright and dark concentric rings on the screen indicates coherence as well as interference.

The interference ring patterns in Fig. 47G illustrate the difference between the kinds of fringes observed when (a) two beams of light are brought together, as in the Michelson interferometer and (b) when a large number of beams are brought together as with the Fabry–Perot interferometer.

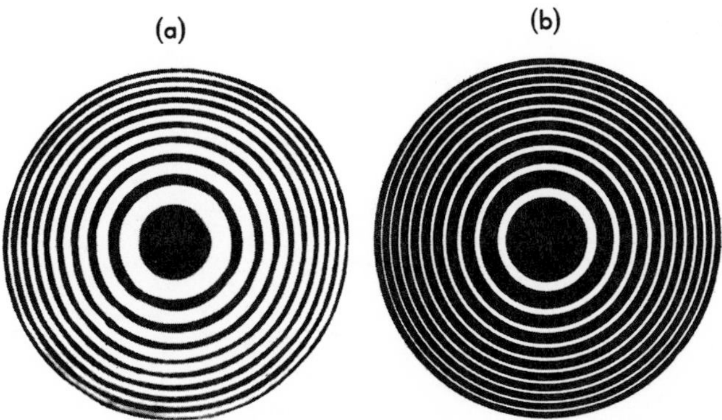

Fig. 47G. Comparison of the types of fringes produced with (a) the Michelson interferometer and (b) the Fabry–Perot interferometer.

Note that in Fig. 47F, for rays entering the interferometer parallel to the axis, that is, with $\theta = 0$, the multiply reflected rays will be brought together at the focal point F, and if these waves arrive in phase, a bright spot will be produced there, and

$$2d = n\lambda \tag{47e}$$

The number n is called the *order of interference*, or in microwave terminology, the *principal oscillation mode* of the cavity.

Example 1. A Fabry-Perot interferometer has a spacing of 6.850 cm. Find the order of interference for red light from a hydrogen discharge tube, if the wavelength is 6561.0 Å.

Solution. The given quantities are $\lambda = 6.561 \times 10^{-7}$ m and $d = 6.850 \times 10^{-2}$ m. Solve Eq.(47e) for n, and substitute the known values:

$$n = \frac{2d}{\lambda} = \frac{2 \times 6.85 \times 10^{-2}\text{m}}{6.561 \times 10^{-7}\text{m}}$$

$$n = 2.0881 \times 10^{5}$$

To derive Eq.(47d) for the bright fringes of a Fabry–Perot interferometer, we refer to Fig. 47H. As ray 1 leaves the point A, ray 3 must travel the extra distance A to B to C to emerge in phase with ray 1. By extending the line BC back to the left, until it intersects the normal AR at the point Q, an isosceles triangle QBA is formed. Since this makes the line QB equal to AB, the total path difference

$$AB + BC = QC$$

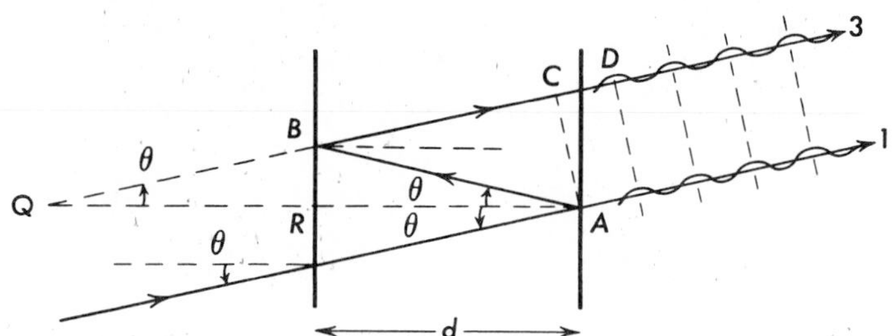

Fig. 47H. Geometry for calculating the path difference between two successive rays of a Fabry–Perot interferometer.

Since QR = AR, and AR = d, we have

$$QA = 2d$$

Since the base of the right triangle QAC is the path difference QC, we obtain

$$QC = 2d \cos \theta$$

For bright fringes, QC must equal $n\lambda$, and this leads directly to Eq.(47d).

Equation (47d) shows that the highest order of interference occurs when $\theta = 0$, that is, for the most central fringe. As θ increases, cos θ decreases, and the path difference QC decreases. If, for example, the central fringe is for $n = 400{,}000$, the next two fringes out will be $n = 399{,}999$ and $n = 399{,}998$, respectively.

47.5. Hyperfine Structure of Spectrum Lines

One of the principal uses of the Fabry–Perot interferometer has been that of resolving what is called the *hyperfine structure* of spectrum lines. Through the study of line structure it has been possible to determine the spin angular momenta and magnetic moments of many atomic nuclei (see Chap. 45).

The ability to resolve lines differing ever so slightly from one another in wavelength is attributed to the great length of the path difference between consecutive rays and the large number of rays producing the interference fringes. Each wavelength produces its own set of fringes as given by Eq.(47d), and because bright fringes are very much sharper than the dark spaces between, several slightly different wavelengths can be seen as separate bright ring systems.

Since the spectrum of most light sources contains many lines, the ring system from a source to be studied is usually focused on the jaw faces of the slit of a prism spectrograph, and photographs are made with the slit wide open or with the slit about a millimeter or two wide.

Figure 47I is a reproduction of a section of the visible spectrum

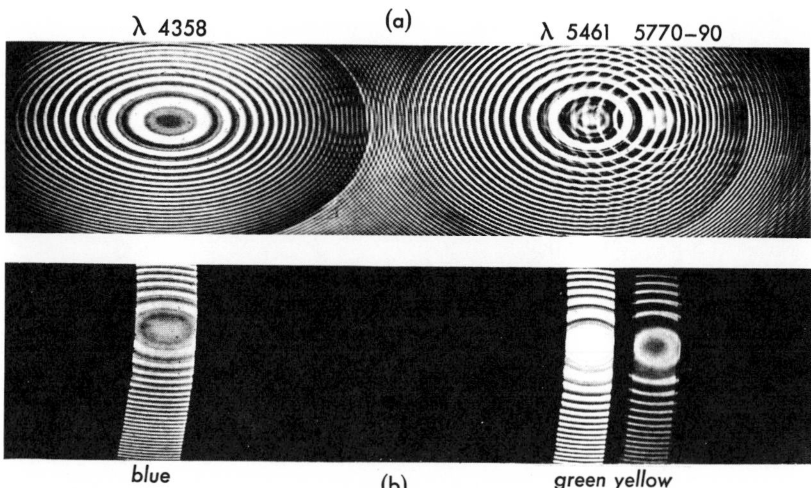

Fig. 47I. Photographs of the visible spectrum of mercury made with a Fabry–Perot interferometer and a prism spectrograph. Spectrograph slit (a) wide open, and (b) 1 millimeter wide.

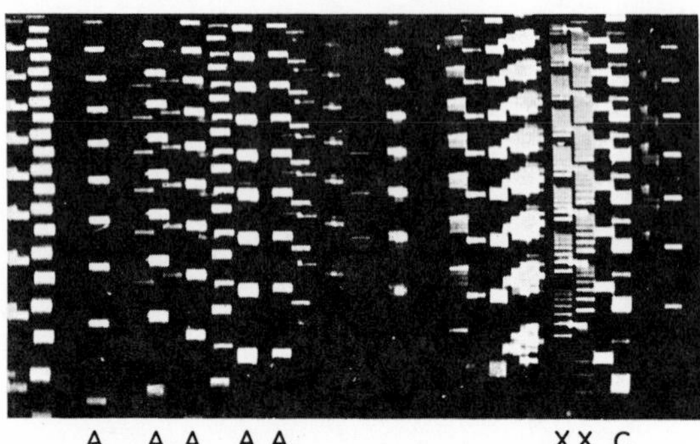

Fig. 47J. Photograph of a section of the lanthanum spectrum made with a Fabry–Perot interferometer and a prism spectrograph. (After D. E. Anderson.)

of mercury. In this relatively simple spectrum the overlapping of interference ring systems in (a) is confusing and the use of a slit to separate interference patterns as in (b) is clearly an improvement. In a complex spectrum like that of lanthanum, $Z = 57$, the slit must be narrowed still further to separate clearly most of the lines and see their ring structure (see Fig. 47J).

By tilting the Fabry–Perot interferometer so the center of the interference ring pattern is just off the lower end of the spectrograph slit, only half of each ring strip is observed. Occasionally it will be found that a line which appears sharp and single in an ordinary spectroscope will yield ring systems that are complex. Examples are found in the lines marked X in the photograph, which upon close examination reveal at least seven components. Those marked A are single sharp lines. Line C is broad and probably composed of several unresolved lines.

Two line patterns selected from the Fabry–Perot spectrum of tantalum, $Z = 73$, and tungsten, $Z = 74$, have been enlarged and turned on their sides as shown in Fig. 47K. The upper pattern shows an eight-component line in the orange part of the spectrum at $\lambda = 5997$ Å, the structure being due to the fact that tantalum atoms of atomic mass 181 have a nuclear spin of $\frac{7}{2}$ $(h/2\pi)$ (see Table 61A).

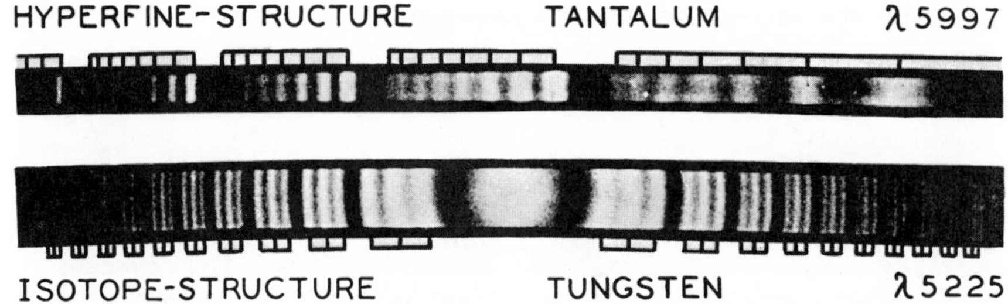

Fig. 47K. Photographs of a section of the Fabry–Perot interferometer pattern of a single line from the spectrum of tantalum and tungsten.

The lower pattern shows a three-component line illustrating what is called *isotope structure.* Tungsten has five isotopes with the following relative abundance:

Isotope	180	182	183	184	186
Abundance, %	0.2	26.4	14.4	30.6	28.4

The even isotope 180 is quite rare and produces too faint a line to be seen. The odd isotope 183 is known to produce a pattern of several lines, and because this pattern is spread over the three single lines produced by the three more abundant even isotopes, they are too faint to show in the reproduction. The inner-most fringe of the three lines in each order is due to isotope 182.

To evaluate the differences in wavelength between the component lines of an otherwise single spectrum line we make use of the general equation, Eq.(47d). Any given fringe of a wavelength λ_1 is formed at such an angle that

$$2d \cos \theta_1 = n\lambda_1 \tag{47f}$$

The next fringe out for this same wavelength is given by

$$2d \cos \theta_2 = (n - 1)\lambda_1 \tag{47g}$$

Note that as θ gets bigger, the path difference $2d \cos \theta$ gets smaller. Suppose now that λ_1 has a component line λ_2 which has a slightly different wavelength than λ_1 and that this component in order n falls on order $n - 1$ of λ_1. We can therefore write

$$2d \cos \theta_2 = n\lambda_2$$

If we now let the small difference in wavelength $\lambda_1 - \lambda_2$ be written as $\Delta\lambda$, that is,

$$\Delta\lambda = \lambda_1 - \lambda_2$$

we may substitute $\lambda_1 - \Delta\lambda$ for λ_2 and obtain

$$2d \cos \theta_2 = n(\lambda_1 - \Delta\lambda)$$

Equating the right-hand side here with that of (47g), we find

$$\lambda_1 = n\Delta\lambda$$

and upon substituting the value of n from Eq.(47f) and solving for $\Delta\lambda$, we obtain

$$\Delta\lambda = \frac{\lambda_1^2}{2d \cos \theta_2}$$

Since θ_2 is practically zero, we can write $\cos \theta_2 = 1$, and obtain the very useful equation

$$\Delta\lambda = \frac{\lambda_1^2}{2d} \tag{47h}$$

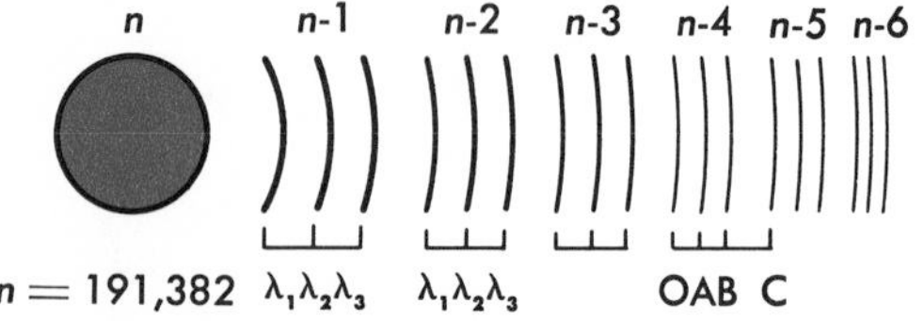

Fig. 47L. Diagram for Example 2, showing the orders of interference and the spacings between component lines.

This is the wavelength interval between the centers of successive fringes and is independent of n. Knowing d and λ_1, we can calculate the wavelength difference of component lines lying in this small range from measured positions.

Example 2. The pattern shown in Fig. 47K for $\lambda = 5225.1600$ Å for the tungsten isotope 182 was made with a Fabry-Perot interferometer with a spacing of 5.0 cm. Calculate (a) the wavelength interval between successive ring patterns of λ_1. Measure the distance intervals between components in the fourth ring on both sides of the center, and from the averages, calculate (b) the wavelength intervals for the two other isotopes 184 and 186. From these intervals, calculate (c) the wavelengths λ_2 and λ_3 for the two isotopes. Make a diagram.

Solution. The given quantities are $\lambda = 5225.1600$ Å and $D = 5.0 \times 10^{-2}$ m $= 5.0 \times 10^8$ Å. Using Eq.(47h), and substituting the known quantities, we obtain

$$\Delta\lambda = \frac{\lambda_1^2}{2d} = \frac{(5225.16 \text{ Å})^2}{2 \times 5.0 \times 10^8 \text{ Å}}$$

$$\Delta\lambda = 0.02730 \text{ Å}$$

Using a millimeter scale we measure the intervals between the components of the *4th* pattern, on each side of the center, and find the average values

$$OA = 1.0 \text{ mm}, \quad OB = 2.2 \text{ mm}, \quad OC = 4.2 \text{ mm}$$

Over these small distances *wavelength intervals* may be assumed to be proportional to *distance intervals.* Making this assumption, we find

$$\Delta\lambda_{OA} = \frac{1.0}{4.2}\, 0.02730 \text{ Å} = 0.00650 \text{ Å}$$

$$\Delta\lambda_{OB} = \frac{2.2}{4.2}\, 0.02730 \text{ Å} = 0.01430 \text{ Å}$$

and adding these to λ_1, we find

$\lambda_1 = 5225.1600$ Å for isotope 182

$\lambda_2 = 5225.1665$ Å for isotope 184

$\lambda_3 = 5225.1743$ Å for isotope 186

See diagram in Fig. 47L.

Suppose the spacing of the plates in a Fabry–Perot interferometer is such that on the axis n comes out a whole integer. Under these conditions the center of the ring pattern will be bright [see Eq.(47e)]. We now count out to ring m, and write

$$2d \cos \theta = (n - m) \lambda \tag{47i}$$

Upon dividing this equation by Eq.(47e), we obtain

$$\frac{2d \cos \theta}{2d} = \frac{(n - m) \lambda}{n\lambda}$$

$$\cos \theta = \frac{(n - m)}{n} \tag{47j}$$

This gives the angle θ at which order $n - m$ will be diffracted out on the other side of the instrument.

Example 3. A Fabry-Perot interferometer has a mirror spacing of 1.0 mm for light of wavelength $\lambda = 5000$ Å. A 1.0-m lens placed behind the instrument focuses the ring pattern on a screen 1.0 m away. Find (a) the order of interference n, and (b) the radius of the 10*th* ring.

Solution. The given quantities are $d = 1.0 \times 10^{-3}$ m, $\lambda = 5.0 \times 10^{-7}$, $m = 10.0$, and $f = 1.0$ m. Using Eq.(47d) we find for n:

$$n = \frac{2d}{\lambda} = \frac{2 \times 1.0 \times 10^{-3}}{5.0 \times 10^{-7}}$$

$$n = 4000$$

If we now use Eq.(47j), we find

$$\cos \theta = \frac{4000 - 10}{4000} = \frac{3990}{4000} = 0.9975$$

$$\theta = 4.052° = 0.07072 \text{ rad}$$

With a lens where $f = 1.0$ m, this angle will produce a circle on the screen of radius

$$R = f\theta = 1.0 \times 0.07072 = 0.07072 \text{ m}$$

$$R = 7.072 \text{ cm}$$

47.7. Lasers

The term *laser* derives its name from the description, *Light Amplification by Stimulated Emission and Radiation.* In principle the laser is a device that produces an intense, concentrated, and highly parallel beam of light. So parallel would be the beam from a visible light laser 1 ft in diameter that at the moon the beam would be no more than a mile wide.

Historically the laser is the outgrowth of the *maser,* a device using *m*icrowaves instead of *l*ight waves. The first successful maser was built by C. H. Townes* at Columbia University in 1953. During the next seven years great strides were made in developing intense microwave beams, the principal contributions being made by the Bell Telephone Research Laboratories and the Lincoln Laboratories at the Massachusetts Institute of Technology.

The first successful laser, using a large synthetic ruby crystal, was built by T. H. Maiman of Hughes Aircraft Company Laboratories in the summer of 1960. Hundreds of extensive researches on laser development have been carried on since that time, and because such devices appear to have great potential in so many different fields of research and development, a brief account of their basic principles will be presented here.

Lasers are of three general kinds, those using solids, those using liquids, and those with gases. For the case of liquid or gas lasers, a Fabry–Perot interferometer, with silvered end plates like the ones shown in Fig. 47F, is filled with a fluid. In the solid laser, the ends of a crystal are polished and silvered as shown in Fig. 47M. Since the first successful laser was made with a large single crystal of ruby, this device will be explained as representative of solid state lasers.

***Charles H. Townes (1915–), American physicist, was born July 28, 1915, in Greenville, South Carolina. He received his Ph.D. from the California Institute of Technology in 1939 and has received honorary degrees from a number of universities. He has served in various capacities in the physics departments at several universities, and is now Professor-at-large at the University of California. He is most noted for his outstanding work in the development of masers and lasers, for which he was awarded the Nobel Prize in physics in 1964 and many national and international awards. He has served on many national science committees, such as, the President's Science Advisory Committee, Chairman of the Science and Technical Advisory Committee on Manned Space Flight, NASA, and the Science Advisory Board of the U.S. Air Force. The author is privileged to know C. H. Townes as a friend and colleague.**

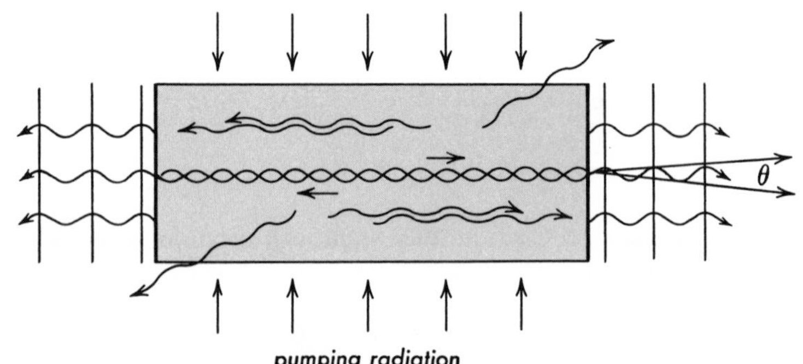

Fig. 47M. Diagram illustrating the coherent stimulation of light waves in a solid state laser such as a ruby crystal.

The atomic lattice structure of a ruby crystal has the properties of absorbing light of certain frequencies ν_0 and, of holding this absorbed energy for a period of time. Then by bouncing light of a different frequency ν_1 back and forth between the silvered ends, the excited atoms may be stimulated to emit their stored energy as light of the same frequency ν_1 and in exact phase with the original light waves. As these intensified waves bounce back and forth, they stimulate others, thus amplifying the original beam intensity.

Because the light waves emerging from the end of the laser are all in phase, the beam is said to be coherent, and the angular spread of the light is given by the relation

$$\theta = \frac{2.440\ \lambda}{d} \tag{47k}$$

where θ is in radians, λ is the wavelength of light, and d is the diameter of the emergent beam. This equation arises from the treatment of the diffraction of light by a circular aperture [see Sec. 36.2 and Eq.(36f)].

Example 4. A ruby laser produces a beam of red light of wavelength 6943 Å with a circular cross section 8.0 mm in diameter. Find the beam width at a distance of 1000 m.

Solution. The given quantities are $\lambda = 6.943 \times 10^{-7}$ m, $d = 8.0 \times 10^{-3}$ m, and $L = 1.0 \times 10^3$ m. Direct substitution of given quantities in Eq.(47k) gives

$$\theta = 2.440\,\frac{\lambda}{d} = \frac{2.440 \times 6.943 \times 10^{-7}}{8.0 \times 10^{-3}}$$

$$\theta = 2.118 \times 10^{-4} \text{ rad}$$

At a distance of 1000 m, the diameter D of the beam will be

$$D = L\theta = 1.0 \times 10^3 \times 2.118 \times 10^{-4}$$

$$D = 0.2118 \text{ m} = 21.18 \text{ cm}$$

47.8. Optical Pumping

A convenient method of describing laser action is to refer to an energy-level diagram of the electronic states involved in light

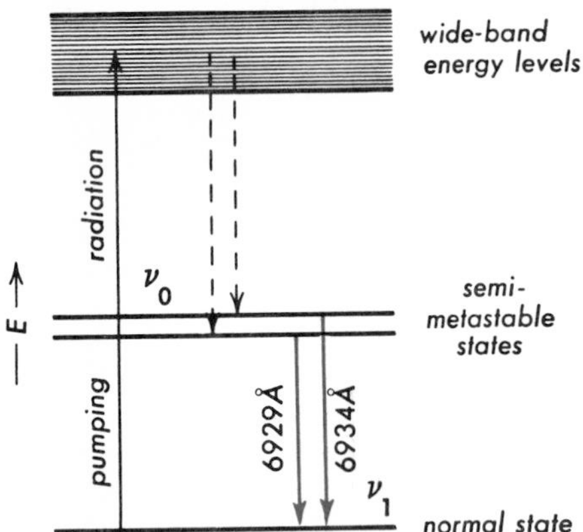

Fig. 47N. Energy-level diagram of the energy states of a ruby crystal.

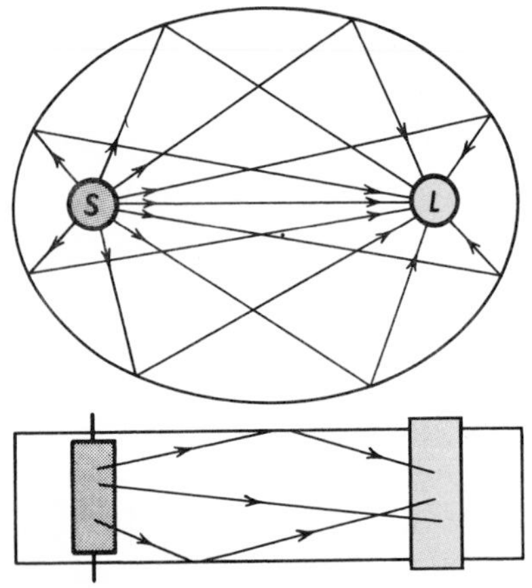

Fig. 47O. Elliptical reflector for concentrating light from a source *S* on a laser *L*.

absorption and emission. An energy-level diagram for the electrons in the atomic lattice of a ruby crystal is given in Fig. 47N. Here there are three sets of levels, the *normal state,* the *semi-metastable states* near the middle, and the top *wide-band energy levels.* (Pink ruby is a crystal lattice of aluminum and oxygen atoms, Al_2O_3, with a small amount of chromium ions as an impurity, 0.04% of Cr^{3+}.)

Semi-metastable states are states in which electron transitions to lower levels are not entirely forbidden, as they are in ionized calcium, but there is a short or long delay in the electrons' jumping down to a lower level.

Normally an electron will remain in an excited state for about 10^{-8} s, before jumping to a lower state. In a metastable state, however, it may stay from 10^{-5} s up to several minutes.

When a beam of white light enters a ruby crystal, strong absorption occurs in the blue and green part of the spectrum, and the transmission of only the red region is what gives the ruby its red color. On shining a strong beam of blue-green light into a ruby crystal the absorption that takes place raises many electrons to the wide-band levels, as shown by the up arrow at the left in Fig. 47N. Because of internal atomic activity the electrons quickly drop down to the intermediate levels, not by the emission of photons, but by the conversion of energy into vibrational kinetic energy of the atoms forming the crystal lattice.

Once in the intermediate levels the electrons remain there for some time and randomly jump back to the normal state emitting visible red light. This *fluorescent light,* as it is called, enhances the red color of the ruby.

Since an incident beam of blue-green light steadily increases the number of electrons in the semi-metastable states, the process is called *optical pumping.* To increase greatly the electron populations in the middle levels, very intense light sources as well as efficient light-gathering systems are frequently used.

One of many systems developed for doing this is shown in Fig. 47O. By placing the exciting light source at one focus of an elliptical reflector and the laser at the other focus, high efficiency can be obtained.

In some lasers, where a steady light beam is required, the random emission of light within the gas, liquid, or solid mass will by chance find some of the waves emitted along the axis (see Fig. 47M). This light, because it may bounce back and forth many times between the highly reflective ends, will stimulate coherent emission parallel to itself and to the axis. These two waves traveling back and forth in step with each other now induce other emission, thereby giving rise to a rapid growth or chain reaction.

Thus by continuous pumping action from a separate light source, a large part of the stored energy is converted into a coherent beam of light of a different wavelength. Under these conditions the device is said to "laze" spontaneously.

If the silvered ends are not highly reflecting, too much light escapes from the ends and spontaneous lazing cannot occur. Under these conditions a beam of light of the stimulating frequency from another laser can be sent into the crystal where it is intensified. By modulating the input beam the greatly intensified output beam will be modulated accordingly. This modulation capability is one of the important properties that gives lasers their promising future applications to the field of communications.

47.9. The Helium–Neon Gas Laser

The first successful optical gas laser was set into operation by Javan, Bennett, and Heriott in 1961. Since that time many different gas lasers, using ten or more gas systems and several different excitation methods, have been made to operate. Because it was the first to function successfully, a helium–neon laser will be described here.

The gas laser shown in Fig. 47P is composed of a glass tube nearly a meter long containing a mixture of 1-mm-Hg pressure of helium and $\frac{1}{10}$-mm-Hg pressure of neon gas. The highly reflecting Fabry–Perot plates on the ends are so sealed as to prevent leakage and so mounted as to be adjustable to a high degree of parallelism.

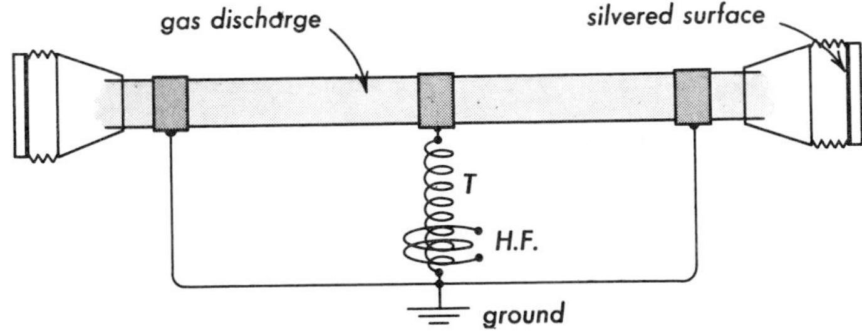

Fig. 47P. Diagram of a helium–neon gas laser showing Fabry–Perot plates at the ends of the discharge tube, and a high-voltage, high-frequency source for excitation.

A high-voltage, high-frequency potential difference, such as that obtained from a Tesla coil, is applied by means of three metal bands around the outside of the tube.

Although there are ten times as many helium atoms present as there are neon atoms, the orange-red color of the gaseous discharge is characteristic of neon. The visible spectrum of helium contains strong lines in the red, yellow, green, and blue, so the discharge in helium alone appears as white light. The spectrum of neon, on the other hand, has so many strong lines in the yellow, orange, and red, and so few in the green, blue, and violet that its gaseous discharge appears orange-red. The neon spectrum also reveals a large number of strong lines in the near-infrared spectrum.

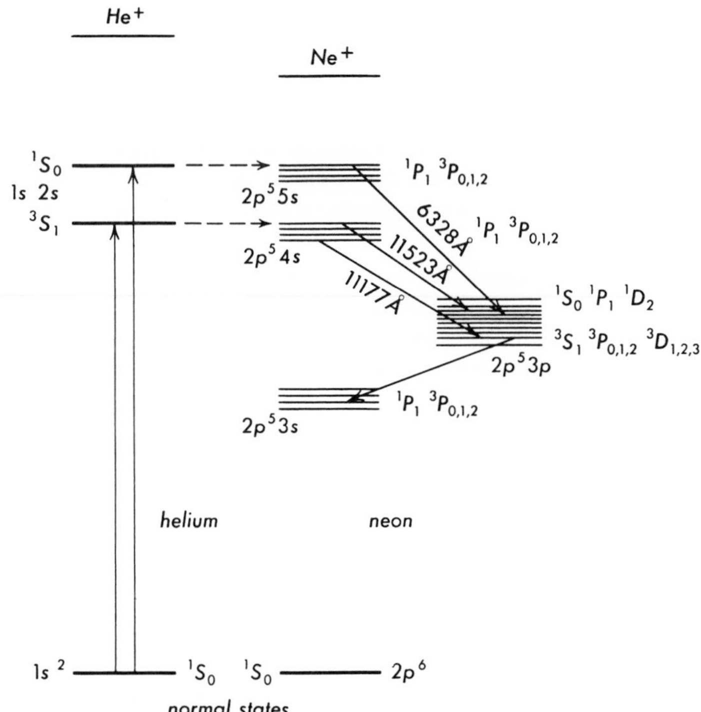

Fig. 47Q. Correlation diagram of the energy levels of helium and neon involved in the helium–neon gas laser.

Simplified energy-level diagrams for helium and neon are shown in Fig. 47Q for the purpose of explaining the atomic processes involved in laser action. The normal state of helium is a $^1S_0$ level arising from two electrons in 1*s* orbits. The excitation of one electron to a 2*s* orbit finds the atom in a $^3S_1$ or a $^1S_0$ state.

Both of these are metastable, since transitions to the normal state are forbidden by selection rules (see Sec. 45.6).

Neon, with $Z = 10$, has ten electrons and in the normal state is represented by the configuration $1s^2\ 2s^2\ 2p^6$. When one of the $2p$ electrons is excited to a $3s$, $3p$, $3d$, $4s$, $4p$, $4d$, $4f$, $5s$, etc., orbit, triplet and singlet levels arise.

A subshell such as $2p^5$, lacking only one electron to form a closed subshell, behaves as though it were a subshell containing only one $2p$ electron. The number and designations of the levels produced are therefore the same as with two electrons.

As free electrons collide with helium atoms during discharge, one of the two bound electrons may be excited to $2s$ orbits, that is, to the $^3S_1$ or $^1S_0$ states. Since downward transitions are forbidden by radiation selection rules, these are *metastable states,* and the number of excited atoms increases. We therefore have optical pumping, out of the normal $^1S_0$ state and into the metastable states $^3S_1$ and $^1S_0$.

When a metastable helium atom collides with a neon atom in its normal state, there is a high probability that the excitation energy will be transferred to the neon, raising it to one of the $^1P_1$ or $^3P_0$, $^3P_1$, $^3P_2$ levels of $2p^5\ 4s$ or $2p^5\ 5s$. The small excess energy is converted to kinetic energy of the colliding atoms.

In this process, called a *collision of the second kind,* each helium atom returns to the normal state as each colliding neon atom is excited to the upper level of corresponding energy.

The probability of a neon atom being raised to the $2p^5\ 3s$ or $2p^5\ 3p$ levels by collisions of the second kind are extremely small because of the energy mismatch. The collision transfer, therefore, selectively increases the population of the upper levels of neon. Since selection rules permit transitions from these levels downward to the ten levels of $2p^5\ 3p$, and these in turn to the four levels of $2p^5\ 3s$, stimulated emission can speed up this process by laser action.

Light waves emitted within the laser at wavelengths such as 6328 Å, 11,177 Å, and 11,523 Å will occasionally be emitted parallel to the tube axis. Bouncing back and forth between the parallel end plates, these waves will stimulate emission of the same frequency from other excited neon atoms, and the initial wave, with the stimulated wave, moves parallel to the axis and in phase.

Most of the amplified radiation emerging from the ends of the helium–neon gas laser are in the near-infrared region of the spectrum, between 10,000 Å and 35,000 Å, with the most intense amplified wavelength in the visible spectrum being the red line at $\lambda = 6328$ Å. The strongest amplified line in the infrared is at $\lambda = 11{,}523$ Å.

problems

1. A helium-neon gas laser is 32.0 cm long and emits light with a wavelength of 6328 Å. Calculate the order of interference to four significant figures.

2. A ruby laser 9.620 cm long emits light of wavelength 6929 Å. Calculate the order of interference to four significant figures.

3. A helium-neon gas laser produces a beam of red light of wavelength 6328 Å. If the emitted beam has a diameter of 1.250 cm, find the diameter of the beam after it has traveled 500 m. [Ans. 6.18 cm in diameter.]

4. A Fabry-Perot interferometer was used to make the photograph in Fig. 47K. This line is attributed to the only stable isotope of tantalum, Ta-181. If the spacer used in the interferometer was 7.0 cm, find the wavelength interval between the successive patterns.

5. The interference pattern shown at the top in Fig. 47K was made with a Fabry-Perot interferometer with a spacing of 7.0 cm. If the wavelength of the strongest of the components is 5997.4680 Å, calculate (a) the wavelength interval between successive patterns. Measure the distant intervals between components, and calculate (b) the wavelength intervals between components, and (c) the wavelengths of all components.

6. A ruby laser with a beam aperture of 0.950 cm in diameter emits red light with a wavelength of 6929 Å. Find the beam width at a distance of 5000 m. [Ans. 89.0 cm.]

7. A Fabry-Perot interferometer has its two highly reflecting surfaces spaced 6.50 cm apart. If yellow light of wavelength 5750 Å is sent through, find (a) the principal oscillation mode, and (b) the equivalent wavelength spacing between orders of inteference.

8. A ring diffraction pattern from a Fabry-Perot interferometer is projected on a screen with a lens having a focal length of 60.0 cm. If green light of wavelength 5400 Å is used, with a mirror spacing of 2.70 mm, find (a) the order of interference, and (b) the radius of the 5*th* bright ring out.

9. Blue light of wavelength 4350 Å is used with a Fabry-Perot interferometer, and a ring pattern is focused on a screen with a lens of focal length 50.0 cm. If the mirror spacing is 4.0 mm, find (a) the order of interference, and (b) the radius of the 10*th* bright ring on the screen. [Ans. (a) 18,391, (b) 1.649 cm.]

10. A Fabry-Perot interferometer with a mirror spacing of 6.55 mm is used with yellow light of wavelength 5750 Å. If a lens with a focal length of 75.0 cm is used to focus the ring pattern on a screen, find (a) the order of interference, and (b) the radius of the 20*th* bright ring.

48 Relativity

The mention of the word "relativity" suggests the name of Albert Einstein,* the scientist to whom we are indebted for the now famous theory. To begin with, Einstein was a realist, and his theory rests upon physical facts which have been verified by repeated observations of well-planned experiments. Reference is made in particular to the Michelson–Morley experiment, described in Chap. 47.

Beginning in Chap. 46 we have seen that moving observers in each of two different frames of reference may make their own simultaneous measurements of some single event, and by the use of transformation equations, determine the observations made by the other observer.

A frame of reference moving with constant velocity has been called an *inertial frame* because Newton's laws are obeyed within it. The term inertial is used to distinguish such a frame from an accelerated frame in which a fictitious force appears to be ever present.

In transforming measurements from one inertial frame to another, distances and accelerations are found to have the same values whether viewed from one frame or the other. For these reasons *distance* and *acceleration* are said to be *invariant* (see Sec. 46.6). Observed velocities, on the other hand, differ from one frame to another and are not invariant.

In deriving the Galilean–Newtonian transformation equations in Chap. 46, it was assumed that light travels with an infinite speed. This means that measurements could be made simultaneously from different frames. Since light has a finite speed, light itself should not be expected to be invariant; the speed of light should be different when measured from different inertial frames.

It should then be possible by accurately observing a single event from two inertial frames to determine this difference in the speed of light and find whether or not the two frames are moving through the ether at different rates.

This was the purpose of the Michelson–Morley experiment, and it failed.

***Albert Einstein (1879–1955), German-Swiss physicist, was born of Jewish parents at Ulm, Württemberg, on March 14, 1879. His boyhood was spent in Munich where his father, a dealer in chemicals, had settled in 1880. When the family moved to Italy in 1894, young Albert went to Switzerland to study. There he worked his way through school, finally taking his Ph.D. degree at the University of Zürich in 1902. He was appointed extraordinary professor of theoretical physics at the University of Zürich in 1909, and in 1913 he was called to Berlin as director of the Kaiser-Wilhelm Institute for Physics. While at this post, he was elected a member of the Prussian Academy of Sciences and a member of the Royal Society of London. In 1921 he received the Nobel prize in physics and, in 1925, the Copley Medal of the Royal Society. From 1933 to 1945 he was with the Institute for Advanced Studies in Princeton, where he died. He is best known for his theory of relativity, the theory and explanation of Brownian motion, the theory of the photoelectric effect, and the quantum theory of radiant heat energy. Twice married, Einstein had several children. For his friends he was a quiet, sincere, and modest man who loved his pipe and violin and disliked formality.**

48.1. Gedanken (Thought) Experiment

Imagine two space ships in the form of two giant rulers, perfectly straight and rigid, precisely marked, and laid out side by side on the ground (see Fig. 48A). Six astronauts A, B, C, and A′, B′, C′, are stationed as shown, and all agree that the rulers are the same length, and that the midpoint markings are truly at the midpoints.

The two space ships take off on a space voyage and later encounter each other in outer space for the purpose of seeing whether the two rulers are still of the same length. As they coast past each other on adjacent and parallel paths at a constant relative velocity u, electric sparks jump across between the points at the two opposite ends [see diagram (b)]. These sparks create light flashes of extremely short duration.

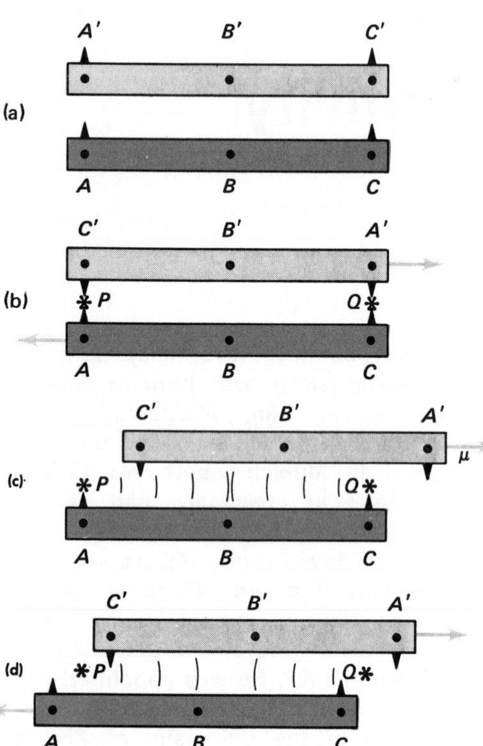

Fig. 48A. Diagrams of a "gedanken" experiment in which two space ships, in the form of two giant rulers, pass each other in free space.

How will observers B and B′ interpret these light flashes? Before the two ships came into sight of each other there were no nearby objects against which B and B′ could determine their ship's motion. As the primed ruler passes, the light flashes are initiated, and B believes that these two events occurred at the two fixed points on his ship where A and C are located.

Since light travels with a constant speed of 3×10^8 m/s in free space, let us assume that the unprimed ruler is at rest and that the two light pulses do indeed reach observer B at the same time [see diagram (c)]. This means that the sparks occurred at an earlier time when B′ was opposite B. Thus at the instant the two pulses reach B, B′ has already moved slightly past. Thus the P pulse has yet to reach B′, whereas the Q pulse has already passed B′. Then B′ must conclude that his primed ruler is longer than the unprimed one. Based on the hypothesis that B thinks the two rulers are still of the same length, B′ disagrees and thinks his own ruler is longer.

But this is impossible. The experiment is completely symmetrical and the two light signals do not arrive at B simultaneously.

Imagine the conditions to be those shown in diagram (d) in which both rulers are in motion and the light pulse P reaches B at the same time light pulse Q reaches B′. A short time Δt later, light pulse P reaches B′ and pulse Q reaches B. Since each observer sees that the light flash from the rear of his ship arrives later than the pulse from the front, each concludes that his ship is longer than the other. Which observer is right?

Since the experiment was absolutely symmetrical, we must conclude they are both right. If there were a tangible medium with respect to which the velocity of each ruler could be specified, and in which the speed of light were constant, one could take this into account and differentiate between the two answers. But the medium is a vacuum, there are no nearby objects, and it is just as meaningful to say one ship is at rest and the other is moving, as it is to say the opposite, or as it is to say they are both moving. Since a vacuum is intangible it is nonsense to talk about the velocity of an object relative to a vacuum.

If you, the reader, imagine yourself to be the observer B, it is very natural for you to consider you are on the stationary ruler and that the primed ruler is moving by at a velocity u [see diagram (c)]. It is also consistent with your common sense to conclude that you and B′ are both moving and that your ruler is longer because the P signal reaches you before the Q signal does [see diagram (d)]. But it is equally natural for me to imagine myself to be observer B′ and come to different conclusions that are equally consistent with common sense.

What makes this experiment seem to be inconsistent is that in our every-day life we do not perceive airplanes becoming shorter as they speed down a runway on take-off, nor trains extending their lengths as they draw up to a stop at a station. The reason for this is that the speed of light is so great compared with the relative velocities of large familiar objects.

The important point of this "gedanken experiment" is to recognize that when there is relative motion between two observers, the time intervals measured between two events as well as lengths measured will differ.

The problem then becomes one of finding a set of equations that will enable the observer in one frame of reference to determine by calculation the measured observations of events as seen by another observer in another frame of reference.

48.2. The Lorentz–Fitzgerald Contraction

From the time Michelson and Morley announced the negative results of their ether-drift experiment, scientists tried to explain why the experiment failed. An ingenious explanation was first advanced by Fitzgerald* in 1890. If objects moving through space have to push against the immovable ether, he suggested, they would be compressed in the direction of motion. This compression would, therefore, shorten the Michelson interferometer arms holding the mirrors and might exactly compensate for an existing ether drift.

Lorentz,† the famous Dutch physicist, studied this problem from an atomic point of view. All matter, he proposed, is made up of atoms, and atoms are made up of charged particles that produce

***George F. Fitzgerald (1851–1901), Irish physicist, was born in Dublin on August 3, 1851. His entire scientific career was spent as professor of natural philosophy at Trinity College in Dublin. His contributions to science were largely related to the electromagnetic properties of light, the magneto-optical phenomena known as the Kerr effect, the oscillatory discharge of a capacitor, the polarization of Hertzian waves, the scattering of X rays, and the validity of Ohm's law in electrolysis. While studying the results of the Michelson-Morley experiment, Fitzgerald worked out the change in length of a body due to its motion. This is known as the Lorentz-Fitzgerald contraction.**

†Hendrik A. Lorentz (1853–1928), Dutch physicist, was born at Arnheim on July 18, 1853. He was educated at the University of Leyden, where he was appointed professor of theoretical physics at the age of 25. Those who knew him never lost the opportunity of mentioning his charming personality and kindly disposition. Of his numerous contributions to science he is best known for (1) a set of four algebraic equations, known as the Lorentz transformation, equations which later came out of Einstein's special theory of relativity, and (2) his theoretical explanation of the Zeeman effect. In 1922 he was awarded, jointly with Zeeman, the Nobel Prize in physics. The author had the good fortune of knowing this great man while a graduate student at Cornell University, and serving as his assistant while giving lectures there in 1927.

electric and magnetic fields. These fields must exert forces on the electromagnetic ether, thus causing the atoms and molecules in moving matter to be pushed closer together. Starting with the well-known principles of electricity and magnetism, Lorentz derived the following formula for the length of any object:

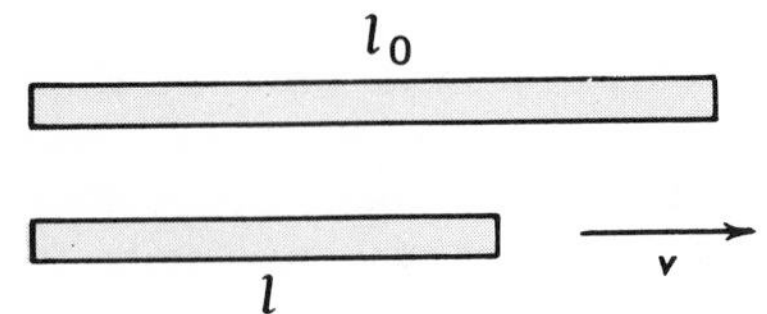

Fig. 48B. Diagram of the Lorentz–Fitzgerald contraction.

$$\ell = \ell_0 \sqrt{1 - \frac{v^2}{c^2}} \tag{48a}$$

where v is the velocity of the object through the ether, ℓ_0 is its length when at rest in the ether, and c is the velocity of light. Note the resemblance of this equation to Eq.(46c). Suppose that an object is at rest, so that $v = 0$. Upon substituting $v = 0$ in Eq.(48a), we find $\ell = \ell_0$, which says the object's length ℓ will be just equal to its rest length ℓ_0. If a rod were moving lengthwise with $\frac{3}{4}$ the speed of light, however, the substitution of $v = \frac{3}{4}c$ into the equation gives $\ell = 0.66\ell_0$. This means that the observer measures the rod to be only $\frac{2}{3}$ as long (see Fig. 48B).

It is interesting to see what this equation reveals if a rod could move lengthwise with the speed of light, i.e., with $v = c$. The result is $\ell = 0$. This means that any object moving with the speed of light would appear to have zero length. The velocity of light, therefore, becomes an upper limit for the velocity of any moving object.

The above formula, when applied to the cross arms of the interferometer used in the Michelson–Morley experiment (see Fig. 47E), shows that the arms are shortened by just the right amount to compensate for the expected drift [see Eq.(46c)]. This shortening of an object cannot be measured, for, if one attempts to measure the length of a moving object, the measuring stick must move with the same velocity, and an equal length of the stick shortens by the same amount.

Example 1. A space ship 25.0 m long passes the earth traveling at 2.650×10^8 m/s. What is its apparent length as seen from the earth?

Solution. The given quantities are $v = 2.650 \times 10^8$ m/s, $c = 2.998 \times 10^8$ m/s, and $\ell_0 = 25.0$ m. Direct substitution of known quantities in Eq.(48a) gives

$$\ell = \ell_0 \sqrt{1 - \frac{v^2}{c^2}} = 25 \sqrt{1 - \frac{(2.650 \times 10^8)^2}{(2.998 \times 10^8)^2}}$$

$$\ell = 11.69 \text{ m}$$

48.3. Einstein's Special Theory of Relativity

Einstein interpreted the failure of the Michelson–Morley experiment to mean that the velocity of light is invariant, that time and distance are relative, and that Galilean–Newtonian mechanics must be modified accordingly. Out of these modifications came the theory of relativity.

Relativity is divided into two parts. One part is called the *special,* or *restricted, theory of relativity,* and the other is called the *general theory.* The special theory, developed by Einstein in 1905, deals with observers and their reference frames moving with constant velocities. The mathematics of the special theory is simple enough, and we will consider several of the relationships that are necessary for the satisfactory explanations of atomic phenomena.

The general theory, proposed by Einstein in 1915, deals with motions of bodies in accelerated frames of reference. The mathematics of the general theory is quite difficult, and the experimental evidence for its validity is not as well founded as for the special theory.

Since the Michelson–Morley experiment fails to provide a fixed frame of reference in space, Einstein's theory assumes that all such experiments will fail, and that at relatively high speeds the laws of Newton are not valid. Einstein's special theory of relativity shows that the laws of physics can be restated so that they will apply to any frame of reference, and that at low relative speeds these laws reduce to Newton's laws of motion. The first postulate for setting up these equations is:

The laws of physics apply equally well for all observers as long as they are moving with constant velocities.

The second postulate follows from the assumption that the velocity of light is *invariant:*

The velocity of light in free space has the same value regardless of the motion of the source and the motion of the observer.

To see the meaning of this second statement, consider a reference frame and observer O at rest as shown in Fig. 48C. A source of light S is set up, and by means of an experiment the velocity of light is measured and found to be 3×10^8 m/s. Another observer O′, moving with a velocity v with respect to O, allows the light from the same source S to pass through his apparatus. Upon measuring the velocity of this same light in his frame, he too finds 3×10^8 m/s.

For these two identical results to be consistent, Einstein derived new transformation equations. To do this he assumed that *distance* and *time* are relative, i.e., they are not *invariant.* His transformation equations may be written down and compared with the nonrelativistic equations as follows:

$$x' = x - vt \qquad x' = \gamma(x - vt) \tag{48b}$$

$$t' = t \qquad t' = \gamma\left(t - \frac{vx}{c^2}\right) \tag{48c}$$

nonrelativistic **relativistic**

where γ is given by

$$\gamma = \frac{1}{\sqrt{1 - \frac{v^2}{c^2}}} \tag{48d}$$

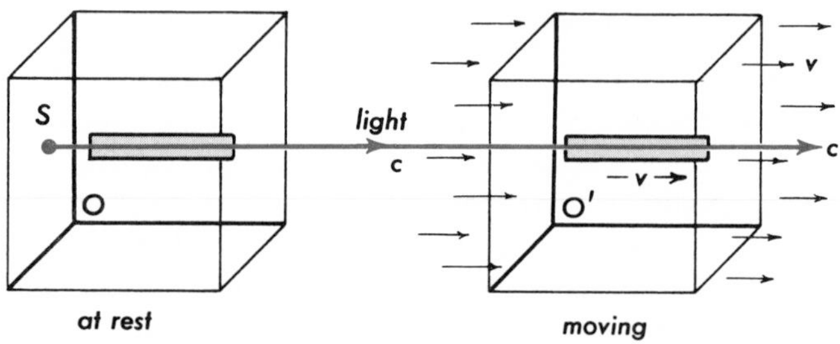

Fig. 48C. The velocity of light is the same to all observers, that is, it is invariant.

Note the similarity of these two sets of equations. By setting $v = 0$ in Eq.(48d), we get $\gamma = 1$, and the relativistic equations reduce to the nonrelativistic, or Newtonian, equations. The value of γ is just the ratio of the two *travel times* for the light paths in the Michelson–Morley experiment.

Classical laws such as Newton's laws of motion can be used in most applications of kinematics and dynamics to the motions of macroscopic bodies; but at speeds above 1 to 10% the speed of light, depending on the accuracy desired the relativistic equations should be used.

Since Eqs.(48b), (48c), and (48d) were first derived by Lorentz in 1895, their use in any problem is referred to as a *Lorentz transformation.* Lorentz arrived at the equations by assuming a contraction of moving objects in an ether, whereas Einstein in 1905 derived the equations by assuming the speed of light as *invariant.*

48.4. Relativistic Velocity Transformation

Suppose the velocity of a body in an observer's frame of reference is u, and we wish to calculate the velocity u' of that same body as measured by an observer moving with a velocity v. For this calculation we use the velocity transformation equations, Eq.(46i):

$$u' = \frac{x'_2 - x'_1}{t'_2 - t'_1} \quad \text{and} \quad u = \frac{x_2 - x_1}{t_2 - t_1} \tag{48e}$$

We now make use of the relativistic transformation equations, Eqs.(48b) and (48c), and substitute unprimed terms for each primed term in the first relation. This gives

$$u' = \frac{\gamma(x_2 - vt_2) - \gamma(x_1 - vt_1)}{\gamma(t_2 - vx_2/c^2) - \gamma(t_1 - vx_1/c^2)} \tag{48f}$$

Upon canceling the γ's, multiplying out, collecting like terms, dividing all terms by $t_2 - t_1$, substituting from the right-hand equation of Eq.(48e), and simplifying, we obtain*

$$u' = \frac{u - v}{1 - uv/c^2} \tag{48g}$$

relativistic

This is the velocity transformation equation in the theory of relativity. It shows that velocity, as in Newtonian mechanics, too, is not *invariant.* Different observers find different velocities:

$$u' = u - v \tag{48h}$$

nonrelativistic

Example 2. An observer on the earth (assumed to be an inertial frame of reference) sees a space ship P receding from him at 2.0 $\times$ 10^8 m/s and overtaking a space ship Q receding at 1.50 $\times$ 10^8 m/s. Find the relative velocity of (a) space ship Q as observed by P,(b) space ship P as observed by Q, and (c) space ship Q relative to space ship P as observed by O. Use $c = 3.0 \times 10^8$ m/s.
Solution. This example is shown schematically in Fig. 48D. The given quantities for (a) are $v = 2.0 \times 10^8$ m/s, $u = 1.50 \times 10^8$

* The algebraic steps from Eq.(48e) to Eq.(48g) are left as a student exercise (see Problem 14).

m/s, and $c = 3.0 \times 10^8$ m/s. Upon substitution in Eq.(48g) we obtain

Part (a)

$$u' = \frac{1.5 \times 10^8 \text{ m/s} - 2.0 \times 10^8 \text{ m/s}}{1 - 1.5 \times 10^8 \times 2.0 \times 10^8/(3 \times 10^8)^2}$$

$$u' = \frac{-0.5 \times 10^8}{1 - 3 \times 10^{16}/9 \times 10^{16}} = -0.750 \times 10^8 \text{ m/s}$$

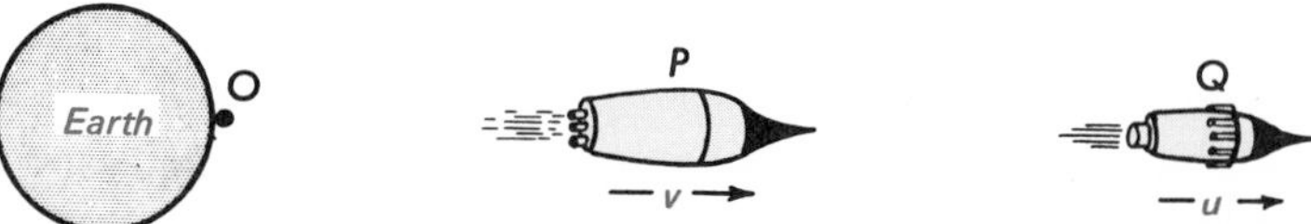

Fig. 48D. Diagram of two space ships receding from the earth with constant velocities.

For (b) we reverse the velocity symbols: $u = 2.0 \times 10^8$ m/s and $v = 1.50 \times 10^8$ m/s. Upon substitution in Eq.(48g), we obtain

Part (b)

$$u' = \frac{2.0 \times 10^8 - 1.5 \times 10^8}{1 - 2.0 \times 10^8 \times 1.5 \times 10^8/(3 \times 10^8)^2}$$

$$u' = \frac{0.5 \times 10^8}{1 - 3 \times 10^{16}/9 \times 10^{16}} = +0.750 \times 10^8 \text{ m/s}$$

For (c) we take just the difference between the two velocities observed by O:

$$u' = 1.5 \times 10^8 - 2.0 \times 10^8 = -0.50 \times 10^8 \text{ m/s}$$

For solving problems using Eq.(48g), make a diagram similar to Fig. 48D, showing observer O, and his reference frame, at rest. The frame from which new observations are to be calculated is selected as body P, and is drawn to the right or left of O, and labeled with an appropriate arrow v. The body to be observed from P is now located in its appropriate position, to the right or left, and labeled Q with its appropriate arrow u.

The sign conventions for use in Eq.(48g) are as follows:

Velocities u or v to the right are positive.
Velocities u or v to the left are negative.
A positive u′ signifies Q is moving to the right with respect to P.
A negative u′ signifies Q is moving to the left with respect to P.

Example 3. Suppose space ship Q in Example 1 (Fig. 48D) is replaced by a beam of light moving from left to right, which observer O measures and finds to be $c = 3.0 \times 10^8$ m/s. What will the velocity of this same light be, as observed by space ship P?
Solution. The given quantities are $u = c$, $v = 2.0 \times 10^8$ m/s, and $c = 3.0 \times 10^8$ m/s. Upon first replacing u by c in Eq.(48g) and solving for u', we obtain

$$u' = \frac{u - v}{1 - uv/c^2} = \frac{c - v}{1 - cv/c^2} = \frac{c - v}{1 - v/c} = \frac{c - v}{\frac{c - v}{c}} = c$$

Hence the observer in P finds the velocity of light to be c regardless of his velocity. Hence the velocity of light is the same to all observers; it is *invariant.*

Fig. 48E. Schematic diagram illustrating the relativistic increase in mass, and the Lorentz–Fitzgerald contraction, due to motion.

48.5. Relativistic Mass

Einstein's special theory of relativity shows that if the mass of an object is measured by two different observers, one moving with respect to the other, the results are different. Mass, therefore, is not invariant. Although the derivation will not be presented here, the special theory gives, for the transformation equation,

$$m = \gamma m_0 \tag{48i}$$

or

$$m = \frac{m_0}{\sqrt{1 - v^2/c^2}} \tag{48j}$$

relativistic

where m_0 is the mass of an object at rest in the observer's reference frame, and m is its mass when it is moving with a velocity v. A schematic diagram of a practical situation is shown in Fig. 48E in which the rest mass m_0 is not moving with respect to the observer, while at the right the same mass m is shown moving with a velocity v.

Table 48A gives the values of the relativistic mass of objects for a large range of velocities.

TABLE 48A
Relativistic mass for different velocities

Velocity ratio v/c in percent	1%	10%	50%	90%	99%	99.9%
Relative mass m/m_0	1.000	1.005	1.15	2.3	7.1	22.3

At 10% the speed of light the mass of a body is only $\frac{1}{2}$ of 1% greater than its rest mass. At 50% the speed of light the mass m has increased 15%, while at 99.9% the speed of light, it has jumped to over 22 times its rest mass. These values are in excellent agreement with experiments on high-speed atomic particles, a subject that will be considered in detail in later chapters.

It is important to note that, as the speed of any given mass increases, the mass rises slowly at first, and then much more rapidly as it approaches the speed of light. No object, however, can move with the speed of light, for by Eq.(48j) its mass would become infinite.

For low velocities v, Eqs.(48d) and (48j) are hard to evaluate, and the following approximation formula should be used*:

$$\frac{1}{\sqrt{1 - v^2/c^2}} \cong 1 + \frac{1}{2}\frac{v^2}{c^2} \qquad (48k)$$

Example 4. A beam of alpha particles, each with a mass of 6.65×10^{-27} Kg, has a velocity of 2.450×10^8 m/s. Find their mass as determined by a stationary observer in the laboratory. Use three significant figures.

Solution. The given quantities are $m_0 = 6.65 \times 10^{-27}$ Kg, $v = 2.450 \times 10^8$ m/s, and $c = 2.998 \times 10^8$ m/s. By direct substitution in Eq.(48j), we find

$$m = \frac{m_0}{\sqrt{1 - \dfrac{v^2}{c^2}}} = \frac{6.65 \times 10^{-27}}{\sqrt{1 - \dfrac{(2.45 \times 10^8)^2}{(2.998 \times 10^8)^2}}}$$

$$m = 11.54 \times 10^{-27} \text{ Kg}$$

---

* The right side of this equation represents the first two terms of a mathematical series expansion, and for relatively low velocities v, the third and all succeeding terms are negligibly small:

$$1 + \frac{1}{2}\frac{v^2}{c^2} + \frac{3}{8}\frac{v^4}{c^4} + \frac{5}{16}\frac{v^6}{c^6} + \cdots$$

48.6. Einstein's Mass–Energy Relation

Just as sound, heat, and light are forms of energy, Einstein's special theory of relativity shows that mass is a form of energy. The expression giving the relation between mass and energy is an equation familiar to everyone. It is

$$E = mc^2 \qquad (48\ell)$$

relativistic

where m is the mass, c is the velocity of light, and E is the energy equivalence of the mass. The validity of this equation is now well established by hundreds of experiments involving atomic nuclei as well as the general subject called *atomic energy.*

If an object has a rest mass of m_0, it has stored within it a total energy m_0c^2. If the same mass is moving with a velocity v, its mass has increased to m and the total stored energy is mc^2. These two masses are related by Eq.(48j).

When a force F is applied to accelerate a given mass, the amount of work done is given by

$$W = F \times x$$

As a result of this *work done*, the object, whose rest mass is m_0, is moving with a velocity and has kinetic energy E_k:

$$F \times x = E_k \qquad (48m)$$

Applying the law of conservation of energy, we can write

$$m_0c^2 + E_k = mc^2$$

Solving for E_k, we obtain for the kinetic energy of a moving mass the relation

$$E_k = mc^2 - m_0c^2 \qquad (48n)$$

Another form for this equation is obtained by substituting Eq. (48j) for m:

$$E_k = \frac{m_0c^2}{\sqrt{1 - v^2/c^2}} - m_0c^2 \qquad (48o)$$

or

$$E_k = m_0c^2\left[\frac{1}{\sqrt{1 - v^2/c^2}} - 1\right] \qquad (48p)$$

In the abbreviated notation,

$$E_k = m_0c^2(\gamma - 1) \tag{48q}$$

The total energy of a moving particle is given by its rest mass, m_0c^2, plus the energy expended to give it motion, E_k. Using Eq. (48o) we can therefore write

$$E_t = \frac{m_0c^2}{\sqrt{1 - v^2/c^2}} \tag{48r}$$

Example 5. A proton, which is the nucleus of a hydrogen atom, has a rest mass of 1.673×10^{-27} Kg. Find its total energy when it is (a) at rest, and (b) when it is moving with a velocity of 2.50×10^8 m/s.

Solution. The given quantities are $m_0 = 1.673 \times 10^{-27}$ Kg, $v = 2.50 \times 10^8$ m/s, and $c = 2.998 \times 10^8$ m/s. The rest mass of any mass m_0 is given by

$$m_0c^2 = 1.673 \times 10^{-27} \times (2.998 \times 10^8)^2$$

$$m_0c^2 = 1.504 \times 10^{-10} \text{ J}$$

Its total energy when moving is given by Eq.(48r). Direct substitution of given quantities results in

$$E_t = \frac{m_0c^2}{\sqrt{1 - \dfrac{v^2}{c^2}}} = \frac{1.504 \times 10^{-10}}{\sqrt{1 - \dfrac{(2.50 \times 10^8)^2}{(2.998 \times 10^8)^2}}}$$

$$E_t = 2.725 \times 10^{-10} \text{ J}$$

---

problems

Assume $c = 2.998 \times 10^8$ m/s for all problems unless otherwise specified.

1. Find the apparent length of a meter stick moving lengthwise at a speed of 2.250×10^8 m/s. Assume a Lorentz-Fitzgerald contraction.

2. If a space ship 45.0 m long passes the earth at a speed of 1.50×10^8 m/s, what would be its apparent length, assuming a Lorentz-Fitzgerald contraction?

3. At what speed would a meter stick be moving if its apparent length is $\frac{2}{3}$ of its real length? [Ans. 2.235×10^8 m/s.]

4. Two space ships are observed from the earth to be receding directly from each other, each with a speed of $\frac{4}{5}$ the speed of light. At what velocity does each ship recede from the other, as seen from either ship?

5. In a laboratory experiment two beams of protons are projected at each other from opposite directions. If each beam has a velocity of $\frac{4}{5}$ the speed of light, find the relative velocities of the particles.

6. An observer on the earth sees a space ship A receding from him at 2.50×10^8 m/s, and another space ship B following it at 2.0×10^8 m/s. Find the relative velocity of (a) space ship B as observed by A, (b) space ship A as observed by B, and (c) space ship B relative to A as observed from the earth. Assume $c = 3.0 \times 10^8$ m/s. [Ans. (a) $+1.1268 \times 10^8$ m/s, (b) -1.1268×10^8 m/s, (c) $+0.50 \times 10^8$ m/s.]

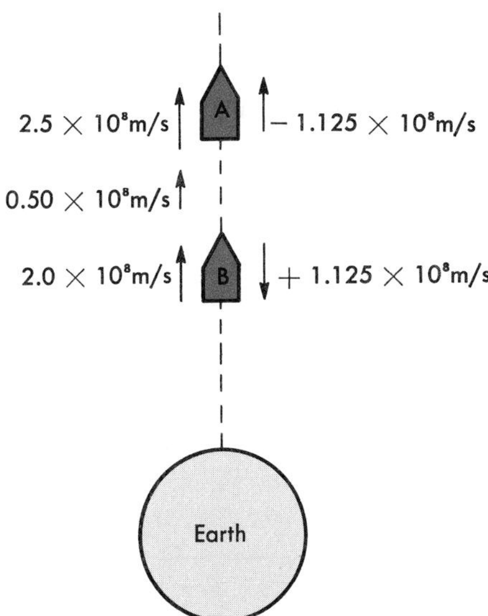

Prob. 6. To observers in space ships, A is receding from B at the same rate of speed that B is receding from A.

7. An observer on the earth sees a space ship approach at $\frac{1}{2}$ the speed of light. It launches an exploration vehicle which from the earth appears to be approaching at $\frac{2}{3}$ the speed of light. What is the velocity of the vehicle with respect to the space ship, as seen from (a) the space ship, and (b) the earth?

8. Two space ships recede from each other, traveling in opposite directions, with speeds of $\frac{2}{3}$ the speed of light. Find (a) the relative velocity of each ship as seen from the other ship, and (b) the relative velocities as seen from the earth.

9.* Two atomic particles approach each other in a head-on collision. If each particle has a mass of 3.60×10^{-25} Kg and a velocity of 2.40×10^8 m/s, what is (a) the velocity of one atom as seen from the other, and (b) their relativistic mass, as seen by the other? [Ans. (a) 2.9252×10^8 m/s, (b) 16.447×10^{-25} Kg.]

10. A space ship A takes off from the earth and heads for a distant planet. Later a second ship B takes off for the same planet. Some time still later, space ship B is observed from the earth to be receding at a speed of $\frac{4}{5}$ the speed of light. Space ship A as observed from ship B is observed to be receding at $\frac{4}{5}$ the speed of light. With what speed is A receding from the earth? Assume all bodies lie along the same straight line.

11. An observer on the earth sees a space ship receding from the earth at 2.40×10^8 m/s launch a projectile in front of it. As seen from the earth this projectile has a speed of 2.60×10^8 m/s. What is the velocity of the projectile with respect to the space ship, as seen from (a) the space ship, and (b) the earth?

12. An atomic particle has a rest mass of 6.64×10^{-27} Kg. Calculate (a) its total rest energy, and (b) its total energy when moving with a velocity of 2.35×10^8 m/s. [Ans. (a) 5.97×10^{-10} J, (b) 9.61×10^{-10} J.]

13. A molecule has a rest mass of 1.455×10^{-25} Kg. Find (a) its total rest energy, and (b) its total energy when moving with a velocity of 2.375×10^8 m/s.

14.* Starting with Eq.(48e), carry out the algebraic steps necessary to obtain Eq.(48g).

Electron optics

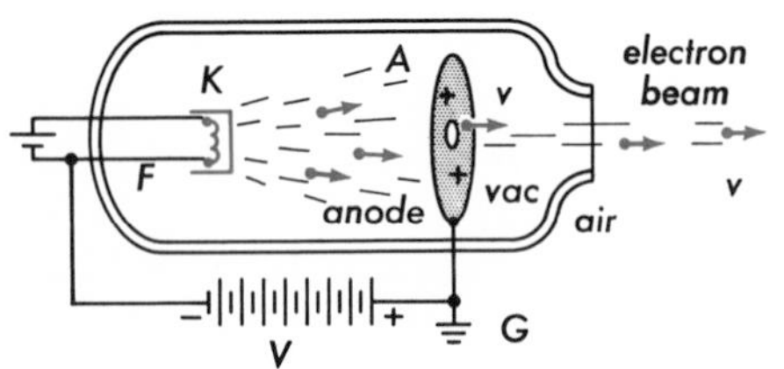

Fig. 49A. Electrons are accelerated by an applied potential difference *V*.

There exists a remarkable similarity between optical systems of prisms and lenses as they act upon light rays, and electric and magnetic fields as they act upon streams of electrons. It is the purpose of this chapter to consider some of these similarities and to treat several practical applications of *electron optics.* To begin with, it is convenient to present one of the standard methods of producing a beam of electrons, and to give the formula for calculating electron velocity.

49.1. An Electron Accelerator

A schematic diagram of an electron accelerator is shown in Fig. 49A. The source of electrons is a cesium-oxide-coated cathode K, heated by a filament F. The cathode and filament are connected to the negative terminal, and the circular disk at the center to the positive terminal of a high-voltage battery V. Starting from rest at the cathode, the electrons are accelerated along the electric lines of force, acquiring at the anode A a velocity v.

By connecting the (+) terminal to the ground, the anode is brought to the potential of the surrounding walls of the room and the electrons are not attracted back toward A, but continue on with constant velocity. With a thin aluminum foil at the end and a high applied voltage V, electrons may be projected into the air beyond.

One of the results of J. J. Thomson's experiments with cathode rays was the discovery that the velocity of electrons depends upon the *potential* applied between the anode and the cathode. The higher the voltage, the higher is the electron velocity:

$$Ve = \tfrac{1}{2}m_0v^2 \qquad (49a)$$

where V is the applied accelerating *potential* in volts, m_0 is the rest mass of the electron in kilograms, v the velocity in meters per second, and e the charge on the particle in coulombs.

Example 1. Calculate the velocity of electrons accelerated by a potential difference of 10,000 V. The electronic charge e is 1.602 $\times 10^{-19}$ C, and $m_0 = 9.11 \times 10^{-31}$ Kg.

Solution. The given quantities are $V = 1.0 \times 10^4$ V, $e = 1.602 \times 10^{-19}$ C, and $m_0 = 9.11 \times 10^{-31}$ Kg. Solving Eq.(49a) for v, and substituting known quantities, gives

$$v = \sqrt{\frac{2Ve}{m_0}} = \sqrt{\frac{2 \times 1.0 \times 10^4 \times 1.602 \times 10^{-19}}{9.11 \times 10^{-31}}}$$

$$v = 5.93 \times 10^7 \text{ m/s}$$

This value is approximately $\frac{1}{5}$ the speed of light ($c = 3.0 \times 10^8$ m/s).

Instead of calculating the velocity of electrons in meters per second, it is customary to refer to their kinetic energy in terms of the applied voltage. For example, in the problem above the energy gained by the electrons is said to be 10,000 *electron volts* (10,000 eV, or 10 KeV). They are also sometimes referred to as 10,000-volt electrons.

If voltages greater than 255,000 V are used in Eq.(49a), the calculated velocities will be greater than the velocity of light. Consequently, for voltages of about 20,000 V or more, the relativistic formula should be used. From the formula for the kinetic energy of a high-speed mass, Eq.(48q), we obtain

$$Ve = m_0c^2(\gamma - 1) \tag{49b}$$

where

$$\gamma = \frac{1}{\sqrt{1 - v^2/c^2}}$$

If Eq.(49b) is solved for v/c, one obtains the very useful equation

$$\frac{v}{c} = \sqrt{1 - \left(\frac{m_0c^2}{m_0c^2 + Ve}\right)^2} \tag{49c}$$

Example 2. A potential difference of 1.0 million volts is applied to an electron gun. Calculate the velocity of the accelerated electrons relative to the speed of light, as well as their velocity in meters per second. Use five significant figures.
Solution. The given quantities to five significant figures are $V = 1.0 \times 10^6$ V, $e = 1.60219 \times 10^{-19}$ C, $m_0 = 9.1095 \times 10^{-31}$ Kg, and $c = 2.99793 \times 10^8$ m/s. To use Eq.(49c), we use the product m_0c^2 given in the table of physical constants (see inside back cover of this text): $m_0c^2 = 8.1873 \times 10^{-14}$ J. Direct substitution gives

$$\frac{v}{c} = \sqrt{1 - \left(\frac{8.1873 \times 10^{-14}}{8.1873 \times 10^{-14} + 1.0 \times 10^6 \times 1.60219 \times 10^{-19}}\right)^2}$$

$$\frac{v}{c} = 0.94108$$

$$v = 2.82129 \times 10^8 \text{ m/s}$$

which is 94.1% the speed of light. Check this answer with Table 51A.

49.2. Refraction of Electrons

When a moving electron, entering an electric field, makes an angle with the electric lines of force, it is bent in its path according to *Bethe's law of refraction* (see Fig. 49B). A correlation of this law with Snell's law in optics is indicated by the following parallel equations:

Snell's Law *Bethe's Law*

$$\frac{\sin i}{\sin r} = \frac{v_1}{v_2} \qquad \frac{\sin \alpha}{\sin \beta} = \frac{v_2}{v_1} \tag{49d}$$

The left-hand diagram shows two metal cylinders lined up end to end with fine wire screens across the ends marked A and B. The lower battery maintains a constant difference of potential $V_2 - V_1$ between these two screens.

Note in Eq.(49d) the reverse order of the velocities v_1 and v_2. When a ray of light enters a denser medium, it is slowed down and at the same time bent toward the normal. Electrons, on the other hand, are deflected toward the normal when, in crossing a potential layer, they are speeded up. If the grid potentials are reversed, the electrons will be retarded in crossing the potential layer and they will be deflected away from the normal. In other words, *reverse the direction of the electrons, keeping their speed the same, and they will retrace their paths exactly.* Such a behavior is analogous to the very useful principle in geometrical optics that *all light rays are retraceable.*

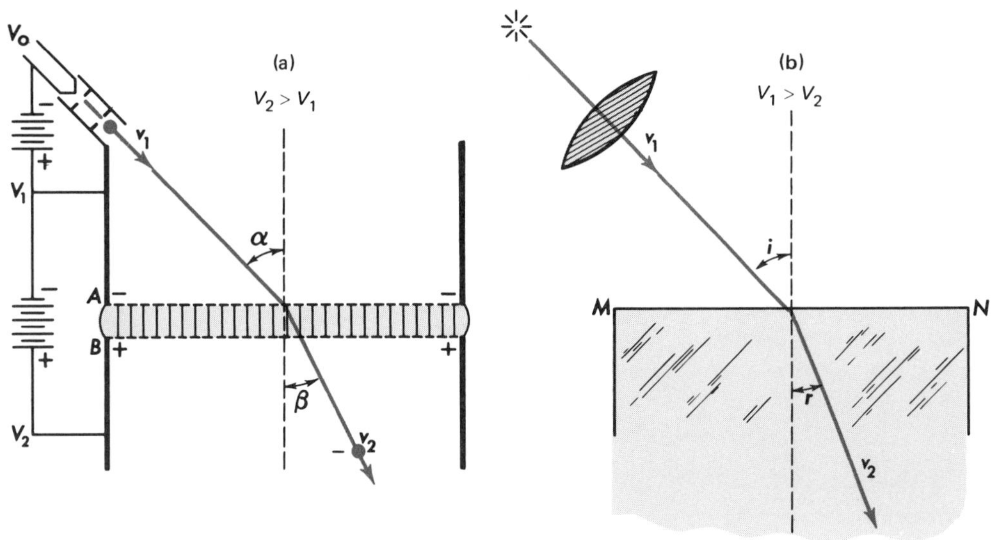

Fig. 49B. The bending of (b) light in refraction is analogous to the bending of (a) the path of an electron.

To carry the refraction analogy a little further, consider the bending of electron paths by electrically charged bodies as shown in Fig. 49C. Attraction by the positively charged wire

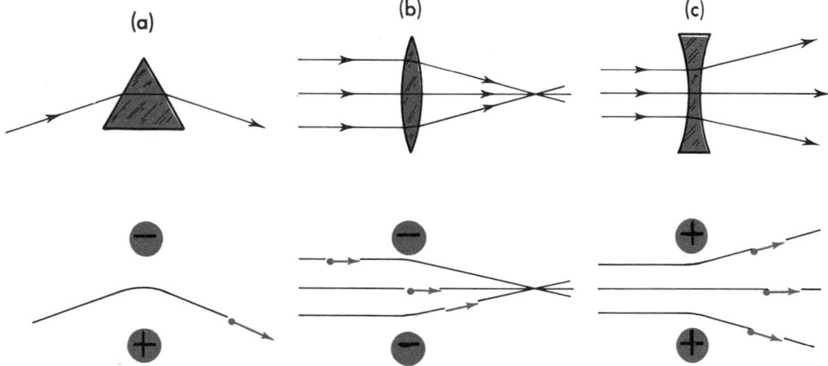

Fig. 49C. Comparison of light optics with electron optics.

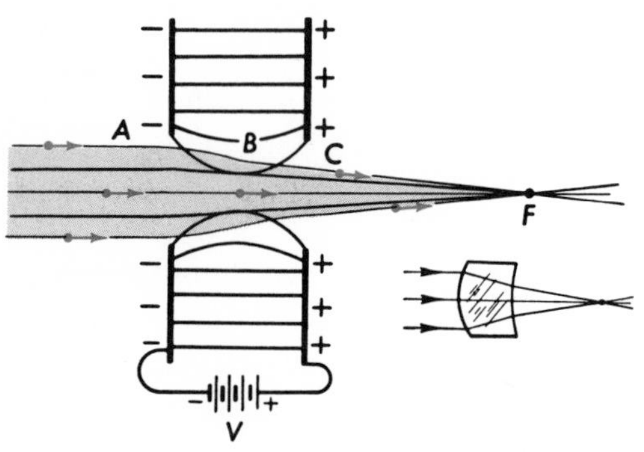

Fig. 49D. Double-aperture electron lens and its optical analog.

and repulsion by the negative produce a prism-like action in case (a). A negatively charged metal ring produces a converging lenslike action in case (b); a positively charged ring produces a diverging lens action in case (c).

Since, by Eq.(49a), $v^2 \propto V$ and $v \propto \sqrt{V}$, the velocities v_1 and v_2 in Bethe's law of electron refraction may be replaced by $\sqrt{V_1}$ and $\sqrt{V_2}$, respectively, giving

$$\frac{\sin \alpha}{\sin \beta} = \frac{\sqrt{V_2}}{\sqrt{V_1}} \tag{49e}$$

V_1 and V_2 are the potentials of the two grids A and B in Fig. 49B, taken with respect to the cathode source of electrons in the electron gun as zero.

Example 3. Electrons accelerated by a potential difference of +1200 V enter the electric field between two parallel grids as shown in Fig. 49B. If the angle of incidence is 40°, and the potential difference applied to the grids is +600 V, find the angle of refraction.

Solution. The given quantities are $V_1 = 1200$ V, $V_2 = 1800$ V, and $\alpha = 40°$. Solving Eq.(49e) for sin β, and substituting known quantities, we obtain

$$\sin \beta = \frac{\sqrt{V_1} \sin \alpha}{\sqrt{V_2}} = \frac{\sqrt{1200} \times 0.643}{\sqrt{1800}}$$

$$\sin \beta = \frac{34.64 \times 0.643}{42.4} = 0.525$$

$$\beta = 31.67°$$

If the grid voltage is reversed so that $V_2 = -600$ V, we obtain

$$\sin \beta = \frac{\sqrt{1200} \times 0.643}{\sqrt{600}} = 0.910$$

$$\beta = 65.4°$$

49.3. Electron Lenses

An electron lens, known as a double-aperture system, is shown in Fig. 49D; it is to be compared in its action to parallel rays of light incident on a converging glass lens as shown at the lower right. While both are converging systems, the essential difference between the two is that whereas light rays are bent only at the two surfaces, electrons are refracted continuously as they pass through the potential layers.

The focal length of a glass lens is fixed in value by the radius of curvature of its two faces and the refractive index for the light used, but the focal length of an electron lens can be varied at will by altering v, the velocity of the electrons, and V, the voltage applied to the system. In this respect, the latter can be compared to the crystalline lens of the eye where the focal length can be changed by altering the lens curvature.

In the diagram, refraction for the upper path is greatest near A and, although it changes sign at some point near B, the gain in velocity due to the electric field produces a lesser deviation over the second half of the path, thereby causing convergence. If the electrons are reversed in direction on the right, they will retrace their paths and emerge parallel at the left. If the electric field is reversed in direction, however, the electron paths will not be the same but the system will still act as a converging lens.

A second type of electron lens, known as a double-cylinder system, is shown in Fig. 49E. In passing through the potential gap, the electric field has a converging action for the first half of the distance and a diverging action during the second half. Because they spend a greater time in the first half of the converging field, and the force on a charged particle is independent of velocity, the impulse (force × time) is greater for the convergence interval than it is for the divergence interval.

By making the second cylinder larger than the first, as in Fig. 49F, the electric lines of force spread out more in the second cylinder. Such spreading weakens the field in the larger cylinder and reduces the divergent action to bring the electrons to a shorter focus.

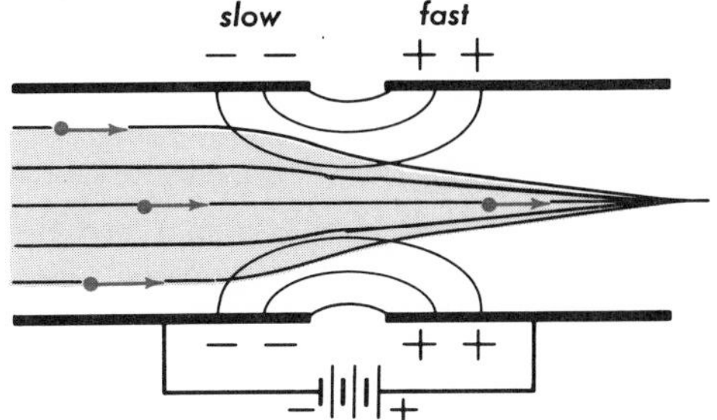

Fig. 49E. Symmetrical electron lens.

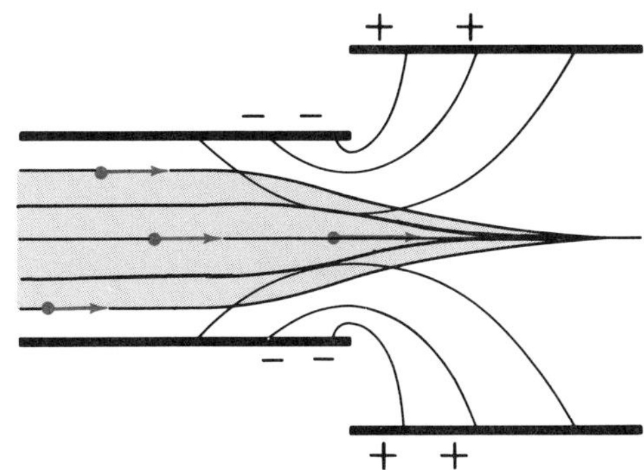

Fig. 49F. Asymmetrical electron lens.

49.4. An Electron Gun

A narrow beam of high-speed electrons, all having as nearly as possible the same velocity, has many practical applications in the field of electronics and atomic research. A device for producing such beams is called an "electron gun" (see Fig. 49G).

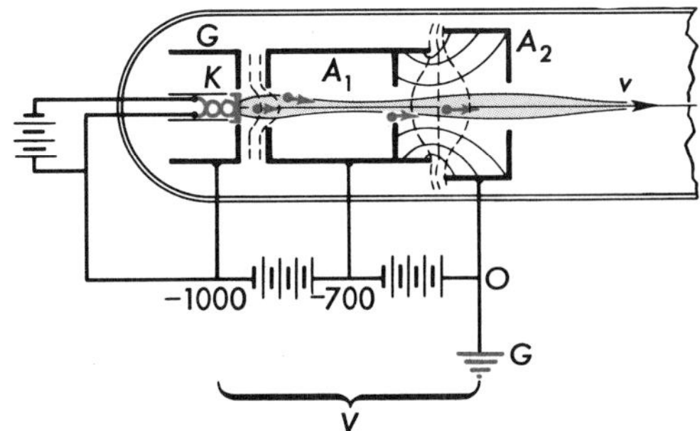

Fig. 49G. Electron gun.

Electrons from a small filament-heated cathode K are accelerated by a difference of potential V applied to the cylinders of an electrostatic lens system, A_1 and A_2. The purpose of the guard ring maintained at the potential of the cathode is to improve the properties of the lens action of the first aperture and thereby collect a maximum number of emitted electrons into the collimated beam.

The function of the second lens is to converge the bundle toward a focus and then introduce enough divergence to straighten the beam out into a narrow pencil. The velocity of the emergent beam is given by Eq.(49a), where V is the over-all voltage from cathode K to anode A_2.

49.5. The Cathode-Ray Oscilloscope

One of the simplest applications of an electron gun is to be found in every *cathode-ray oscilloscope,* an instrument whose purpose is to reveal the detailed variations in rapidly changing electric currents, potentials, or pulses (see Fig. 49H). In appearance this device looks like J. J. Thomson's cathode-ray tube (see Fig. 41F), and is actually the important element in one type of television receiver.

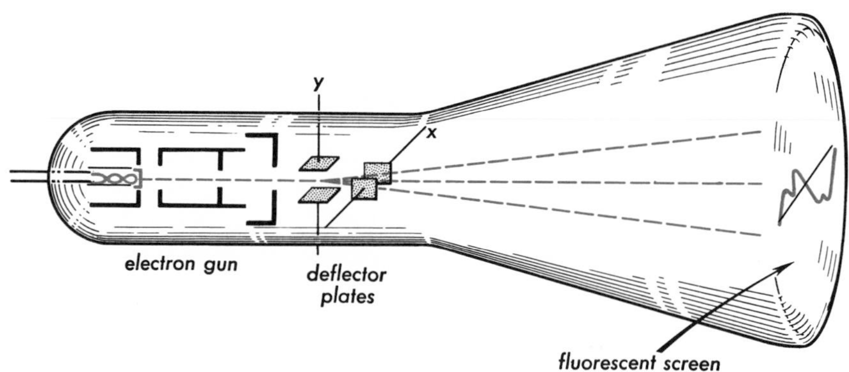

Fig. 49H. Cathode-ray oscilloscope.

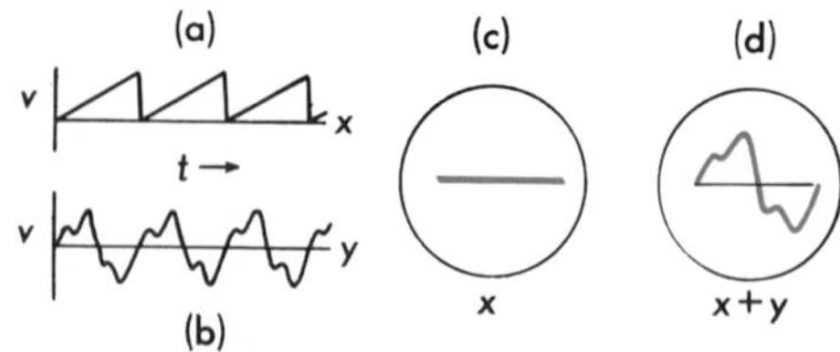

Fig. 49I. Potentials applied to a cathode-ray tube, and graphs appearing on a fluorescent screen.

A cathode-ray oscilloscope is a vacuum tube containing *an electron gun* at one end, two pairs of *deflector plates* (or magnetic coils) near the middle, and a *fluorescent screen* at the other end. When an alternating voltage is applied to the *x plates,* the electron beam bends back and forth from side to side and, when applied to the *y plates,* it bends up and down. The luminous spot produced where the beam strikes the fluorescent screen traces out a horizontal line in the first instance and a vertical line in the second.

It is customary to apply a *saw-tooth potential difference* to the *x* plates [see Fig. 49I(a)] and the unknown potential difference to be studied, (b), to the y plates. The saw-tooth potential difference supplied by a special radio tube circuit, called a "sweep circuit," causes the beam spot to move from left to right across the screen at constant speed and then jump quickly back from right to left to repeat the motion, (c). When the vertical deflections occur at the same time, the spot draws out a graph of the varying potential difference as in diagram (d). By varying the sweep circuit frequency until it matches the frequency of the studied signal, repeated graphs will be drawn out, one on top of the other, and persistence of vision and the fluorescent screen will present a stationary graph.

Green fluorescent screens are used for visual observation since the eye is most sensitive to this color; blue screens are used for photographic purposes since films and plates are most sensitive to blue.

The oscilloscope has many practical applications, and is to be found in every research laboratory as well as in every radio and television repair shop. Its principal function is to analyze, or diagnose, rapidly changing potential differences whose frequencies may be as low as a fraction of a cycle per second or as high as thousands of megacycles per second. Periodic or transient potential differences as small as a fraction of a microvolt may also be studied by first amplifying them with standard vacuum-tube or transistor circuits (see Chaps. 38 and 39).

Another valuable feature of the oscilloscope is its ability to measure time intervals between electrical impulses less than a microsecond apart. One microsecond is equal to one-millionth of a second.

49.6. Infrared Telescope

A telescope for seeing objects in the dark illuminated by infrared light is diagrammed in Fig. 49J. An image of the object to

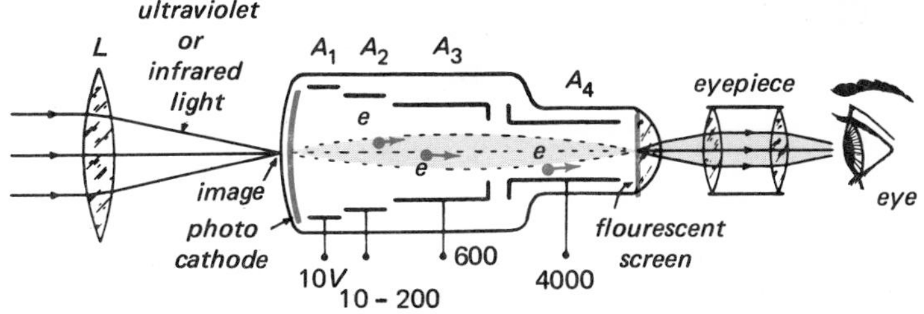

Fig. 49J. Ultraviolet and infrared telescope employing an electron-image tube.

be observed is focused on the photocathode of the vacuum tube by means of an ordinary glass lens L. The cesium-oxide-coated cathode under infrared illumination emits photoelectrons which, accelerated to the right by A_1, A_2, A_3 and A_4, are brought to a focus on the green fluorescent screen at the right. The visible light they produce there by their impact is then observed by means of a magnifying eyepiece.

Electron focusing is accomplished by varying the potential difference applied to the second anode A_2; the infrared light image is focused by moving the lens L; and the visible light image is focused by moving the eyepiece.

49.7. Magnetic Lenses

When electrons cross a magnetic field and their paths make an angle with the magnetic lines, they are deflected in spiral-like paths which, if properly controlled, may bring them to a focus. Such focusing properties of magnetic fields, illustrated by the cross section of a flat coil in Fig. 49K, were first demonstrated and proved mathematically by Busch in 1926. It can be shown that the focal length of such a lens, the magnetic field strength, and the electron velocity fit into well-known formulas in optics.

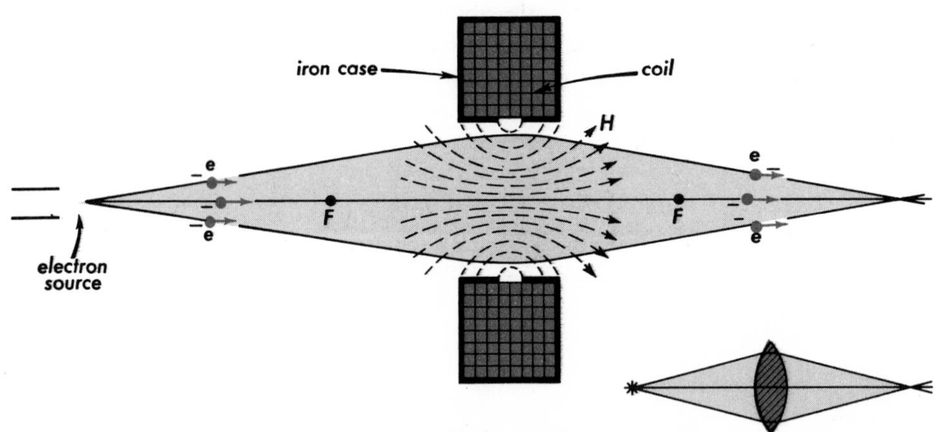

Fig. 49K. Magnetic lens for electrons. (Optical analog, lower right.)

By encasing a flat coil in a hollow iron ring, the magnetic field becomes more concentrated and the refraction of electrons becomes more abrupt as they pass through the field. As a consequence the refraction more nearly resembles that of optical lenses. Still greater concentration is brought about by providing a small narrow gap on the inside of the iron casing, as shown in the diagram.

If electron paths diverge too far from the principal axis of a coil lens, aberrations of the kind found with light and glass lenses arise. For this reason *diaphragms* are often used to confine electron beams to the center of the coil, as an *iris diaphragm* is used to confine light rays to the center of a lens.

49.8. Electron Microscope

The electron microscope, like the optical microscope, is an instrument used principally in the research laboratory for magnifying small objects to such an extent that their minutest parts may be observed and studied in detail. The importance of this device in the field of medical research cannot be overestimated. To illustrate, many viruses known to medical science as being responsible for certain human diseases lie beyond the range of the optical microscope. With the electron microscope, magnifications of from 10 to 100 times that of the finest optical microscopes make many of these viruses, and some of their detailed structure, visible to the eye. While the highest magnification obtained with the best optical microscope is about 2000×, electron microscopes have already been made that give magnifications as high as 100,000×.

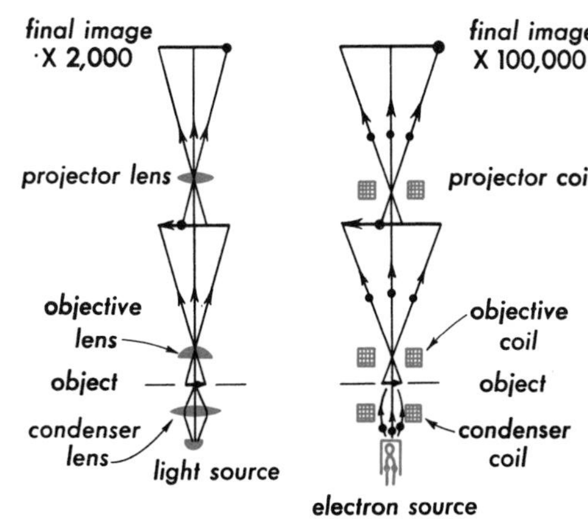

Fig. 49L. Optical microscope compared with an electron microscope.

A schematic diagram of an electron microscope employing magnetic lenses is shown in Fig. 49L. At the bottom, a source of electrons is concentrated on the object (small arrow) by a condenser coil. Passing through or around the object, these electrons focus a magnified image of the object just below the projector coil. Only a small central section of these electrons pass into the projector coil, to be brought to focus in a further magnified image at the top. There the image of only a small section of the object can be seen directly on a fluorescent screen or can be photographed with ordinary photographic plates.

Electrons, like light waves, are stopped by metallic films; only when the films are extremely thin can transmitted rays be employed. For opaque objects the light, or electrons, may be reflected from the surface and only surface structures may be observed.

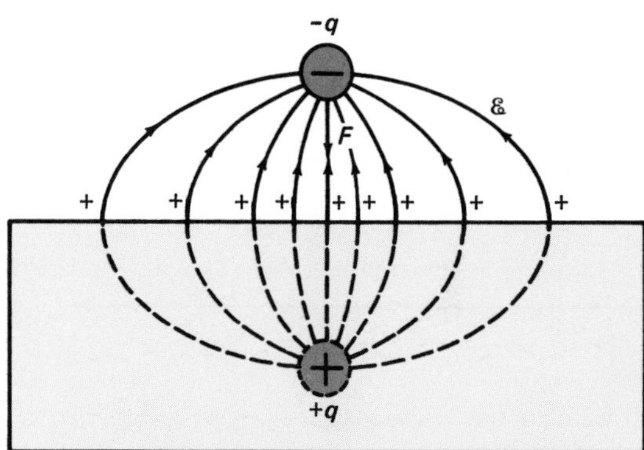

Fig. 49M. Diagram of the electric field between a negative charge $-q$ and a good metallic conductor.

49.9. Visible Light from Unbound Electrons

When an isolated charged body is located close to a metallic conductor as shown in Fig. 49M, Coulomb forces of attraction and repulsion set up surface charges as shown. Under these conditions the electric field between the two takes the form shown by the solid lines.

A comparison of these lines with Fig. 23A(c) shows their general shape to be the same as though an equal but opposite charge $+q$ was located an equal distance beyond the metal surface. In other words, the field outside the conductor is essentially that of an electric dipole. Furthermore, the total plus charge at the conducting surface is equal to $+q$ and exerts a force F on the isolated charge $-q$.

Suppose now that an electron moving with a velocity v passes close to a metallic conductor with a corrugated surface as shown in Fig. 49N. The field between the two will be the same as though an equal positive charge moved along with the same forward velocity v but oscillated up and down. Since the force on the electron varies with distance from the surface, it too moves up and down as shown and the accompanying field is the same as that of an oscillating electric dipole. As a result of these oscillations, electromagnetic waves will be radiated as if from a moving Hertzian dipole (see Sec. 38.5).

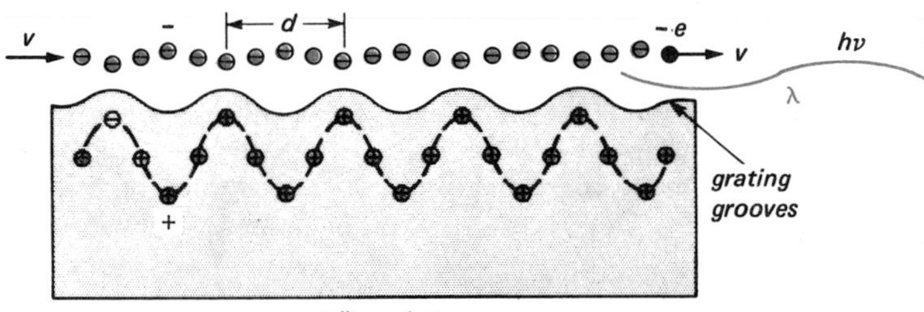

Fig. 49N. Electrons passing over a metallic diffraction grating at right angles to the surface grooves generate electromagnetic waves of very short wavelength.

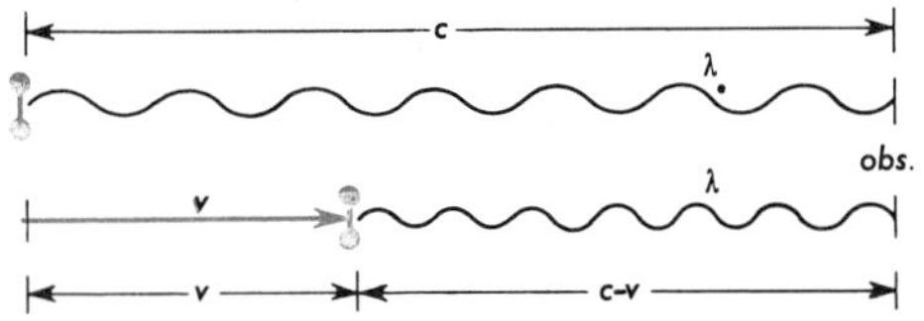

Fig. 49O. Geometry for derivation of Doppler wavelength of electromagnetic waves from a moving electric dipole. Diagram constructed for distances traveled per second of time.

To calculate the frequency of the emitted radiation and the wavelength observed by a stationary observer, the principles of the Doppler effect must be employed. The top diagram in Fig. 49O represents the waves emitted in 1 s from a stationary dipole source, and we can write

$$c = \nu\lambda_e \tag{49f}$$

where c is the speed of light, ν is the source frequency, and λ_e is the wavelength.

The bottom diagram shows the same number of waves emitted in 1 s by the source as it moves toward the observer with a velocity v. Since the waves are crowded into a distance $c - v$, we may write

$$\nu\lambda = c - v \tag{49g}$$

where λ is now the wavelength measured by the stationary observer. Substituting $\nu\lambda_e$ for c in this second equation, we obtain

$$\nu\lambda = \nu\lambda_e - v$$

and, therefore,

$$\lambda = \lambda_e - \frac{v}{\nu}$$

Since $\nu = c/\lambda_e$, substitution gives

$$\lambda = \lambda_e - \lambda_e \frac{v}{c}$$

from which

$$\lambda = \lambda_e\left(1 - \frac{v}{c}\right)$$

If the observer is not in the forward direction but is in some direction making an angle θ with v, only the component of v should be used in this formula, and we write for the general case

$$\lambda = \lambda_e\left(1 - \frac{v}{c}\cos\theta\right) \tag{49h}$$

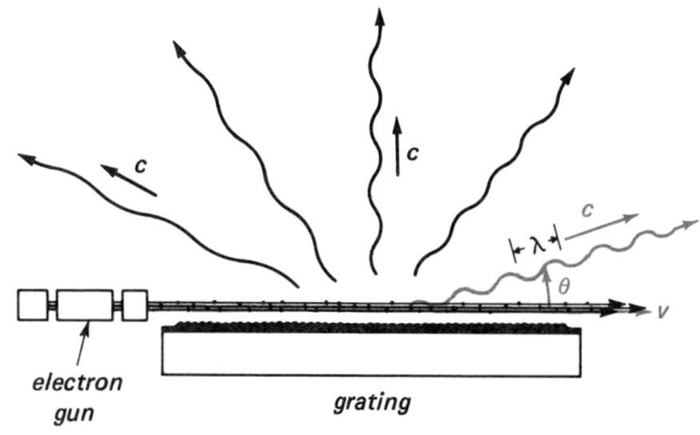

Fig. 49P. Moving electron sources give rise to Doppler effect and different wavelengths of light.

The first proposal that electromagnetic waves in the microwave and infrared region of the spectrum could be generated by projecting a beam of electrons over the surface of a diffraction grating was made by W. W. Salisbury in 1949 (see Fig. 49P). The first experimental generation of visible light by this method was performed by Smith and Purcel.

If d represents the grating spacing, as shown in Fig. 49N, the vibration frequency of each moving electron will be given by

$$\nu = \frac{v}{d} = \frac{c}{\lambda_e}$$

Since this gives

$$\lambda_e = d\,\frac{c}{v}$$

direct substitution of dc/v for λ_e in Eq.(49h) yields

$$\lambda = d\left(\frac{c}{v} - \cos\theta\right) \tag{49i}$$

Example 4. A beam of 300,000-volt electrons is projected across a diffraction grating at right angles to the rulings. If the grating contains 20,000 lines per centimeter, find the wavelength of the light emitted at right angles to the grating face. Use atomic constants to four significant figures.

Solution. The given quantities are $V = 3.0 \times 10^5$ V, $m_0 = 9.110 \times 10^{-31}$ Kg, $e = 1.6022 \times 10^{-19}$ C, $c = 2.9979 \times 10^8$ m/s, $m_0c^2 = 8.187 \times 10^{-14}$, and $\theta = 90°$. The electrons' relative velocity v/c is first obtained by use of Eq.(49c). Following the method used in Example 2, we find for v/c

$$\frac{v}{c} = \sqrt{1 - \left(\frac{m_0c^2}{m_0c^2 + Ve}\right)^2}$$

$$\frac{v}{c} = \sqrt{1 - \left(\frac{8.187 \times 10^{-14}}{8.187 \times 10^{-14} + 3.0 \times 10^5 \times 1.6022 \times 10^{-19}}\right)^2}$$

$$\frac{v}{c} = 0.7765$$

We next find the distance between grating lines in meters, as follows:

$$d = \frac{1}{2.0 \times 10^6} = 5.0 \times 10^{-7}\ \text{m}$$

Direct substitution of known quantities in Eq.(49i) gives

$$\lambda = d\left(\frac{c}{v} - \cos\theta\right) = 5.0 \times 10^{-7}\left(\frac{1}{0.7765} - 0\right)$$

$$\lambda = 6.439 \times 10^{-7}\ \text{m}$$

$$\lambda = 6439\ \text{Å}$$

---

problems

Use c = 2.9979 × 10⁸ m/s in the following problems.

1. A potential of 1000 V is applied to an electron gun. Calculate (a) the speed relative to the velocity of light, and (b) the real velocity of the electrons.

2. A difference of potential of 2500 V is applied to an electron gun. Find (a) the speed relative to the velocity of light, and (b) the real velocity of the electrons.

3. If 5000 V is applied to an electron gun, find (a) the speed relative to the velocity of light, and (b) the actual velocity of the electrons. Use nonrelativistic equations. [Ans. (a) 0.13989, (b) 4.194×10^7 m/s.]

4. An electron gun designed for high voltage has 50,000 V applied to its terminals. Find (a) the speed relative to the velocity of light, and (b) the actual velocity of the electrons.

5. A potential difference of 250,000 V is applied to an electron gun. Find (a) the speed relative to the velocity of light, and (b) the actual velocity of the electron beam.

6. If 100,000 V is applied to an electron gun, find (a) the speed relative to the velocity of light, and (b) the actual velocity of the electron beam. Check your answer with Table 51A. [Ans. (a) 0.5482, (b) 1.6435×10^8 m/s.]

7. An electron gun has a potential difference of 5000 V applied to its electrodes. The beam produced enters an electric field between two grids as shown in Fig. 49B. If the angle of incidence is 30°, and a potential difference of 2000 V is applied to the grids, find (a) the electron beam velocity, and (b) the angle of refraction when the grid voltage accelerates the electrons passing through.

8. A potential difference of 10,000 V is applied to an electron gun. The beam produced enters the electric field between two grids as shown in Fig. 40B. If the angle of incidence is 20°, and a potential difference of 2000 V is applied to the grids, find (a) the incident electron beam velocity, and (b) the angle of refraction of the beam if the grid voltage retards the electrons.

9. A potential difference of 3000 V is applied to an electron gun. The beam produced enters the electric field between two grids as shown in Fig. 49B. If the angle of refraction is 32° when a potential difference of 1000 V is applied to the grids, find (a) the incident electron beam velocity, and (b) the angle of incidence, if the voltage accelerates the electrons. [Ans. (a) 3.248×10^7 m/s, (b) 37.73°.]

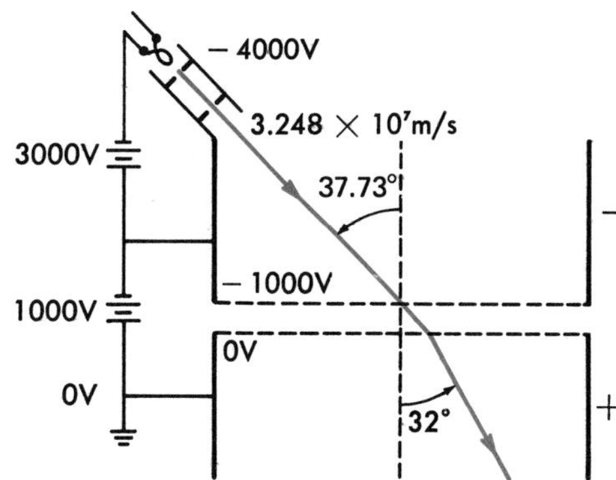

Prob. 9. A beam of electrons is refracted by an electric field between parallel grids.

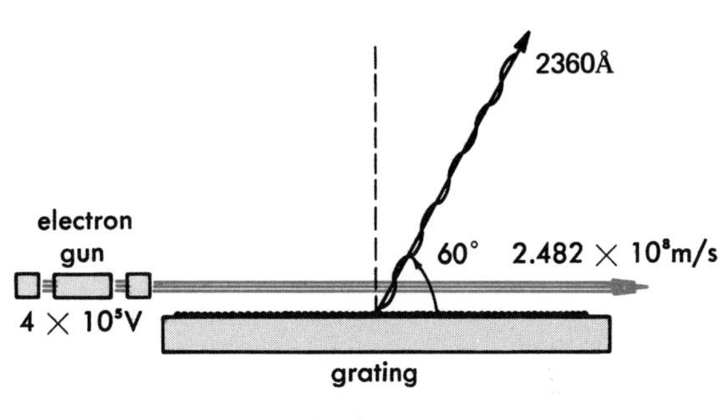

Prob. 12.

10. A beam of 100,000-V electrons is projected across a diffraction grating at right angles to the rulings. If the grating contains 30,000 lines/cm, find (a) the electron beam velocity *v*, and (b) the wavelength of the light emitted at right angles to the grating face.

11.* A beam of 250,000-volt electrons is projected across a diffraction grating at right angles to the rulings. If the grating contains 25,000 lines/cm, find (a) the electron beam velocity, and (b) the wavelength of the light emitted at 45° to the grating face.

12.* A beam of 400,000-volt electrons is projected across a diffraction grating at right angles to the rulings. If the grating contains 30,000 lines/cm, find (a) the electron beam velocity, and (b) the wavelength of the light emitted at 60° to the grating face. [Ans. (a) 2.482×10^8 m/s, (b) 2.360×10^{-7} m, or 2360 Å.]

50 X rays

One of the most interesting episodes in the history of modern science began with the accidental discovery of X rays by Wilhelm Röntgen* in 1895. While studying the green fluorescent stage of an electrical discharge in a Crookes tube, Röntgen observed the bright fluorescence of some nearby crystals of barium platino-cyanide. Even though the discharge tube was in a darkened room, and entirely surrounded with black paper to prevent the escape of visible light, a distant screen covered with crystals would fluoresce brightly when the discharge was turned on. Röntgen reasoned, therefore, that some kind of invisible, yet penetrating, rays of an unknown kind were being given out by the discharge tube. These rays he called *X rays,* the letter *X* meaning, as it so often does in algebra, an unknown.

In the short series of experiments that followed his discovery, Röntgen found that the unknown rays were coming from the glass walls of the tube itself and, in particular, from the region where the most intense part of the cathode ray beam was striking the glass. So great was the importance of this discovery that, within only a few weeks of Röntgen's announcement, X rays were being used as an aid in surgical operations in Vienna.

Today X rays are used in hundreds of different ways. In the post offices metallic and other materials can be observed in packages without opening them. In foundaries, metallic castings of all sizes and shapes can be examined for blowholes without damage of any kind to the product. X rays are also used to identify minerals in soils, as well as in mine ores. In the field of medicine they are widely used after surgery to destroy undetected cancer remnants, thus avoiding the spread of the disease throughout the body.

These, and other practical applications and uses that can be made of scientific discoveries are good examples of the role of modern science in the rapid advancement of civilization.

50.1. X-Ray Tubes

The Crookes tube with which Röntgen made his discovery bears very little resemblance to the modern X-ray tube. In form it

* See Introduction, Chapter A, for biography of Röntgen.

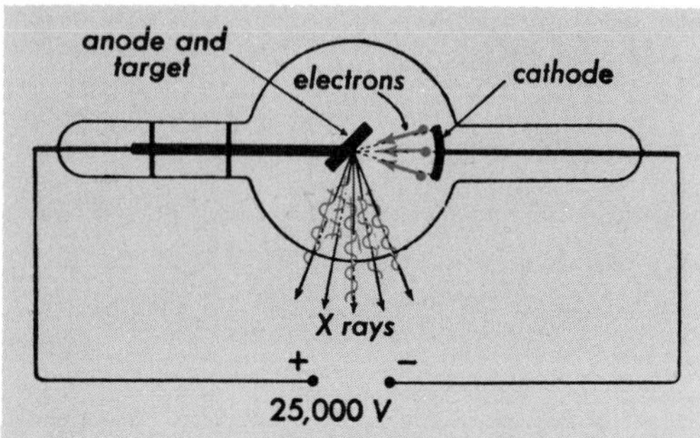

Fig. 50A. Diagram of early form of X-ray tube.

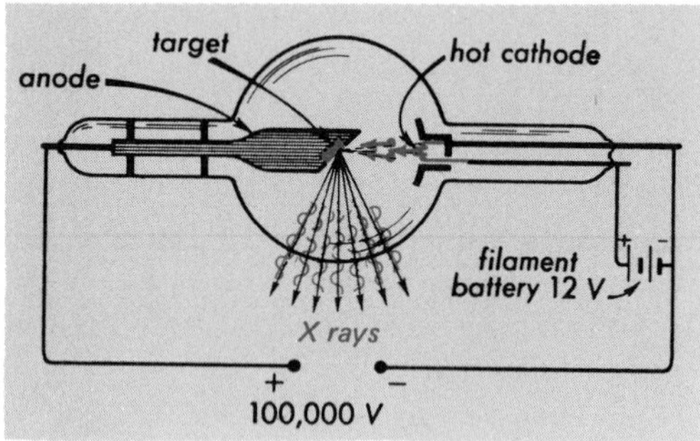

Fig. 50B. Diagram of a Coolidge X-ray tube employing a hot cathode.

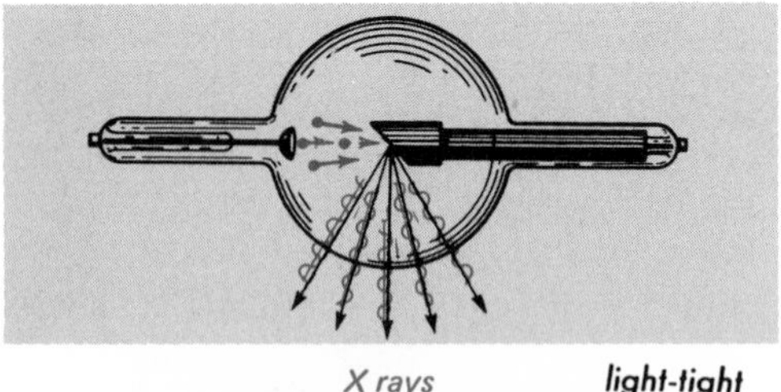

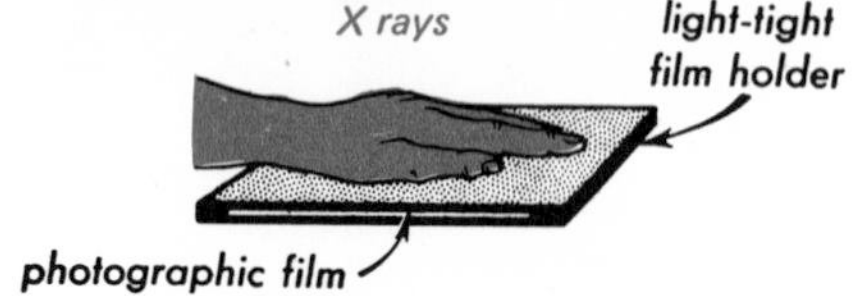

Fig. 50C. Arrangement for taking X-ray photographs of the bones of the hand.

had somewhat the appearance of the tube shown in Fig. 41C. Within a short period of time after Röntgen's discovery, quite a number of noteworthy improvements upon tube design were made. The first important contribution in this direction came immediately after the discovery that it is the sudden stopping of electrons that gives rise to X rays.

In X-ray tubes of early design, the electrons from the cathode were not allowed to strike the glass walls, but were directed toward the anode as a target, as shown in Fig. 50A. By curving the cathode like a concave mirror, it was found that it was possible to focus the electrons on one spot on the target, thus making of that spot a localized source of X rays. Radiating outward in all possible directions, these "Röntgen rays," as they are sometimes called, have no difficulty in passing through the glass walls of the tube.

The biggest improvement in X-ray tube design was made by Coolidge, an American physicist, in 1913. In the Coolidge tube, now a commercial product (see Fig. 50B), a tungsten-wire filament is placed at the center of the cathode and heated to incandescence by a storage battery or low-voltage transformer. This filament, being a copious source of electrons, gives rise at the target to a far more intense source of X rays than was previously possible with a cold cathode. Under the terrific bombardment of the target by so many electrons, most metals will melt. To overcome this difficulty, a metal with a high melting point, like tungsten or molybdenum, is embedded in the face of a solid copper anode to become the target. Copper, being a good heat conductor, helps to dissipate the heat.

The early sources of high voltage applied to the anode and cathode of X-ray tubes were induction coils of various descriptions. Although some of these sources are still in use, they have been almost entirely supplanted by a more efficient high-voltage transformer. The emf generated by these transformers varies between 50,000 and 2,000,000 V. The normal emf used for surgical work is about 100,000 V, whereas for the treatment of diseases a higher emf is employed. The high-voltage alternating emf supplied by a transformer is not applied directly to the X-ray tube, but is first changed into direct current by means of rectifier tubes.

50.2. Penetration of X Rays

Four useful and important properties of X rays are their ability (1) to penetrate solid matter, (2) to cause certain chemical compounds to fluoresce, (3) to ionize atoms, and (4) to affect a photographic plate. The penetration of X rays depends upon two things:

first, the voltage applied between the anode and cathode of the X-ray tube; and second, the density of the substance through which the rays must travel. The higher the voltage applied to the tube, the greater is the penetration. *X rays of great penetrating power are called hard X rays, whereas those having little penetrating power are called soft X rays.*

The relation between density and penetration may be illustrated in several ways. When X rays are sent through a block of wood containing nails, or a closed leather purse containing coins, a clear and well-defined image of the nails, or coins, can be formed and observed on a fluorescent screen. The experimental arrangement is the same as that shown in Fig. 50C. When X rays are sent through the hand or any part of the body to obtain photographs of the bones, it is the difference in penetration between the flesh and the bones that permits a picture to be made. Materials like paper, wood, flesh, etc., composed principally of light chemical elements like those at the beginning of the periodic table, are readily penetrated by X rays. In other words, they are poor absorbers of X rays. For materials like brass, steel, bone, gold, etc., composed partly of heavy elements, like those farther along and near the end of the periodic table, the penetration of X rays is very poor. Hence, heavy elements, or dense substances, are good absorbers.

The bones of the body, which contain large amounts of calcium, are relatively good absorbers of X rays, whereas the soft tissue, composed principally of much lighter elements—hydrogen, oxygen, carbon, and nitrogen—is a poor absorber. This explains the general appearance of X-ray photographs. X-ray pictures like the ones in Fig. 50D are similar to shadows cast by the objects being photographed. The focus point on the X-ray target, being bombarded by high-speed electrons, acts as a point source of rays. These rays spread out in straight lines as shown in Fig. 50C. On passing through the hand to the photographic film, more X rays are absorbed by the bones than by the flesh. The shadow cast by the bones is therefore lacking in X rays, and the photographic film for these areas becomes transparent upon development.

Where only flesh is traversed, the X rays penetrate through to the photographic film, causing it to develop out black. The bones therefore appear white against a darker background. If this "negative film," as it is called, is printed on paper as in Fig. 50D, it becomes a "positive," the bones appearing black.

If the photographic film is placed farther away from the hand than shown in the diagram, the shadow picture will be larger and less distinct. The best pictures are obtained by placing the film

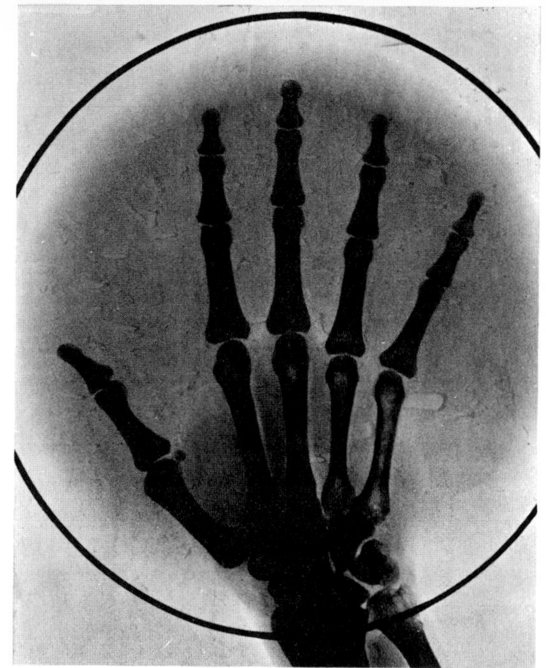

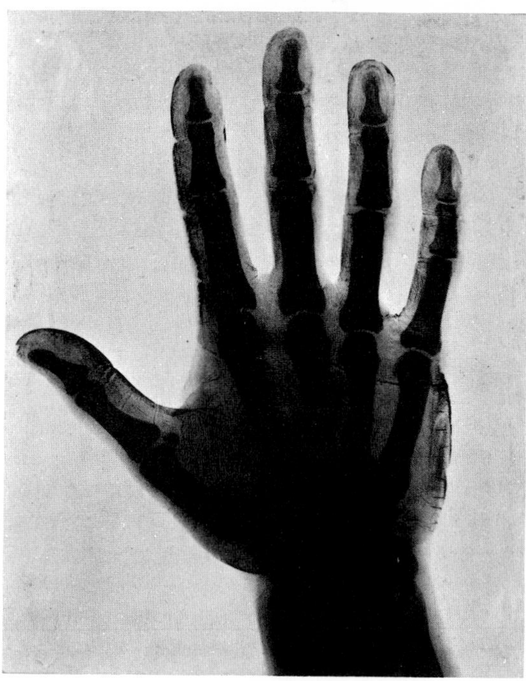

Fig. 50D. X-ray photographs of the wrist bones of the hand. Above, with hand in water. Below, with lead oxide ointment spread on hand. (Courtesy, Stamford Research Laboratories, American Cyanamid Co.)

as close in contact with the object to be photographed as is physically possible. Whenever a film is being exposed for an X-ray picture, it is mounted in a black paper envelope or thin aluminum box. This prevents visible light from reaching the film but allows the X rays to pass through.

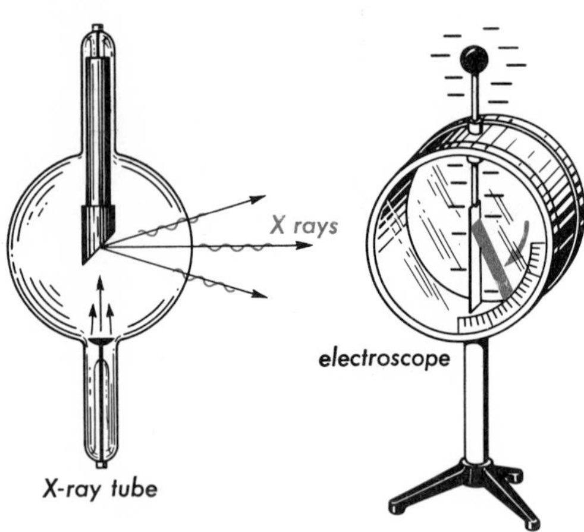

Fig. 50E. X rays discharge an electroscope.

50.3. Ionizing Power

As X rays pass through matter in the solid, liquid, or gaseous state, they are found to *ionize* atoms and molecules. This can be shown by charging a gold-leaf electroscope positively or negatively and placing it some 10 to 15 ft away from an X-ray tube. When the X-ray tube is turned on (see Fig. 50E), the gold leaf falls, showing discharge.

The explanation of this experiment is as follows. X rays pass through the electroscope and ionize the air by removing electrons from many of the oxygen and nitrogen molecules. Leaving these particular molecules with a net positive charge, the freed electrons move about until they are picked up by other neutral molecules, which thus take on a net negative charge. The result is that the passage of X rays through matter produces both *positively charged* and *negatively charged ions.* If the electroscope is negatively charged, it attracts the positively charged ions to the gold leaf, neutralizing the charge and repelling the negatively charged ions to the "grounded" walls where they, too, become neutralized. If the electroscope is positively charged, it attracts the negative ions to it, again neutralizing the charge. The positive ions in this case are repelled to the walls. In either case, whether the electroscope is positively or negatively charged, the gold leaf falls, showing discharge.

It is the ionization of atoms and molecules in a substance that limits the penetrating power of X rays. Heavy elements contain more electrons than light elements, thus placing more electrons in the path of the X rays to stop them. The stopping power of a thin sheet of lead, for example, is equivalent to the stopping power of a sheet of aluminum many times thicker. Lead atoms each contain 82 electrons, whereas aluminum atoms each contain only 13.

50.4. Practical Applications

During the first few weeks following Röntgen's discovery of X rays, reports from all over the world were received by the editors of scientific journals telling how the new rays could be put to practical use. A few examples of the first applications were (1) the location of a bullet in a patient's leg, (2) the observation and photography of the healing of a broken bone, (3) the detection of contraband in baggage, (4) the distinction between artificial and real gems, (5) the detection of pearls in oysters, and (6) the examination of the contents in parcel post. In 1897 Dr. Morton exhibited in New York an X-ray picture of the entire skeleton of a living and fully clothed adult.

The biological effects became important when it was found that X rays killed off some forms of animal tissue more rapidly than others. This made them a possible means of cure for certain skin diseases. In particular, the application to the treatment of well-known forms of cancerous growths in animals and human beings has yielded amazing results, and oftentimes a cure. When an internal cancer is treated by sending a beam of X rays directly through the body, the cancerous tissue as well as the normal tissue is slowly killed off. It is principally because the normal tissue grows in again more rapidly than the cancerous tissue that it is possible to bring about a cure. Periodic radiation allows the normal tissue to build up in the intervals.

Although only certain diseases can be successfully treated by X rays, a great deal of research work is still being carried on with extremely high voltage X rays in the hope of discovering new and more effective medical aids. It is generally believed that the killing-off of cell tissue of X rays is due in part to ionization and in part to the formation of free radicals of the molecules within the individual cells.

The importance of X rays in some phases of the field of engineering cannot be overestimated. This can be appreciated when it is realized that metal castings or welded joints sometimes contain internal flaws or blowholes that otherwise escape detection. Because of the disastrous results that might occur by the insertion of defective castings or welded joints into a bridge or building, many such metal parts are examined by X rays before they are used.

50.5. X Rays Are Waves

Not long after Röntgen's discovery of X rays, there arose in scientific circles two schools of thought concerning the nature of these penetrating rays. One school held to the belief that X rays are highspeed particles like cathode rays, but more penetrating; and the other school held to the idea that they are electromagnetic waves of extremely high frequency. Although many experiments were performed to test these two hypotheses, sev-

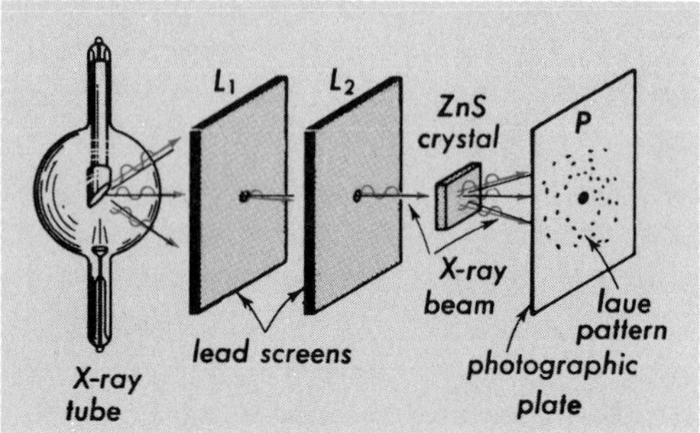

Fig. 50F. Experimental demonstration of the wave property of X rays. Diffracted by the atoms in a crystal, a Laue pattern is photographed.

eral years passed before the wave theory was proven to be correct.

The crucial experiment came in 1912 when von Laue* suggested to his associates, W. Friedrich and P. Knipping, that they try diffracting X rays by sending them through a thin crystal. Believing that the ultramicroscopic structure of a crystal is a three-dimensional array of regularly spaced atoms, von Laue reasoned that the equally spaced layers of the atoms would act like a diffraction grating.

The experiment, as it was performed, is shown diagrammatically in Fig. 50F. X rays from a cold-cathode X-ray tube, and limited to a narrow pencil of rays by a pinhole in each of the two lead screens L_1 and L_2, are shown passing through a thin crystal to a photographic film or plate at P. In addition to the central beam, the major part of which goes straight through to produce a blackened spot at the center of the film, there are many other weaker beams emerging in different directions to produce other spots on the same film. The pattern of spots obtained in this way is always quite symmetrical, and is referred to as a *Laue pattern.*

Photographs of two Laue patterns obtained with single crystals are reproduced in Fig. 50G. The small number of spots in (a) is indicative of a relatively simple crystal structure for zinc sulfide, ZnS, and the large number of spots signifies a relatively complex crystal structure for sugar, $C_{12}H_{22}O_{11}$. While the picture for sugar was being taken, the central beam was masked off by a small lead disk placed just in front of the film to prevent excessive blackening. Simple Laue patterns in general arise from simple crystal structures. Common salt is an example of a simple crystal, containing sodium ions $(Na)^+$ and chlorine ions $(Cl)^-$ in equal numbers arranged in a three-dimensional cubic lattice. Figure 50H is a cross section through such a crystal, showing the alternation of ions in two of the three directions. Here, in this two-dimensional array, the origin of the different spots on a Laue pattern is illustrated.

Each spot arises from the reflection of some of the incident X rays from one of the various sets of parallel crystal planes, three of which are shown by the sets of parallel lines. Always, the rays obey the law of reflection that the angle of incidence equals the angle of reflection. While the reflection planes shown in the diagram are all perpendicular to the plane of the page, there are many other planes in a three-dimensional lattice to reflect the rays off in other directions.

The success of the Laue experiment proves the correctness of two postulates: (1) that X rays are light rays of very short wavelength, and (2) that the ions of a crystal are arranged in a

*Max von Laue (1879–1960) was born near Coblenz, Germany, in 1879, and was educated in the German universities of Strasbourg, Göttingen, and Munich. Following this, his teaching and research work carried him to the university at Munich, Zurich, Frankfurt on the Main, and finally Berlin. Since he was interested in theoretical physics, his early attentions were confined to various phases of Einstein's theory of relativity and to Bohr's quantum theory of atomic structure. His chief contribution to physics, however, was the instigation and supervision of experiments leading to the diffraction of X rays by crystals. For this work, which proved the wave nature of X rays, he was granted the Nobel Prize in 1914.

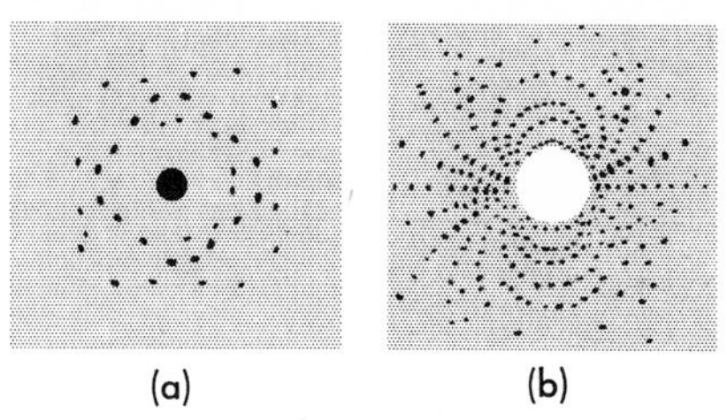

Fig. 50G. X-ray diffraction patterns from crystals: (a) zinc sulfide crystal (face-centered cubic crystal); (b) sugar crystal (a complex crystal structure).

regular three-dimensional lattice. These are the results for which von Laue was granted the Nobel Prize in physics in 1914. As a direct result of the Laue experiment, two new and important fields of experimental physics were opened up: (1) the study and measurement of X-ray wavelengths, and (2) the study of crystal structures by their action on X rays.

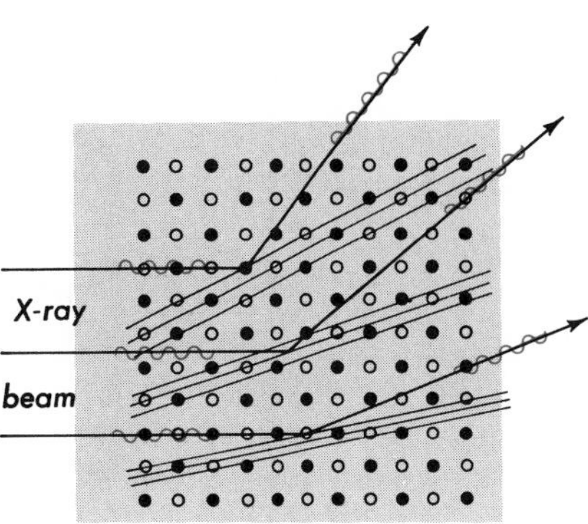

Fig. 50H. Illustration of the reflection of X rays from the various atomic planes in a cubic crystal lattice.

50.6. The X-Ray Spectrograph

No sooner had von Laue, Friedrich, and Knipping announced the results of their experiments than many investigators began a study of the various phases of *X-ray diffraction* by crystals. The most outstanding of these experiments are those of W. H. Bragg* and his son, W. L. Bragg; they also developed the X-ray spectrometer and spectrograph.

A diagram of an X-ray spectrograph is shown in Fig. 50I. Instead of having pinhole screens, as in Fig. 50F, and sending a narrow pencil of rays through a crystal, the early spectrographs used screens with narrow slits and reflected the rays from one face of a crystal. The crystal is not fixed tightly in place but can be turned back and forth about a pivot C at the center of the front face. As this rocking motion takes place, the crystal acts somewhat like a mirror and causes the reflected X-ray beam to sweep back and forth along the photographic film from one end to the other. After the photographic film has been exposed to the rays for some time, and then developed, it is found to have the general appearance of the reproduction in Fig. 50J. This unusually clear photograph was originally taken by De Broglie, who used an X-ray tube containing a tungsten-metal anode target. Instead of a general blackening from end to end, the film shows *bands* and *lines,* indicating that at certain orientation angles of the crystal the reflected rays were unusually intense, while at others there

***Sir William Henry Bragg (1862–1942), British physicist, was professor at the University of London. Bragg's researches on radioactive phenomena brought him early recognition from scientific societies at home and abroad. Joint work with his son, William Lawrence Bragg, (1890–1971), on the arrangement of ions in crystals, and the development of the X-ray spectrograph are his greatest scientific contributions. In 1915, father and son were jointly granted the Nobel Prize in physics, as well as the Barnard Gold Medal from Columbia University.**

were apparently none. The lines, which are particularly noticeable at points marked K_α, L_α, L_β, and L_γ, are called *X-ray spectrum lines.*

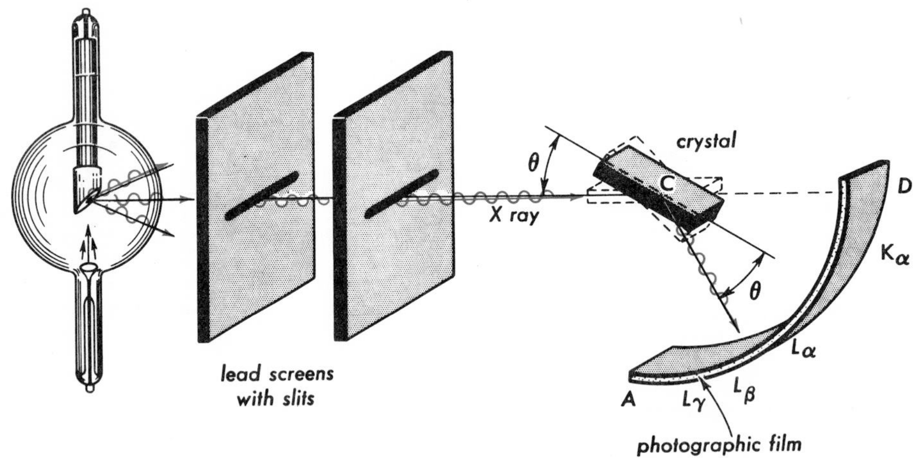

Fig. 50I. Schematic diagram of a Bragg X-ray crystal spectrograph.

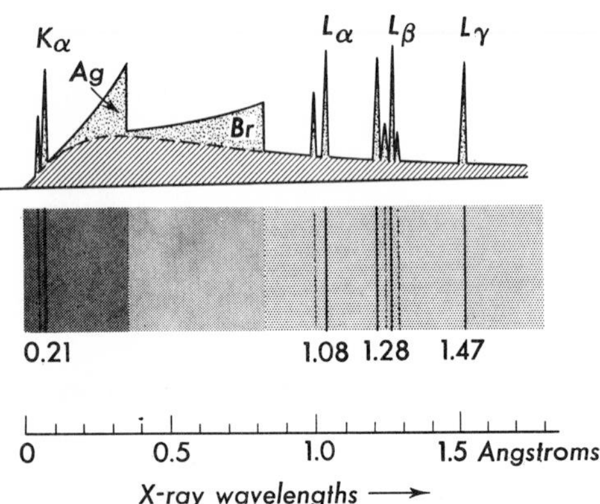

Fig. 50J. X-ray spectrogram taken with an X-ray tube containing a tungsten metal target. (After De Broglie.)

The origin and interpretation of these spectrum lines are illustrated by a detailed diagram in Fig. 50K. To reflect X rays of one given wavelength from a crystal, a certain relation must exist between the direction of the incident rays and the distance d between surface layers of the crystal. This relation, known as *the Bragg rule,* requires the waves to be incident on the crystal face, at such an angle θ that the crests of the waves reflected from adjacent atomic layers move off together. This occurs when the additional distance traveled by ray (2), AMB in the diagram, is exactly one whole wavelength greater than that traveled by the ray (1) next above it. When the angle is adjusted so that this is true, other rays like (3), belonging to the same wave train as (1) and (2), will be reflected from the third crystal layer to be "in step" with the others.

Suppose now that the X-ray tube in Fig. 50I emits X rays of only one wavelength; then, as the crystal rocks back and forth, there will be no reflection except at one particular angle θ, and this will occur where the conditions of Bragg's rule are satisfied. At this particular position on the photographic plate, a single dark line will appear. If now the distance d between crystal layers is known, and the angle θ for the X-ray line measured, the wavelength of the X rays can be calculated. One wavelength, it will be noted in Fig. 50K, is equal to twice the length of the side AM of the right triangle AMC. Thus, with one side and two angles of a triangle known, either of the other sides can be calculated. Bragg's rule therefore becomes

$$2d \sin \theta = \lambda \qquad (50a)$$

In the case of a sodium chloride crystal, NaCl, the atomic spacing is 2.8140 Å, or 2.8140×10^{-10} m.

Since several spectrum lines appear in the photograph in Fig. 50J, there are several different wavelengths emitted by the same X-ray tube. The two fluted-appearing bands between the K and L X-ray lines are not of interest here because they appear on all X-ray spectrograms; they are due to the strong absorption of X rays of many other wavelengths by the silver and bromine atoms in the photographic plate itself. Had the original photographic film been exposed for a much longer time, the spectrogram would have shown a general blackening over the whole plate. This blackening, illustrated by the shaded area in the curve of Fig. 50J, is due to X rays of all different wavelengths being emitted by the X-ray tube; it is these which, although not very intense, strongly affect the photographic plate at the two bands, Ag and Br.

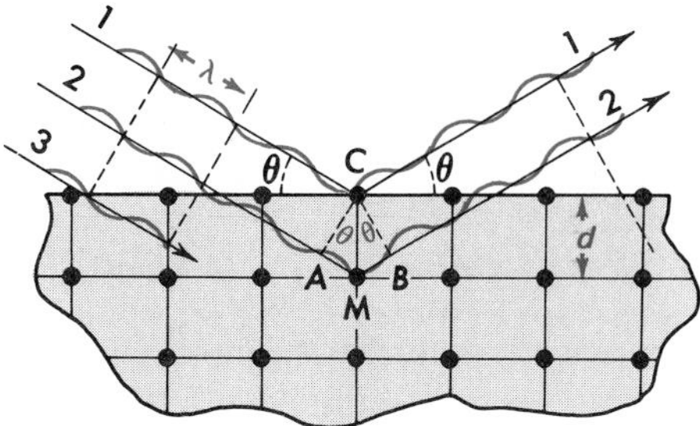

Fig. 50K. Illustration of the Bragg rule of reflection for X rays from the surface layers of a crystal.

TABLE 50A
Grating spacings for various common crystals used for x-ray diffraction

Crystal	*Plane*	*d (angstroms)*
Calcite	Cleavage	3.0290
Gypsum	Cleavage	7.5791
Mica	Cleavage	9.9276
Quartz	Prism	4.2449
Rock Salt	100	2.8140
Sugar	100	10.5700

Example 1. X-ray L lines are photographed with a rocking crystal spectrograph. If a calcite crystal with an effective atomic spacing of 3.0290×10^{-10} m is used, and two prominent lines are observed at angles of 43.20° and 40.42°, what are the wavelengths in angstroms of the lines?

Solution. The given quantities are $d = 3.0290 \times 10^{-10}$ m, $\theta_1 = 43.20°$, and $\theta_2 = 40.42°$. By direct substitution of the given quantities in Eq.(50a), we obtain

$$\lambda_1 = 2d \sin \theta_1 = 2 \times 3.0290 \times 10^{-10} \text{ m} \times 0.6845$$

$$\lambda_1 = 4.147 \times 10^{-10} \text{ m} = 4.147 \text{ Å}$$

$$\lambda_2 = 2d \sin \theta_2 = 2 \times 3.0290 \times 10^{-10} \text{ m} \times 0.6484$$

$$\lambda_2 = 3.928 \times 10^{-10} \text{ m} = 3.928 \text{ Å}$$

50.7. The Origin of X Rays

X rays, like visible light, originate from the jumping of an electron from one orbit to another. When high-speed electrons from the cathode of an X-ray tube strike the target, they ionize many of the atoms composing the surface layers of the metal.

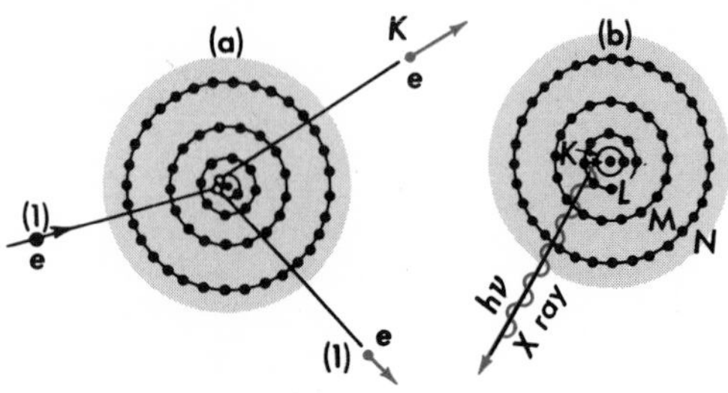

Fig. 50L. Schematic diagram illustrating (a) the ionization of an atom by a high-speed electron, and (b) the subsequent jumping of an inner electron with the simultaneous emission of an X ray.

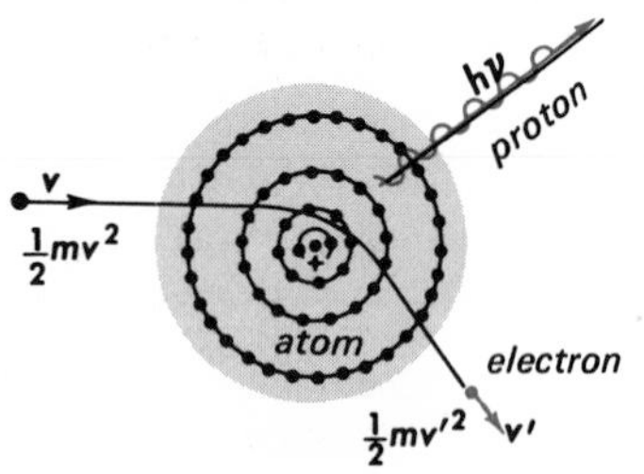

Fig. 50M. Diagram illustrating the production of a photon by a high-speed electron as it passes through an atom close to the nucleus ("bremsstrahlung").

Owing to their very high speeds (about $\frac{1}{10}$ the velocity of light), the electrons penetrate the atoms and remove an electron from the inner shells by collision. This is illustrated in Fig. 50L where an electron is knocked out of the K shell. The designations K, L, M, N, O, P, etc., for the various electron shells originated with the X-ray spectroscopist and are identical with the quantum numbers $n = 1, 2, 3, 4, 5, 6$, etc. When an electron is missing in the innermost K shell, a nearby electron from the next shell beyond jumps into the vacant space, simultaneously emitting a photon of energy $h\nu$. Such X rays, arising from millions of atoms, produce the K lines shown in Fig. 50J.

Since the L shell now has one less electron, the M electron can jump into the L shell vacancy, with the consequent emission of another but different X-ray frequency. These are the L lines in Fig. 50J. The jumping process continues until the outermost shell is reached, where an electron jumping in gives rise to visible light. Thus we see how it is possible for a single atom to emit X rays of different wavelengths.

The continuous X-ray spectrum, illustrated by the shaded area under the curve in Fig. 50J, is due to another phenomenon often referred to as "bremsstrahlung." These radiations are due to the slowing down of high-speed electrons as they pass close to the nuclei of the atoms within the target of the X-ray tube. The process is illustrated in Fig. 50M. As the electron passes through the atom, it is attracted by the positive charge of the nucleus and deflected in its path.

During the deflection of the electron in the strong electric field of the nucleus, a light wave of energy $h\nu$ is emitted. Since the law of conservation of momentum must hold for such a collision, the electron is deflected off to one side of the atom, and the photon off to the other. Since the law of conservation of energy must hold, some of the energy of the incoming electron $\frac{1}{2}mv^2$ is given up to the newly created photon $h\nu$, and the remainder $\frac{1}{2}mv'^2$ is retained by the electron. Thus the electron is slowed down to a velocity v' by the encounter. The closer the electron comes to the nucleus, the greater is its loss in velocity and energy, and the greater is the frequency and energy of the radiated photon. By the conservation of energy,

$$\frac{1}{2}mv^2 - \frac{1}{2}mv'^2 = h\nu \tag{50b}$$

The highest frequency that is possible is one in which the electron is completely stopped by the atom. In this special case,

$$\frac{1}{2}mv^2 = h\nu_{\max} \tag{50c}$$

Since the kinetic energy of the electrons in the beam striking the target is given by the voltage V applied to the tube, we may use Eq.(43b),

$$Ve = \tfrac{1}{2}mv^2 \tag{50d}$$

and obtain

$$Ve = h\nu_{\max} \tag{50e}$$

While Eq.(50d) must be replaced by the relativistic equation, Eq.(49b), when electrons reach speeds comparable to that of light, Eq.(50e) holds true for all voltages.

Example 2. If 50,000 V is applied to an X-ray tube, what is (a) the maximum frequency in hertz, and (b) the minimum wavelength in angstroms emitted by the tube? Use three significant figures.

Solution. The known quantities are $V = 5.0 \times 10^4$ V, $e = 1.602 \times 10^{-19}$ C, and $h = 6.63 \times 10^{-34}$ Js. Solving Eq.(50e) for $\nu_{\max}$, and substituting known quantities, we obtain

$$\nu_{\max} = \frac{Ve}{h} = \frac{5.0 \times 10^4 \times 1.602 \times 10^{-19}}{6.63 \times 10^{-34}}$$

$$\nu_{\max} = 1.208 \times 10^{19} \text{ Hz}$$

Using the wave equation, $c = \nu\lambda$, we find for the wavelength

$$\lambda = \frac{c}{\nu} = \frac{2.998 \times 10^8 \text{ m/s}}{1.208 \times 10^{19} \text{ Hz}}$$

$$\lambda = 0.2482 \text{ Å}$$

---

questions and problems

1. What are hard X rays? What are soft X rays? How is hardness or softness related to X-ray wavelengths?

2. What contribution did Coolidge make to the design and construction of X-ray tubes?

3. Which of the following materials is the best absorber of X rays: (a) beryllium, (b) magnesium, (c) calcium, (d) copper, (e) gold, (f) lead, or (g) uranium?

4. How is X-ray absorption related to the periodic table of elements?

5. Why does the skin show so clearly in the X-ray photograph in Fig. 50D(b)?

6. What is the process of ionization by X rays? What happens to the liberated free electrons?

7. How is the penetrating power of X rays related to the voltage applied to the tube?

8. If a small child swallowed a safety pin, why would an X-ray photograph clearly show the location of the pin?

9. An X-ray photograph of a closed leather purse will easily show silver coins or other metal articles inside. Explain.

10. Briefly explain why an X-ray photograph of the hand shows the bones more clearly than the flesh surrounding them.

11. A rocksalt crystal is used with an X-ray spectrometer to photograph the L series lines of the element gold. Three strong lines are observed on the photographic plate, at angles of 13°6′, 11°0′, and 9°28′. Find (a) the wavelengths in angstrom units, and (b) the frequencies in hertz of these X-ray lines.

12. A rocking crystal X-ray spectrometer is used to photograph the X-ray spectrum of the element zinc. If the wavelengths determined are 1.436 Å, 1.432 Å, 1.293 Å, and 1.281 Å, what are the observed angles? Assume the crystal to be rocksalt, with its atomic spacing of 2.814 Å. [Ans. 14.78°, 14.74°, 13.28°, and 13.16°.]

13. A rocking crystal X-ray spectrometer is used to photograph the L series lines in the X-ray spectrum of the element tungsten. If the angles at which the strongest lines occur are 14°4′, 11°50′, and 10°25.5′, find (a) the wavelengths in angstroms, and (b) the frequencies in Hz. The crystal used in the spectrograph was calcite, with a grating space of 3.029×10^{-7} m.

14. Prominent M lines in the X-ray spectrum of the element platinum are observed with a crystal spectrometer using a calcite crystal. If the crystal spacing is 3.029×10^{-7} m, and the angles are 49°50′, 61°31′, and 73°45′, what are (a) the wavelengths in angstroms, and (b) the frequencies in hertz?

15. What is (a) the maximum frequency in hertz, and (b) the minimum wavelength in angstroms emitted by an X-ray tube when 20,000 volts is applied to it? [Ans. (a) 4.836×10^{18} Hz, (b) 0.6199 Å.]

16. What is (a) the maximum frequency in hertz, and (b) the minimum wavelength in angstroms emitted by an X-ray tube when 50,000 volts is applied to it?

17. If 100,000 volts is applied to an X-ray tube, what is (a) the highest frequency in hertz, and (b) the shortest wavelength in angstroms emitted?

18. If 1 million volts is applied to an X-ray tube, what is the maximum frequency in hertz, and (b) the minimum wavelength in angstroms emitted? [Ans. (a) 2.418×10^{20} Hz, (b) 0.01240 Å.]

51 Photon collisions and atomic waves

In the preceding chapters we have seen that light waves consist of small finite bundles of energy, called *quanta* or *photons,* and that they too, like atomic particles, may be made to collide with atoms of one kind or another. This was the case both in the *photoelectric effect* (Chap. 43) and in the production of X rays (Chap. 50). The first part of the present chapter deals with the *corpuscular nature of light,* and the last part with the *wave nature of atomic particles.*

This last statement suggests a sort of Dr. Jekyll and Mr. Hyde existence for light waves as well as for atoms. Under some conditions, light and atoms may both act as though they were waves, whereas under other conditions they may both act like small particles.

51.1. Photoelectric Effect with X Rays

When a beam of X rays is allowed to shine on the surface of a thin sheet of metal like gold, several different phenomena may be observed to take place. Acting like waves, the X rays may be scattered at different angles to produce a diffraction pattern (see Fig. 50F), or acting like particles, they may collide with atoms and eject electrons as in the photoelectric effect (see Chap. 43).

Even though a beam of X rays may contain waves all of the same frequency, not all of the ejected photoelectrons acquire the same velocity, but they are divided into several well-defined groups. These different groups are illustrated schematically by the lengths of the arrows in Fig. 51A.

Careful measurements of the velocities of the photoelectrons, first made by Robinson and his collaborators in 1914, have shown that each velocity group is to be associated with the various shells of electrons within the atoms. The slowest electrons, all with the same velocity v_K, are ejected from the K shell, the next faster group with a velocity v_L from the L shell, the next group with a velocity v_M from the M shell, etc.

The closer an electron is to the nucleus [see diagram (b)], the greater is the attracting force and the greater is the force and energy necessary to liberate it from the atom. The velocity of the electrons in each group is given by Einstein's photoelectric equation:

$$h\nu = W + \tfrac{1}{2}mv^2 \qquad (51a)$$

where W, the work function, is the energy necessary to free an electron from any one of the different electron shells (see Sec. 43.6).

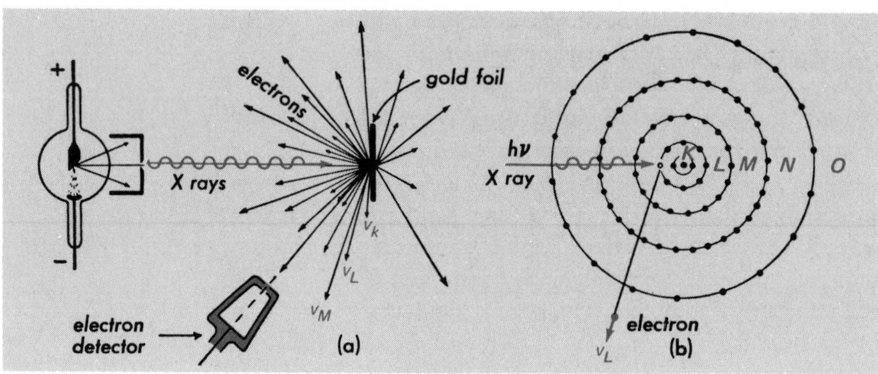

Fig. 51A. (a) Photoelectric effect produced with X rays gives rise to electrons with several different velocities. (b) Detail of an X ray ejecting an *L* electron from a heavy atom.

While all of the incident X-ray photons have the same energy $h\nu$, more energy W will be used in liberating a K electron than there will be in liberating an L electron. This being the case, a photon liberating a K electron will have less energy left over for the electron than would another photon liberating an L electron from a similar atom. This experiment shows as well as one could wish that electrons exist in shells within the atom.

It should be pointed out that the energy W, used up in ejecting a photoelectron, is not lost by the atom but is later given out again in the form of X rays of various frequencies. In atoms where a K electron has been ejected, an L electron may jump into the vacated K shell, with the simultaneous emission of a K X ray. This may be followed immediately by an M electron's jumping into the vacated L shell and the emission of an L X ray.

51.2. The Compton Effect

While making a spectroscopic study of scattered X rays in 1923, A. H. Compton* discovered a new phenomenon, now known as the Compton effect. After considerable controversy with other experimenters, Compton proved quite conclusively that an X ray may collide with an electron and bounce off with reduced energy in another direction. This is analogous to the collision of two billiard balls.

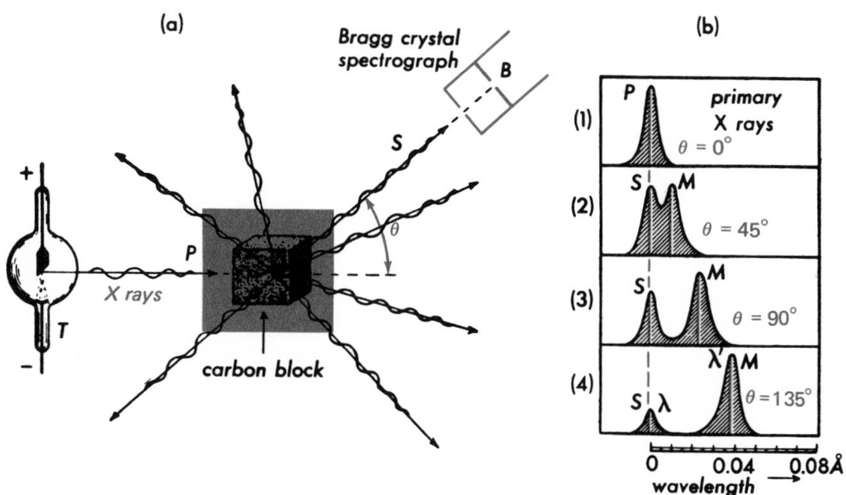

Fig. 51B. The Compton effect: (a) schematic diagram of Compton's experiment; (b) graphs of the X-ray spectrum lines observed with a Bragg crystal spectrograph.

Compton's historic experiment is illustrated schematically in Fig. 51B. X rays from a tube T were made to strike one face of a small carbon block and scatter out in various directions. With an X-ray spectrograph at one side of the block, he measured the wavelength of the X rays S scattered in a direction θ. These wavelengths he then compared with those of the incident beam P.

The comparisons are illustrated by graphs in diagram (b). The top curve (1) represents the wavelength λ of the X rays in the beam P, before striking the block. The other three curves, (2), (3), and (4), represent the two wavelengths λ and λ' observed when the spectrograph is located at the angles $\theta = 45°$, 90°, and 135°, respectively. These graphs show that some of the scattered X rays have changed their wavelengths whereas others have not. They further show the important result that as the angle increases the change in wavelength of the modified rays M increases.

***Arthur H. Compton (1892–1962), American physicist, was born in Wooster, Ohio, on September 10, 1892. He received the degree of Doctor of Philosophy at Princeton University in 1920. In 1923 he discovered the change in wavelength of X rays when scattered by carbon, the phenomenon now known as the Compton effect. In recognition of this important discovery, in 1927 he was awarded the Nobel Prize in physics jointly with C. T. R. Wilson of England.**

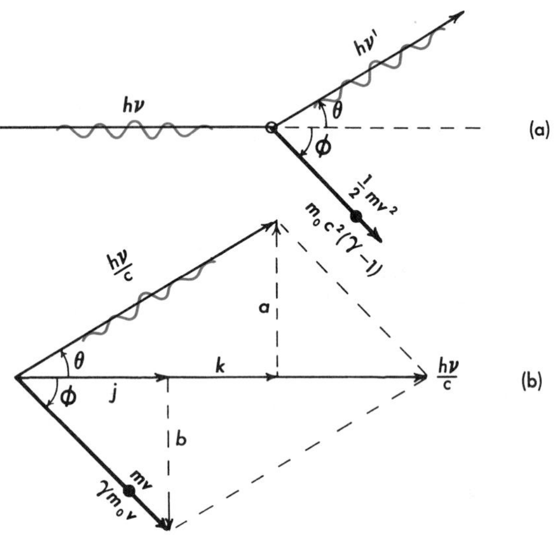

Fig. 51C. The Compton effect: vector diagrams for the collision between an X-ray photon and a free electron.

Carbon was used because it is a very light element (At. No. 6) with only two shells of electrons. X rays passing through heavy elements were known to produce fluorescent X rays of longer wavelengths by electrons jumping between outer electron shells.

To explain the modified wavelengths M, Compton invoked the quantum theory of light and proposed that a single X-ray photon, acting as a material particle, may collide with a free electron and recoil as though it were a perfectly elastic sphere [Fig. 51C(a)]. Applying the law of conservation of energy of the collision, Compton assumed that the energy $\frac{1}{2}mv^2$ imparted to the recoiling electron must be supplied by the incident X-ray quantum $h\nu$. Having lost energy, the X ray moves off in some new direction with a lower frequency ν' and energy $h\nu'$. By applying conservation of energy, we obtain

$$h\nu = h\nu' + \tfrac{1}{2}mv^2 \tag{51b}$$

Since in most cases the velocity of the recoiling electron is so near the velocity of light c, the relativistic equations must be applied. Using Eq.(48q) for the kinetic energy of a moving mass, we write

$$h\nu = h\nu' + m_0c^2(\gamma - 1) \tag{51c}$$

conservation of energy

where

$$\gamma = \frac{1}{\sqrt{1 - v^2/c^2}} \tag{51d}$$

and m_0 is the *rest mass* of the electron.

As with two perfectly elastic balls, Compton also applied the law of conservation of momentum and derived an equation from which he could calculate the change in wavelength λ' of the scattered X ray. These calculated changes were found to agree exactly with those observed by the experiment.

The fact that a beam of light has the equivalence of a momentum mv, and can exert a pressure on a wall on which it falls, has long been known. According to the quantum theory the momentum of a single photon is given by the energy $h\nu$ divided by the speed of light c:

$$\text{momentum of a photon} = \frac{h\nu}{c} \tag{51e}$$

Compton's experiment is considered a proof of this equation.

Since momentum is a vector quantity, we construct a vector diagram as shown in Fig. 51C(b). The momentum of the X ray before impact is $h\nu/c$, while its momentum after impact is $h\nu'/c$, and the momentum of the electron is mv.

For electrons close to the speed of light the momentum mv is written in the relativistic form $\gamma m_0 v$ [see Eq.(48i)]. By resolving the two momenta into two components, we obtain ***a*** and ***k*** as components of $h\nu'/c$ and ***b*** and ***j*** as components of $\gamma m_0 v$.

Conservation of momentum requires the vector sum of ***j*** plus ***k*** to equal the initial momentum $h\nu/c$, and the vectors ***a*** and ***b*** to cancel each other. As equations,

$$\frac{h\nu}{c} = \frac{h\nu'}{c} \cos\theta + \gamma m_0 v \cos\phi \tag{51f}$$

and

$$0 = \frac{h\nu'}{c} \sin\theta + \gamma m_0 v \sin\phi \tag{51f'}$$

conservation of momentum

Solve the first equation and the second equation for $\gamma m_0 v \times \cos\phi$, and then divide the second relation by the first to obtain

$$\frac{\sin\phi}{\cos\phi} = \frac{-\dfrac{\nu'}{c}\sin\theta}{\dfrac{\nu}{c} - \dfrac{\nu'}{c}\cos\theta} = \frac{-\dfrac{\sin\theta}{\lambda'}}{\dfrac{1}{\lambda} - \dfrac{\cos\theta}{\lambda'}} = \frac{-\dfrac{\sin\theta}{\lambda'}}{\dfrac{\lambda' - \lambda\cos\theta}{\lambda\lambda'}}$$

From trigonometry

$$\tan\phi = -\frac{\lambda \sin\theta}{\lambda' - \lambda\cos\theta} \tag{51g}$$

Knowing λ and λ', Eq.(51c) can be used to find the velocity of the recoiling electron. Solving Eq.(51c) for v, we find

$$v = c\sqrt{1 - \left(\frac{m_0 c}{\dfrac{h}{\lambda} - \dfrac{h}{\lambda'} + m_0 c}\right)^2} \tag{51g'}$$

By combining Eqs.(51c), (51f), and (51f′), and changing from frequencies ν and ν' to wavelengths by λ and λ', respectively, Compton derived the equation

$$\lambda' - \lambda = \frac{h}{m_0 c}(1 - \cos\theta) \qquad (51h)$$

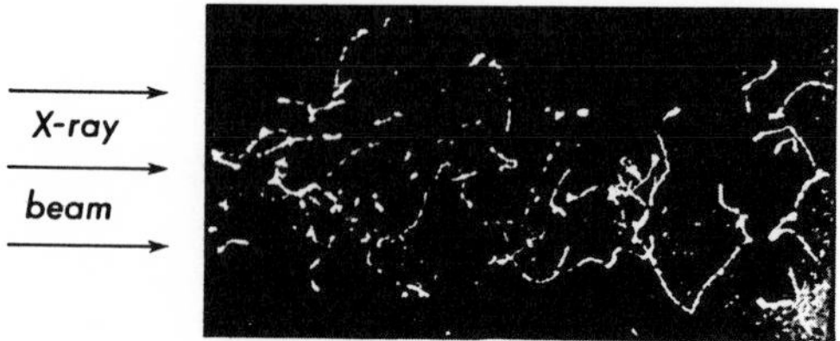

Fig. 51D. The Compton effect: recoil electrons from X rays passing through the air in a Wilson cloud chamber. (After C. T. R. Wilson.)

The quantity h/m_0c is called the *Compton wavelength,* and is equal to

$$\frac{h}{m_0 c} = 2.4263096 \times 10^{-12} \text{ m}$$

For those X rays that are scattered at an angle of 90°, the observed or calculated change in wavelength is just this amount and is the same for all X-ray wavelengths incident on the scatterer.

Compton's success is to be attributed to the exact agreement he found between the wavelength shift calculated from this application of the quantum theory and the values measured by experiment.

Example 1. An X-ray photon with a wavelength of 1.250×10^{-12} m collides with an electron, and is scattered at an angle of 40°. Calculate the wavelength of the modified wavelength λ'.

Solution. The known quantities are $\lambda = 1.250 \times 10^{-12}$ m, $\theta = 40°$, and $h/m_0c = 2.426 \times 10^{-12}$ m. Solving Eq.(51h) for λ', we obtain

$$\lambda' = \lambda + \frac{h}{m_0 c}(1 - \cos\theta)$$

Substituting known quantities, we find

$$\lambda' = 1.250 \times 10^{-12} + 2.426 \times 10^{-12}(1 - 0.7660)$$

$$\lambda' = 1.250 \times 10^{-12} + 0.568 \times 10^{-12}$$

$$\lambda' = 1.818 \times 10^{-12} \text{ m}$$

The first discoveries of the recoil electrons from the Compton effect were made by C. T. R. Wilson, and by Bothe and Becker. The existence of these collision products is readily shown by sending a beam of X rays through a Wilson cloud chamber just prior to its expansion (Fig. 51D).

When an X ray collides with a free electron the Compton effect can be expected, since the recoiling photon and electron are able to conserve energy and momentum. But when an X ray collides with an electron bound to an atom, the photoelectric effect takes place, since the atom can now recoil and conserve energy and momentum with the electron.

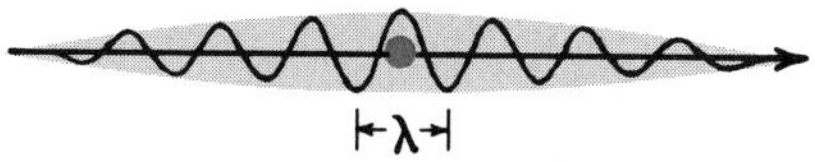

Fig. 51E. Schematic diagram of a De Broglie wave.

51.3. De Broglie's Electron Waves

In 1924 De Broglie,* a French theoretical physicist, derived an equation predicting that all atomic particles have associated with them waves of a definite wavelength. In other words, a beam of electrons or atoms should, under the proper experimental conditions, act like a train of light waves or a beam of photons. The wavelength of these waves, as predicted by De Broglie, depends upon the mass and velocity of the particles according to the following relation:

$$\lambda = \frac{h}{mv} \tag{51i}$$

This is known as *De Broglie's wave equation.* For an electron moving at high speed, the denominator mv is large and the wavelength is small. In other words, the faster an electron moves, the shorter is the wavelength associated with it (see Fig. 51E).

Example 2. A voltage of 50,000 V is applied to an electron gun. Find (a) the beam velocity, (b) the relativistic mass, and (c) the De Broglie wavelength of the electrons.

Solution. The known quantities are assumed to be $V = 50{,}000$ V, $m_0 = 9.110 \times 10^{-31}$ Kg, $e = 1.6022 \times 10^{-19}$ C, $h = 6.626 \times 10^{-34}$ Js, $m_0c^2 = 8.187 \times 10^{-14}$ J, and $c = 2.9979 \times 10^8$ m/s. Solving Eq.(49c) for the velocity, we obtain

$$v = c\sqrt{1 - \left(\frac{m_0c^2}{m_0c^2 + Ve}\right)^2}$$

$$v = 2.9979 \times 10^8 \sqrt{1 - \left(\frac{8.187 \times 10^{-14}}{8.187 \times 10^{-14} + 5 \times 10^4 \times 1.6022 \times 10^{-19}}\right)^2}$$

$$v = 1.2372 \times 10^8 \text{ m/s}$$

To find the relativistic mass m we substitute in Eq.(48j), and find

*Louis V. P. R. Duc De Broglie (1892-), French physicist, was born in Dieppe, France, August 15, 1892. After being educated at the Sorbonne, Paris, he served as instructor and later as professor at the same institution from 1926–62. He received many national and international awards and was elected to membership in many science societies. He has written a number of books, particularly on microphysics, and is best known for his theory that all moving objects have wave properties associated with them. For this now-proven theory, which laid the ground work for wave mechanics, he was awarded the Nobel Prize in physics for 1929.

$$m = \frac{m_0}{\sqrt{1 - \frac{v^2}{c^2}}} = \frac{9.110 \times 10^{-31}}{\sqrt{1 - \frac{(1.2372 \times 10^8)^2}{(2.998 \times 10^8)^2}}}$$

$$m = 10.001 \times 10^{-31}\ \text{Kg}$$

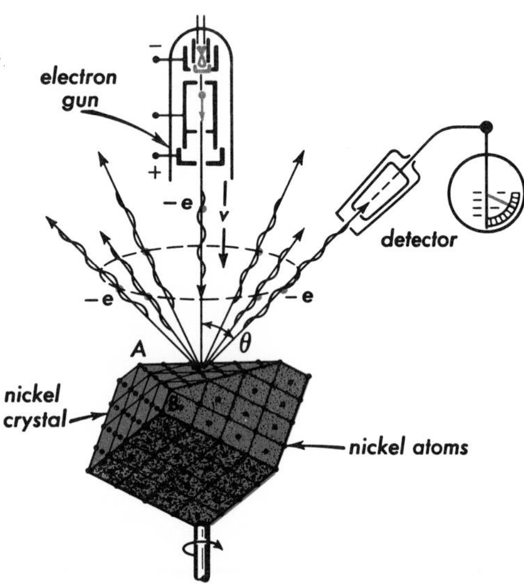

Fig. 51F. The Davisson–Germer experiment. Electrons striking the surface layers of a crystal are diffracted at different angles just as if they were waves with a very short wavelength.

By direct substitution in the De Broglie wave equation, we obtain

$$\lambda = \frac{h}{mv} = \frac{6.626 \times 10^{-34}}{10.001 \times 10^{-31} \times 1.2372 \times 10^8}$$

$$\lambda = 5.355 \times 10^{-12}\ \text{m}$$

which is

$$\lambda = 0.5355\ \text{Å}$$

TABLE 51A
Relative velocities, masses, and wavelengths for electrons

V (volts)	v/c (%)	m/m_0	λ (m)
1	0.1976	1.0000	1.229×10^{-9}
10	0.6255	1.0000	3.879×10^{-10}
100	1.9781	1.0000	1.226×10^{-10}
1 KeV	6.2472	1.0020	3.876×10^{-11}
10 MeV	19.4993	1.0201	1.220×10^{-11}
100 KeV	54.8238	1.1955	3.702×10^{-12}
1 MeV	94.1086	2.9570	8.720×10^{-13}
10 MeV	99.8818	20.570	1.181×10^{-13}
100 MeV	99.9987	196.64	1.234×10^{-14}
1 GeV	99.9992	1958.3	1.239×10^{-15}
10 GeV	99.9999	19569.0	1.240×10^{-16}

TABLE 51B
Relative velocities, masses, and wavelengths for protons

V (volts)	v/c (%)	m/m_0	λ (m)
1 KeV	0.1455	1.000	9.086×10^{-13}
10 KeV	0.4616	1.000	2.862×10^{-13}
100 KeV	1.4599	1.000	9.121×10^{-14}
1 MeV	4.6134	1.002	2.861×10^{-14}
10 MeV	14.4851	1.011	9.027×10^{-15}
100 MeV	42.8213	1.107	2.788×10^{-15}
1 GeV	87.5039	2.066	7.310×10^{-16}
10 GeV	99.6315	11.66	1.138×10^{-16}
100 GeV	99.9957	174.8	7.561×10^{-18}
1 TeV	99.9984	1066.	1.239×10^{-18}

A few values for the *velocities, masses,* and *wavelengths* of electrons and protons moving with a wide range of speeds have been computed and assembled in Tables 51A and 51B. These values take into account the relativistic increase in mass and velocity of the moving particle [see Eqs.(48j) and (49b)].

The voltages V listed in column 1 are those required to accelerate the particles to the relative velocities given in column 2. The wavelengths at the right are similar to those for X rays and γ rays.

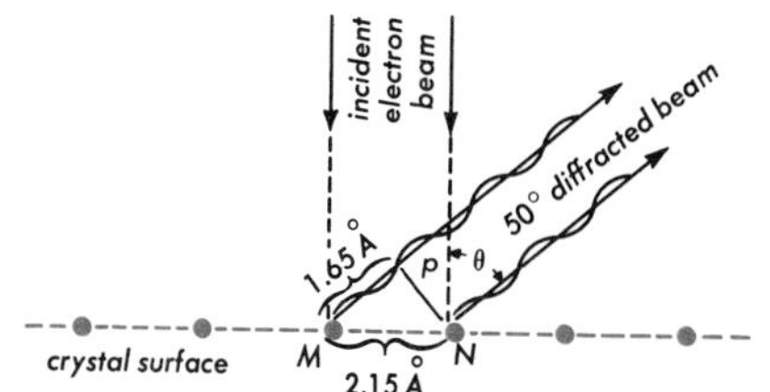

Fig. 51G. Diagram of electron diffraction from the surface layer of a nickel crystal. The regular spacing of the atoms makes the crystal act like a diffraction grating.

51.4. The Davisson–Germer Experiment

The first experimental proof of the wave nature of atomic particles was demonstrated in 1927 by two American physicists, C. J. Davisson, and his collaborator, L. H. Germer. Their experiment is illustrated schematically in Fig. 51F. Electrons from a hot filament are accelerated toward an anode, where, upon passing through a system of pinholes, they emerge as a narrow beam as indicated. This source acts as an electron gun from which electrons of any desired velocity may be obtained by applying the proper potential difference V.

Upon striking one of the polished faces of a nickel crystal, the electrons, acting like waves, are diffracted off in certain preferred directions. These preferred directions are located by means of a detector in which the electrons are collected and their accumulated charge measured. The detector is mounted so that it may be turned to an angle θ, and the crystal is mounted so it may be turned about an axis parallel to the incident beam.

With the electron-beam incident perpendicular to the crystal surface shown in Fig. 51F, the preferred direction of diffraction for 54-volt electrons was found to be 50°. Under these conditions the surface rows of atoms parallel to AB act like the rulings of a diffraction grating, producing the first-order spectrum of 54-volt electrons at $\theta = 50°$. This is illustrated in a cross-sectional detail in Fig. 51G. The waves reflected from one row of atoms M must travel one whole wavelength farther than the waves from the adjacent row N.

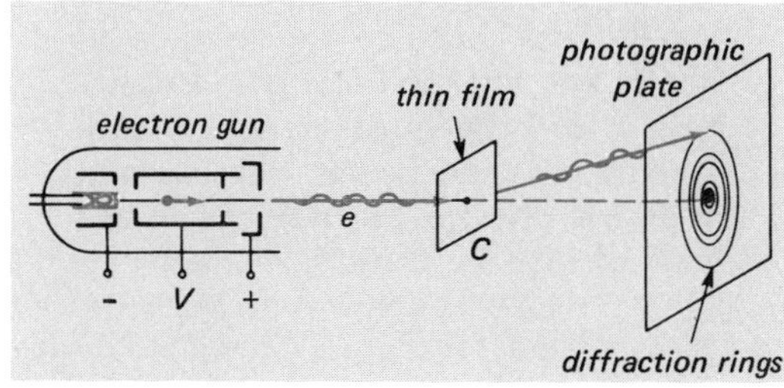

Fig. 51H. Experimental arrangement for observing the diffraction of electron waves by thin films or crystals.

51.5. Electron Diffraction Patterns

Experiments analogous to von Laue's X-ray diffraction experiments were first performed in 1928 by the English physicist G. P. Thomson, and independently by the Japanese physicist Kikuchi (see Fig. 50F). A schematic diagram of their experimental apparatus is given in Fig. 51H. Electrons of known velocity from an electron gun are projected at the front face of a thin metal film or crystal at C. A short distance farther on, the diffracted electrons strike a photographic plate where they produce patterns of the type reproduced in Fig. 51I.

Kikuchi's photograph (b) was made by projecting 68,000-volt electrons through a thin mica crystal. In this instance we have the exact analog to the X-ray diffraction patterns of Friedrich, Knipping, and von Laue (see Figs. 50F and 50G). The electrons, in passing through the crystal, are diffracted by the atom centers in such a way that the various crystal planes act like mirrors to reflect them the same as they do with X rays of an equivalent wavelength. Because high-speed electrons had to be used to penetrate the crystal, the diffraction spots are closer together; the reason for this is that the equivalent electron wavelength, $\lambda = 0.047$ Å, is about $\frac{1}{50}$ of the crystal spacing.

51.6. Electron Waves within the Atom

It is now known that the Bohr picture of the atom with sharply defined electron orbits is not correct. The newer and more accepted theories do not discard the Bohr theory entirely, but modify it to the extent that the electron does not behave as though it were a particle. The electron behaves as if it were made up of waves of the type described in preceding sections.

A very useful theory of the hydrogen atom was worked out independently by the two German physicists Heisenberg* and Schrödinger in 1925, and was later modified by the English theoretical physicist Dirac in 1928.†

Schrödinger, making use of De Broglie's idea of electron waves, pictures the single electron in the hydrogen atom as moving around the nucleus as a kind of *wave packet.* This wave packet is formed in somewhat the same way that standing waves are set up and maintained in sound waves.

We have seen in Sec. 20.2 how a stretched string may be set vibrating with a number of different natural modes. The frequencies ν of these different modes are called *harmonics* and are given by

$$\nu = n\nu_1 \tag{51j}$$

where ν_1 is the frequency of the *first harmonic,* or *fundamental,* and

$$n = 1, 2, 3, 4, 5, \ldots \tag{51k}$$

To set up similar conditions in a Bohr circular orbit of hy-

***Werner Karl Heisenberg (1901–), German physicist, was awarded the Nobel Prize in physics in 1932 for "the creation of quantum mechanics," and is best known for his uncertainty principle. He was born at Würtzburg, where his father was a professor. He studied under Arnold Sommerfeld at Munich, where he obtained his doctor's degree in 1923. He studied under Max Born at Göttingen in 1924, and from 1927 to 1941, he was professor of theoretical physics at Leipzig. He became director of the Max Planck Institute for Physics at Berlin, and later in Göttingen. Heisenberg's work on quantum theory profoundly influenced the development of atomic physics. The author met him first in 1930 in Leipzig, Germany.**

†Paul Adrien Maurice Dirac (1902–), British mathematical physicist, received the Nobel Prize in physics in 1933 at the age of 31 for his pioneer work in the quantum mechanics of the atom. He developed the transformation theory of quantum mechanics and was the co-discoverer of the Fermi–Dirac statistics. He replaced the conventional single second-order Schrödinger wave equation by four first-order equations, the solutions of which solved various properties of the electron spin and anomalous magnetic moment in an almost miraculous fashion. These equations suggested the possible existence of the positron, a particle later discovered by C. D. Anderson.

drogen, we visualize the electron as a wave with a De Broglie wavelength long enough to extend more than once around the atom. With a complete overlap of waves the system should stabilize into one of standing waves. A little reasoning applied to such a system will show that each wave pattern should contain an even number of nodes and loops.

Since the circumference of a circle is $2\pi r$, and the De Broglie wavelength $\lambda = h/mv$, the conditions for standing waves may be written: Circumference $= n\lambda$,

$$2\pi r = n\frac{h}{mv} \tag{51ℓ}$$

where

$$n = 1, 2, 3, 4, 5, \ldots \tag{51m}$$

Multiplying both sides of this equation by $mv/2\pi$, we obtain

$$mvr = n\frac{h}{2\pi} \tag{51n}$$

which is exactly the equation first given by Bohr in his theory [see Eq.(44b)].

A schematic diagram of this standing-wave model for the first three orbits of hydrogen is shown in Fig. 51J. Note that the first orbit has two nodes and a circumference of $1\lambda_1$, the second has four nodes and a circumference of $2\lambda_2$, and the third has six nodes and a circumference of $3\lambda_3$.

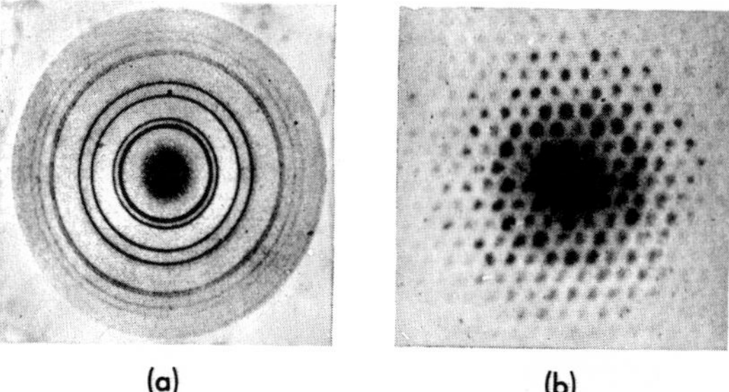

Fig. 51I. Photographs of electron diffraction patterns demonstrating the wave nature of electrons. (a) 36,000-volt electrons from a thin silver foil (after G. P. Thomson). (b) 68,000-volt electrons from a thin mica crystal (after Kikuchi).

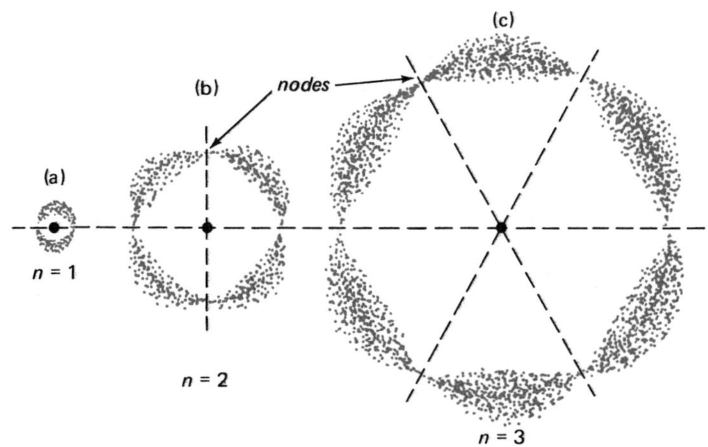

Fig. 51J. Schematic diagrams of the waves of the orbital electron in the first three quantum states of the hydrogen atom.

For increasing n, from 1 to 2 to 3, the wavelengths increase from $1\lambda_1$ to $2\lambda_1$ to $3\lambda_1$, the radii increase from $1r_1$ to $4r_1$ to $9r_1$, while the wave velocity decreases from $1v_1$ to $\frac{1}{2}v_1$ to $\frac{1}{3}v_1$.

51.7. The Schrödinger and Dirac Wave Equations

Introducing the De Broglie wavelength in a more general way into the theory of the hydrogen atom, Schrödinger,* in Germany, in 1926 made a new and important contribution to atomic structure. His contribution is most briefly expressed by what is called the *Schrodinger wave equation:*

$$\nabla^2\psi + \frac{m^2v^2}{\hbar^2}\psi = 0 \qquad (51o)$$

Two years later Dirac, in England, introduced the spin of the electron into this wave mechanics, and replaced Schrödinger's equation by four quite similar equations.

Although the methods used in solving these differential equations are beyond the scope of this book, we will discuss the results of the solutions since they lead to a better understanding of the structure and behavior of atoms.

A vibrating string represents a one-dimensional system of standing waves, and the integral numbers n specifying the allowed frequencies, as given by Eq.(51j), are analogous to the quantum numbers n of the allowed Bohr circular orbits [see Eqs.(20a) and (51j)].

When a thin metal plate is set into vibration, nodes and antinodes are formed, and we have a two-dimensional system of standing waves (see Fig. 20N). In all of the natural modes that may be produced with such plates, the nodes formed, whether they are radial, circular, or of any other shape, are even in number. Furthermore, the classical theory of vibrating plates shows that all natural modes may be presented by combination of two series of whole numbers n and m.

Dirac's and Schrödinger's wave equations for the hydrogen atom are set up as models in which the electron may be thought of as spread out around the nucleus as a kind of cloud. Because of its wave nature, this negatively charged cloud takes the form of a three-dimensional system of standing waves.

The many vibration modes of such a cloud are called *spherical harmonics,* and the nodes they exhibit take the forms of lines, planes, cones, and spheres. In other words, the standing-wave

***Erwin Schrödinger (1887–1961), Austrian physicist, was awarded the Nobel Prize in physics in 1933 for his work on wave mechanics and its application to atomic structure. He was educated at the University of Vienna and later served as professor of physics in Stuttgart, Breslau, and Zurich. He succeeded Max Planck as professor of physics at the University of Berlin in 1927. His famous wave equation, which carries his name, applied the De Broglie matter waves to the electron of the hydrogen atom, by assuming that the electron waves are an exact multiple of the orbital length. These then led to a form of spherical harmonics with nodes and antinodes for the electron cloud around the nucleus.**

patterns of the allowed states of hydrogen are more complex than those shown in Fig. 51J.

In our earlier studies we have seen that the energy involved in vibrations is proportional to the square of the amplitude (see Sec. 17.11). Since ψ in any of the wave equations represents the amplitude of the electron-cloud vibrations at any point P, the square of the amplitude ψ^2 has been interpreted to be proportional to the charge density of the cloud at that point.

To visualize the different allowed vibration states of the cloud, it is convenient to locate the nodes and loops in *polar coordinates* (see Fig. 51K). The vertical line MN represents a fixed direction in space and is set up by imagining the atom located in a magnetic field B and then slowly reducing the field intensity to zero. Any point in the space is then located with respect to this line, and the nucleus at the center, by specifying the values of ϕ, θ, and r.

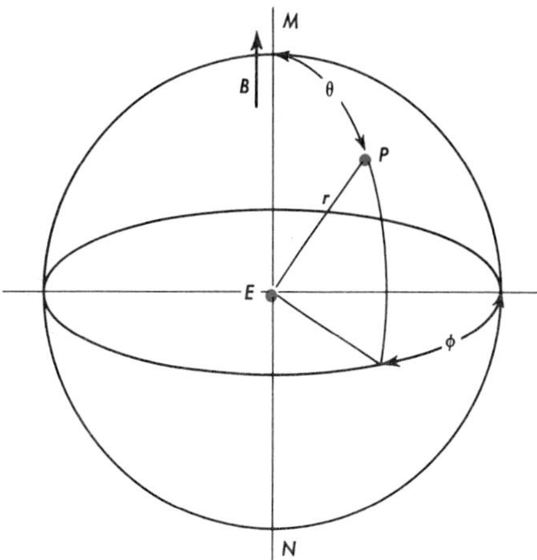

Fig. 51K. Diagram illustrating the position of a point P in polar coordinates.

It is not surprising to learn that the solutions of the wave equation give the exact same energies for the various allowed states of the hydrogen atom, as does the Bohr theory of orbits [see Eq.(44n)]:

$$E = -\frac{2\pi^2 me^4 Z^2 k^2}{n^2 h^2} \tag{51p}$$

where n takes integral values only. Furthermore all allowed states are determined by four quantum numbers [see Eq.(45r)]:

$$\left.\begin{aligned} n &= 1, 2, 3, 4, 5, \ldots \infty \\ \ell &= 0, 1, 2, 3, 4, \ldots n-1 \\ j &= \tfrac{1}{2}, \tfrac{3}{2}, \tfrac{5}{2}, \tfrac{7}{2}, \tfrac{9}{2}, \ldots \ell + \tfrac{1}{2} \\ m &= \pm\tfrac{1}{2}, \pm\tfrac{3}{2}, \pm\tfrac{5}{2}, \pm\tfrac{7}{2}, \ldots \pm j \end{aligned}\right\} \tag{51q}$$

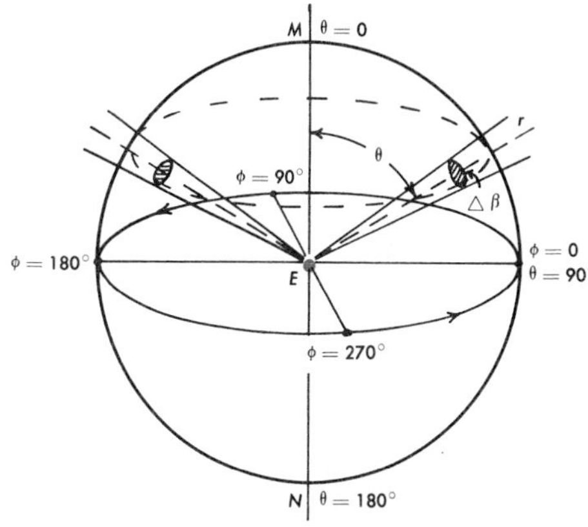

Fig. 51L. Diagram in polar coordinates illustrating the symmetry of the D_ϕ density distribution of the electron cloud in hydrogen.

We will now see how these allowed states may be represented by graphs, and how closely these graphs may be correlated with the simpler but less accurate orbital models of Bohr.

The D_ϕ Density Distribution. For any fixed value of θ the total charge density is a constant for all values of ϕ from 0° to 360° (see Fig. 51L). This means that if we select a small angle $\Delta\beta$ making an angle θ with the polar axis, and sum all of the charge within it from $r = 0$ to $r = \infty$, an equal amount of charge will be found within as we rotate it around the axis:

$$D_\phi = \text{constant} \tag{51r}$$

We say, therefore, that the D_ϕ distribution is symmetrical around the polar axis for all values of n, ℓ, j, and m.

The D_θ Density Distribution. The electron cloud density is not constant for all values of the azimuth angle θ, except for the s and p states where $j = \frac{1}{2}$. For all other values of j and m the charge density varies with θ.

If in Fig. 51L we turn the small solid angle $\Delta\beta$ from $\theta = 0°$ through 90° and on to $\theta = 180°$, the total negative charge found within this narrow cone at the different angles θ varies according to the polar graphs shown in Fig. 51M.

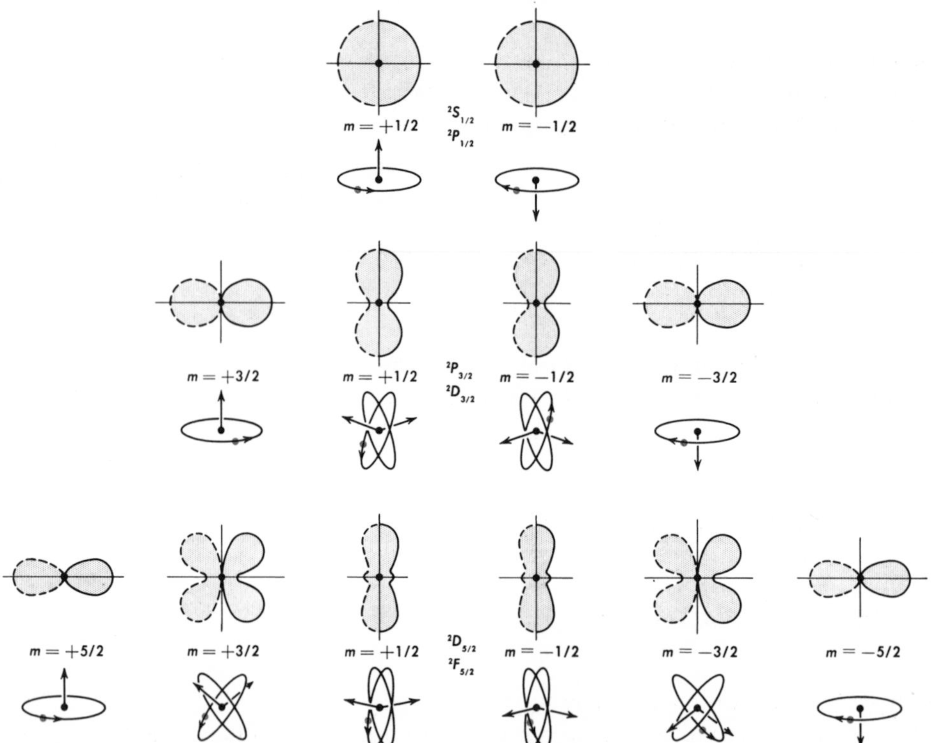

Fig. 51M. The D_θ charge-density distribution of the electron cloud for several of the lower states of the hydrogen atom, according to the Dirac wave equations.

These graphs, shown as solid lines at the right of each polar axis, should now be rotated 360° around the axis, to produce a three-dimensional surface. The dashed lines on the left in each figure are drawn in to show this surface in cross section, and the polar symmetry of the D_ϕ distribution.

It is important to note that the electron cloud is not confined to the color-shaded areas inside these graphs. The length of any straight line, drawn from the center of any one of these diagrams to any point on its surface, is proportional to the charge found in the small solid angle $\Delta\phi$ when its axis is at that angle θ.

The corresponding Bohr orbits are shown below each density graph for comparison purposes only. Rotating the orbit around the polar axis corresponds to the space quantization and orbit precession described in Sec. 45.8.

The two top figures, representing all of the s and p states of the hydrogen atom with $j = \frac{1}{2}$ ($^2S_{1/2}$ and $^2P_{1/2}$), are spherically symmetrical. The first and fourth diagrams in the second row, when rotated, are similar in shape to smoke rings, while the second and third, when rotated, are similar to dumbbells. These angular distributions are the same for all principal quantum numbers n.

The D_r Density Distribution. The D_r density distribution specifies the relative amount of the electron charge to be found at a distance r from the nucleus. If we sum up the total charge within a thin spherical shell of thickness Δr and of radius r, and repeat the summing process for many other shells of the same thickness but different r, we can plot graphs as shown in Fig. 51N.

In the case of the 3s graph, for the $3^2S_{1/2}$ state, for example, the maximum at $r = 12r_1$ means that more of the electron's charge is found to be at that distance than at any other. The points $r = 2r_1$ and $r = 7r_1$, where the curve goes almost to zero, correspond to spherical nodes within the electron cloud. The value r_1 is the radius of the first Bohr circular orbit, and is equal to 0.529 Å.

It should be noted that all graphs go to zero only at $r = 0$ and at $r = \infty$. The corresponding Bohr–Sommerfeld electron orbits are shown below each density-distribution curve for comparison purposes. Note how closely each charge-density graph and its corresponding orbit compare with each other in size.

Photographs representing a number of the possible states of a single electron are shown in Fig. 51O. These are not pictures of real atoms but are made to represent them. They were made by *time-exposure photography* of a specially designed mechanical top whose shape and spinning motion combine the D_ϕ, D_θ, and D_r distributions described above.

Where the electronic charge density is large, the figure is white; where it is zero or nearly zero at the nodes, the figure is dark. The three-dimensional distributions can be visualized by imagining each photograph to be rotating about a vertical axis through the center. The relative sizes of these patterns are given approximately by n^2.

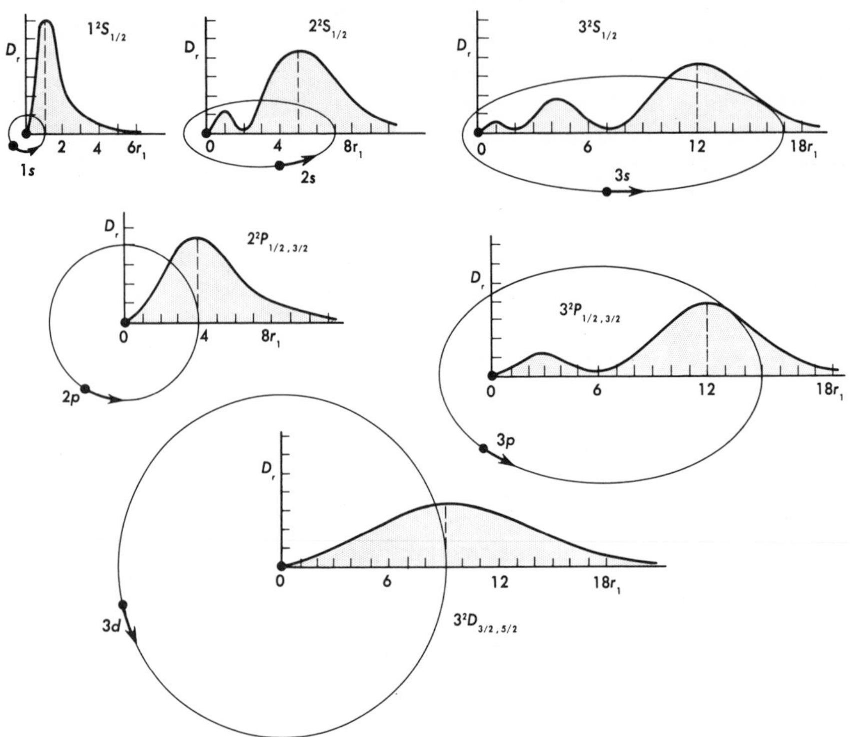

Fig. 51N. The D_r density distribution of the electron cloud for several of the lower states of the hydrogen atom, according to the Dirac wave equations.

Even though the new theory of the hydrogen atom is an improvement upon the older Bohr orbit theory, and gives a more satisfactory explanation of all known phenomena, it is difficult to form a mental picture of what an atom might look like. Indeed, the modern theoretical physicist goes so far as to say that the question, "What does an atom look like?" has no meaning much less an answer. There are others, however, who still maintain that only those things that can be pictured are the things that are understood and that all mental thought processes are made in terms of things we detect by sight, sound, and touch.

There are some scientists who prefer to think of the electron as a particle rather than a wave, and to interpret the quantity ψ^2 as a probability factor. Following this interpretation, the graphs

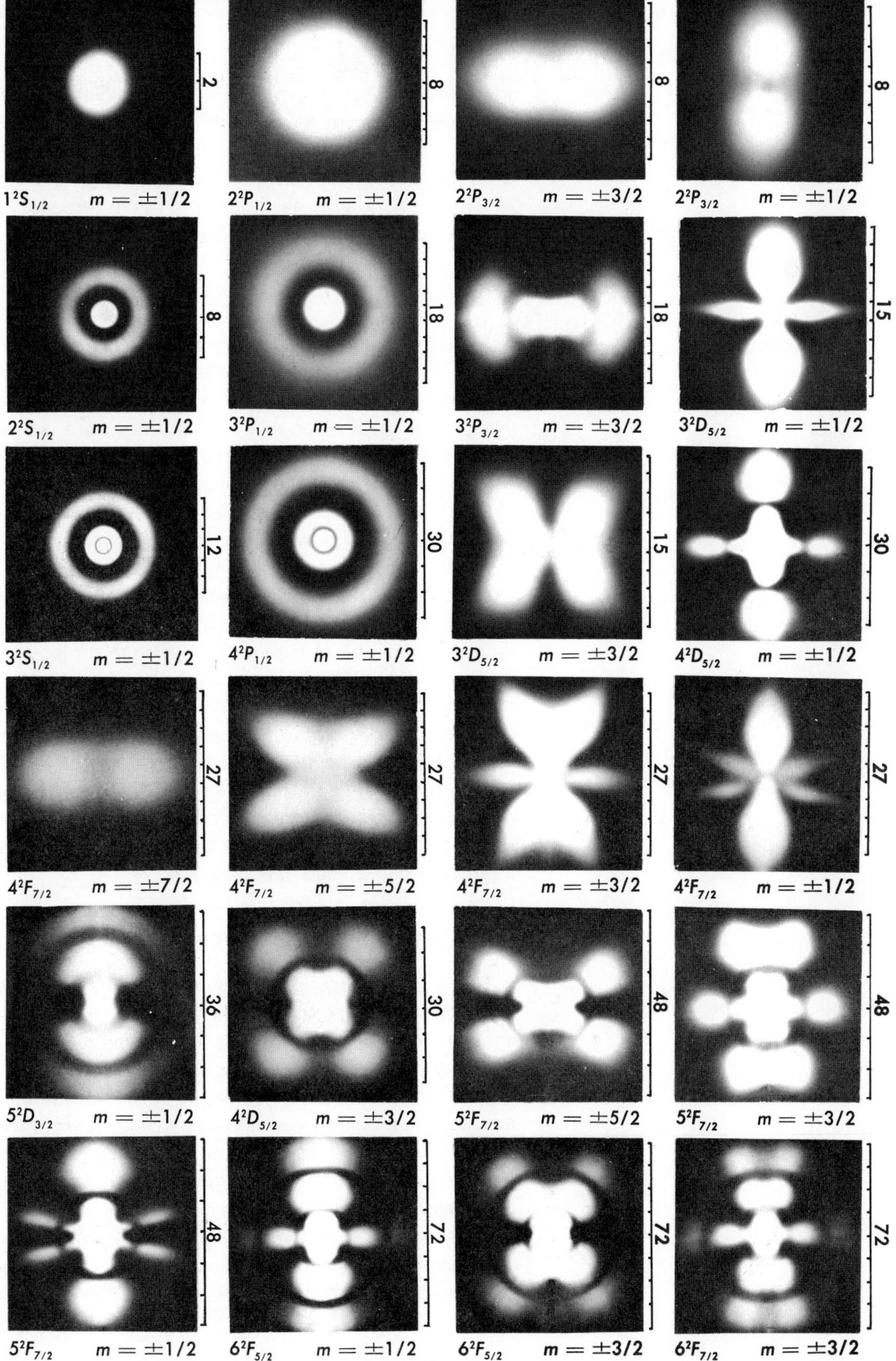

Fig. 51O. Electron-density distribution figures representing the single electron states of the hydrogen atom. The rotation of each figure about a vertical axis through its center generates the three-dimensional distribution. The scale on the right of each figure gives the dimensions in angstrom units: 1 angstrom unit = 10^{-10} meters.

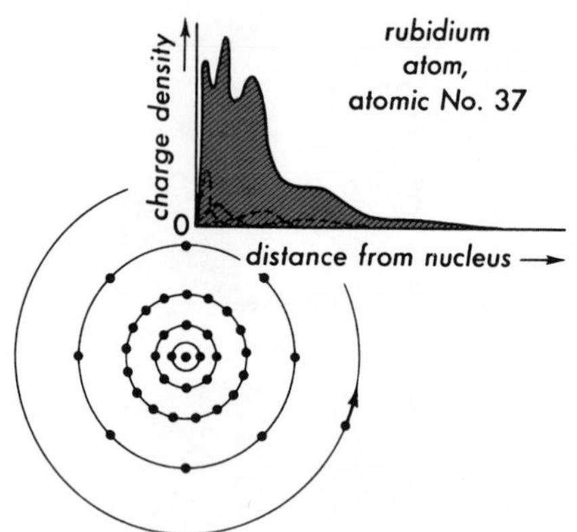

Fig. 51P. Diagrams comparing the new and the old theories of atomic structure, according to wave mechanics and the Bohr–Stoner model.

in Figs. 51M and 51N represent the relative probability of finding the electron at any given time in that direction and at that distance, respectively. In other words, there are regions in the space around the nucleus where the probability of finding the electron at any given instant is high, and other regions like the nodes where the probability is very low or zero.

51.8. The New Atomic Picture

Although the Bohr atom has been replaced by the more satisfactory model of a *nucleus surrounded by electron waves,* it is still customary, for convenience only, to talk about electron *shells* and *orbits.* The reason for this is that there is a close analogy between the old and the new models. When the Bohr–Stoner scheme of the building up of the elements is extended to the new theory of electron waves, the electrons are found to distribute their charge in such a way that something analogous to shells is formed.

This is illustrated by the graph for a rubidium atom, atomic number 37, in Fig. 51P. The shaded area above represents the distribution of the charge of 37 electrons on the new theory, and the lower orbital model represents the electron shells on the old theory. The new model is represented by a graph because it is spherically symmetrical in space, while the old model is represented by orbits because it is confined to one plane. Proceeding out from the nucleus it is seen that the charge rises to several maxima at distances corresponding closely to the discrete K, L, M, N, and O shells of the orbital model. In other words, the new atom also has a shell-like structure.

51.9. Heisenberg's Uncertainty Principle

The quantum theory description of a light beam as being made up of discrete packages of energy $h\nu$, called photons, would seem to rest upon our ability to determine for a given photon both the *position* and the *momentum* that it possesses at a given instant. These are usually thought of as measurable quantities of a material particle. It was shown by Heisenberg, however, that for particles of atomic magnitude it is in principle impossible to determine both position and momentum simultaneously with perfect accuracy. If an experiment is designed to measure one of them exactly, the other will become uncertain, and vice versa.

An experiment can measure both position and momentum but only within certain limits of accuracy. These limits are specified by the *uncertainty principle* (sometimes called the *principle of indeterminacy*), according to which

$$\Delta x \cdot \Delta p \cong h \tag{51s}$$

Here Δx and Δp represent the variations of the value of position and the corresponding momentum of a particle which must be expected if we try to measure both at once, i.e., the uncertainties of these quantities ($h = 6.6262 \times 10^{-34}$ J s).

Heisenberg's uncertainty principle is frequently written in terms of energy and time. Converting Δx and Δp into these units, Eq. (51s) is written

$$\Delta E \times \Delta t = h \tag{51t}$$

The uncertainty principle is applicable to photons, as well as to all material particles from electrons up to sizable bodies dealt with in ordinary mechanics. For the latter, the very small magnitude of h renders Δx and Δp entirely negligible compared to the ordinary experimental errors encountered in the measuring of its position x and its momentum p.

When p is very small, as it is for an electron or a photon, the uncertainty may become a large percent of the momentum itself, or else the uncertainty in the position is relatively large.

According to Bohr the uncertainty principle of Heisenberg provides complementary descriptions of the same phenomenon. That is, to obtain the complete picture of any event we need both the wave and corpuscular properties of matter, but because of the uncertainty principle it is impossible to design an experiment that will show both of them in all detail at the same time. Any one experiment will reveal the details of either the wave or corpuscular character, according to the purpose for which the experiment is designed.

The interference fringes in Young's double-slit experiment, shown in Fig. 35G, constitute one of the simplest manifestations of the wave character of light. Identical fringe patterns, however, can be obtained by sending a beam of electrons or protons through the same slits. On the wave theory a small part of the incident wave goes through one slit and another small part goes through the other, and these when they come together produce constructive and destructive interference at different areas on the screen (see Fig. 51Q).

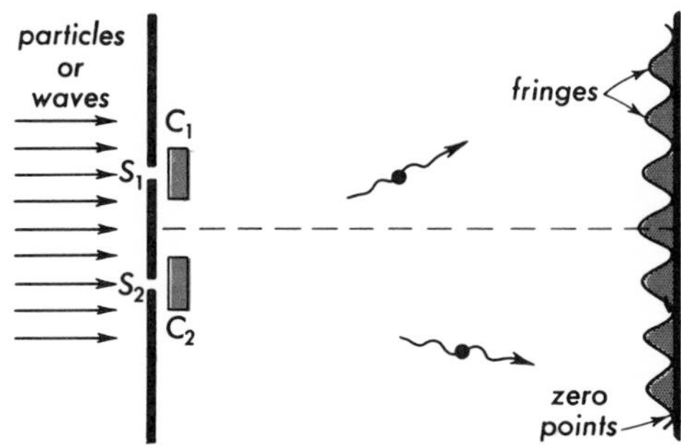

Fig. 51Q. Young's double-slit experiment modified to demonstrate both wave and corpuscular properties of matter.

If on the corpuscular theory, however, a photon $h\nu$, or a particle m, goes through one slit, how can it be affected by the other slit, and hence go to one of the appropriate fringe areas on the screen, and never to one of the zero points?

To answer this question let us suppose small sensitive detectors, such as scintillation counters (see Figs. 54H and 54I), are placed behind the two slits as shown in Fig. 51Q. These detectors C_1 and C_2 can register each photon or particle that goes through one slit or the other. But, in so doing, the fringe pattern will have been destroyed because of the deflections suffered by the corpuscles in producing scintillations. Because of a change in direction the momentum p is charged so that its new momentum is uncertain.

Hence, when we use slit detectors to make Δx small, we introduce a large change in momentum p, and destroy the fringe pattern. When we do without the slit counters to restore the fringe pattern making Δp small, Δx becomes large because we do not know what slit the corpuscle went through.

Some philosophers regard the uncertainty principle as one of the profound principles of nature. Some physicists, on the other hand, are inclined to believe it to be an expression of our inability thus far to formulate a better theory of radiation and matter.

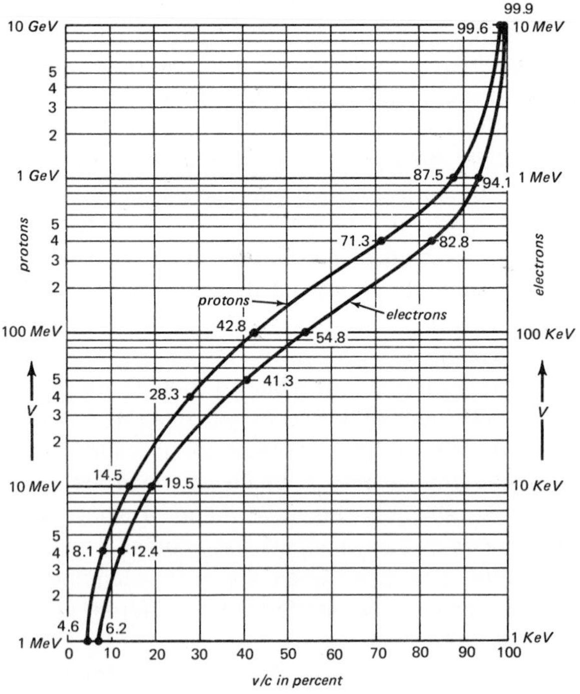

Fig. 51R. Graphs of the relative velocities of protons and electrons for a large range of voltages. See Table 51A.

51.10. Graphs for High Energy Particles

Because of the difficulty in calculating the velocities of protons or electrons for high voltages, it is convenient to refer to graphs of the kind shown in Fig. 51R. At the very bottom of the curves, below 10-MeV protons and 10-KeV electrons, nonrelativistic equations apply, but for all applied voltages above these the relativistic equations must be used.

problems

1. Find the De Broglie wavelengths in angstroms of a proton moving with $\frac{1}{20}$ *th* the speed of light.

2. Calculate the wavelength of a 2500-Kg automobile traveling at 30 m/s.

3. An X ray has a wavelength of 0.010 Å. Calculate (a) its momentum, and (b) its energy. [Ans. (a) 6.626×10^{-22} Kg m/s, (b) 1.986×10^{-13} J.]

4. An X ray has a wavelength of 0.0580 Å. Calculate (a) its momentum, and (b) its energy.

5.* The electron beam forming the image on a television picture tube is accelerated by 15,000 volts. What is (a) the velocity of the beam, and (b) the De Broglie wavelength of the electrons? Neglect any relativistic effect.

6. The De Broglie wavelength of a moving electron is 0.360 Å. What is (a) the electron's velocity, and (b) the voltage applied between two grids that will just stop the electrons? Use nonrelativistic equations. [Ans. (a) 2.020×10^{7} m/s, (b) 1161 V.]

7. An alpha particle has a rest mass of 6.64×10^{-27} Kg and a charge of 3.204×10^{-19} C. Find (a) the velocity, and (b) the De Broglie wavelength of this particle if it was accelerated by 20,000 volts. Use nonrelativistic equations.

8. The electron beam in a TV picture tube is accelerated by 12,000 V. What are (a) the electrons' velocity, and (b) their De Broglie wavelength. Use nonrelativistic equations.

9. Find (a) the energy, and (b) the momentum of a photon of green light of wavelength 5000 Å. [Ans. (a) 1.325×10^{-27} Kg m/s, (b) 3.973×10^{-19} J.]

10. An X ray with a wavelength of 2.250×10^{-2} Å collides with an electron at rest, and scatters it at an angle of 55°. Calculate the wavelength of the modified X ray.

11. A compton recoil electron is scattered at an angle of 60°. If the scattered X ray has a wavelength of 0.0580 Å, what is the wavelength of the incident X ray?

12. X rays with a wavelength of 2.250 Å fall on a metal plate. Find (a) the velocity, and (b) the wavelength

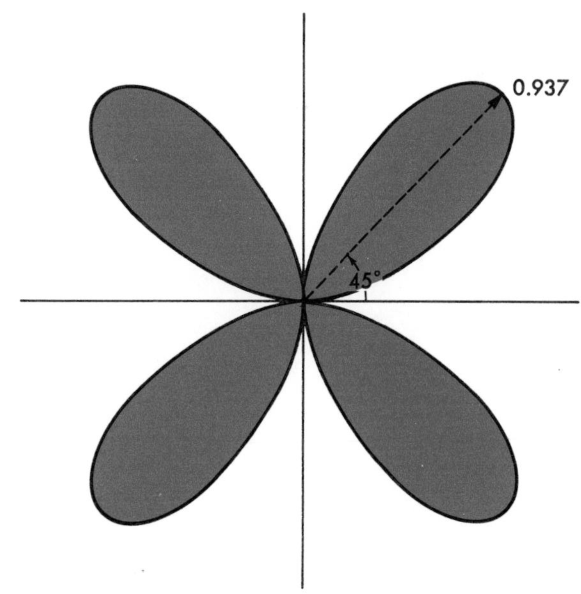

Prob. 15. Polar graph of the D_θ distribution of mass and charge of the atomic state of hydrogen, $\ell = 2$, $m = \pm 1$.

associated with the photoelectrons. Neglect the metal's work function. Use nonrelativistic equations. [Ans. (a) 4.40×10^7 m/s, (b) 0.1653 Å.]

13. A beam of X rays impinge on a metal plate, causing the emission of photoelectrons. If the X-ray wavelength is 7.50 Å, what are (a) the photoelectrons' velocity, and (b) their De Broglie wavelength in angstroms?

14.* Plot a polar graph of the D_θ distribution for the atomic state of hydrogen, $^2P_{3/2}$, where $j = \frac{3}{2}$ and $m = \frac{3}{2}$. $D_\theta = \frac{3}{2} \sin^2 \theta$. Calculate values for every 10-degree interval from 0° to 90°, and use the same set of resultant values for 360°.

15.* Plot a polar graph of the D_θ distribution for the atomic state of hydrogen $\ell = 2$ and $m = \pm 1$. Assume $D_\theta = \frac{15}{4} \sin^2 \theta \cos^2 \theta$. Calculate values of every 10° interval from 0° to 90°, and use the same set of values to complete the graph for 360°. [Ans. See diagram.]

16.* With the data given in Example 1, use Eq.(51c) to (a) find the velocity of the recoiling electron, and (b) use Eq.(51g) to find its direction. [Ans. (a) 2.446×10^8 m/s, (b) $\phi = 43.05°$.]

17.* An X ray with a wavelength of 2.8560×10^{-12} m collides with an electron at rest, and scatters the modified X-ray at an angle of $\theta = 56.5°$. Calculate (a) the wavelength of the scattered X ray, (b) the velocity of the recoiling electron, and (c) its direction.

18.* Starting with the energy given in Eq.(51c), and the momentum relations of Eq.(51f), derive Eq.(51h).

52 Radioactivity

Radioactivity may be defined as a spontaneous disintegration of the nucleus of one or more atoms. The phenomenon was discovered originally by Becquerel* in 1896 and is confined almost entirely to the heaviest elements in the periodic table, elements 83 to 102. What Becquerel discovered was that uranium, element 92, gave out some kind of rays that would penetrate through several thicknesses of thick black paper and affect a photographic plate on the other side. When the same phenomenon was confirmed several months later by Pierre and Marie Curie† these rays became known as Becquerel rays.

The story of the discovery of radioactivity by Becquerel has been told as follows. During the research period of the 1890's, many experimenters were studying the phenomena of *fluorescence* and *phosphorescence.* It was well known at the time that various chemical compounds of uranium formed some of the best fluorescent materials with which to experiment.

One day Becquerel opened a drawer in his work table and removed a photographic plate from a cardboard box, and used the plate to take a picture. Upon development of the plate, however, he found an unaccounted-for image of a key in the center of the picture. Thinking back, he recalled that a key was lying on top of the box of plates when he removed it from the drawer. Curious as to how the image could have transferred to the plate, he noted uranium ores on the table top only a few inches above the box.

Röntgen had just discovered X rays and their penetrating power, and Becquerel wondered if the uranium ore was giving off penetrating radiation. He set up the experiment as it was, and placed a key on top of a box containing a fresh photographic plate. Above that he placed some uranium ore, and after some time, developed the plate and found, surely enough, an image of the key.

52.1. Discovery of Radium

Unlike the discovery of many new phenomena, the discovery of radium by Pierre and Madame Curie in 1898 was brought about

***Antoine Henri Becquerel (1852–1908), French physicist, was born in Paris on December 15, 1852. He succeeded to his father's chair at the Museum of Natural History in 1892. In 1896 he discovered radioactivity, the phenomenon for which he is most famous. The invisible but penetrating rays emitted by uranium and other radioactive elements are now called Becquerel rays. For these researches he was granted the Noble Prize in physics in 1903.**

†Pierre Curie (1859–1906), French, and Marie Curie (1867–1936), Polish, worked as physicist and physical chemist, respectively. Pierre Curie was educated at Sorbonne where he later became professor of physics. Although he experimented on piezoelectricity and other subjects, he is chiefly noted for his work on radioactivity performed jointly with his wife, Marie Sklodowska, whom he married in 1895. Marie was born in Poland on November 7, 1867, where she received her early scientific training from her father. Becoming involved in a students' revolutionary organization, she left Poland for Paris where she took a degree at the university. Two years after the discovery of radioactivity by Becquerel, Pierre and Madame Curie isolated polonium and radium from pitchblende by a long and laborious physical-chemical process. In 1903 they were awarded

intentionally by a set of carefully planned experiments. Having found that pitchblende was active in emitting Becquerel rays, the Curies chemically treated a ton of this ore in the hope of isolating from it the substance or element responsible for the activity. The first concentrated radioactive substance isolated was called *polonium* by Madame Curie, a name chosen in honor of her native country, Poland. Five months later came the isolation of a minute quantity of *radium,* a substance that was a powerful source of Becquerel rays. Continued experiments by the Curies, and others, soon led to the isolation of many other substances now recognized as radioactive elements. Some of the more common of these are *radon* and *thorium.*

the Davy Medal of the Royal Society, and (jointly with Becquerel) the Nobel Prize in physics. Professor Curie, who was elected to the Academy of Sciences in 1905, was run over and killed by a carriage in 1906. Succeeding him as professor at the university, Madame Curie in 1911 was awarded the Nobel Prize in chemistry. She has the unique distinction of having had a share in the awards of two Nobel Prizes.

52.2. The Properties of Becquerel Rays

It is to the experimental genius of Rutherford* that we owe the complete unraveling of the mystery surrounding the nature of Becquerel rays. As the result of an extensive series of experiments, Rutherford and his co-workers discovered that these penetrating rays are of three quite different kinds. A simplified experiment demonstrating this is illustrated in Fig. 52A. A small sample of radium is dropped to the bottom of a small drill hole made in a block of lead. This produces a narrow beam of rays emerging from the top of the block, since rays entering the walls of lead are absorbed before reaching the surface. When electrically charged plates are placed at the side of this beam as shown in diagram (a), the paths of some rays are bent to the left, some to the right, and some are not bent at all. A magnetic field as shown in diagram (b) exhibits the same effect. Paths bending to the left indicate positively charged particles called *α rays* or *α particles,* those bending to the right indicate negatively charged particles called *β rays* or *β particles,* and those going straight ahead indicate no charge and are called *γ rays* or photons.

Rutherford, by a series of experiments, was able to show that each *α ray* is in reality a *doubly ionized helium atom,* i.e., a helium atom with both of its electrons removed. Such a particle is nothing more than a bare helium nucleus with double the positive charge of a hydrogen nucleus or proton, and a mass number or atomic weight four times as great. The *β rays* he found are ordinary electrons with a mass of $\frac{1}{1836}$ the mass of a *proton* or $\frac{1}{7360}$ the mass of an *α particle,* while *γ rays* are electromagnetic waves of about the same or a little higher frequency than X rays. Although γ rays all travel with exactly the velocity of X rays and visible light, α rays are ejected with a speed of from $\frac{1}{10}$ to $\frac{1}{100}$ the

***Lord Rutherford (1871–1937), British physicist, was born in New Zealand where he attended the university. In 1898 he became Macdonald professor of physics at McGill University, Montreal, Canada, and in 1907 professor of physics at Manchester University. In 1919 he became professor and director of experimental physics at the University of Cambridge, and in addition held a professorship at the Royal Institution in London. He is most famous for his brilliant researches establishing the existence and nature of radioactive transformations and the electrical structure of the atom. For this work, and until the time of his death in 1937, he was acclaimed by many as the greatest living experimental physicist. He was awarded the Nobel Prize in chemistry in 1908, and was knighted in 1914. The author had the good fortune of being shown around the Cavendish Laboratory in 1930 by Lord Rutherford.**

velocity of light; β particles move faster than α particles, some of them traveling with 99% the velocity of light.

52.3. Identification of Alpha Particles

The first conclusive evidence that alpha particles are helium nuclei was obtained by Rutherford and Royds in England in 1909. A special glass tube as shown in Fig. 52B was used for this purpose. A thin-walled glass tube A containing radon gas was sealed inside a thick-walled tube B containing mercury. At the top was a glass capillary tube C with two metal electrodes D and E sealed through the glass as shown.

Tubes B and C were evacuated through the side tube P, and then mercury was raised to the level shown. After maintaining this condition for some time, some of the alpha rays emitted by the radon gas atoms passed through the thin glass walls of tube A to be collected in tube B. Here these particles acquire electrons and become neutral atoms. After standing for six days the mercury was raised to the level L, forcing the helium into the capillary. A high voltage was applied to the electrodes, and the light from the discharge was observed with a spectroscope. The line spectrum observed was found to be identical with that obtained when a discharge was sent through another tube containing regular helium gas.

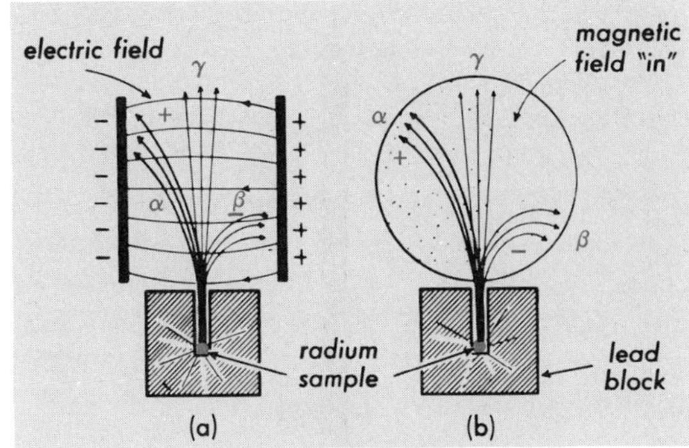

Fig. 52A. The bending of Becquerel rays in (a) an electric field, and (b) a magnetic field.

52.4. Ionizing Power

When Becquerel rays penetrate matter in the gaseous, liquid, or solid state, they do not continue to move indefinitely, but are brought to rest slowly by ionizing atoms all along their path. Being ejected from their radioactive source with tremendously high speeds, all three types of rays collide with electrons and knock them free from atoms. They are, therefore, *ionizing agents.* The relative number of ionized atoms created along the path of an α particle, however, is much greater than the number created by a β particle or γ ray. If, in traveling the same distance in a given material, a γ ray products one ionized atom, a β particle will, on the average, produce approximately 100, and an α particle will produce about 10,000. Thus α particles are powerful ionizing agents, while γ rays are not.

As stated above, an α particle, ejected from a radioactive atom, is only a nucleus of a helium atom and lacks the two electrons necessary to make of it a neutral atom. As this particle speeds through matter, it picks up and loses electrons at a rapid rate. No sooner does an electron become attached than it is swept off again by other atoms. Finally, upon coming to rest, however, each α particle collects and retains two electrons, becoming a *normal helium atom.*

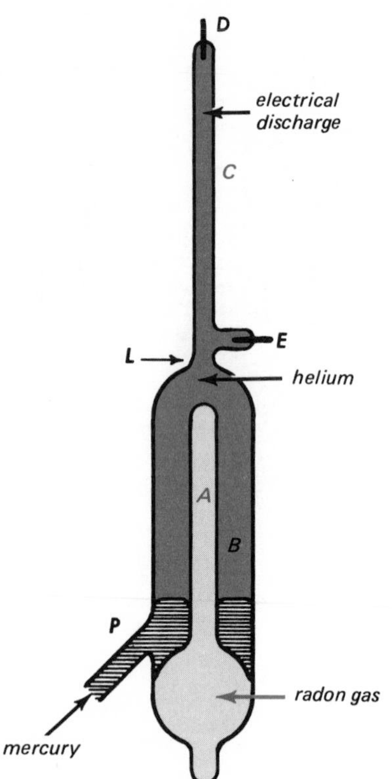

Fig. 52B. Special discharge tube used in proving that alpha particles are helium nuclei.

52.5. Penetrating Power

At each collision with an atom, α and β rays lose, on the average, only a small part of their initial energy. Usually an α particle or β particle will make several thousand collisions before being brought to rest. At each collision, some of the kinetic energy is expended in ionizing the atom encountered while giving that same atom a certain amount of kinetic energy. Since α particles produce the greatest number of ions in a given path, they penetrate the shortest distance and therefore have the poorest penetrating power. The penetrating powers of the three kinds of rays are roughly inversely proportional to their ionizing power:

	α	β	γ
Relative ionizing power	10,000	100	1
Relative penetrating power	1	100	10,000

52.6. Methods of Detecting Becquerel Rays

There are several well-known methods for detecting and measuring radioactivity; the most common of these are

Electroscopes	**Geiger-Müller counters**
Electrometers	**Scintillation counters**
Cloud chambers	**Ionization chambers**
Bubble chambers	**Photographic emulsions**
Semiconductors	**Spark chambers**

We have already seen how X rays passing through an electroscope cause the charge to disappear and the gold leaf to fall. This same action may be demonstrated with α, β, and γ rays. The stronger the source of rays or the nearer the sample is brought to the electroscope, the more rapid is the discharge. Experiments show that, if the walls of the electroscope are too thick, only the γ rays get through to produce ionization on the inside. For this reason specially designed electroscopes made with thin windows of light material like aluminum are used for measuring α and β rays.

The Braun type of electrometer is convenient for demonstration purposes. This device uses a lightweight metal pointer, pivoted a trifle above its center of gravity and insulated from its ring support by a nonconductor 1 as shown in Fig. 52C. In principle, the electrometer operates exactly like an electroscope; when charged positively or negatively, the needle rises and the pointer indicates the acquired potential on a scale.

If a radioactive source is brought close to the knob or terminal of a charged electrometer, the needle slowly returns to the vertical, or no charge, position. The α particles produce many ions in the air close to the source; oppositely charged ions are drawn toward the nob and there neutralize the charge.

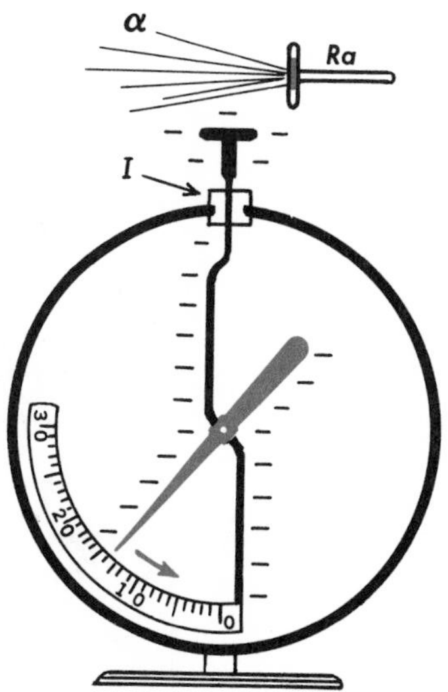

Fig. 52C. Diagram of a Braun-type electrometer—used here to detect radioactivity.

52.7. The Wilson Cloud Chamber

In 1912 C. T. R. Wilson* devised a method by which one may actually observe the paths of α and β particles. As will be seen in the following chapters, this method is used extensively in modern atomic physics as a means of studying many different atomic processes. The device by which this is accomplished consists of an expansion chamber in which water vapor is made to condense upon ions produced by the high-speed particles that have previously passed through it.

To begin with, the conditions under which water in the vapor state will condense into fogdrops are quite critical. These conditions are (1) there must be water vapor present, (2) there must be dust particles or ions on which the drops can form, and (3) the temperature and pressure must be brought to a definite value. That water drops will condense only upon ions or dust particles can be demonstrated with an ordinary glass jar containing a little water as shown in Fig. 52D. If allowed to stand for a short period of time, some of the water will evaporate and fill the bottle with vapor. Ions are next formed in the bottle by momentarily inserting a small gas flame as shown in diagram (a). Compressed air is then injected into the bottle through a tube, so that when the stopper is quickly removed the sudden expansion will produce a dense fog as shown in diagram (b). If the flame is not first inserted to produce ions, no appreciable fog can be formed.

The purpose of the compressed air and subsequent expansion of the chamber is to lower the temperature, thus causing the air to become supersaturated with water vapor. Under these conditions the vapor will condense on all ionized molecules present.

When an α or β particle shoots through the air, positive and negative ions are formed all along its path. The removal, by collision, of each electron from a neutral atom or molecule leaves a positively charged ion. The electron that attaches almost immedi-

***Charles Thomson Rees Wilson (1869–1959), Scottish physicist, was awarded the Nobel Prize in physics in 1927 for his development of the so-called Wilson cloud chamber. This device causes the formation of fog drops on ionized atomic particles, thereby making visible the paths of electrically charged particles as well as their collisions with other particles. The cloud chamber led to the discovery of recoil electrons from X rays, the so-called Compton recoils, the tracks of alpha particles, and the discovery by C. D. Anderson of positrons and mesons. C. T. R. Wilson was educated at Owens College, Manchester, and Sidney Sussex College, Cambridge. He was elected to the Royal Society and served for years as lecturer in physics and professor of natural history at Cambridge.**

ately to another neutral atom or molecule forms a negatively charged ion. If immediately after an α particle has gone through a cloud chamber an expansion takes place, fog drops will form on the newly created ions, revealing clearly the path the particle

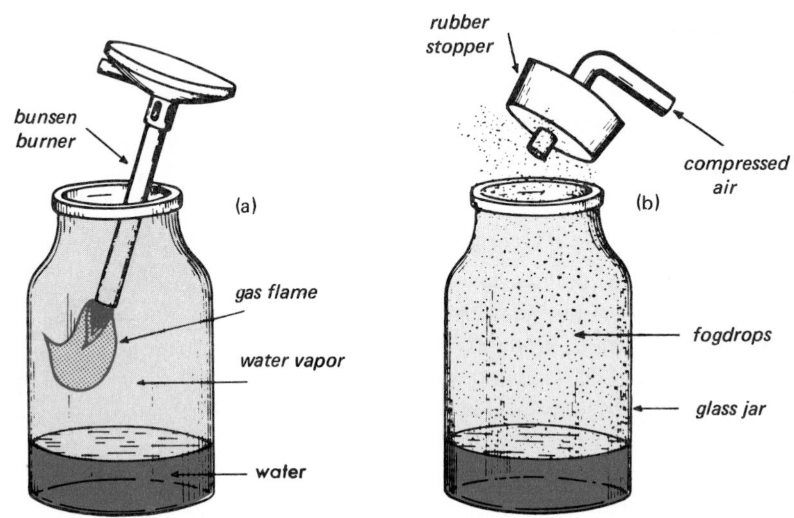

Fig. 52D. Experiment demonstrating the formation of fog drops on ions in a glass jar.

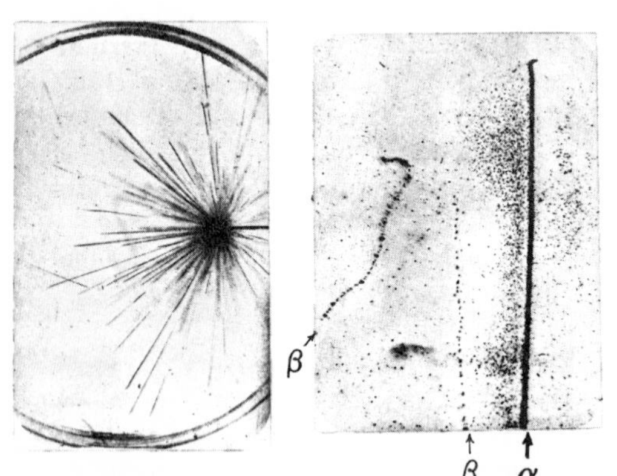

Fig. 52E. (a) α-ray tracks from radium as seen in a Wilson cloud chamber. (b) One α-ray and two β-ray tracks. [After C. T. R. Wilson, Proc. Roy. Soc. (London), **87,** 292 (1912).]

has taken. As illustrated by the photographs in Fig. 52E, such α-ray tracks are straight and quite dense, whereas the β-ray tracks are crooked and sparsely lined with drops. The β rays, being very light particles, are easily deflected by collision, while the relatively heavy α particles "plow" right through thousands of atoms with only an occasional deflection.

Gamma rays are never observed in a cloud chamber, since they produce so few ions. In passing through several feet of air a single γ ray will, on the average, produce only one or two ions. This is not enough to produce a recognizable cloud track. If a very strong source of γ rays is available, however, their presence can be observed in a cloud chamber by the chance collisions some of them have made with electrons. These recoiling electrons are called "Compton electrons" and were explained in Sec. 51.2, and shown in Fig. 51D.

A diagram of a simple type of Wilson cloud chamber is shown in Fig. 52F. The arrangement is made from an ordinary flat-bottomed flask with a rubber bulb attached to the neck. A tiny deposit of radium or polonium is inserted in the end of a thin-walled glass tube as indicated. When the rubber bulb is squeezed to compress the air in the top, and then released to cause an expansion, fog drops will form on the ions created by the α particles. The battery and the wires leading to the wire ring in the top of the chamber and the water below are for the purpose of quickly removing ions previously formed in the chamber. This clears the field of view for newly formed tracks.

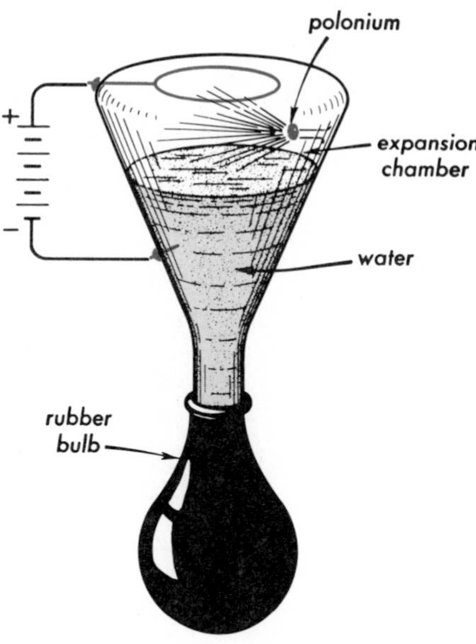

Fig. 52F. Diagram of a small laboratory-type Wilson cloud chamber.

Another type of cloud chamber, one that is readily made in any laboratory workshop, is shown in Fig. 52G. This is the so-called *diffusion cloud chamber,* a device that is continuously sensitive to track formation. A glass cylinder separates and insulates a shallow metal pan below from a metal ring and glass disk above. The bottom pan contains alcohol and rests on a slab of dry ice (solid CO_2).

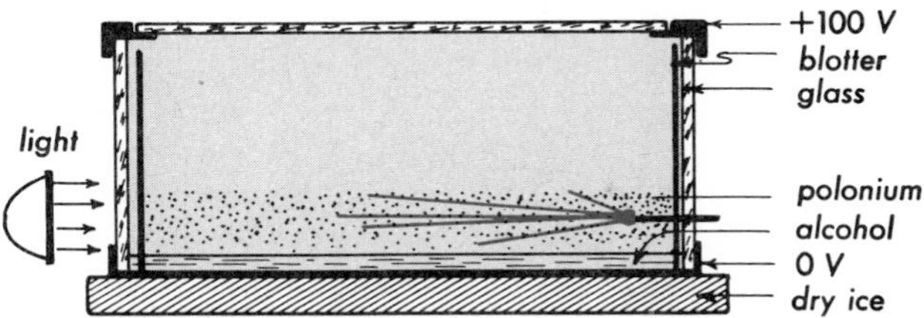

Fig. 52G. Cross-sectional diagram of a diffusion cloud chamber.

A blotter, extending 80% of the way around the walls, rests with its lower edge in the alcohol. Evaporated alcohol around the warm upper edge of the blotter mixes with the air and slowly settles as it cools. In the dotted region, alcohol vapor is saturated and small droplets will form on any ions present. Alpha particles shooting out through this space create positive and negative ions, and hence tracks are observed.

A potential difference of 100 V or so between the bottom pan and the top ring will clear the field of ions so that newly formed tracks are not masked by a dense fog of droplets. A strong source of light shining through the 20% open space through the blotter wall illuminates the tracks, thus making them visible.

52.8. *Isotope Designations*

Within a period of a few years following the discovery of radioactivity, a large number of radioactive elements were found. Soon after J. J. Thomson's discovery of isotopes in 1912, it was realized that the actual number of radioactive elements was few in number and that the many different kinds of activities are to be attributed to the isotopes of only a few elements.

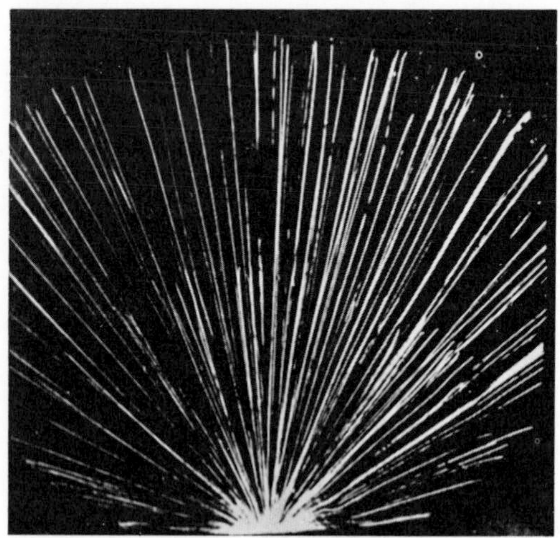

Fig. 52H. Wilson cloud-chamber tracks from $_{83}Bi^{212}$ and $_{84}Po^{212}$. (After Rutherford, Chadwick, and Ellis, courtesy of Cambridge University Press.)

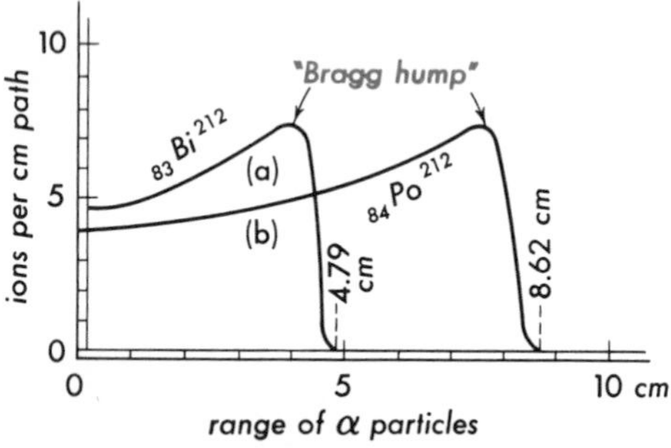

Fig. 52I. Graphs of the relative number of ions produced at various points along the path of an α particle (a) from $_{83}Bi^{212}$, and (b) from $_{84}Po^{212}$.

The early designations and the present-day assignments of radioactive isotopes are given in Appendix X. Note for example that Ra A, Ra C′, Ac A, Ac C′, Th A, and Th C′ are all isotopes of the 84th element, *polonium.*

It is common practice among scientists today to designate all isotopes of all elements in an abbreviated form. The isotopes of radium, for example, are written

$$_{88}Ra^{223} \quad _{88}Ra^{224} \quad _{88}Ra^{225} \quad _{88}Ra^{226} \quad _{88}Ra^{228}$$

instead of

Ac X   Th X   Ra   Ms I

The subscript to the left of the chemical symbol gives the value of the atomic number Z, i.e., the number of positive charges in the nucleus, the number of orbital electrons in the neutral atom, and the position of the element in the periodic table. The superscript on the right gives the atomic mass number A, i.e., the whole number nearest in value to the atomic mass when that quantity is expressed in atomic mass units (amu).

52.9. Range

The range of an α particle is defined as the distance such a particle will travel through dry air at normal atmospheric pressure. In a partial vacuum where there are fewer air molecules per centimeter to bump into, the distance traveled before coming to rest will be greater, whereas in air under higher than normal atmospheric pressure there are more molecules per centimeter and the distance will be diminished. Experiments show that some radioactive elements eject α particles with a higher speed than others. The higher the initial speed, the greater is the range. The range of the α particles from $_{88}Ra^{226}$ is 3.39 cm, whereas the range of those from $_{84}Po^{212}$ is 8.62 cm.

The ranges of α particles in general have been determined in three different ways: (1) by the Wilson cloud chamber, (2) by the number of ions produced along the path, and (3) by scintillations produced on a fluorescent screen.

In the Wilson cloud-chamber photograph of Fig. 52H, α particles of two different ranges are observed. The radioactive sample used to obtain this picture was a mixture of $_{83}Bi^{212}$ and $_{84}Po^{212}$. The shorter tracks with a 4.79 cm range are due to the α particles from $_{83}Bi^{212}$, which disintegrates to become $_{81}Tl^{208}$, and the longer tracks of 8.62 cm range are due to the α particles from $_{84}Po^{212}$, which disintegrates to become lead (see Appendix X).

When one measures the number of ions produced along the path of an α particle, curves similar to those in Fig. 52I are obtained. At the end of each track the number is seen to reach a maximum and then drop to zero within a very short distance. This maximum on the graph is called the "Bragg hump" in honor of W. H. Bragg, who discovered the phenomenon. The maximum number of ions is therefore produced just before the particles are stopped, i.e., where they are moving at relatively low speeds. The point at which the ion density drops rapidly to zero gives the range as shown in the figure. Although the experimental method by which ion density is usually determined will not be presented here, another method is presented. This is the well-known method of counting fog drops. An enlarged photograph of a cloud track, as reproduced in Fig. 52J, reveals the individual fog drops separated sufficiently to enable the number of drops per centimeter of path to be counted. In measurements of this kind, it is assumed that each ion produces one fog drop.

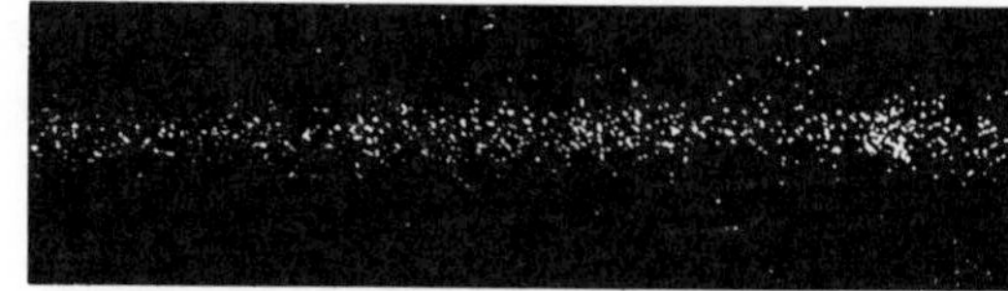

Fig. 52J. Enlarged photograph of a cloud-chamber track showing individual fog drops. (After Brode.)

The third method used in measuring the range is illustrated in Fig. 52K. When each α particle strikes a fluorescent screen, a tiny flash of light is produced. These flashes, called *scintillations,* are observed by means of a microscope. When the sample is moved farther and farther away, by pulling the rod R back, a point is reached where scintillations are no longer observed. The distance *d*, where the α particles just fail to reach the screen, is a direct measure of the range.

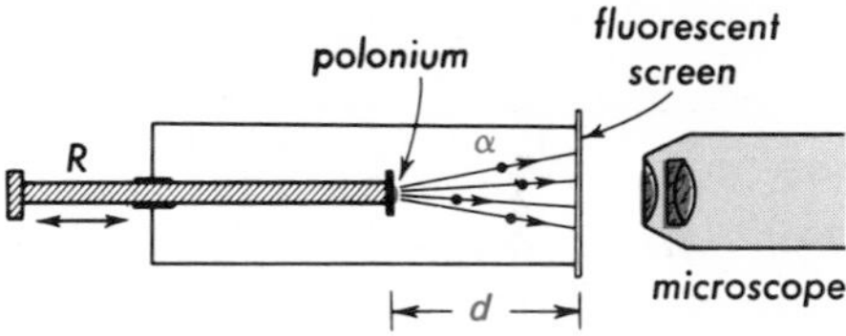

Fig. 52K. Experimental method of measuring the range of α particles.

52.10. Range of Alpha Particles—Experiment

A simple laboratory experiment for measuring the range of α particles is shown in Fig. 52L. It involves the use of a radioactive source obtained from any physics supply house, a Braun-type electrometer, and an ionization chamber made from ordinary sheet metal. The ionization chamber, about the size of the most common tin can, has a hole in the bottom and a sliding disk plunger for a top. The radioactive source is placed on the Braun electrometer, and a small metal clamp is used to ground the needle to the frame when it swings about 3 cm from its zero position. A 600-V radio battery of small capacity is a convenient source of high potential.

The plunger distance *r* is first set at about 8 cm. In this position the needle rises steadily, hits a small metal clamp stop, and quickly drops back to zero. The needle rises again and drops back quickly at a regular rate, due to the continual collection of charge from the ions in the chamber above. With a stop watch the time *t* required for any given number *n* of discharges of the

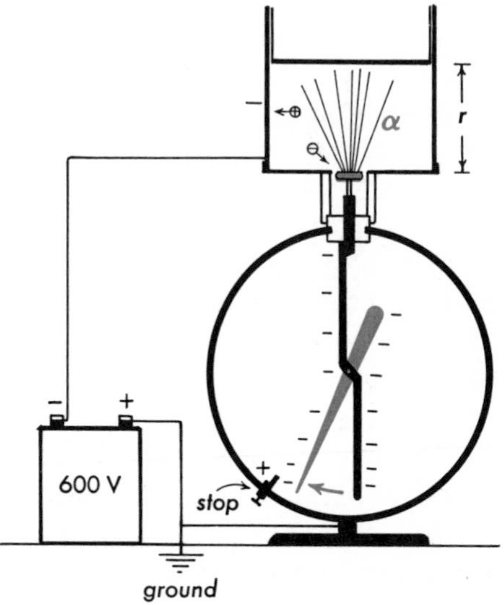

Fig. 52L. An experimental arrangement for measuring the ranges of α particles.

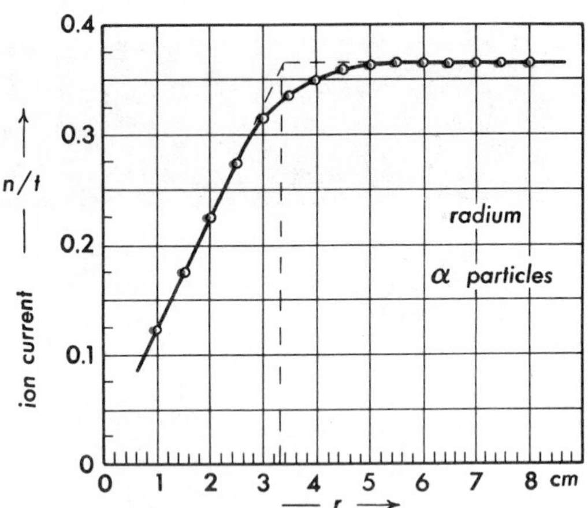

Fig. 52M. Graph of the ion current from the α-particle range experiment (see Fig. 52L).

needle is recorded. The plunger is then lowered 5 mm and the discharge time again measured. This process is repeated for distances diminishing by 5-mm steps, and the discharge rate determined.

The quantity n/t for each setting of the plunger distance r is a direct measure of the ion current, that is, to the number of ions produced per second. If n/t is plotted against r, a curve similar to that shown in Fig. 52M is obtained. The drop in ion current at distances less than the *range* is due to the fact that α particles hit the plunger before they reach the end of their range in air and are prevented from creating their full quota of ions. The leveling-off of the current at larger values of r signifies that all α particles reach the end of their range in air and create their full ion quota. From the intersection of the dotted lines the α-particle range is found to be approximately 3.3 cm, in good agreement with the accurately known value of 3.39 cm.

The ranges of α particles from some of the natural radioactive elements are given in Chap. 53, Tables 53A and 53B.

questions

1. What is a Wilson cloud chamber? How does it work?

2. What kinds of particles do not leave tracks in a Wilson cloud chamber? Why not?

3. Define or briefly explain each of the following: (a) scintillations, (b) the Bragg hump, (c) penetrating power, (d) ionizing power, and (e) an ionized atom.

4. Who discovered radioactivity? What were the circumstances?

5. Who discovered radium, polonium, and thorium?

6. What names are given to the different radioactive rays? Who unraveled this mystery?

7. What are α rays, β rays, and γ rays?

8. What are the relative ionizing powers and penetrating powers of the different rays?

9. Why does the α particle-range graph of Fig. 52M round off at the top instead of showing a sharp break in the curve?

10. What effect would β and γ rays from a radium source have upon the measured ion current and the α-particle range measurements described in Sec. 52.9?

11. What is the purpose of the dry ice in the operation of a diffusion cloud chamber (see Fig. 52G)?

12. What is meant by the range of an α particle?

13. From your knowledge of atomic structure, explain how an α particle loses energy as it passes through matter, such as a gas.

14. Draw a graph showing how the specific ionization along the path of an α particle varies with distance. Indicate the range of the particle on the plot.

53 Spontaneous disintegration and transmutation

We have seen in the preceding chapter how the heaviest naturally occurring elements in the periodic table spontaneously emit three kinds of radiation, *alpha particles* which are positively charged helium nuclei, *beta particles* which are negatively charged electrons, and *gamma rays* which are electromagnetic waves of extremely high frequency called photons. Such emission is called *radioactivity.*

53.1. Transmutation by Spontaneous Disintegration

A careful study of radioactivity indicates that α, β, and γ rays originate from within the nucleus of the atom and are the result of a nuclear disintegration. When a radium atom disintegrates by ejecting an α particle, the nucleus loses a net positive charge of 2. Since the number of positive charges on the nucleus determines the exact number of electrons outside of the atom, and this in turn determines the chemical nature of an atom, the loss of an α particle, with two positive charges, leaves a new chemical element. Thus a *radium atom,* for example, in disintegrating, changes into a new atom called *radon.* We say that there has been a *transmutation.* Not only does a nucleus lose a double charge by emitting an α particle and thereby *drops down two places in atomic number,* but it also loses a weight of four mass units and thus *drops down four units in atomic weight,* or four *atomic mass units.*

The disintegration of radioactive nuclei may be written in the form of simple equations, as follows. For radium

$$_{88}\mathrm{Ra}^{226} \rightarrow {}_{86}\mathrm{Rn}^{222} + \alpha \qquad \text{(53a)}$$

or

$$_{88}Ra^{226} \rightarrow {}_{86}Rn^{222} + {}_2He^4 \quad (53b)$$

As another example, for polonium

$$_{84}Po^{210} \rightarrow {}_{82}Pb^{206} + {}_2He^4 \quad (53c)$$

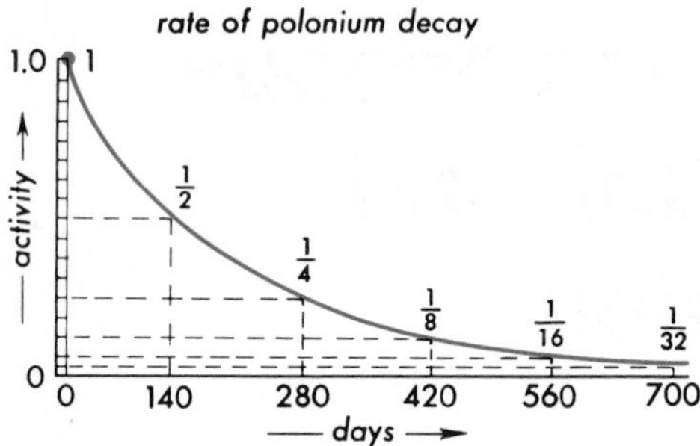

Fig. 53A. Decay curve for the radioactive element polonium. $_{84}Po^{210}$ has a half-life of 140 days.

When a nucleus like $_{82}Pb^{214}$ disintegrates by ejecting a β particle (an electron) to become $_{83}Bi^{214}$, the nuclear positive charge *increases by one unit.* Such a transmutation yields a new element one atomic number higher in the chemical table. Since an electron weights only $\frac{1}{1836}$ part of a hydrogen atom or proton, the change in mass due to a β particle leaving a nucleus is too small to change the atomic mass number. Although the loss in weight is measurable, it changes the atomic weight so slightly that for most purposes of discussion it can be, and is, neglected. For $_{82}Pb^{214}$

$$_{82}Pb^{214} \rightarrow {}_{83}Bi^{214} + {}_{-1}e^0 + \gamma \text{ ray}$$

In each equation the sum of the subscripts on the right side of the equation is equal to the subscript on the left. The same is true for the superscripts. The designation $_2He^4$ represents the α particle, and $_{-1}e^0$ represents the β particle. In nearly all radioactive disintegrations where a β particle is emitted, one finds a γ ray also. In such cases, as shown by the example, $_{82}Pb^{214}$ ejects a β particle and a γ ray to become $_{83}Bi^{214}$, a nucleus higher in atomic number by unity, but with the same mass number.

A γ ray, like the β-ray particle, changes the weight of a nucleus by a negligible amount, and, since it has no charge, it does not alter either the atomic number or the mass number.

53.2. Half-Life

The half-life of a radioactive element is the time required for half of a given quantity of that element to disintegrate into a new element. For example, it takes 1600 years for $\frac{1}{2}$ of a given quantity of $_{88}Ra^{226}$ to change into $_{86}Rn^{222}$. In another 1600 years, $\frac{1}{2}$ of the remainder will have disintegrated, leaving $\frac{1}{4}$ of the original amount. The half-life of $_{88}Ra^{226}$ is therefore said to be 1600 years.

The rate at which a given quantity of a radioactive element disintegrates, that is, *decays,* is found by observing the activity of a given sample over a period of time and plotting a graph of the type shown in Fig. 53A. Here, for $_{84}Po^{210}$, the activity drops to $\frac{1}{2}$ of its original value in 140 days. In another 140 days it again drops to half value, etc. The term "activity" may be defined as the number of rays given off per second of time, or as the number of ionized atoms produced each second by the rays.

The only difference between the decay curve of one element and that of another is the horizontal time scale to which they are plotted. To turn Fig. 53A into a decay curve for $_{84}Ra^{226}$, the times 140, 280, 420 days, etc., need only be changed to read 1600, 3200, 4800 years, etc., respectively. Since, therefore, all radioactive decay curves follow the same law, one does not have to wait for half of a given sample to disintegrate to be able to calculate how long it will be before half will have changed. This would require too many years of waiting for some elements.

A decay curve for the radioactivity of any given substance is best shown on what is called a *semilog graph.* Such a graph involves the use of cross-section paper in which the spacings on the horizontal scale are uniform, while on the vertical scale they are proportional to the logarithms of numbers. Such cross-section paper can be purchased, or made by using the B or C scale on the slipstick of a slide rule.

In Fig. 53B, the fractions $\frac{1}{1}$, $\frac{1}{2}$, $\frac{1}{4}$, $\frac{1}{8}$, $\frac{1}{16}$, etc., are plotted on semilog graph paper with the polonium *time scale* plotted horizontally.

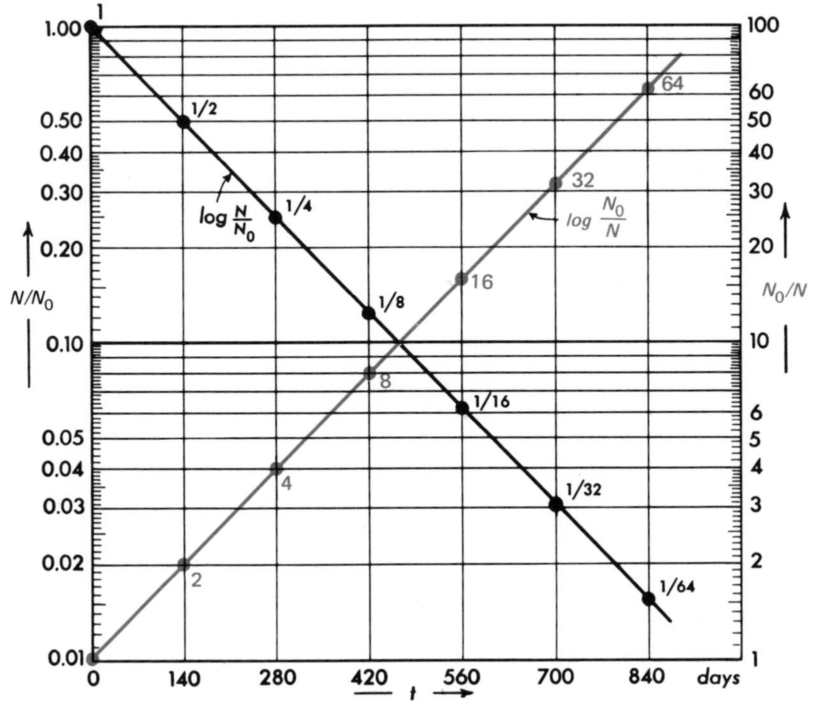

Fig. 53B. Semilog graphs of the α-particle activity of polonium, $_{84}Po^{210}$.

Note that a straight line is the result. If a semilog graph is plotted for the activity of any other radioactive element, it too will be a straight line, but with a different slope.

Suppose that for a given sample of radioactive material the initial number of particles given off per minute is N_0. After a time t, the number of atoms yet to disintegrate will have decreased and the reduced number of particles given off per minute will be N. Hence, the ratio N/N_0 will decrease with time t. If the logarithm of the inverse ratio N_0/N is plotted against t, as shown by the dotted line in Fig. 53B, it too will produce a straight line. The latter shows that the Napierian logarithm of N_0/N is proportional to t. We can therefore write

$$\ln \frac{N_0}{N} = \lambda t \tag{53d}$$

where λ is the proportionality constant and is called the *decay constant.*

To find the half-life of an element from the semilog graph we find the point where $N = \frac{1}{2}N_0$, and call the corresponding time the *half-life T.* For this graph point, Eq.(53d) gives

$$\ln \frac{N_0}{\frac{1}{2}N_0} = \lambda T$$

or

$$\ln 2 = \lambda T$$

Looking up the Napierian logarithm of 2, we find 0.693147 (see Appendix IX). Hence

$$0.693147 = \lambda T \tag{53e}$$

or

$$T = \frac{0.693147}{\lambda} \tag{53f}$$

This is the relation between the decay constant λ and the half-life T of any element.

The mean life of a radioactive element is defined as the average time single atoms or particles exist before disintegrating, and can be shown to be given by the reciprocal of the decay constant:

$$\tau = \frac{1}{\lambda} \tag{53g}$$

As shown by Eq.(53f) the half-life T is just slightly over $\frac{2}{3}$ the mean life τ:

$$T = 0.693147\tau \tag{53h}$$

Example 1. A count-rate meter is used to measure the activity of a given quantity of a radioactive element. At one instant the meter shows 475 counts per minute (C/M). Exactly 5.0 minutes later it shows 270 C/M. Find (a) the decay constant, (b) the mean life, and (c) the half-life of the element.

Solution. The given quantities are $t = 5.0$ min, $N_0 = 475$ C/M, and $N = 270$ C/M. To find the decay constant λ, we use Eq.(53d). First we find the value of N_0/N:

$$\frac{N_0}{N} = \frac{475}{270} = 1.759$$

To find the logarithm to the base e of any number we look up the logarithm to the base 10 of the number and multiply by 2.30258509. From the table of ordinary logarithms in Appendix IX, we find

$$\log 1.759 = 0.2453$$

which upon multiplying by 2.3026 gives

$$\ln 1.759 = 0.565$$

Using Eq.(53d), we obtain

$$\lambda = \frac{0.565}{5 \text{ min}} = 0.1130 \text{ min}^{-1}$$

By direct substitution in Eq.(53g), we find for the mean life

$$\tau = \frac{1}{\lambda} = \frac{1}{0.1130} \text{ min} = 8.85 \text{ min}$$

And by direct substitution in Eq.(53h), the half-life is found to be

$$T = 0.693\ \tau = 6.13 \text{ min}$$

53.3. Radioactive Series

It was Rutherford and his colleagues who discovered that when one radioactive atom disintegrates by ejecting an α or β particle, the remaining atom is still radioactive and may sooner or later eject another particle to become a still different atom. This process they found to continue through a series of elements,

TABLE 53A
Uranium-238 series

Element	*Symbol*	*Atomic no.*	*Mass no.*	*Particle ejected*	*Range in air*	*Half-life*
Uranium	$_{92}U^{238}$	92	238	α	2.70 cm	4.5×10^9 y
Thorium	$_{90}Th^{234}$	90	234	β	....	24.5 days
Protoactinium	$_{91}Pa^{234}$	91	234	β	....	1.14 min
Uranium	$_{92}U^{234}$	92	234	α	3.28	3×10^5 y
Thorium	$_{90}Th^{230}$	90	230	α	3.19	83,000 y
Radium	$_{88}Ra^{226}$	88	226	α	3.39	1600 y
Radon	$_{86}Rn^{222}$	86	222	α	4.12	3.82 days
Polonium	$_{84}Po^{218}$	84	218	α	4.72	3.05 min
Lead	$_{82}Pb^{214}$	82	214	β	....	26.8 min
Bismuth	$_{83}Bi^{214}$	83	214	α, β	....	19.7 min
Polonium	$_{84}Po^{214}$	84	214	α	6.97	10^{-6} s
Thallium	$_{81}Tl^{210}$	81	210	β	....	1.32 min
Lead	$_{82}Pb^{210}$	82	210	β	....	22 y
Bismuth	$_{83}Bi^{210}$	83	210	β	....	5 days
Polonium	$_{84}Po^{210}$	84	210	α	3.92	140 days
Lead	$_{82}Pb^{206}$	82	206	stable	....	infinite

TABLE 53B
Plutonium series*

Element	*Symbol*	*Atomic no.*	*Mass no.*	*Particle ejected*	*Range in air*	*Half-life*
Plutonium	$_{94}Pu^{241}$	94	241	β	. .	. . .
Americium	$_{95}Am^{241}$	95	241	α	4.1†	500 y
Neptunium	$_{93}Np^{237}$	93	237	α	3.3†	2.25×10^6 y
Protoactinium	$_{91}Pa^{233}$	91	233	β	. .	27.4 days
Uranium	$_{92}U^{233}$	92	233	α	3.3†	1.63×10^5 y†
Thorium	$_{90}Th^{229}$	90	229	α	3.3	7×10^3 y
Radium	$_{88}Ra^{225}$	88	225	β	. .	14.8 days
Actinium	$_{89}Ac^{225}$	89	225	α	4.4	10 days
Francium	$_{87}Fa^{221}$	87	221	α	5.0	4.8 min
Astatine	$_{85}At^{217}$	85	217	α	5.8	0.018 s
Bismuth	$_{83}Bi^{213}$	83	213	β(94%) α(4%)	4.6	47 min
Polonium	$_{84}Po^{213}$	84	213	α	7.7	10^{-6} s
Lead	$_{82}Pb^{209}$	82	209	β	. .	3.3 h
Bismuth	$_{83}Bi^{209}$	83	209	stable	. .	infinite

* See J. M. Cork, *Radioactivity and Nuclear Physics* (D. Van Nostrand Co., Inc., Princeton, New Jersey, 1957).
† See F. Hagemann, L. I. Katzin, M. H. Studier, A. Ghiorso, and G. T. Seaborg. *Phys. Rev.*, **72,** 252 (August 1947).

ending up finally with a type of atom that is stable and not radioactive. It is now known that nearly all natural disintegration processes, occurring among the heaviest elements of the periodic table, finally end up with *stable lead atoms.*

There are at least four known radioactive series or chains of elements, one starting with uranium-238, a second with thorium-232, a third with uranium-235, and a fourth with plutonium-241. The first and fourth of these series are given in Tables 53A and 53B. All four series are given, along with man-made heavier radioactive elements, in a graphical tabulation in Appendix X.

When a uranium atom ${}_{92}U^{238}$ of mass number 238 and atomic number 92 disintegrates by ejecting an α particle, the remainder is a new atom, ${}_{90}Th^{234}$, of mass number 234 and atomic number 90. When a ${}_{90}Th^{234}$ atom disintegrates by ejecting a β particle to become ${}_{91}Pa^{234}$, the mass number remains unchanged at 234, whi'e the atomic number increases by 1 to become 91. This increase of 1 positive charge is attributed to the loss of 1 negative charge. These processes of successive disintegration continue until ${}_{82}Pb^{206}$, a *stable* lead atom, is the end result.

As explained in Secs. 42.4 and 52.8, all atoms with the same atomic number but different mass number are called isotopes of the same element. For example, ${}_{82}RaB^{214}$, ${}_{82}ThB^{212}$, ${}_{82}AcB^{211}$, ${}_{82}RaD^{210}$, ${}_{82}Pb^{209}$, ${}_{82}Pb^{208}$, ${}_{82}Pb^{207}$, and ${}_{82}Pb^{206}$ are isotopes of the same chemical element, lead (see Appendix X). Even though the first five of these are radioactive, i.e., unstable, the other three are stable. Chemically they behave exactly alike and are separated only with difficulty. The isotopes 214, 210, and 206 belong to the uranium-238 series; 212 and 208 belong to the thorium series; 211 and 207 belong to the uranium-235 series; and 209 belongs to the neptunium series.

53.4. Daughter Products

When an element disintegrates by emitting α or β rays, it produces a new chemical element. Such "offspring" atoms are referred to as the *daughter element,* an element which itself may or may not be radioactive. Consider as an example the radioactive e'ement radon, $Z = 86$. Of the several known isotopes of this element (see Appendix X), isotope 220 is a derivative of the thorium series beginning with ${}_{90}Th^{232}$.

Thoron-220 is a gas and is α-active, that is, it disintegrates by giving off α particles. The daughter product, polonium-216, is α active, and has an extremely short half-life of 0.158 s. The daughter product of this element, however, has the relatively long half-life of 10.6 h. The reactions involved here are as follows:

$$
\begin{aligned}
{}_{86}\mathrm{Rn}^{220} &\rightarrow {}_{84}\mathrm{Po}^{216} + {}_{2}\mathrm{He}^{4} \quad (T = 54.5\ \mathrm{s}) \\
{}_{84}\mathrm{Po}^{216} &\rightarrow {}_{82}\mathrm{Pb}^{212} + {}_{2}\mathrm{He}^{4} \quad (T = 0.158\ \mathrm{s}) \\
{}_{82}\mathrm{Pb}^{212} &\rightarrow {}_{83}\mathrm{Bi}^{212} + {}_{-1}e^{0} \quad (T = 10.6\ \mathrm{h})
\end{aligned}
\tag{53i}
$$

If a given quantity of ${}_{86}Rn^{220}$ gas is confined to a closed vessel, the gas nuclei that disintegrate will tend to accumulate as ${}_{84}Po^{216}$. Not much of this daughter product can accumulate, however, since with the short half-life of 0.158 s, most of the nuclei quickly disintegrate into ${}_{82}Pb^{212}$. In the period of 10 to 15 min, few of these ${}_{82}Pb^{212}$ nuclei disintegrate, and they do accumulate. A graph of this decrease of parent element ${}_{86}Rn^{220}$ and the accumulation of daughter element ${}_{84}Po^{216}$ and its daughter element ${}_{82}Pb^{212}$ is shown in Fig. 53C.

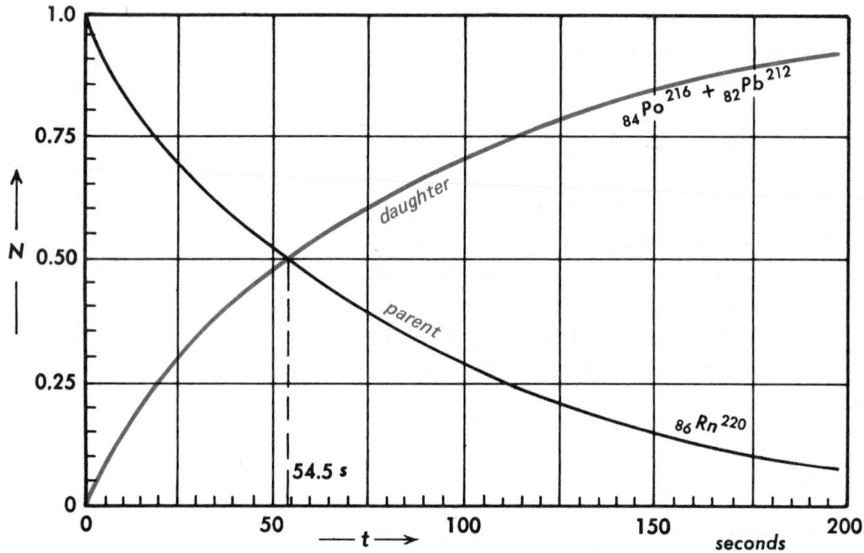

Fig. 53C. Decay curve for ${}_{86}Rn^{220}$ (radon) and the growth curve for the daughter products, ${}_{84}Po^{216} + {}_{82}Pb^{212}$.

53.5. Half-Life Experiment

A relatively simple experiment for measuring the half-life of a radioactive element is shown in Fig. 53D. Radon gas ${}_{86}Rn^{220}$ from a small glass vessel A, injected into an ionization chamber C, is detected by the ion current *I* as it flows through the electrometer E into the ground G.

Immediately upon squeezing the rubber bulb B and injecting the radon, the electroscope needle rises and falls, discharging intermittently through the stop S. The time t is recorded from a seconds clock each time a discharge occurs, and these are recorded against the discharge number n. A typical set of recorded times is plotted in Fig. 53E. The leveling-out of the graph after some time signifies that little radon gas is left, and a reasonably horizontal line is drawn at $n = 14$ as the last discharge that could be obtained. Coming down, therefore, to the point $N = 7$, where the activity was at half value, the time $t = 56$ s is read from the graph as the half-life of ${}_{86}Rn^{220}$.

The decay curve of Fig. 53E can be plotted as a semilog graph by plotting the difference between the line $N = 14$ and the curve value at each 10-s interval, and plotting these as shown in Fig. 53F. When the best possible straight line is drawn through the points, the half-value point comes at $t = 56$ s.

Mathematically, this value can be computed from the graph and Eq.(53d) as follows. At time $t = 0$ we obtain $N_0 = 14$. Choosing any other point far down on the graph, such as the one at $t = 150$ s, we find $N = 2.2$. Dividing one value by the other gives $N_0/N = 6.36$. Looking up this number in a table of logarithms we find ln 6.36 = 1.850 (see Appendix IX). Substitution of this value in Eq.(53d), along with $t = 150$ s, gives as the value for the decay constant:

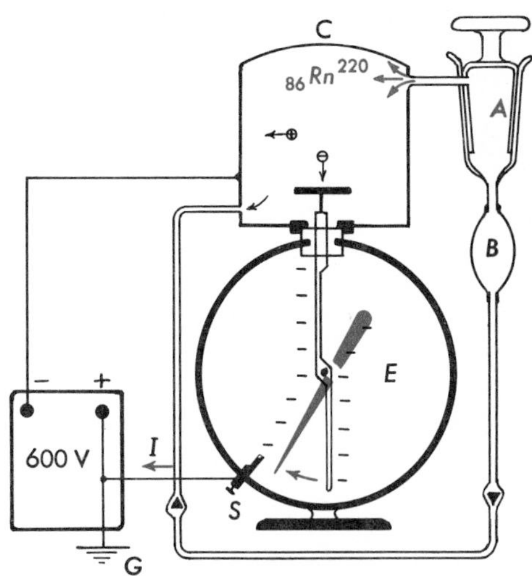

Fig. 53D. Simple apparatus for determining the half-life of a radioactive gas like radon, ${}_{86}Rn^{220}$.

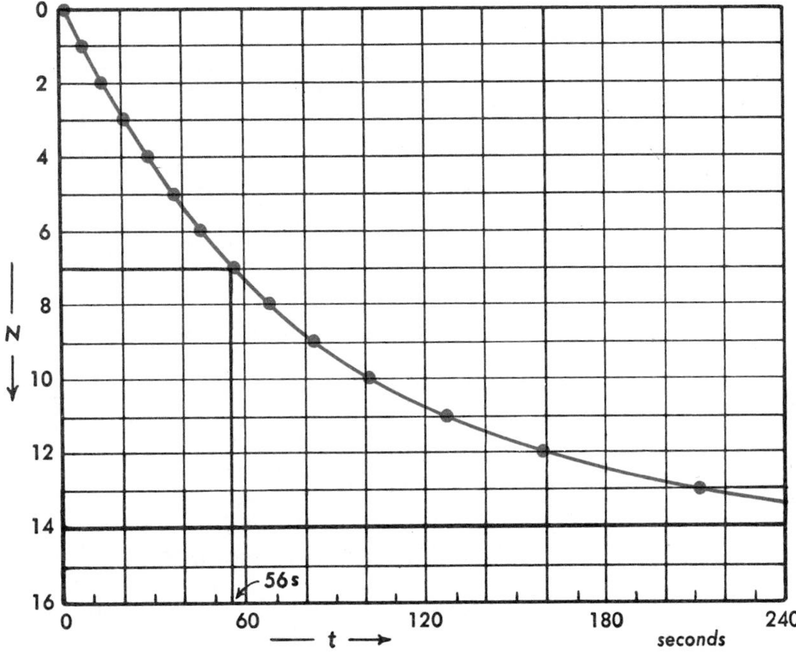

Fig. 53E. Experimental decay curve for radon (${}_{86}Rn^{220}$), obtained using the apparatus shown in Fig. 53D.

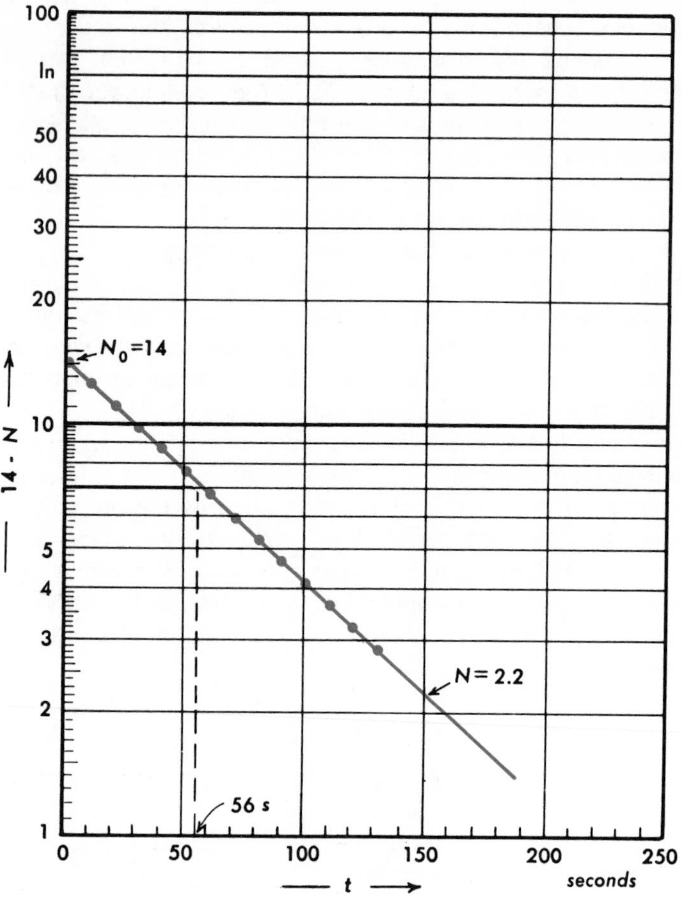

Fig. 53F. Semilog graph for finding the half-life of radon, $_{86}Rn^{220}$.

$$\lambda = \frac{1.850}{150} = 0.01233$$

When this is substituted in Eq.(53f), we obtain

$$T = \frac{0.693}{0.01233} = 56.2 \text{ s}$$

as the half-life.

53.6. Different Forms of Energy

Einstein, in working out the theory of relativity, arrived at a number of simple equations concerning the nature of the physical world. One of these equations, having to do with the increase in mass of a moving object, was presented in Sec. 48.5. It is important at this point to consider this mass–energy equation again:

$$E = mc^2 \tag{53j}$$

where m is the mass, c is the velocity of light, and E is the energy equivalent.

From this relation we can predict that mass can be turned into energy, or energy into mass. In other words, mass is a form of energy, for if a quantity of mass m could be annihilated, a definite amount of energy E would become available in some other form. To illustrate this, suppose that a 1-g mass could be completely annihilated and the liberated energy given to some other body in the form of kinetic energy:

$$E = 1 \times 10^{-3} \text{ Kg} \times 9 \times 10^{16} \text{ m}^2/\text{s}^2$$

$$E = 9 \times 10^{13} \text{ J}$$

In the English system of units this is equivalent to 7×10^{13} ft-lb or enough energy to propel the largest ship around the world.

The annihilation of mass then is a source of staggeringly immense energy. In the following chapters we will see that disintegration is one means whereby mass can be annihilated or created through planned laboratory experiments.

In the following chapters we will see that if an atom, a part of an atom, or an electron is annihilated, the energy may either be transformed into kinetic energy and given to another atomic particle in the form of a velocity, or it may appear as a γ ray of specified frequency ν and energy $h\nu$. To find the equivalence between mass energy, $\gamma =$ ray energy, and kinetic energy, all of the following quantities are equated to each other:

$$E = mc^2 = h\nu = \tfrac{1}{2}mv^2 = Ve \tag{53k}$$

It is customary among physicists to express each of these energies in terms of V in volts. Thus one speaks of a one-million volt γ ray, a three-million volt electron, or a 12.5-million volt proton, etc. This terminology is used for convenience only, and denotes the value of V in the above equation which, with the electronic charge substituted for e, gives the energy of the γ-ray photon, or the energy of the moving atomic particle. For all energies, m in the second term is the relativistic mass given by Eq.(48j), and the fourth term is the kinetic energy of any particle whose rest mass is m_0. At very high velocities the fourth term must be replaced by the relativistic kinetic energy $m_0c^2(\gamma - 1)$ [see Eq.(48q)].

When an atomic nucleus ejects an α or β particle, the mass of that nucleus diminishes not only by the rest mass of the ejected particle, but by an amount called the *annihilation energy.* A small part of the nuclear mass is annihilated and given to the ejected particle as kinetic energy. While the annihilated mass varies from isotope to isotope, it is usually less than 1% of one atomic mass unit.

As a convenient figure to use in disintegration problems, we will calculate the energy equivalent to the annihilation of unit atomic mass, namely, $1.6605311 \times 10^{-27}$ Kg. Using the second and last terms of Eq.(53k), we find

$$Ve = mc^2 \qquad (53\ell)$$

$$V = \frac{1.6605311 \times 10^{-27} \times 8.9875543 \times 10^{16}}{1.6021917 \times 10^{-19}}$$

$$V = 931.48113 \text{ V}$$

The annihilation energy of 1 amu equals 931.48113 million electron volts. Abbreviated,

$$1 \text{ amu} = 931.48113 \text{ MeV} \qquad (53m)$$

When a γ ray is ejected from a nucleus, it carries with it an energy $h\nu$. This energy may be expressed by the mass equivalence as given by the second and third terms of Eq.(53k), or by the voltage equivalence as given by the third and fifth terms. It is customary to use the latter relation and write

$$Ve = h\nu \qquad (53n)$$

Similarly for the kinetic energy of any moving mass m:

$$Ve = \tfrac{1}{2}mv^2$$

For velocities over ten percent the speed of light, this equation should be written in relativistic form:

$$Ve = m_0c^2(\gamma - 1) \tag{53o}$$

where
$$\gamma = \frac{1}{\sqrt{1 - \dfrac{v^2}{c^2}}}$$

Example 2. A γ ray has a wavelength of 4.50×10^{-13} m. Calculate its energy in million electron volts. Use four significant figures. **Solution.** The known quantities are $\lambda = 4.50 \times 10^{-13}$ m, $h = 6.626 \times 10^{-34}$ Js, $c = 2.9979 \times 10^8$ m/s, and $e = 1.6022 \times 10^{-19}$ C. To use Eq.(53n) the frequency ν is replaced by its equivalent c/λ. Solving the equation for the voltage V, we obtain

$$V = \frac{hc}{e\lambda}$$

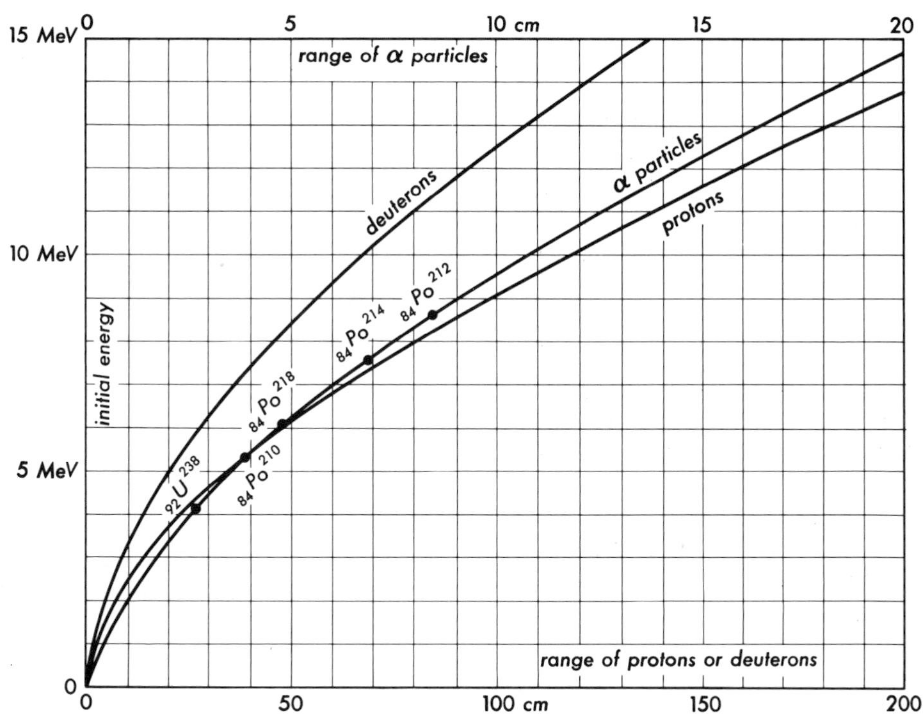

Fig. 53G. Graphs giving the range of protons, deuterons, and α particles in dry air at standard pressure for different initial energies in million electron volts.

Upon substituting known quantities, we find

$$V = \frac{6.626 \times 10^{-34} \times 2.9979 \times 10^{8}}{1.6022 \times 10^{-19} \times 4.50 \times 10^{-13}}$$

$$V = 2.7551 \times 10^{6}\ \text{V}$$

$$V = 2.7551\ \text{MeV}$$

It is common practice to express the initial energy of α particles by specifying either their range in air or their energy equivalence in MeV. This applies to other high-speed particles as well, particles such as protons and deuterons which are the nuclei of the two hydrogen isotopes. A graph like the one shown in Fig. 53G is useful for converting the observed range of an α particle to its equivalent in MeV, or vice versa.

problems

1. Write down the nuclear reaction for the emission of an α particle by americium-243. See Appendix X.

2. Write down the nuclear reaction for the emission of an α particle by fermium-254. See Appendix X.

3. Write down the nuclear reaction for the emission of an α particle by curium-246. See Appendix X.

4. Write down the nuclear reaction for the emission of a β particle by plutonium-246. See Appendix X.

5. What is meant by (a) the half-life, and (b) the mean life of a radioactive element?

6. Define, or briefly explain, each of the following: (a) range of α particles, (b) β emission, (c) spontaneous disintegration, (d) decay constant, and (e) daughter product.

7. If the activity of a radioactive element drops to $\frac{1}{64}$*th* of its initial value in 2 h and 45 min, find (a) its mean life, and (b) its half-life.

8. If the activity of a radioactive element drops to $\frac{1}{32}$*nd* of its initial value of 32.0 s, find (a) mean life, and (b) the half-life.

9. A count-rate meter, used to measure the activity of a radioactive element, shows 895 C/M, and 10.0 min later 327 C/M. Find (a) the decay constant, (b) the mean life, and (c) the half-life. [Ans. (a) 0.1007 min^{-1}, (b) 9.93 min, (c) 6.88 min.]

10. The half-life of a piece of polonium-218 is 3.05 min. Find (a) the decay constant, (b) the mean life, and (c) the time required for the activity to decrease to 1.0%.

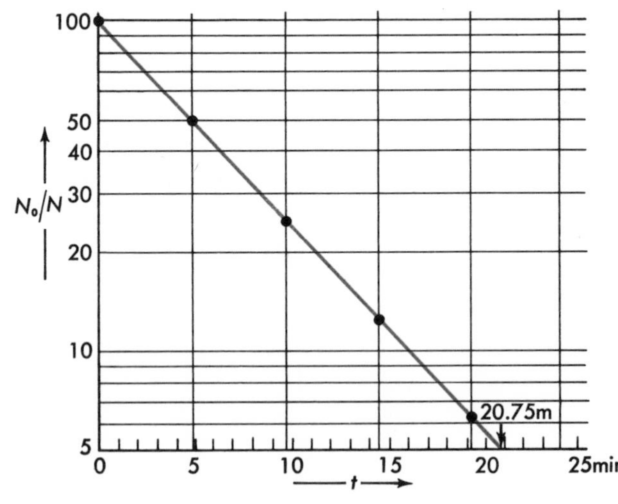

Prob. 12.

11. The half-life of a sample of actinium-225 is 10.0 days. Find (a) the decay constant, (b) the mean life, and (c) the time required for the activity to decrease to 10.0%.

12. The half-life of a radioactive sample of francium-221 is 4.80 min. Find (a) the decay constant, (b) the mean life, and (c) the time required for the activity to decrease to 5.0%. [Ans. (a) 0.1444 min^{-1}, (b) 6.93 min, (c) 20.75 min.]

13. The half-life of a radioactive sample of radon-222 is 3.820 days. Find (a) the decay constant, (b) the mean life, and (c) the time for the activity to decrease to 2.0%

14. If 100 g of iron could be completely annihilated, how many joules would be produced?

15. If 25 g of copper could be completely annihilated, how many joules would be produced? [Ans. 2.247×10^{15} J.]

16. Calculate the mass equivalent to an energy of 5.82 MeV, in (a) kilograms, and (b) atomic mass units.

17. Calculate the mass equivalent to an energy of 9.25 MeV, (a) in kilograms, and (b) in atomic mass units.

18. A gamma ray has a wavelength of 2.640×10^{-13} m. Calculate its energy in MeV. [Ans. 4.70 MeV.]

19. A γ ray has a wavelength of 1.296×10^{-13} m. Calculate its energy in MeV.

54 Beta and gamma rays

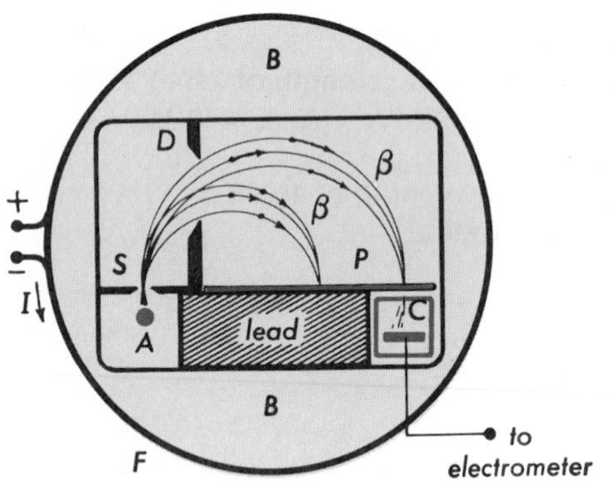

Fig. 54A. Diagram of a β-ray spectrograph.

Beta rays emitted by the natural radioactive elements have been studied by many people. It was Becquerel who first found them to be comparable to cathode rays. Today we know them as electrons. One of the greatest mysteries of atomic physics has been the origin of these particles. The great mass of experimental evidence shows that most of them come from the nucleus, yet they do not exist in the same form inside any of the known nuclei. Furthermore, unlike α particles and γ rays, they do not emerge from the nuclei with the same energy and range, but with a wide band of velocities.

54.1. Beta-Ray Spectrograph

This is an instrument by which one can experimentally determine the velocity of β particles from a radioactive source. Figure 54A is a diagram of one such instrument, developed in principle by Robinson in England. Beta particles from a small radioactive source A, consisting of a fine wire with a deposit of material on its surface, are allowed to pass through a slit S. With the entire vacuum tube located in a uniform magnetic field, the β particles follow circular paths and are brought to focus on a photographic plate P or at the open slit of an ionization chamber C. Each of the three semicircular paths in any one group shown in the diagram has the same radius and diameter. The focusing action indicated can be demonstrated by using a compass and drawing several semicircles with the same radius, but slightly displaced centers. The velocity of any group of electrons is given by Eq.(51e), as

$$Bev = \frac{mv^2}{r} \tag{54a}$$

where r is the path radius, B the magnetic induction, and e, m, and v the electron's charge, mass, and velocity, respectively.

If the field B is constant, and a photographic plate P is located as shown in the figure, its development after a time t will result in a photograph like the drawing in Fig. 54B. In addition to a darkened background all along the plate, one finds several lines parallel to the slit. The background indicates β particles present with all different velocities, while the lines signify groups with discrete and definite velocities. Not all spectrograms with such a continuous background contain these lines, however.

In some β-ray spectrographs, the β particles are collected in an ionization chamber C as shown in Fig. 54A. Different velocities are determined by slowly and continuously changing the magnetic induction B. This is accomplished by changing the current I in the field coils F. If measurements of electrometer current are recorded for different values of B, a graph similar to that shown in Fig. 54C can be plotted.

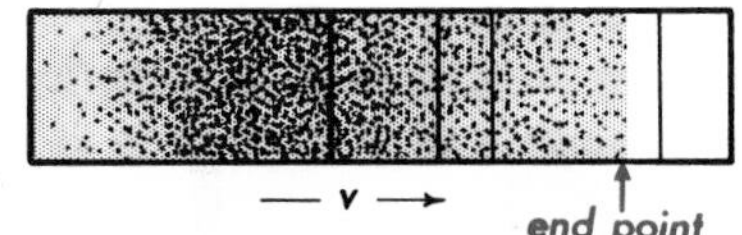

Fig. 54B. Diagram of a β-ray spectrogram.

TABLE 54A
End-point energies for β rays

Nuclide	End point E	Half-life
$_{82}Pb^{214}$	0.72 MeV	26.8 min
$_{83}Bi^{210}$	1.16 MeV	5.0 days
$_{87}Fr^{223}$	1.15 MeV	22.0 min
$_{88}Ra^{225}$	0.350 MeV	15 days
$_{89}Ac^{228}$	1.18 MeV	6.1 h
$_{90}Th^{231}$	0.28 MeV	25.6 h
$_{90}Th^{234}$	0.193 MeV	24 days

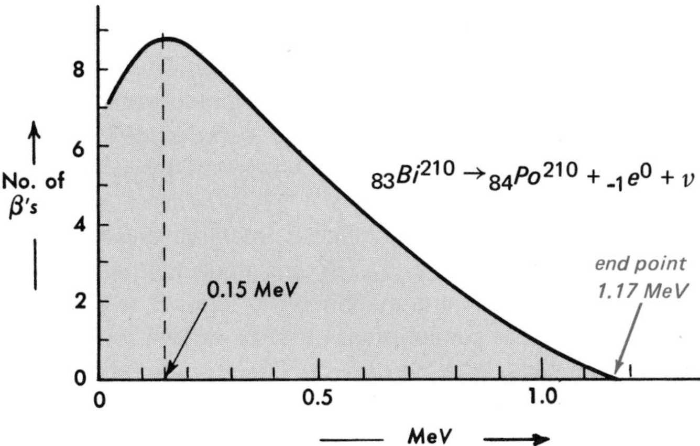

Fig. 54C. Graph of β-ray energies from $_{83}Bi^{210}$.

The measured ion current is plotted as the number of β particles, and the coil current I is plotted as the energy the particles would need to enter the slot at C. This curve, which is for the radioactive bismuth isotope $_{83}Bi^{210}$, shows β particles with a maximum number of 0.15 MeV, and an *end-point* energy of 1.17 MeV. The end point, or cut-off, at the high-energy end of this curve, signifies a velocity limit or maximum. As shown by Table 54A, such end-point energies have different values for different isotopes.

54.2. The Neutrino Postulate

In 1931 Pauli, of Germany, suggested that in β-ray emission all nuclei of the same isotope emit the same amount of energy, and that this is the *end-point energy* shown in Fig. 54C (see also Table 54A). To account for the observed fact that some β particles emerge with much less energy than others, he made the following postulate. The emission of a β particle by any nucleus is accompanied by a companion particle having a variable energy E. While the β particle is an ordinary negatively charged electron, the companion particle, now called a *neutrino,* has no charge. In some respects a neutrino is like a photon; it has no rest mass, it has energy E, and it travels with the speed of light c. Hence, the reaction for β emission by a nucleus like ${}_{83}\mathrm{Bi}^{210}$ can be written

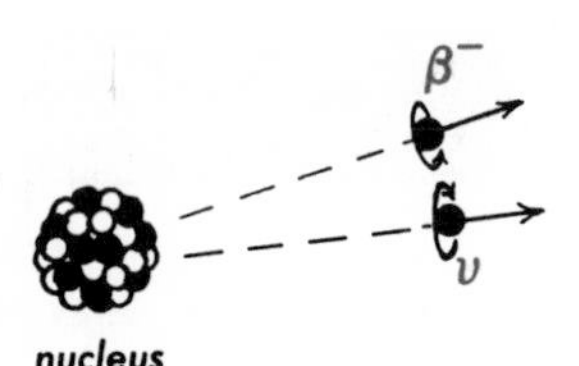

Fig. 54D. Each β particle from a nucleus is accompanied by a neutrino.

$${}_{83}\mathrm{Bi}^{210} \rightarrow {}_{84}\mathrm{Po}^{210} + {}_{-1}e^{0} + \nu \tag{54b}$$

where ${}_{-1}e^{0}$ represents the beta particle and ν represents the neutrino.

The neutrino postulate has served another important function in atomic processes; it permits the retention of conservation of angular momentum. All even-numbered nuclei, *even A,* are known to have an angular momentum given by an integral quantum number, $I = 0, 1, 2, 3, 4, \ldots$, all odd-numbered nuclei, *odd A,* are known to have an angular momentum given by a half-integral quantum number, $I = \frac{1}{2}, \frac{3}{2}, \frac{5}{2}, \frac{7}{2}, \ldots$. Furthermore, all electrons are known to have a spin angular momentum given by a half-integral quantum number, $s = \frac{1}{2}$. By assigning the neutrino a spin angular momentum equal in magnitude to that of the electron, the two spins can either cancel each other as shown in Fig. 54D, or add together, thus keeping the nuclear spin integral or half-integral valued as the case may be.

Only recently have experiments been performed that appear to establish the existence of these phantom particles, neutrinos. Since nuclei are composed of neutrons and protons, the two ejected particles are created by the nucleus, a neutron transforming into a proton as it emits an electron of mass m_0, charge $-e$, and spin $\frac{1}{2}\hbar$, and a neutrino of energy E, no charge and spin $\frac{1}{2}\hbar$ [see Eq.(45h)].

54.3. Conservation of Nuclear Energy

The simultaneous emission of a β particle and a neutrino from the nucleus of an atom requires energy. The disintegrating nucleus gives up not only the mass of the electron, but also some additional mass which it converts into kinetic energy. By adding up all this energy in the form of mass, the total loss in the mass of an atom can be calculated.

Consider as an example the β emission of $_{83}Bi^{210}$ as represented by Eq.(54b). The masses of the two atoms involved are known to be

$$
\begin{array}{rl}
{}_{83}\mathrm{Bi}^{210} & 209.984110 \text{ amu} \\
{}_{84}\mathrm{Po}^{210} & \underline{209.982866 \text{ amu}} \\
\Delta m = & 0.001244 \text{ amu}
\end{array}
$$

To convert this mass into MeV, we multiply Δm by the value 931.5 MeV given by Eq.(53m), which gives

$$E = 1.159 \text{ MeV}$$

This is just the end-point energy derived from experiment and shown in Fig. 54C. The mass of the ejected electron need not be included here, since the two masses above are for the neutral atoms. $_{83}Bi^{210}$ has 83 orbital electrons included in its mass of 209.984110 amu, while $_{84}Po^{210}$ includes 84 electrons. When $_{83}Bi^{210}$ ejects an electron from the nucleus, the daughter product $_{84}Po^{210}$ picks up a stray electron to become a neutral atom.

54.4. Gamma Rays

For many radioactive elements the emission of an α or β particle from a nucleus is immediately followed by the emission of a γ ray. It has been shown by crystal diffraction spectrographs that γ rays are electromagnetic waves and that they consist of sharp lines of discrete wavelengths. Just as visible light, ultraviolet and infrared radiation, and X rays are known to be emitted from the outer structure of the atom by an electron's jumping from one energy level to another, so γ rays are believed to arise from a transition of a nucleon from one energy state to another within the nucleus. (Neutrons and protons as constituents of nuclei are called *nucleons.*)

There is good evidence that γ rays are emitted by the daughter element, that is, that they are preceded by particle emission. A good example is to be found in the case of $_{82}Pb^{210}$. This nucleus is the lead isotope with a beta half-life of 22 years. The reaction is written

$$_{82}\mathrm{Pb}^{210} \rightarrow {}_{83}\mathrm{Bi}^{210} + {}_{-1}e^{0} + \nu + \gamma \text{ ray} \tag{54c}$$

These emissions are represented on a nuclear energy-level

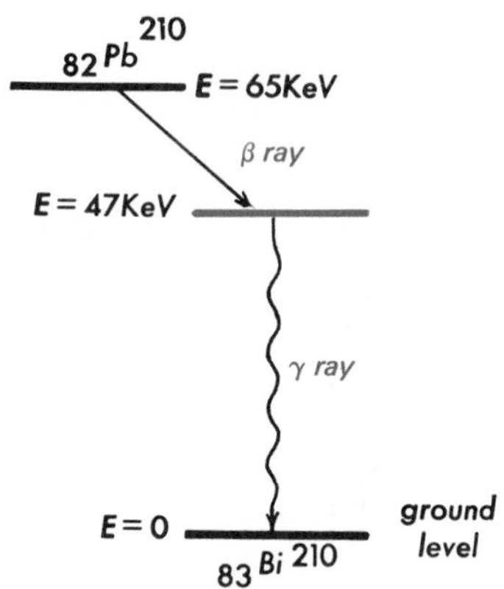

Fig. 54E. Energy-level diagram illustrating β-ray emission followed by γ-ray emission.

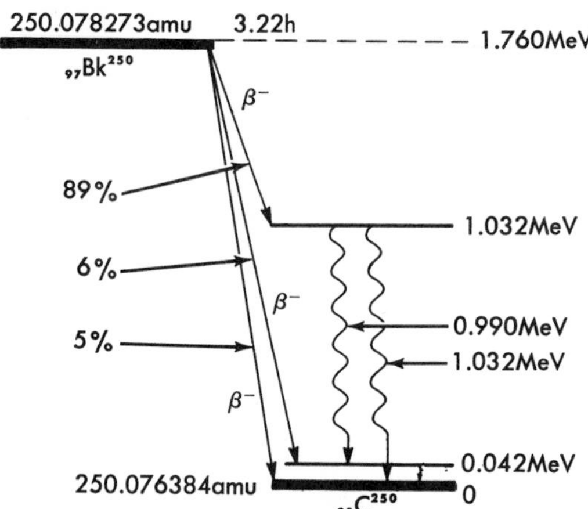

Fig. 54F. Energy level diagram for the β^- decay of berkelium-250. Part (b) of Example 1.

diagram in Fig. 54E. When a $_{82}\text{Pb}^{210}$ nucleus emits a β particle and a neutrino, the end-point energy is found to be 18,000 electron volts (18 KeV). This leaves a $_{83}\text{Bi}^{210}$ nucleus in what is called an *excited state* or energy level. A transition down to the ground level is accompanied by the emission of a γ ray with an energy $h\nu$. This energy is equivalent to 47 KeV. Although it is not shown in this diagram, this nucleus, too, is radioactive and emits another β ray to become $_{84}\text{Po}^{210}$ [see Eq.(54b)].

Example 1. Eighty-nine percent of the radioactive isotope berkelium-250 decays by β^- emission with an end-point energy of 0.728 MeV, followed by three γ rays carrying them to the ground state of the daughter product. Six percent decays by β^- emission with an end-point energy of 1.718 MeV, followed by a γ ray with an energy of 0.042 MeV, and five percent decays by β^- emission with an end-point energy of 1.760 MeV, ending on the ground state without the emission of γ rays. (a) Write down the first reaction, and (b) make an energy level diagram.

Solution. The reaction is

$$_{97}\text{Bk}^{250} \rightarrow {}_{98}\text{Cf}^{250} + {}_{-1}e^0 + \nu + \gamma \text{ rays}$$

The diagram is shown in Fig. 54F.

54.5. Internal Conversion

In certain radioactive atoms the emission of a γ ray frequently gives way to the expulsion of an electron from the $n = 1, 2, 3, 4$, etc., outer shells of the neutral atom. Energetically this process follows the photoelectric equation, Eq.(43a):

$$h\nu = W + \tfrac{1}{2}mv^2 \tag{54d}$$

Part of the energy that would otherwise have gone into the emission of a γ ray is used to get the electron away from its bound orbit and out of the atom. The remainder is imparted to it as kinetic energy. As a rule this kinetic energy is relatively large and $\frac{1}{2}mv^2$ must be replaced by the relativistic term $m_0c^2(\gamma - 1)$ [see Eq.(48q)].

The process is *not* to be visualized as the emission of a γ ray, followed by the photoelectric effect, but as an energy conversion inside or close to the nucleus. The process is shown schematically in Fig. 54G, where only one of the many orbital electrons is shown according to the wave-mechanics picture treated in Sec. 51.7 (see Fig. 51N).

The probability density distribution D_r shows part of the innermost loop of the curve overlapping the nucleus. The greater the amount of this overlap, and the greater the change in nuclear spin involved in a nuclear transition, the greater is the probability for internal conversion. Overlapping increases with increasing atomic number.

The ratio of *internal conversion* events to *γ-ray emission* differs from 0 to 100% between nuclides. For some the ratio is very high favoring internal conversion, while for others it is very low and γ-ray emission is the more probable.

Since the energy required to remove an electron from an atom will differ from one shell to another, the ejected electrons can be expected to have any one of several discrete energies. The definite sharp lines shown in Fig. 54B supply the evidence for this assumption.

If by internal conversion an electron is ejected from the innermost K shell, leaving a vacancy there, another electron from the L shell or M shell falls in to take its place and, in so doing, emits an X ray. Confirmation of such a process is assured since the measured wavelengths of such X rays are identical with those emitted by the same element in an X-ray tube (see Fig. 51A).

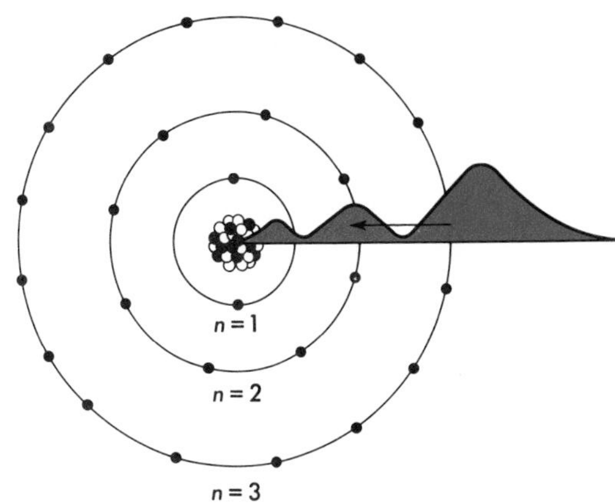

Fig. 54G. Schematic diagram of an atom showing only one of its outer electrons in terms of its probability density, and used in explaining internal conversion.

54.6. Scintillation Counters

A scintillation counter is a sensitive device used in nuclear physics studies for the detection and measurement of high-energy atomic radiation. In principle it is based upon the earliest discoveries in radioactivity that α particles upon striking a fluorescent material, like zinc sulfide, produce a tiny flash of light (see Fig. 52K). These flashes, called *scintillations,* can be seen by the dark-adapted eye, or they can be detected by a photomultiplier tube and amplified.

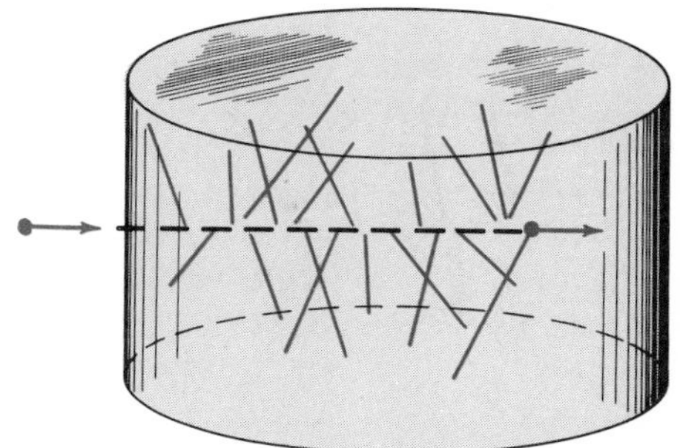

Fig. 54H. Diagram of the fluorescent light developed by an atomic particle traversing a transparent crystal or plastic fluor.

It is now well known that when high-energy-charged atomic particles pass through certain transparent materials, fluorescent light is produced all along the path (see Fig. 54H). As the fast-moving particle collides with atoms and molecules, electrons are raised to excited energy levels and in returning to their ground states emit light. For many crystals and plastics this *fluorescent light* is blue or violet in color, while for others it is ultraviolet or infrared.

A typical scintillation counter tube is shown in Fig. 54I. A block of fluorescent material is mounted on the flat end of a special photomultiplier tube and then encased in a thin-walled, light-tight

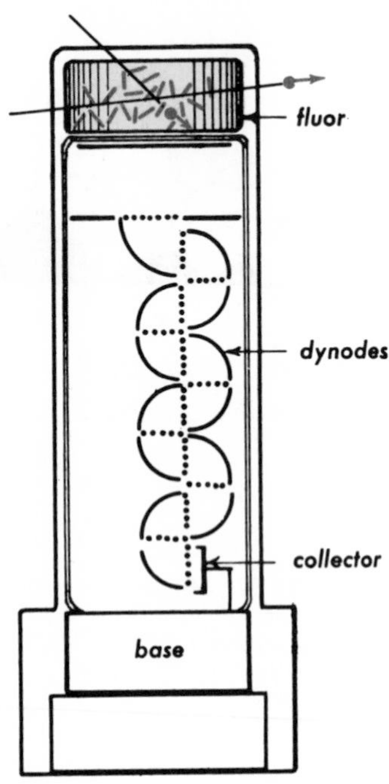

Fig. 54I. Scintillation detector tube using a photomultiplier tube with a fluorescent block.

aluminum shield. When a particle traverses the fluor, the light ejects electrons from the photocathode by the photoelectric effect. The charge multiplication built up by the eight or more dynodes makes a sizeable voltage pulse that activates some electronic counting device (see Fig. 54J).

When γ rays are to be detected, the fluorescent materials frequently used are crystals of sodium iodide, NaI, and cesium iodide, CsI. For high-energy β rays, such plastics as polystyrene, impregnated with anthracene, are used. These are inexpensive and very effective and can be quite large in size. For α particles with their relatively low penetrating power, a thin layer of zinc sulfide deposited on the photomultiplier tube or a plastic surface is commonly used.

The principal advantages of scintillation counters over other detectors of nuclear radiation are these: (1) They operate in air or in a vacuum; (2) they deliver an electrical impulse which is proportional to the energy lost by the traversing particle; and (3) they can count at amazingly high speeds.

While the duration of a single pulse from a NaI crystal counter will last about one microsecond, the pulse time from an anthracene counter can be as short as one thousandth of a microsecond (10^{-9} s).

54.7. Cerenkov Radiation

In 1934 Cerenkov, in Russia, discovered that fast-moving electrons, such as β particles from radioactive materials, will produce light within a transparent medium if their velocity is greater than the speed of light in that medium. In a medium like glass or plastic, the speed of light is about $\frac{2}{3}$ to $\frac{3}{4}$ the speed of light in a vacuum, yet many β particles are ejected at speeds greater than this, and some of them are close to $c = 3 \times 10^8$ m/s.

The phenomenon of Cerenkov radiation is analogous to (a) the production of the V-shaped wave from a ship when the ship travels through water at a speed greater than the wave velocity or (b) the shock waves from a missile traveling through the air at a speed greater than sound.

In Fig. 54K a particle is shown generating a conical wave as it travels with a velocity V through a medium of refractive index μ. While the conical wave front makes an angle with the particle's direction, the light travels outward at right angles to the wave front.

The principle of Cerenkov radiation is frequently used to detect high-energy atomic particles. A Cerenkov counter has the same general construction as shown in Fig. 54I, except that the fluor is replaced by a transparent medium, liquid or solid, and with a refractive index specified for the particular particle speeds to be detected.

54.8. Semiconductor Detectors

Recent experiments show that semiconducting materials like those used in transistors are useful detectors of α rays and other heavy atomic particles. One type of semiconductor detector used is shown in Fig. 54L. A thin layer of gold metal is deposited on the two surfaces of a thin wafer of very pure silicon and the two conducting surfaces are connected to a 1- to 20-V battery and amplifier. When a charged particle enters the crystal, free electrons and holes develop, increasing the number of free electric charges. The sudden current pulse thereby created is amplified and then measured or counted.

54.9. Radiation Absorption

As high-energy-charged particles travel through matter in the solid, liquid, or gaseous state, their energy is gradually dissipated in a number of different ways, principally by the excitation and ionization of atoms and molecules. Gamma rays, on the other hand, have a far greater range because they have no electric charge. Unless their energy is over 1 MeV, their absorption is due to the photoelectric effect or the Compton effect. In either case, ions are formed in the process, and, in relation to those produced by charged particles, are far apart.

A diagram representing the absorption of γ rays is presented in Fig. 54M. If I_0 represents the intensity of the beam as it enters the medium, there will be some depth d_1 at which the intensity will have dropped to $\frac{1}{2}I_0$. Imagine now that we divide the medium into layers, each of thickness d_1. The beam intensity $\frac{1}{2}I_0$ entering the second layer will be reduced to $\frac{1}{2}$ of this initial value and emerge to enter the third layer with an intensity $\frac{1}{4}I_0$. Upon traversing the third layer, the entering beam $\frac{1}{4}I_0$ will be reduced to half value, or to $\frac{1}{8}I_0$, etc.

If we now plot a graph of the beam intensity I against the number of absorbing layers, or the depth x, we obtain the curve shown in Fig. 54N. While the absorption curves for different γ-ray energies, and different absorbers, are not identical, they are alike in that they follow the same law. Just as in the case of the half-lives of radioactive isotopes (see Fig. 53B), if we plot the absorption on a semilog graph, we obtain a straight line. From this straight line we can write

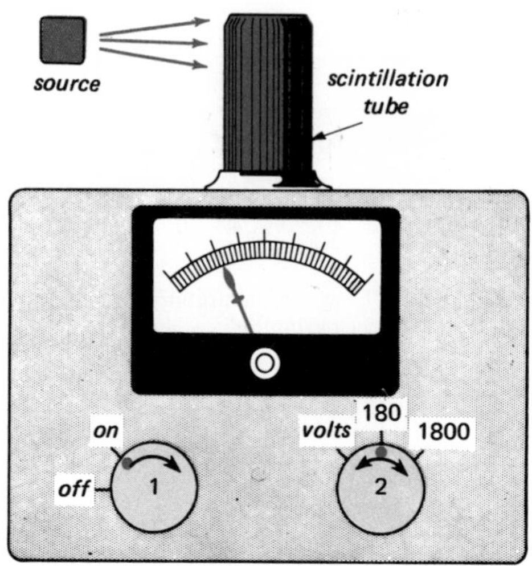

Fig. 54J. One type of scintillation counter with a counter-rate meter, two ranges, and an on–off switch.

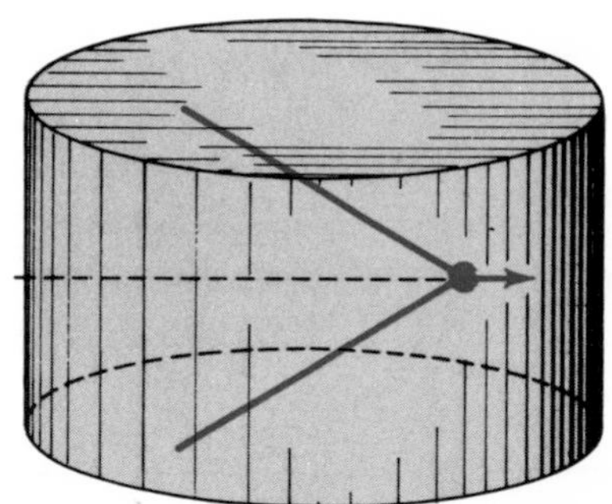

Fig. 54K. The conical wave from a high-speed atomic particle in a transparent medium: Cerenkov radiation.

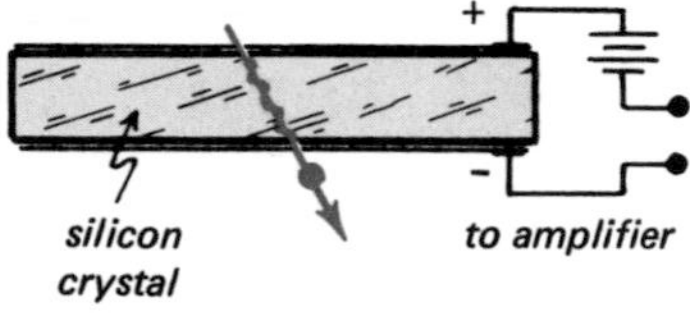

Fig. 54L. Semiconductor detector using silicon.

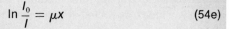

$$\ln \frac{I_0}{I} = \mu x \qquad (54e)$$

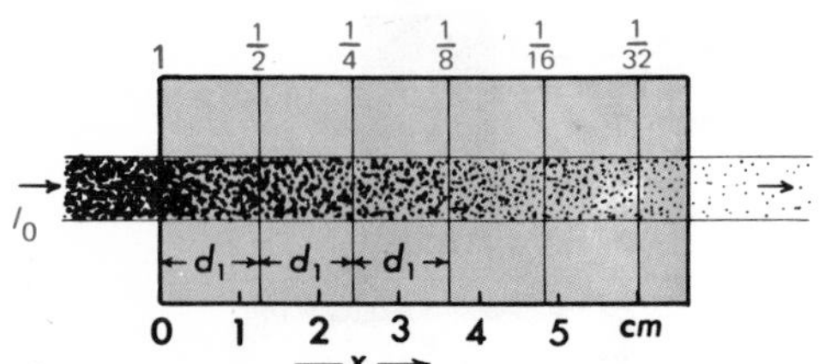

Fig. 54M. Diagram illustrating the absorption of γ rays by matter.

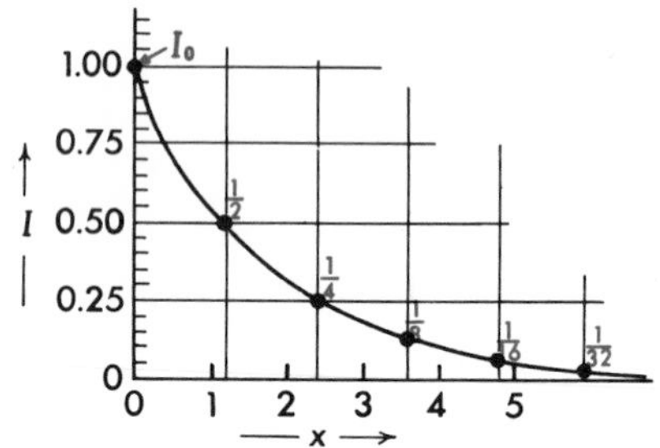

Fig. 54N. Absorption curve for γ rays.

TABLE 54B
Absorption coefficients for two wavelengths of five common metals

Atomic number	Element	$\mu(m^{-1})$ $\lambda = 0.064$ Å	$\lambda = 0.098$ Å
13	Aluminum	35	42
29	Copper	176	289
47	Silver	208	1100
74	Tungsten	256	5380
92	Uranium	337	7290

The proportionality constant μ is often called the *absorption coefficient* and represents the fraction of the beam absorbed from the beam per centimeter path. The calculation of μ can be made from the experimental data by selecting any two values of I from the straight-line section of such a semilog graph.

If a beam of β and γ rays, emitted by a radioactive source, is allowed to enter an absorbing medium, the β rays are absorbed within a much shorter distance than are the γ rays. A schematic diagram of the relative absorptions is shown in Fig. 54O.

Suppose we perform an experiment, using a small sample of radium as a radiation source, a scintillation counter as a detector, and aluminum or lead sheets as absorbers (see Fig. 54P). Radiation from a radium source S, in passing through absorbers at A, enters the fluor block C, and the signal developed is amplified by the photomultiplier tube PM.

The number of counts per minute (C/M), detected by the scintillation counter, is shown here being recorded with an electronic amplifier called a *scaler.*

The five circles represent the end view of electronic tubes, each having ten small pins. Only one pin at a time in each tube will glow orange-red in color, the light arising from a neon gas discharge around it. Each pulse from the scintillator will cause the glow to jump to the next pin clockwise in tube "1." When the tenth pulse arrives and the glow jumps from pin 9 to 0, the glow in the next tube "10" will jump from pin 0 to pin 1. The next time around for tube "1," the glow in tube "10" will jump to 2, thus indicating a total count of 20. This process continues, thus activating the third tube for hundreds, the fourth for thousands, etc. The reading showing in the diagram is 12,631.

By depressing the *RESET* switch, all five tubes return to their zero positions. To determine the number of counts per minute from any setting, the *COUNT* switch is raised at the same time the button on a stop-watch is pressed. At the end of one minute, by the watch, the *COUNT* switch is depressed, stopping the counting process. The total counts are then read directly from the tubes.

Such scalers as these are usually equipped with a dual-purpose milliammeter as shown at the right. When the accompanying switch is thrown to the V position, the knob N can be turned to adjust and set the total voltage applied to the photomultiplier tube. When it is thrown to the C/M position, the meter pointer will read directly the counts per minute. As one observes this meter for a fixed set of counting conditions, the pointer will fluctuate about some median position, and the observer must estimate the average value. It is for this reason that, for accuracy, the tube readings are preferred.

With no absorbers in place, and the source far removed from the scintillation counter, stray radiation from nearby objects and cosmic rays can and should always be measured and recorded as "background C/M." After the source is inserted in the holder, absorbers are inserted one at a time between the source and the counter, and the C/M determined for each. The results of this experiment, using first a series of lead absorbers and then a series of aluminum absorbers, are shown on a semilog graph in Fig. 54Q.

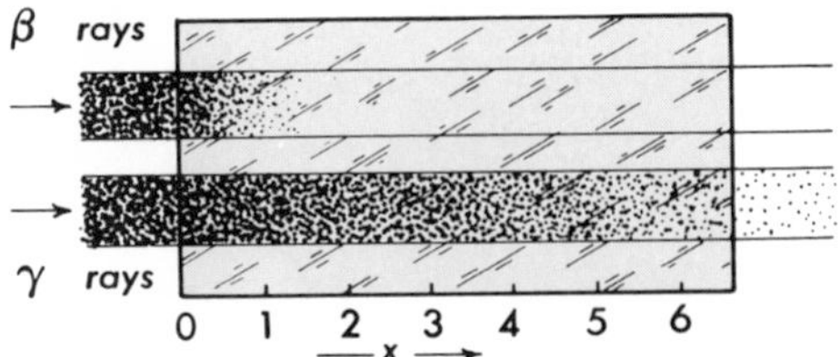

Fig. 54O. Schematic diagram showing the relative absorption of β and γ rays.

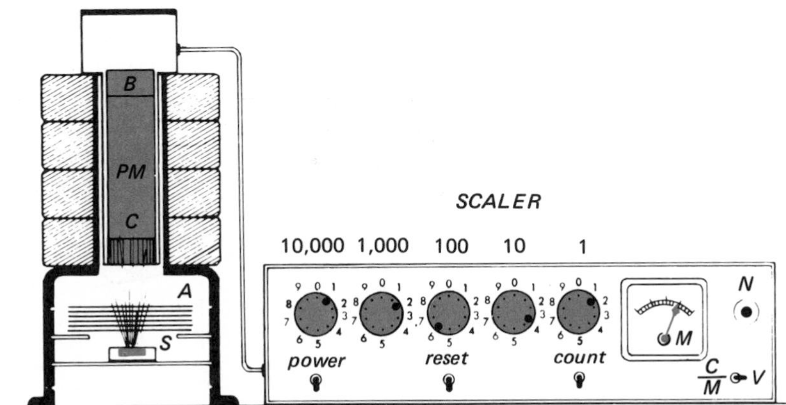

Fig. 54P. Scintillation tube with scaler counter for radiation absorption measurements.

Since β rays from a radioactive source have a range of velocities, the upper part of each graph is curved. At the point where each curve straightens out, the β rays are completely absorbed and only the more penetrating γ rays are left. The straight section signifies that γ-ray absorption follows Eq.(54e), and that absorption coefficients can be determined for both lead and aluminum.

Example 2. A beam of γ rays with a wavelength of 0.0980 Å is measured with a count-rate meter and found to have an intensity of 12,600 counts per minute. If a silver absorber 1.250 mm thick is placed in the beam, reducing the intensity to 3,186 C/M, what is the value of the absorption coefficient of silver?

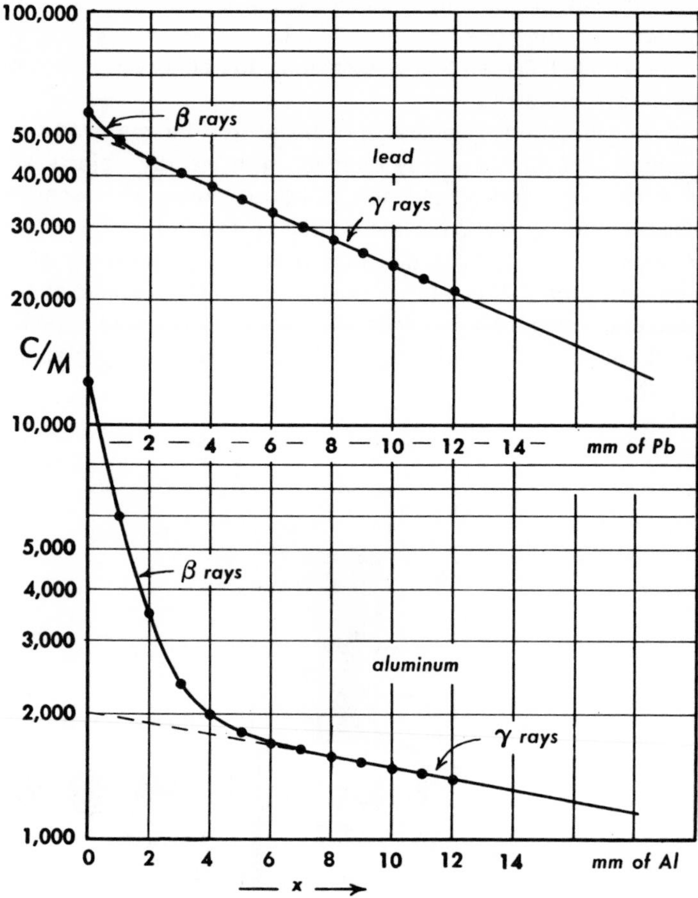

Fig. 54Q. Semilog graphs of β-ray and γ-ray absorption by lead (Pb) and aluminum (Al).

Solution. The given quantities are $x = 1.250 \times 10^{-3}$ m, $I_0 = 12{,}600$ C/M, and $\lambda = 9.80 \times 10^{-12}$ m. Since we will use Eq.(54e) we first find the ratio I_0/I, as follows:

$$\frac{I_0}{I} = \frac{12{,}600}{3{,}186} = 3.955$$

Looking up the logarithm of 3.955 in Appendix IX, we find

$$\log_{10} 3.955 = 0.5971$$

Multiplying by the factor given at the top of Appendix IX, we obtain

$$\ln 3.955 = 0.5971 \times 2.3026 = 1.3750$$

By Eq.(54e) we now equate this value to μx, and obtain

$$\mu = \frac{1.3750}{x} = \frac{1.3750}{1.250 \times 10^{-3}\text{ m}}$$

$$\mu = 1100\text{ m}^{-1}$$

Check this result with Table 54 B.

---

problems

1. All radioactive nuclei of the isotope thallium-206 emit β particles with an end-point energy of 1.524 MeV. (a) If the mass of these atoms is 206.041576 amu, find the mass of the stable atoms into which they decay. (b) Write down the nuclear reaction, and (c) make an energy level diagram.

2. One hundred percent of the radioactive nuclei of the isotope lead-209 emits β^- particles with an end-point energy of 0.640 MeV. If the accurately known mass of this nuclide is 209.047543 amu, (a) find the mass of the daughter product. (b) Write down the reaction. (c) Make an energy level diagram.

3. Atoms of the radioactive nuclide thorium-234 have a mass of 234.043570 amu. Eighty-one percent decays by β^- emission with an end-point energy of 0.1932 MeV, while 12% decays by β^- emission with an end-point energy of 0.1001 MeV, and 7.0% by β^- emission with an end-point energy of 0.0997 MeV. The last two modes of decay are followed by one γ ray each. All modes of decay end with the same daughter product. (a) Make an energy level diagram. Find (b) the energies of the γ rays emitted, and (c) the mass of the daughter product. [Ans. (a) See diagram, (b) 0.0931 MeV and 0.0935 MeV, (c) 234.043363 amu.]

4. Nineteen percent of the radioactive nuclei of bismuth-214 decays by β^- emission with an end-point energy of 3.280 MeV. (a) Write down the reaction. (b) If the mass of the daughter product is 213.995192 amu, find the mass of the bismuth-214 nuclide. (c) Make an energy level diagram.

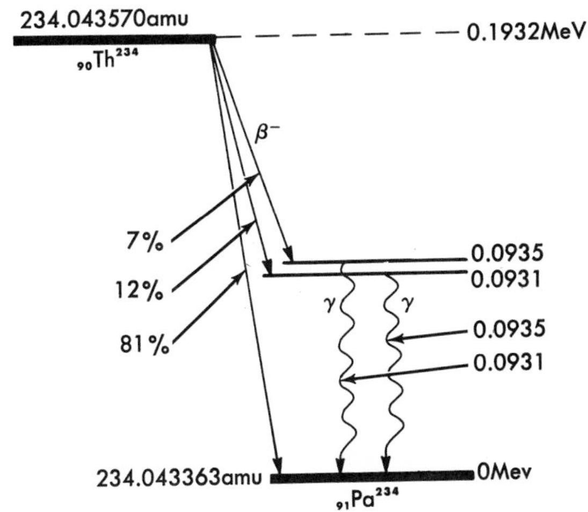

Prob. 3.

5. Nineteen percent of the radioactive atoms of bismuth-214 decays by β^- emission with an end-point energy of 3.280 MeV. Another nineteen percent decays by β^- emission with an end-point energy of 1.551 MeV, followed by a γ ray. (a) Write down the two reactions. (b) If the mass of bismuth-214 is 213.998713 amu, find the mass of the daughter product. (c) Make an energy level diagram.

6. Calculate the absorption coefficient for γ rays in lead, as given by the experimental graph in Fig. 54Q. [Ans. 366.5 m^{-1}.]

7. Find the absorption coefficient for γ rays in aluminum, as given by the experimental curve in Fig. 54P.

8. Gamma rays from a radioactive source are measured with a count-rate meter. The initial reading is 16,000 C/M. When a 2.50 mm sheet of copper is placed in front of the counter the meter shows a reading of 3,100 C/M. Find the absorption coefficient.

9.* Protoactinium-233 atoms decay to the ground state of uranium-233 by several routes: 5% by β^- emission with an end-point energy of 0.571 MeV directly; 27% by β^- with an end-point energy of 0.259 MeV, followed by a 0.312 MeV γ ray; 26% by β^- emission with an end-point energy of 0.231 MeV, followed by a 0.340 MeV γ ray; 26% by β^- emission with an end-point energy of 0.155 MeV, and a 0.416 MeV γ ray; and 13% by β^- emission with an end-point energy of 0.172 MeV, and a 0.399 MeV γ ray. Draw an energy level diagram, and show all these transitions and energies. Label all energy levels. [Ans. See diagram.]

10.* A beam of γ rays with a wavelength of 6.40×10^{-12} m is measured with a count-rate meter, and found to be 25,500 C/M. If a sheet of tungsten 1.0 mm thick is placed in the beam, find the intensity in C/M.

11.* A beam of γ rays of wavelength 6.4×10^{-12} m is measured with a count-rate meter, and found to have an intensity of 62,500 C/M. If a sheet of silver 1.50 mm thick is put in front of the counter, find the C/M. See Table 54B.

12.* A radioactive sample of protoactinium-232 is found to decay in four different ways. Twenty-seven percent emits a β^- with an end-point energy of 0.289 MeV, followed by a 0.894 MeV γ ray. Seventy-one percent emits a β^- with an end-point energy of 0.323 MeV, followed by a 0.949 MeV γ ray. Eight-tenths of one percent emits a β^- with an end-point energy of 1.183 MeV, followed by a 0.1566 MeV γ ray. Seven-tenths of one percent emits a β^- with an end-point energy of 1.292 MeV, followed by a 0.0476 MeV γ ray. (a) Make an energy level diagram. (b) If the accurate mass of protoactinium-232 is 232.038612 amu, find the mass of the daughter product. (c) Write down the reaction that satisfies all four modes. [Ans. (a) See diagram, (b) 232.037168 amu, (c) ${}_{91}Pa^{232} \rightarrow {}_{92}U^{232} + {}_{-1}e^0 + \nu + \gamma$ rays.]

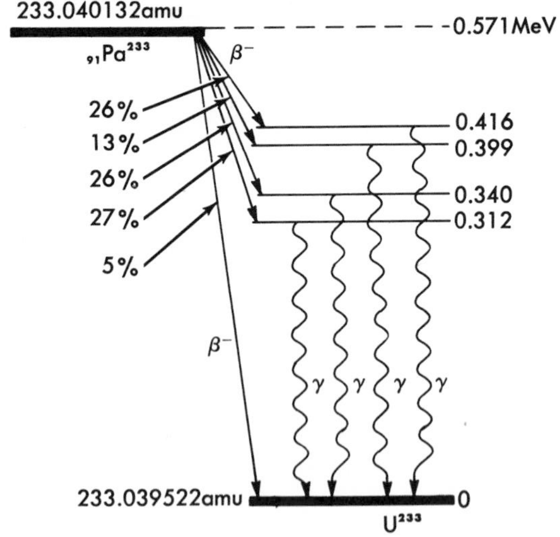

Prob. 9.

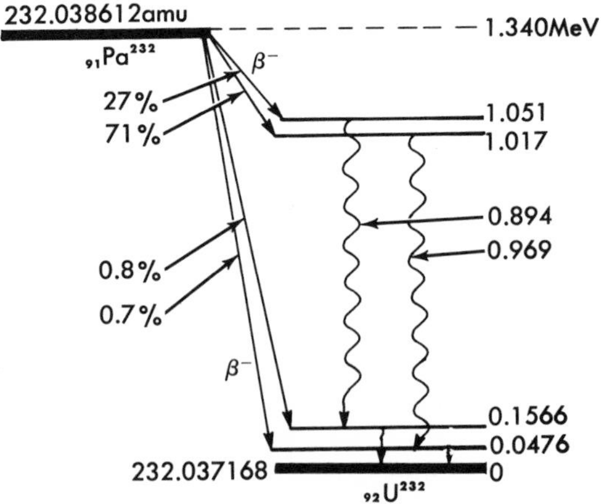

Prob. 12.

55 Atomic collisions and nuclear disintegration

For centuries past it has been the dream of the alchemists to discover a process for changing base metals into gold. At long last this transmutation of one element into another has been accomplished by the physicists, but not on the kind of paying basis dreamed of by so many.

The continual search of the scientists for some knowledge of the ultimate particles into which all matter may be subdivided has led within the last 60 years to the discovery of still smaller particles than molecules and atoms: protons, neutrons, mesons, neutrinos, etc. These discoveries are only the first step toward solving the age-old mystery of why all solids, large or small, do not fall apart.

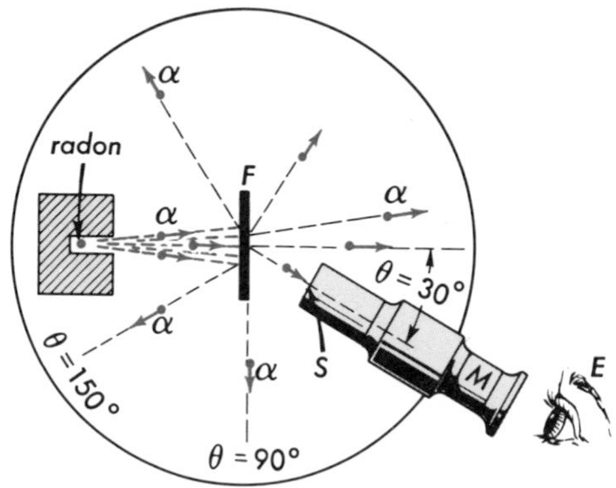

Fig. 55A. Diagram of the Rutherford scattering experiments.

55.1. Rutherford's Scattering Experiments

As early as 1903 P. Lenard sent cathode rays through thin films of metal and measured their penetration and absorption in matter. He concluded from his experiments that the mass associated with solid matter is not distributed uniformly throughout the body, but is concentrated upon myriads of tiny isolated centers which he called *dynamics*. It was for these experiments that he was awarded the Nobel Prize in physics in 1905.

During the following decade Sir Ernest Rutherford, and his collaborators H. Geiger and E. Marsden, performed a series of ingenious experiments on the scattering of α particles, the results of which implied that the positive charge and mass of every atom are confined to a particle smaller than 10^{-12} cm in diameter. Historically this marks the beginning of the idea of a nuclear atom proposed formally by Niels Bohr several years later. A schematic diagram of the scattering experiments is given in Fig. 55A.

High-speed α particles from the radioactive element radon, confined to a narrow beam by a hole in a lead block, were made to strike a very thin gold foil F. While most of the α particles go straight through the foil as if there were nothing there, some of them collide with atoms of the foil and bounce off at some angle. The latter phenomenon is known as *Rutherford scattering.*

The observations and measurements made in the experiment consisted of counting the number of particles scattered off at different angles θ. This was done by the scintillation method of observation. Each α particle striking the fluorescent screen S produces a tiny flash of light, called a *scintillation,* and is observed as such by the microscope M. With the microscope fixed in one position the number of scintillations observed within a period of several minutes was counted; then the microscope was turned to another angle, and the number was again counted for an equal period of time.

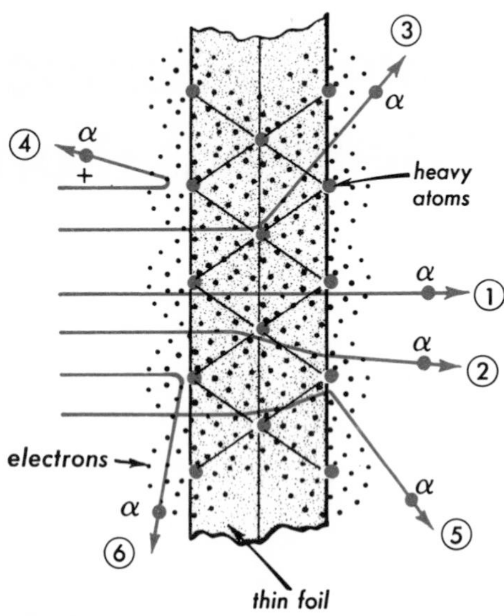

Fig. 55B. Schematic diagram of α particles being scattered by the atomic nuclei in a thin metallic film.

In the schematic diagram of Fig. 55B, α particles are shown passing through a foil three atomic layers thick. Although the nuclear atom was not known at the time the experiments were performed, each atom is drawn in the figure with the positively charged nucleus at the center and surrounded by a number of electrons. Since most of the film is *free space,* the majority of the α particles go through with little or no deflection as indicated by ray (1). Other α's like (2) passing relatively close to an atom nucleus are deflected at an angle of a few degrees. Occasionally, however, an almost *head-on collision* occurs as shown by (4) and the incoming α particle is turned back toward the source.

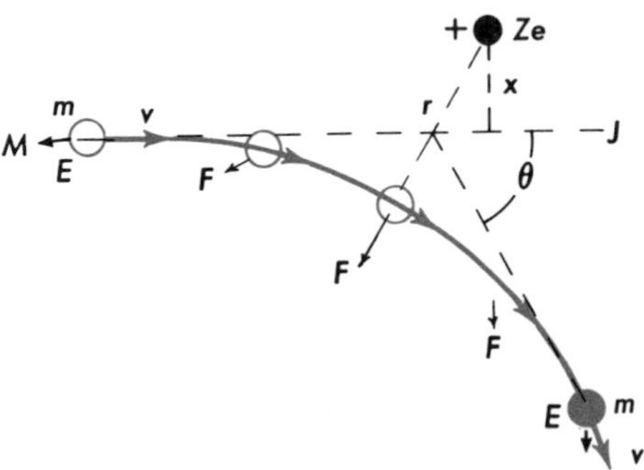

Fig. 55C. Diagram of the deflection of an α particle by a nucleus: Rutherford scattering.

As an α particle approaches an atom, as represented by ray (6) in Fig. 55B, it is repelled by the heavy positively charged nucleus and deflected in such a way as to make it follow a curved path. The magnitude of the repulsive force is at all times given by Coulomb's law [see Eq.(21a)]:

$$F = k\frac{QQ'}{r^2} \tag{55a}$$

Whatever the force of repulsion may be at one distance r, it becomes 4 times as great at $\frac{1}{2}$ the distance, 9 times as great at $\frac{1}{3}$ the distance, 16 times as great at $\frac{1}{4}$ the distance, etc. We see, therefore, that at very close range the mutual repulsion of the two particles increases very rapidly and finally becomes so great that the lighter α particle is turned away. The repelling force, still acting, gives the particle a push, causing it to recede with the same velocity as that with which it approached. The actual trajectory is in every case a hyperbolic orbit with the nucleus at the focus (see Fig. 55C).

55.2. The Rutherford Scattering Experiments

To see how the principles of mechanics and Coulomb's law, Eq.(55a), are applied to the deflection of α particles passing by an atomic nucleus, we refer to Fig. 55C. The α particle of mass m, charge $2e$, moving with a velocity r along the line MJ would, in the absence of Coulomb's law, pass within a distance x of a relatively heavy nucleus of charge Ze. Owing to the mutual repulsion of the two positive charges, the force F, expressed by

$$F = k\,\frac{Ze \cdot 2e}{r^2} \tag{55b}$$

and acting on the α particle at all points, gives rise to a hyperbolic trajectory as shown.

Approaching along one asymptote, and receding along the other, the α particle is deflected through a total angle θ.

By applying these principles to find the numbers of particles scattered at different angles Rutherford obtained the following formula:

$$N = N_0\,\frac{nt(Ze)^2(2e)^2}{2^4r^2(\frac{1}{2}mv^2)^2 \sin^4 \frac{1}{2}\theta} \tag{55c}$$

where
N = number of α's striking the screen
N_0 = number of α's striking the foil
n = number of atoms per unit volume
t = foil thickness
Z = atomic number
e = charge on electron
$\frac{1}{2}mv^2$ = kinetic energy of α particle
θ = angle scattered

While this formula looks quite complicated, it can be separated into parts as follows:

1. Foil thickness	$N = k_1t$	
2. Kinetic energy	$N = k_2/(\frac{1}{2}mv^2)^2$	(55d)
3. Scattering angle	$N = k_3/\sin^4 \frac{1}{2}\theta$	
4. Nuclear charge	$N = k_4(Ze)^2$	

Repeated experiments with different films made of light and heavy elements, like copper, silver, and gold, showed that the relative number of the wide-angle deflections increases with atomic number. From all of these results and numerous calculations, Rutherford came to the following conclusions.

1. *An increase in film thickness t increases proportionately the number of target nuclei to be hit, and hence the number of particles scattered out.*
2. *The higher the energy of the incident particle, the smaller will be the number deflected through a given angle.*
3. *A single impact can deflect a particle through a large angle and by head-on collision reverse its direction.*
4. *Increased deflections resulting from foils of increasing atomic number Z are the result of stronger Coulomb forces arising from increased nuclear charge Ze.*
5. *Deflections resulting from nuclear collisions are perfectly elastic and obey the laws of conservation of mechanical energy and momentum.*
6. *All of the positive charge of an atom is confined to a particle smaller than 10^{-12} cm in diameter.*
7. *Practically all of the weight of an atom is confined to this same particle.*
8. *The amount of positive charge in atomic units is approximately equal to half the atomic weight.*

Although an α particle (mass number 4) is light compared with an atom of a metal like gold (mass number 197), it is 7000 times heavier than a single electron. For this reason the electrons surrounding the atomic nucleus are pushed to either side as the α particle goes speeding through, and they have little effect upon the shape of the trajectory.

Example 1. In a Rutherford scattering experiment with gold foil, 238 scintillations per minute are observed at an angle of 30°. Calculate the number of scintillations that are expected at an angle of 60°.

Solution. The given quantities are $N = 238$, $\theta_1 = 30°$, and $\theta_2 = 60°$. Using the third relationship in Eq.(55d), we write

$$N = k_3 \frac{1}{\sin^4 \frac{1}{2}\theta}$$

where k_3 is a constant of proportionality. Solving for this constant, we find

$$k_3 = N \sin^4 \tfrac{1}{2}\theta$$

and upon substituting the known values of $N = 238$ and $\theta = 30°$, obtain

$$k_3 = 238 \sin^4 15° = 238(0.2588)^4$$

$$k_3 = 1.068 \text{ scint./min}$$

Using the same equation to find the number N for the angle $\theta = 60°$, we find

$$N = k_3 \frac{1}{\sin^4 \frac{1}{2}\theta} = 1.068 \frac{1}{(0.500)^4}$$

$$N = 17.09 \text{ scint./min}$$

A graph representing the force of repulsion between an α particle and a positively charged nucleus is illustrated in Fig 55D. Diagram (a) shows the rapid increase in force as the distance decreases, while diagram (b) shows the rapid rise in potential energy. The energy between two electric charges is given by Eq.(23ℓ):

$$E_p = k \frac{QQ'}{r} \tag{55e}$$

The reason for giving this equation, and the potential-energy curve in Fig 55D, is that an interesting mechanical model for demonstrating Rutherford scattering can be derived from it. Such a model is illustrated in Fig. 55E, where the circular peak at the right represents the nucleus of an atom and has a form generated by rotating curve (b) of Fig. 55D about its vertical axis at $r = 0$.

Marbles representing α particles roll down a chute and along a practically level plane where they approach the potential hill. Approaching the hill at various angles, the marbles roll up to a certain height and then off to one side or the other. The paths they follow, if watched from above, are *hyperbolic* in shape. Approaching the hill in a head-on collision, the ball rolls up to a certain point, stops, then rolls back again. Thus the potential energy of the α particle close to the nucleus is analogous to the potential energy of a marble on the hillside, and the electrostatic force of repulsion is analogous to the component of the downward pull of gravity.

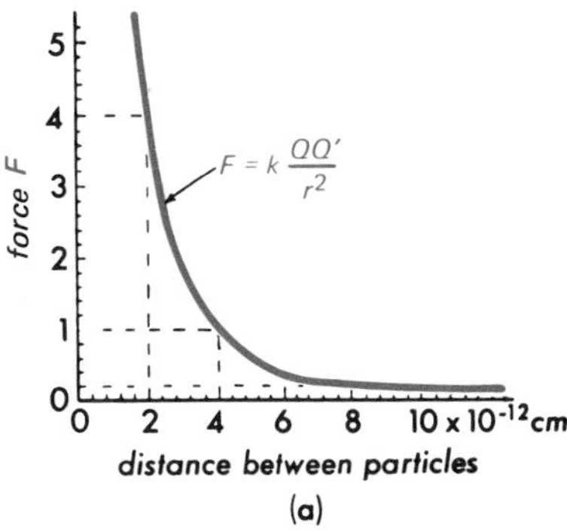

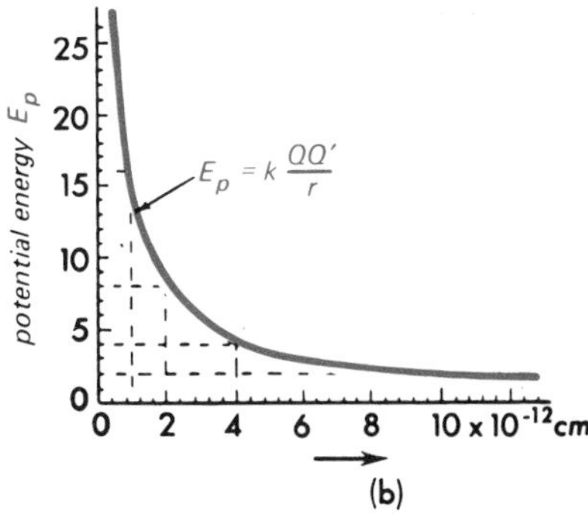

Fig. 55D. Graphs representing the repulsion between a positively charged nucleus and an α particle. (a) Coulomb's law giving the repelling force F, and (b) the potential curve giving the energy.

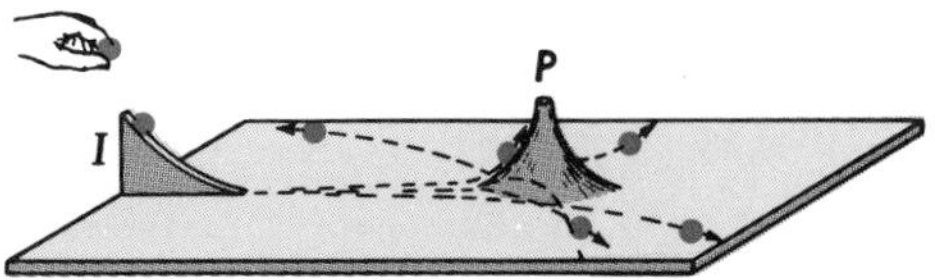

Fig. 55E. Mechanical model of an atomic nucleus for demonstrating Rutherford scattering.

55.3. Elastic Collisions between Atoms

Collisions between free atomic particles were first studied by Rutherford with apparatus as shown in Fig 55F. A long glass tube, containing a small sample of radioactive material R, was first thoroughly evacuated by means of a vacuum pump and then filled with a gas of known constitution. Alpha particles from the radioactive source were then permitted to travel through the gas to the other end of the tube where, upon passing through a thin aluminum foil to a fluorescent screen S, they could be observed as scintillations in the field of view of a microscope M. This is exactly the arrangement used by Rutherford in measuring the range of α particles from different radioactive elements (see Fig 55K).

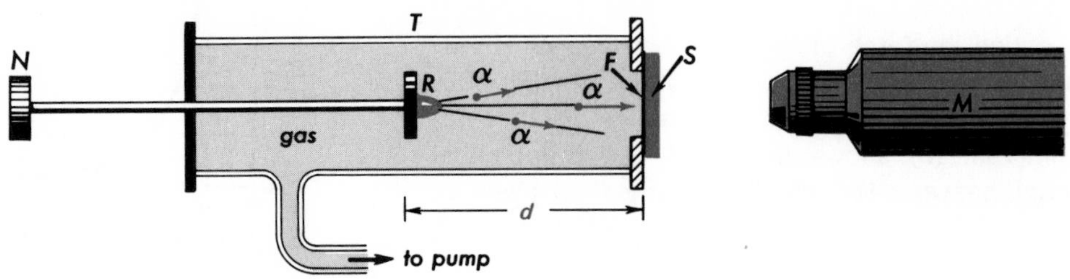

Fig. 55F. Rutherford's apparatus used in observing atomic collisions between α particles from radium and the atoms of a gas like hydrogen, helium, nitrogen, oxygen, etc.

With air in the tube T and $_{84}Po^{214}$ as a source of α particles, scintillations could be observed with the screen as far back as 7 cm. With hydrogen in the tube it was found that the distance *d* could be greatly increased. Inserting thicker and thicker aluminum foils between F and S in front of the fluorescent screen, the range of the particles was calculated to be equivalent to 28 cm of air.

The conclusion Rutherford drew from this result was that an α particle occasionally collides with a hydrogen atom, much as a large ball collides with a lighter one, imparting to it a greater velocity and hence a greater penetrating power. Of the many recoil hydrogen atoms from collisions with α particles, some undergo head-on collisions and go shooting off in a forward direction again with over half (more accurately 1.6 times) the speed of the incident α particle.

The enormous increase in range is due principally to a higher velocity. Each hydrogen nucleus, called a *proton,* is stripped of its orbital electron, and, with only a single positive charge, produces fewer ions per centimeter of path than an α particle with its double positive charge. Curiously enough, protons or α particles having the same velocity have about the same range. The reason for this is that, whereas an α particle has double the charge of a proton and produces more ions per centimeter of its path, which tends to slow it down more rapidly, it also has four times the mass and therefore four times the energy. The range curves in

Fig. 53G show that for *protons* and α *particles* with the same kinetic energy, the protons have about ten times the greater range.

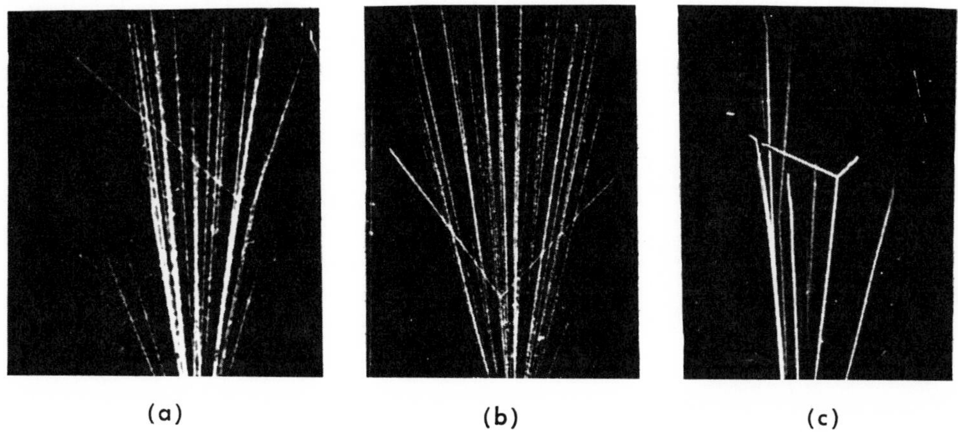

Fig. 55G. Wilson cloud-chamber photographs of collisions between α particles and (a) a hydrogen atom, (b) a helium atom, and (c) an oxygen atom. (After Rutherford, Chadwick, and Ellis.)

A more convincing study of such atomic collisions can be made with a Wilson cloud chamber. In the thousands of cloud-chamber photographs of the ion tracks made by α particles from radioactive elements, one occasionally observes forked tracks of the type reproduced in Fig. 55G. When each of these pictures was taken, the cloud chamber contained different gases. For photograph (a) the cloud chamber contained hydrogen, for (b) it contained helium, and for (c) it contained oxygen. Schematic diagrams of these same collisions are illustrated in Fig. 55H. Note in (b) that the angle between the two recoiling particles is 90°, a right angle.

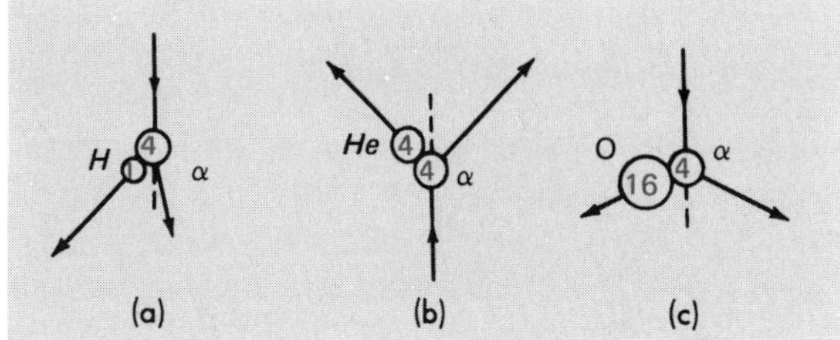

Fig. 55H. Diagrams of collisions between α particles and other nuclei of different mass.

Most elastic collisions between atoms are not head-on collisions, but ones in which the incident particle strikes the other a glancing blow. When an α particle having a mass of 4 units collides with a hydrogen atom of 1 unit, the α particle is deviated only a little from its path, whereas the hydrogen atom nearly always recoils off at quite a large angle. This is in agreement with the laws of conservation of energy and momentum applied to two perfectly elastic spheres.

When an α particle collides with a helium atom, both particles have the same mass of 4 units each, and the two always glance off at right angles to each other. The laws of mechanics show that for a head-on collision between perfectly elastic spheres of equal mass, one moving and one at rest, the incident particle is stopped by the collision and the second body goes on in the forward direction with all of the velocity.

When an α particle collides with an oxygen atom having a mass of 16 units, the oxygen atom recoils to one side with a relatively low velocity, and the α particle glances off to the other side with a high or low velocity depending upon the angle of recoil. The oxygen atom with its greater mass and charge ionizes more particles per centimeter path and therefore leaves a heavier track.

Atom collisions involving such high velocities take place between the heavy nuclei of the atoms and are little affected by the light orbital electrons. As a particle passes through matter many electrons are hit and knocked free from their atoms all along the path. With each such collision the heavy particle loses about 32 electron volts of its energy. Barring collision with a heavy nucleus, it is this loss in energy that causes the particle to slow down and stop. If a nucleus is hit hard by a collision it will be partly or wholly denuded of its electrons, and when it comes to rest will pick up enough electrons to become a neutral atom.

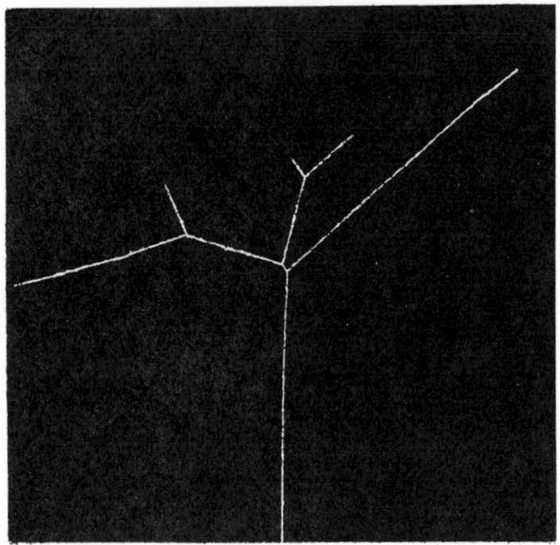

Fig. 55I. Multiple elastic scattering of protons in a liquid hydrogen bubble chamber.

When protons or alpha particles enter a denser medium like a liquid or solid there are approximately 1000 more nuclear targets per cubic centimeter, and through elastic scattering, the energy is divided between many particles within a very short distance (see Fig. 55I).

55.4. The Discovery of Nuclear Disintegration

Upon repeating the range experiments illustrated in Fig 55F with a heavy gas in the tube T, Rutherford made a new and startling discovery in 1919. When nitrogen gas (atomic weight 14) was admitted to the tube, scintillations could be observed at a distance of 40 cm or more from the source. No such long-range particles had ever been observed before. What were these long-range particles? They could not be electrons or γ rays, for these were not capable of producing visible scintillations. Rutherford allowed the new rays to pass through a magnetic field and discovered from their deflection that they had the mass and charge of protons. In other words, the long-range particles were hydrogen nuclei.

Rutherford was not long in coming forward with the correct explanation of the phenomenon. An α particle, near the beginning of its range where its velocity is high, may make a head-on collision with a nitrogen nucleus and be captured. This capture is then followed immediately by a disintegration in which a proton is ejected with high speed. The process is illustrated in Fig. 55J, and the transformation can be represented by the following simple reaction:

$$_2He^4 + {}_7N^{14} = ({}_9F^{18}) = {}_8O^{17} + {}_1H^1 \qquad (55f)$$

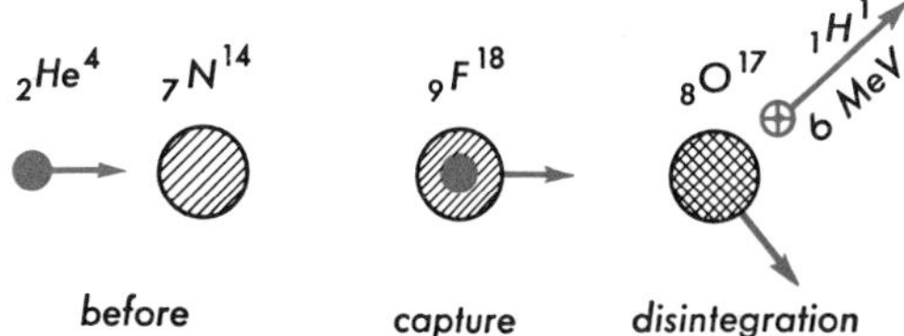

Fig. 55J. The disintegration of a nitrogen nucleus by a high-speed α particle.

When the α particle, with a charge of +2 and mass 4, collides with the nitrogen nucleus with a charge of +7 and mass 14, they form a single particle with a charge of +9 and mass 18. Since an atom with a nuclear charge of +9 would be expected to have all the chemical properties of *fluorine*, atomic number 9, the newly formed nucleus is labeled $_9F^{18}$.

An examination of the table of isotopes, however (see Appendix VIII), shows that no such isotope exists in nature. The reason becomes apparent when it is realized that such a combination of particles is not stable. A fluorine nucleus of mass 18 is unstable and disintegrates by discharging a proton, a particle with a charge of +1 and a mass of 1. This leaves behind a residual nucleus with a charge of +8, and a mass of 17. Under atomic number 8 in the same Appendix VIII, an oxygen isotope of mass 17 is seen to have been found in nature.

Thus the above disintegration process started with two stable nuclei, *helium* and *nitrogen*, and out of them were created two new stable nuclei, *oxygen* and *hydrogen*. This is called a *transmutation* of elements. Because the intermediate step indicates only a momentary existence of a fluorine nucleus, $_9F^{18}$, this step is often omitted from any discussion of the above process and the disintegration reaction is simply written

$$_2He^4 + {}_7N^{14} = {}_8O^{17} + {}_1H^1$$

Such transformation reactions are like equations and must balance: first, the total amount of charge must remain the same, and second, the mass numbers must balance. The first of these is accomplished by having the sum of the subscripts on one side of the reaction equal to the sum of the subscripts on the other side, and the second by having the sum of the superscripts the same on both sides. In every known atom the subscript, representing the nuclear charge, is the sole factor determining the chemical element to which the atom belongs.

55.5. Chadwick's Identification of the Neutron

In 1932 Chadwick, in England, performed an experiment for which he was awarded the Nobel Prize in physics in 1935.* As

***Sir James Chadwick (1891–), British physicist, received the Nobel Prize in physics in 1934 for the discovery of the neutron. He was born in Manchester and educated there where he came under the influence of Ernest Rutherford at Victoria University. In 1913, he studied at the Charlottenburg Institution, Berlin, under Hans Geiger, a former associate of Rutherford's, and at the outbreak of World War I, was detained in a concentration camp in Ruhleben, Germany. After the war, he returned to England and worked under Rutherford at the Cavendish Laboratory in Cambridge. It was there in 1930 that the author met Chadwick for the first time. Chadwick became professor of physics at the University of Liverpool in 1935, was knighted in 1945, awarded the Copley Medal in 1950, and the Franklin Medal in 1951.**

diagrammed in Fig. 55K his experiment consisted of bombarding a beryllium target with α particles. Penetrating particles emerging from the beryllium were permitted to impinge upon a block of paraffin from which protons were found to emerge with high speed. From energy calculations he was able to show that the penetrating rays were uncharged particles with the mass of protons; these he called *neutrons*. The disintegration taking place in the metal target is the following (see Fig. 55L):

$$_2\text{He}^4 + {_4\text{Be}^9} = {_6\text{C}^{12}} + {_0n^1} \tag{55g}$$

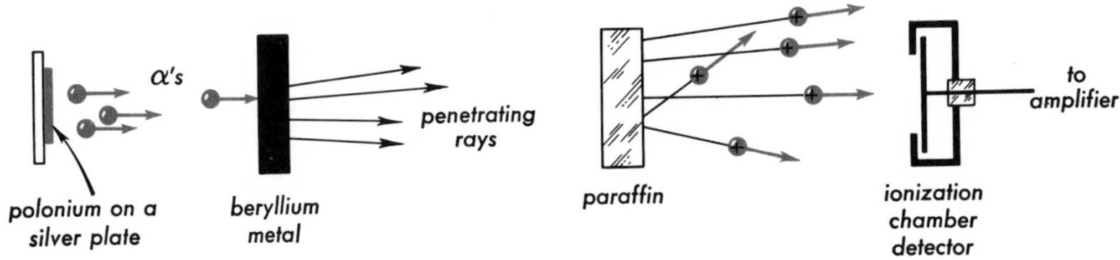

Fig. 55K. The experiment by which Chadwick discovered the neutron. The penetrating rays are neutrons and α particles.

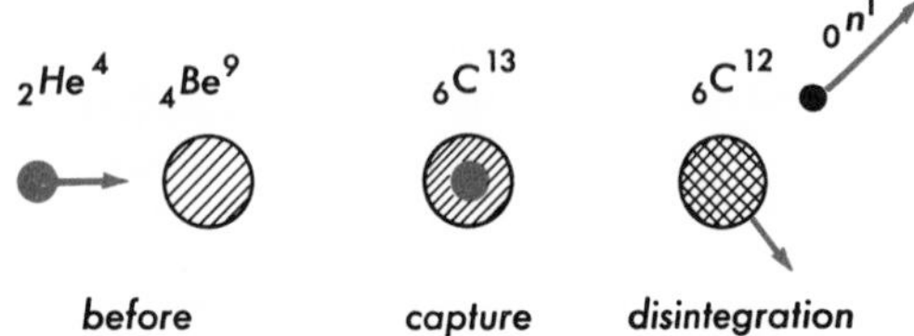

Fig. 55L. The neutron process discovered by Chadwick (see Fig. 55K).

The α particle, $_2\text{He}^4$, makes a collision and unites with a beryllium nucleus $_4\text{Be}^9$, causing a disintegration, whereupon a neutron, $_0n^1$, is expelled with high velocity. The residual particle with a charge of +6 and mass of 12 units is a stable carbon nucleus such as found in nature.

The penetrating rays from the beryllium block in Fig. 55K are mostly neutrons which, in bombarding the paraffin block, collide elastically with hydrogen atoms, knocking them out on the other side. An elastic head-on collision between two particles of the same weight, like a neutron and proton, finds the entire velocity of one transferred to the other; the neutron is stopped and the proton goes on. The protons, having a positive charge, can be observed by their tracks in a Wilson cloud chamber, whereas neutrons cannot.

The reason fast neutrons have such a high penetrating power is that they are not slowed down by ionizing atoms as they pass close by them. A proton, electron, or α particle has a charge and can ionize atoms by attracting or repelling electrons from a distance, but a neutron without a charge cannot do this. It must make a direct collision with another particle to be slowed down or stopped.

Neutrons can now be produced in such intense beams that they are often used in place of X rays wherever radiations of high penetrating power are desired.

55.6. The Nucleus Contains Neutrons and Protons

Since the time of Chadwick's identification of the neutron as an elementary particle, our ideas concerning the nucleus of the atom have had to be modified. We now believe that the nucleus contains two basic kinds of particles, neutrons and protons, plus a number of lighter particles called pions, to be considered later. Each neutron has a mass of one unit and no charge, whereas each proton has a mass of one unit and a positive charge of one unit. This differs from the older idea that the nucleus contains protons equal in number to the atomic weight and enough electrons to neutralize the surplus charge in excess of the amount specified by the atomic number.

Since only the proton has a charge, any given nucleus of atomic number Z and mass number M is now believed to have Z protons and $M - Z$ neutrons, and in a neutral atom the number of protons is believed to be equal to the number of orbital electrons. The nuclear particles of a few of the elements of the periodic table are given in Table 55A, as examples. Schematic diagrams of the nucleus of five different atoms are given in Fig. 55M.

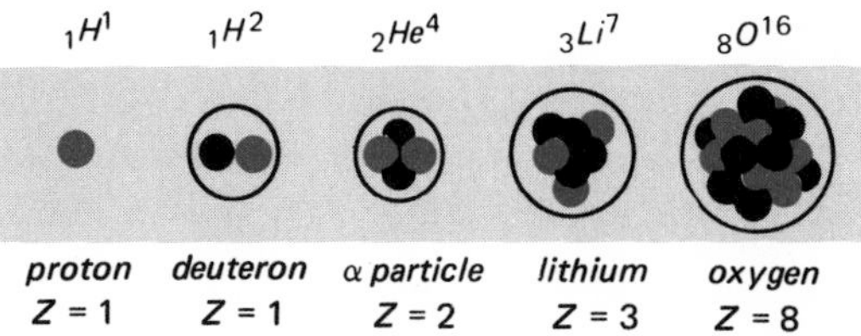

Fig. 55M. The number of protons and neutrons in the nuclei of hydrogen, deuterium, helium, lithium, and oxygen.

TABLE 55A
Neutrons and protons in the nuclei of a few elements

Atom	*Protons*	*Neutrons*
$_1H^1$	1	0
$_1H^2$	1	1
$_2He^4$	2	2
$_3Li^6$	3	3
$_3Li^7$	3	4
$_4Be^9$	4	5
$_4Be^{10}$	4	6
$_5B^{11}$	5	6
$_7N^{13}$	7	6
$_8O^{16}$	8	8
$_{11}Na^{23}$	11	12
$_{29}Cu^{65}$	29	36
$_{80}Hg^{200}$	80	120
$_{92}U^{238}$	92	146

55.7. Atomic Masses Are Not Whole Numbers

When an α particle collides with the nucleus of an atom and produces a disintegration as shown in Fig. 55I, the total energy before collision must be equal to the total energy after collision. To verify this, all forms of energy involved in the process must be included: (1) *the kinetic energy of all particles,* (2) *the energy of a γ ray if one is involved,* and (3) *the mass energy.* The latter is necessary since disintegration experiments show that the total mass of the two colliding particles is not in general equal to the total mass after disintegration. To test this change, it is necessary that we know the exact masses of all atoms individually.

Mass spectrographic measurements by Aston, Bainbridge, and others (see Chap. 42) show that the masses of atoms are not exactly whole-number values as previously suspected and given in Appendix VII. A list of the most recent mass determinations of some of the lighter elements of the periodic table is given in Appendix VIII. These values are all based upon the carbon isotope 12 as having a mass of exactly 12.000000.

55.8. Conservation of Energy in Nuclear Disintegrations

To illustrate the law of conservation of energy as it applies to nuclear disintegrations, consider Rutherford's first experiment, shown in Figs. 55F and 55J, where α particles from ${}_{84}Po^{214}$ passing through nitrogen gas make collisions with, and disintegrate, nitrogen nuclei. The total energy of any two particles before impact will be the sum of the masses of the two nuclei, ${}_{2}He^{4}$ + ${}_{7}N^{14}$, plus their kinetic energy E_{k1}. The total energy after impact will be the sum of the masses of the two nuclei, ${}_{8}O^{17}$ and ${}_{1}H^{1}$, plus their kinetic energy E_{k2}. If we insert accurately known masses, the reaction becomes

$$ {}_{2}He^{4.002604} + {}_{7}N^{14.003074} + E_{k1} = {}_{8}O^{16.999133} + {}_{1}H^{1.007825} + E_{k2} \tag{55h}$$

It is customary to express the energies E_{k1} in *atomic mass units* or in *million electron volts*, MeV. The kinetic energy before impact is confined to the α particle from ${}_{84}Po^{214}$, which has been measured and found to be equivalent to 7.70 MeV. Dividing this value by 931, from Eq.(53m), gives the equivalent of 0.00827 atomic mass unit. Adding mass-energy for both sides of Eq.(55f), we must obtain the same total.

Using mass values given in Appendix VIII we obtain

$$\begin{array}{rlrl} {}_{2}He^{4} = & 4.002604 & {}_{8}O^{17} = & 16.999133 \\ {}_{7}N^{14} = & 14.003074 & {}_{1}H^{1} = & 1.007825 \\ E_{k1} = & 0.008270 & E_{k2} = & ? \\ \hline \text{Total} = & 18.013948 & & 18.013948 \end{array} \tag{55i}$$

Simple addition and subtraction show that, to yield the proper sum for the right-hand column, E_{k2} must be equal to 0.006990 mass unit. Multiplying by 931 gives, this time, 6.51 MeV as the energy liberated. This is the energy liberated in the "explosion" which drives the proton and oxygen nuclei apart.

In general, when an atomic nucleus disintegrates by splitting up into two particles, the annihilation energy is divided between them. Experiments show that this division takes place according to the ordinary laws of mechanics, that *the kinetic energies of the two particles are approximately inversely proportional to their respective masses* (see Example 2, Chap. 58).

Example 2. A sulfur nucleus ${}_{16}S^{33}$ disintegrates by ejecting a proton ${}_{1}H^{1}$, leaving behind a phosphorus nucleus ${}_{15}P^{32}$. If 9.24

MeV energy is liberated as kinetic energy that drives the two fragments apart, how much of the energy goes into each particle?
Solution. The given particles have masses of 33 amu, 32 amu, and 1 amu, and the energy is 9.24 MeV. Since the total mass is 33 amu, we divide the available energy by this mass, and obtain

$$\frac{9.24 \text{ MeV}}{33 \text{ amu}} = 0.280 \frac{\text{MeV}}{\text{amu}}$$

Since the energy divides inversely as the masses of the fragments, we multiply this energy by the masses of the two fragments:

$$0.280 \times 32 = 8.960 \text{ MeV}$$

$$0.280 \times 1 = 0.280 \text{ MeV}$$

The proton recoils with 8.960 MeV, while the phosphorus nucleus recoils in the opposite direction with 0.280 MeV.

When, in the above example, the available energy is divided between an oxygen nucleus of mass 17 and a proton of mass 1, the $_8O^{17}$ nucleus acquires an energy of 0.36 MeV, and the proton an energy of 6.15 MeV. A proton with this kinetic energy and velocity has a range of 49 cm in air. Recent repetitions of Rutherford's experiment give measured ranges of 48 cm and an energy of 6 MeV, in good agreement with the calculation.

Graphs showing the ranges of protons, deuterons, and α particles for different energies are drawn in Fig. 53G.

55.9. The Cockcroft–Walton Experiment

Believing that the disintegration of atomic nuclei might be accomplished by using other than α particles as projectiles, Rutherford instigated in 1930 the construction of a high-voltage, dc generator at the Cavendish Laboratory. The purpose of this *million-volt* source of potential difference was to accelerate hydrogen nuclei, *protons*, to high speeds and then cause them to strike known substances. In this way he hoped to produce new and various kinds of disintegrations.

Becoming impatient with the relatively slow progress of the project, however, Rutherford suggested to Cockcroft and Walton that lower voltages be tried in the meantime to see if, by chance, disintegrations might occur. In 1932 Cockcroft* and Walton† announced that they had successfully disintegrated lithium atoms

***Sir John D. Cockcroft (1897–1967), British physicist, was born in Yorkshire, England, May 27, 1897. Educated at Manchester University and St. John's College, Cambridge, Sir Cockcroft won the Nobel Prize in physics, jointly with E. T. S. Walton, in 1951. These two men, working in the Cavendish Laboratory with Rutherford, were the first to transmute atomic nuclei by artificially accelerated atomic particles. Cockcroft served his country in several capacities: as Chief Superintendent, Air Defense Research and Development, Director of the Atomic Energy Ministry of Supply, and several other posts. He was elected a fellow of the Royal Society in 1936 and was knighted in 1948, and created Knight Commander of the Bath in 1953. The author had the good fortune to meet Sir Cockcroft in the Cavendish Laboratory in 1930.**

†Ernest T. S. Walton (1903–), Irish physicist, was born October 6, 1903. He was educated at Bainbridge, County Down, at Cookstown, County Tyrone, and in the Methodist College, Belfast. While working with Sir John D. Cockcroft, under Rutherford, at the Cavendish Laboratory, the first transmutation experiments with laboratory accelerated atomic particles were performed. He was awarded the Hughes Medal of the Royal Society in 1938, and elected Erasmus Smith Professor of Natural Philosophy at the University of Dublin in 1946. He was awarded, jointly with Sir Cockcroft, the Nobel Prize in physics for 1951.

with protons accelerated by relatively low voltages. Their apparatus is schematically represented in Fig. 55N.

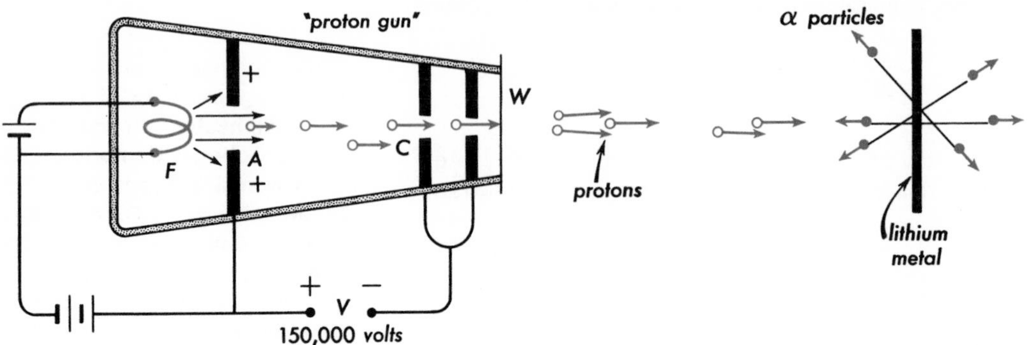

Fig. 55N. Schematic diagram of the Cockcroft–Walton experiment. Lithium is disintegrated by 150,000-volt protons.

Electrons from a hot filament F, passing through hydrogen gas in the region of A, ionize many hydrogen atoms. These protons with their positive charge are then accelerated toward the other end of the tube by a potential difference V of 150,000 V. Upon passing through the opening C and a window W, they emerge from the acceleration chamber as a narrow beam of protons.

This tube, acting as a "proton gun," is aimed at a target consisting of lithium metal. Cockcroft and Walton observed and measured α particles emanating from the metal with a range of 8 cm, an energy equivalent to 8.5 MeV. Considering the relatively low energy of the bombarding protons of only 0.15 MeV, this is tremendous release in atomic energy. The transmutation taking place here is written as follows:

$$_1\mathrm{H}^1 + {}_3\mathrm{Li}^7 + E_{k1} = {}_2\mathrm{He}^4 + {}_2\mathrm{He}^4 + E_{k2} \qquad (55j)$$

This reaction, illustrated in Fig. 55O, shows a proton, $_1\mathrm{H}^1$, of energy $E_{k1} = 0.15$ MeV, entering a lithium nucleus, $_3\mathrm{Li}^7$, to form a new but stable beryllium nucleus, $_4\mathrm{Be}^8$. Being unstable, this compact structure of eight particles splits up into two α particles which are driven apart with great violence. Since the measured energy of each α particle is equivalent to 8.5 MeV, each disintegration involves the liberation of 17.0 MeV energy. The source of energy is to be found in the annihilation of a part of the total atomic mass.

The loss in mass can be calculated from the table of atomic

weights, given in Appendix VIII. Listing the involved masses in two columns and adding, we obtain

$$\begin{array}{rlrl} {}_1H^1 = & 1.007825 & & \\ {}_3Li^7 = & 7.016005 & {}_2He^4 = & 4.002604 \\ E_{k1} = & 0.000161 & {}_2He^4 = & 4.002604 \\ \hline & 8.023991 & & 8.005208 \end{array}$$

E_{k1} is the mass equivalent to the energy of the incident proton and is obtained by dividing 0.15 MeV by 931 [see Eq.(53m)]. The difference between the two sums, $8.023991 - 8.005208 = 0.018783$ mass unit, represents the loss in mass by the disintegration. When multiplied by 931, this gives 17.48 MeV as the liberated energy, a value in good agreement with the experimentally determined value of 17.0 MeV.

It might be thought that such a disintegration as the one described above could be used as a source of energy, but as yet it has not been feasible to use it so. While each nuclear collision and disintegration liberates at least one hundred times as much energy as that supplied to the proton, it takes many particles to make a few collisions. In other words, only a small percentage

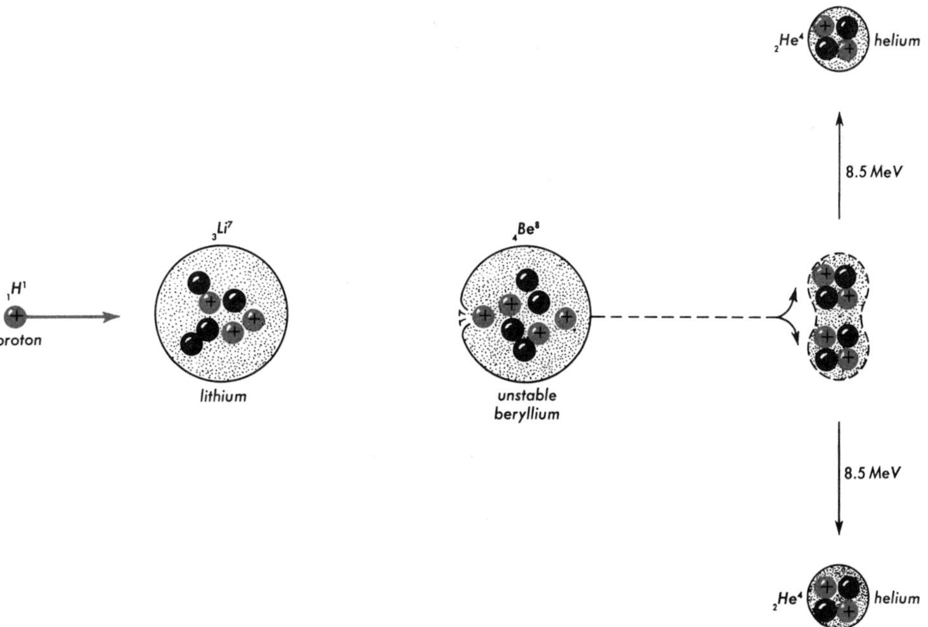

Fig. 55O. Disintegration of a lithium nucleus by a proton of 0.15 MeV energy: the Cockcroft–Walton experiment.

of the proton bullets hit the tiny nuclear targets as they pass through matter. Most of them are slowed down by electron collisions and the ionization of atoms. To a proton bullet the lithium nuclei, as targets in the lithium metal, present an area millions of times smaller than the space between them.

Example 3. An α particle with a kinetic energy of 7.58 MeV is captured by an aluminum-27 nucleus. The compound nucleus is unstable and disintegrates by ejecting a proton. (a) Write down the reaction. Find the energy of (b) the recoiling proton, and (c) the recoiling heavy nucleus.

Solution. The given quantities are $E_{k1} = 7.58$ MeV, combining particles $_2He^4$ and $_{13}Al^{27}$, and one of the two disintegrating products, $_1H^1$. Calling the other disintegration particle X, we obtain for the reaction

$$E_{k1} + {_2He^4} + {_{13}Al^{27}} \rightarrow {_1H^1} + {_{14}X^{30}} + E_{k2}$$

Using the table in Appendix VIII, the unknown nucleus with atomic number 14 must be silicon-30. The reaction is therefore written

$$E_{k1} + {_2He^4} + {_{13}Al^{27}} \rightarrow {_1H^1} + {_{14}Si^{30}} + E_{k2}$$

We now convert the α particle kinetic energy to mass in atomic mass units:

$$\frac{7.58}{931} = 0.007057 \text{ amu}$$

Using masses given in Appendix VIII, we add as follows:

$$\begin{aligned} E_{k1} &= 0.007057 \\ {_2He^4} &= 4.002604 \\ {_{13}Al^{27}} &= 26.981535 \\ \hline &\quad 30.991196 \text{ amu} \end{aligned} \qquad \begin{aligned} {_1H^1} &= 1.007825 \\ {_{14}Si^{30}} &= 29.973761 \\ \hline &\quad 30.981586 \text{ amu} \end{aligned}$$

The difference in mass $m = 0.009610$ amu, converted to MeV, gives for the liberated energy

$$E_{k2} = 0.00961 \times 931 = 8.95 \text{ MeV}$$

Dividing this energy by the total mass number 31, we obtain

$$\frac{8.95}{31} = 0.2887 \frac{\text{MeV}}{\text{amu}}$$

Since the liberated energy of 8.95 MeV is divided between the two particles, in the inverse ratio of their masses, the energies imparted are divided:

$$_1H^1 = 8.661 \text{ MeV}$$

$$_{14}Si^{30} = 0.289 \text{ MeV}$$

problems

1. In a Rutherford scattering experiment 325 α-particle scintillations per minute are observed at an angle of 20°. Find the number of scint./min expected to be scattered at angles of (a) 30°, and (b) 50°.

2. The Rutherford scattering experiment is performed with a thin silver foil. If 295 α-particle scintillations per min are observed at 25°, find the number to be expected at (a) 30°, and (b) 40°.

3. If a Rutherford scattering experiment is performed using a thin copper foil, and 28.0 scintillations per minute are observed at 90°, find the number to be expected at an angle of 25°. [Ans. 3190.]

4. When a thin copper foil is used to scatter α particles from a radium source, 155 scint./min are observed at an angle of 30°. When the foil is changed to (a) a silver foil, and (b) a gold foil, find the number of scint./min to be expected at the same angle.

5. A gold foil 5.0×10^{-7} m thick is used to scatter α particles. At an angle of 30°, 245 scint./min are observed. If the foil is changed to one with a thickness of 8.60×10^{-7} m, find the number of scint./min at the same angle.

6. If the following mass is annihilated, and 95% of the energy is imparted as kinetic energy to an α particle, find (a) its energy in MeV, and (b) its range in air. $\Delta m = 0.00886$ amu. See Fig. 53G. [Ans. (a) 7.84 MeV, (b) 7.25 cm.]

7. An α particle with an energy of 10.6 MeV is captured on impact by an oxygen-16 nucleus. If a proton is observed recoiling from the compound nucleus, (a) write down the reaction, and calculate (b) the kinetic energy liberated in MeV, (c) the recoil energy of the proton, and (d) the proton's range in air (see Fig. 53G).

8.* In a nuclear disintegration reaction, a mass of 0.0126 amu is annihilated, and 92% of the liberated energy is imparted as kinetic energy to an α particle. Find (a) its energy in MeV, and (b) its range in air. See Fig. 53G.

9.* A mass of 0.00692 amu is annihilated in a nuclear reaction, and 97.5% of the liberated energy is imparted to a proton. Find (a) its energy in MeV, and (b) its range in air. [Ans. (a) 6.28 MeV, (b) 52.0 cm.]

10.* The energy of the α particles scattered from a silver foil as in Rutherford's experiment is equivalent to 4.58 MeV. If the energy of the incident beam is raised to 7.28 MeV, find the ratio of the number of scintillations/min in the two cases, observed at the same angle.

11.* Alpha particles with an energy of 5.30 MeV were used by Chadwick when he discovered the neutron. Using the masses of the different particles involved in the reaction, calculate (a) the mass in amu converted into kinetic energy, (b) the energy in MeV imparted to the neutron, and (c) the energy of the carbon-12 recoil. See Eq. (53g), Fig. 55L, and Appendix VIII.

12.* If the incident α particle in Eq.(55h) has an energy of 12.50 MeV, find (a) the mass equivalent to the α particle's kinetic energy, (b) the total energy liberated by mass conversion, and (c) the energy imparted to the proton. See Eqs. (55h) and (55i). [Ans. (a) 0.01343 amu, (b) 11.31 MeV, (c) 10.68 MeV.]

56 Cosmic rays

There are few who know that living at or near sea level an average of twenty-eight cosmic rays pass through the typical human being per second. This has been going on for many thousands of years, yet no one knows whether such low intensity radiation has cumulative beneficial or detrimental effects.

Karl K. Darrow has described the subject of cosmic rays "as unique in modern physics for the minuteness of the phenomena, the delicacy of the observations, the adventurous excursions of the observers, the subtlety of the analysis, and the grandeur of the inferences." It is impossible for anyone to say when and by whom cosmic rays were first studied. From the time of the discovery of radioactivity by Becquerel (in 1896) and the discovery of radium by the Curies only two years later, the radioactive rays from the ground, air, and outer space have been investigated by many scientists. Extending over a period of some 50 years, these investigations have led to some of the most interesting and important discoveries in the structure of atomic nuclei.

56.1. Early Experiments

It has long been known that a charged electroscope, if left standing for some little time, will discharge regardless of how well the gold leaf is insulated. Realizing that the rays from radioactive materials can be stopped by a sufficient thickness of heavy matter, Rutherford and Cooke (in Canada, 1903) surrounded an electroscope with a thick wall of brick and found very little decrease in the rate of discharge. McLennan and his co-workers (also in Canada) lowered an electroscope into a lake, hoping that the thick layer of water would screen off the rays. This experiment, like the other, failed.

In 1910 Glockel, with an electroscope, rose nearly 5 Km (3 mi) in a balloon in order to get away from the ground radiation, but to his astonishment he found that the rate of discharge did not decrease, but increased, the higher he went. The same effect was observed by Hess (in Austria, 1911) and Kolhörster (in Germany,

1914). Rising to heights as great as 9 Km ($5\frac{1}{2}$ mi), both of these observers independently found that the intensity of these unknown radiations became greater the higher they went.

Because in one of his scientific publications concerning these results Hess* suggested the possibility that some kind of penetrating rays were entering the earth's atmosphere from outer space, he is usually credited with the discovery of cosmic rays. For this reason he was granted the Nobel Prize in physics for the year 1936.

56.2. Millikan and Bowen's Discovery

Soon after World War I (1922), R. A. Millikan, with the help of I. S. Bowen, constructed several small, self-recording string electroscopes. Making use of their war-time experiences with sounding balloons, they sent these electroscopes high into the stratosphere by fastening each one to two sounding balloons. As shown in Fig. 56A, the string electroscope E consists of two gold-covered quartz fibers insulated and mounted with their ends together. When they are charged, the fibers spread apart in mutual repulsion, and as they discharge they slowly come together.

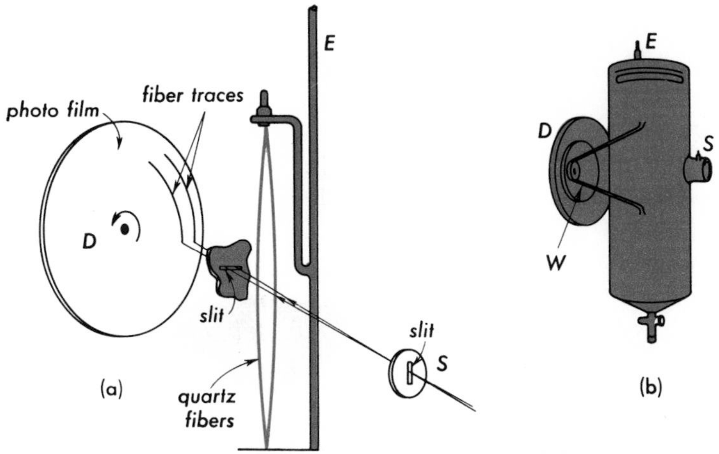

Fig. 56A. Diagrams of one of the sensitive electroscopes sent up into the stratosphere by Millikan and Bowen to measure cosmic rays: (a) schematic diagram; (b) scale drawing of entire instrument 15.2 cm high.

Daylight, passing through a narrow vertical slit S in the instrument case, casts a shadow of the center section of the fibers on a rotating disk D which contains a photographic film. As the films

*Victor Francis Hess (1883–1964), Austrian physicist, shared the 1936 Nobel Prize with C. D. Anderson for his discovery of cosmic rays. Born at Schloss, Waldstein, he was educated at Graz, Vienna, performed experiments on radioactivity of the Institute for Radium Research of the Vienna Academy of Sciences, Vienna, and lectured in physics at the Vienna Veterinary College. He became Director of the U. S. Radium Corporation in 1921, and consultant to the U. S. Department of the Interior, Bureau of Mines. In 1938, he became professor of physics at Fordham University, New York, and became a naturalized citizen of the U. S. A. in 1944.

turns slowly and the fibers come together, they leave a double trace, as indicated in the diagram. On the same film, a small oil manometer recorded the height of ascent and a small thermometer recorded the temperature. The film was driven by a watch W, the whole apparatus weighing only 200 g. On one of the best record flights, only one of the balloons burst at a height of 16 Km (10 mi) and the other brought the instruments safely to earth.

Like the earlier results obtained by other experimenters, Millikan and Bowen found the ionization to increase with increasing altitude. After extending the observations of previous workers to higher altitudes, Millikan and Bowen became convinced, and announced their belief, that the rays were coming from interstellar space.

56.3. The Penetration of Cosmic Rays

In order to determine the nature of the new rays, Millikan and his co-workers, Otis, Cameron, and Bowen, in the fall of 1922 began an extensive study of the penetrating power of cosmic rays. Since cosmic rays penetrate our atmosphere of many kilometers of air, how far might they penetrate beyond?

Self-recording electroscopes were lowered to various depths in snow-fed lakes as illustrated schematically in Fig. 56B. Meas-

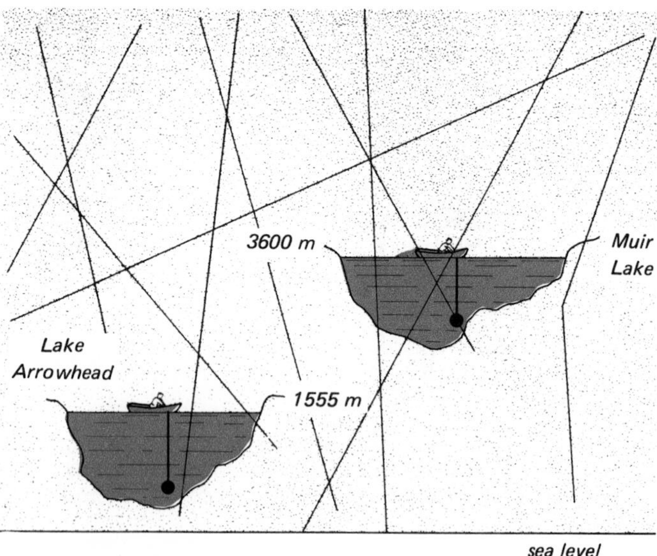

Fig. 56B. Illustrating the lowering of self-recording electroscopes into deep, snow-fed lakes to measure the absorption of cosmic rays by the water.

urements taken at Arrowhead Lake in Southern California (at an elevation of 1555 m) agreed approximately with those taken at Muir Lake near Mt. Whitney (at an elevation of 3600 m), provided one took into account the increased air path for the lower elevation. The extra 2045 m of air is equivalent in weight to 1.8 m of water.

As cosmic rays penetrate deeper and deeper below the surface of water, their number decreases, until at a depth of 30 m the intensity is reduced to about one ten-thousandth of that at the surface. With very sensitive electroscopes, cosmic radiation capable of penetrating 600 m of water has more recently been detected. This is a far greater penetrating power than that possessed by any known X rays or γ rays from radioactivity.

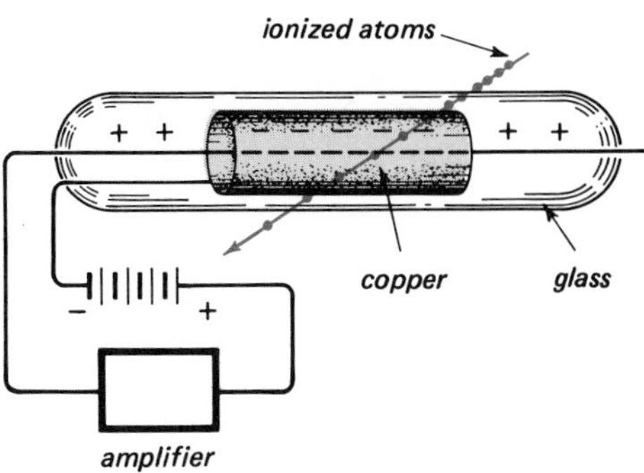

Fig. 56C. Diagram of a Geiger–Müller tube.

56.4. The Geiger–Müller-Tube Counter

There are at least nine methods of observing and measuring cosmic rays. These are

(a) Geiger–Müller-tube counters
(b) Wilson cloud chambers
(c) Ionization chambers
(d) Photographic emulsions
(e) Scintillation counters
(f) Bubble chambers
(g) Electroscopes
(h) Semiconductors
(i) Spark chambers

The Geiger–Müller tube, named after its inventors, is one of the simplest electrical instruments ever designed (see Fig. 56C). It consists of an open-ended copper cylinder from 1 cm to 1 m long, fitted inside a thin-walled glass cylinder with a fine tungsten wire stretched along the middle. After the tube has been partially evacuated (a pressure of from 5 to 10 cm of mercury is convenient), a potential difference of about 1000 V is applied, the positive to the center wire and the negative to the cylinder.

When a single cosmic ray or high-speed particle from a radioactive source goes through a Geiger–Müller tube, ions are created by the freeing of electrons from air molecules. These freed electrons are attracted by the positively charged wire and move toward it, acquiring within a very short distance a high velocity of their own. Because of this velocity they, too, can ionize other atoms, thus freeing more electrons.

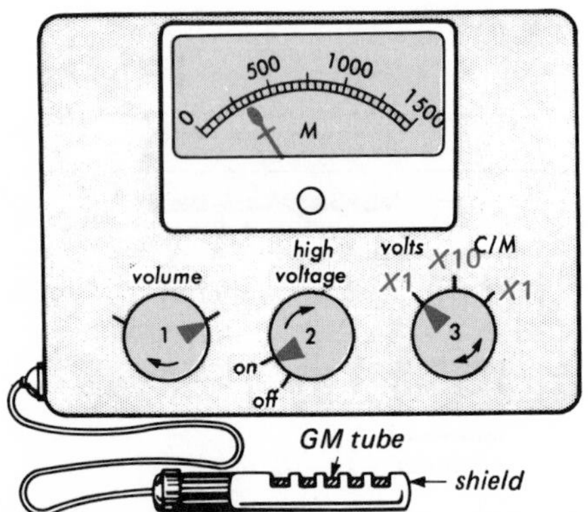

Fig. 56D. Geiger counter instrument complete with G–M tube and counting-rate meter.

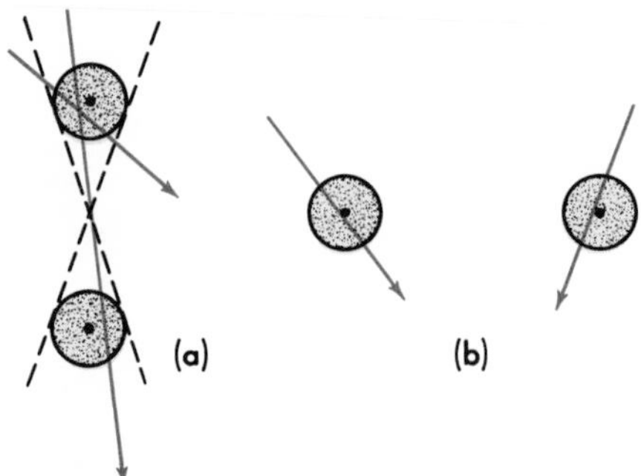

Fig. 56E. Diagram of two Geiger counters. Connected in coincidence they form a cosmic-ray telescope.

The multiplication of charges repeats itself in rapid succession, producing within a very short interval of time an *avalanche of electrons toward the central wire*. This sudden surge of charge is equivalent to a small current impulse along the electrical circuit. When this current has been intensified by an amplifier, it may be made to operate an electric switch, a radio loud-speaker, or any kind of electrical device.

Quite frequently, the impulses of a Geiger–Müller tube are made to operate a small counting device. Each cosmic ray particle passing through the tube is therefore counted automatically. The number of counts received per second depends upon the size of the counter tube. An average-sized tube 2 cm in diameter and several centimeters long, at sea level, gives from 50 to 100 counts per minute.

A common form of Geiger counter is shown in Fig. 56D. It consists of a G–M-counter tube about 10 cm long connected to a box containing vacuum-tube circuits, a small loud-speaker, and a counting-rate meter M.

Dial (1) operates the speaker and permits the individual ray pulses to be heard. Dial (2) turns on the vacuum tubes as in any radio or TV receiver, and turning it clockwise increases the voltage supplied to the G–M tube. Dial (3) has three position points to which it can be turned. The position marked volts connects the meter M so that it shows the voltage on the G–M tube. When in the $\times 1$ position, under C/M, the meter M directly reads counts per minute, and in the $\times 10$ position the meter reading should be multiplied by 10.

56.5. Directional Effects

To observe the direction of the greatest cosmic-ray intensity, a cosmic-ray telescope is used. Such a telescope is made by connecting two or more Geiger–Müller tubes *in coincidence,* and mounting them on a common support some distance apart. Tubes in coincidence are so connected electrically that a current will flow in the accompanying electric circuit only when both tubes discharge within a short period of time.

When one tube is set above the other, as shown in Fig. 56E(a), a single cosmic ray, on going through both cylinders, will cause a current pulse and a count to be made. If, however, a particle goes through one and not the other, no count is recorded. Experiments at sea level show that, when the telescope is mounted in the horizontal position (b), few counts are made, whereas when it is mounted in a vertical direction many more counts are recorded. The interpretation to be made, therefore, is that cosmic rays come principally from overhead.

As a verification of the telescope method, a Wilson cloud chamber is frequently inserted between two Geiger counter tubes as shown in Fig. 56F, and a photograph of the path of each cosmic ray is taken. Thousands of such photographs are made automatically by having a single cosmic ray take its own picture. This is accomplished by allowing the sudden electric current from the counter tubes, produced by a ray in transit, to open and close a camera shutter, to cause the cloud chamber to expand, and to flash a light, illuminating the fog track that forms.

In the reproduction of Fig. 56F, either one of the two cosmic rays would have tripped the electrical devices and taken the picture. It should be noted that both rays passed right through a 1.2-cm lead plate without being deviated. Cloud-chamber pictures are not photographs of cosmic rays, but of the path traversed by the rays.

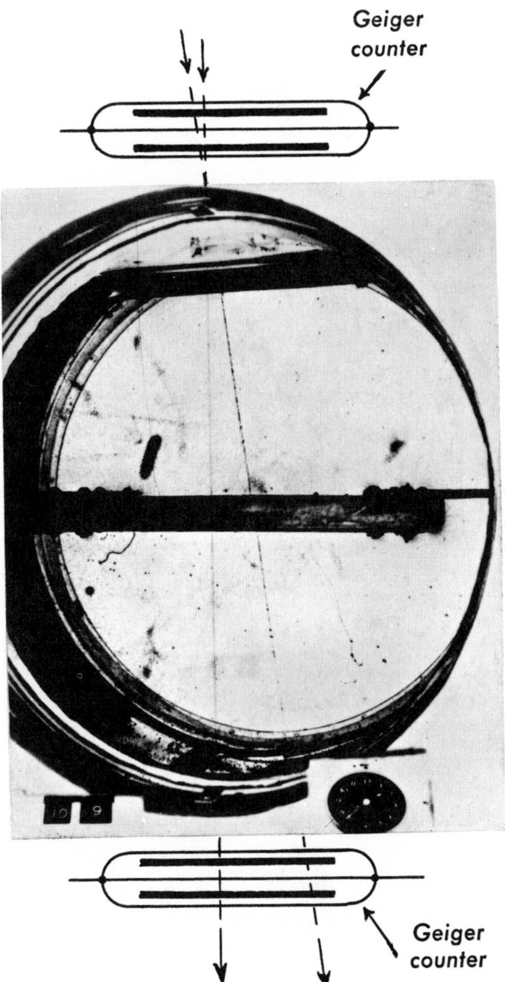

Fig. 56F. With a Wilson cloud chamber mounted between two Geiger tubes connected in coincidence, the cosmic rays are made to take their own picture. (After R. B. Brode.)

56.6. The Altitude Effect

The results of airplane and balloon flights into the stratosphere have shown that the intensity of cosmic rays increases up to a height of from 18 to 25 Km, and then decreases again. In 1935 Stevens and Anderson, for example, rose to a height of nearly 22 Km carrying with them, among other scientific instruments, Geiger–Müller tube counters. With these instruments they measured the cosmic-ray intensity at various altitudes on both their ascent and descent.

The compiled experimental results of various observers taken at different elevations are illustrated by the curves in 56G. Near the city of Omaha, at a magnetic latitude of 51°N, the maximum is found at a height of 25 Km where an intensity 170 times as great as that at sea level has been measured. From that altitude to the highest points that observations have been made, about 27 Km, there is a gradual decrease in total intensity .

The four different curves in the figure show, from altitude measurements made by observers all over the world, that in nearing the magnetic equator the cosmic-ray intensity decreases at high altitudes, as well as at sea level.

56.7. Primaries and Secondaries

Experimental observations show that the cosmic rays entering our atmosphere are almost entirely composed of positively charged atomic nuclei. Of these so-called *primary cosmic rays,* 89% are protons, and another 10% are about 90% α particles and 10% heavier nuclei like carbon, nitrogen, oxygen, iron, etc. (see Table 56A in Sec. 56.13).

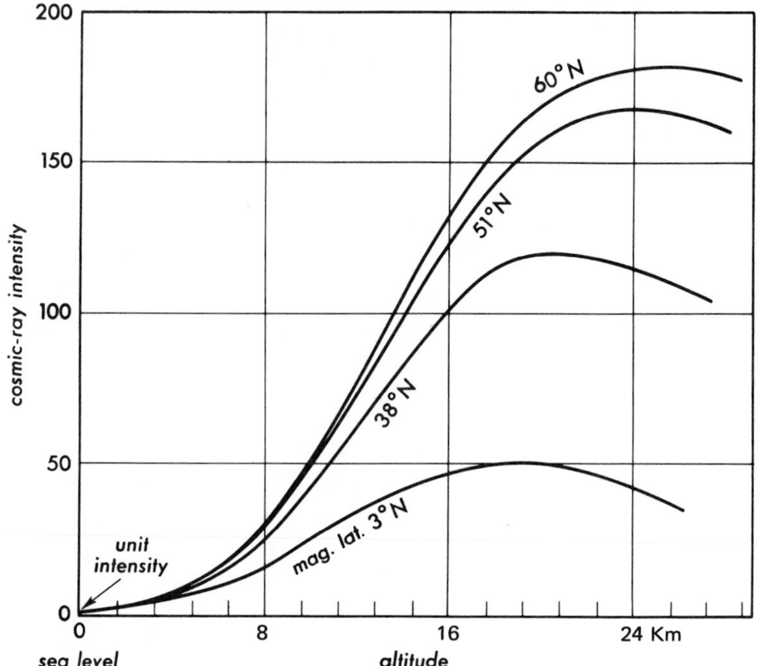

Fig. 56G. The intensity of cosmic rays increases with altitude up to a height of 16 to 24 Km, and then decreases.

Upon entering the atmosphere, a high-energy primary particle soon collides with another atomic nucleus, splitting one or both particles into a number of smaller nuclear fragments, each one of which carries away some of the primary's energy. These high-speed particles in turn collide with other nuclei, further dividing their energy to produce other high-speed particles. All of these rays, with the exception of the primary particle, are called *secondary cosmic rays.*

One of the results of cosmic-ray collision processes is the creation of very high frequency and highly penetrating gamma rays. These photons, too, are included in the classification, secondary cosmic rays.

At a height of some 25 Km, about ten to fifteen times as many secondary cosmic rays exist as have entered the atmosphere as primaries. At this level, where more than $\frac{9}{10}$ of the earth's atmosphere still lies below, as many rays are observed moving in a horizontal direction as in the vertical. From the diagram presented in Fig. 56H it becomes quite clear why the primaries are difficult to distinguish from the far greater number of secondaries.

At lower altitudes the total intensity decreases, since many of the secondaries produced above are stopped by collision. In other words, so much energy is lost by successive collisions that the energy is gradually absorbed as heat motion by the air molecules. By the time sea level is reached, the remaining rays consist principally of a few high-speed secondaries and primaries. Even at sea level, some of these rays have enough energy left to penetrate several hundred, and even several thousand, feet of earth and water.

It should be borne in mind that, between collisions of the type indicated in Fig. 56H, each cosmic-ray particle is continually being slowed down as it "plows through" thousands of air molecules, knocking electrons free to produce ions. These are the ions on which fog drops form, revealing the path in a cloud chamber.

Although γ rays also lose energy by collisions with atoms to produce Compton electrons, the γ rays themselves do not leave visible tracks in a Wilson cloud chamber. The reason for this is that collisions are few and far between, and the resulting fog drops are too far apart.

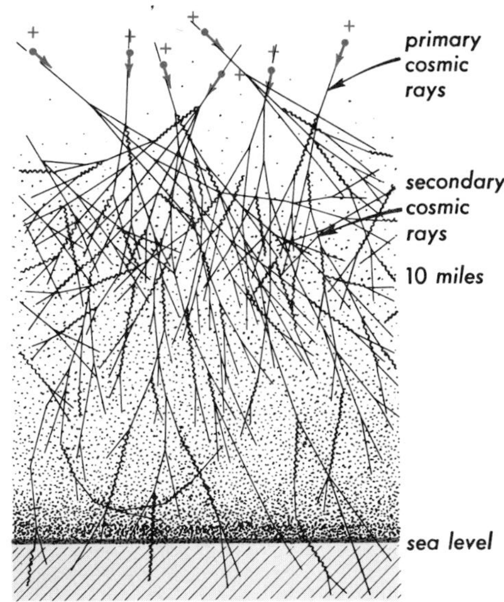

Fig. 56H. Schematic illustration of secondary cosmic rays produced from primaries entering the earth's atmosphere.

56.8. The Latitude Effect

By the year 1930, studies of cosmic-ray intensities by Millikan indicated that the number of cosmic rays arriving at the earth's surface was constant at all latitudes. This led him to the conclusion that the primary cosmic radiation entering the atmosphere must be γ rays of very high energy. He reasoned that, if they were charged atomic particles, they would be deflected by the earth's magnetic field, and fewer would reach the earth near the magnetic equator.

In 1931 the Dutch physicist Clay, sailing from Amsterdam in the Northern Hemisphere to Jakarta, Indonesia, in the Southern Hemisphere, carried Geiger counters with him aboard ship. Measuring the cosmic-ray intensity daily en route, he obtained the results shown by the graph in Fig. 56I. The curve shows that as one proceeds from magnetic north to magnetic south, at sea level, the cosmic-ray intensity remains quite constant, until a magnetic latitude of about 42° is reached. In this region the intensity begins to drop appreciably, reaches a minimum at the equator, and rises again to symmetrical intensities in the Southern Hemisphere.

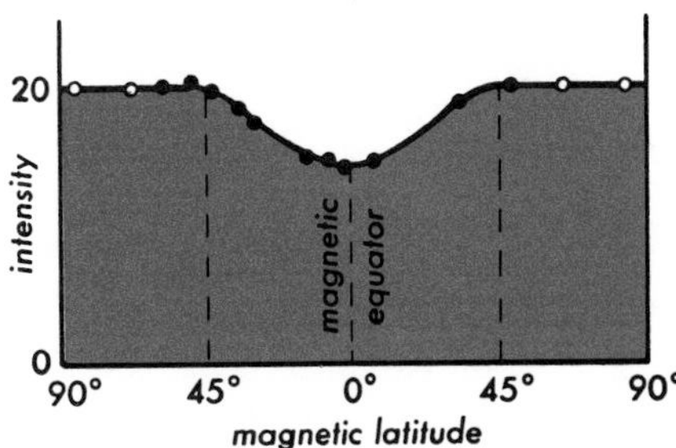

Fig. 56I. Graph of the cosmic-ray intensity at various latitudes of the earth's surface.

56.9. Effect of the Earth's Magnetic Field

The decrease in cosmic-ray intensity at the earth's magnetic equator (see Fig. 56I) is now explained as being due to the earth's magnetic field. This is illustrated in Fig. 56J. The paths of all charged particles crossing the earth's magnetic field are bent by a force that is perpendicular to the direction of the field.

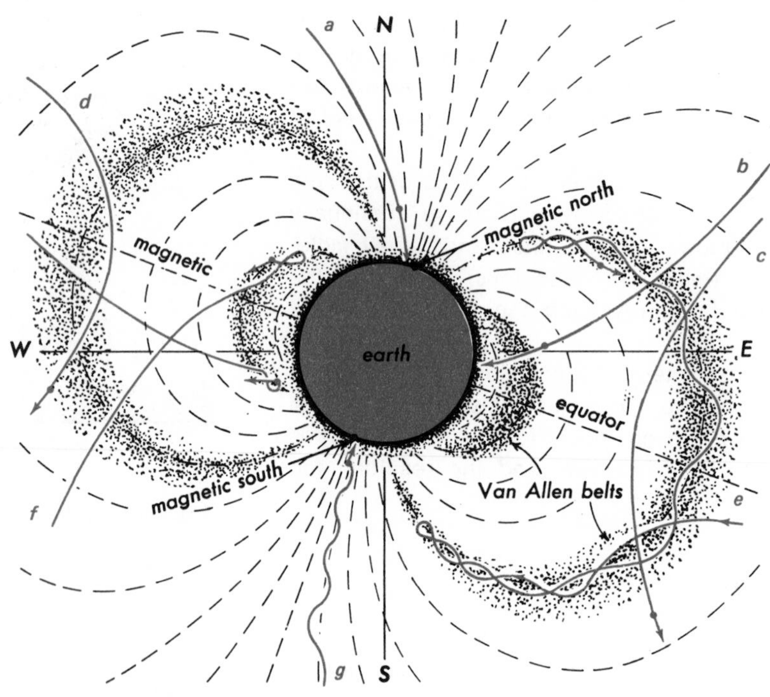

Fig. 56J. The behavior of primary cosmic rays in the earth's magnetic field. The shaded arches are the Van Allen belts.

Because of these forces, many charged particles from the sun and outer space are trapped by the field in two belts. The discovery of these belts by Van Allen and his colleagues at State University of Iowa was made from instruments carried into space by American earth-circling satellites. These belts surround the earth, except at the regions of the magnetic poles, the outer one being caused largely by the slower particles, protons and electrons, from the sun. The inner Van Allen belt is formed by more energetic particles from outer space, and is centered about 4,000 Km above the magnetic equator.

If the primary energy is very large, little deflection will occur, and particles like a and b will reach our atmosphere and perhaps the ground. At somewhat lower energies they will be deflected back into space as c and d. At still lower energies they may follow paths like e, f, and g.

Particle e spirals around the field lines and follows them in toward the earth. As the field gets stronger, a point is reached where the particle is turned back, and spiraling around the field lines approaches the earth again on the other side. Such particles running back and forth are trapped; they account for the larger number of ionized particles that form the Van Allen belts.

Slow particles, such as g, entering the earth's field parallel to the lines of force from far away, will be guided by the field and reach the earth's surface. A day or two after an active display of solar flares, so many particles become trapped in the outer Van Allen belt that they spill out into the earth's atmosphere, creating auroras. Since particles with only the highest of energies can get down to the earth's atmosphere near the magnetic equator, the cosmic-ray latitude effect is well understood.

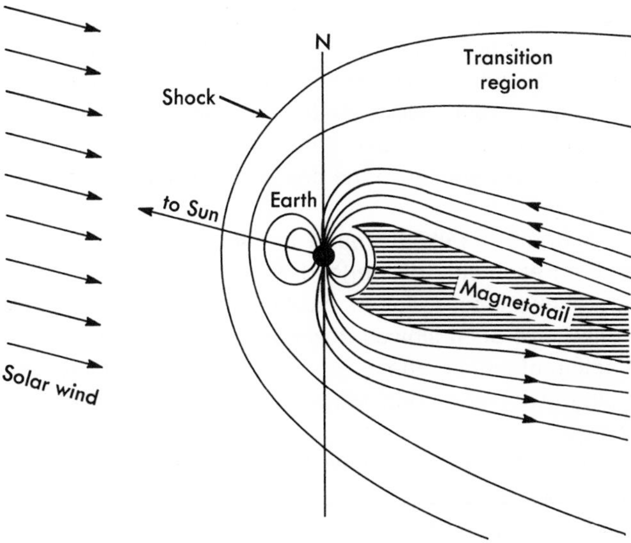

Fig. 56K. Diagram of the solar· wind and its effect upon the earth's magnetic field. (Los Alamos Scientific Laboratory, from measurements made with satellites orbiting the earth at approximately 120,000 Km above the surface.)

56.10. The Solar Wind

The "solar wind" is a good example of the *plasma state.* It arises from streams of ions, composed of equal numbers of protons and electrons, flowing radially outward from the sun, with a speed of approximately 400 Km/s. As this wind, containing about 5 ions per cubic centimeter, streaks past the earth it drags with it the earth's magnetic field.

The distorted field, as shown in Fig. 56K, forms a concentrated region called a "magnetotail." The earth's field tends to retard the charged wind and form a kind of ion *shock wave.* This "transition region," on the leading side, is from 80,000 to 100,000 Km above the earth's surface. Large solar flares increase the intensity of the solar wind and help fill the Van Allen belts. Spilling out they account for all natural geomagnetic storms.

56.11. Discovery of the Positron

The positron, or positive electron, was discovered by Anderson* in 1932 by photographing the tracks of cosmic rays in a Wilson cloud chamber. Under the influence of a strong magnetic field applied perpendicular to the face of the cloud chamber, positively charged particles should bend to the right and negatively charged particles should bend to the left. In order to be certain that those bent one way were not all coming from above, and those bent the other way were particles of the same kind and charge coming from below, Anderson inserted a block of lead in the chamber to slow down the particles. Under these conditions photographs similar to the one shown in (a) of Fig. 56L were obtained.

Here Anderson could be quite certain, from the curvature of the track on each side of the lead, that the particle entered from the side shown above, for in passing through the lead plate it could only have been slowed down and not speeded up. Knowing the direction of motion, the direction of the field, and the direction of bending, Anderson concluded that such a particle had a positive charge.

Comparing the track with well-known electron tracks and α particle tracks, he concluded that the new particle had about the same mass as the electron. Later experiments continued to give more positive proof of the existence of a positive electron. Now, very strong beams of positrons can be produced in the laboratory.

It should be pointed out here that near sea level most cosmic rays come from above, whereas a few come from other angles and the horizontal, and some even from below.

***Carl David Anderson (1905–), American physicist, was born in San Marino, California, September 3, 1905. He obtained his Ph.D. in physics at the California Institute of Technology in 1930 and has remained there ever since. He became professor of physics in 1939 and Chairman of the Division of Physics, Mathematics, and Astronomy in 1962. He has received many medals and honorary degrees, including the Nobel Prize in physics in 1936. He is best known for his discovery of mesons, as well as positively charged electrons in cosmic rays. The author has had the good fortune of meeting C. D. Anderson on various occasions.**

56.12. Creation of Electron Pairs

Soon after Anderson's discovery of the positron, several theoretical physicists attempted to calculate the conditions under which a positron might exist in nature. An extension of the quantum theory of the electron, proposed earlier by P. Dirac, led them to the prediction that if a high-energy photon, i.e., a high-frequency γ ray, were to come close enough to the nucleus of an atom, the electric field of the nucleus would be strong enough to annihilate the γ ray and create in its place a *pair of particles, an electron and a positron.* These two particles, the theory predicts, should have the same mass, and equal but opposite charges. A schematic diagram of pair production is given in Fig. 56M.

Blackett, Anderson, and others, looking for such pairs in a cloud chamber, soon found them exactly as predicted. Gamma rays from a radioactive element like $_{81}Tl^{208}$, in passing through matter, were observed to produce pairs of electrons. Three photographs of such incidents are shown in Fig. 56L. In (b) three different pairs are seen emerging from the points marked X on the lower side of a lead plate, and in (c) and (d) a pair is seen having been produced apparently in mid-air. As usual the γ rays that produced these pairs do not show up in the cloud chamber.

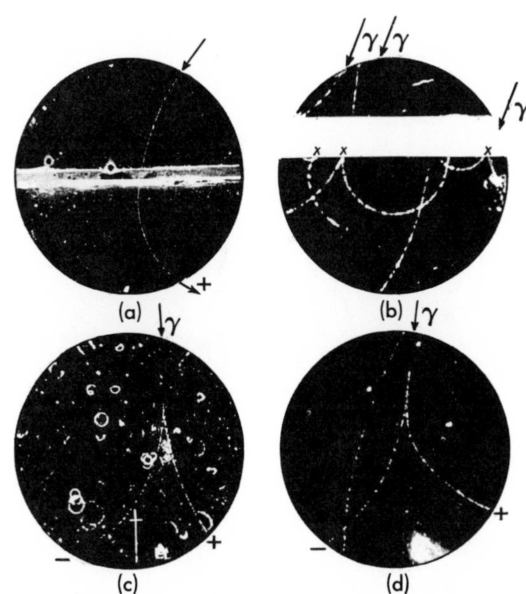

Fig. 56L. Wilson cloud-chamber photographs of pair production. An X ray coming close to the nucleus of an atom produces a pair of electrons, one positive and one negative. (a) Discovery of a positron (after Anderson), (b) three pairs of electrons produced by X rays (after Anderson), (c) pair produced in air by X rays (after Lauritson and Fowler), (d) pair produced in air by X rays from $_{81}Tl^{208}$ (after Simons and Zuber).

When an electron pair is created, *conservation of energy and momentum* requires the two particles to move almost straight forward. Without a magnetic field applied to the cloud chamber, the particles travel side by side in almost parallel paths, but with a magnetic field the path of the positron bends to one side and that of the electron to the other.

The reason positrons were not discovered earlier in the history of physics is that they do not exist long in the free state. As soon as a positron meets with an electron, the two are annihilated. Because a positron can annihilate an electron it is called an *antiparticle.*

Experiments indicate that all electrons and positrons spin around an axis through their center of mass. There is good evidence that when a positron and an electron come close together, they frequently combine by revolving around each other like a double star, with their spin axes parallel to one another. As such a pair they are called *positronium.*

Positronium is very short lived, for soon the two particles annihilate each other; in their place γ rays are created. If the particles were spinning in the same direction, they would disintegrate into three γ rays of different energies, whereas, if they were spinning in opposite directions, they would produce two γ rays. Conservation of energy and momentum requires each of these latter rays to have an energy of $\frac{1}{2}$MeV [see Eq.(53k)]. As reactions we can write, for pair production

$$\gamma \rightarrow e^- + \bar{e}^+ \tag{56a}$$

and for pair annihilation into two gamma rays,

$$e^- + \bar{e}^+ \rightarrow \gamma + \gamma \tag{56b}$$

The bar over any given symbol signifies that it is an antiparticle. The subject of particles vs antiparticles is given in detail in Chaps. 64 and 65.

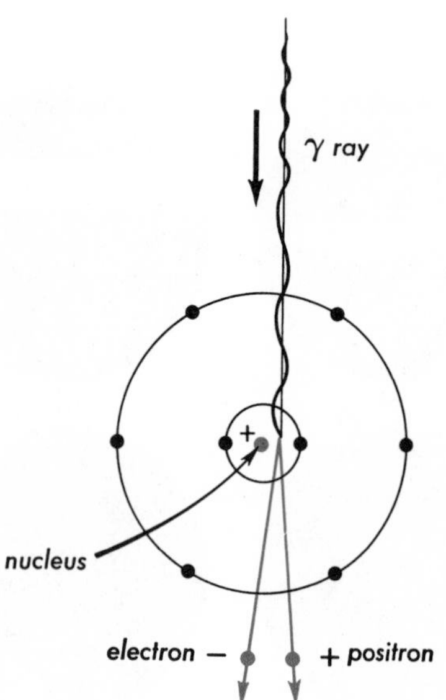

Fig. 56M. Schematic diagram of electron pair production.

56.13. Cosmic-Ray Showers

Out of hundreds and hundreds of cloud-chamber photographs of cosmic rays, the experimenter is occasionally rewarded with a picture of a cosmic-ray shower. Instead of one or two tracks in the picture, he finds anywhere from half a dozen or more to several hundred. As shown by the photographs in Fig. 56N, most of the tracks of a shower seem to come from one localized region, usually within a solid piece of matter like a lead plate or the wall of the cloud chamber.

An extensive study of showers by both the experimental and theoretical physicists has led to the conclusion that each shower is produced by a single, high-energy cosmic ray. A charged particle of very high energy upon entering a solid block of matter, where atoms are packed very close together, carries out the multiple-collision process illustrated in Fig. 56H. Here, within a short distance of 1 or 2 cm of lead, enough atoms are encountered to yield many secondaries. These secondaries, emerging from the lower face of the metal, result in the observed photographs.

In a thin sheet of metal, relatively small showers are usually found, whereas with a thick metal block showers of many tracks are occasionally photographed. The first five photographs in Fig. 56N were taken without a magnetic field so that the tracks are all straight, while the last photograph was taken with a magnetic field. The bending of three tracks to the right and three to the left indicates equal numbers of positrons and electrons.

In photograph (a), a single high-speed particle is seen to enter the lead plate from above and to produce some twenty or more secondary particles, each with enough energy to get through and into the air space below. In (b), two small showers of particles enter the top surface of the lead plate, whereas a single larger shower emerges from the bottom. Apparently one or two of the particles at the center of the one shower above have the necessary high energy to produce the lower shower, whereas the others of lower energy are stopped by the lead. Note particularly the fanning out of the rays below. In (c), a small shower of very high energy particles enters the chamber from above, having been produced far above the cloud chamber in a shower-producing process, probably by a single particle of extremely high energy. As some of these secondaries pass through the lead, each produces a shower of its own.

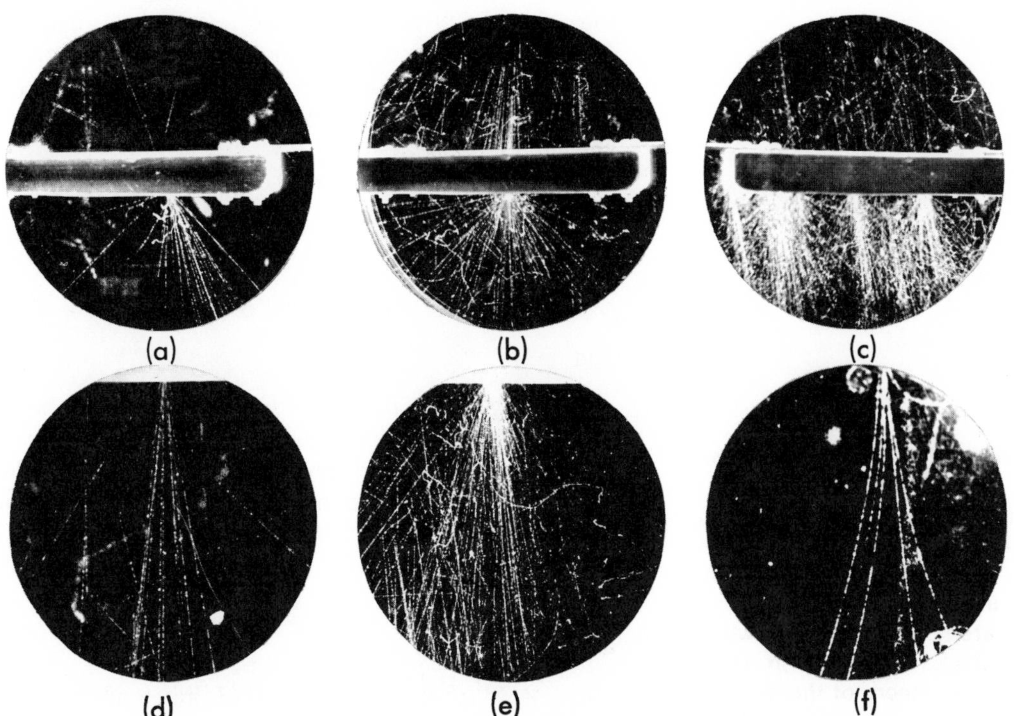

Fig. 56N. Wilson cloud-chamber photographs of cosmic-ray showers. (The first three photographs are reproduced through the courtesy of R. B. Brode and the last three through the courtesy of C. D. Anderson and the *Physical Review*.)

Direct evidence that some showers originate with a single high-energy particle is shown in Fig. 56O. Here, in a cloud chamber with 13 equally spaced lead plates, a relatively large shower is seen to have grown from only one or possibly two particles at the top. Not only does this avalanche grow in numbers with each traversal of a lead plate, but the relatively small spread of the tracks indicates how nearly each new particle recoils along with the others in the forward direction. In this picture, one observes in the small space of several inches the process that, in Fig. 56H, requires several miles of air.

56.14. Mesons

The presence in cosmic rays of charged particles having a mass several hundred times that of an electron, yet considerably lighter than a proton, was discovered by Anderson and Nedermeyer in 1938. These particles, called *mesons,* are of several kinds, and experimental data taken in balloons and airplanes show that most of them are produced high in the atmosphere by the collisions of primary cosmic rays with air nuclei.

High in the atmosphere high-energy atomic particles collide with atomic nuclei, and as a result transfer large amounts of energy by knocking out protons, neutrons, and π mesons, as shown in Fig. 56P.

When a high-energy proton collides with a nucleus transferring energy to another proton within, the following typical reactions occur:

$$p^+ + p^+ \rightarrow p^+ + p^+ + \pi^+ + \pi^0 + \pi^- \tag{56c}$$

and

$$p^+ + p^+ \rightarrow p^+ + n^0 + \pi^+ + \pi^+ + \pi^- \tag{56d}$$

When the incoming proton collides and transfers a large amount of energy to a neutron the following typical reactions occur:

$$p^+ + n^0 \rightarrow p^+ + p^+ + \pi^+ + \pi^- + \pi^- \tag{56e}$$

and

$$p^+ + n^0 \rightarrow p^+ + n^0 + \pi^+ + \pi^0 + \pi^- \tag{56f}$$

The π mesons, each with a mass of about 273 m_e, along with other nucleons, recoil forward with speeds close to that of light (m_e = mass of an electron). The term nucleon is here applied to only those particles believed to exist in atomic nuclei and consist of protons and neutrons.

The possible existence of mesons and their spontaneous disintegration were first predicted by H. Yukawa* in 1935, and first photographed by Williams and Roberts in 1940.

All charged π mesons are now known to have a half-life of

***Hideki Yukawa (1907–), Japanese physicist, won the Nobel Prize for physics in 1949 for "investigations in theoretical physics, especially the theory of elementary particles." He was born in Tokyo, graduated from Kyoto University in 1929, and while lecturer at Osaka University in 1935, proposed a new theory of the nuclear forces that bind atomic nuclei together. Through this work, he predicted the existence of mesons, later discovered in cosmic rays by C. D. Anderson. He served as professor of physics at Kyoto from 1939 to 1950; Director of the Research Institute for Fundamental Physics in 1953; visiting professor at the Institute for Advanced Studies, Princeton, N.J. in 1948; and lecturer at Columbia University 1949–1953.**

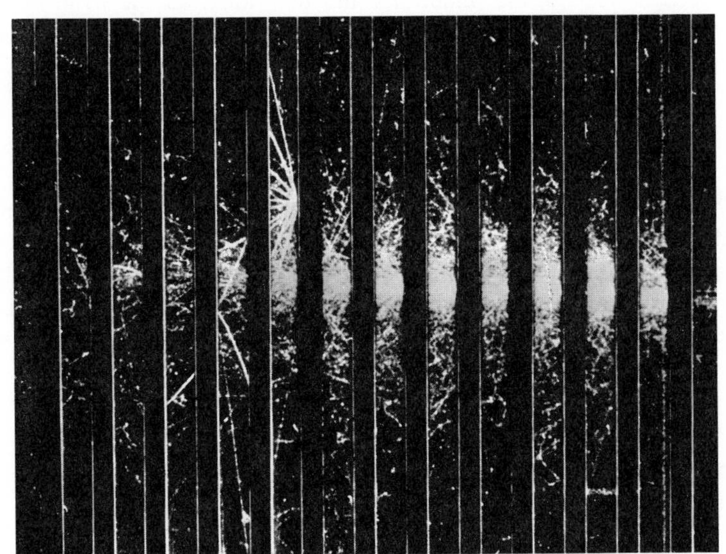

Fig. 56O. Cloud-chamber photograph showing cascade shower of cosmic rays developed in 13 lead plates, each 1.3 cm thick. (Courtesy, Wm. B. Fretter.)

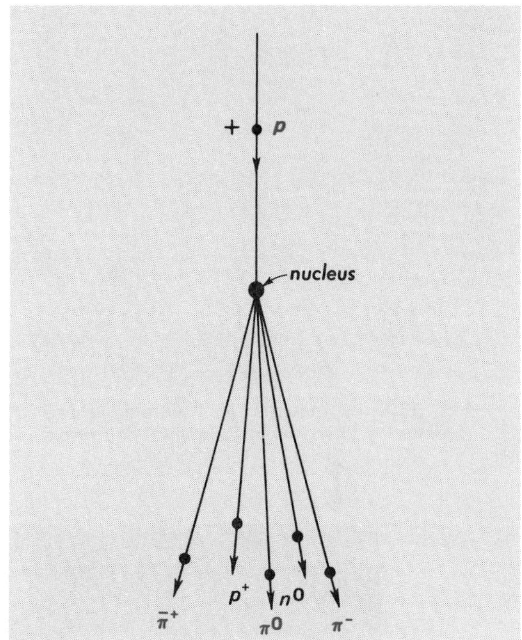

Fig. 56P. Primary cosmic ray produces π mesons by nuclear collision.

2.604×10^{-8} s, and each one decays into a charged μ particle called a *muon,* and a lightweight neutral particle called a *neutrino* (see Sec. 54.2).

The neutrino ν is an uncharged particle, postulated first by Pauli in order to explain nuclear phenomena in keeping with the fundamental laws of the conservation of energy and of momentum.

The decay of π mesons, more commonly called *pions,* may be written as interactions as follows:

$$\pi^- \rightarrow \mu^- + \bar{\nu}_\mu \tag{56g}$$

$$\bar{\pi}^+ \rightarrow \bar{\mu}^+ + \nu_\mu \tag{56h}$$

The uncharged π mesons are very unstable. With a half-life of 8.9×10^{-17} s, they decay into two γ rays. In the upper atmosphere these γ rays create cascade showers of electrons by electron pair-production and bremsstrahlung (see Fig. 56O).

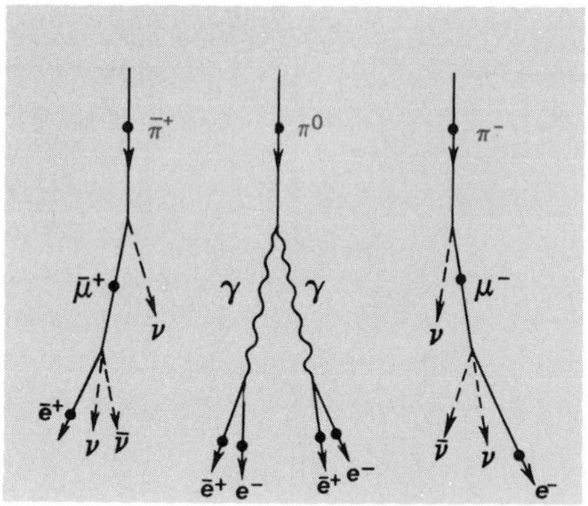

Fig. 56Q. π mesons disintegrate into μ mesons, γ rays, electrons, and neutrinos.

The decay of a neutral pion can be written

$$\pi^0 \rightarrow \gamma + \gamma \tag{56i}$$

It is now well known that muons decay, with half-lives of 2.1983×10^{-6} s, into electrons and neutrinos, as shown in Figs. 56Q and 56R. The decay of the muons may be written as follows:

$$\mu^- \rightarrow e^- + \bar{\nu}_e + \nu_\mu \tag{56j}$$

$$\bar{\mu}^+ \rightarrow \bar{e}^+ + \nu_e + \bar{\nu}_\mu \tag{56k}$$

In the above reactions we see that there are four different kinds of neutrinos, ν_μ, $\bar{\nu}_\mu$, ν_e, and $\bar{\nu}_e$. These particles will be treated in detail in Chaps. 64 and 65. The neutrino subscripts indicate the electrons and muons with which they were associated, while the bar over a particle signifies it is an *antiparticle*.

Many of the charged muons, with their mass of about 210 m_e,

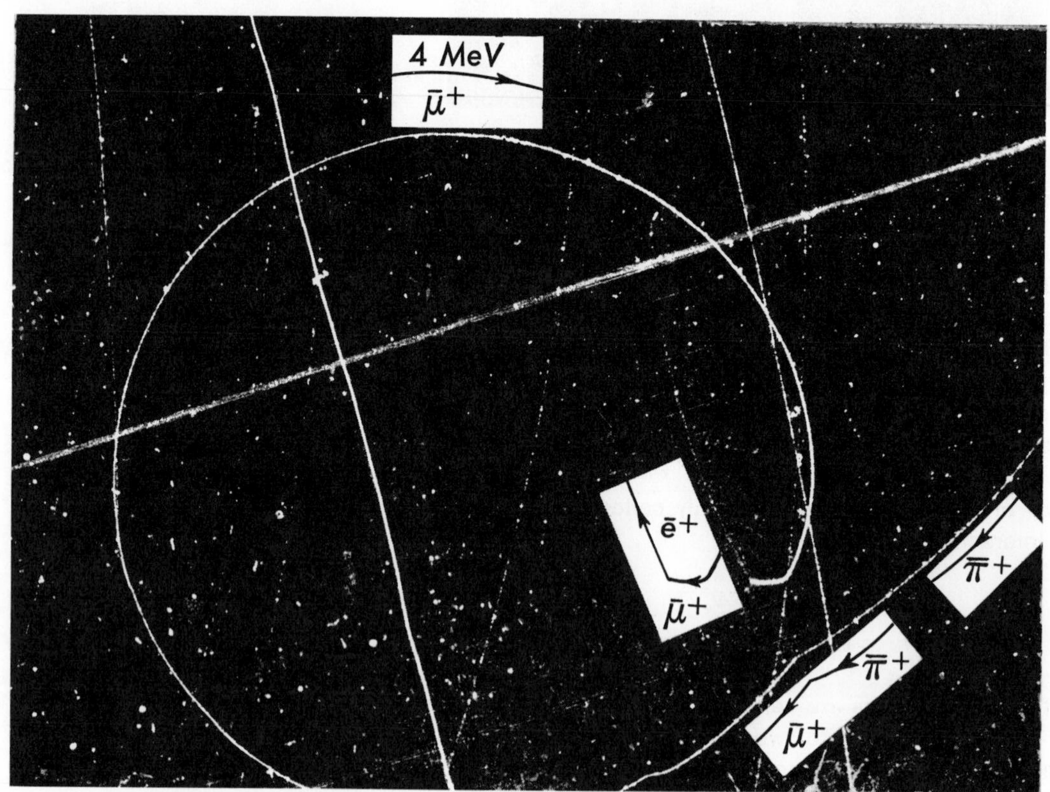

Fig. 56R. Wilson cloud chamber photographed in a magnetic field of 8000 gauss showing decay of a π meson (pion) into a μ meson (muon) and of the μ meson into a positron.

traverse the atmosphere before decaying, and reach the surface of the earth. At sea level the charged cosmic rays are about 70% muons and 29% electrons and positrons, with about 1% heavier particles like protons, deuterons, α particles, etc.

In traversing solid matter, negatively charged π mesons frequently slow down to such a speed that, upon an encounter with a nucleus, they are attracted by the + charge and captured. In this process the meson mass is transformed into energy exciting the nucleus to such a state that it literally explodes by shooting out a number of heavier particles like protons, deuterons, α particles, etc. Figure 56S shows such a "star" event in a photographic emulsion.

Recent studies of cosmic-ray tracks made in photographic emulsions and cloud chambers indicate the presence of particles with various other masses and charges (to be discussed in Chap. 64). Most recent cosmic-ray observations at high altitudes and at sea level are shown in Table 56A.

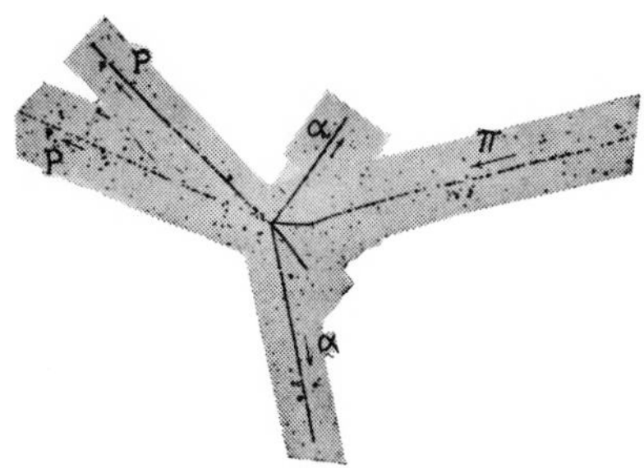

Fig. 56S. "Star" in photographic emulsion showing the explosion of a nucleus resulting from the capture of a slow π meson. (Courtesy, C. F. Powell's laboratory, University of Bristol, England.)

TABLE 56A
Composition of primary and secondary cosmic rays

Primaries		*Sea level*	
H	89%	Muons	70%
He	9%	$\bar{e}^+$ and e^-	29%
Li, Be, B	0.5%	Heavier particles	1%
C, N, O	0.5%		
Ne, Mg, Si	0.1%		
Fe	0.03%		

questions

1. Make a diagram of a string-electroscope. Explain how you could charge it for recording cosmic rays. How do cosmic rays cause it to discharge?

2. Make a diagram of a Geiger–Müller-tube counter, and briefly explain how it is able to be used to detect atomic particles of high energy.

3. Who was awarded the Nobel Prize in physics for the discovery of cosmic rays? What was his experimental observation?

4. How does the intensity of cosmic rays vary with altitude?

5. Explain why the intensity of cosmic rays is a minimum near the equator.

6. Make a diagram.

7. How was the positron discovered, and by whom?

8. Under what conditions are electron pairs created?

9. What is a cosmic-ray telescope, and how is it made?

10. What are primary cosmic rays, and of what are they composed?

11. What are the secondary cosmic rays, and of what are they composed?

12. Make a list of all the atomic particles found in cosmic rays.

13. Make diagrams to show the disintegration of π mesons.

14. What is the solar wind composed of? What effect does it have on the earth's magnetic field?

57 Atomic particle accelerators

*Ernest O. Lawrence (1901–1958), American experimental physicist, obtained the A.B. degree at the University of South Dakota in 1922, the master's degree at Minnesota in 1923, and the Ph.D. at Yale University in 1925. After two years as National Research Fellow he became, at the early age of 26, assistant professor of physics at Yale University. The following year he was appointed associate professor of physics at the University of California, and in 1930 was made full professor. Having built up the Radiation Laboratory at the same institution, he became its director in 1936. In 1937 he was awarded the Comstock Prize of the National Academy of Sciences, the Cresson Medal of the Franklin Institute, and the Hughes Medal of the Royal Society of London. Lawrence was a member of the National Academy of Sciences and was noted principally for his invention and development of the cyclotron and its application to the production of induced radioactivity. For these discoveries he was granted the Nobel Prize in 1939. During World War II he directed one of the main research projects leading to the isolation of uranium-235 used in atomic bombs.

At the time Cockcroft and Walton were performing their first disintegration experiments (see Fig. 55M), E. O. Lawrence,* an American physicist, and his assistant M. S. Livingston were developing a new type of atomic accelerator which soon attracted the attention of the leading physicists the world over. So successful was this "atomic machine gun" in producing high-speed atomic projectiles for disintegration experiments that a new and larger instrument was soon constructed and put into operation. Because the principles of this accelerator involved the cyclic motion of charged atomic particles in a uniform magnetic field, the device was appropriately called a *cyclotron.* Today a cyclotron of considerable size occupies a most prominent position in many of the leading physics laboratories of the world.

One of the early cyclotrons built at the University of California, called the "sixty-inch," was an instrument capable of producing intense beams of protons, deuterons (isotopes of hydrogen with mass 2 and missing their electron), or α particles having energies of 12, 24, and 48 MeV, respectively. The purpose of these high-speed particles, as is the case with all such instruments, is to subject various known substances to bombardment and thus produce disintegrations and transmutations of all kinds.

57.1. The Lawrence Cyclotron

Although the operation of a large cyclotron requires an elaborate outlay of apparatus and equipment, the principles upon which it operates are quite simple. As a means of explaining these principles, cross-sectional diagrams of a cyclotron are shown in Figs. 57A and 57B.

The very heart of the instrument consists of two short, hollow, half-cylinders, D_1 and D_2, mounted inside of a vacuum chamber V, between the poles of a powerful electromagnet, and connected on the outside to the two terminals of a high-frequency alternating-current generator. This generator is really a shortwave radio transmitter supplying energy to the "dees" (D_1 and D_2) instead of to the antenna.

When a trace of hydrogen gas is admitted to the evacuated chamber, the hot-wire filament F ionizes some of the hydrogen atoms, thereby producing the protons to be used as atomic bullets. At the particular instant when D_1 is charged positively and D_2 is charged negatively, a proton in the neighborhood of F will be accelerated toward D_2. Moving through the strong magnetic field of the huge magnet, this positively charged particle traverses a circular path as shown in the diagram.

If, after making a half-turn, the potential difference is reversed so that D_1 becomes negatively charged and D_2 positively charged, the proton will be attracted by one and repelled by the other, causing it to increase its speed. With added speed it therefore moves in the arc of a larger circle as shown.

After this second half-turn, the potential difference again reverses, making D_1 positive and D_2 negative, and again the proton speeds up. Thus, as the potentials reverse periodically, the proton travels faster and faster, moving in ever-expanding circles, until, reaching the outer edge, it passes through a narrow open window W.

Upon leaving W all protons must pass close to a negatively charged plate P where, by attraction, their paths are straightened out and they become a separated beam of projectiles. Whatever substance is to be bombarded is then placed in this beam, and the disintegrated fragments are studied by means of various detective devices.

The fundamental principle that makes the cyclotron work at all is the fact that *the time required for a charged particle to make one complete turn within the dees is the same for all speeds.* The faster a particle travels the larger is the circle it must traverse, thus keeping the time constant. Hence, with a constant frequency of the alternating current supply, some particles may be just starting their acceleration near the center while others farther out have already acquired higher speeds. The result is a pulsed stream of protons emerging from the window W.

If the ac voltage applied between the *dees* of the cyclotron is 200,000 V, with each half-turn a particle obtains an added velocity equivalent to 200,000 V. If a proton makes 30 complete revolutions before leaving the chamber at W, it will have acquired a velocity equivalent to 200,000 times 30 times 2, or 12,000,000 V. Here, then, is a beam of 12 MeV protons acquired by the application of a potential difference only $\frac{1}{60}$ as great.

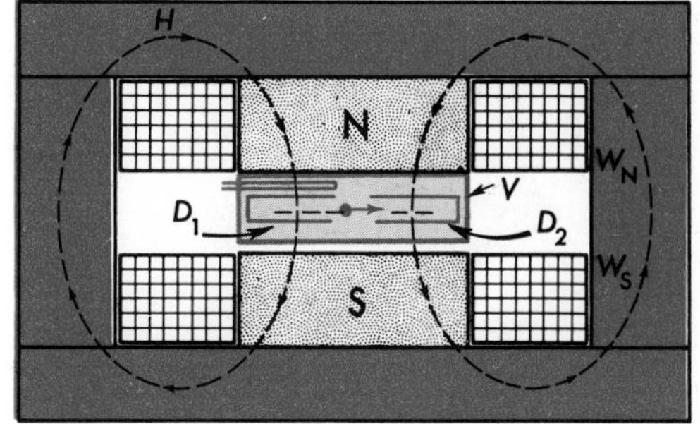

Fig. 57A. Cross-sectional diagram of a cyclotron.

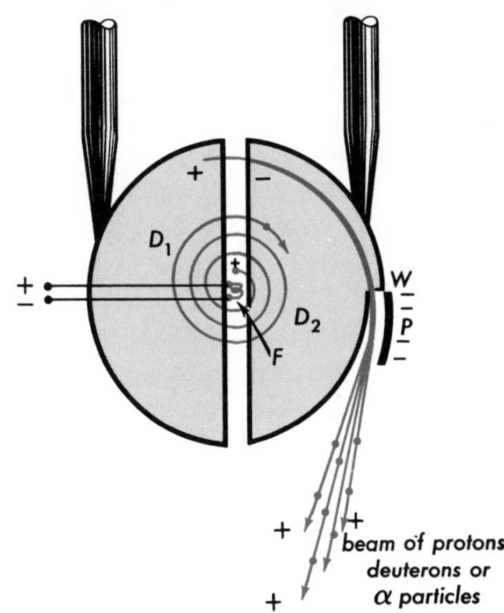

Fig. 57B. Detailed diagram of the "dees" of a cyclotron.

Fig. 57C. Photograph by Paul Donaldson of an 11-MeV deuteron beam from the Harvard cyclotron. (Courtesy, Harvard University Press and A. K. Solomon.)

Deuterium is a gas composed of atoms of mass 2, the heavy isotope of hydrogen (see Appendix VIII). A deuterium atom without its one and only orbital electron is called *deuteron.* When hydrogen in the evacuated chamber of the 60-in. cyclotron is replaced by *deuterium* and the magnetic field strength is doubled, a beam of high-energy deuterons is obtained. Having twice the mass, but the same unit positive charge as protons, these particles acquire twice as much energy. If helium gas is used in place of deuterium, many of the atoms become doubly ionized at the source and after acceleration emerge from the cyclotron window as alpha particles with an energy of about 40 MeV. By increasing or decreasing the frequency of the potential applied to the dees, and properly adjusting the magnetic field, protons, deuterons, or α particles of 12, 24, and 48, MeV, respectively, can be produced.

Some of the details of the cyclotron shown in Fig. 57A are as follows: The dimension, 60 in., refers to the diameter of the poles of the cyclotron magnet; this in turn limits the size of the dees and therefore the maximum energy available in the form of atomic projectiles. Most of the instrument's total weight of 200 tons lies in the solid iron core and the pole pieces located inside the field windings. The latter, consisting of many turns of thick copper wire, are encased in tanks W_S and W_N through which cooling fluid is continually circulated.

A photograph of an 11-MeV deuteron beam from the Harvard University cyclotron is shown in Fig. 57C. From the point where the particles emerge from the cyclotron window at the left center to where they come to rest in mid-air at the lower right, they ionize the air molecules and atoms, causing them to emit visible light.

57.2. Theory of the Cyclotron

The theory of the cyclotron involves simple classical laws describing the motion of a charged particle in a uniform magnetic field. By Eq.(41e), the force on a particle in a magnetic field is given by *Bev,* and this is equal to the centripetal force Mv^2/r:

$$Bev = \frac{Mv^2}{r} \tag{57a}$$

Here *e* is the charge on the particle in coulombs, *M* is its mass in kilograms, *v* is its velocity in meters per second, and *r* is the radius of its circular path in meters. To find the time required for any charged particle to make one complete circle the formula

$x = vt$ from mechanics is employed. The distance traveled in one turn is represented by x, and T represents the time:

$$T = \frac{x}{v} = \frac{2\pi r}{v} \tag{57b}$$

By solving Eq.(57a) for v, and substituting Eq.(57b), we obtain

$$v = \frac{Ber}{M} \tag{57c}$$

and

$$T = \frac{2\pi M}{Be} \tag{57d}$$

Since the frequency of revolution ν is just the reciprocal of the period,

$$\nu = \frac{Be}{2\pi M} \tag{57e}$$

Equation (57d) shows that the period is independent of r and v and for like particles (that is, the same e and M) varies with the magnetic induction B. The alternating potential difference E applied to the cyclotron dees must therefore match in frequency the particles' motion due to the field B. It is customary in practice to apply a fixed frequency to the dees and adjust the current in the magnetic field coils until resonance occurs. In the 60-in. cyclotron, $B = 1.30$ T.

To complete the relationships given above we use Eq.(49a) to obtain the energy of the accelerated particles in volts:

$$Ve = \tfrac{1}{2}Mv^2 \tag{57f}$$

The masses of particles commonly accelerated are

electron $= 9.109558 \times 10^{-31}$ Kg
proton $= 1.672614 \times 10^{-27}$ Kg
deuteron $= 3.343569 \times 10^{-27}$ Kg
α particle $= 6.644625 \times 10^{-27}$ Kg

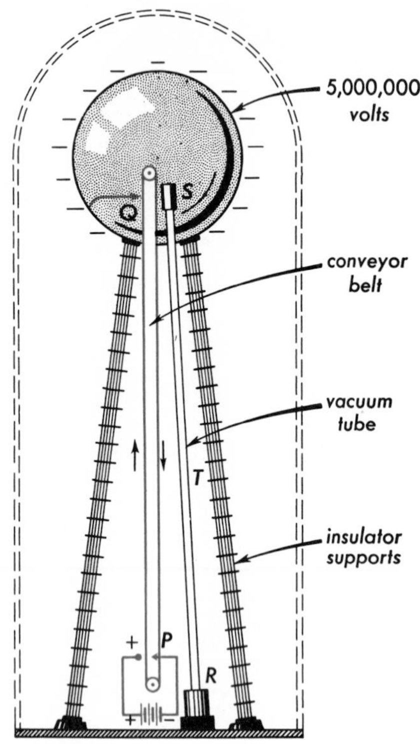

Fig. 57D. Diagram of a Van de Graaff generator of high voltage.

Example 1. The diameter of the D's in the 60-inch cyclotron is 1.524 m. If deuterons, each with a mass of 3.344×10^{-27} Kg, are accelerated in a field of 1.30 T, find (a) the period of the particles, (b) the frequency applied to the D's, (c) the velocity of the emerging particles in m/s, and (d) the energy of the emerging deuterons in MeV.

Solution. The given quantities are $B = 1.30$ T, $e = 1.602 \times 10^{-19}$ C, $M = 3.344 \times 10^{-27}$ Kg, and $r = 0.762$ m. By direct substitution of known quantities in Eq.(57c), we obtain

$$T = \frac{2\pi M}{Be} = \frac{2\pi \times 3.344 \times 10^{-27}}{1.30 \times 1.602 \times 10^{-19}}$$

$$T = 1.009 \times 10^{-7} \text{ s}$$

Since the frequency is the reciprocal of the period, we find

$$\nu = \frac{1}{T} = 9.91 \text{ MHz}$$

Using the first relation in Eq.(57c), we find

$$v = \frac{Ber}{M} = \frac{1.30 \times 1.602 \times 10^{-19} \times 0.762}{3.344 \times 10^{-27}}$$

$$v = 4.75 \times 10^{7} \text{ m/s}$$

Using Eq.(57f), solving for V, and substituting known quantities, we obtain

$$V = \frac{\frac{1}{2}Mv^2}{e} = \frac{\frac{1}{2}\cdot 3.344 \times 10^{-27} (4.75 \times 10^{7})^2}{1.602 \times 10^{-19}}$$

$$V = 23.55 \text{ MeV}$$

57.3. The Van de Graaff Generator

This machine, developed in 1931 by R. Van de Graaff at Princeton University, employs the principle of the electrostatic generator discovered many years ago. A typical installation, as shown in Fig. 57D, consists of a large hollow sphere, supported on insulating columns and charged by a belt conveying electrical charges from a battery at ground potential and depositing it inside the sphere. The fabric conveyor belt, a foot or more in width and running over well-aligned rollers, travels about 25 m/s.

As the belt passes between the metallic surface and row of

needle points at P, electrons from the points jump toward the positive electrode and are caught by the belt. Upon entering the sphere at the top, the electrons jump to the needle points Q where they go quickly to the outside surface of the sphere. The "spraying" of electrons *to* and *from* the points is ensured by keeping the battery potential high (about 50,000 V) to maintain a "brush discharge." As more and more electrons arrive at the sphere, its negative potential rises higher and higher until leakage into the surrounding air and through the insulators becomes equally fast.

Atomic particles to be accelerated are generated inside a vacuum-tube source S inside the sphere. Starting at the top of a long straight vacuum tube T, electrons are accelerated downward toward ground potential, where, acquiring the full energy of the available voltage, they are allowed to bombard whatever target is being studied. Where installations are designed for accelerating protons, deuterons, or α particles, the battery potential is reversed and the sphere acquires a high positive potential with respect to the ground.

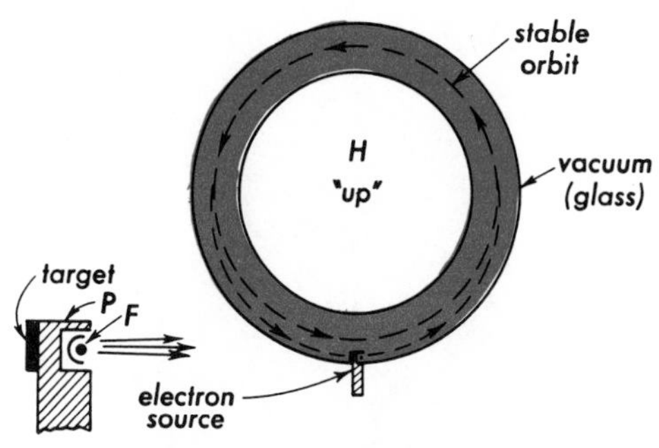

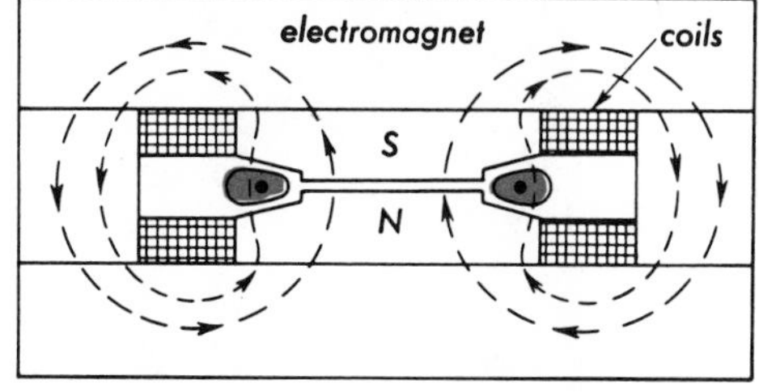

Fig. 57E. Cross-sectional diagrams of an electron accelerator, called a betatron.

57.4. The Betatron

The *betatron,* invented in 1941 by D. W. Kerst* at the University of Illinois, is an electron accelerator capable of producing electron beams of high energy as well as X rays of extremely high penetrating power. This ingenious device differs from the cyclotron in at least two fundamental respects: first, the electrons are accelerated by a rapidly changing magnetic field, and, second, the circular orbit of the particles has a constant radius.

A cross-sectional diagram of a 20-MeV betatron is shown in Fig. 57E. A glass vacuum tube in the shape of a *doughnut* and containing an *electron gun* is mounted between the poles of an electromagnet. An alternating current (180 Hz) applied to the coils causes some of the magnetic lines of force to pass through the vacuum tube at the electron orbit and the remainder through the orbit center, as shown below in the figure. Electrons are injected only at the beginning of each quarter cycle when the field begins to increase in the "up" direction. The increasing field through the center of the orbit gives rise to an electromotive force, tangent to the orbit, speeding up the electrons; whereas the increasing field at the orbit is just sufficient to increase the centripetal force and keep the electrons from spiraling outward. The stability of such an orbit is brought about by properly shaping the pole faces of the magnet, adjusting the frequency and strength of the magnetic field, and injecting the electrons at the proper voltage at the appropriate time.

***Donald William Kerst (1911–), American physicist, was born in Galena, Illinois. Educated at the University of Wisconsin, he began his career as an X-ray tube developer with the General Electric X-ray Corporation in 1937, and became an instructor in physics at the University of Illinois in 1938, and served as professor from 1942–57. After this, he spent five years with the Atomic Division of the General Dynamics Corporation, and, in 1962, became professor of physics at the University of Wisconsin. He is a member of the National Academy of Science and has been awarded their Comstock Prize and the Scott Award of the Franklin Institute. He is most noted for his invention of the betatron while at the University of Illinois.**

Fig. 55F. Photograph of the 184-in., 4000-ton, synchro-cyclotron at the University of California, Berkeley, California.

During World War II, a 350-ton betatron was constructed by the General Electric Company and put into use as a source of extremely penetrating X rays. In this instrument electrons accelerated to 100-MeV energy, and impinging upon a target, give rise to X rays capable of penetrating many feet of solid iron and lead.

57.5. The Synchro-Cyclotron

The firm belief that new and fundamental discoveries in nuclear physics can be made with atomic projectiles having greater and greater energies has led scientists and engineers in various institutions to combine their efforts in groups to design and construct larger and larger atomic accelerators. One such instrument is the *synchro-cyclotron* shown in Fig. 57F.

The fundamental differences between this and the orthodox cyclotron are the use of one dee in place of two and the use of an applied alternating-current potential whose frequency is made to rise and fall periodically instead of remaining constant. The principles of operation are illustrated in Fig. 57G. Starting at the center, protons, deuterons, or α particles are made to move in circles of increasing radius, the acceleration taking place as they enter and leave the lips of the dee. At the outer edge they are deflected out of the field, as in the cyclotron, or allowed to strike a suitable target inside the vacuum chamber.

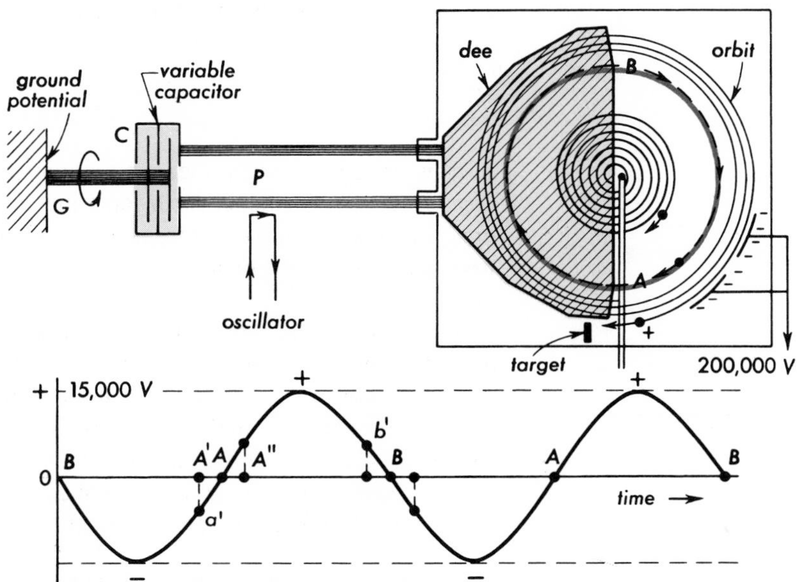

Fig. 57G. Illustration of "phase stability" as applied to the synchro-cyclotron.

The theory of the synchro-cyclotron is based upon "phase stability," a principle fundamental to nearly all high-energy accelerators.* This relatively new idea can be derived from the well-founded theory that, as a particle is accelerated and approaches the speed of light, continued acceleration increases the mass, while the speed approaches a nearly constant value. In other words, as more and more energy is given to a particle, more and more of it is stored as *increased mass* and less and less as *increased speed.*

To apply this principle to an accelerator like the synchro-cyclotron, consider the conditions that exist when a positively charged particle in a uniform magnetic field is moving with constant speed in an orbit of constant radius and at the same time in synchronism with an applied high-frequency potential difference. Such an orbit is represented by the dotted circle in Fig. 57G, with the particle entering and leaving the lips of the dee at A and B when the potential (see graph below) is zero. By Eq.(57a), $Bev = Mv^2/r$. Since, from mechanics, angular velocity $\omega = v/r$, and the frequency of revolution $f = \omega/2\pi$, direct substitution in Eq.(57a) gives $M = Be/2\pi f$. Multiplying both sides of this equation by the square of the speed of light c^2 gives

$$Mc^2 = \frac{Bec^2}{2\pi f}$$

where Mc^2 represents the total energy E of the particle:

$$E = \frac{Bec^2}{2\pi f} \tag{57g}$$

It may be shown from these equations that Mc^2 includes the *rest mass* m_0c^2 of the particle, and that to increase E the magnetic induction can be *increased* as in the betatron and synchrotron (see Sec. 57.6), or *the frequency can be decreased* as in the synchro-cyclotron.

Returning now to the high-speed but stationary orbit AB in Fig. 57G, assume that a particle is a little early in entering the dee. Arriving there, as shown by A′ in the graph below, the dee has a negative potential a′ and the particle is accelerated by attraction. Being accelerated, the mass increases with little increase in speed. Owing principally to increased mass, the particle now describes a larger circle, and the next time around it has dropped

* The theory of phase stability of atomic accelerators of high energy was first developed in 1945 by V. Veksler [*J. Phys.*, USSR, **9,** 153 (1945)], and independently by E. M. McMillan [*Phys. Rev.* **68,** 143 (1945)].

back to arrive more nearly at the time of *zero potential.* Hence, if the magnetic induction B were to be increased or the frequency f were to be decreased, the particle might be made to continually enter and leave the dee ahead of the zero phase and receive a forward push each time around.

If a particle gets behind the zero phase (A to A″ in the graph), it will not receive a forward pulse and, moving with nearly constant speed, will permit a decreasing frequency of an applied potential difference to catch up and get ahead again. Hence phase stability is ensured and forward impulses will occur as the particle spirals outward with increasing energy.

In the 184-in. synchro-cyclotron, the high-frequency potential difference of 7 to 9 KV is applied to the dee stem at P, and the variable capacitor C, composed of a fast rotating set of "fan blades" passing between a set of stationary blades, varies the frequency up and down through relatively wide limits. In producing 460 MeV deuterons, the frequency of the dee potential rises and falls 120 times/s between the limits of 18.0 and 13.6 MHz.

The positive ions are pulsed into the center of the dee when the frequency is 18.0 MHz, and they arrive at the outer edge when it has dropped to about 13.6 MHz. Having made 110,000 turns around the chamber in a period of only 4.5 thousandths of a second, the deuterons have an energy of 460 MeV. The target, located inside the vacuum chamber, is therefore bombarded by pulses coming at the rate of 120 per second.

A drop from 18.0 to 13.6 MHz decreases f [see Eq.(57g)] by about 25%, thereby increasing a deuteron's energy E and mass m by 25%, or 0.50 atomic mass unit (amu). Such an increase, by Eq.(53m), is equivalent to 450 MeV.

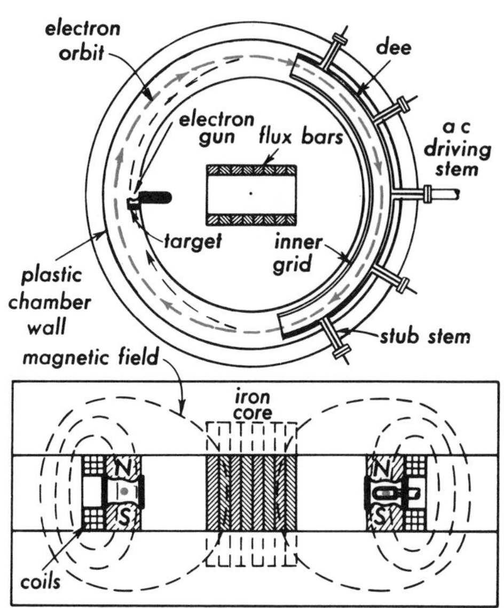

Fig. 57H. Cross-sectional diagrams of a 300-MeV synchrotron.

57.6. The Synchrotron

This device is an electron accelerator employing the principles of the *cyclotron* and *phase stability.* A cut-away diagram of such an instrument is shown in Fig. 57H. As in the betatron, electrons are injected into a doughnut-shaped vacuum chamber by an electron gun. Operating first as a betatron, the electrons are accelerated in an orbit of fixed radius by a rapidly increasing magnetic field. The rising field is produced by discharging a large capacitor bank through the magnet coils. Part of the field goes through the relatively small *flux bars* near the orbit center, and part through the pole faces and vacuum chamber.

As the electrons quickly approach the speed of light, their mass begins to increase rapidly; from about 2 MeV on, they move at almost constant speed (between 98% and 100% the speed of light). Increasing energy is added in this *second phase* by an alternating potential difference applied to the *sector dee* shown in the diagram. Instead of decreasing the frequency, as in the synchro-cyclotron, the magnetic induction B is increased [see Eq.(57d)] and as the electron *mass* increases, the stronger field maintains the beam orbit constant.

Upon reaching a maximum energy of 300 MeV, for example, the electrons, with a mass some 600 times their *rest mass,* are caused to spiral inward to strike a tungsten target, where they produce 300-MeV X rays.

57.7. The Proton Linear Accelerator

Although linear accelerators were proposed as early as 1929, and several were constructed, they did not prove satisfactory until 16 years later. Applying the principles of tubular wave guides and resonant cavities, L. Alvarez* and his collaborators, immediately after World War II, constructed the first successful linear accelerator (linac). Since a giant machine employing the same principles is functioning quite successfully at Stanford University, the ideas involved are of considerable importance.

A cut-away diagram of part of the Alvarez Lineac is given in Fig. 57I. Protons are initially produced and accelerated to 4 MeV by a pressure Van de Graaff generator (see Fig. 57D) and then

*Luis W. Alvarez (1911–) was born June 13, 1911, the son of a famous American physician and author, Dr. Walter C. Alvarez. He obtained his Ph.D. degree in physics at the University of Chicago in 1936, under the direction of A. H. Compton. He joined the physics staff of the University of California in 1936 and began his postgraduate research career in nuclear physics with Ernest O. Lawrence of the Radiation Laboratory. During World War II, he developed the Ground Control Approach Radar System widely used at major airports for landing planes in dense fog cover. For this he received the National Collier Trophy in 1946. Since then, he has won the Medal of Merit, the Einstein Medal, and the Michelson Award. His greatest contribution to physics is the development of the liquid hydrogen bubble chamber, and with his colleagues, his use of it to identify a large number of elementary atomic particles. For this and other work, he was awarded the Nobel Prize in physics for 1968.

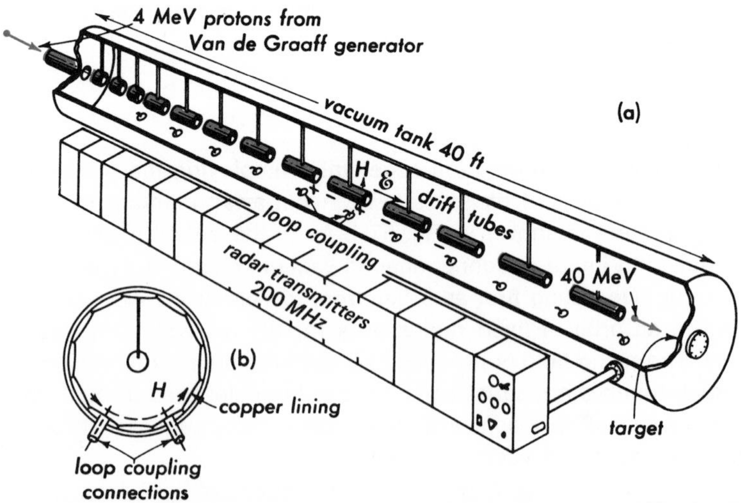

Fig. 57I. Diagrams showing the first section of a linear accelerator.

injected at that energy into one end of a 40-ft tank, as shown at the upper left. Once inside they are further accelerated as they pass through a series of "drift tubes," and arrive at the other end with an energy of about 40 MeV.

The tank cavity within the copper lining, fed by 30 radar transmitting oscillators, is set resonating at its *dominant mode* at a frequency of 200 MHz. The "standing-wave" conditions set up are such that the electric field $\mathcal{E}$ is parallel to the tube axis and is everywhere rising and falling together. The lengths of the drift tubes gradually increase so that the protons cross each gap when the field $\mathcal{E}$ is to the right. The protons are inside the tubes, in a field-free space, when the field between adjacent tube ends is to the left. It now seems possible that additional tank sections can be added end to end to this system to obtain almost any desired energy. Calculations indicate 1 MeV per lineal foot can be expected from such a system.

57.8. The 6.3-GeV Bevatron

The design and construction of accelerators capable of producing particles with energies in the range of thousands of millions of electron volts involve many problems and many people. Not the least of the problems is the economic factor concerned with the cost of building the equipment, as well as the projected cost of its maintenance and operation over a period of years.

The first of the giant machines to be constructed to accelerate atomic particles to the GeV range (1 GeV $= 1 \times 10^9$ electron volts) is the bevatron, a facility located at the Lawrence Radiation Laboratory, University of California, Berkeley, California. The bevatron was originally built to produce high velocity protons with sufficient energy to create pairs of protons by the process of collision and *pair production.* That they were produced is discussed in detail in Sec. 64.3.

The giant magnet of the bevatron consists of quadrant segments so spaced that the particle orbit is made up of four quarter-circles connected by four 6-m straight sections (see Fig. 57J). The electrical power supplied to the 10,000 ton magnet is provided by motor generators with large fly wheels. During buildup of the magnetic field, a peak power of 100,000 KW is drawn from the flywheels, and stored as a magnetic field in the magnet. As the field decreases between beam pulses, the generators act as motors and return the energy as mechanical energy to the flywheels.

The protons from a source S are first accelerated by a *Cockcroft-Walton* accelerator and injected at low energy, 500 KeV, into a *linear accelerator*. From there with an energy of 20 MeV they enter the race track proper. As they pass through the accelerator electrode in one of the straight sections, and are speeded up by the high-frequency potential differences, the magnetic field increases at the proper rate to keep the beam in the same orbit.

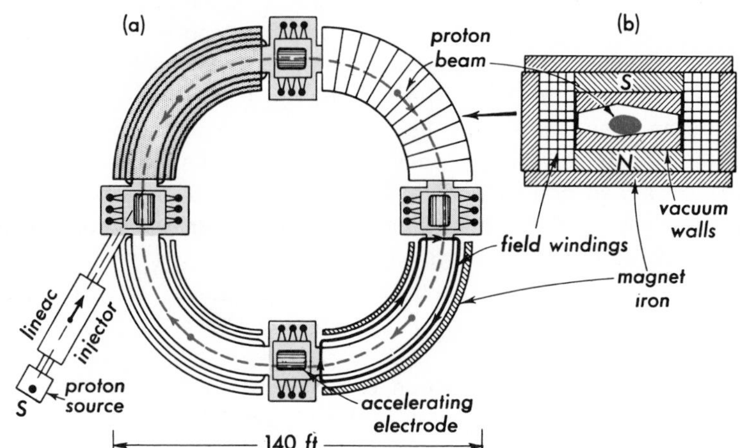

Fig. 57J. Berkeley bevatron designed to produce 6.2-BeV protons.

The output beam from the bevatron consists, as it does in all high-energy accelerators, of a series of pulses. From the time of injection, each pulse of protons takes about two seconds to acquire its final speed, and in so doing makes about four million revolutions of the orbit and travels about 480,000 Km (see Fig. 57K). Note for sake of comparison that this is greater than the distance to the moon (see Chap. 64).

57.9. *The 200-GeV Accelerator at Batavia*

The largest accelerator in the world today is located at the National Accelerator Laboratory near Batavia, Illinois. Funded by the United States Atomic Energy Commission, this machine produces proton pulses with energies in the 200 GeV range. An aerial photograph of the laboratory is reproduced in Fig. 57L. Note the relative sizes of the large and small circular tracks in relation to the automobiles in the parking lot near the bottom of the picture.

A schematic diagram of this facility in Fig. 57M shows how the protons are accelerated by four different units. Hydrogen ions are first produced and accelerated to 750 KeV by the Cockcroft-

Walton (C-W) accelerator at the bottom. Upon entering a long straight tube of a linear accelerator they are speeded up to an energy of 200 MeV, and injected into the circular booster, 150 m (500 ft) in diameter. Here they acquire an energy of 8 GeV, and are injected into the main ring, 2 Km ($1\frac{1}{4}$ mi) in diameter.

Emerging from the main ring with an energy of approximately 200 GeV, the beam is deflected along a straight path parallel to the linac. There the protons, traveling with 99.999% the speed of

THE BEVATRON

Fig. 57K. A six-billion volt accelerator of atomic particles, located at the University of California, Berkeley. (Photographed by K. Hildebrand and G. Kagawa. Courtesy of E. Lofgren, D. Cooksey, the Berkeley Laboratory at the University of California, and the Atomic Energy Commission.) Just behind the two men on the platform, at the far right and center, can be seen the rectangular housing of the atomic source and the Cockcroft-Walton accelerator. The cylindrical tank section containing the linear accelerator is clearly seen leading into the inflector assembly between quadrants 1 and 4. The main accelerating electrode assembly with the yellow colored ducts leading to it is seen farther back between quadrants 3 and 4. Note the overhead crane used for assembling, repairing, and the handling of massive apparatus and equipment.

light and a mass over 300 times their rest mass, are deflected into three or more laboratory areas. Area A is called the *proton laboratory,* area B the *neutrino laboratory,* and area C the *meson laboratory.*

Much, in the way of new discoveries, can be expected from this laboratory in the realm of elementary particle physics in the years that lie ahead.

Fig. 57L. Aerial photograph of the National Accelerator Laboratory, near Batavia, Illinois. The large main ring accelerator measures 2000 meters, or 1¼ miles in diameter, and produces 200-GeV protons.

The largest linear accelerator in the world today is located at Stanford University, Stanford, California. This facility consists of a 3000-m (10,000 ft) copper tube, through which electrons are accelerated to an energy of 20,000 MeV, or 20 GeV. Completed in 1966 the Stanford Linear Accelerator Center (SLAC) was funded, and today is operated, under a contract with the United States Atomic Energy Commission.

A photograph of the accelerator, with its related research and administration buildings, is shown in Fig. 57N. Over 240 klystron amplifier tubes are regularly spaced 12 m apart along the accelerator, and when the machine is turned on, oscillate with the same frequency of 2856 MHz.

Starting from rest at the far end in the photograph, electrons are propelled by radio waves through the 10 cm diameter tube to

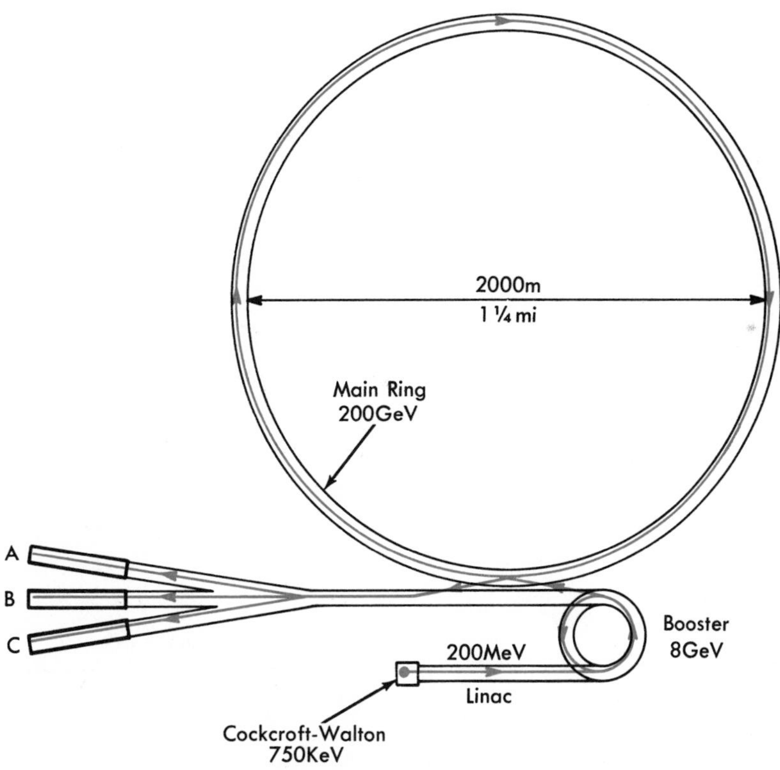

Fig. 57M. Schematic diagram of the largest accelerator in the world, located at the National Accelerator Laboratory, near Batavia, Illinois. The colored path shows the protons starting from rest in the Cockcroft–Walton accelerator, then being speeded up by the Linac and booster, and finally by the main ring. Leaving the main ring with 200-GeV energy, the protons are deflected into three or more laboratory areas: A, B, and C.

Fig. 57N. The Stanford Linear Accelerator Center (SLAC) facility, a two-mile long electron accelerator at Stanford, California. Note the different accompanying laboratories in the immediate foreground, the administration buildings at the right, and the divided highway crossing the landscape.

the near end, in much the same way that a surf rider on his board rides the incoming waves at the beach. At this end they emerge with a velocity of 99.99990% the speed of light, and a relativistic mass of ~40,000 times their rest mass. Here in the laboratory they may be made to strike a metal target and produce 20-GeV photons by the X-ray process.

The long accelerator tube is made up of a series of nearly one thousand identical 3-m *sections,* each containing more than 80 accurately machined cavities. Each section is constructed by alternately welding short copper tube sections, 10 cm in diameter and 3.5 cm long, to disks with a hole in the center, as shown in Fig. 57O. Copper tubing is then welded along the sides to produce water cooling for the section.

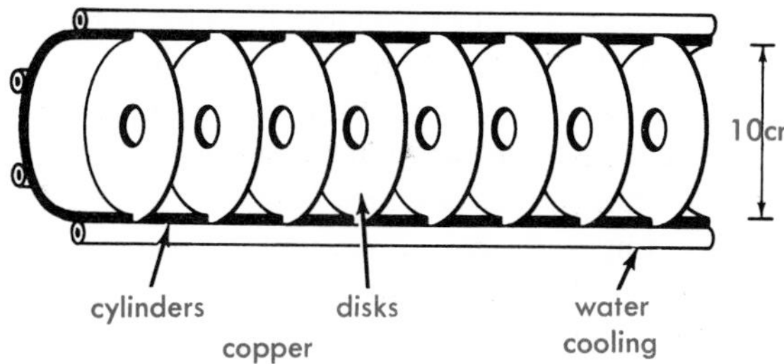

Fig. 57O. Drawing showing the construction of the 3000-meter (two-mile) copper accelerator tube of the Stanford LINAC.

The klystrons used for accelerating the electrons are radio vacuum tube oscillators, about one meter long, which work on the *principle of electron bunching* (see Fig. 57P). A steady stream

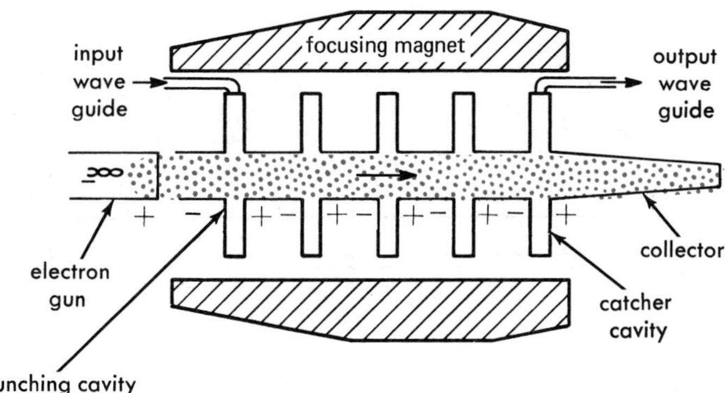

Fig. 57P. Schematic diagram of a klystron vacuum tube oscillator for producing radio waves by the process of electron bunching.

of electrons from a hot filament and anode are made to pass by the openings of the first cavity, called the *buncher.* The electric and magnetic field oscillations (standing waves) set up within the cavity give rise to oscillating potentials at the openings that speed up the electrons for one-half cycle, and slow them down for the other. In this manner the fast electrons catch up with the slower ones, causing a bunching of the electrons.

As regularly spaced bunches of electrons pass each cavity, resonance sets it oscillating, thus narrowing and refining the bunches. The strong oscillations of the electromagnetic field in the *output cavity,* called the *catcher,* are led off by the output wave guide as shown.

At the far end of the accelerator, 80-KeV electrons for the beam are produced by a hot filament and anode as in an ordinary *electron gun* (see Fig. 49G). Leaving the gun with about 50% the speed of light, the electrons pass through a buncher much the same as in the klystrons. They then pass through a drift tube where a radio wave, traveling at 75% the speed of light, further bunches the electrons, and raises their energies to 250 KeV. Next they enter a 3-m accelerator section where radio waves, traveling with the speed of light, further bunch and focus the electrons, and their speed is raised to 99.98% the speed of light, and the energy to 30 MeV. With this speed and energy they enter the long accelerator tube.

The basic unit of the accelerator proper is a 12-m "module" divided into four 3-m "sections." Power to each module is supplied by an individual klystron. There are 240 modules and 240

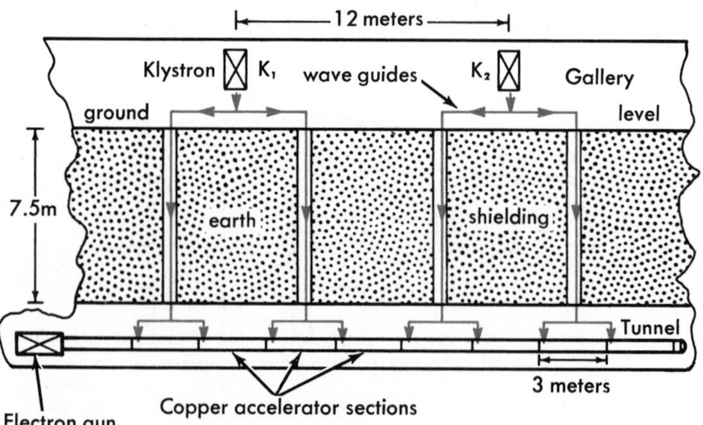

Fig. 57Q. Schematic diagram showing the first two of the 240 modules of the SLAC electron accelerator. Each klystron produces the traveling waves in four sections of the 3000-meter tube.

klystrons located at regular intervals in the two-mile underground tunnel, and in the two-mile klystron gallery at ground level (see Fig. 57Q).

Output power from each klystron is divided into two halves,

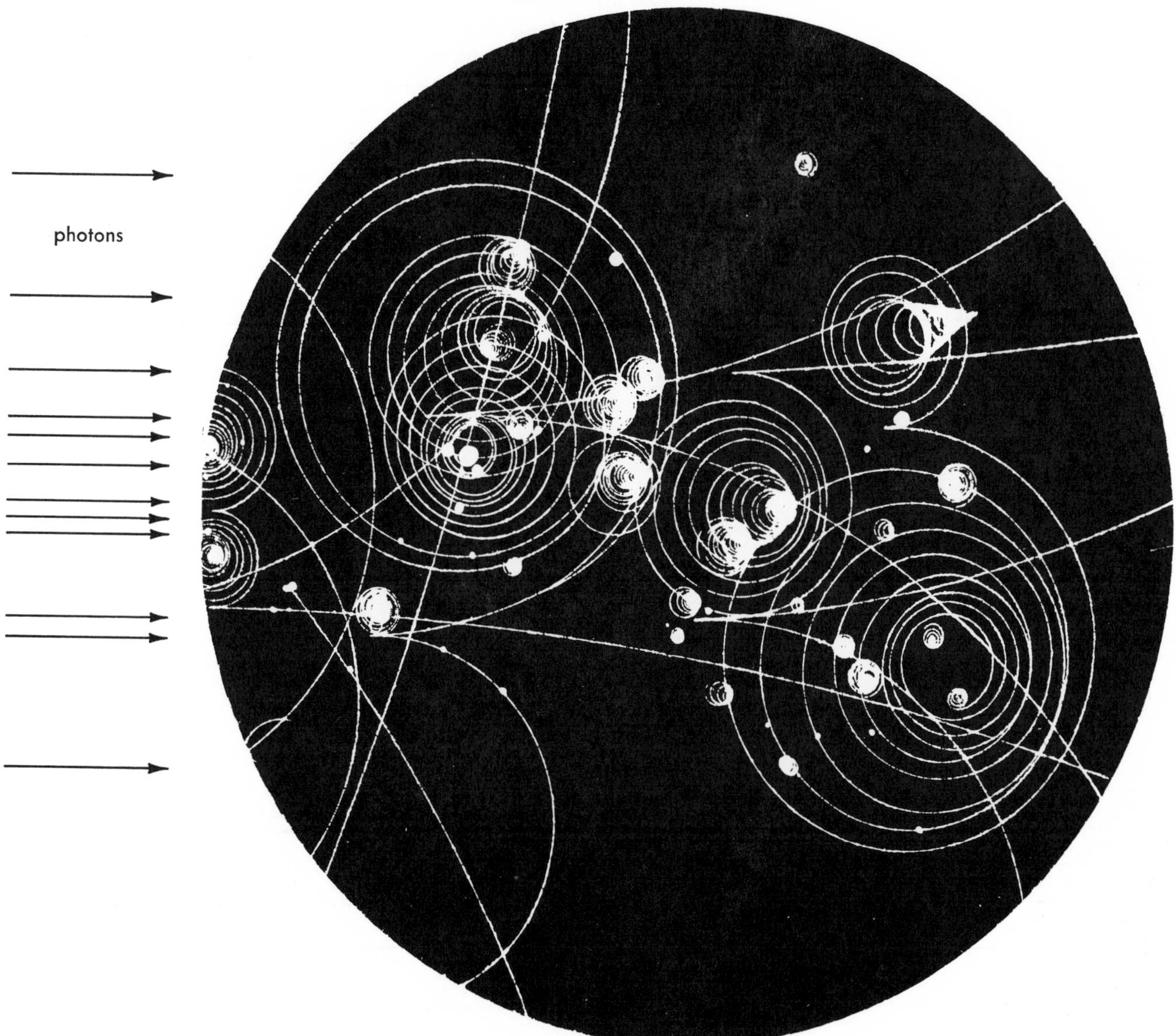

Fig. 57R. Reproduction of a liquid-hydrogen bubble chamber photograph made using the 20-GeV photons from the Stanford Linear Accelerator Center facility (SLAC). Observe the large number of electron pairs, and the even larger number of Compton recoil electrons (small spirals). (Photograph taken by the SLAC staff and prepared for artistic reproduction by Walter Zawojski.)

and transmitted down through the 7.5-m deep earth shield, to the accelerator tunnel below. In the tunnel the 2856 MHz *rf power* is again divided into two, so that 6 MW of power is supplied to each 3-m section.

After 3 m of acceleration in each section the radio wave has lost a large part of its energy in the form of heat. The remaining energy is dumped into and dissipated by a water-cooled copper load. Meanwhile the accelerated electrons enter the next 3 m through a small hole where a new radio wave picks them up for another 3-m acceleration.

A high voltage modulator at the starting end of the accelerator turns on the klystrons for 2.5 μs, and at a rate of 360 times/s.

TABLE 57A
GeV accelerators in operation in 1972

Location	*Name*	*Particle*	*GeV Energy*	*Completion*
United States				
LRL Berkeley, California	Bevatron	deuterons	6.2	1954
Princeton, New Jersey	PPA	deuterons	3.0	1963
ANL, Illinois	ZGS	deuterons	12.5	1963
Brookhaven, New York	AGS	deuterons	33.0	1960
Stanford, California	Mark III	electrons	1.2	1950
Stanford, California	SLAC I	deuterons	20.0	1966
Cal. Tech., California	Synchrotron	deuterons	1.5	1952
Cornell, New York	DO	electrons	2.2	1955
Cornell, New York	Synchrotron	deuterons	10.0	1968
Cambridge, Massachusetts	CEA	deuterons	6.0	1962
Batavia, Illinois	GeV	protons	200.0	1971
France				
Saclay	Saturne	deuterons	3.0	1958
Orsay	Linac	electrons	1.3	1961
Germany, Hamburg	DESY	deuterons	6.0	1964
Italy, Rome	Synchrotron	deuterons	1.1	1959
Japan, Tokyo	DO	deuterons	1.3	1960
Sweden, Lund	DO	deuterons	1.2	1962
Switzerland, CERN	PS	protons	28.0	1959
United Kingdom				
Birmingham	Synchrotron	deuterons	1.1	1953
Daresburg	NINA	electrons	5.0	1967
Harwell	NIMROD	deuterons	8.0	1963
USSR				
Moscow, ITER	Synchrotron	deuterons	7.0	1961
Dubna, JINR	DO	deuterons	10.0	1957
Kharkov	Linac	electrons	2.0	1965
Serpukov	70	protons	70.0	1966
Yerevan	Synchrotron	electrons	6.0	1965

Since these "trigger" pulses to the klystrons travel with the speed of light, each klystron is turned on at just the right time to accelerate the electrons passing through.

The Linac's great energy of 880 KW of power make it one of the most important scientific tools available for exploring the basic constituents of matter (see Sec. 65.12). Figure 57R is a liquid hydrogen bubble chamber photograph made by a pulse of photons as it passes through the chamber. Note the large number of electron pairs produced, and the even larger number of Compton recoil electrons (small spirals).

questions and problems

1. What is the purpose of a cyclotron? What are the principal kinds of atomic particles used in accelerators?

2. What is a betatron?

3. What is a linear accelerator? What are its advantages over a cyclotron?

4. What is a Van de Graaff generator? Can it be used to accelerate atomic particles? What kinds of particles can be accelerated?

5. Find the frequency of the oscillating potential differences that must be applied to a cyclotron in which protons are accelerated. Assume a magnetic induction of 0.95 T, and the proton mass to be 1.6726×10^{-27} Kg.

6. Find the magnetic induction that must be applied to a cyclotron accelerating deuterons, if the applied voltage has a frequency of 6.80 MHz. [Ans. 0.892 T.]

7. The frequency applied to the D's of a cyclotron is 7.80 MHz. What must be the value of the magnetic induction B if α particles are to be accelerated?

8. What magnetic induction is required in a cyclotron if it is to accelerate protons with an oscillating emf frequency of 8.75 MHz?

9.* A cyclotron with D's 0.60 m in diameter is designed to accelerate protons. If the magnetic induction is to be 1.250 T, find (a) the period, (b) the frequency of the alternating voltage to be applied, (c) the maximum velocity reached by the protons, and (d) their energy in MeV. [Ans. (a) 5.24×10^{-8} s, (b) 19.06 MHz, (c) 3.592×10^{7} m/s, (d) 6.74 MeV.]

10.* The D's in a cyclotron chamber have a diameter of 0.860 m. If deuterons are to be accelerated, and the magnetic induction is to be 1.20 T, calculate (a) the period of the oscillating voltage, (b) the frequency, (c) the maximum deuteron velocity, and (d) the deuteron energy in MeV.

11.* A cyclotron with D's 1.250 m in diameter accelerates deuterons to an energy of 4.2 MeV. What is (a) their maximum velocity, (b) the magnetic induction B, and (c) the frequency of the applied voltage?

12.* Protons are accelerated to an energy of 3.550 MeV by a cyclotron with D's that are 0.50 m in diameter. Find (a) their velocity, (b) the magnetic induction, and (c) the frequency of the applied voltage. [Ans. (a) 2.608×10^{7} m/s, (b) 1.089 T, (c) 16.60 MHz.]

58 Transmutation of the elements

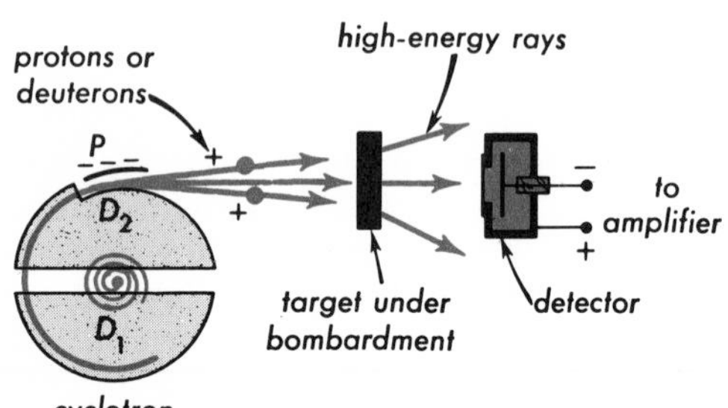

Fig. 58A. Experimental arrangement generally used for bombarding known substances with high-speed deuterons from the cyclotron and for detecting the disintegration products with an ionization chamber as a detector.

The use of high-speed atomic particles, whether they come from radioactive materials, from cyclotrons, or from cosmic rays, has led in recent years to the discovery of many secrets that lie hidden within the atomic nucleus. While the thousands of experiments performed have led to the discovery of many new elementary particles, several hundred radioactive isotopes of the known elements have been produced by the process of nuclear bombardment.

58.1. Proton and Deuteron Disintegrations

When high-energy protons or deuterons are used to bombard different known elements, various disintegration products are formed. An experimental arrangement in which the cyclotron acts as the source of high-speed particles is shown in Fig. 58A. To determine the nature of the disintegration taking place within the substance under bombardment, it is common practice to identify the penetrating rays emerging from the other side by the use of suitable detectors.

Numerous experiments have shown that the disintegration products to be looked for may be *protons*, *α particles*, *neutrons*, *γ rays*, *mesons*, *electrons*, *positrons*, etc. For some of these penetrating rays, one kind of detector may be more suitable than another. Scintillation counters are in widespread use today, and special designs are employed for the different kinds of particles. Solid-state counters are frequently used for protons and alpha particles.

The detector shown at the right in Fig. 58A represents an ionization chamber. When a Wilson cloud chamber is used to identify disintegration products, charged particles can be identified by the density of their fog tracks, and their energy can be determined by the curvature of the tracks when a magnetic field is applied.

This is illustrated in Fig. 58H for positrons. Once the nature of the emerging rays from a bombarded target is known, the recoil product of the disintegration also becomes known by writing down a reaction equation. Sixteen examples of such reaction equations are given by the following:

Reaction	*Q values,* (MeV)	
${}_1H^1 + {}_9F^{19} = {}_8O^{16} + {}_2He^4$	8.113	(58a)
${}_1H^1 + {}_5B^{11} = {}_6C^{12} + \gamma$ ray	15.955	(58b)
${}_1H^2 + {}_7N^{14} = {}_6C^{12} + {}_2He^4$	13.574	(58c)
${}_1H^2 + {}_8O^{16} = {}_7N^{14} + {}_2He^4$	3.110	(58d)
${}_1H^2 + {}_3Li^6 = {}_3Li^7 + {}_1H^1$	5.028	(58e)
${}_1H^2 + {}_4Be^9 = {}_5B^{10} + {}_0n^1$	4.362	(58f)
${}_1H^1 + {}_{29}Cu^{63} = {}_{30}Zn^{63} + {}_0n^1$	−4.148	(58g)
${}_1H^1 + {}_{19}K^{39} = {}_{18}A^{36} + {}_2He^4$	1.287	(58h)
${}_1H^2 + {}_{12}Mg^{26} = {}_{12}Mg^{27} + {}_1H^1$	4.213	(58i)
${}_1H^2 + {}_{14}Si^{29} = {}_{13}Al^{27} + {}_2He^4$	6.012	(58j)
${}_1H^2 + {}_{32}Ge^{72} = {}_{32}Ge^{73} + {}_1H^1$	4.560	(58k)
${}_1H^1 + {}_{14}Si^{30} = {}_{13}Al^{27} + {}_2He^4$	−2.378	(58ℓ)
${}_1H^2 + {}_{46}Pd^{108} = {}_{46}Pd^{109} + {}_1H^1$	3.925	(58m)
${}_1H^1 + {}_{42}Mo^{95} = {}_{43}Tc^{95} + {}_0n^1$	−2.440	(58n)
${}_1H^2 + {}_{23}V^{50} = {}_{22}Ti^{48} + {}_2He^4$	9.978	(58o)
${}_1H^2 + {}_{34}Se^{76} = {}_{34}Se^{77} + {}_1H^1$	5.190	(58p)

It is customary to omit the *kinetic energy* of the bombarding particle from the left-hand side of all reaction equations and to designate the total energy by the disintegration as shown at the right above. The values of Q given above therefore represent the experimentally determined values of the energy over and above that supplied by the incident projectile.

A negative Q value means that the total mass created is greater than the masses of the colliding particles, and that more than that energy must be provided by the incident particle to make the reaction go. Consider the fifth reaction, which can be taken to represent an experiment in which a beam of 2-MeV deuterons from the cyclotron bombards a target of lithium metal. From the other side of the target a stream of high-energy protons would be detected. If they are sent through a Wilson cloud chamber in a magnetic field, for example, their tracks could be identified as proton tracks and their energy determined by the curvature of the tracks to be 6.0 MeV. The lithium atoms in the target would recoil with the remaining 1 MeV. When the accurate weights of the four nuclei involved are taken into account, there is a total loss of 0.00540 atomic mass units. Multiplying by 931, this is equivalent to 5.0 MeV energy. This value plus the energy of the incident bombarding particle gives 7.0 MeV.

As a second example consider Eq.(58f) in which deuterons, bombarding beryllium metal, produce high-speed neutrons and recoiling boron nuclei. This particular disintegration is important experimentally because it is used as a means of obtaining intense beams of neutrons for use as projectiles in other disintegrations. The nuclear changes are illustrated schematically in Fig. 58B. The available energy from the loss in mass alone is equivalent to 4.4 MeV, so that, if deuterons with an energy of 7 MeV are used to bombard the beryllium target, the available energy becomes 11.4 MeV, 1 MeV going to the recoil boron nucleus and approximately 10.4 MeV to the neutron.

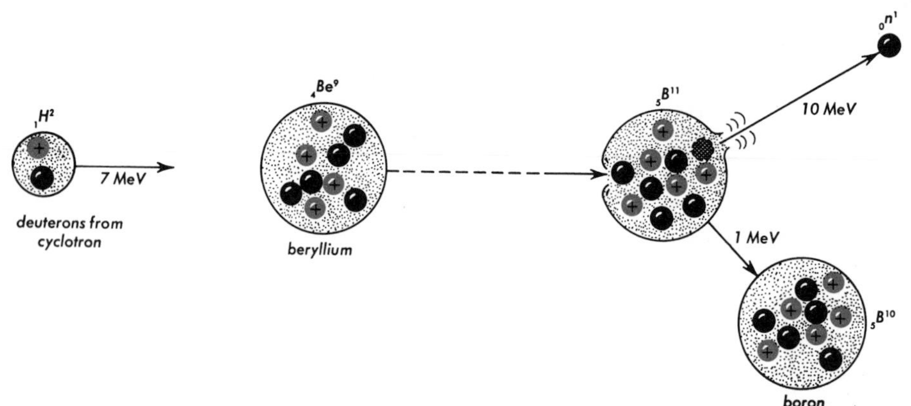

Fig. 58B. Deuteron disintegration of a beryllium nucleus to produce high-speed neutrons.

The table of accurately known masses of nuclides given in Appendix VIII includes a column 3 of excess mass values in MeV. These values represent the difference between the mass of each nuclide and its *mass number*. These numbers have been multiplied by 931.48113 to give the equivalent energy in MeV.

As a practical matter column 3 of mass excess energies is very useful. Consider as an illustration the following example.

Example 1. Find the Q value for the reaction shown in Eq.(58e), using the mass energies given in column 3 of Appendix VIII.

Solution. The *mass excesses* for the two nuclides coming together are first added:

${}_1H^2$	13.135 MeV
${}_3Li^6$	14.089 MeV
	27.224 MeV

The *mass excesses* for the two separating nuclides are added, and give

${}_3Li^7$	14.908 MeV
${}_1H^1$	7.288 MeV
	22.196 MeV

The difference between these totals gives directly

$$Q = +5.028 \text{ MeV}$$

58.2. Multiple Disintegrations

A study of certain disintegration experiments shows that some of the unstable nuclei created by the capture of a proton or deuteron by a stable nucleus split up into more than two stable nuclei. Examples of this arise when boron is bombarded by protons and when nitrogen is bombarded by deuterons. In the case of boron (see Fig. 58C), the proton is first captured by a ${}_5B^{11}$ nucleus to form an unstable carbon nucleus, ${}_6C^{12}$. This composite structure,

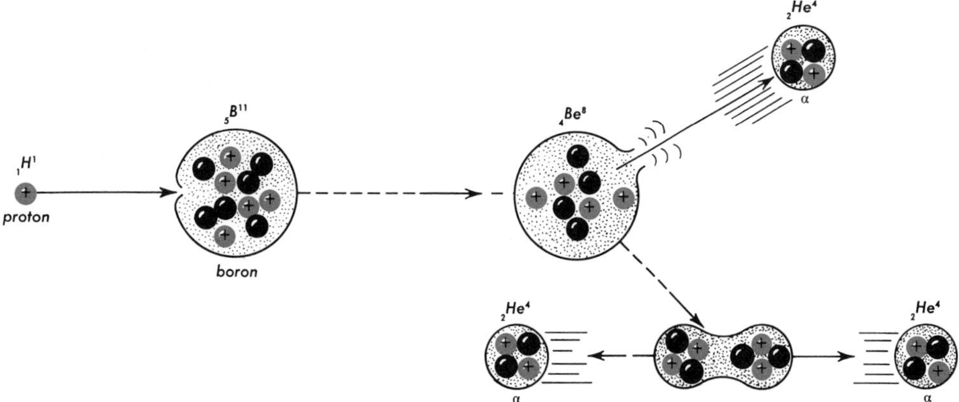

Fig. 58C. Disintegration of a boron nucleus of mass 11 by a proton to produce three α particles.

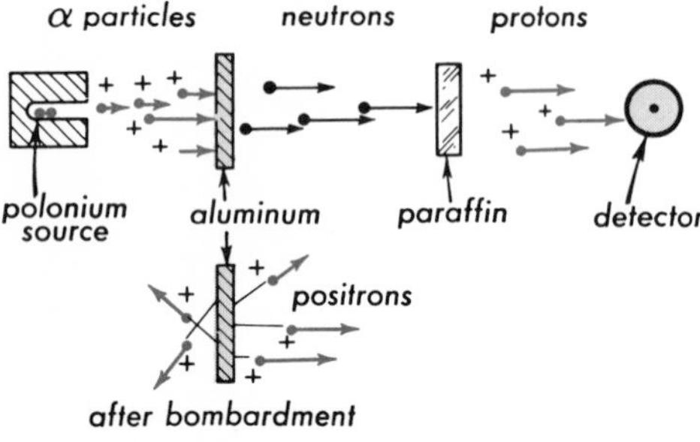

Fig. 58D. Experimental arrangement used by the Curie–Joliots when they discovered induced radioactivity.

as we will see in a later chapter, has too much mass to be a stable $_6C^{12}$ nucleus, and it disintegrates by the expulsion of an α particle with several million volts energy, leaving behind a beryllium nucleus, $_4Be^8$:

$$_1H^1 + {}_5B^{11} = {}_4Be^8 + {}_2H^4 \qquad (58q)$$

This nuclear combination is still unstable and splits apart into two more α particles:

$$_4Be^8 = {}_2He^4 + {}_2He^4$$

When the phenomenon was first observed, it was thought that all three α particles came apart simultaneously, but further observations showed that first one and then two were ejected. The total energy liberated has been measured to be about 11 MeV, which checks almost exactly with the value obtained from the loss in mass.

58.3. Branch Disintegrations

It so happens that when certain atoms are bombarded with high-speed particles, any one of several disintegration processes may take place. As an illustration of this phenomenon of *branch disintegration,* consider the proton bombardment of beryllium in which the following two types of disintegration have been identified:

$$_1H^1 + {}_4Be^9 = {}_3Li^6 + {}_2He^4$$

$$_1H^1 + {}_2Be^9 = {}_5B^{10} + \gamma \text{ ray} \qquad (58r)$$

When a proton is captured by a beryllium nucleus to form an unstable boron nucleus, $_5B^{10}$, there are two ways in which it may split up. The instability of the boron in the first place is due to the presence of too much mass. Such an atom is said to be in an *excited state*, for by the emission of a γ ray it gives up its surplus energy and becomes a stable $_5B^{10}$ nucleus, or by splitting up into two particles it gives up its surplus in the form of kinetic energy to become $_2He^4$ and $_3Li^6$, two stable nuclei.

An abbreviated notation for nuclear reactions is illustrated by the following examples:

$_1H^1 + {}_9F^{19} = {}_8O^{16} + {}_2He^4$	$F^{19}(p, \alpha)O^{16}$
$_1H^2 + {}_7N^{14} = {}_6C^{12} + {}_2He^4$	$N^{14}(d, \alpha)C^{12}$
$_1H^2 + {}_3Li^7 = {}_2He^4 + {}_2He^4 + {}_0n^1$	$Li^7(d, 2\alpha n)\alpha$
$_2He^4 + {}_{14}Si^{28} = {}_1H^1 + {}_{15}P^{31}$	$Si^{28}(\alpha, p)P^{31}$
$_2He^4 + {}_{28}Ni^{60} = {}_0n^1 + {}_{30}Zn^{63}$	$Ni^{60}(\alpha, n)Zn^{63}$

The discovery of induced radioactivity was made in 1934 by F. Joliot* and I. Curie Joliot.† For years the Curie–Joliots, as they are now often called, had been exposing various substances to the α rays from naturally radioactive elements and had been studying the various disintegrations that took place. In the specific instance referred to above, they bombarded aluminum with *α particles from polonium* and measured the energies of the ejected neutrons by the recoiling of protons from paraffin (see Fig. 58D). They observed that, even after the polonium source was taken away, the detector continued to respond to some kind of penetrating radiation. Upon investigating the nature of these rays, they found positively charged electrons coming from the aluminum.

Repeating the experiments to make certain of the results, they came to the conclusion that, under the bombardment of α particles, the aluminum had become radioactive in its own right. What was happening has since been verified: α particles striking aluminum nuclei are captured, and the resulting nuclei disintegrate with the violent ejection of neutrons:

$$_2\text{He}^4 + {}_{13}\text{Al}^{27} = [{}_{15}\text{P}^{30}] + {}_0n^1 \tag{58s}$$

The newly created recoil particles, with a charge of + 15 and mass 30, have been identified as phosphorus nuclei which are not stable but radioactive. Spontaneously disintegrating, these radioactive phosphorus nuclei $_{15}\text{P}^{30}$ shoot out positrons, leaving behind them stable silicon atoms of charge + 14 and mass 30:

$$[{}_{15}\text{P}^{30}] = {}_{14}\text{Si}^{30} + {}_1e^0 + \nu_e \tag{58t}$$

The *half-life* of this activity, which measures the rate of decay of the phosphorus into silicon (for the meaning of half-life see Sec. 53.2), is only 2.5 min. The emission of a positively charged electron is accompanied by a neutrino, just as in the case of β emission. Oftentimes, however, the neutrino is omitted from the reaction since it carries no charge and no rest mass.

Although the mass of the electron is not zero, it is so small compared with unit mass (the mass of one electron, it will be remembered, is $\frac{1}{1836}$*th* of the mass of the proton) that e is written with a zero superscript. According to this notation, a positron is written $_1e^0$ and an electron $_{-1}e^0$.

***Frederic J. Joliot (1900–1958), French physicist, was also known with Irene Curie as Joliot-Curie, after his marriage in 1926. Born in Paris, March 19, 1900, he was appointed to the staff of the Paris Radium Institute in 1925, where he later became professor. In bombarding boron, aluminum, and magnesium with alpha particles, he produced radioactive isotopes of nitrogen, phosphorus, and aluminum. In 1935, he was awarded, jointly with his wife, the Nobel Prize in chemistry for the discovery of new radioactive elements prepared artificially. In 1944, he was appointed Director of the French Centre Nationale des Recherches Scientifiques, Paris; and in 1946, was made High Commissioner for Atomic Energy, but he was removed by the government in 1950 because of his strong Communist views.**

†Irene Curie (1897–1956), daughter of the most famous woman physicist, Marie Curie, was the wife of Frederic Joliot. Because of the now famous name of Curie, the physicists of the world hyphenate the name and call them Mme. Curie-Joliot and F. J. Joliot, or for short the Curie-Joliots. For years they worked with radioactive substances in the famous laboratory of the late Mme. Marie Curie at the Radium Institute in Paris.

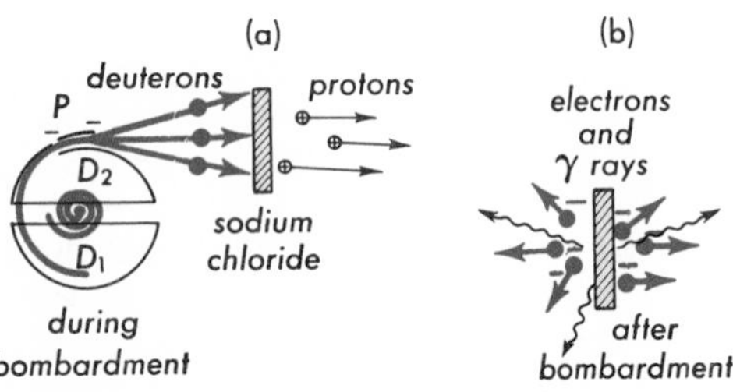

Fig. 58E. Experimental arrangement used by Lawrence in discovering radioactive sodium.

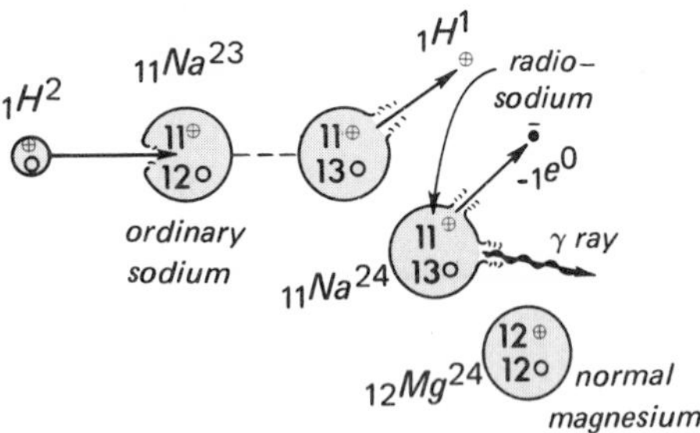

Fig. 58F. The production and disintegration of radiosodium.

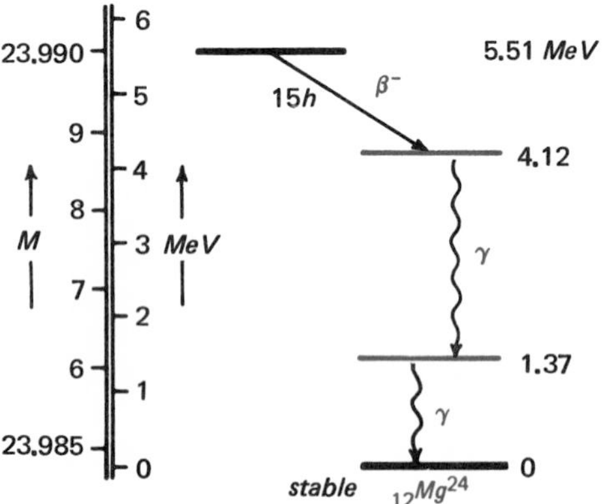

Fig. 58G. Energy-level diagram for radioactive decay of sodium-24.

Because the phosphorus does not all disintegrate immediately, it has been possible to identify the activity as coming from the newly created phosphorus atoms in the following way. A piece of aluminum metal, immediately after being bombarded, is dissolved in hydrochloric acid together with some ordinary inactive phosphorus, and then a standard chemical separation is made. Testing each part separately, the radioactivity is found to be present with the phosphorus residue, and not with the aluminum.

58.5. The Discovery of Radioactive Sodium

Immediately after the discovery of induced radioactivity by the Curie–Joliots, Lawrence bombarded sodium with 2-MeV deuterons from the cyclotron and found that it too, like aluminum, became radioactive (see Fig. 58E). Upon testing for the nature of the rays given off during bombardment, Lawrence found protons with an energy of about 7 MeV. When the sodium target was removed from the deuteron beam, as shown in diagram (b), and then tested for activity, it was found to be emitting both electrons and γ rays. The bombarding reaction, therefore, is

$$_1\text{H}^2 + {}_{11}\text{Na}^{23} = [{}_{11}\text{Na}^{24}] + {}_1\text{H}^1 \tag{58u}$$

followed by the radioactive decay of the unstable sodium nuclei,

$$[{}_{11}\text{Na}^{24}] = {}_{12}\text{Mg}^{24} + {}_{-1}\text{e}^0 + \nu_e + \gamma \text{ ray} \tag{58v}$$

The first stage of the disintegration process is shown at the left in Fig. 58F, and the radioactive decay is shown at the right.

The residual nucleus $_{11}\text{Na}^{24}$ of the first disintegration is called *radiosodium*. Having a charge of +11 and mass of 24, it must be an isotope of sodium not found in nature. Since measurements of the activity of radiosodium give a *half-life* of only 15 h, it is clear why such atoms are not found in nature. If they were formed some time in the ages past, they would all have disintegrated by this time.

An energy-level diagram for the decay of radioactive sodium is shown in Fig. 58G. The left-hand energy scales are given equally well in *amu* or in MeV. After emitting an electron, the nuclear charge increases by unity, and we have a magnesium nucleus in an excited state or energy level. With two successive transitions in which 2.75-MeV and 1.37-MeV γ rays are emitted, the nucleus becomes a stable system, a normal isotope of magnesuim $_{12}\text{Mg}^{24}$.

Up to the present time more than 600 different kinds of radioactive atoms have been produced in the laboratory. Two examples, in addition to those already given, are illustrated by the following reactions:

$$
\begin{aligned}
{}_1H^2 + {}_{15}P^{31} &= [{}_{15}P^{32}] + {}_1H^1, \\
[{}_{15}P^{32}] &= {}_{16}S^{32} + {}_{-1}e^0 + \bar{\nu}_e
\end{aligned}
\tag{58w}
$$

$$
\begin{aligned}
{}_1H^2 + {}_6C^{12} &= [{}_7N^{13}] + {}_0n^1, \\
[{}_7N^{13}] &= {}_6C^{13} + {}_1\bar{e}^0 + \nu_e
\end{aligned}
\tag{58x}
$$

The first of these reactions forms *radioactive phosphorus* ${}_{15}P^{32}$, which is *electron active* with a half-life of 15 days.

A cloud-chamber photograph of the positrons emitted by radioactive nitrogen ${}_7N^{13}$ is reproduced in Fig. 58H. The magnetic field bends all the rays in the same direction, indicating that all are positive charges. The low-density fog drops forming the tracks indicate particles with the mass of an electron.

Fig. 58H. Photograph of the Wilson cloud-chamber tracks of positrons ejected by radio nitrogen, ${}_7N^{13}$.

58.6. Electron Capture

Many radioactive nuclei, when created by some collision process, are unstable to the extent of one extra positive charge. Although many such nuclei disintegrate and become stable by the emission of a positron, others draw to them an orbital electron from the K shell of the same atom. Inside the nucleus this negative charge neutralizes a positive charge, whereas outside an L or M electron jumps into the K shell vacancy with the simultaneous emission of a characteristic X ray (see Fig. 58I). Beryllium-7 and gallium-65 are specific examples of unstable nuclei in which *K capture* occurs. The reactions for these are

$$
\begin{aligned}
{}_4Be^7 + {}_{-1}e^0 &= {}_3Li^7 + \bar{\nu}_e \\
{}_{31}Ga^{65} + {}_{-1}e^0 &= {}_{30}Zn^{65} + \bar{\nu}_e
\end{aligned}
\tag{58y}
$$

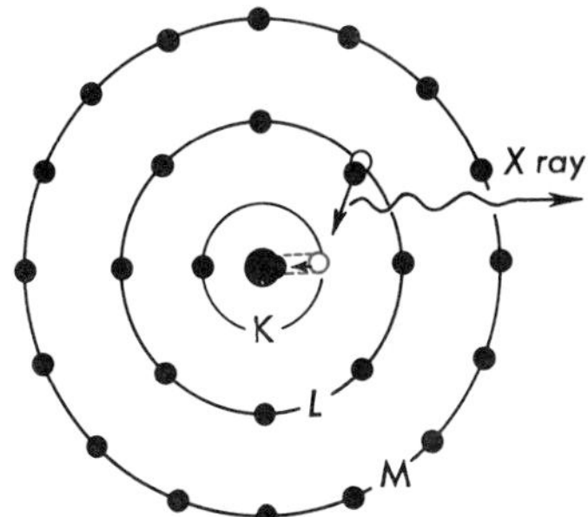

Fig. 58I. Unstable nucleus captures an electron from the K shell of orbital electrons. As a consequence, an X ray is emitted.

An energy-level diagram involving the radioactive decay of actinium-226 is shown in Fig. 58J. This nucleus is β-active; 80% of its atoms disintegrate by emitting β particles with an end-point of approximately 1 MeV, each followed by the emission of one or two γ rays to become thorium-226. The other 20% of the atoms capture an electron from the K shell, and immediately emit one or two γ rays to become radium-226.

It is more appropriate to visualize *electron capture* (*abbr*. E.C.) from a quantum-mechanical picture similar to that shown in Fig. 54F. The overlapping of the probability density D_r of a 1*s* electron

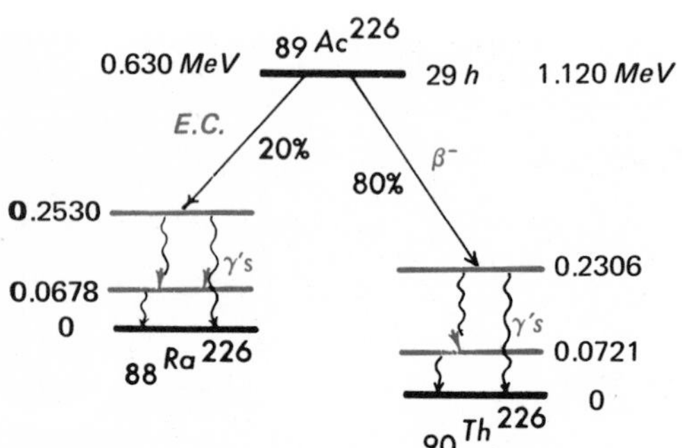

Fig. 58J. Energy-level diagram of the two-way radioactive decay of actinium-226.

(see Fig. 51N) with the nucleus provides the conditions for easy capture of the electron. In some few isotopes, E.C. is the only means of radioactive decay.

58.7. Nuclear Stability

We know that if we bombard targets with atomic particles of sufficiently high energy, every known stable element can be converted into radioactive isotopes of that element or of neighboring elements. Furthermore, a number of isotopes can be produced for any one element, some with masses smaller than any kind of its stable isotopes, and some with greater masses. In the case of copper, for example, the following isotopes have been produced.

Copper Z = 29

Mass	*Activity*	*Half-Life*	
58	β^+	3 s	
59	β^+	81 s	
60	β^+	24 min	
61	β^+	3.3 h	
62	β^+	10 min	
63	Stable	— 70%	
64	$\beta^-/\beta^+ = 2$	12.8 h	42% E.C.
65	Stable	— 30%	
66	β^-	5.1 min	
67	β^-	58 s	
68	β^-	32 s	

The first five isotopes have too many protons to be stable nuclides, and by positron emission convert a proton into a neutron and become an isotope of nickel. The last three isotopes have too few protons, and by electron emission convert a neutron into a proton and become an isotope of zinc.

Isotope $_{29}Cu^{64}$, lying between two stable isotopes, is an interesting combination of nucleons, since these nuclei are found to decay in any one of four different ways. All four processes are illustrated in an energy-level diagram in Fig. 58K.

Approximately 38% of the copper-64 nuclei decay by the emission of a β^- and a neutrino, to become zinc-64:

$$_{29}Cu^{64} = {}_{30}Zn^{64} + {}_{-1}e^0 + \bar{\nu}_e \qquad +0.573 \text{ MeV}$$

The β^- end-point energy of 0.573 MeV corresponds to a decrease in nuclear mass of 0.000616 amu. *The masses of all atoms include the masses of all orbital electrons for the neutral atoms.* When $_{29}Cu^{64}$ ejects an electron from the nucleus, the daughter product $_{30}Zn^{64}$ picks up a stray electron to become a neutral atom. The term *nuclide* is applied to any known assembly of nuclear particles called a nucleus.

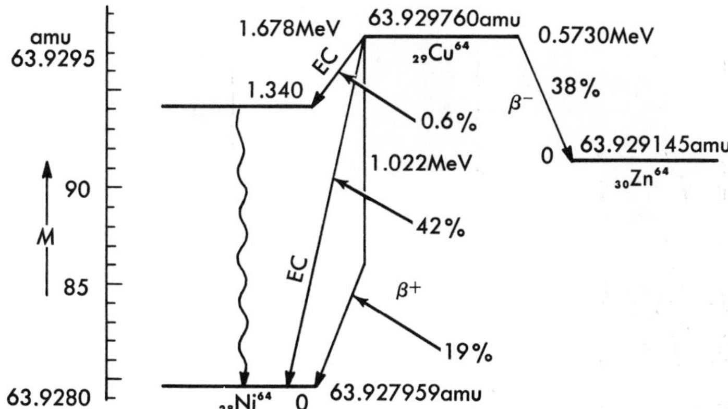

Fig. 58K. Energy level diagram of the 4-way radioactive decay of copper-64.

Approximately 42% of the copper-64 nuclei decay by *electron capture* with the simultaneous emission of a neutrino:

$$_{29}Cu^{64} + {}_{-1}e^0 = {}_{28}Ni^{64} + \nu_e \qquad +1.678 \text{ MeV}$$

The end-point energy of this process is 1.678 MeV, and the neutrino spin of $\frac{1}{2}\hbar$ compensates for the spin of $\frac{1}{2}\hbar$ given the nucleus by the captured electron.

Some 19% of the copper-64 nuclei emit a β^+ and a neutrino to become stable nuclei, nickel-64:

$$_{29}Cu^{64} = {}_{28}Ni^{64} + {}_{+1}\bar{e}^0 + \nu_e \qquad +0.656 \text{ MeV}$$

The end-point energy for these positrons is 0.656 MeV. The difference between the two end-point energies of 1.678 MeV and 0.656 MeV, or 1.022 MeV, is just the mass-energy equivalence of two electrons. When $_{29}Cu^{64}$ ejects a positron from the nucleus, the nuclear charge decreases by one and the daughter product also drops one of its orbital electrons to become a neutral atom. The

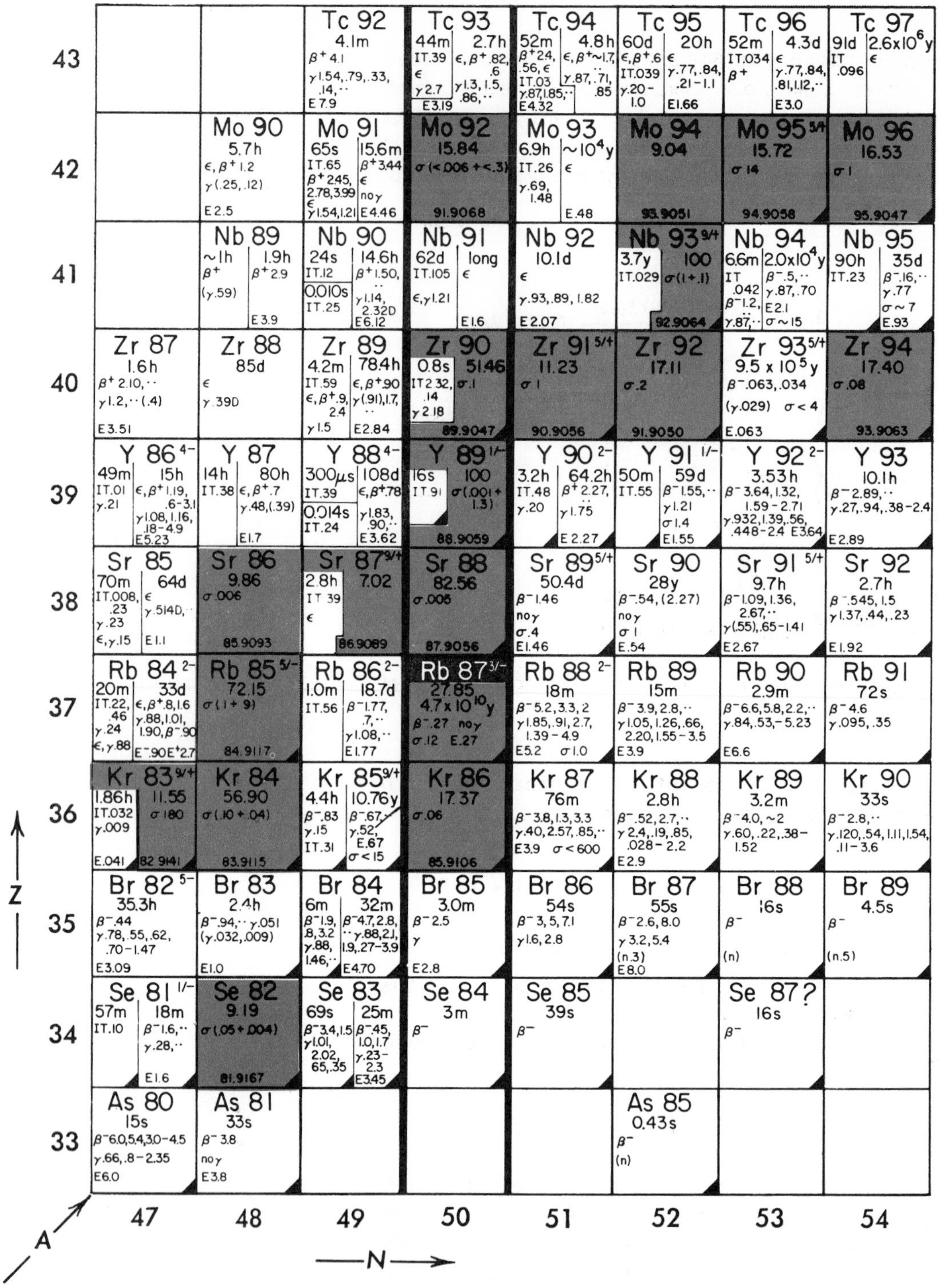

Z \ N	47	48	49	50	51	52	53	54
43			Tc 92 4.1m β^+ 4.1 γ1.54,.79,.33,.14,·· E7.9	Tc 93 44m | 2.7h IT.39 ε γ2.7 | ε,β^+.82,.6 γ1.3,1.5,.86,·· E3.19	Tc 94 52m | 4.8h β^+2.4,.56,ε IT.03 γ.87,1.85,·· \| ε,β^+~1.7, γ.87,.71,.85 E4.32	Tc 95 60d | 20h ε,β^+.6 IT.039 γ.20-1.0 | ε γ.77,.84,.21-1.1 E1.66	Tc 96 52m | 4.3d IT.034 β^+ | ε γ.77,.84,.81,1.12,·· E3.0	Tc 97 91d | 2.6×10^6y IT .096 | ε
42		Mo 90 5.7h ε,β^+1.2 γ(.25,.12) E2.5	Mo 91 65s | 15.6m IT.65 β^+2.45, 2.78,3.99 ε γ1.54,1.21 | β^+3.44 ε noγ E4.46	Mo 92 15.84 σ(<.006+<.3) 91.9068	Mo 93 6.9h | ~10^4y IT.26 γ.69,1.48 | ε E.48	Mo 94 9.04 93.9051	Mo 95 5/+ 15.72 σ14 94.9058	Mo 96 16.53 σ1 95.9047
41		Nb 89 ~1h | 1.9h β^+ (γ.59) | β^+2.9 E3.9	Nb 90 24s | 14.6h IT.12; 0.010s IT.25 | β^+1.50, γ1.14, 2.32D E6.12	Nb 91 62d | long IT.105 ε,γ1.21 | ε E1.6	Nb 92 10.1d ε γ.93,.89,1.82 E2.07	Nb 93 9/+ 3.7y | 100 IT.029 | σ(1+.1) 92.9064	Nb 94 6.6m | 2.0×10^4y IT .042 β^-1.2, γ.87,·· | β^-.5,·· γ.87,.70 E2.1 σ~15	Nb 95 90h | 35d IT.23 | β^-.16,·· γ.77 σ~7 E.93
40	Zr 87 1.6h β^+2.10,·· γ1.2,··(.4) E3.51	Zr 88 85d ε γ.39D	Zr 89 4.2m | 78.4h IT.59 ε,β^+.9, 2.4 γ1.5 | ε,β^+.90 γ(.91),1.7,·· E2.84	Zr 90 0.8s | 51.46 IT2.32,.14 γ2.18 | σ.1 89.9047	Zr 91 5/+ 11.23 σ1 90.9056	Zr 92 17.11 σ.2 91.9050	Zr 93 5/+ 9.5×10^5y β^-.063,.034 (γ.029) σ<4 E.063	Zr 94 17.40 σ.08 93.9063
39	Y 86 4- 49m | 15h IT.01 γ.21 | ε,β^+1.19,.6-3.1 γ1.08,1.16,.18-4.9 E5.23	Y 87 14h | 80h IT.38 | ε,β^+.7 γ.48,(.39) E1.7	Y 88 4- 300μs | 108d IT.39; 0.014s IT.24 | ε,β^+.78 γ1.83,.90,·· E3.62	Y 89 1/- 16s | 100 IT.91 | σ(.001+1.3) 88.9059	Y 90 2- 3.2h | 64.2h IT.48 γ.20 | β^-2.27, γ1.75 E2.27	Y 91 1/- 50m | 59d IT.55 | β^-1.55,·· γ1.21 σ1.4 E1.55	Y 92 2- 3.53h β^-3.64,1.32,1.59-2.71 γ.932,1.39,.56,.448-2.4 E3.64	Y 93 10.1h β^-2.89,·· γ.27,.94,.38-2.4 E2.89
38	Sr 85 70m | 64d IT.008,.23 γ.23 ε,γ.15 | ε γ.514D,·· E1.1	Sr 86 9.86 σ.006 85.9093	Sr 87 9/+ 2.8h | 7.02 IT.39 ε 86.9089	Sr 88 82.56 σ.005 87.9056	Sr 89 5/+ 50.4d β^-1.46 noγ σ.4 E1.46	Sr 90 28y β^-.54,(2.27) noγ σ1 E.54	Sr 91 5/+ 9.7h β^-1.09,1.36,2.67,·· γ(.55),.65-1.41 E2.67	Sr 92 2.7h β^-.545,1.5 γ1.37,.44,.23 E1.92
37	Rb 84 2- 20m | 33d IT.22,.46 γ.24 ε,γ.88 | ε,β^+.8,1.6 γ.88,1.01,1.90,β^-.90 E^-.90 E^+2.7	Rb 85 5/- 72.15 σ(1+9) 84.9117	Rb 86 2- 1.0m | 18.7d IT.56 | β^-1.77,.7,·· γ1.08,·· E1.77	Rb 87 3/- 27.85 4.7×10^{10}y β^-.27 noγ σ.12 E.27	Rb 88 2- 18m β^-5.2,3.3,2 γ1.85,.91,2.7,1.39-4.9 E5.2 σ1.0	Rb 89 15m β^-3.9,2.8,·· γ1.05,1.26,.66,2.20,1.55-3.5 E3.9	Rb 90 2.9m β^-6.6,5.8,2.2,·· γ.84,.53,-5.23 E6.6	Rb 91 72s β^-4.6 γ.095,.35
36	Kr 83 9/+ 1.86h | 11.55 IT.032 γ.009 E.041 | σ180 82.9141	Kr 84 56.90 σ(.10+.04) 83.9115	Kr 85 9/+ 4.4h | 10.76y β^-.83 γ.15 IT.31 | β^-.67,·· γ.52, E.67 σ<15	Kr 86 17.37 σ.06 85.9106	Kr 87 76m β^-3.8,1.3,3.3 γ.40,2.57,.85,·· E3.9 σ<600	Kr 88 2.8h β^-.52,2.7,·· γ2.4,.19,.85,.028-2.2 E2.9	Kr 89 3.2m β^-4.0,~2 γ.60,.22,.38-1.52	Kr 90 33s β^-2.8,·· γ.120,.54,1.11,1.54,.11-3.6
35	Br 82 5- 35.3h β^-.44 γ.78,.55,.62,.70-1.47 E3.09	Br 83 2.4h β^-.94,·· γ.051 (γ.032,.009) E1.0	Br 84 6m | 32m β^-1.9,.8,3.2 γ.88,1.46,·· | β^-4.7,2.8,·· γ.88,2.1,1.9,.27-3.9 E4.70	Br 85 3.0m β^-2.5 γ E2.8	Br 86 54s β^-3,5,7.1 γ1.6,2.8	Br 87 55s β^-2.6,8.0 γ3.2,5.4 (n.3) E8.0	Br 88 16s β^- (n)	Br 89 4.5s β^- (n.5)
34	Se 81 1/- 57m | 18m IT.10 | β^-1.6,·· γ.28,·· E1.6	Se 82 9.19 σ(.05+.004) 81.9167	Se 83 69s | 25m β^-3.4,1.5 γ1.01,2.02,.65,.35 | β^-.45,1.0,1.7 γ.23-2.3 E3.45	Se 84 3m β^-	Se 85 39s β^-		Se 87? 16s β^-	
33	As 80 15s β^-6.0,5.4,3.0-4.5 γ.66,.8-2.35 E6.0	As 81 33s β^-3.8 noγ E3.8				As 85 0.43s β^- (n)		

Z (increasing upward) — A (diagonal) — N (increasing to the right)

Fig. 58L. A typical section from a "Chart of Nuclides," published by the Knolls Atomic Power Laboratory, operated by the General Electric Company, under the direction of Naval Reactors, U. S. Atomic Energy Commission. Revised 1964.

atom's total mass therefore decreases to the mass of two electrons. The mass-energy equivalence of one electron ($m = 0.00549$ amu) is 0.511 MeV.

Finally, a few copper-64 nuclei, approximately 0.6%, capture an orbital electron and emit a neutrino, leaving the daughter product, ${}_{28}Ni^{64}$, in an *excited state*. This process is immediately followed by the emission of a 1.34-MeV gamma ray:

$$ {}_{29}Cu^{64} + {}_{-1}e^{0} = {}_{28}Ni^{64} + \nu_e + \gamma \text{ ray} + 1.678 \text{ MeV} $$

The end-point energy for this electron capture process alone is only 0.338 MeV.

A small section of a chart of the known nuclides of all the elements is shown in Fig. 58L.* Each square represents one nuclide, and includes such information as relative abundance, atomic number, mass, half-life, activity, etc. *Isotopes,* nuclides having the same number of protons, lie along a horizontal line. *Isotones,* nuclides having the same number of neutrons, lie along vertical lines. *Isobars*, nuclides having the same number of nucleons, i.e., the same A, lie along 45° lines. The small shaded rectangles represent the stable nuclides; all others are radioactive.

The stability of every nucleus is associated with the relative numbers of neutrons and protons bound together. If N represents the number of neutrons and Z the number of protons in any nucleus, and we plot a graph for all the known stable nuclides, we obtain a chart like the one shown in Fig. 58M. It will be noted that along any isobaric line, constant A ($A = Z + N$), there is only one nuclide for *odd A*. There are only two exceptions to this rule, and these are found at $A = 113$ and $A = 123$. These pairs are

$$ {}_{48}Cd^{113} \quad \text{and} \quad {}_{49}I^{113} $$

$$ {}_{51}Sb^{123} \quad \text{and} \quad {}_{52}Te^{123} $$

For *even A*, there are usually two, and occasionally three, stable nuclides having the same A.

If, in Fig. 58M, we plotted vertically upward out of the page, as a third dimension, the accurately known atomic masses M for all known stable as well as radioactive nuclides, we would obtain a kind of valley running diagonally up the chart, with the lowest points near the center of the stable nuclides. This is illustrated by a cross-sectional diagram in Fig. 58N for $A = 87$. These isobars are given along the diagonal in Fig. 58L:

* A complete "Chart of the Nuclides" including all known nuclides may be obtained by writing to General Electric Co., Knolls Atomic Power Laboratory, Schenectady, New York.

$_{35}Br^{87}$	86.927310 amu	β^-
$_{36}Kr^{87}$	86.919311 amu	β^-
$_{37}Rb^{87}$	86.915410 amu	β^-
$_{38}Sr^{87}$	86.915130 amu	Stable
$_{39}Y^{87}$	86.916820 amu	E.C.
$_{40}Zr^{87}$	86.920330 amu	β^+
$_{41}Nb^{87}$	86.926380 amu	β^+

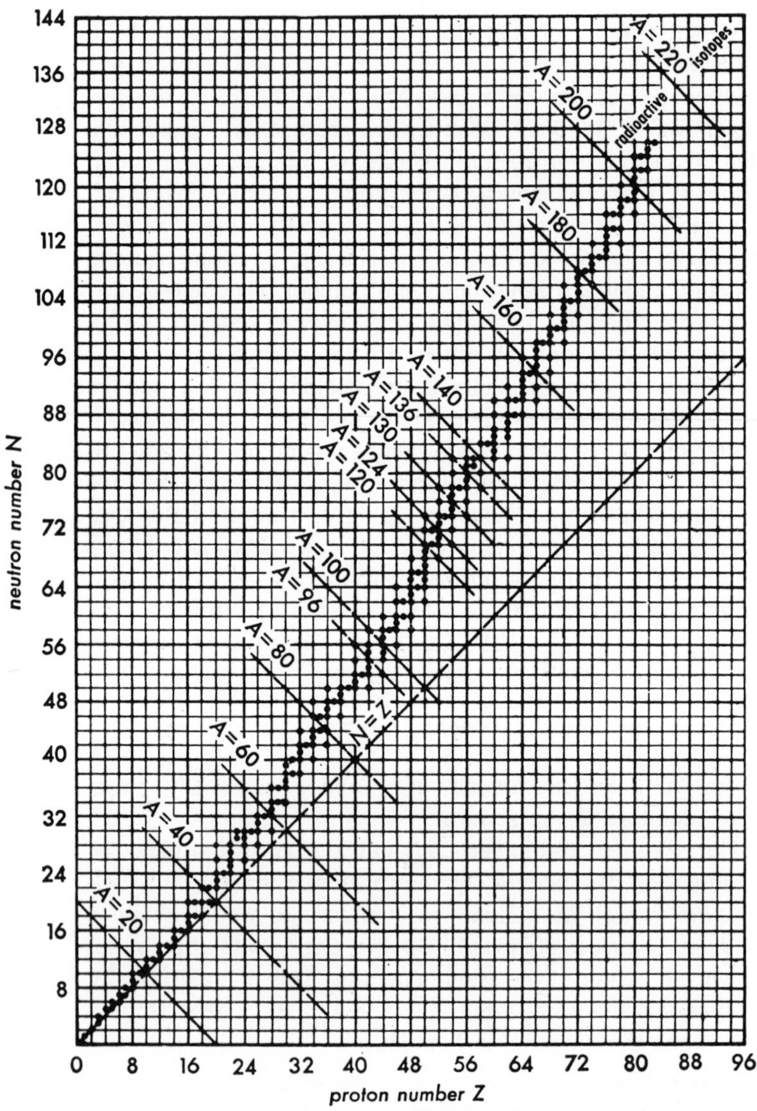

Fig. 58M. Neutron–proton diagram of stable nuclei.

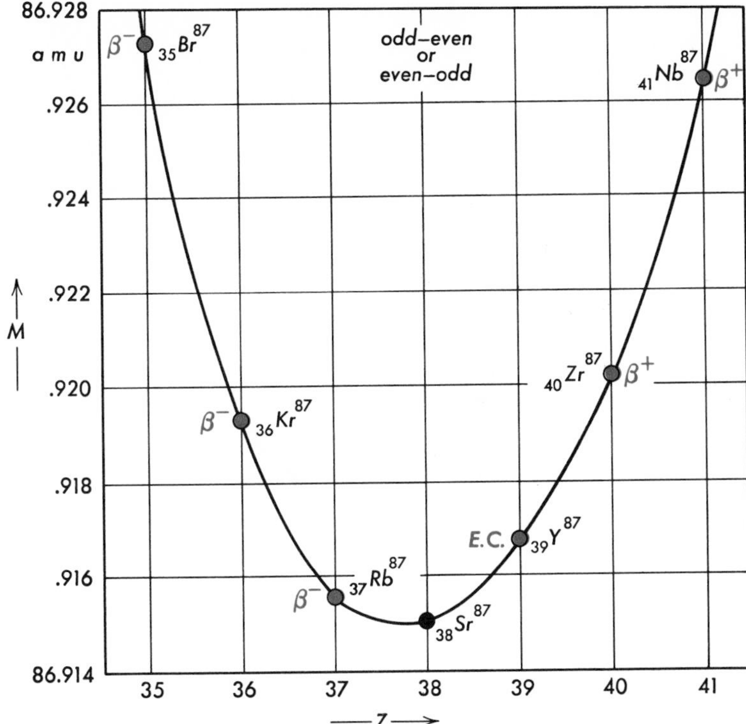

Fig. 58N. Atomic mass relations for nuclides with $A = 87$: odd Z and even N nuclides fall on the same parabola with even Z and odd N.

Note that the only stable nuclide, $_{38}Sr^{87}$, lies deepest in the valley curve.

Figure 58O is a typical atomic mass graph for isobars of *even A*. The isobars of *even Z* and *even N* fall on the lower parabola and therefore represent more tightly bound nuclear structures than the *odd Z odd N* isobars.

Among the stable nuclides there are 54 pairs of *even–even* isobars and only two cases of three. The latter are: $_{50}Sn^{124}$, $_{52}Te^{124}$, $_{54}Xe^{124}$, and $_{54}Xe^{136}$, $_{56}Ba^{136}$, $_{58}Cs^{136}$.

The isobar parabolas given in Fig. 58O are drawn from the following known masses:

$_{38}Sr^{92}$	91.916650 amu	β^-
$_{39}Y^{92}$	91.914730 amu	β^-
$_{40}Zr^{92}$	91.911130 amu	Stable
$_{41}Nb^{92}$	91.913210 amu	E.C.
$_{42}Mo^{92}$	91.912720 amu	Stable
$_{43}Tc^{92}$	91.919100 amu	β^+

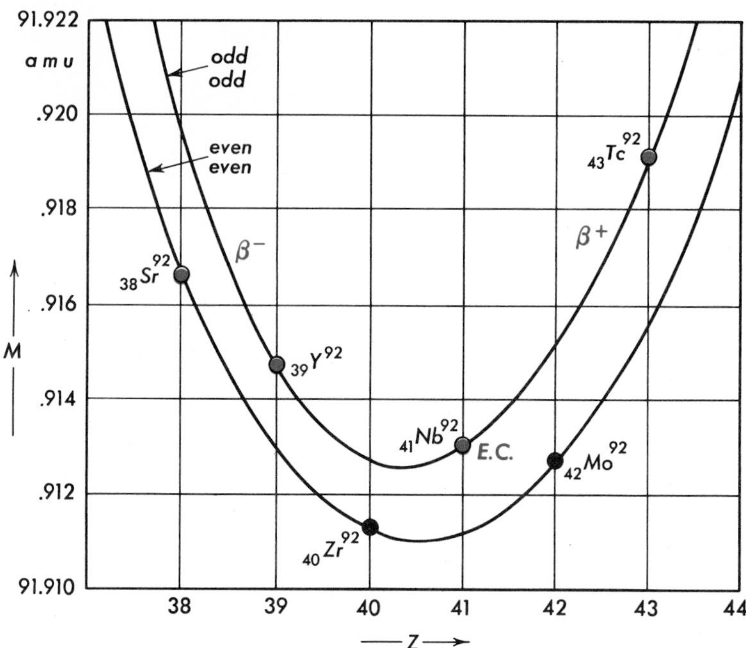

Fig. 58O. Atomic mass relations for nuclides with $A = 92$: odd Z and odd N nuclides form one parabola and even Z and even N nuclides form another.

Since mass is a form of energy, the stable and unstable nuclei on the graphs in Figs. 58N and 58O represent energy levels, which are the ground states for these nuclides. In general, the levels above these ground states are relatively simple for the lighter elements, and become more complex for the heavier elements. The transitions between these levels are governed partly by different nuclear spin values, and account for the various β rays and γ rays emitted by the radioactive nuclides.

A scale diagram of the energy levels of the five known isobars, $A = 67$, are given in Fig. 58P. Note how the vertical drop from ${}_{32}Ge^{67}$ of 1.022 MeV accounts for the loss of two electrons (0.511 MeV each) from the mass when a β^+ is emitted. The only stable nuclide is ${}_{30}Zn^{67}$ at the bottom. When a nucleus captures an electron from the outside structure of the atom (E.C.), or emits a β^-, no such drop occurs, since the number of electrons held by that atom, inside the nucleus or out, remains unchanged.*

* C. M. Lederer, J. M. Hollander and I. Perlman, Table of Isotopes (John Wiley and Sons, Inc., New York), 6th Edition.

58.8. The Mechanics of Recoiling Particles

When a nucleus disintegrates by ejecting a particle, classical laws of mechanics are found to apply to the resultant motions. Consider, for example, a radioactive nucleus as shown in Fig. 58Q.

If the compound nucleus is initially at rest, and the masses of the two fragments after disintegration are m_1 and m_2, conservation of momentum requires that

$$m_1 v_1 = m_2 v_2 \tag{58z}$$

If an amount of energy E is liberated by the disintegration

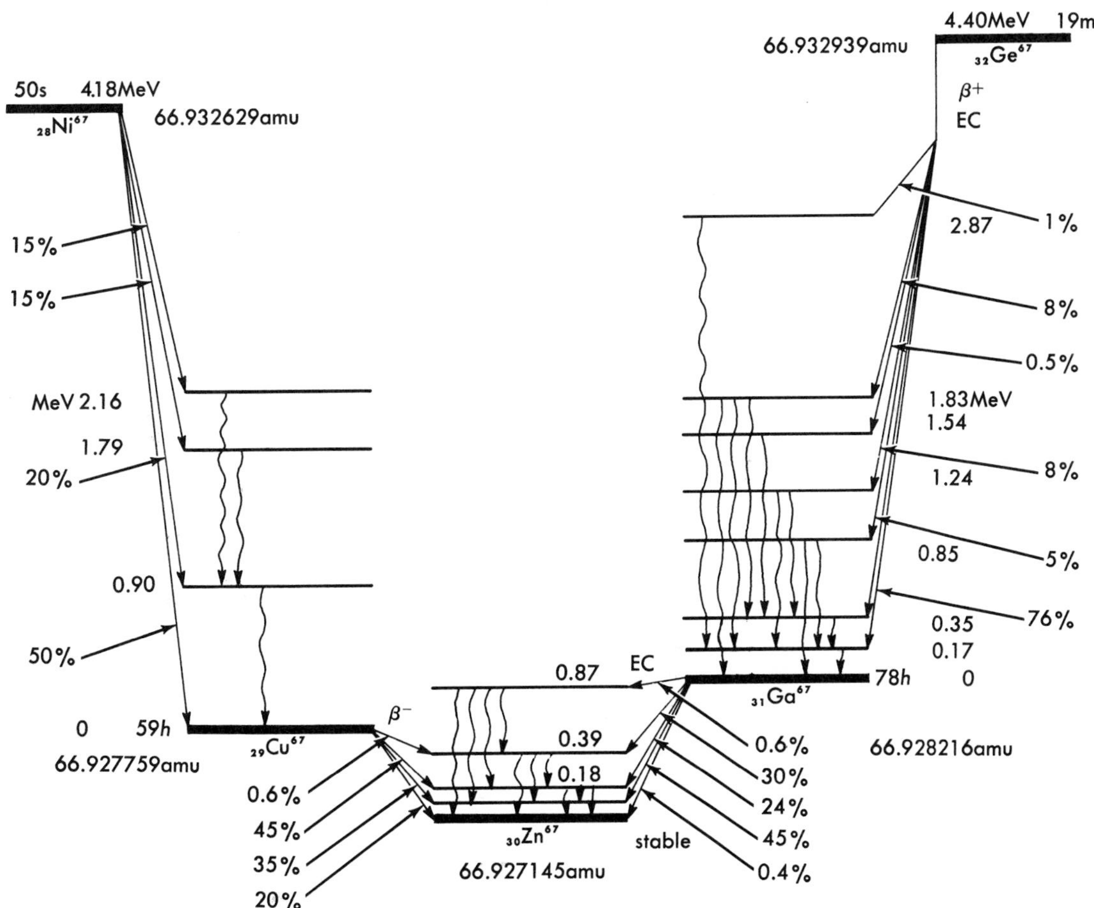

Fig. 58P. Energy level diagrams for the even-odd, odd-even nuclides with $A = 67$. Energies are in MeV.

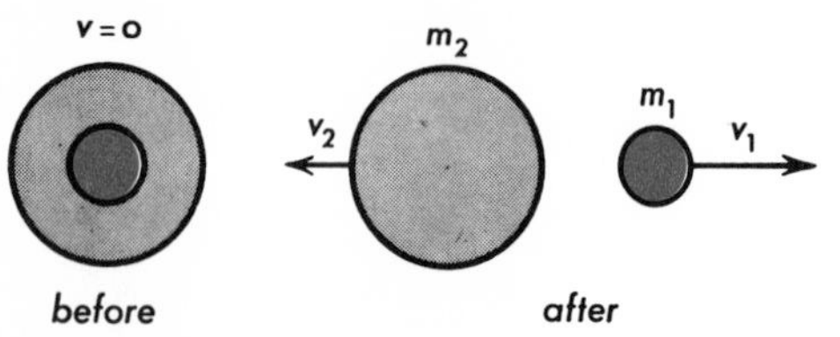

Fig. 58Q. Mechanics involved in the disintegration of a compound nucleus.

process, the law of conservation of energy requires that

$$E = E_1 + E_2 \qquad (58aa)$$

where

$$E_1 = \tfrac{1}{2}m_1v_1^2$$

and

$$E_2 = \tfrac{1}{2}m_2v_2^2$$

The ratio of the two energies is, therefore,

$$\frac{E_1}{E_2} = \frac{\frac{1}{2}m_1v_1^2}{\frac{1}{2}m_2v_2^2} \qquad (58bb)$$

If we solve Eq.(58z) for v_1, we can substitute m_2v_2/m_1 for v_1 in Eq.(58bb), and obtain

$$\frac{E_1}{E_2} = \frac{m_2^2}{m_1m_2} = \frac{m_2}{m_1} \qquad (58cc)$$

Example 2. If an energy of 20.0 MeV is liberated in a reaction in which the nuclear recoil mass is 100 times the mass of the ejected particle, find (a) the energy ratio of the two recoiling particles, and (b) the energy given each particle.

Solution. Since $m_2 = 100m_1$, direct substitution in Eq.(58t) gives

$$\frac{E_1}{E_2} = 100$$

or

$$E_1 = 100E_2$$

By substituting $100E_2$ for E_1, and 20.0 MeV for E, in Eq.(58aa), we obtain

$$20.0 \text{ MeV} = 100E_2 + E_2$$

or

$$E_2 = 0.19802 \text{ MeV}$$

and

$$E_1 = 19.802 \text{ MeV}$$

In all such nuclear reactions the momentum imparted to both sides is always equal, yet approximately 99% of the energy in this example is carried away by the lighter particle. In other words, conservation of energy and momentum divides the energy approximately inversely as the masses.

If the compound nucleus is moving with a velocity v at the time of disintegration, the above equations apply to a *center of mass* point continuing on with the same initial velocity v.

58.9. Radiation Damage

Energy absorbed by the passage of radiation through matter gives rise to structural changes called *radiation damage.* The nature and amount of damage produced are closely related to the number of ion pairs created, and this in turn depends upon the absorbing material and the characteristic of the radiation.

Since biological effects vary widely between body tissues and different types of radiation, it is customary to measure radiation absorption by the number of ion pairs produced in air. The exposure of specimens to any and all kinds of radiation is measured in terms of a unit called the *roentgen.*

Roentgen. The roentgen unit, abbreviated 1 R, is that quantity of X or γ radiation that produces one electrostatic unit of negative, or positive, charge in 0.001293 g of dry air. Under standard conditions air has a density of 0.001293 g/cm^3, and one coulomb $= 3 \times 10^9$ esu. Since the charge of a single electron, or ion, is 1.60×10^{-19} C, the roentgen can also be defined as the quantity of X or γ radiation which, under standard conditions, produces in air:

$$\frac{1}{3 \times 10^9 \times 1.6 \times 10^{-19}} = 2.08 \times 10^9 \text{ ion pairs/cm}^3$$

Experimental measurements show that on the average it takes 32.5 eV to produce one ion pair. Consequently,

$$1 \text{ R} = 2.08 \times 10^9 \times 32.5 = 67.6 \text{ BeV}$$

This energy is equivalent to 0.108×10^{-7} J, or 0.108 ergs. In one gram of air 1 R would produce

$$\frac{0.108 \times 10^{-7} \text{ J}}{0.001293} = 83.5 \times 10^{-7} \text{ J}$$

This same radiation will produce 93×10^{-7} J per gram of water (the main constituent of tissue), approximately 4×10^{-3} J/Kg in fat, and 9×10^{-2} J/Kg in bone.

A dose of any ionizing radiation producing the same biological effect in tissue as that produced by 1 *roentgen* of high-voltage X radiation called 1 Rem.

The roentgen is frequently divided into one thousand equal parts called the *milliroentgen:*

$$1 \text{ roentgen} = 1000 \text{ milliroentgens}$$

$$1 \text{ R} = 1000 \text{ mR}$$

Curie. The *curie,* Ci, as a unit of radioactivity, was originally defined as the number of disintegrations per second emanating from one gram of radium. Because of experimental difficulties the unit was redefined by the International Commission on Radiological Units (July 1953) as follows: The curie is a unit of radioactivity defined as the quantity of any radioactive nuclide in which the number of disintegrations per second is 3.700×10^{10}. The *millicurie,* mCi, and *microcurie,* μCi, are smaller units in frequent use. Medical doses are usually expressed in millicurie-hours.

problems

1. If 9.50-MeV deuterons strike a magnesium-25 target, they produce α particles. (a) Write down the reaction. (b) Find the total energy liberated. If the total energy liberated is divided between the two recoiling particles in the inverse ratio of the masses, what is (c) the maximum energy of the α particles, and (d) their range in air? See Fig. 53G.

2. When a 4.20-MeV deuteron collides with a silicon-28 nucleus, an α particle is produced. If the available energy is divided between the two recoiling particles, in the inverse ratio of the masses, what is (a) the reaction, (b) the total kinetic energy liberated, (c) the maximum energy of the α particle, and (d) its range in air? See Fig. 53G.

3. When 8.60-MeV deuterons bombard boron-10, α particles, neutrons, and protons are observed as disintegration products. Assuming these particles arise from three different reactions as branch disintegrations, what are (a) the three reactions, and (b) the three Q values to three figures? [Ans. (a) ${}_1\text{H}^2 + {}_5\text{B}^{10} = 3{}_2\text{He}^4, = {}_6\text{C}^{11} + {}_0n^1, = {}_5\text{B}^{11} + {}_1\text{H}^1$, (b) 17.91 MeV, 6.47 MeV, 9.23 MeV.]

4. A beam of 12.50-MeV protons from a cyclotron is incident on a calcium-44 metal target. If α particles are emitted from the target, what is (a) the reaction, (b) the total energy liberated, (c) the energy of the α particles, and (d) their range in air? See Fig. 53G.

5. A beam of 15.30-MeV protons is incident on a sulfur-34 target, and neutrons are detected as coming off the target during bombardment. (a) Write down the nuclear reaction, (b) calculate the liberated energy and (c) the energy of the neutrons.

6. A beam of 8.85-MeV deuterons from a cyclotron bombards chlorine-37, and protons are emitted. (a) Write down the nuclear reaction. What is (b) the value of the liberated energy, (c) the energy of the protons, and (d) their range in air? See Fig. 53G. [Ans. (a) ${}_1\text{H}^2 + {}_{17}\text{Cl}^{37} = {}_{17}\text{Cl}^{38} + {}_1\text{H}^1$, (b) + 4.965 MeV, (c) 4.83 MeV, (d) 32.5 cm.]

7. If the accurately known mass of copper-64 is 63.929760 amu, find the accurate masses of the stable isobars nickel-64 and zinc-64. See Fig. 58K for the energy level diagram.

8. If the accurately known mass of $_{32}Ge^{67}$ is 66.932940 amu, find the accurate masses of the isobars $_{31}Ga^{67}$, $_{30}Zn^{67}$, $_{29}Cu^{67}$, and $_{28}Ni^{67}$. See Fig. 58P.

9.* There are seven known isobars with atomic mass number 129. Their masses are:

$_{51}Sb^{129}$	128.909260 amu
$_{52}Te^{129}$	128.906575 amu
$_{53}I^{129}$	128.904987 amu
$_{54}Xe^{129}$	128.904784 amu stable
$_{55}Cs^{129}$	128.905960 amu
$_{56}Ba^{129}$	128.908590 amu
$_{57}La^{129}$	128.912882 amu

(a) Plot an atomic mass vs. atomic number graph for these nuclides, similar to that shown in Fig. 58N. (b) Extrapolate the graph to find the approximate mass of $_{50}Sn^{129}$.

10.* There are seven known isobars with the atomic mass number 201. Their masses are:

$_{78}Pt^{201}$	200.974770 amu
$_{79}Au^{201}$	200.971920 amu
$_{80}Hg^{201}$	200.970308 amu stable
$_{81}T1^{201}$	200.970750 amu
$_{82}Pb^{201}$	200.972860 amu
$_{83}Bi^{201}$	200.977370 amu
$_{84}Po^{201}$	200.983020 amu

(a) Plot an atomic mass vs. atomic number graph for these nuclides, similar to that shown in Fig. 58N. (b) Extrapolate the graph to find the approximate mass of $_{77}Ir^{201}$.

11.* There are seven known isobars with atomic mass number 92. Their masses are:

$_{37}Rb^{92}$	91.919140 amu
$_{38}Sr^{92}$	91.910980 amu
$_{39}Y^{92}$	91.908926 amu
$_{40}Zr^{92}$	91.905031 amu stable
$_{41}Nb^{92}$	91.907211 amu
$_{42}Mo^{92}$	91.906910 amu stable
$_{43}Tc^{92}$	91.915460 amu

(a) Plot an atomic mass vs. atomic number graph for these nuclides, similar to that shown in Fig. 58O. (b) Extrapolate the graph to find the approximate mass of $_{44}Ru^{92}$.

12.* There are seven known isobars with the atomic mass number 154. Their masses are:

$_{62}Sm^{154}$	153.922282 amu stable
$_{63}Eu^{154}$	153.923053 amu
$_{64}Gd^{154}$	153.920929 amu stable
$_{65}Tb^{154}$	153.924500 amu
$_{66}Dy^{154}$	153.924350 amu
$_{67}Ho^{154}$	153.931250 amu
$_{68}Er^{154}$	153.932760 amu

(a) Plot an atomic mass vs. atomic number graph for these nuclides, similar to that shown in Fig. 58O. (b) Extrapolate the graph to find the approximate masses of $_{60}Nd^{154}$ and $_{61}Pm^{154}$.

59 Neutron and gamma-ray reactions

While the bombardment of all targets by high-energy charged atomic particles, such as protons, deuterons, and alpha particles, is found to produce disintegrations and transmutations of various kinds, it is also possible to bring about similar reactions with neutrons and gamma rays.

59.1. Neutron Reactions

The first disintegrations produced by high-speed neutrons as atomic projectiles were announced in 1932 by the English physicist Feather. Immediately following Chadwick's discovery of these neutral particles, Feather allowed neutrons from beryllium (see Fig. 59A) to enter a Wilson cloud chamber containing pure nitrogen gas. Numerous expansions of the chamber and the simultaneous clicks of a camera shutter gave many photographs of the ion tracks left by recoiling nitrogen atoms.

Although most of the photographs indicated elastic collisions between nitrogen atoms and neutrons, an occasional photograph showed a forked track, indicating a disintegration of a nitrogen nucleus:

$$ {}_0n^1 + {}_7N^{14} = {}_6C^{14} + {}_1H^1 \qquad (59a)$$

Two photographs of several such disintegrations are reproduced in Fig. 59A. Although hundreds of neutrons enter the cloud chamber every second, they do not ionize atoms as charged particles do, and hence leave no tracks. When a head-on nuclear collision occurs, however, the disintegrated nuclei, possessing as they do high speeds and positive charges, leave a trail of ions behind them. The fork in each photo shows a proton track of considerable length originating at the same point as the more dense, short-ranged track of the recoiling carbon nucleus.

Strong sources of neutrons are produced by inserting a thin plate of beryllium metal in the intense beam of deuterons coming from the cyclotron as shown in Fig. 59B. The disintegration process, giving rise to the neutrons, is the reaction Eq.(58f).

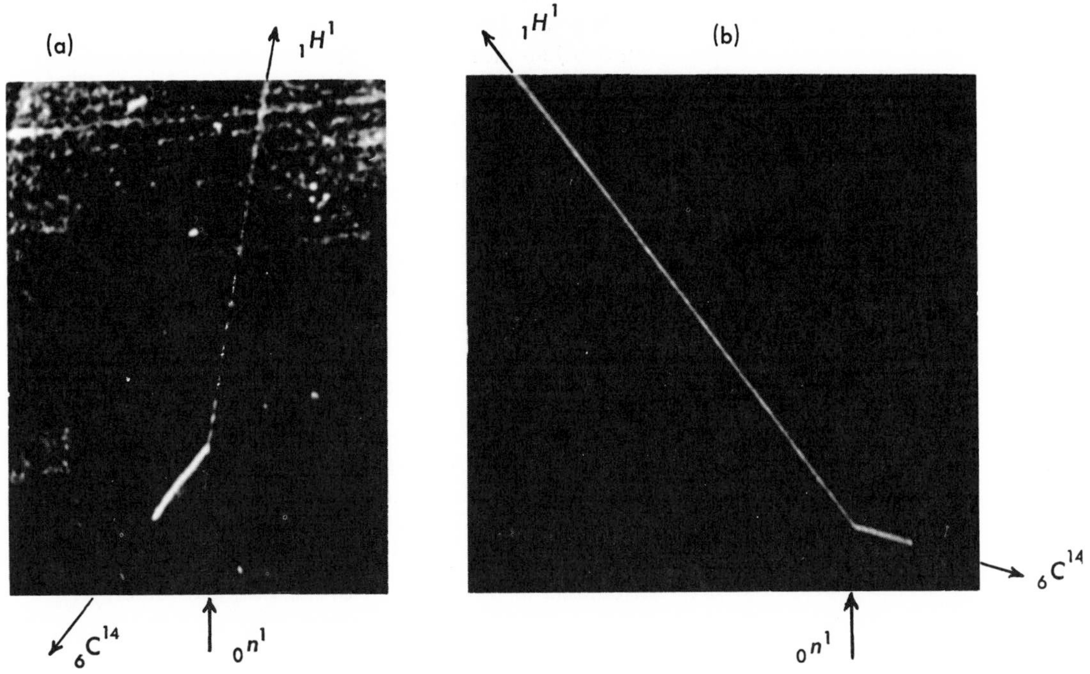

Fig. 59A. Cloud-track photographs of neutron disintegrations of nitrogen. (After Feather and Rasetti.)

Into such a beam of chargeless particles, numerous substances of known chemical constitution have been inserted, and the disintegration products studied with suitable detectors. To illustrate by an example, suppose that a thin sheet of aluminum is inserted into the beam of neutrons as shown in the figure. In this particular instance, α particles are observed emerging from aluminum, thus enabling one to write down the following neutron reaction:

$$_0n^1 + {}_{13}\text{Al}^{27} = {}_{11}\text{Na}^{24} + {}_2\text{He}^4 \tag{59b}$$

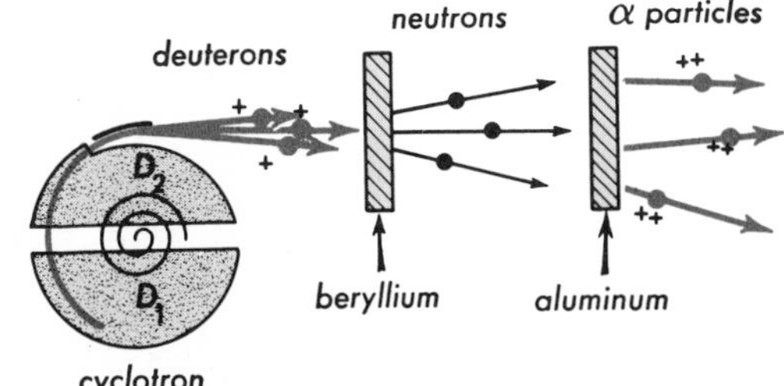

Fig. 59B. Experimental arrangement for producing intense beams of neutrons by bombarding beryllium with deuterons. The neutrons are then used as projectiles for further disintegrations, as illustrated here for aluminum.

Thus *radioactive sodium,* produced originally by the deuteron bombardment of ordinary sodium, is here produced by a different reaction [see Eq.(58u)]. As proof of the result, the bombarded aluminum target is found to be β-ray and γ-ray active with a half-life of 15 h. There are at least two other known disintegration processes by which radiosodium is produced: one by the neutron bombardment of silicon, and the other by the α-particle bombardment of magnesium.

This is but one example of the many known radioactive elements that can be manufactured in four different ways. As a matter of fact, with sufficiently energetic atomic bullets, it is now possible to produce hundreds of atomic nuclei not found in nature. While most of them have short half-lives and do not last very long, there are many with long half-lives, some extending into thousands of years.

Examples of other neutron disintegrations, followed by radioactive β^- emissions, are illustrated by the following reactions:

$$\begin{gathered} {}_0n^1 + {}_9\mathrm{F}^{19} = [{}_7\mathrm{N}^{16}] + {}_2\mathrm{He}^4 \\ [{}_7\mathrm{N}^{16}] = {}_8\mathrm{O}^{16} + {}_{-1}e^0 + \bar{\nu}_e + \gamma \end{gathered} \tag{59c}$$

$$\begin{gathered} {}_0n^1 + {}_{20}\mathrm{Ca}^{42} = [{}_{19}\mathrm{K}^{42}] + {}_1\mathrm{H}^1 \\ [{}_{19}\mathrm{K}^{42}] = {}_{20}\mathrm{Ca}^{42} + {}_{-1}e^0 + \bar{\nu}_e \end{gathered} \tag{59d}$$

Equation (59d) represents a typical case of the capture of a neutron to form a radioactive isotope ${}_{19}\mathrm{K}^{42}$ which, by the ejection of an electron, reverts back to the original stable element, ${}_{20}\mathrm{Ca}^{42}$. Many such reactions are known, particularly among the heavier elements in the first half of the periodic table.

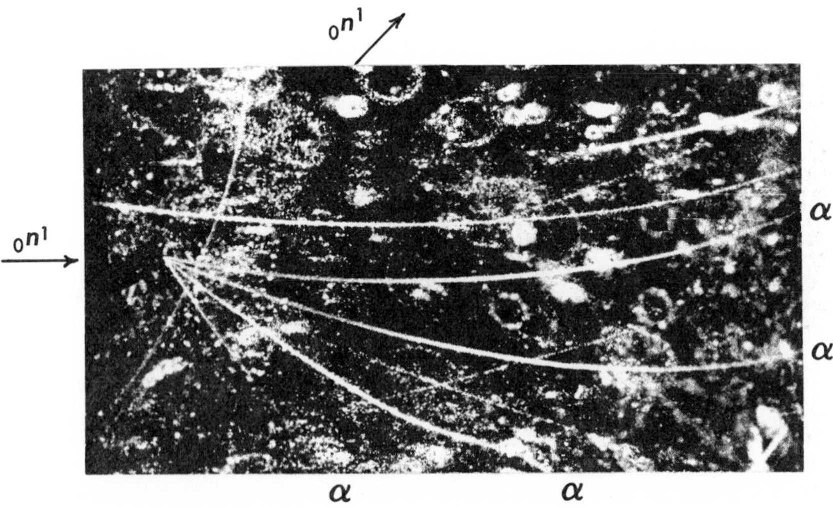

Fig. 59C. Wilson cloud-chamber photograph showing the result of a 100-MeV neutron impact on an oxygen nucleus. (Courtesy of W. Powell.)

When 100- to 200-MeV deuterons from a large cyclotron strike almost any target, neutrons with energies of 100 MeV or more are produced. Figure 59C is a Wilson cloud-chamber photograph showing the result of a 100-MeV neutron impact with an oxygen nucleus. The paths of the recoiling fragments, four α particles, are bent in the magnetic field.

Not all disintegration processes liberate more energy than that required to produce them. This is illustrated by the following example:

$$_0n^1 + {}_6C^{12} = {}_4Be^9 + {}_2He^4 \qquad Q = -5.704 \text{ MeV} \tag{59e}$$

To carry out this disintegration, the bombarding neutrons must have an energy of 5.7 MeV or greater. The sum of the masses produced is greater by this amount than those that went to make them. This is an example of what is called a fast-neutron reaction. This reaction is the reverse of the reaction by which neutrons were first produced in large quantity [see Sec. 55.5 and Eq.(55g)].

59.2. Slow Neutron Reactions

The fact that neutrons, slowed down to very low speeds, have the ability to disintegrate certain atoms was first discovered and investigated by the Italian physicist, Enrico Fermi,* and his collaborators. A neutron approaching the nucleus of an atom does not experience a repulsive force, as does a proton, deuteron, or α particle, and consequently its chances of penetration into a nucleus and of being captured by it are relatively large. It is for this reason that slowly moving neutrons are able to bring about disintegrations that slowly moving charged particles cannot.

The customary method of producing *slow neutrons* is to surround a source of fast neutrons with paraffin or some material containing large quantities of hydrogen or deuterium. As neutrons pass through this "moderator" material, elastic collisions with hydrogen nuclei continually slow them down, until at a distance of several centimeters from the source most of them have lost all of their original energy. What little energy they do have is picked up by regular thermal collisions with other atoms.

Since their resultant motions become quite the same as the random motions of the atoms and molecules of the moderator, they are called *thermal neutrons.* Thermal neutrons are defined as neutrons in equilibrium with the substance in which they exist, i.e., neutrons of average kinetic energy of 0.0253 eV. Compared with fast neutrons moving with almost the speed of light, like those from a target of beryllium bombarded by the beam from a

***Enrico Fermi (1901–1954), American physicist, was born in Italy. He studied at Pisa, Göttingen, and Leiden, and later taught physics at the universities of Florence and Rome. He was professor of physics at Columbia University (1939–1945) and the University of Chicago (1945–1954). For his experimental discoveries of disintegration, induced by slow neutrons, Fermi was awarded the 1938 Nobel Prize in physics. His creation of the first self-sustaining uranium chain reaction at Chicago in 1942 led to the development of the atomic bomb. He later worked on the hydrogen bomb and served on the General Advisory Committee of the Atomic Energy Commission. The element fermium (At. No. 100) was named after him.**

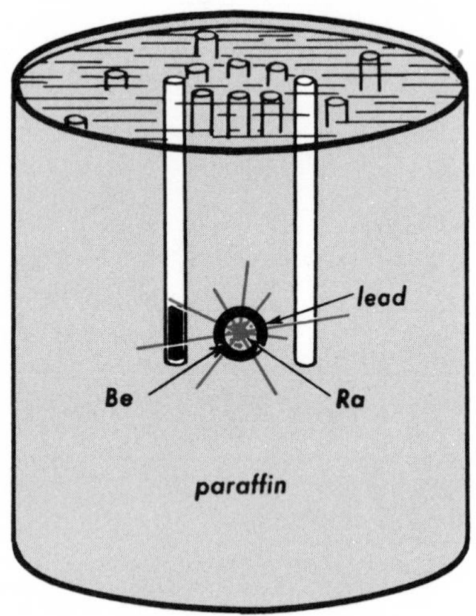

Fig. 59D. Diagram of a Ra–Be source of thermal neutrons for laboratory experiments.

cyclotron, thermal neutrons have a velocity of only 2200 m/s. This is essentially the velocity of hydrogen molecules in a gas at normal temperature and pressure.

One of the many known slow-neutron reactions is one in which boron-10 captures a neutron and ejects an α particle:

$$_0n^1 + {}_5B^{10} \rightarrow {}_3Li^7 + {}_2He^4 \tag{59f}$$

59.3. A Thermal-Neutron Source

A very good laboratory source of thermal neutrons can be made with a small quantity of radium and beryllium. The radium sample is surrounded by a thin jacket of beryllium metal and an outer jacket of lead, and then this unit is imbedded at the center of several cubic feet of paraffin (see Fig. 59D). The α particles from radium produce neutrons by the reaction

$$_2He^4 + {}_4Be^9 \rightarrow {}_6C^{12} + {}_0n^1 \qquad Q = 5.6 \text{ MeV}$$

The fast neutrons given off by the beryllium metal bounce around in the paraffin, quickly slowing down to thermal velocities, while the unwanted β and γ rays from the radium are absorbed by the lead.

Any source to be radiated by slow neutrons is placed in a holder and lowered through any one of several ports shown in the top surface.

An effective demonstration of slow-neutron reactions can be made by rolling a thin sheet of silver metal into a hollow cylinder, about 1 in. in diameter and 4 in. long, and subjecting it to the Ra–Be source (Fig. 59D). After several minutes the cylinder is withdrawn and quickly placed around a Geiger-counter tube, or near the fluor of a scintillation counter. The activity detected will be strong at first and then will slowly die out over a period of several minutes.

If a scaler counting system like the one shown in Fig. 54O is employed, and the number of counts registered on the tube faces is recorded at 10 s intervals, a decay curve like the one shown in Fig. 59E can be plotted. Such a graph with two distinct straight sections is found to be a composite of two half-life curves, one for 24 s and the other for 2.3 min. These two half-lives are attributed to the two radioactive isotopes of silver, one of mass 108 amu and one of 110 amu:

$$_0n^1 + {}_{47}Ag^{107} \rightarrow {}_{47}A^{108} + \gamma \text{ ray}$$

$$_0n^1 + {}_{47}Ag^{109} \rightarrow {}_{47}Ag^{110} + \gamma \text{ ray}$$

The capture of a neutron by each of these nuclides produces the radioactive isotopes, silver-108 and silver-110. Both of these are electron active, and produce stable cadmium nuclides as follows:

$$_{47}Ag^{108} \rightarrow {}_{48}Cd^{108} + {}_{-1}e^0 + \bar{\nu}_e \qquad (2.42 \text{ min})$$

$$_{47}Ag^{110} \rightarrow {}_{48}Cd^{110} + {}_{-1}e^0 + \bar{\nu}_e \qquad (24.4 \text{ s})$$

The procedure for finding the two half-lives from the graph in Fig. 59E is to start with the lower straight section and extrapolate back to zero time. This straight line is then subtracted from the upper curve at two points of time, such as $t = 0$ and $t = 100$ s, and the other straight line drawn in as shown. The summation

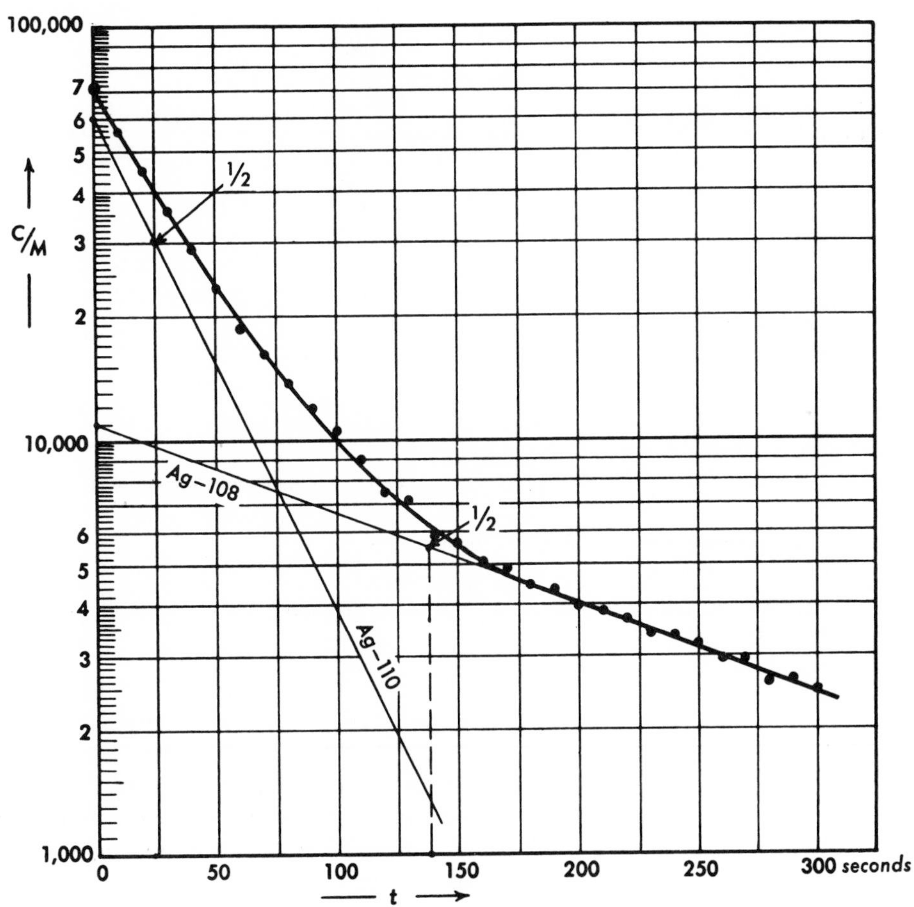

Fig. 59E. Semilog graph of the β rays from the two silver isotopes, made active by thermal neutrons.

of these two straight lines should produce the observed curve. Note that the straight lines drop to half their initial values at $t =$ 24 s and $t =$ 138 s.

Both radioactive silver isotopes belong to isobaric groups of odd-odd, even-even nuclei. Like niobium-92 in Fig. 58O, they both decay to stable nuclei: to the right by β^- emission, and to the left by β^+, or E.C. An energy level diagram for the decay of silver-108 is shown in Fig. 59F. Note that 96% of the $_{47}Ag^{108}$ nuclei decays to the ground state by the emission of a β^-, but that the remaining 4% decays by the emission of β^- to excited states of $_{48}Cd^{108}$, or by β^+ emission, or by electron capture, to the ground or excited states of $_{46}Pd^{108}$, followed by the emission of γ rays.

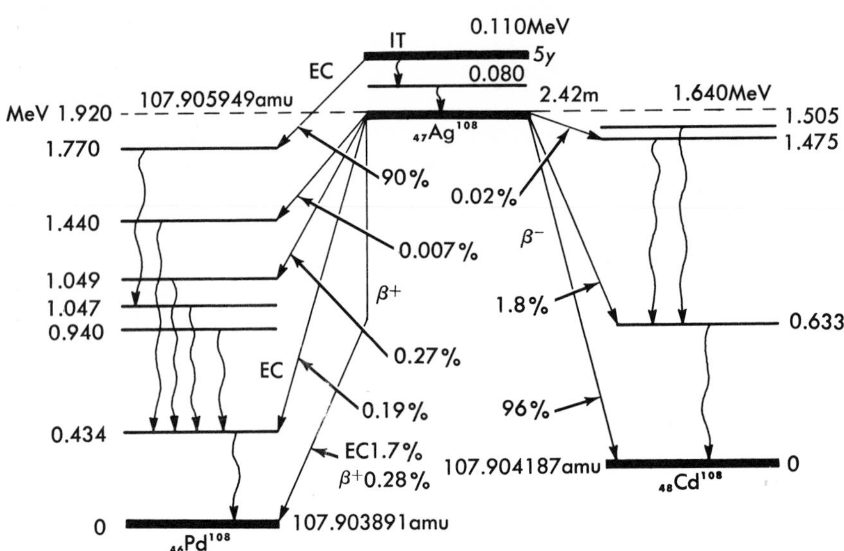

Fig. 59F. Energy level diagram for the radioactive decay of the silver isotope $_{47}Ag^{108}$. Note the long half-life of 5 years for the Isomeric Transition, IT, at the top.

Another effective demonstration of slow-neutron reactions is to roll a thin sheet of indium metal into a hollow cylinder, subject it to the slow neutron source (Fig. 59D), and then place it over a Geiger-counter tube or scintillation counter. Like silver, it too will show a strong activity at first and then die out over a period of several minutes.

Indium has two stable isotopes, $_{49}In^{113}$ and $_{49}In^{115}$. Upon neutron capture they will become the radioactive isotopes $_{49}In^{114}$ and

${}_{49}\mathrm{In}^{116}$. Both of these nuclides decay by electron emission into stable tin isotopes. ${}_{49}\mathrm{In}^{116}$ decays in either one of two ways, as follows:

$$ {}_{49}\mathrm{In}^{114} \rightarrow {}_{50}\mathrm{Sn}^{114} + {}_{-1}e^0 + \bar{\nu}_e \qquad (72\ \mathrm{s}) $$

$$ {}_{49}\mathrm{In}^{116} \rightarrow {}_{50}\mathrm{Sn}^{116} + {}_{-1}e^0 + \bar{\nu}_e \qquad (54\ \mathrm{min}) $$

$$ {}_{49}\mathrm{In}^{116} \rightarrow {}_{50}\mathrm{Sn}^{116} + {}_{-1}e^0 + \bar{\nu}_e \qquad (14\ \mathrm{s}) $$

The longer-lived In^{116} is an excited state of the nucleus, called an *isomeric state,* and beta decay with an end-point energy of 1 MeV is followed by several gamma rays. The shorter-lived In^{116} is the normal state of the nucleus, and beta decay with an end-point energy of 2.9 MeV takes it directly to the normal state of Sn^{116} without the emission of gamma rays.

Fig. 59G. Neutron diffraction pattern of sodium chloride. (Courtesy, E. O. Wollan and C. G. Shull.)

59.4. Neutron Diffraction

We have seen in a preceding chapter that wave properties are associated with all moving bodies. The De Broglie wavelength of any mass m is given by Eq.(51i) as

$$ \lambda = \frac{h}{mv} \qquad (59g) $$

which for thermal neutrons with a velocity of 2200 m/s gives $\lambda = 1.80 \times 10^{-10}$ meters, or 1.80 Å. This value is comparable to the spacings of atoms in solids and suggests the possibilities of diffraction, as in the case of X rays and Laue patterns (see Figs. 50F and 50G).

The diffraction of strong beams of neutrons by the atoms of a crystal has been studied by many people. Wollan and Shull, using a sodium chloride crystal and an experimental arrangement similar to that shown for X rays in Fig. 50F, obtained the picture reproduced in Fig. 59G. Since neutrons have little or no effect upon photographic films, the front face of the film was covered with a sheet of indium metal 0.5 mm thick.

Neutrons captured by the indium nuclei produce radioactive isotopes, as shown in the preceding section. These unstable isotopes disintegrate, with the emission of electrons. Electrons do affect a photographic emulsion and upon development produce the spots shown. Neutrons, like X rays, therefore, become useful tools in the study of the atomic structure of matter.

TABLE 59A
Photon relations

V (volts)	λ (m)	ν (Hz)
1 KeV	1.241×10^{-9}	2.416×10^{17}
1 MeV	1.241×10^{-12}	2.416×10^{20}
1 GeV	1.241×10^{-15}	2.416×10^{23}

Example 1. A fast neutron has an energy equivalent to 2.0 MeV. Calculate (a) its kinetic energy in joules, (b) its velocity in m/s, and (c) its De Broglie wavelength in angstroms.

Solution. The known quantities needed are $E = 2.0$ MeV, $M_n = 1.649 \times 10^{-27}$ Kg, $e = 1.602 \times 10^{-19}$ C, and $h = 6.626 \times 10^{-34}$ J. To find the energy we use the basic energy equation $Ve = \frac{1}{2}mv^2$, and find Ve:

$$Ve = 2.0 \times 10^6 \times 1.6022 \times 10^{-19}$$

$$Ve = 3.2044 \times 10^{-13} \text{ J}$$

Solving the above energy equation for the velocity, we find

$$v = \sqrt{\frac{2\,Ve}{M_n}} = \sqrt{\frac{2 \times 3.2044 \times 10^{-13}}{1.6749 \times 10^{-27}}}$$

$$v = 1.9561 \times 10^7 \text{ m/s}$$

which is approximately 1/15 the velocity of light. We are therefore justified in using the nonrelativistic equations.

We now find the De Broglie wavelength by direct substitution in Eq.(59g):

$$\lambda = \frac{h}{mv} = \frac{6.626 \times 10^{-34}}{1.6749 \times 10^{-27} \times 1.9561 \times 10^7}$$

$$\lambda = 2.0224 \times 10^{-14} \text{ m}$$

$$\lambda = 0.00020224 \text{ Å}$$

59.5. Photon Interactions

The term "photon interaction" refers to the disintegration of atomic nuclei brought about by photons. In general, the photons to be used must have a very high energy $h\nu$, and this means their frequency ν must be high and their wavelength λ short ($c = \nu\lambda$).

X rays and γ rays are electromagnetic waves in character, and both are composed of photons. The terms X ray or γ ray only signify their origin and, in reactions with nuclei, are of no consequence.

Instead of specifying a photon by giving its frequency ν, it is customary in nuclear reactions to express its energy in electron volts. By the general energy equation, Eq.(53k), we have

$$Ve = h\nu \qquad \text{or} \qquad V = h\nu/e \tag{59h}$$

For reference purposes, only the following wavelengths and frequencies are calculated from this equation.

To obtain sources of high-energy photons, it is common practice to use γ rays from radioactive sources, or to produce X rays with the high-energy electron beam of a betatron or synchrotron. ${}_{81}\text{Tl}^{208}$, for example, produces 2.62-MeV γ rays that are useful for several kinds of experiments.

As an example of the production of high-energy photons with the beam from a large electron accelerator, consider the 1.3-GeV electrons of the Cornell synchrotron (see Fig. 59H). Each time the beam in this machine is allowed to strike a metal target inside the vacuum chamber, the 1.3-GeV electrons produce X rays of very high energy. Target composition is of some importance in this process, and the phenomenon called "bremsstrahlung" is responsible for the high-energy X-ray beam that emerges (see Fig. 50M). In such a beam one finds a continuous band of photons ranging in energy from practically 0 up to 1.3 GeV.

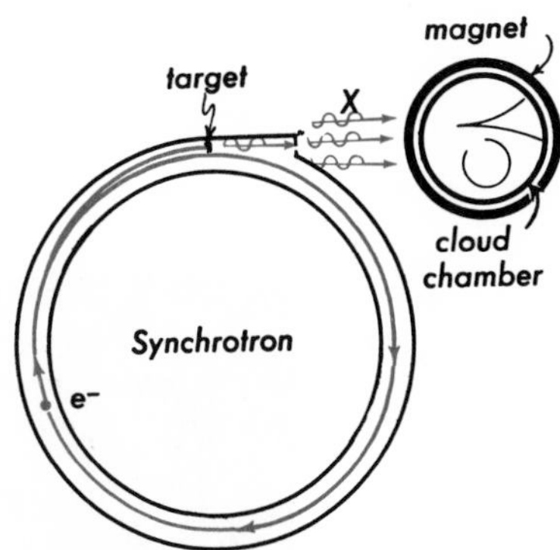

Fig. 59H. Photons produced by the electron beam from a synchrotron are used to study photon reactions in a cloud chamber.

As such a beam is made to traverse any form of matter, there are several processes by which the rays are absorbed or scattered from the beam. These, as shown in Fig. 59I, are:

- Photoelectric effect
- Compton effect
- Pair production

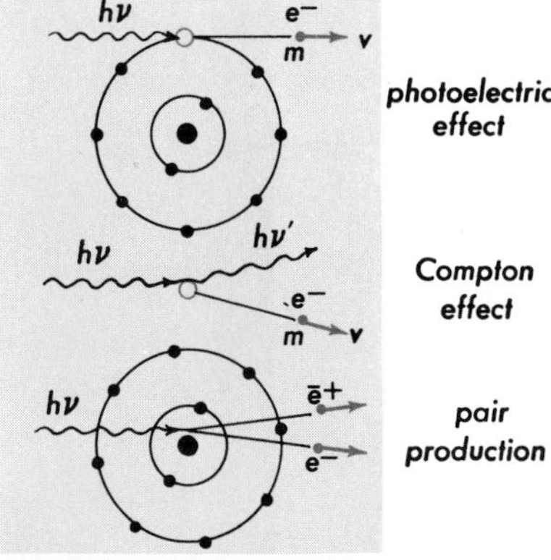

Fig. 59I. The three major processes responsible for the absorption of high-energy photons in matter.

For photons of low energy the photoelectric effect is chiefly responsible for absorption. As the energy increases, the Compton effect becomes more and more important until, at energies of 1 MeV, pair production sets in and eventually becomes predominant.

A diffusion cloud-chamber photograph of a Compton recoil electron and an electron pair is shown in Fig. 59J. The hundreds of photons that passed through this gas-filled cloud chamber, from left to right, left no tracks since they were electrically neutral. One photon, however, collided with an atomic electron near the upper center of the field, and the forward recoiling electron, in the magnetic field applied to the chamber, made $1\frac{3}{4}$ turns around a circle. Another photon, coming close to a nucleus at the upper left, created an electron pair. From the curvatures of the tracks it is clear that the positron curving upward had more energy than the Compton electron, but less energy than its electron associate.

The production of a pair of electrons by a photon passing close to an atomic nucleus can also occur in the region close to an electron (see Fig. 59K). In both of these processes, the force exerted by the photon on the charged particle during the pair creation causes that particle to recoil forward. Because of its relatively small mass, the electron recoil may be large enough to appear as a third track in a cloud chamber, whereas with the far heavier nucleus the recoil energy is small and a track is seldom observed.

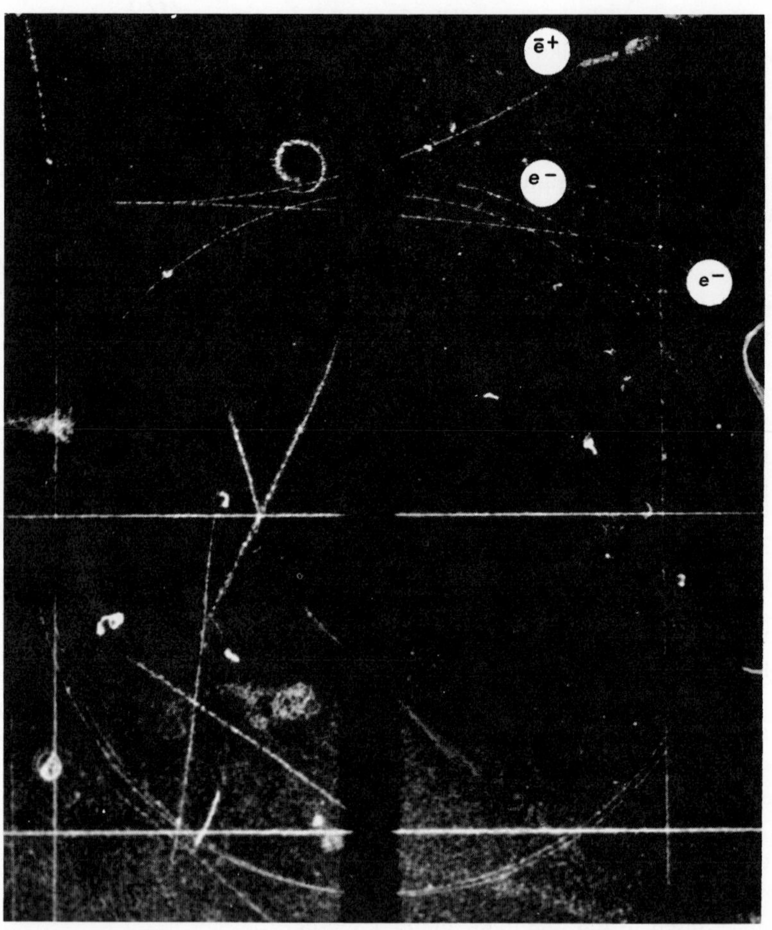

Fig. 59J. Cloud-chamber photograph showing a Compton recoil electron (circle) and an electron pair (V track) produced by photons. (Courtesy of Cornell Laboratory.)

A bubble-chamber photograph showing an electron triplet and an electron pair is reproduced in Fig. 59L. Of the many photons traversing the chamber from left to right, one came extremely close to an atomic electron, and there in the strong electric field created a pair, the positron bending upward, the slower electron downward, and the still slower recoiling electron spiraling around in a small circle. The second photon coming close to the nucleus of a hydrogen atom produced another pair, the positron bending upward and the electron downward.

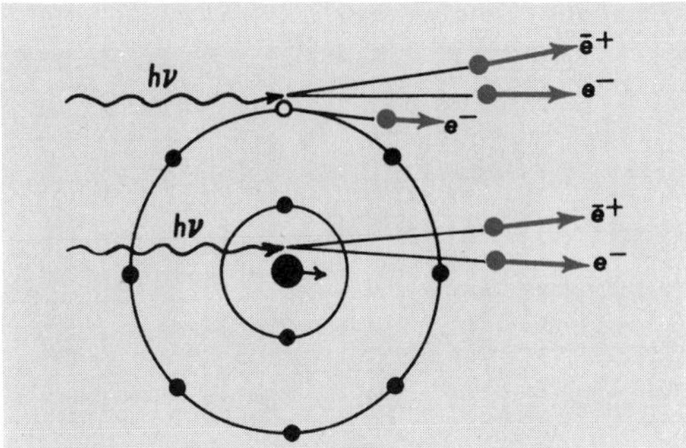

Fig. 59K. High-energy photons can produce electron pairs by collision with a nucleus or an orbital electron.

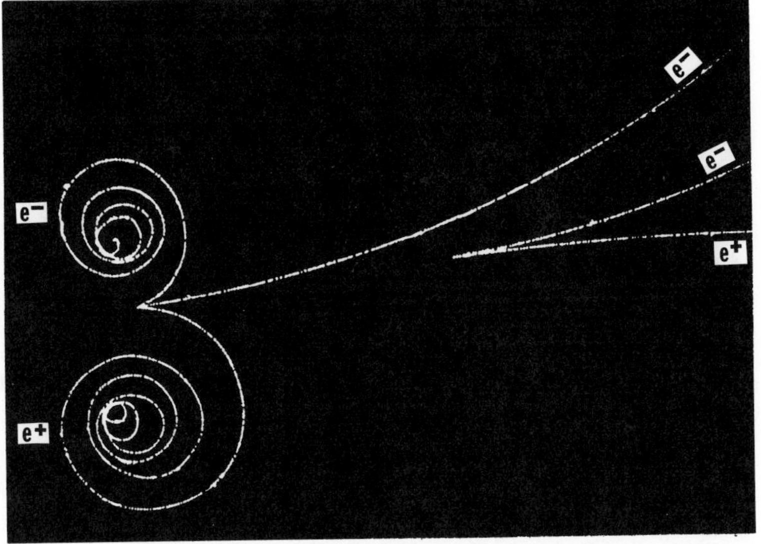

Fig. 59L. Cloud-chamber photograph showing an electron triplet and an electron pair produced by high-energy photons (see Fig. 59K).

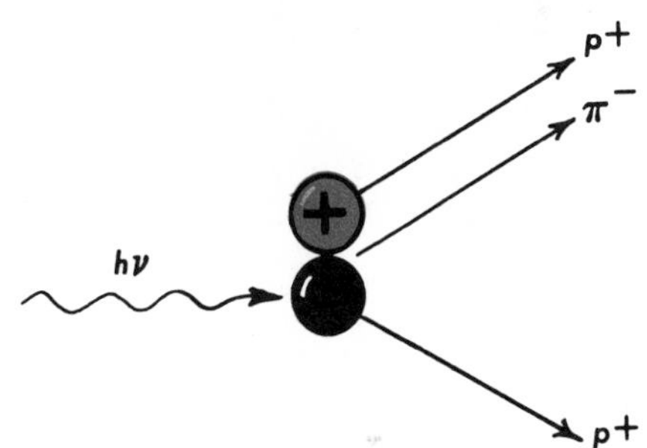

Fig. 59M. One type of reaction produced by photon collisions with deuterons (see Fig. 59N).

59.6. Photon-Deuteron Interactions

If a cloud chamber is filled with deuterium, that is, with gas in which all molecules are composed of the heavy hydrogen atoms, ${}_1H^2$, interesting photon interactions can be observed. One process is shown in Fig. 59M. A deuteron, the nucleus of a deuterium atom, is composed of one neutron and one proton.

If a photon collides with the neutron of a deuteron, it may produce a proton p and a pi-minus meson, π^-, as shown. Since the two particles leave so quickly after the collision, the remaining "spectator proton" continues on with whatever momentum it had at the moment of impact. The reaction for this can be written

$$h\nu + d^+ \rightarrow p^+ + \pi^- + \underbrace{p^+}_{\text{spectator}} \tag{59i}$$

Such an explanation accounts for the cloud-chamber event shown in Fig. 59N. A photon entering from the left collides with the neutron of a deuteron. The neutron is split into a proton p^+ and a π^- meson, with the low momentum "spectator proton" stopping in the chamber.

Since it is generally accepted that a proton or deuteron has unit positive charge, and neutrons and neutrinos have none, their charge exponents are usually omitted in reactions.

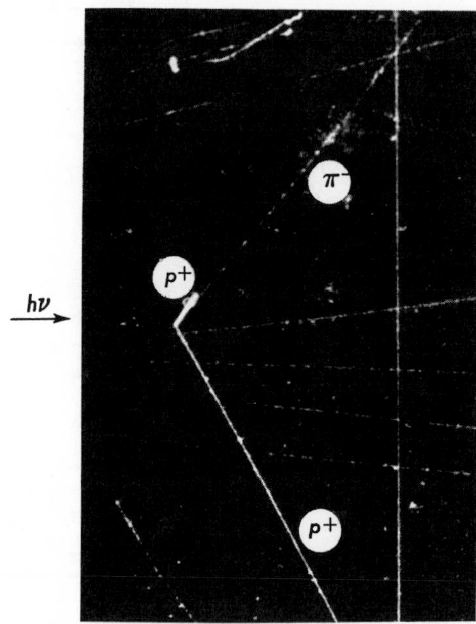

Fig. 59N. Cloud-chamber photograph showing one type of photon reaction (see Fig. 59M). (Courtesy of Cornell Laboratories.)

59.7. Photon Production of Meson Pairs

If a high-energy photon comes close enough to a proton in a nucleus, a π meson pair may be created in much the same way that an electron pair is produced with a photon of lower energy. If the nucleus is a deuteron, as shown in Fig. 59O, the proton recoils from the impact while the neutron continues on with whatever momentum it had at the moment of impact.

As a reaction, we can write

$$h\nu + d^+ \rightarrow p^+ + \pi^- + \pi^+ + \underbrace{n^0}_{\text{spectator}} \tag{59j}$$

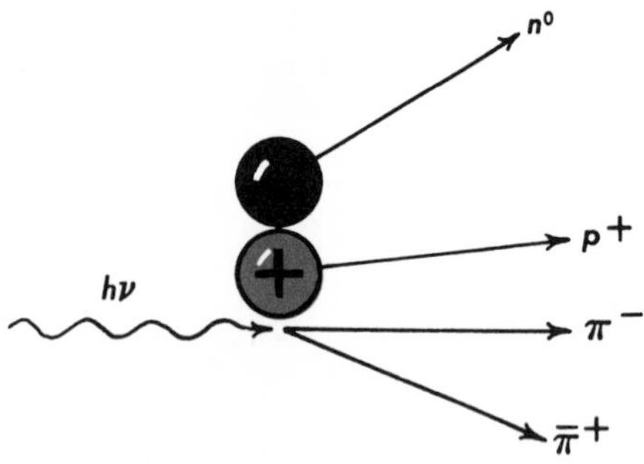

Fig. 59O. Diagram of a photon collision with the proton of a deuteron, producing a pair of π mesons (see Fig. 59P).

This reaction accounts for the cloud-chamber event shown in Fig. 59P. A photon, entering from the left, comes close to the proton of a deuteron. A pair of π mesons is created, the proton recoils under the impact, and the neutron "spectator," not being able to form a track, goes on in some unknown direction.

In all such reactions the conservation laws of energy, momentum, and charge must hold. Measurements of track curvatures give velocities and momenta of particles, and calculations are made to see that the conservation of energy and momentum hold. We have seen previously that approximately 1 MeV is required to create an electron pair. Since a π meson has a mass 273 times that of an electron, an energy of approximately 273 MeV is required to create a pair of π mesons. This is the threshold energy for meson pair-production.

Another interesting reaction involving the impact of a high-energy photon with a deuteron is one in which the processes shown in Figs. 59M and 59O are combined. As shown schematically in Fig. 59Q, a photon collides with the neutron, splits it apart into a proton, p^+, and a π^- meson, and simultaneously creates a π meson pair, while the proton "spectator" continues on with its relatively low energy. The reaction is written

$$h\nu + d^+ \rightarrow p^+ + p^+ + \pi^- + \pi^+ + \pi^- \tag{59k}$$

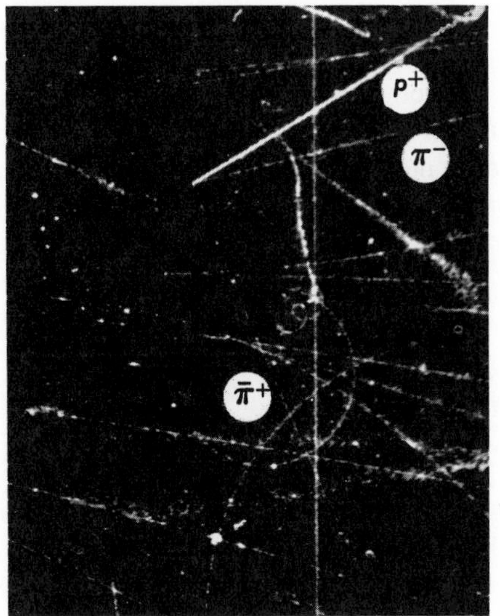

Fig. 59P. Photograph of a photon collision with the proton of a deuteron, producing a pair of π mesons. (Courtesy of Cornell Laboratories.)

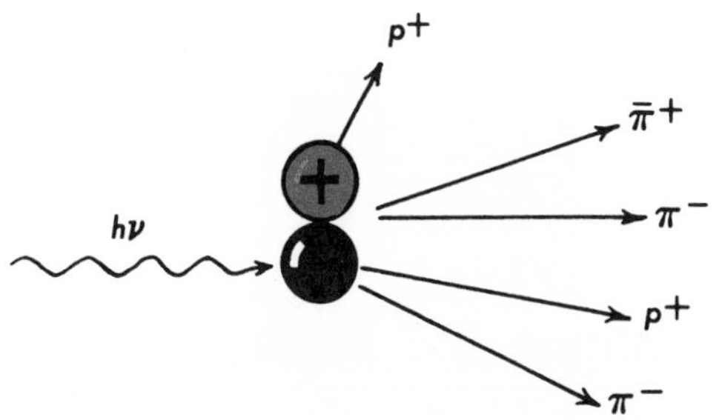

Fig. 59Q. Diagram of a photon collision with a deuteron, splitting the neutron and producing a pair of π mesons (see Fig. 59R).

All five of these particles have a charge and may be identified in the cloud-chamber event reproduced in Fig. 59R. The laboratory-measured angles, the ionization along the tracks of the five particles, as well as the momentum calculations, readily verify the dynamics of this event.

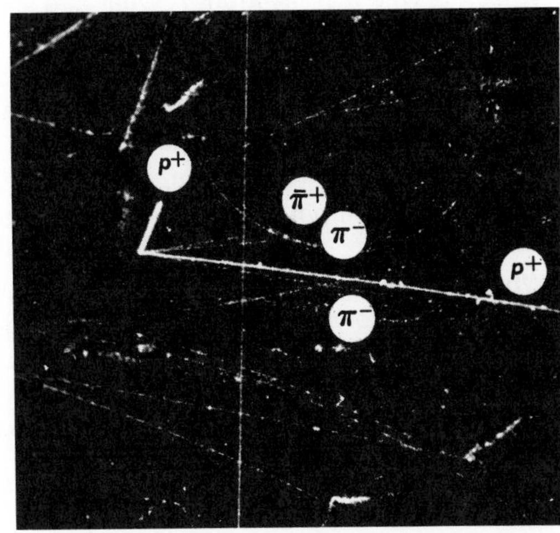

Fig. 59R. Cloud chamber photograph of a photon collision with a deuteron, splitting the neutron and producing a pair of π mesons. (Courtesy of Cornell Laboratories)*

59.8. Mean Life of a Neutron

Numerous laboratory experiments show that a free neutron has an average life of 15 min 32 s, or 932 s, before it spontaneously decays. The neutron decays into a proton, an electron, and an antineutrino. In the form of a reaction,

$$n^0 \to p^+ + e^- + \bar{\nu}_e \qquad (59\ell)$$

In relation to the time scale in which atomic particles interact with each other during a collision (about 10^{-8} to 10^{-15} s), the mean life of a neutron is extremely long.

* The photographs in Figs. 59J, 59N, 59P, and 59R were supplied by the diffusion cloud chamber research group, B. Chasan, G. Cocconi, V. Cocconi, E. Hart, R. Schectman, and D. White, at Cornell University.

The mean life of a neutron is so long that even a thermal neutron will, on the average, travel more than 1600 Km before decaying. A 2 MeV neutron will travel 16 million kilometers.

By comparing the decay of a neutron with the radioactive decay of unstable nuclei, we can speak of the above equation as one of beta decay.

questions and problems

Use the following values in the problems below, and calculate answers to three significant figures:

$M_n = 1.675 \times 10^{-27}$ Kg $\qquad e = 1.602 \times 10^{-19}$ C

$M_\pi = 2.448 \times 10^{-28}$ Kg $\qquad h = 6.626 \times 10^{-34}$ Js

$c = 2.998 \times 10^8$ m/s $\qquad M_p = 1.673 \times 10^{-27}$ Kg

1. What are thermal neutrons? What are slow neutrons? What are their velocities in m/s?

2. Make a diagram of a radium-beryllium source of thermal neutrons. Explain the function of each substance used.

3. When silicon-28 is bombarded by neutrons, protons are found coming from the target. Write down the resultant reaction.

4. When neutrons collide with oxygen-16 nuclei, α particles are observed to be given off. Write down the reaction.

5. Charged particles show their tracks in a Wilson cloud chamber. Neutrons and γ rays do not. Why?

6. How are strong beams of neutrons produced? Can neutrons be accelerated in a cyclotron?

7.* A fast neutron has an energy equivalent to 0.450 MeV. Calculate (a) its kinetic energy in joules, (b) its velocity in m/s, and (c) its De Broglie wavelength in angstroms.

8.* In a nuclear reaction a neutron is emitted with an energy of 1.850 MeV. Find (a) its energy in joules, (b) its velocity in m/s, and (c) its De Broglie wavelength in angstroms.

9.* The De Broglie wavelength of a neutron is 0.0550 Å. Calculate (a) its velocity in m/s, (b) its kinetic energy in joules, and (c) its energy in electron volts. [Ans. (a) 7.19×10^4 m/s, (b) 4.33×10^{-18} J, (c) 27.03 eV.]

10.* A diffraction experiment is performed with neutrons having a De Broglie wavelength of 0.250 Å. Find (a) their velocity in m/s, (b) their kinetic energy in joules, and (c) their energy in electron volts.

11.* Find (a) the minimum energy in MeV, (b) the frequency in Hz, and (c) the wavelength in angstroms of a γ ray that will produce an electron pair.

12*. Find (a) the minimum energy in MeV, (b) the frequency in Hz, and (c) the wavelength in angstroms of a pair of pions. Assume their mass to be 273.2 m_e each. [Ans. (a) 279.2 MeV, (b) 6.75×10^{22} Hz, (c) 4.44×10^{-5} Å.]

60 Special atomic and nuclear effects

It is well known from detailed observations of spectrum lines that whether radiant energy arises from the external structure of atoms or from the nucleus, the breadths of most lines are independent of the spectrograph used to observe them. In many cases narrow and broad lines are observed in the same spectrum. The sharp and diffuse series of the optical spectra of the alkali metals and alkaline earth elements are good examples of this. Although special sources of light have been devised that are capable of sharpening most lines to within the limits of the resolving power of the finest spectrographs, some lines have resisted all efforts to make them narrow.

In this chapter we are concerned with the principal causes of the observed breadth of lines, and with certain atomic and nuclear processes associated with the emission and absorption of photons. The principal causes for the breadth of spectrum lines are:

- Doppler effect
- Natural breadth
- Stark effect

60.1. Doppler Broadening

One of the most classical of all atomic phenomena is the Doppler principle as it applies to the observed frequencies of light. This is well illustrated by certain lines in the solar spectrum shown in Fig. 37M. The rays emitted from atoms on the side of the sun approaching the earth are shifted to higher frequencies, while rays emitted from atoms on the side receding from the earth are shifted to lower frequencies.

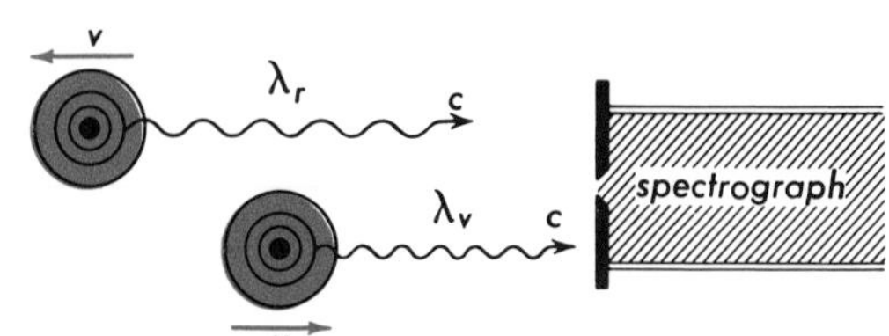

Fig. 60A. Diagram of the Doppler effect for light emitted by excited atoms, receding from, and approaching, the slit of a stationary spectrograph.

Figure 60A gives a classical representation of two identical atoms emitting photons of the same frequency ν_0 while they are moving with respect to the slit of a spectrograph. The wavelength emitted by the atom receding from the spectrograph is lengthened, while that emitted by the approaching atom is shortened. Although the velocity of light c is the same for both waves, the frequency of the waves passing through the slit will be different in the two cases. From the theory of relativity the observed frequency will be given by

$$\nu = \nu_0 \frac{\sqrt{1 - (v^2/c^2)}}{1 - (v/c)}$$

Relativistic

This is the relativistic Doppler equation, where ν is the observed frequency, ν_0 is the emitted frequency, and v is the relative velocity of the atom with respect to the spectrograph, $+v$ for an approaching atom and $-v$ for the receding atom.

By a mathematical expansion this equation can be written in the more useful form of a series, as follows:

$$\nu = \nu_0 \left(1 + \frac{v}{c} + \frac{1}{2}\frac{v^2}{c^2} + \frac{1}{2}\frac{v^3}{c^3} + \cdots\right) \tag{60a}$$

For velocities that are less than 1% the speed of light, the third and succeeding terms of this series are extremely small and can be neglected. The equation then becomes

$$\nu = \nu_0 \left(1 + \frac{v}{c}\right) \tag{60b}$$

Nonrelativistic

which is just the Doppler formula derived for sound waves. For velocities where v is high and not greatly different from c, the first three or four terms are also required for calculations and the Doppler formula from Newtonian mechanics is not valid.

When the spectrum lines from most of the distant stars are observed and measured with a spectrograph, they are found to be shifted to longer wavelengths than those found and observed from appropriate light sources in the laboratory. This *red shift* as it is called is attributed to the Doppler effect of an apparent expanding universe. Numerous measurements show that the more distant the stars the higher is their velocity away from our galaxy. A relatively few stars, however, are approaching the earth, and the shift of their spectrum lines is to shorter wavelengths. This seems to imply either a "big bang" theory or a "pulsating universe" theory for the creation of the universe.

Example 1. The iron lines of the spectrum of a distant star are shifted to longer wavelengths. The green line $\lambda = 5270.0$ Å, for example, is observed to have a wavelength of 5295.0 Å. Find (a) the frequency of the normal unshifted green line, (b) the frequency of the same line from the star, (c) the frequency shift, and (d) the velocity of the star with respect to the earth. Use five significant figures.

Solution. The given quantities are $\lambda_0 = 5.2700 \times 10^{-7}$ m, $\lambda = 5.2950 \times 10^{-7}$ m, and $c = 2.99793 \times 10^8$ m/s. To find the frequencies of λ_0 and λ we use the wave equation $c = \nu\lambda$. Solving for the frequency, we obtain

$$\nu_0 = \frac{c}{\lambda_0} = \frac{2.99793 \times 10^8 \text{ m/s}}{5.2700 \times 10^{-7} \text{ m}}$$

$$\nu_0 = 5.6887 \times 10^{14} \text{ Hz}$$

$$\nu = \frac{c}{\lambda} = \frac{2.99793 \times 10^8 \text{ m/s}}{5.2950 \times 10^{-7} \text{ m}}$$

$$\nu = 5.66176 \times 10^{-14} \text{ Hz}$$

The difference in frequency is

$$\nu - \nu_0 = 0.02690 \times 10^{14} \text{ Hz}$$

Using the first two terms in Eq.(60a), we find

$$\nu = \nu_0\left(1 + \frac{v}{c}\right)$$

and solving for v, we obtain

$$v = \frac{c(\nu - \nu_0)}{\nu_0} = -\frac{2.99793 \times 10^8 \times 0.02690 \times 10^{14}}{5.6887 \times 10^{14}}$$

$$v = -\,1.4176 \times 10^6 \text{ m/s away}$$

The minus sign signifies a receding star.

Quite similar effects are well known to exist in the case of an electrical discharge tube where, owing to thermal agitation, most of the atoms emitting light have high velocities. The random motions of the atoms and molecules in a gas, however, produce a net broadening of the line with no apparent shift in its central maximum.

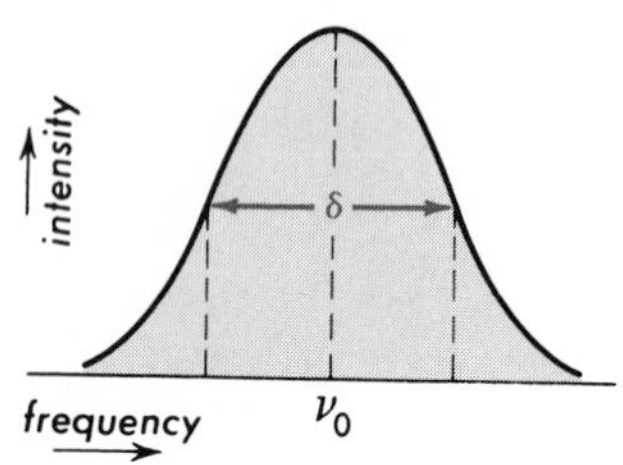

Fig. 60B. Intensity contour of a spectrum line broadened by the Doppler effect.

Since the emitting atoms and molecules of a gas are moving with random velocities, the thousands of photons entering the slit of a spectrograph produce a broadened spectrum line having an intensity contour like that shown in Fig. 60B.

The frequency spread of this line is called the *half-intensity breadth,* and is given by the formula

$$\delta = 2\,\frac{\nu_0}{c}\sqrt{\frac{2RT}{m}\ln 2}$$

$$\delta = \frac{1.66511}{\lambda}\sqrt{\frac{2RT}{m}} \qquad (60c)$$

where T is the absolute temperature of the gas, m is the atomic weight, λ is the wavelength in m and R is the universal gas constant. In the *MKSA* system of units,

$$R = 8.3143435\,\frac{\text{J}}{\text{mole }^\circ\text{K}}$$

The half-intensity breadth δ is defined as the interval between two points on opposite sides of the line where the intensity drops to half its maximum value, as shown in Fig. 60B. This equation shows that the Doppler broadening is (1) proportional to the frequency ν_0, (2) proportional to the square root of the temperature, and (3) inversely proportional to the square root of the atomic weight. As an illustration of the use of Eq.(60c), consider the following example.

Example 2. The brightest of the two yellow lines in the spectrum of sodium has a wavelength of 5890.0 Å. If a sodium lamp is operated at a temperature of 500°K, find (a) the half-intensity breadth in hertz, (b) in wave numbers, and (c) in angstroms. Use five significant figures.

Solution. The general gas constant R has the value R = 8.3143435 J/mole °K. See the table of constants on the inside back cover. To five significant figures the value is R = 8.3143 Kg m^2/s^2/mole/°K. The molecular weight of sodium from Appendix VI is 22.9898×10^{-3} Kg/mole.* The wavelength given is $\lambda = 5.890 \times 10^{-7}$ m. Direct substitution of these quantities in Eq.(60c) gives

$$\delta = \frac{1.66511}{5.890 \times 10^{-7}\text{ m}} \sqrt{\frac{2 \times 8.3143 \dfrac{\text{Kg m}^2}{\text{mole }^\circ\text{K s}^2} \times 500^\circ\text{K}}{22.9898 \times 10^{-3} \dfrac{\text{Kg}}{\text{mole}}}}$$

$$\delta = \frac{1.66511}{5.890 \times 10^{-7}\text{ m}} \sqrt{36.1652 \times 10^4 \frac{\text{m}^2}{\text{s}^2}}$$

$$\delta = 1.7001 \times 10^9 \text{ Hz}$$

This represents the difference between two frequencies, one on each side of the line at half the intensity of the central maximum. To change this difference to wave numbers, we must divide by the speed of light in cm/s:

$$\delta_\nu = \frac{1.7001 \times 10^9 \text{ Hz}}{2.99793 \times 10^{10} \dfrac{\text{cm}}{\text{s}}}$$

$$\delta_\nu = 0.056709 \text{ cm}^{-1}$$

We now use the direct proportion

$$\frac{\delta_\lambda}{\delta_\nu} = \frac{\lambda}{\nu} \qquad \text{or} \qquad \delta_\lambda = \delta_\nu \frac{\lambda}{\nu}$$

and upon substituting, we obtain

$$\delta_\lambda = 0.056709 \text{ cm}^{-1} \frac{5890.0 \text{ Å}}{16{,}977.9 \text{ cm}^{-1}}$$

$$\delta_\lambda = 0.019674 \text{ Å}$$

Experimental observations are in keeping with Eq.(60c); to produce sharper lines in any given spectrum the temperature must be lowered. Furthermore the lines produced by the lighter

* A mole is defined as a mass of a substance in grams equal to the molecular weight. Since sodium is monatomic, and has an atomic and molecular weight of 22.9898, 1 mole of pure sodium weighs 22.9898 g, and 1 Kg mole weighs 22.9898 Kg. The number of sodium atoms in 1 Kg mole of substance is given by Avogadro's number, i.e., 6.022×10^{26}/Kg mole. This is the number of sodium atoms in 22.9898 Kg of sodium metal.

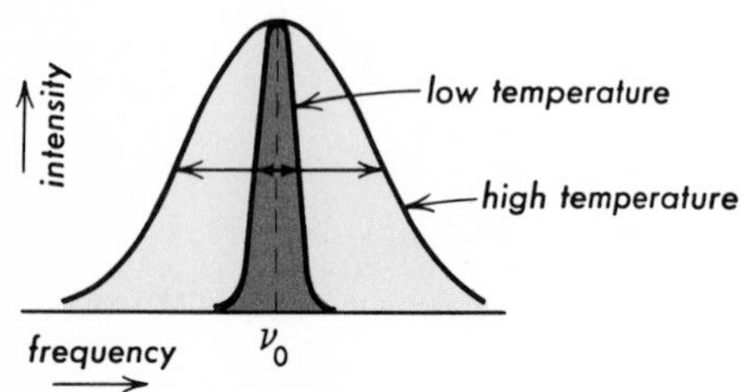

Fig. 60C. Comparison of Doppler line widths for spectrum lines from a hot and cold light source.

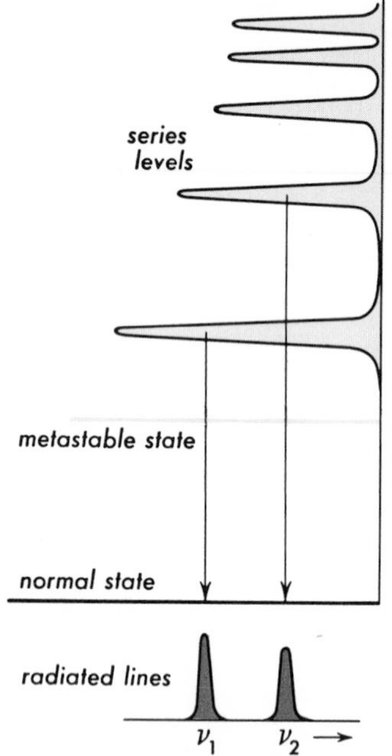

Fig. 60D. Schematic diagram illustrating the natural breadths of atomic energy levels and spectrum lines.

elements in the periodic table are in general broader than those produced by the heavy elements.

Figure 60C is a graph of the same spectrum line produced by a high-temperature source such as an electric spark, and a low-temperature source such as a liquid-air-cooled gaseous discharge.

60.2. Natural Breadths of Spectrum Lines

According to quantum mechanics, an energy-level diagram of an atom is not to be thought of as a set of sharp discrete levels but a sort of continuous distribution of energy possibilities with pronounced peaks as shown in Fig. 60D. This is a kind of graph in which the energy is plotted vertically and the probability of an electron being excited to that energy is plotted horizontally.

When an electron is excited to higher energy, it has a high probability of arriving at an energy value at or near one of the peaks before it returns to the normal state and emits light. Since there is a high probability it may go slightly higher or lower than the center of each peak, the spectrum lines arising from transitions to lower levels will give rise to a so-called *natural breadth* of the observed spectrum lines.

The longer an electron remains in an excited state, the greater is the probability it will arrive at the peak energy value before jumping back down. For this reason *metastable states,* with their relatively long average lifetime t, will be quite narrow, as is the *normal state.* The shorter the average lifetime in an excited state, the wider it will be. The natural half-value widths of energy levels are given by the simple relation

$$\delta_n = \frac{1}{2\pi t} \tag{60d}$$

where for many levels in neutral atoms, t is approximately 10^{-8} s and δ_n represents the frequency for the normal state. For the yellow lines of the sodium spectrum the natural half-intensity breadth is only 0.000116 Å, a value a hundred times smaller than the Doppler width from normal gas discharge tubes. In most spectrum lines the natural width is so narrow as to be completely masked by Doppler broadening.

An explanation of the natural breadth of energy levels is to be found in *Heisenberg's uncertainty principle* [see Eq.(51t)]:

$$\Delta E \times \Delta t \cong h \tag{60e}$$

In this equation ΔE represents the uncertainty of the energy when the uncertainty of the time is Δt. If an atom remains in the normal state for a long time, the uncertainty of the energy value is small and the level is sharp. If the electron is excited to an upper level where it remains for an extremely short time, the uncertainty of the energy value is greater and the level is widened. In other words, an electron excited toward an upper level may have little time to settle into the peak position before jumping down again.

Except for the ground states and metastable states, where Δt is a long time, the time Δt in an excited state is approximately 10^{-8} s.

Fig. 60E. Observed Stark-effect pattern for the red line of hydrogen, H_α, λ = 6562 Å.

60.3. The Stark Effect

Although the splitting up of spectrum lines in a magnetic field was discovered by Zeeman as early as 1897, some 16 years elapsed before anyone succeeded in showing that a similar effect is produced when a source of light is placed in an electric field.

In 1913 J. Stark demonstrated that every line of the Balmer series of hydrogen, when the source was located in a uniform electric field of 100,000 V/cm, is split into a number of components. A greatly enlarged photograph of the red hydrogen line λ = 6562 Å is shown in Fig. 60E.

The origin of the Stark effect is to be found in energy levels themselves. In an electric field many of the energy levels that are otherwise single are split up into a number of component levels. As in the Zeeman effect, where the atoms are in a magnetic field, the levels form a pattern that is symmetrical about the field-free level. The stronger the electric-field intensity, the wider is the splitting.

Not all levels of the same atoms are split the same amount in any given field. Some levels are widely spaced, while others are close together and some remain single. In general, the widest splitting occurs for levels arising from nonpenetrating electron orbits. These are the orbits of valence electrons that are nearly circular on the orbital model and correspond to the D and F levels of the elements in the first two columns of the periodic table.

In an ordinary arc, where no external electric field is applied to the light source, many ions are produced which upon collision with other atoms give rise to strong electric fields. The effect of these intermolecular heterogeneous fields is to produce varying amounts of splitting of the energy levels of atoms, resulting in a broadening of the observed spectrum lines. This is the origin of the diffuseness of the so-called *diffuse series* of lines observed in many spectra. The sharp series, on the other hand, involves levels that show little or no splitting in strong electric fields.

60.4. Gamma-Ray Spectrum Lines

Gamma rays emitted by radioactive nuclei, like visible light emitted by the external electron structure of atoms, show a finite breadth when photographed with an appropriate γ-ray spectrograph. Gamma-ray spectrographs are identical in principle and similar in construction to X-ray spectrographs, and γ-ray spectrograms are similar in appearance to X-ray spectrograms (see Figs. 50I and 50J). In a gas at room temperature, radioactive atoms, like stable atoms, move about with different velocities. The emission of γ rays by randomly moving nuclei will, therefore, give rise to a Doppler broadening as shown in Fig. 60B.

Because γ rays have extremely high frequencies, their photon energies $h\nu$ and momenta $h\nu/c$ are thousands of times greater than for visible light, and upon emission by a nucleus give rise to an appreciable recoil energy and momentum. This is illustrated schematically in Fig. 60F.

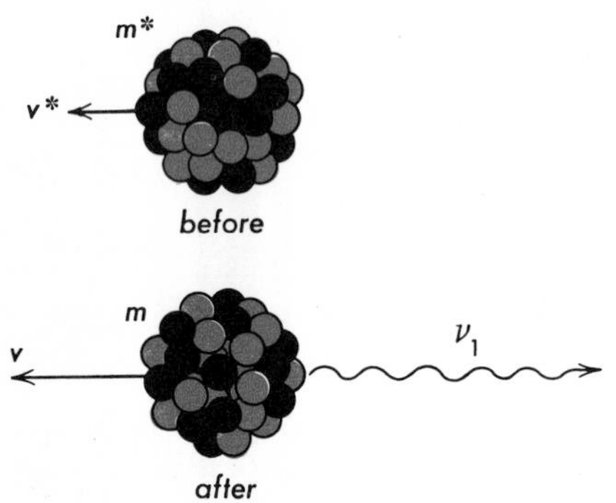

Fig. 60F. Diagram of γ-ray frequency change due to Doppler effect and nuclear recoil.

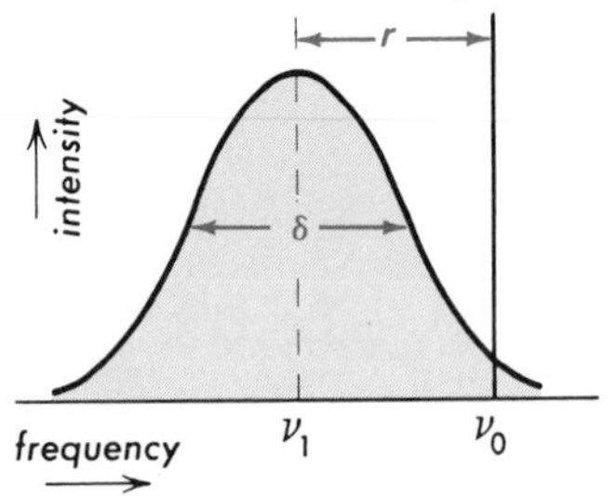

Fig. 60G. Frequency–intensity graph for γ-ray emission showing Doppler width δ and recoil frequency shift r.

Before disintegration the excited nucleus of mass m^* is moving with a random velocity v^*. As a result of γ-ray emission the recoiling nucleus acquires additional momentum and the γ ray loses momentum. Momentum balance therefore requires

$$\underset{\textbf{before}}{m^*v^*} = \underset{\textbf{after}}{mv + \frac{h\nu_1}{c}} \tag{60f}$$

Conservation of energy also applies to the process, giving

$$E^*_n = E_n + E_\gamma$$

or

$$\underset{\textbf{before}}{\tfrac{1}{2}m^*v^{*2}} = \underset{\textbf{after}}{\tfrac{1}{2}mv^2 + h\nu_1} \tag{60g}$$

It is important to note that the frequency ν_1 is not the frequency ν_0 that would be observed if the nuclear mass were at rest.

Since the nuclei producing any given line all have the same mass, and emit γ rays of the same energy $h\nu_0$, the observed frequency loss r due to recoil and the broadening δ due to the Doppler effect have the result shown in Fig. 60G. If a nuclear mass could be steadily increased, momentum and energy balance would still hold, but the energy of nuclear recoil would decrease, and the maximum of ν_1 would approach ν_0.

60.5. Optical and Gamma-Ray Resonance Absorption

When a beam of yellow light from a sodium lamp is made to pass through a glass vessel containing sodium vapor, strong absorption occurs. The atomic processes taking place under these conditions are a kind of resonance phenomenon commonly observed with sound waves.

A good demonstration in sound is shown in Fig. 60H. Two tuning forks with exactly the same natural frequency, that is, with the same pitch, are mounted on separate sounding boards. Fork A is set vibrating for a moment and then stopped. Fork B will then be found to be vibrating.

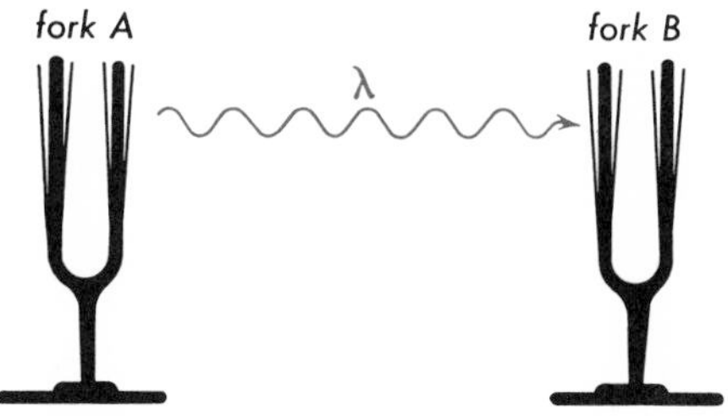

Fig. 60H. An experiment for demonstrating resonance between two identical tuning forks.

Each sound pulse that emerges with each wave from fork A passes by the other fork, pushing with just the right frequency to set fork B vibrating. Such resonance absorption will fail if there is a frequency mismatch between the second fork and the passing waves. If fork A is moved rapidly away from or toward fork B, such a mismatch due to the Doppler effect will prevent resonance.

An analogous demonstration of resonance absorption with visible light is shown in Fig. 60I. Light from a sodium lamp in passing through a sodium flame of a Bunsen burner casts a pronounced dark shadow on a nearby screen. A small piece of asbestos paper soaked in common table salt, NaCl, and placed in an ordinary gas flame can be used to produce an abundance of free sodium atoms.

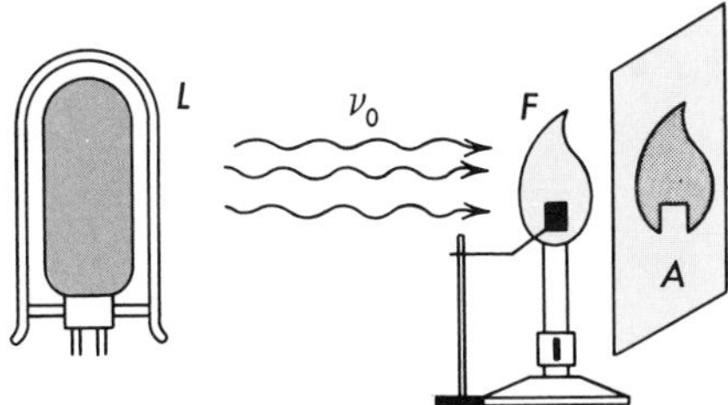

Fig. 60I. An experiment for demonstrating resonance between sodium atoms.

The atomic process of resonance absorption taking place in this experiment is shown in Fig. 60J. An excited atom in the sodium lamp emits, for example, a wave $\lambda = 5890$ Å by the downward transition from the $3^2P_{3/2}$ excited level to the $3^2S_{1/2}$ normal state (see Fig. 45G).

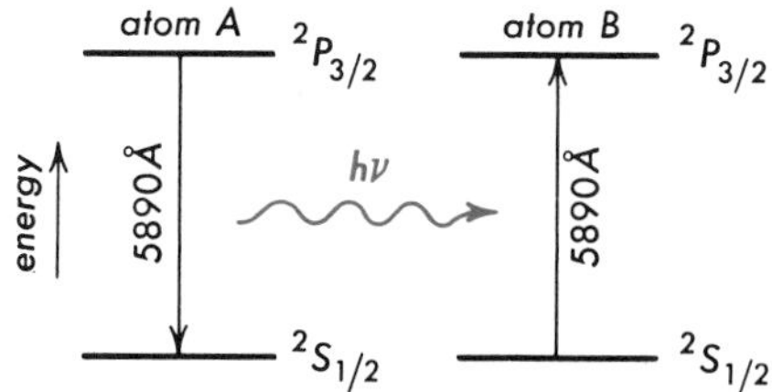

Fig. 60J. Energy-level diagram illustrating light emission and resonance absorption between two sodium atoms.

This wave on coming close to a normal sodium atom in the flame will be absorbed and raise the single valence electron to the $3^2P_{3/2}$ level. This second atom will in turn emit the same frequency again, to be absorbed by another atom in the flame, or to escape from the flame in some random direction. Because reemission will be in a random direction and seldom in the original direction from the lamp, a shadow will be cast.

When an experiment analogous to this is performed with gamma rays, various difficulties are encountered. Because an appreciable amount of the energy of a gamma ray emitted by a radioactive atom is given up to the recoiling nucleus, the frequency of the emitted wave is reduced sufficiently from ν_0 to

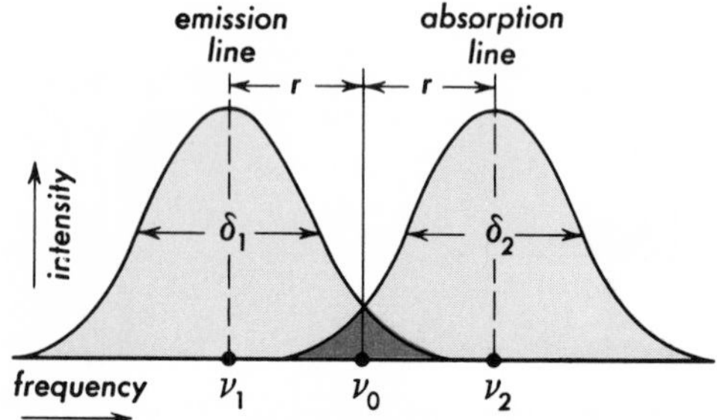

Fig. 60K. Frequency–intensity graphs for γ-ray emission and absorption lines, showing Doppler widths δ, recoil shifts r, and overlap frequencies in color.

cause a mismatch between the gamma-ray frequency ν and the natural frequency ν_0 of another nucleus of the same isotope (see Fig. 60G). Furthermore, the recoil of a second nucleus resulting from a gamma-ray impact would give rise to an even greater mismatch.

Intensity–frequency graphs for gamma emission and absorption by identical nuclides are given in Fig. 60K. If the radioactive source, and the target on which the γ rays impinge, are at the same temperature, the Doppler broadening will be the same for both.

The area of overlap of the two curves indicates conditions where resonance absorption might be expected to occur. For example, a point at ν_0 corresponds to an event in which a radioactive nucleus is approaching the target at the time of emission and has sufficient kinetic energy to compensate for the energy loss required for recoil. If this emitted γ ray of frequency ν_0 encounters a normal target nucleus moving toward the oncoming wave with an appropriate kinetic energy, resonance absorption can occur. The small overlap area would indicate, however, that resonance absorption under the conditions described should be very small.

60.6. The Mossbauer Effect

The phenomenon of resonance absorption with γ rays was predicted by W. Kuhn in 1921 and first observed by P. B. Moon in 1951. A major breakthrough occurred in 1958, when the phenomenon of recoilless nuclear resonance absorption was discovered by R. L. Mossbauer.

This new absorption effect provided a means for eliminating the energy losses by recoil, both at the source and at the receiver. As an additional feature of the discovery, gamma-ray spectrum lines of extreme narrowness have been produced, which may be useful for other research experiments.

According to the principles described in Sec. 60.4, the loss of energy to a recoiling nucleus could be suppressed by rigidly fastening the emitting nuclei, as well as the absorbing nuclei, to an infinitely heavy mass. An experimental method for doing this is the binding of nuclei to a crystal lattice.

To reduce Doppler broadening, the γ-ray source and absorber are cooled to extremely low temperatures. This is accomplished by immersing the radioactive crystal source and the crystal absorber in a liquid helium bath.

At temperatures close to absolute zero, atomic vibrations

within the crystal lattice are reduced to practically zero, so that during emission or absorption the atoms have little or no motion. Under these conditions Doppler broadening is reduced to practically zero and the observed line reveals its natural line breadth (see Figs. 60C and 60D).

The elimination of atomic vibrations within the crystal lattice has another important effect. Atomic vibrations are quantized, that is, vibration energies have discrete values which may be represented by spaced energy levels. When atoms are in their lowest vibrational energy state, as they are when the crystal is at absolute zero, the recoil energy of a gamma ray is not always sufficient to raise an atom to the next vibrational state. Under these conditions the binding of a nucleus with its neighbors is such that an appreciable part of the crystal lattice takes up any γ-ray recoil momentum. Because the crystal mass is so large, the recoil energy is practically zero, and the value of r in Fig. 60K is reduced to zero. Gamma-ray emission or absorption under these conditions is said to be *recoilless.*

With the Doppler effect and nuclear recoil both reduced to zero, only the natural line breadths are involved in nuclear resonance absorption.

A diagram of Mossbauer's apparatus is shown in Fig. 60L. Gamma rays from a source at M pass through a narrow channel C and a thin target A, to where they fall on a scintillation counter S. The lead shielding around the source and the detector is for the purpose of reducing all extraneous radiation to a minimum.

To detect resonance absorption in A, the source is set into rotation as indicated by an arrow and the detector turned on only when the source is moving in line with the absorber. This motion introduces a Doppler shift *d,* that is, a slight increase or decrease in the frequency of the gamma rays. The effect is illustrated by shifting the red curve in Fig. 60M to the right or to the left. The mismatch in frequency between the γ rays from the moving source and the nuclei in the stationary absorber reduces the number of photons absorbed. The faster the source moves toward or away from the target, the greater the Doppler shift is and the greater the number of γ rays reaching the counter.

Figure 60N is a graph from Mossbauer's original experiment, performed by using the 0.1290-MeV gamma rays from iridium-191. Note that the greatest absorption occurs when the source is at rest. Observe also the extremely low velocities required to produce a Doppler mismatch in frequency. The latter is a clear indication of the narrowness of γ-ray spectrum lines and shows that one is observing natural line breadths rather than Doppler broadening (see Figs. 60B and 60D). The mean lifetime of the Ir^{191}

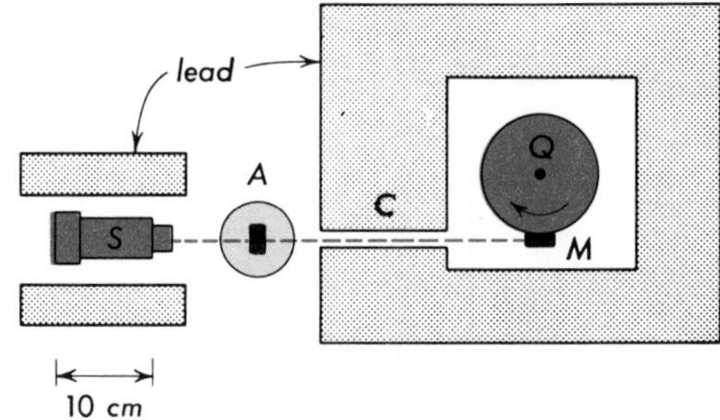

Fig. 60L. Diagram of Mossbauer's apparatus with which he discovered recoilless emission and absorption of γ rays.

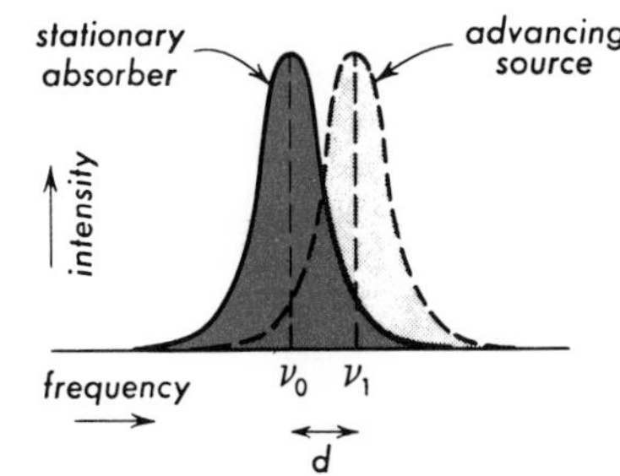

Fig. 60M. Graphs of the natural breadths of γ-ray lines from radioactive crystals at low temperatures near absolute zero.

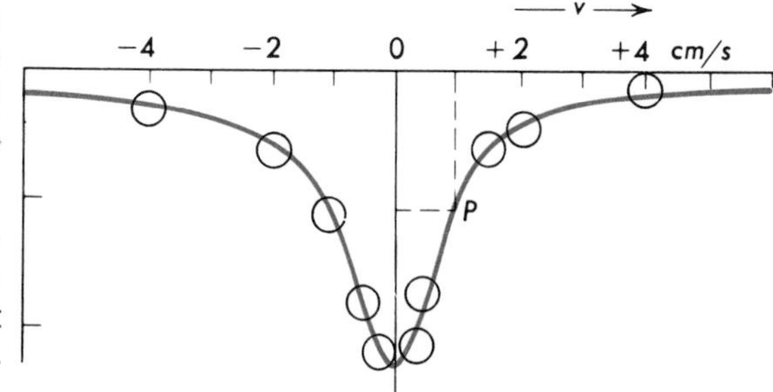

Fig. 60N. Transmission of the 0.129-MeV γ radiation through a resonance absorber of iridium-191, measured at different velocities of the source. (After Mossbauer.)

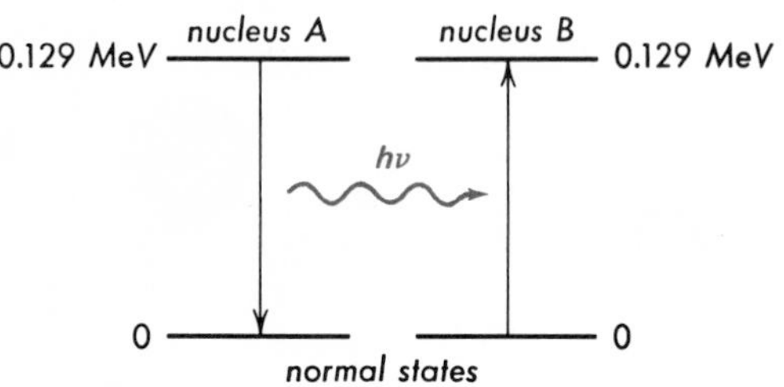

Fig. 60O. Energy-level diagram illustrating γ-ray emission and resonance absorption between two iridium-191 nuclei.

transition can be calculated from the half-width of the curve in Fig. 60N and Eq.(60e). See Example 3.

The nuclear energy levels of Ir^{191} involved in Mossbauer's experiment are shown in Fig. 60O.

Many experimenters have confirmed Mossbauer's discovery and recoilless γ-ray transitions have been observed in fifteen or more radioactive nuclei. For his discovery Mossbauer was awarded, jointly with Hofstader, the 1961 Nobel Prize in physics.

Example 3. If the Mossbauer experiment is performed with the 0.12939-MeV γ ray from iridium-199, and the half-width at half-intensity of the velocity resonance curve is 0.90 cm/s, find (a) the γ-ray frequency, (b) the Doppler shift in Hz, and (c) the mean life of the excited energy level. Use five significant figures.

Solution. The known quantities are $V = 1.29390 \times 10^5$ V, $e = 1.60219 \times 10^{-19}$ C, $h = 6.6262 \times 10^{-34}$ Js, and $v = 9.0 \times 10^{-3}$ m/s. To find the γ-ray frequency we use the energy equation, $Ve = h\nu_0$:

$$\nu_0 = \frac{Ve}{h} = \frac{1.29390 \times 10^5 \times 1.60219 \times 10^{-19}}{6.6262 \times 10^{-34}}$$

$$\nu_0 = 3.12860 \times 10^{19} \text{ Hz}$$

We next use the Doppler formula, Eq.(60b), to find the difference in frequency from the center of the line at ν_0 and the frequency at half-intensity. If we call this difference $\Delta\nu$, we have

$$\nu - \nu_0 = \Delta\nu = \nu_0 \frac{v}{c}$$

Upon substituting known quantities, we find

$$\Delta\nu = 3.12860 \times 10^{19} \frac{9.0 \times 10^{-3}}{2.99793 \times 10^8}$$

$$\Delta\nu = 9.3923 \times 10^8 \text{ Hz}$$

We now use Heisenberg's uncertainty principle, Eq.(60e), to find the mean life Δt. Solving for Δt,

$$\Delta t = \frac{h}{\Delta E} = \frac{h}{h\,\Delta\nu} = \frac{1}{\Delta\nu}$$

and substituting known quantities, we obtain

$$\Delta t = \frac{1}{9.3923 \times 10^8 \text{ Hz}} = 1.0647 \times 10^{-9} \text{ s}$$

$$\Delta t = 1.0647 \text{ ns}$$

The mean life of this excited γ-ray state is approximately one nanosecond.

---

problems

Using the following values for the problems of this chapter, calculate all answers to five significant figures, and then round off answers to four significant figures:

$c = 2.99793 \times 10^8$ m/s $\quad h = 6.6262 \times 10^{-34}$ Js
$R = 8.3143$ J/mole °K $\quad e = 1.60219 \times 10^{-19}$ C

1. The strongest of the two yellow lines in the sodium spectrum has a wavelength of 5890.0 Å. This same line from a distant star is found to have a wavelength of 5936.40 Å. Find (a) the frequencies of the two wavelengths, (b) their frequency difference, and (c) the star's velocity with respect to the earth.

2. The red line of the hydrogen spectrum has a wavelength of 6562.1 Å in the laboratory. This same line from a distant star is observed to have a wavelength of 6625.60 Å. Find (a) the frequencies of these two wavelengths, (b) the red shift of the line in Hz, and (c) the star's velocity relative to the earth.

3. A distant star is found to be approaching the earth at a speed of 1.865×10^6 m/s. In the laboratory the strong line of the calcium spectrum is observed to have a wavelength of 3968.12 Å. Find (a) the frequency of this light, (b) the Doppler difference in frequency in Hz, (c) the observed frequency of the light coming from the star, and (d) its wavelength in angstroms. [Ans. (a) 7.5550×10^{14} Hz, (b) 4.700×10^{12} Hz, (c) 7.6020×10^{14} Hz, (d) 3943.59 Å.]

4.* A source of light is operated at a temperature of 2500°K. Find the Doppler half-intensity breadth of the hydrogen red line at $\lambda = 6562.1$ Å (a) in Hz, (b) in wave numbers, and (c) in angstroms. Assume the molecular weight of hydrogen to be 2.016×10^{-3} Kg/mole.

5.* A light source containing mercury is operated at 3000°K. Find the Doppler half-intensity breadth of the green line at $\lambda = 5461.2$ Å (a) in Hz, (b) in wave numbers, and (c) in angstroms.

6.* A light source containing potassium is operated at a temperature of 1200°K. For a spectrum line with a wavelength of 7.667×10^{-7} m, find (a) the frequency of the line in wave numbers, (b) the Doppler half-intensity breadth in wave numbers, and (c) its half-intensity breadth in angstroms. [Ans. (a) 13,043 cm^{-1}, (b) 0.05175 cm^{-1}, (c) 0.03042 Å.]

7.* If the Mossbauer experiment is performed with a 0.603-MeV γ ray from a tellurium-124 source, and the half-width at half-intensity of the resonance curve is 1.65 cm/s, find (a) the frequency of the γ ray, (b) the Doppler shift in Hz, and (c) the mean life of the excited γ ray state.

8.* A 1.230-MeV γ ray is used in performing the Mossbauer experiment. The source of the radiation is the radioactive tin-118 isotope, and the resonance curve is found to have a half-intensity half-breadth at a velocity of 1.150 cm/s. Find (a) the frequency of the γ ray, (b) the Doppler shift in Hz, and (c) the mean life of the excited nuclear energy level.

9.* The Mossbauer experiment is performed with a 0.3250-MeV γ ray from a radioactive source of ruthenium-101. The half-width at half-intensity of the velocity resonance curve is 1.350 cm/s. Find (a) the frequency of the γ ray, (b) the Doppler shift $\nu - \nu_0$ in Hz, and (c) the mean life of the excited γ-ray state. [Ans. (a) 7.858×10^{19} Hz, (b) 3.5387×10^9 Hz, (c) 0.28259 ns.]

61 The atomic nucleus

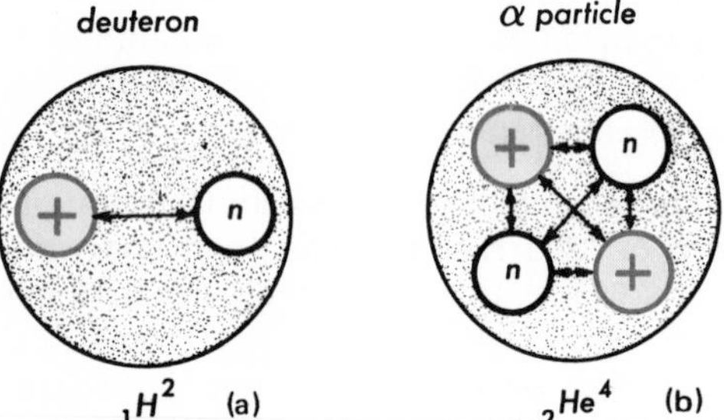

Fig. 61A. Schematic diagram of the nucleus for (a) a deuterium atom, and (b) a helium atom.

Although the disintegrations of different nuclei give rise to many different kinds of particles of units of energy, it would appear that we need assume only two kinds of particles exist within the nucleus—*neutrons* and *protons.* If this is correct, our task becomes the difficult one of explaining not only the disintegration mechanism of an unstable nucleus but the binding forces that hold a stable nucleus together. An answer to the latter question will serve as a starting point for the following presentations.

61.1. Nuclear Binding Forces

According to the *neutron–proton theory* of the atomic nucleus (see Fig. 61A), the deuteron nucleus contains only one neutron and one proton. Let us compare, therefore, the mass of one free proton and one free neutron with their mass when combined as a deuteron (for masses, see Appendix VIII):

Neutron mass	$_0n^1 = 1.008665$
Hydrogen mass	$_1H^1 = 1.007825$
	Sum $= 2.016490$
Deuteron mass	$_1H^2 = 2.014103$

The difference in mass of 0.002387 atomic mass unit (amu) is not due to inaccurate measurements of mass but is a real difference to be accounted for as the annihilation energy that binds the two particles together. When a neutron and proton come together to form a deuteron, a small part of their mass—namely, 0.002387 amu (equivalent to 2.22 MeV energy)—is radiated from the newly formed nucleus. At close approach, in other words, the two particles attract each other so strongly that once together, it takes the equivalent of a little more than 2 MeV of energy to pull them apart. This has been confirmed by a nuclear photoelectric effect, an experiment in which γ rays of 2.22 MeV energy or greater are found to break up deuterium nuclei into their constituent parts, while γ rays of lower energy have no effect. How neutrons and protons attract each other when very close together is a question of great importance, for we now realize that the stability of all the universe as we konw it depends upon these forces.

Consider as a second example, the attractive forces between the four nucleons of a helium nucleus, i.e., the two neutrons and two protons of an α particle as shown in Fig. 61A. By combining the masses of the four free particles and comparing them with the mass of the helium atom, we obtain

$$
\begin{aligned}
2\,{}_0n^1 + 2\,{}_1H^1 &= 4.032980 \text{ amu} \\
He^4 &= 4.002604 \text{ amu} \\
\hline
\text{Mass difference} &= 0.030376 \text{ amu} \\
E &= 28.3 \text{ MeV}
\end{aligned}
$$

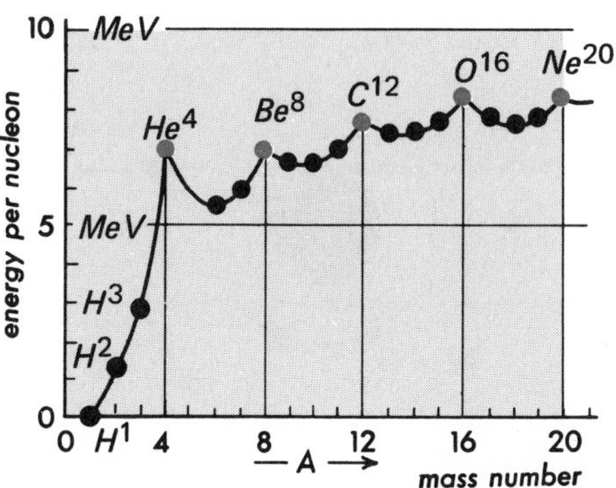

Fig. 61B. Binding energy per nucleon for the lightest elements in the periodic table.

This value of 28.3 MeV indicates a binding energy of approximately 7 MeV per nucleon, a value considerably higher than 1.11 MeV for the deuteron. This is a measure of the energy that must be expended in breaking the attractive bonds shown in the diagram.

If we make similar calculations for other nuclides near the beginning of the periodic table, and plot a graph of the binding energy per nucleon, E/A, where A is the mass number, we obtain Fig. 61B. If this same procedure is carried out for the entire periodic table, a graph like the one shown in Fig. 61C is obtained.

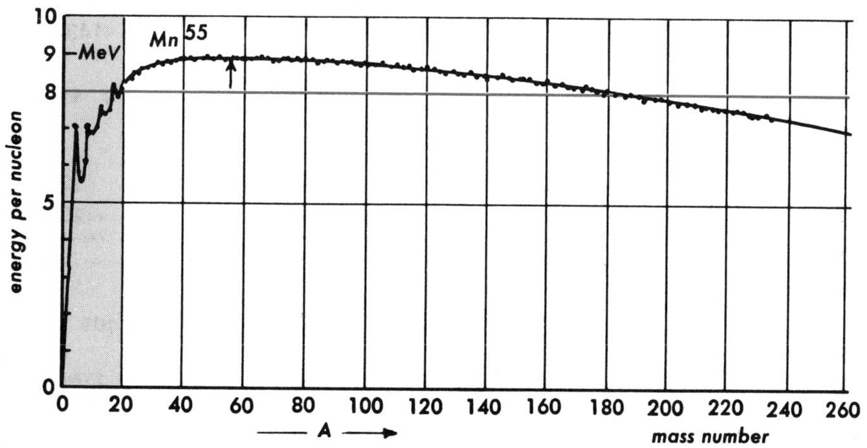

Fig. 61C. Binding energy per nucleon for the stable isotopes of the periodic table.

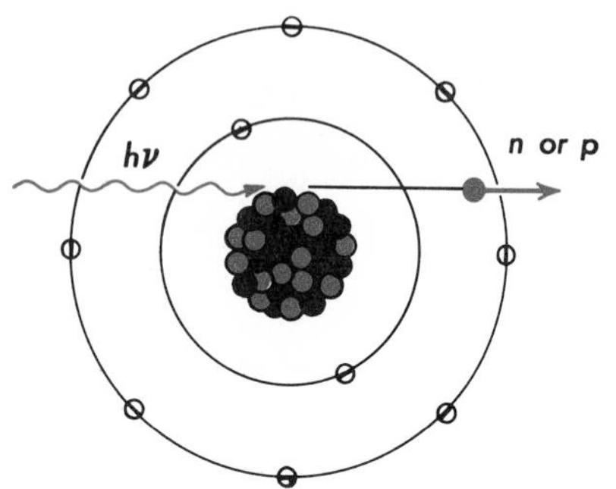

Fig. 61D. The nuclear photoelectric effect.

By drawing a horizontal line across the upper part of the graph at 8 MeV, as shown by the colored line, we obtain a kind of average binding energy per nucleon for nearly all the elements. This value is approximately the difference between unit atomic mass and the mass of a free neutron or proton.

Collisions between high-energy photons and nuclei, giving rise to several kinds of reactions, are given in the preceding chapter. One process not described there, and called the *nuclear photoelectric effect,* is shown in Fig. 61D. A photon of energy $h\nu$, passing close to a nucleus, is absorbed; part of the energy is used to remove a neutron or proton from the nucleus, and the remainder given to the particle as kinetic energy [see Eq.(43a)]:

$$h\nu = W + \tfrac{1}{2}mv^2 \tag{61a}$$

The work function W, as we have seen above, is about 8 MeV and is essentially the energy required to create the extra mass needed by the nucleon to set it free.

Example 1. Calculate the binding energy per nucleon for thorium-232, if its accurately known mass is 232.038211 amu.

Solution. Since thorium has the atomic number 90, it contains 90 protons and 142 neutrons. Since a free hydrogen atom has a mass of 1.007825 amu, and a free neutron has a mass of 1.008665 amu, an entirely dissociated thallium-232 nucleus would have the following mass:

$$\begin{array}{r} 1.007825 \text{ amu} \\ \times\ 90 \\ \hline 90.704250 \text{ amu} \end{array} \qquad \begin{array}{r} 1.008665 \text{ amu} \\ \times\ 142 \\ \hline 143.230430 \text{ amu} \end{array}$$

Summing these two results, and subtracting the mass of thorium-232 gives

$$\begin{array}{r} 143.230430 \text{ amu} \\ 90.704250 \text{ amu} \\ \hline 233.934680 \text{ amu} \end{array} \qquad \begin{array}{r} 233.934680 \text{ amu} \\ -232.038211 \text{ amu} \\ \hline 1.896469 \text{ amu} \end{array}$$

Multiplying this mass by 931.48 gives

$$1.896469 \times 931.48 = 1766.52 \text{ MeV}$$

which divided by 232, the number of nucleons in thallium-232, yields

$$\frac{1766.523}{232.0} = 7.6143 \frac{\text{MeV}}{\text{nucleon}}$$

Compare this result with Fig. 61C.*

61.2. The Packing Fraction

An informative method of displaying the mass differences and binding energies of stable nuclei is to plot a graph of all packing fractions. The *packing fraction P* of any nuclide is obtained from the relation

$$P = \frac{M - A}{A}$$

where $M - A$ for any nuclide is called its *mass defect:*

$$M = \text{mass of nuclide}$$
$$A = \text{mass number}$$

In other words, P is the difference between the average nucleon mass for that nuclide and unit atomic mass. It will be seen in Fig. 61E that the very light and the heavy nuclides have an average mass per nucleon greater than unity, whereas those near the middle of the graph have a mass per nucleon less than unity. In the next chapter we shall see that these differences are directly related to the availability of nuclear energy.

61.3. The Nuclear Potential Barrier

Early in the development of ideas concerning nuclear disintegration, Gamow proposed a model by which one might represent the atomic nucleus. This model is based upon the forces acting between two positive charges and is an extension of the nuclear model described in Sec. 55.2, and illustrated in Figs. 55D and 55E.

Picture again a proton or an α particle, with its positive charge, approaching a positively charged nucleus. As the two charges come closer and closer together, they repel each other with

* The reason for using the mass of the *hydrogen atom = 1.007825 amu,* in place of the mass of the *proton = 1.007276 amu,* in the calculations above, is that the masses of all nuclides, such as thorium-232, include the external orbital electrons equal in number to the number of protons in the nucleus.

greater and greater forces as given by Coulomb's law. This repulsion cannot continue to increase all the way to zero separation, however, for as the two charges come very close together we know, from what has been said in the preceding section, there must be an attraction. Gamow proposed, therefore, that at close approach there is another law of force that comes into play and that this force is one of attraction for neutrons as well as protons and is very strong.

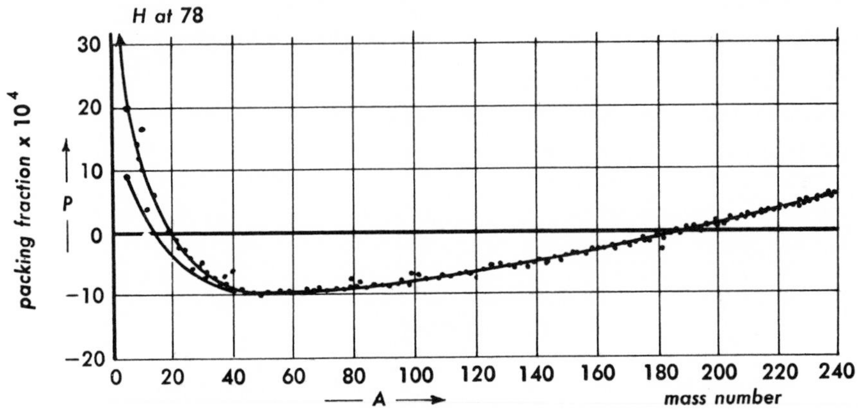

Fig. 61E. Graph of the packing fraction for stable nuclei.

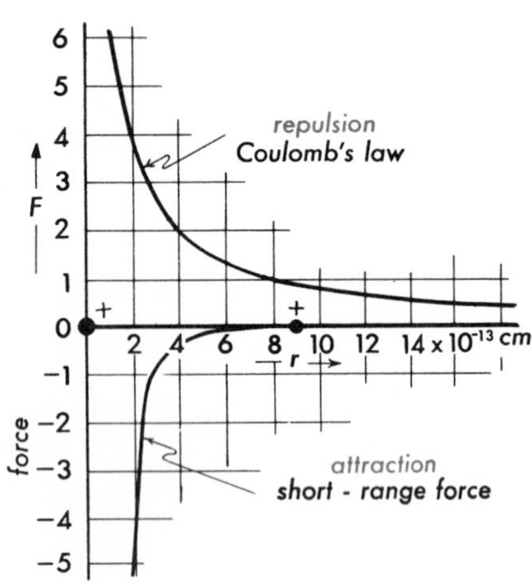

Fig. 61F. The two force laws for a positive charge to a nucleus.

Since Coulomb's law is known to hold quite accurately at large distances, this added factor is called a *short-range force.* Graphs of Coulomb's law for repulsion and the short-range for attraction are shown in Fig. 61F. Note that when the particle is at the distance shown, 9×10^{-13} cm, Coulomb's law of repulsion is predominant, whereas, at a distance less than 2×10^{-13} cm, the short-range force of attraction predominates. Since both of these forces are effective for all distances, they should be combined into one graph as shown by the F curve in Fig. 61G. If instead of the force F we plot the potential energy stored between the two particles, we obtain the E_p curve shown by the dotted line. Such a curve represents what is called the *potential barrier* of the nucleus. The highest point of the barrier is frequently called the edge of the nucleus which, for heavy atoms in the periodic table, occurs at, and gives a nuclear radius of, from 1 to 8×10^{-15} cm (see Table 63A).

A very good model of the nucleus, having the form of a *well* or the *crater of a volcano,* can be made by rotating the dotted line around the vertical axis. When this is done we obtain the cross-sectional diagram in Fig. 61H. With this model the electrical potential energy, E_p, between the positively charged particles is analogous to the potential energy of a ball at any point on the side of the hill, and the electrostatic force of repulsion is analogous to the force of gravity.

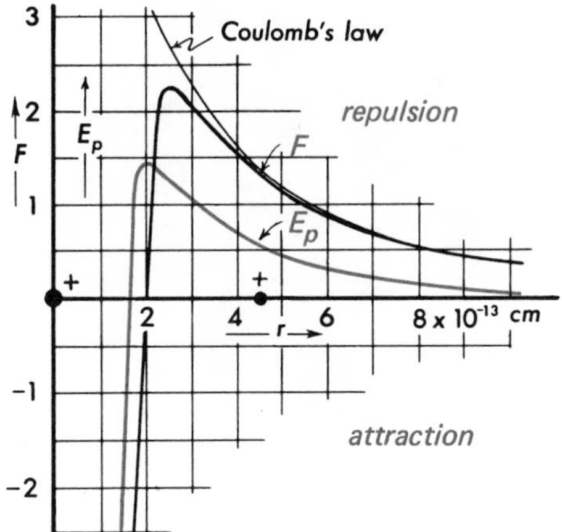

Fig. 61G. Graphs of the force and potential energy of a positively charged particle close to a nucleus.

61.4. Bohr's Nuclear Model

In 1937 Niels Bohr, the famous Danish physicist, made another outstanding contribution to modern physics when he improved Gamow's model of the nucleus by extending what is sometimes called the *waterdrop model* of the nucleus. Bohr and his collaborator Kalkar imagined the many particles in a heavy nucleus as moving about within a spherical enclosure with motions analogous to the molecules in a drop of water. The forces at the surface of the spherical enclosure, which is the top of the potential barrier as represented in Fig. 61I, are analogous to the surface tension which holds a small waterdrop to its spherical form.

Just as the rapid motion of the molecules in water is a measure of the temperature, so Bohr speaks of the rapid motion of the neutrons and protons within the spherical boundary of the nucleus as a sort of *pseudotemperature*. To explain disintegration, the analogy is drawn that the ejection of a particle from the nucleus is like the evaporation of a water molecule from a drop of water. Just as a rise in temperature brings about a more rapid evaporation of water, so an increase in the motions within the nucleus gives rise to a higher probability of disintegration.

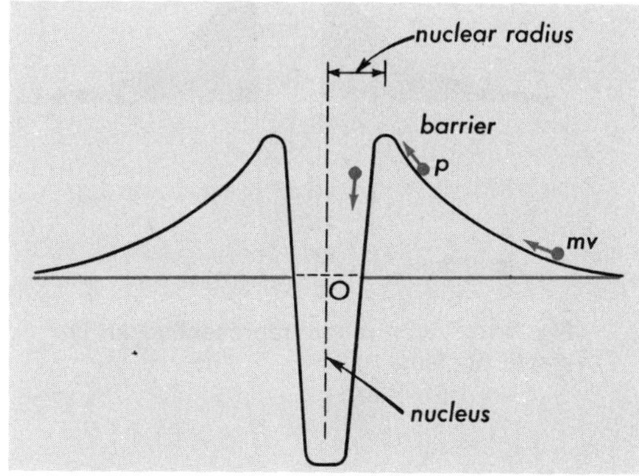

Fig. 61H. A graphical model of the atomic nucleus as proposed by Gamow. The potential barrier of a nucleus to an approaching positive charge is analogous to the crater of a volcano.

In a stable nucleus, the particles within are moving about with very little kinetic energy and are in the analogous state of a relatively low temperature. When a high-speed particle from outside penetrates the potential barrier, it is accelerated toward the center of the nucleus and acquires a very high kinetic energy before it collides with one or more of the particles inside. Soon the energy becomes divided among the many particles, and the nucleus takes on a higher temperature state. The potential-well model of this same condition is shown in Fig. 61J.

Now, as the particles move about inside, there is a certain probability or chance that, within a given interval of time, some one particle will be hit by several particles, giving it a sufficiently high velocity in an outward direction to permit an escape through the potential barrier. The more rapid the internal motions, that is, the higher the temperature, the greater is this chance of escape.

A direct disintegration may be described in this way: If upon entering the nucleus a high-speed particle like a proton adds sufficient energy to give the nucleus a high temperature, another particle like a neutron or an α particle may be ejected immediately. Since such an ejected particle has to be supplied with a certain minimum energy to get free, the remaining particles will be slowed down, and the nucleus will have a lower temperature.

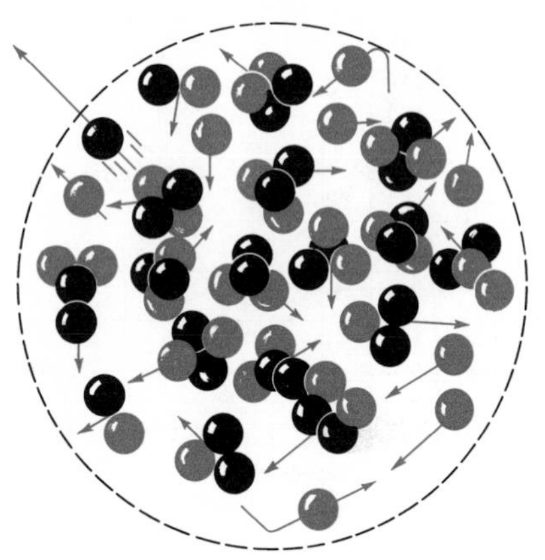

Fig. 61I. Nucleus in the act of ejecting a neutron, based upon the Bohr–Gamow waterdrop model.

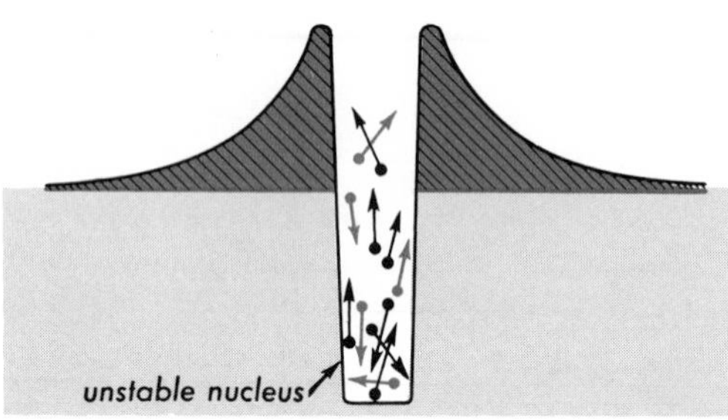

Fig. 61J. Well model representing an unstable nucleus.

61.5. Nuclear Demonstration Models

A demonstration model illustrating the capture of a high-speed proton or an α particle by a nucleus, prior to disintegration, is shown in Fig. 61K. Marbles rolled down the incline represent the speeding-up of atomic projectiles by an accelerator like the cyclotron. Approaching the potential barrier, a marble may roll part way up and then be deflected off to one side, illustrating elastic scattering of the kind observed by Rutherford. If the initial velocity is high enough the marble may go over the top of the barrier and drop into the crater opening at the top, representing a capture prior to disintegration.

A demonstration of what happens inside the nucleus is illustrated by another model as shown in Fig. 61L. In this case the vertical scale of the barrier has of necessity been reduced, i.e., flattened out. When a marble is rolled down the incline and into the group of marbles at the center of the barrier, there may be several collisions before another particle usually goes bouncing out on the other side. This corresponds to a direct disintegration where one particle like a proton goes in and a neutron comes out.

If a single particle does not emerge, most of the particles inside take on random motions, colliding with each other much the same as do the molecules or atoms in a gas or liquid. To prevent friction from stopping them (there is no friction in an atom), the marbles are continually agitated by a small pin protruding from underneath the barrier. This pin is mounted slightly off center at the end of the shaft of a small electric motor. If the motor is left running for some time, a single marble will eventually be hit by

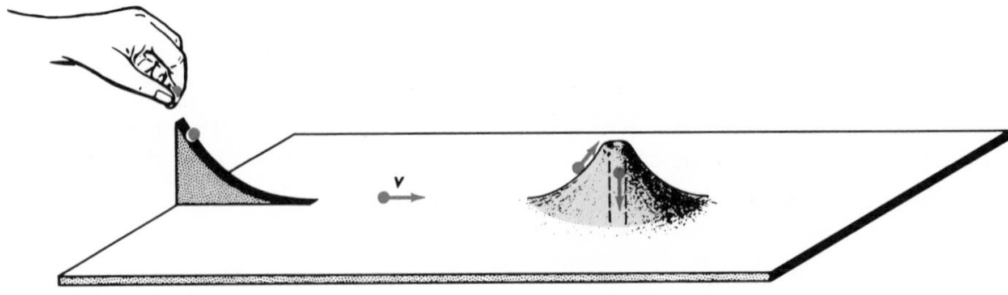

Fig. 61K. Mechanical model of a nucleus for demonstrating the capture of a high-speed proton, deuteron, or α particle. prior to disintegration.

several particles moving in the same direction and will recoil with sufficient speed to carry it over the barrier and out. This corresponds to a disintegration or radioactive decay, which takes place according to the *laws of chance*, and to the resultant drop in "temperature" of the nucleus.

The faster the motor runs, the greater is the internal agitation and chance of ejection, and the shorter is the so-called half-life of the element.

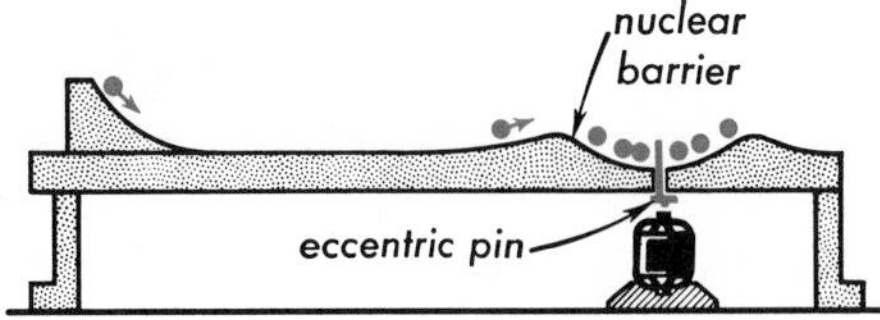

Fig. 61L. Mechanical model of a nucleus for demonstrating (a) the increased kinetic energy of nuclear particles after a capture and (b) the chance probability of radioactive decay or disintegration by the ejection of a particle.

61.6. Nuclear Model for Neutron Disintegrations

When a neutron approaches a nucleus prior to a disintegration, it does not encounter a potential barrier of the type already described for protons and α particles. A neutron has no charge, so that at large distances it is not repelled by the positively charged nucleus. It may, therefore, approach a nucleus with very little speed of its own and be captured when it comes too close. At very close range the short-range attractive force shown in Fig. 61F sets in, and draws the two together.

To an approaching neutron, the nucleus acts as though it were a pit into which the particle will fall. This is illustrated by the flat potential curve in Fig. 61M. The marble rolling along the horizontal plane toward the pit represents the influence of the nucleus upon the neutron's motion, whereas the marble rolling up the hill (dotted line) represents the influence of the same nucleus upon the motion of a proton. A mechanical model patterned after Fig. 61K, and made with the neutron-barrier shape, offers an excellent demonstration of neutron scattering and capture.

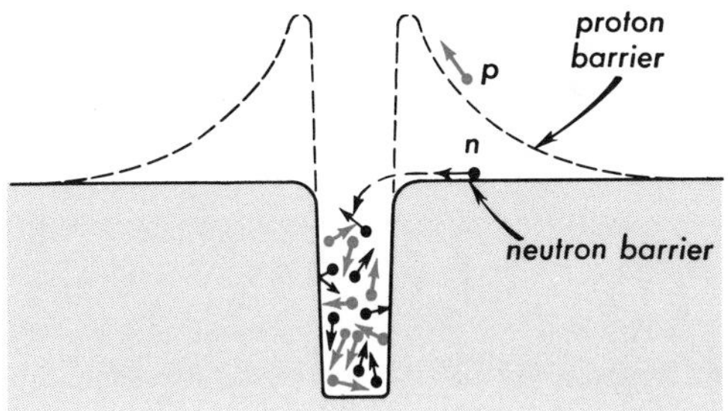

Fig. 61M. A graphical model of the nucleus as it is presented to an approaching neutron or proton.

61.7. Nuclear Spin

Approximately $\frac{1}{3}$ of all known stable nuclei, and many of the radioactive nuclides, are known to have a mechanical moment p_J and a magnetic moment μ_J. The earliest evidence for a nuclear spin, as it is called, was found in atomic spectra. Many spectrum lines show a fine structure which in Sec. 45.4 was explained as being due to electron spin. Many of these fine-structure lines show a still finer structure, now known to be due to a nuclear spin (see Sec. 47.5, and Figs. 47J and 47K).

As an additional example of this *hyperfine structure*, as it is called, several of the spectrum lines of the element praseodymium are shown in Fig. 61N. In a normal spectrogram these look like single lines, but under the high dispersion and magnification shown here, each line reveals six hyperfine components. The six components signify that the nucleus of praseodymium has a spin angular momentum $p_J = \frac{5}{2}\hbar$ and a large magnetic moment.

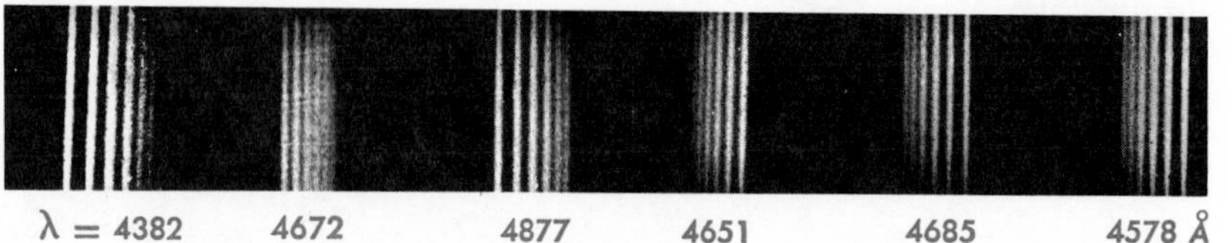

Fig. 61N. Photographs of the hyperfine structure of a few of the spectrum lines of the element praseodymium, $Z = 59$. Wavelengths are in angstrom units; structure produced by nuclear spin.

The angular momenta of nuclei in general are given by

$$p_J = J\hbar \tag{61b}$$

where J is the nuclear spin quantum number, and $\hbar$ represents unit angular momentum given by $h/2\pi$ [see Eq.(45b)]. Quantitative experiments show that this *quantum number*, J, can take half-integral as well as whole-number values (see Table 61A).

The magnetic moments of nuclei in general are extremely small as compared with those associated with electrons in the outer structures of atoms. For all nuclei the magnetic moment is given by the relation

$$\mu_J = g\hbar \frac{e}{2M_p} \tag{61c}$$

where the g factor varies from nucleus to nucleus, $\hbar$ is unit angular momentum, and M_p is the mass of the proton. The last two factors involve fixed atomic constants, and combined are called the *nuclear magneton*. One nuclear magneton is given by

$$\mu_N = \hbar \frac{e}{2M_p} \tag{61d}$$

or

$$\mu_N = 5.0509515 \times 10^{-27} \text{ ampere meters}^2$$

The g factor therefore gives the nuclear magnetic moment in nuclear magnetons. *Note that one nuclear magneton is* $\frac{1}{1836}$ *of one Bohr magneton* [see Eq.(45f)].

A list of a few nuclides in Table 61A shows typical values of the nuclear spin quantum number J, and the measured magnetic moments in nuclear magnetons.

61.8. Proton and Neutron Spin

Every proton, whether it is bound to an atom or is free, has a spin angular momentum of $\frac{1}{2}\hbar$ (see Fig. 61O):

$$p_{\text{proton}} = \tfrac{1}{2}\hbar \tag{61e}$$

Having a positive charge, the magnetic field around a proton is parallel to its mechanical moment, instead of oppositely directed as is the case with an electron (see Fig. 45F). Furthermore, since the mass of a proton is 1836 times the mass of an electron, it maintains the same angular momentum by spinning much slower, and this reduces its magnetic moment to a relatively small value. The magnetic moment of a proton is found by precision experimental measurements to be

$$\mu_{\text{proton}} = 2.792763 \text{ nuclear magnetons} \tag{61f}$$

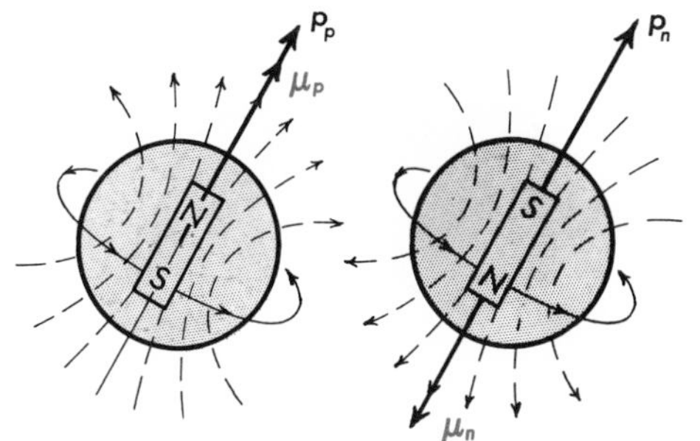

Fig. 61O. Schematic diagrams showing proton and neutron spins and associated magnetic moments.

TABLE 61A
Typical nuclear spins and magnetic moments

Nuclide	*J*	*g Factor*
$_1H^1$	½	+2.792
$_1H^2$	1	+0.857
$_3Li^6$	1	+0.82
$_3Li^7$	3/2	+3.26
$_4Be^9$	3/2	−1.18
$_5B^{10}$	3	+1.80
$_7N^{14}$	1	+4.01
$_8O^{16}$	0	0
$_8O^{17}$	5/2	−1.89
$_8O^{18}$	0	0
$_{23}V^{51}$	7/2	+5.15
$_{25}Mn^{55}$	5/2	+3.47
$_{50}Sn^{119}$	½	−1.05
$_{55}Cs^{135}$	7/2	+2.73
$_{73}Ta^{181}$	7/2	+2.1
$_{80}Hg^{198}$	0	0
$_{80}Hg^{199}$	½	+0.50
$_{80}Hg^{200}$	0	0
$_{80}Hg^{201}$	3/2	−0.56
$_{83}Bi^{209}$	9/2	+4.08

The neutron, like the proton and electron, has a spin angular momentum of $\frac{1}{2}\hbar$:

$$p_{\text{neutron}} = \tfrac{1}{2}\hbar \tag{61g}$$

Having no net charge, the neutron might well be expected to have zero magnetic moment. Experimentally, however, its spin does produce a magnetic field, and one that is oppositely directed to angular momentum (see Fig. 61O). The neutron's magnetic moment is

$$\mu_{\text{neutron}} = -1.913148 \text{ nuclear magnetons} \tag{61h}$$

A negative magnetic moment is a clear indication that the neutron is a complex particle containing negative and positive charges in equal amounts, and that the negative charge is, on the average, farther from its axis of rotation.

61.9. The Deuteron

The deuteron is a nuclear particle composed of one proton and one neutron. Its known spin of $J = 1$ (see Table 61A) indicates that the spins of the two particles are parallel to each other as shown in Fig. 61P. Since the two magnetic moments are oppositely directed, the resultant magnetic moment of the combination

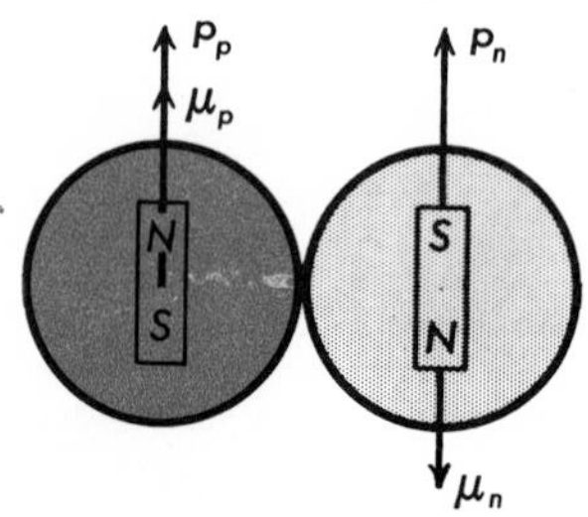

Fig. 61P. Schematic diagram of the deuteron, showing proton and neutron spins parallel and magnetic moments opposing.

should be 2.792 − 1.913, or 0.879 nuclear magnetons. Precision measurements, however, show that μ_d is slightly smaller than this, and is

$$\mu_{\text{deuteron}} = 0.857 \text{ nuclear magnetons} \tag{61i}$$

61.10. Nuclear Shell Model

A reasonably successful theory* of nuclear spins and magnetic moments is based upon the electron spin–orbit model so successful in explaining the outer structure of atoms (see Sec. 45.5). Experimental evidence for this idea stems in large measure from a classification of all stable nuclides as to their odd or even numbers of protons and neutrons (see Table 61B).

TABLE 61B
Classification of known stable nuclides

Z *protons*	*N* *neutrons*	*Known stable nuclides*	*Nuclear spin J*
odd	odd	4	1, 2, 3, 4
odd	even	50	½, 3⁄2, 5⁄2, 7⁄2, 9⁄2
even	odd	55	½, 3⁄2, 5⁄2, 7⁄2, 9⁄2
even	even	165	0

While all nucleons have a spin of $\frac{1}{2}\hbar$, neutrons and protons appear to pair off with opposing spins, thus canceling both the mechanical moments and magnetic moments. While the positive magnetic moments (see Table 61A) are probably due to *odd protons*, and the negative magnetic moments to *odd neutrons*, the wide range in values and the half-integral values of J in the *odd–even* and *even–odd* nuclides suggests orbital motions.

By analogy with the electron structure of atoms, orbital quantum numbers $\ell = 0, 1, 2, 3, 4, . . ,$ for $s, p, d, f, g, . . . ,$ respectively, are assigned to all nucleons. If the odd orbital nucleon is a proton, its positive charge and spin will give rise to two positive magnetic moments (see Fig. 61Q). If ℓ and s are parallel as in the diagram, so that $j = \ell + s$, the magnetic moments will add; if ℓ and s are oppositely directed, $j = \ell - s$, the magnetic moments will subtract.

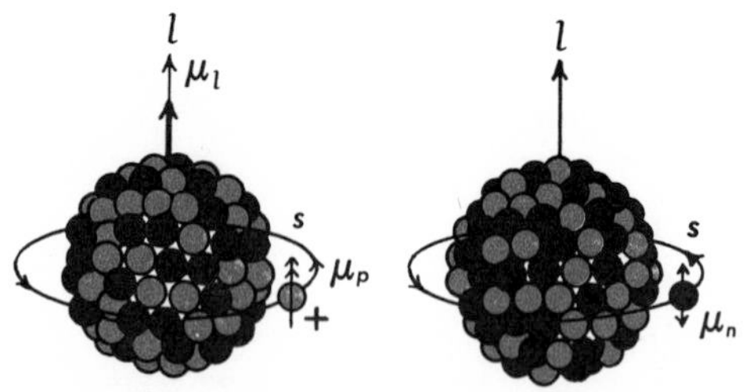

Fig. 61Q. Schematic diagrams of proton and neutron orbits around nuclei.

For a proton the orbital angular momentum is given by

$$p_l = \ell\hbar$$

and the associated orbital magnetic moment by

$$\mu_l = \ell\hbar \frac{e}{2M}$$

By adding or subtracting the spin magnetic moment μ_{proton} [see Eq.(61f)], we obtain the expected total nuclear magnetic moment

* For their development of the theory of the nature of the shell structure of the atomic nucleus, Maria Goeppert-Mayer of California, J. Hans D. Jensen of Heidelberg, and Eugene Wigner of Princeton were jointly awarded the 1963 Nobel Prize in physics.

μ_J. While experimentally determined values of μ_J do not agree exactly with the values calculated by this simple model, they are in surprisingly good agreement.

If the orbital nucleon is a neutron, its orbital motion cannot give rise to an orbital magnetic moment (see Fig. 61Q). Neutron spin, however, does have a negative magnetic moment, and the magnitude of its contribution to the entire nucleus will depend upon its orientation with respect to the nuclear spin axis.

Some success with the application of the Pauli exclusion principle, applied to the filling of proton and neutron subshells, has been achieved (see Sec. 45.9). The experimental evidence that such closed subshells exist in nuclei is to be found in a number of nuclear properties. If the binding energy, angular momentum, or magnetic moment is plotted against proton number Z or neutron number N, discontinuities occur when either Z or N has any of the following values:

$$2, 8, 14, 20, 28, 50, 82, \text{ or } 126$$

nuclear magic numbers

While these so-called "magic numbers" seem to represent closed shells and subshells, much is yet to be learned about the structure of atomic nuclei.

Example 2. A nucleus has an odd proton in a g orbit. The spin angular momentum is parallel to the orbital angular momentum. Find (a) the nuclear angular momentum, and the nuclear magnetic moment (b) in nuclear magnetons, and (c) in absolute units. Use five significant figures.

Solution. Since a g orbit has an orbital angular momentum of $4\hbar$, and a spin angular momentum of $\frac{1}{2}\hbar$, and these are parallel to each other, the total angular momentum is just the vector sum of the two:

$$p_J = J\hbar = 4\hbar + \frac{1}{2}\hbar$$

$$p_J = \frac{9}{2}\hbar$$

The orbital magnetic moment is given by Eq.(61k), and the spin magnetic moment by Eq.(61f). Since ℓ and s are parallel, and both give rise to a positive magnetic moment, the resultant magnetic moment is given by the sum of the two:

$$\mu_J = 4.0\,\hbar\,\frac{e}{2M} + 2.79276\,\hbar\,\frac{e}{2M}$$

$$\mu_J = 6.7928 \text{ nuclear magnetons}$$

or in absolute units

$$\mu_N = 6.7928 \times 5.0510 \times 10^{-27}$$

$$\mu_N = 3.43104 \times 10^{-26} \text{ ampere meters}^2$$

Although elastic scattering experiments similar to those first performed by Rutherford show that most nuclei throughout the periodic table are spherical in shape, a number of the heaviest elements are found to have nuclei with the shape of a football. The odd-shaped nuclei shown in Fig. 61R were drawn by Stevens from the experimental work of Hendrie, Harvey, Mahoney, and Glendenning. Their experiments consisted of scattering 50-MeV α particles from targets of the stable elements *yttrium* and *samarium*.

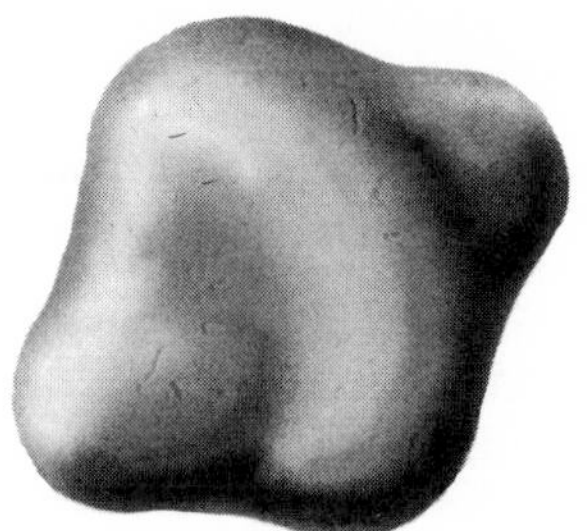

Fig. 61R. Model drawings of two stable nuclei: (left) yttrium-176, and (right) samarium-154. (Drawn by R. Stevens from experimental results of D. Hendrie, B. Harvey, J. Mahoney, and N. Glendenning.)

problems

1. Using the atomic mass table given in Appendix VIII, calculate the binding energy per nucleon for chlorine-35.

2. Calculate the binding energy per nucleon for potassium-39. Use the mass given in Appendix VIII.

3. If the odd proton in a nucleus is in an *f* orbit, with its spin direction parallel to ℓ, what would you expect for (a) the nuclear spin value J, and (b) the nuclear magnetic moment μ_J? [Ans. (a) $\frac{7}{2}$, (b) +5.793 nuclear magnetons, or $+2.926 \times 10^{-26}$ Am^2.]

4. If the odd proton in a nucleus is in a *d* orbit, with its spin antiparallel to 1, what would you expect for the value of (a) the nuclear spin *J*, and (b) the nuclear magnetic moment.

5. If the odd neutron in a nucleus is in a *d* orbit, with its spin parallel to ℓ, what would you expect for the value of (a) the nuclear spin *J*, and (b) the nuclear magnetic moment?

6. Calculate the ratio between the angular velocity of the electron spin and the proton spin. Assume uniform homogeneous spheres of equal size. [Ans. 1836 : 1.]

Fission and  fusion

In 1937 Fermi, Segré, and their collaborators subjected uranium to the bombardment of neutrons. From the radioactivity produced they believed they had succeeded, for the first time, in producing a series of new elements, 93, 94, 95, etc., beyond uranium 92. The reason for their belief was that the uranium, after bombardment, gave off electrons with a number of different half-lives. If one attributed these different half-lives to the successive disintegrations of the same atoms, a single nucleus should emit several electrons, one after the other. With each emission the nuclear charge would increase by unity, thus producing an atom of higher and higher atomic number. Similar observations were later made by the Curie–Joliots, in France.

62.1. The Discovery of Fission

In 1939, just prior to World War II, Otto Hahn in Germany, with his two associates, Lise Meitner and F. Strassmann, made a new and important discovery. After bombarding uranium metal with neutrons they carefully performed a series of chemical separations of the uranium sample to determine the element to which the newly produced radioactivity belonged. To their amazement they found the radioactive atoms to be identical chemically with a number of different elements, nearly all of which are near the center of the periodic table. In other words, a uranium nucleus, after the capture of a single neutron, seemed to be splitting apart into two nearly equal fragments, as illustrated in Fig. 62A.

In the few weeks that followed this discovery, many observers in different laboratories the world over not only confirmed the results, but extended the observations by studying in detail the products of the disintegrations. To explain the phenomenon in simple words, consider the details of the process illustrated in Fig. 62A. An original uranium nucleus, ${}_{92}U^{235}$, with its 92 protons and 143 neutrons, is shown in (a) as it captures a slowly moving neutron.

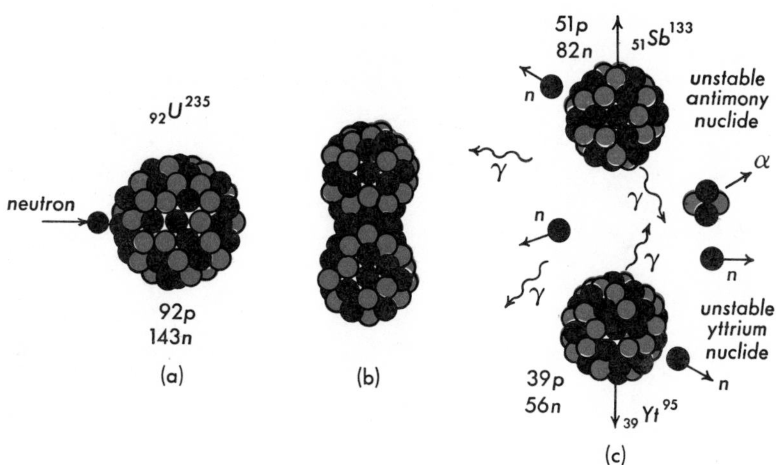

Fig. 62A. Diagrams of the fission of a uranium nucleus into two unstable nuclides, four neutrons, four gamma rays, and one alpha ray.

In diagram (b), the newly formed nucleus is unstable and starts to separate into two nearly equal parts. Because this process resembles cell division in the science of biology, the phenomenon is called *fission*. In coming apart, the uranium nucleus, behaving like the analogous waterdrop, splashes out small drops, that is, alpha particles, neutrons, and γ rays. So great is the energy liberated by this explosion of the nucleus that each of the two heavy nuclei fly apart in opposite directions with tremendous speeds. That they do so has been confirmed by many Wilson cloud-chamber photographs, one of which is reproduced in Fig. 62B.

To obtain this photograph the cloud chamber contained a thin film of material coated with uranium. The fission of one uranium nucleus reveals two tracks of the same density, showing clearly that the particles traveled outward in opposite directions. The heavy forks near the ends of the tracks are characteristic of highly charged fission fragments that have made several collisions with other nuclei before coming to rest.

Not all of the uranium nuclei divide into antimony and yttrium as shown in Fig. 62A, but into any one of many pairs of fragments corresponding to elements near the center of the periodic table. The experimental evidence seems to favor pairs of slightly unequal mass, accompanied by from one to five or more neutrons, as shown in diagram (c).

Fig. 62B. Wilson cloud-chamber photograph showing a pair of fission fragments recoiling in opposite directions. Note the δ-ray forks near the ends. Fission was produced by a neutron beam from a cyclotron. (Courtesy of I. K. Bogg.)

Numerous measurements of the masses of fission fragments have made it possible to construct the graph shown in Fig. 62C. The fission fragment yield is plotted vertically to a logarithmic scale, and the mass number A is plotted horizontally to a uniform scale. The curve is seen to rise sharply between $A = 75$ and 90 and to drop equally fast between $A = 145$ and 160. The most probable values for the mass numbers of the two fragments are 95 and 139 with a minimum of $\frac{1}{10}$ of 1% at $A = 117$.

In general, fission fragments are not stable nuclei but contain an excess number of neutrons.

As an illustration of typical fission events, consider what happens to the two fragments shown in Fig. 62A. As they first separate and fly apart, two neutrons, an alpha particle, and two gamma rays splash out as shown. Within less than a millisecond after separation, each of the two massive fragments is shown ejecting another neutron and a gamma ray. All four of the neutrons are called *prompt neutrons*. As a reaction, we may write

$${}_0n^1 + {}_{92}U^{235} \rightarrow {}_{51}Sb^{133} + {}_{39}Yt^{95} + {}_2He^4 + 4({}_0n^1) + 4\gamma$$

Although the two massive fragments, ${}_{51}Sb^{133}$ and ${}_{39}Yt^{95}$, are not stable, they will collide with other atoms and slow down to thermal energies before continuing to decay toward stability. To become stable, each massive fragment undergoes a series of beta emissions until it becomes a stable nucleus. This is illustrated for ${}_{51}Sb^{133}$ in Fig. 62D. The reaction shown in this figure may be written

$${}_{51}Sb^{133} \xrightarrow{\beta^-} {}_{52}Te^{133} \xrightarrow{\beta^-} {}_{53}I^{133} \xrightarrow{\beta^-} {}_{54}Xe^{133} \xrightarrow{\beta^-} {}_{55}Cs^{133}$$

The diagram starts at the left immediately after the nuclide ${}_{51}Sb^{134}$ has emitted a prompt neutron, leaving behind ${}_{51}Sb^{133}$. With a half-life of 5 min, ${}_{51}Sb^{133}$ emits an electron and becomes ${}_{52}Te^{133}$. With a half-life of 60 min, ${}_{52}Te^{133}$ emits an electron to become ${}_{53}I^{133}$. This process continues until ${}_{54}Xe^{133}$ emits an electron to form the stable nucleus ${}_{55}Cs^{133}$. The neutrino and gamma rays emitted with each beta decay are not shown.

A similar series of beta emissions occurs with the other fission fragment:

$$\begin{array}{ccccccc} {}_{39}Yt^{95} & \rightarrow & {}_{40}Zr^{95} & \rightarrow & {}_{41}Nb^{95} & \rightarrow & {}_{42}Mo^{95} \\ 10.9\text{m} & \beta^- & 65\text{d} & \beta^- & 35\text{d} & \beta^- & \text{stable} \end{array}$$

The final nuclide is a stable isotope of molybdenum.

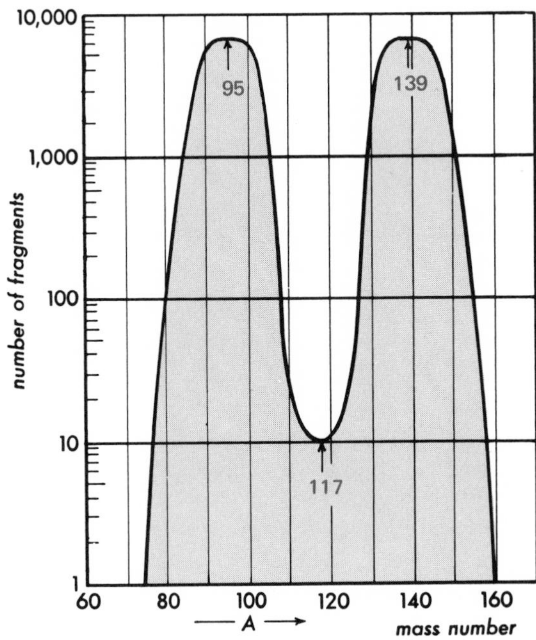

Fig. 62C. Semilog graph showing the fission fragment yield for slow neutrons on uranium-235.

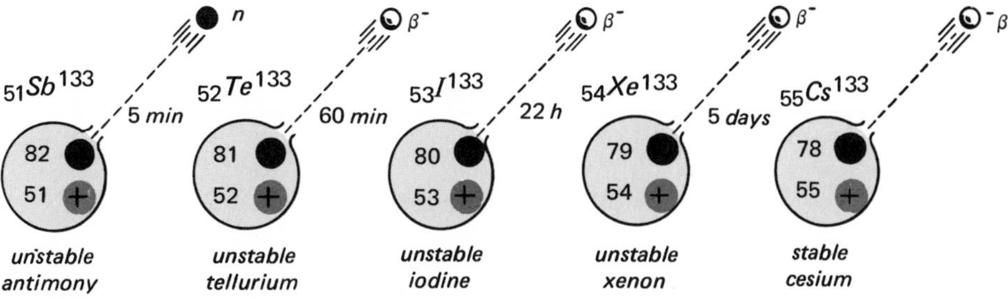

Fig. 62D. Disintegration series starting with unstable antimony, one of the fragments of the fission of a uranium-235 nucleus.

As proof that the above series is produced by fission, previously bombarded uranium has been chemically analyzed for elements near the center of the periodic table. After each chemical separation is performed, a test of the β-ray activity is made by a measurement of the half-life. A comparison of this measured half-life with the values already known for the same element from other disintegration experiments has made it possible to identify some of the radioactive nuclei produced. Such tests, for example, have been made by C. S. Wu for the series of four elements in Fig. 62D. Note the increasing half-lives she identified for this series, indicating increased stability as the stable nucleus cesium is approached.

In carrying out such a series of beta decays, some fission fragments suddenly emit a neutron to become stable. In Fig. 62D, for example, the $_{54}Xe^{133}$ nucleus may emit a neutron, in place of an electron, to form a stable xenon nucleus, $_{54}Xe^{132}$. Similarly in the $_{39}Yt^{95}$ series the $_{40}Zr^{95}$ nucleus may emit a neutron to become stable zirconium $_{40}Zr^{94}$.

Because such neutrons are emitted a relatively long time after fission, they are called *delayed neutrons*. About 99% of the neutrons ejected as the result of fission are prompt neutrons while only one out of a hundred are delayed neutrons.

Example 1. The capture of a neutron by a uranium-235 nucleus is followed by fission into two fragments, one of which is krypton-95. This radioactive nuclide is the start of a series of nuclides which, after a series of $\beta-$ emissions, ends with a stable nucleus. Write down the series of nuclides involved.

Solution. The starting point in this series of nuclides is $_{36}Kr^{95}$. We first look in Appendix VI for the lightest stable nuclide with the atomic mass number 95. This turns out to be molybdenum. Starting with $_{36}Kr^{95}$ and ending with $_{42}Mo^{95}$, and including all of the elements in between, we can write the sequence as:

$$_{36}Kr^{95} \underset{\beta^-}{\longrightarrow} {_{37}Rb^{95}} \underset{\beta^-}{\longrightarrow} {_{38}Sr^{95}} \underset{\beta^-}{\longrightarrow} {_{39}Y^{95}} \underset{\beta^-}{\longrightarrow} {_{40}Zr^{95}} \underset{\beta^-}{\longrightarrow} {_{41}Nb^{95}} \underset{\beta^-}{\longrightarrow} {_{42}Mo^{95}}$$

62.2. Fission Energy

The energy liberated in the fission of uranium is due largely to the U-235 isotope. Uranium found in the earth's crust has three isotopes with the following relative abundance:

U-238	99.280%	4.51×10^9 y
U-235	0.714%	7.10×10^8 y
U-234	0.006%	2.48×10^5 y

All three of these nuclides are radioactive and decay by α emission (see Appendix X).

When a slow or fast neutron is captured by a U-235 nucleus, the two fission fragments as well as the neutrons fly apart with a tremendous amount of kinetic energy. This energy release can best be illustrated by graphs. In Fig. 62E the number of fission fragments from a given quantity of U-235 is plotted vertically, and their kinetic energy in MeV is plotted horizontally. The result is a double-peaked curve with maxima at 67 MeV and 100 MeV. While the greatest probability is for a particle of 100 MeV, the areas under the two peaks represent the total numbers of particles produced, and these are approximately equal.

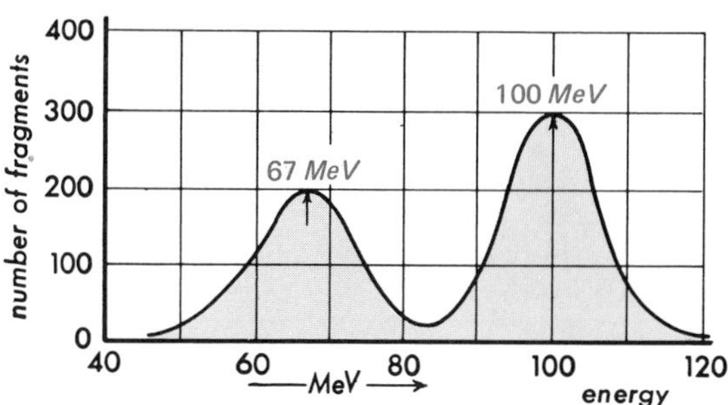

Fig. 62E. Graph of the energies of the fission fragments from uranium-235.

When U-235 nuclei undergo fission as the result of slow-neutron capture, the average number of neutrons liberated is found to be 2.5 neutrons per fission. Some may yield as many as five neutrons, but two and three are the most probable numbers. When the initial kinetic energies of prompt neutrons are measured, a graph of the kind shown in Fig. 62F is obtained. Although the maximum probability is for a neutron of 0.7 MeV, the median energy is approximately 2.0 MeV.

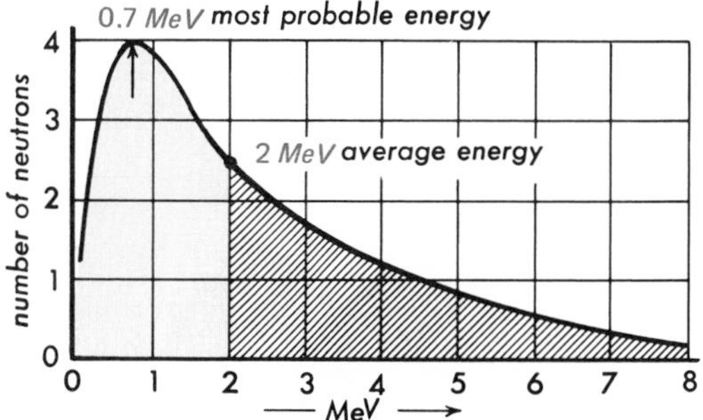

Fig. 62F. Graph of the prompt neutron energies from uranium-235 fission.

The average γ-ray energy emitted in the fission of U-235 is approximately 23 MeV.

A rough calculation of the average energy liberated in the fission of U-235 can be made from known atomic masses. For U-235, the atomic mass, $M = 235.043933$ amu, gives a mass defect $M - A$ of 0.043933 amu. The incoming neutron with a mass of 1.008665 amu has a mass defect of 0.008665 amu. The average mass defect $M - A$ for isotopes near the middle of the periodic table is approximately -0.094 amu. If the fission products, for example, have mass numbers 100 and 133, and these are accompanied by three prompt neutrons, the mass belance gives the following:

Before Fission		*After Fission*	
U-235	235.043933	2 frag.	232.812000
n	1.008665	3 *n*	3.025995
	236.052598		235.837995

The total mass converted is the difference, 0.214603 amu. After multiplying by 931 MeV/amu, we find the energy released to be

200 MeV. This is consistent with the measured energies given in Figs. 62E and 62F. For the two fragments the average measured energy is 171 MeV. For the three neutrons the average measured energy is 6 MeV. These, added to the γ-ray energy release of 23 MeV, give a measured total of 200 MeV.

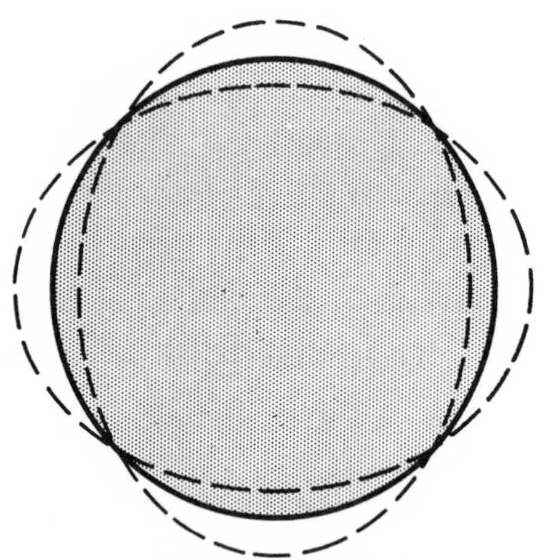

Fig. 62G. Diagram of the oscillations of a waterdrop. Bohr's model for the nuclei of heavy atoms.

62.3. Bohr's Liquid Drop Model

It was Bohr who first proposed that a heavy nucleus behaves like a liquid drop, and that fission may be explained as the result of oscillations brought about by the impinging neutron (see Fig. 62G). Attractive forces between nucleons, like the attractive forces between liquid molecules, give rise to surface tension and the spheroidal state. As raindrops grow in size while falling through the air, their spherical stability decreases; they respond more readily to disruptive forces of the air stream and break up into smaller drops. A similar instability could be expected in heavy nuclei where the attractive forces give rise to a similar kind of surface tension.

Consider a nucleus like ${}_{92}U^{235}$, containing 92 protons and 143 neutrons, closely packed so that attractive forces between neighboring nucleons are all the same. This nucleus should be slightly larger than six nucleons in diameter, as shown in Fig. 62A(a). Each nucleon in the interior of such a system will be in contact with, and therefore will be bound by, 12 others, as shown in Fig. 62H. Since the binding energy U between each pair of nucleons belongs equally to both, the total binding energy of each nucleon should be $6U$:

Fig. 62H. With a large number of closely packed spheres, each will be in contact with twelve others: six around, three above, and three below.

$$B_v = +6U \tag{62a}$$

This quantity B_v applies only to the interior of the nucleus and is called the *volume binding energy*. Experimentally, B_v is about 14 MeV per nucleon for heavy nuclides.

Nucleons on the surface of the sphere are attracted by only half as many neighbors as those on the interior. For this reason the *surface binding energy* per nucleon should be approximately half as great as the volume binding energy. As more and more particles are added to build up larger and larger nuclides, the numbers inside and on the surface both increase, but the number inside increases more rapidly. The surface area of a sphere is proportional to the square of the radius, while the volume is proportional to the cube of the radius.

If, therefore, we assign the volume binding energy B_v to all nucleons, we must subtract some surface binding energy B_s to take care of surface nucleons. The relative amount to be subtracted will decrease as A, the total number of nucleons, increases (see Fig. 62I).

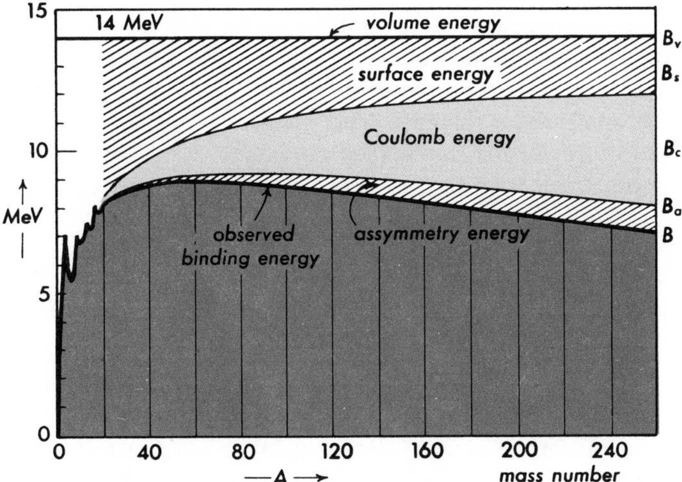

Fig. 62I. Graph of the binding energy factors for the liquid-drop model of atomic nuclei.

While the short-range forces of attraction between nucleons account for nuclear stability, the weaker Coulomb forces between protons are also present. Since these Coulomb forces are repulsive, the binding energy per nucleon is further reduced. The amount by which it is reduced is called the *Coulomb energy*.

Finally, the total binding energy is also reduced in heavy nuclei by the preponderance of neutrons. If we tried to construct a heavy nucleus out of equal numbers of protons and neutrons, the repulsive Coulomb forces between protons would not be overcome by the attractive short-range forces between all nucleons, and the nucleus would be unstable. The excess number of neutrons provides the additional attractive forces necessary to ensure stability. However, since subshells of neutrons and protons are filled according to the Pauli exclusion principle (see Sec. 61.10), the excess neutrons must be placed in higher energy levels. Being in higher energy levels means they are less tightly bound to the nucleus, thus reducing the average binding energy per nucleon.

Hence there are four factors affecting the stability of nuclei:

$+B_v$ = volume binding energy

$-B_s$ = surface binding energy

$-B_c$ = Coulomb energy

$-B_a$ = asymmetric energy

The curves and their shaded areas in Fig. 62I show how, starting with the volume binding energy of 14 MeV for each nucleon, each of the other three factors reduces this value in going to heavier and heavier nuclides. This gives only a rough accounting of the experimentally determined curve shown by the heavy line, and reproduced from Fig. 61C.

62.4. The Transuranic Elements

All elements with atomic numbers greater than 92 are called the *transuranic elements*. The first transuranic element, neptunium, atomic number 93, was identified in 1939 by McMillan* and Abelson. A beam of neutrons incident on a target of uranium metal gave rise to several known nuclear reactions. A neutron captured by one of the most abundant nuclei, U-238, forms U-239 and a γ ray, followed by β emission, to yield neptunium, element 93:

$$_0n^1 + {}_{92}U^{238} \rightarrow {}_{92}U^{239} + \gamma \text{ ray}$$

$$_{93}U^{239} \rightarrow {}_{93}Np^{239} + {}_{-1}e^0 + \nu + \gamma$$

Ten different radioactive isotopes of neptunium are now known. Ranging in mass number from 231 to 240, isotope $_{93}Np^{237}$ emits α particles and has the longest half-life, 2.2 million years. While slow or fast neutron capture by U-238 is almost always followed by β emission, about one out of a hundred fast neutrons will cause fission.

Plutonium (Pu), element 94, was first identified by Kennedy, McMillan, Seaborg, Segrè, and Wahl, as arising from the spontaneous emission of β particles from $_{92}Np^{239}$:

$$_{92}Np^{239} \rightarrow {}_{94}Pu^{239} + {}_{-1}e^0 + \nu + \gamma$$

Schematic diagrams of the above processes are given in Fig. 62J. Fifteen different radioactive isotopes of plutonium are now known. Ranging in mass numbers from 232 to 246, several have

*Edwin M. McMillan (1907–), American physicist, was born at Redondo Beach, California, September 18, 1907. He was educated at the California Institute of Technology and Princeton University, where he obtained his Ph.D. in 1932. His science career began as research associate in 1934, and as professor of physics in 1946 at the University of California, Berkeley. With the death of E. O. Lawrence in 1958, he became Director of the Lawrence Berkeley Laboratory. During World War II, he carried on research at the Massachusetts Institute of Technology, the Radio and Sound Laboratory of the U. S. Navy, and the Los Alamos Scientific Laboratory, where the first atomic bomb was developed. He has received many awards, as well as the Atoms for Peace Award, and the Nobel Prize in 1951 for chemistry.

long half-lives:

$_{94}Pu^{239}$	α-active	24,360 y
$_{94}Pu^{240}$	α-active	6760 y
$_{94}Pu^{242}$	α-active	380,000 y
$_{94}Pu^{244}$	α-active	7.6×10^7 y

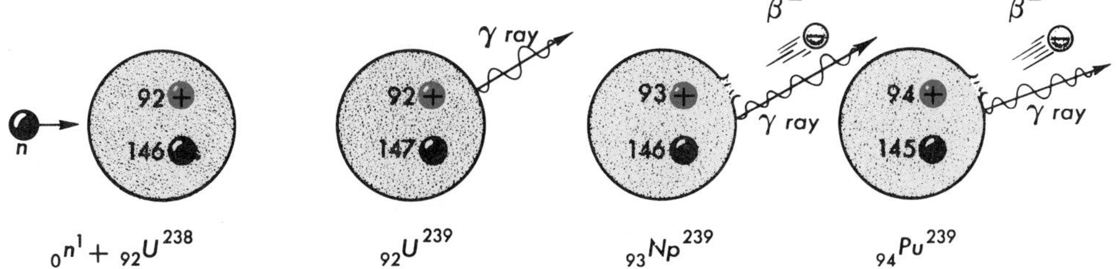

Fig. 62J. Neutron capture by uranium-238 produces, by radioactive β decay, neptunium and plutonium.

Each of the succeeding elements of the transuranium series has been produced by several of a large group of scientists, headed by Glenn Seaborg* and Albert Ghiorso, at the Lawrence Berkeley Laboratory of the University of California, Berkeley. In each case the group making the discovery has named the element.

There are ten known radioactive isotopes of americium (Am), element 95; thirteen known isotopes of curium (Cm), element 96; eight known isotopes of berkelium (Bk), element 97; eleven known isotopes of californium (Cf), element 98; nine known isotopes of einsteinium (Es), element 99; nine known isotopes of fermium (Fm), element 100; two known isotopes of mendelevium (Md), element 101; and four known isotopes of nobelium (No), element 102; and at least one known isotope of lawrencium (Lr), element 103.

This completes what is called the *actinide series* in the table of chemical elements, and the next series begins with 104 in the seventh period as shown in Appendix IV. Starting a new series called the *transactinide elements*, there are four known unstable isotopes of rutherfordium (Rf), element 104, and at least one known unstable isotope of hahnium, element 105. Both of these new elements were also discovered at the Lawrence Berkeley Laboratory.

It is interesting to trace out the genetic relationships of the

***Glenn T. Seaborg (1912–), American chemist, was born in Ishpeming, Michigan, April 19, 1912. He obtained his Ph.D. at the University of California, Berkeley, in 1937. He has been awarded many honorary D.Sc. degrees since then from other universities. He became research associate at California in 1937, professor in 1941, and Chairman of the United States Atomic Energy Commission in 1961. From 1946 to 1958, he served as director of nuclear chemistry at the Lawrence Berkeley Laboratory, where he and his colleagues discovered ten or more of the transuranium elements. From 1958–1961, he served as Chancellor of the Berkeley campus of the University of California. He has received numerous National and International awards, including the Fermi Award in 1959, and the Nobel Prize in chemistry in 1951.**

entire group of transuranium elements and see how they link up with the natural radioactive elements. All of the known nuclides fall naturally into four main series as shown in Appendix X. The four principle activities common to all series are alpha emission (α), beta emission ($\beta-$), electron capture (E.C.), and spontaneous fission (S.F.). While small percentages of some transuranium nuclides spontaneously fission, note that practically all californium-254, fermium-256, and rutherfordium-258 nuclei decay in this way.

It is now known that all heavy nuclei, starting approximately with Th-232, are fissionable, i.e., under proper excitation conditions they split apart with great violence into almost equal pair fragments. Some of them, like U-233, U-235, and Pu-239, fission by the capture of a slow neutron as well as a fast neutron, whereas others like U-238 and Pu-241 fission only by the capture of fast neutrons. The capture of a slow neutron by U-238 is followed by β decay to produce Np and Pu, whereas fast-neutron capture is followed by fission.

62.5. *Photofission of Heavy Nuclei*

The fission of uranium and thorium initiated by γ rays was first discovered by Haxley, Schoupp, Stevens, and Wells in 1941. These experimenters bombarded a uranium target with 6.2-MeV γ rays and observed fission fragments. Later experiments by others have shown that photofission can be demonstrated with many of the heavy elements, and that the threshold energy for nuclides Th-230, U-233, U-235, U-238, and Pu-239 is just over 5 MeV.

The discovery that some nuclei undergo fission spontaneously was made by Petrzhak and Flerov in 1940. Many of the heavier isotopes of the transuranic elements show spontaneous fission.

62.6. *The Meson Theory of the Nucleus*

The possible existence of mesons was first proposed by the Japanese mathematical physicist Yukawa in 1935. He proposed that the short-range forces between protons and neutrons inside the nucleus are to be attributed to relatively smaller particles.

According to Yukawa, nucleons emit and absorb mass-quanta, called *mesons*, just as electrons in the outer structure of the atom emit and absorb photons. The fact that the nuclear forces extend over only a short range can be shown to mean that the meson, unlike the massless photon, would have a finite rest mass. Furthermore, some mesons are charged, and some are neutral (see Fig. 56P).

The present concept of nucleons is that they consist of some sort of common mass core surrounded by a pulsating cloud of π mesons, or *pions*.

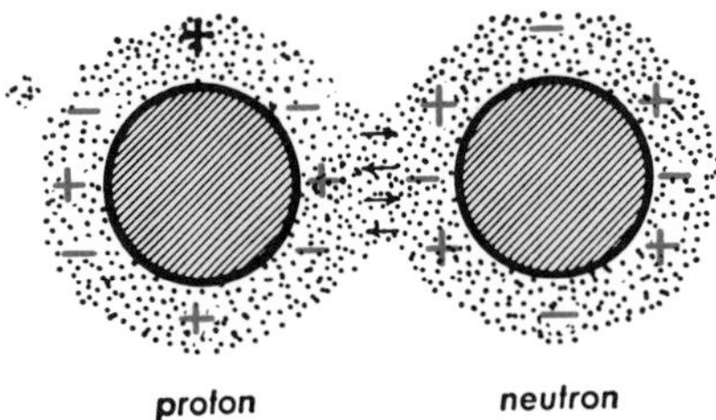

Fig. 62K. Schematic diagram of the meson clouds around each of two nucleon cores, the charge exchange accounting for the strong attractive force U.

Since pions are charged $+1$, 0, or -1, the rapid jumping back and forth between nucleons changes the nucleon identity equally fast and at the same time binds the two nucleons together (see Fig. 62K). This diagram might well represent a deuteron, with both spins in the same direction to give $I = 1$, and the negative pion charge at a greater distance from the center of the neutron to produce its negative magnetic moment (see Fig. 61P).

To liberate two pions as free particles, sufficient energy must be imparted to the nucleus to create their rest mass of 273 m_e each, or a total of 0.27 GeV (see Fig. 59N).

The exchange of a single pion between two nucleons may be written

$$n \rightleftarrows p + \pi^-$$

$$p \rightleftarrows n + \pi^+$$

62.7. Fusion

Measurements of solar radiation reaching the earth each day not only make it possible to calculate the surface temperature of the sun but also to determine its total radiation. The fact that the sun, over a period of many years, shows no signs of cooling off, has long been an unsolved mystery. With the discovery of nuclear disintegration and the development of methods of producing many new types of atoms, this mystery has in a measure been recently solved.

Although there is no direct way known of observing the interior of a star like our sun, mathematical calculations based upon well-established physical laws show that down deep within such a mass the temperature is so extremely high that matter must be in the plasma state—a conglomeration of ions, electrons, and light waves, all moving about at tremendously high speeds.

Near the center of the sun where the temperature is about 20 million degrees, the atoms are stripped of their electrons and the light waves produced are of such high frequencies that they should be classified as γ rays and X rays. Here, where the average particle velocity is so high, nuclear reactions must be taking place on a large scale and the liberated energy must be filtering up through to cooler and cooler layers as light waves of lower and lower frequency. At the surface, most of the radiations escaping are of sufficiently low frequency to be classified as *visible*, *ultraviolet*, and *infrared*.

A careful study of all known nuclear reactions led Bethe in 1938 to propose the following set of chain processes as those most probably responsible for the generation of energy at the sun's central core:

$$
\begin{aligned}
&(1)\quad {}_1H^1 + {}_6C^{12} = {}_7N^{13} + \gamma \text{ ray}\\
&(2)\quad {}_7N^{13} \rightarrow {}_6C^{13} + {}_1e^0 + \nu_e\\
&(3)\quad {}_1H^1 + {}_6C^{13} = {}_7N^{14} + \gamma \text{ ray}\\
&(4)\quad {}_1H^1 + {}_7N^{14} = {}_8O^{15} + \gamma \text{ ray}\\
&(5)\quad {}_8O^{15} \rightarrow {}_7N^{15} + {}_1e^0 + \nu_e\\
&(6)\quad {}_1H^1 + {}_7N^{15} = {}_6C^{12} + {}_2He^4
\end{aligned}
\qquad (62b)
$$

By summing up the equations it will be seen that four hydrogen atoms are consumed and that two positrons, three γ rays, and one helium nucleus are created. The other nuclei cancel out, since the original carbon atom in the first reaction is returned unaltered in the last reaction. Hence hydrogen is burned and helium is liberated. The loss in mass for each such cycle of reactions is, therefore, as follows:

$$4{}_1H^1 = 4.031300$$

$${}_2He^4 = 4.002604$$

$$2{}_1e^0 = 0.001098$$

Subtracting gives 4.031300 − 4.002604 − 0.001098 = 0.027598 amu. This is equivalent to 25.7 MeV energy.

Further experiments and calculations (in 1952) indicate that the proton–proton cycle given below is of even greater importance in the creation of solar and stellar energy than the above carbon cycle:

$${}_1H^1 + {}_1H^1 \rightarrow {}_1H^2 + {}_1e^0 + \nu_e + 0.93 \text{ MeV} \qquad (62c)$$

$${}_1H^1 + {}_1H^2 \rightarrow {}_2He^3 + \gamma \text{ ray} + 5.5 \text{ MeV} \qquad (62d)$$

$${}_2He^3 + {}_2He^3 \rightarrow {}_2He^4 + 2{}_1H^1 + 12.8 \text{ MeV} \qquad (62e)$$

The net result is the same as before; four hydrogen atoms have been converted into one helium atom. Note that since two ${}_2He^3$ nuclei are involved in the reaction, Eq.(62e), two proton reactions of the type of Eqs.(63c) and (62d) are required to form one $_2He^4$ nucleus. Six protons are used and two are returned.

The rates at which these reactions should take place are not only consistent with the temperature of 20 million degrees, calculated from other considerations, but hydrogen and helium are known to be the most abundant elements of which stars are made.

In order for the sun to radiate 3.8×10^{26} joules of energy per second, Einstein's equation $E = mc^2$ shows that mass must be annihilated at the rate of 4.218×10^9 Kg/s (or 4,650,000 tons/s). While this result indicates that the sun is losing mass at a tremendous rate, the amount is small when compared with the sun's total mass of 1.98×10^{30} Kg. To illustrate, in 14.92 million years the sun should lose one millionth of its total mass.

62.8. White Dwarfs, Neutron Stars, and Black Holes

In stellar evolution even stars grow old, and what happens has in recent years become of great interest to astrophysicists and astronomers alike. Stars continue to change because they are constantly radiating energy. Their energy is produced, as in our sun, by the conversion of mass to energy by thermonuclear fusion reactions at the stellar center. When all the fuel supply has been converted to heavy elements the star begins to collapse, and the final outcome is believed to be one of three end states: the white dwarf, the neutron star, or the black hole.

The *white dwarf* is possibly the most commonly observed end state of stellar evolution, and has been known for many years. The *neutron star* is a more recent discovery through the advent of radio astronomy, and is considerably less understood. The sixty or more *pulsars* that have been identified since 1967 are now regarded to be rotating neutron stars. Mesons and other short-lived particles of the kind produced in the laboratory with accelerators are apparently common throughout the structure, which has a radius of about 10 Km. The superdense composition (10^{14} to 10^{18} Kg/cm^3) of the neutron star can be said to be the fifth state of matter—the *nucleonic state.*

The *black hole* is the least understood and the strangest of the proposed stellar end states of matter. Although there is some evidence of their existence, none have yet been identified. Theoretically, the collapse of a neutron star into a black hole may take place. To a distant observer the limit of collapse is known as the Schwartzschild radius, a few kilometers or more in diameter, at which point the relativistic geometry associated with that region of space is so curved that neither electromagnetic radiation nor mass can escape from the star (hence the name "black hole"). The black hole has, according to relativistic theory, the phenomenal characteristic of time and distance exchanging properties. For example, the distance of a particle from the center must always decrease (as the radius of mass contracts indefinitely toward the Schwartzschild limit). The density of matter in a black hole would probably be of the order of 10^{19} Kg/m^3, one hundred times more dense than that of the average nucleus. Black holes should be characterized by their mass, charge, and angular momentum, and it is these properties that hopefully will lead to their eventual detection and study.*

* For a more thorough and quite readable treatment of stellar terminal states, see Allen L. Hammond, "Stellar Old Age," *Science,* March 12, 14, and 26, 1971 issues.

problems

1. One of the two fragments of the fission of uranium-235 is the radioactive nuclide $_{35}Br^{90}$. Write down the series of nuclides, each decaying by β^- emission, ending with a stable nucleus.

2. One of the fission fragments of uranium-235 is the radioactive nuclide $_{36}Kr^{93}$. Write down the series of nuclides, each decaying by β^- emission, ending with a stable nuclide.

3. As the result of the fission of a plutonium-239 nucleus one of the principal fragments is a radioactive nuclide of iodine. If the mass number of this nuclide is 139 amu, write down the series of nuclides, each decaying by β^- emission, ending with a stable nucleus. [Ans. $_{53}I^{139} \xrightarrow[\beta^-]{} {}_{54}Xe^{139} \xrightarrow[\beta^-]{} {}_{55}Cs^{139} \xrightarrow[\beta^-]{} {}_{56}Ba^{139} \xrightarrow[\beta^-]{} {}_{57}La^{139}$.]

4. As the result of the fission of a plutonium-239 nucleus one of the principal fragments is a radioactive nuclide of xenon. If the mass of this nuclide is 141 amu, write down the series of nuclides, each decaying by β^- emission, ending with a stable nucleus.

5. The capture of a neutron by a plutonium-239 nucleus is followed by fission. One of the radioactive fragments is xenon-143. Write down the series of nuclides, each decaying by β^- emission, that ends with a stable nucleus.

6. A neutron is captured by a uranium-238 nucleus, causing it to fission. If the two fragments are the radioactive nuclides $_{36}Kr^{93}$ and $_{56}Ba^{143}$, find (a) the number of prompt neutrons, and (b) the two sequences of radioactive nuclides that follow from these two fragments to become stable nuclides. (c) Make a fission diagram similar to Fig. 62A.

7. A neutron is captured by a plutonium-239 nucleus causing it to fission. If the two principal fragments are nuclides $_{37}Rb^{93}$ and $_{57}La^{144}$, find (a) the number of prompt neutrons, and (b) the two sequences of radioactive nuclides that follow these two fragments to become stable nuclides. (c) Make a fission diagram similar to Fig. 62A.

8.* The solar radiant energy falling on one square meter of area, at normal incidence, outside the earth's atmosphere at the mean distance of 1.495×10^{11} m equals 19.38 Kcal/m^2/min. Calculate the total radiant energy given out in all directions by the sun in one second's time, (a) in kilocalories per second, and (b) in joules per second.

9.* Measurements of the total radiant energy from the sun give a value of 3.792×10^{26} J/s. Using Einstein's equation $E = mc^2$, (a) calculate the total mass in Kg lost per second by the sun. (b) If the sun's total mass is 1.986×10^{30} Kg, how long will it take the sun to lose one-millionth of its mass? [Ans. (a) 4.218×10^9 Kg, or 4.65 million tons, (b) 1.492×10^7 y.]

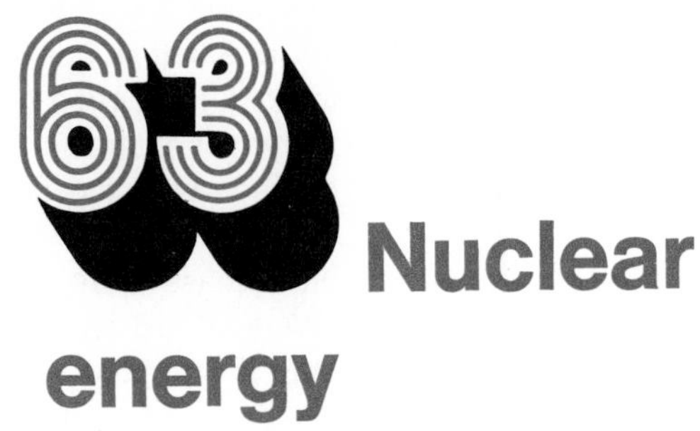

63 Nuclear energy

Not long after the discovery of fission in 1939, it became evident to many scientific groups in America and in Europe that if a sufficient quantity of pure uranium-235 (U-235) could be isolated from its more abundant isotope unranium-238 (U-238), it might have explosive powers many times greater than anything heretofore known. The reasons for believing this appeared at the time to be somewhat as follows.

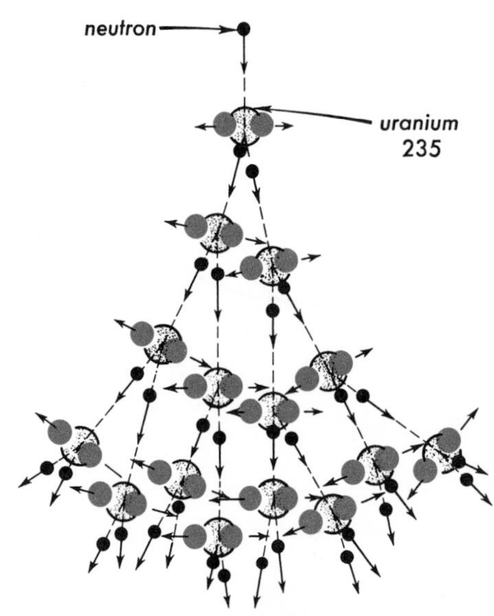

Fig. 63A. Schematic diagram of a chain reaction in pure uranium-235.

63.1. A Chain Reaction

Suppose that a given mass of uranium metal, composed entirely of U-235 atoms, was brought together into one lump. The first cosmic ray that penetrated this mass and produced a neutron might well set off the chain reaction shown schematically in Fig. 63A. A U-235 nucleus would capture the neutron and in splitting apart with great violence would liberate one or more additional neutrons. These in turn would be quickly absorbed by other nearby atoms, which in turn would split up, at the same time liberating other neutrons. Hence a rapidly growing kind of avalanche might occur, a kind which, if fast enough, would have the characteristics of an explosion.

A graph showing the rate of growth of such a chain process is given in Fig. 63B. Since even the slowest of neutrons in solid matter will have average speeds of hundreds of thousands of centimeters per second, about the same as hydrogen atoms in a gas at ordinary temperatures, and since many neutron collisions will, on the average, occur within several centimeters, the graph shows how quickly the growth reaches gigantic proportions. The *time* scale is of the order of microseconds.

The escape of neutrons from any quantity of uranium is a *surface effect* depending on the area of the surface, whereas fission capture occurs throughout the body and is therefore a *volume effect.*

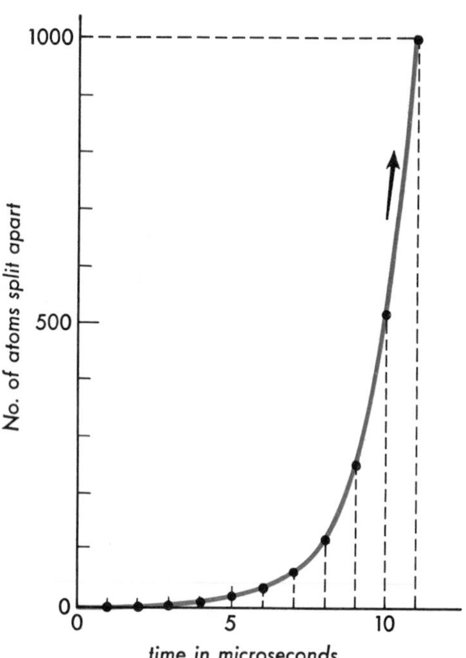

Fig. 63B. Growth curve of fission in pure uranium-235.

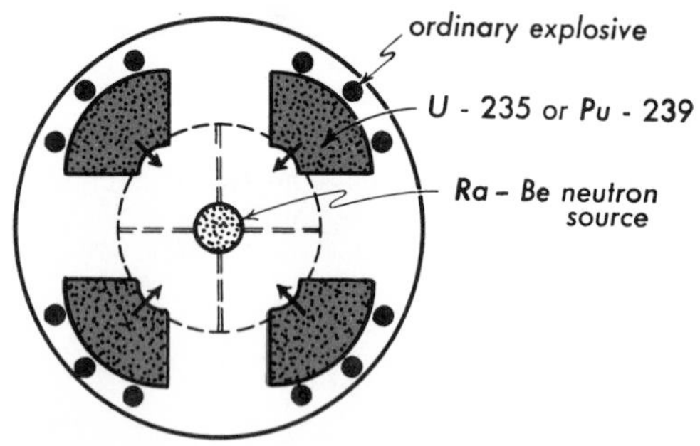

Fig. 63C. A schematic diagram of a hypothetical atomic explosion device, based upon a fast chain reaction in pure uranium-235 or plutonium-239.

If the assembled mass of uranium is too small, the probability that most neutrons liberated by fission would escape through the surface before being captured might well be so large that a growing chain reaction could not occur. Since the volume of a sphere increases with the cube of the radius while the surface area increases with the square of the radius, the *probability of escape* would decrease with increasing size. In other words, if the uranium mass were too small, the growth process shown in Figs. 63A and 63B would be cut off before it became very large, and only if the mass were greater than some critical value would an explosion take place.

Consider, therefore, a large quantity of U-235 in two or more units, each smaller than the critical size, and separated by a short distance (see Fig. 63C). Because of the relatively large surface area of each unit, neutrons readily escape and a chain reaction cannot develop. Suddenly, an explosive like TNT is detonated behind the separated blocks, driving them together as indicated at the center of the diagram. Neutrons entering this greater-than-critical mass from a Ra–Be source will now initiate a rapid chain reaction which results in a violent explosion. The tremendous energy release of such a device can only be fully realized by those who have actually seen and heard one detonated.

The first atomic bomb ever produced was assembled by scientists under the Manhattan Project at Los Alamos, and was successfully detonated at Alamogordo, New Mexico, on July 16, 1945. This device was composed of practically pure U-235. Many of the atomic devices exploded since that time have used plutonium-239 as the fissionable material.

Various peaceful uses are now being studied by many. One such promising development makes use of the tremendous amount of heat energy liberated. Repeated explosions underground can be confined to relatively small volumes of space, and the heat can be tapped off through some heat-transfer system, such as circulating steam pipes.

63.2. Nuclear Radius and Geometrical Cross Section

Many experiments concerned with the collisions between atomic particles indicate that a nucleus may be considered a conglomerate of closely packed spheres of the same size. The average nucleon radius is now believed to be

$$r_0 = 1.20 \times 10^{-15} \text{ m} \tag{63a}$$

A unit of length frequently used for specifying the relative sizes of atomic nuclei is called the *fermi* (*abbr*. F):

$$1 \text{ fermi} = 1 \times 10^{-15} \text{ meter}$$

which gives

$$r_0 = 1.20 \text{ F} \tag{63b}$$

If spheres of this size are packed together into a ball-like structure as shown in Fig. 62A(a), the approximate radius of the combination will be given by

$$R = r_0\sqrt[3]{A} \tag{63c}$$

where the number of nucleons is given by the mass number A. For a uranium nucleus, U-238, for example, $A = 238$ and $R = 7.4 \times 10^{-15}$ m, a value only six times that of the proton.

The concept of nuclear cross section is one of considerable importance in nuclear studies. If a nucleus is set up as a target for other atoms to hit, its *geometrical cross section* serves as a reasonably good measure of the target size, and is given by

$$\sigma_g = \pi R^2 \tag{63d}$$

For U-238 this cross section is approximately

$$\sigma_g = 1.73 \times 10^{-28} \text{ m}^2$$

The unit area for nuclei has been arbitrarily set at 1×10^{-28} m^2, and is called the *barn*. The geometrical cross section for U-238, for example, would be written $\sigma_g = 1.73$ barns:

$$1 \text{ barn} = 1 \times 10^{-28} \text{ m}^2$$

$$1 \text{ barn} = 1 \times 10^{-24} \text{ cm}^2 \tag{63e}$$

Calculated cross sections for a few nuclides are given in Table 63A, along with the heights of the nuclear barrier B for incident α particles (see Fig. 61H).

TABLE 63A
Nuclear radii, geometrical cross sections, and potential barrier heights

Nuclide	R (10^{-15} m)	σ_g (*barns*)	B (MeV)
$_2He^4$	1.905	0.1140	2.4
$_8O^{16}$	3.024	0.2873	6.0
$_{30}Zn^{64}$	4.80	0.724	14.0
$_{48}Cd^{113}$	5.80	1.057	19.0
$_{100}Fm^{252}$	7.58	1.805	29.0

Example 1. Find the geometrical cross section of the mercury-200 nucleus.

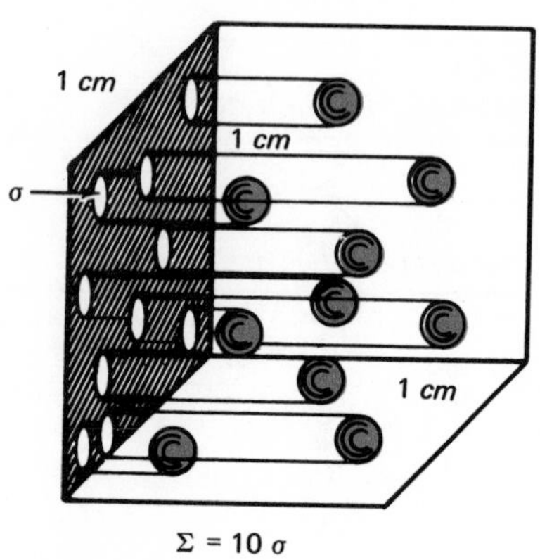

Fig. 63D. Diagram showing the microscopic cross section and the meaning of the macroscopic cross section.

Solution. The given quantity is $A = 200$. By direct substitution in Eq.(63c), we obtain for the radius of the nucleus

$$R = r_0\sqrt[3]{A} = 1.20 \times 10^{-15}\ \text{m}\sqrt[3]{200}$$

$$R = 7.02 \times 10^{-15}\ \text{m}$$

and by direct substitution in Eq.(63d), we find

$$\sigma_g = \pi R^2 = \pi(7.02 \times 10^{-15}\ \text{m})^2$$

$$\sigma_g = 1.548 \times 10^{-28}\ \text{m}^2 = 1.548\ \text{barns}$$

63.3. Cross Sections and Mean Free Path

When neutrons are incident upon some material, each nucleus within the target area does not always behave as though its cross section is a constant. For example, in the capture of a neutron prior to radioactive decay, the nuclear size may appear to be quite different from its calculated geometric cross section. For fast neutrons, a nuclear cross section might be relatively small, while for slow neutrons it may be quite large.

With this explanation we see that cross section is not a target area in the literal sense, but is a figurative concept expressing the *interaction probability.*

The probability of interaction between a neutron and a nucleus is called the *microscopic cross section* σ, and is regarded as the effective target area of a nucleus. If a beam of neutrons is incident on 1 cm^3 of material, the total effective target area will be $n\sigma$, where n is the total number of atoms per cm^3 (see Fig. 63D). This product is called the *macroscopic cross section*, and is designated Σ:

$$\Sigma = n\sigma \tag{63f}$$

The total cross section σ_t of a single nuclide is the sum of several cross sections, one for each different kind of process that alters the bombarding particles' energy or momentum:

$$\sigma_t = \sigma_s + \sigma_c \tag{63g}$$

where σ_s is the effective nuclear area that produces measurable scattering, and σ_c is the effective area for radiative capture. A nuclear capture process whose prompt result is the emission of electromagnetic radiation only is called *radiative capture.* The designation σ_c therefore represents the *radiative cross section.* If fission is also one of the effects of capture, as it is with some of the heaviest nuclides like U-235 and Pu-239, we have

$$\sigma_t = \sigma_s + \sigma_c + \sigma_f \quad (63h)$$

As an illustration of these various σ's, the cross sections for U-235 for fast neutrons (2 MeV) and thermal neutrons (0.0253 eV) are given in Table 63B. U-235 is one of a number of exceptional nuclei, for most cross sections are small and comparable with geometrical cross sections. The whole subject of nuclear energy and the design of nuclear reactors and explosives is very dependent upon the smallness of the cross sections of some elements and the largeness of others.

TABLE 63B
Cross sections for pure U-235

Cross sections in barns	*Fast neutrons 2 MeV* $\left(\frac{2\times10^7}{\text{m/s}}\right)$	*Slow neutrons 0.0253 eV* $\left(\frac{2200}{\text{m/s}}\right)$
Scattering $\sigma_s =$	5.0	10
Capture $\sigma_c =$	0.25	107
Fission $\sigma_f =$	1.27	580

The average distance a neutron travels between nuclear events is given by the reciprocal of the macroscopic cross section. This average distance is called the *mean free path:*

$$\text{Mean free path } \lambda = \frac{1}{\Sigma} \quad (63i)$$

Example 2. Find (a) the total macroscopic cross section, and (b) the mean free path for 2-MeV neutrons in pure U-235. The density of uranium metal is 18.70×10^3 Kg/m^3.

Solution. The known quantity is $\rho = 18.70 \times 10^3$ Kg/m^3, and the cross sections are given in Table 63B. We first add the three cross sections, to obtain

$$\sigma_t = 6.52 \times 10^{-28} \text{ m}^2$$

To find n for use in Eq.(63f), we take the density of uranium ρ, and divide by the mass of one uranium atom. Since unit atomic mass is 1.660×10^{-27} Kg, the mass of one U-235 atom is

$$M = 235.0 \times 1.660 \times 10^{-27} = 3.901 \times 10^{-25} \text{ Kg}$$

Dividing ρ by M gives

$$n = \frac{\rho}{M} = \frac{18.70 \times 10^3}{3.901 \times 10^{-25}} = 4.79 \times 10^{28} \frac{\text{atoms}}{\text{m}^3}$$

Substituting the values for n and σ in Eq.(63f), we obtain

$$\Sigma_t = n\sigma = 4.79 \times 10^{28} \times 6.52 \times 10^{-28}$$

$$\Sigma_t = 31.23\ \text{m}^{-1}$$

$$\Sigma_t = 0.3123\ \text{cm}^{-1}$$

To find the mean free path, we use Eq.(63i) to obtain

$$\lambda_t = \frac{1}{\Sigma_t} = 3.202\ \text{cm}$$

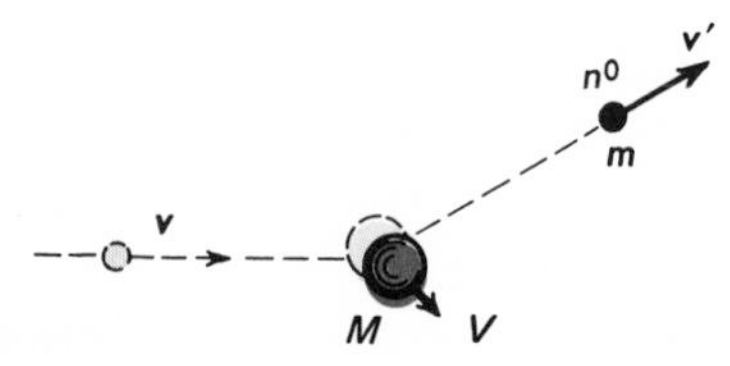

Fig. 63E. Elastic scattering of a neutron by a nucleus.

By using the separate value σ_s, σ_c, or σ_f alone, and the procedure given in Example 2, the mean free paths for scattering, radiative capture, or fission alone can be calculated. For the scattering and fission of U-235 by 2-MeV neutrons, for example,

$$\lambda_s = 4.175\ \text{cm} \tag{63j}$$

and

$$\lambda_f = 16.44\ \text{cm} \tag{63k}$$

Since the scattering cross section of U-235 is four times the fission cross section, secondary neutrons will collide several times with U-235 nuclei before producing fission. A schematic diagram of this process is illustrated in Fig. 63E.

63.4. Neutron Scattering

There are, in general, two ways in which particles may be scattered by impacts with atomic nuclei; one is by *elastic scattering*, and the other is called *inelastic scattering*. In cases of elastic scattering, the total kinetic energy as well as the total momentum before impact are equal, respectively, to the total kinetic energy and the total momentum after impact. In mechanics this means that the coefficient of restitution $r = 1$.

If a fast neutron collides elastically with a light particle like a proton, deuteron, or an α particle, considerable energy may be imparted to the recoiling nuclide. If the neutron collides with a heavy nucleus, on the other hand, conservation laws show that little kinetic energy can be imparted to the recoiling heavy nucleus and that the neutron will rebound in some new direction with most of its original energy (see Fig. 63E).

If, therefore, fast neutrons are to be slowed down to relatively low velocities by elastic scattering, materials composed of large quantities of atoms of low atomic weight, such as hydrogen, will be most effective. Any material used for this purpose is called a *moderator*.

Since the function of a moderator is to reduce the speeds of fast neutrons to low velocities by elastic collisions, the material used to do this will best serve its purpose if the nuclei scatter elastically and have small capture cross sections. Furthermore, the lighter the atoms the greater will be the recoil energy of the moderator nuclei when they do collide, and the fewer will be the impacts necessary to reduce the neutrons to thermal energies (see Table 63C).

TABLE 63C
Number of impacts to reduce 2-MeV neutrons to thermal energies, 0.0253 eV

Element	*No. of impacts*
Hydrogen	18
Deuterium	25
Beryllium	87
Carbon	115
Uranium	2160

Capture cross sections of a few moderators are given in Table 63D.

TABLE 63D
Neutron capture cross sections of moderators and structural materials

Element	σ_c *(barns)*
Hydrogen	0.33
Deuterium	0.00046
Carbon	0.0032
Beryllium	0.010
Aluminum	0.23
Zirconium	0.18
Molybdenum	2.4
Iron	2.5
Copper	3.6

Note the extremely low cross section and atomic mass of the second, third, and fourth elements.

When fast neutrons collide with uranium nuclei, either U-235 or U-238, some of them are scattered inelastically, while others are captured. The inelastic scattering process is illustrated in Fig. 63F. In passing close to one of these heavy nuclei, the neutron may lose a considerable amount of energy, and the nucleus is raised to an excited state. The neutron leaves the nucleus in some new direction, with perhaps less than half its initial kinetic energy.

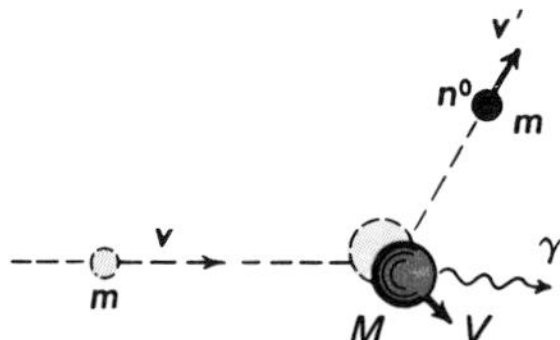

Fig. 63F. Inelastic scattering of a neutron by a uranium nucleus.

The excited nuclei, in returning to their normal state, emit γ rays. While inelastic impacts always obey the law of conservation of momentum, thus giving rise to the heavy-particle recoil shown, *conservation of kinetic energy does not hold.*

63.5. Explosive Chain Reactions

Uranium metal as it is usually refined is composed of three radioactive isotopes:

Uranium Isotope	*Relative Abundance*
$A = 238$	99.280%
235	0.714%
234	0.006%

Since both U-235 and U-238 undergo fission with fast neutrons, one might think ordinary uranium in a large enough mass might explode. One good reason for believing this is that fission cross sections for both isotopes are about the same for fast neutrons. (σ_f for U-235 is 1.27 barns; see Table 63B.) Another reason is that fast neutrons might be expected to shorten the time between fission events.

TABLE 63E
Thermal neutron cross section for fissionable materials (in barns, at 2200 m/s)

Nuclide	σ_s	σ_c	σ_f
U-235	10	107	580
Pu-239	9.6	315	750
U-233	—	52	533
U-238	8.3	3.50	0

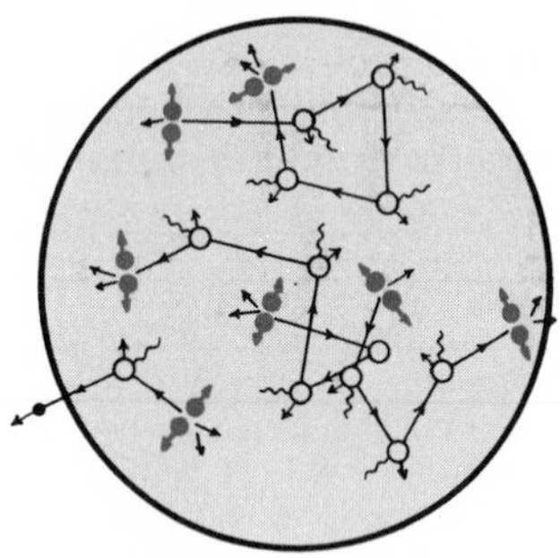

Fig. 63G. Schematic diagram of inelastic scattering between fission events in uranium-235 or plutonium-239.

The reason that ordinarily refined uranium in a mass of any size will not explode is that the scattering cross sections are larger than fission cross sections, thus making the mean free path between scattering events relatively small. After one or two elastic impacts with uranium nuclei, the secondary neutrons have lost most of their initial energy of 2 MeV, and the fission capability of U-238 has dropped to an extremely low value. The fission cross section of U-238 for slow neutrons is practically zero.

Since the fission cross section for U-235 increases as the neutron velocity decreases and becomes extremely large at thermal energies (see Table 63B), only relatively pure U-235 can develop an explosive chain reaction. Thermal-neutron cross sections for fissionable nuclides are given in Table 63E.

63.6. Critical Mass Factors

For a mass of fissionable material like pure U-235 or Pu-239 to be explosive, the time between fission events must be very small, and relatively few neutrons must escape through the surface, or be lost somewhere by capture. A schematic diagram of possible paths of neutrons between two consecutive fission events is shown in Fig. 63G.

Starting out as fast neutrons, the neutrons lose energy with each elastic impact. As the neutron velocity decreases, the U-235 fission cross section increases and fission capture becomes more and more probable.

To find the time T_f between fission events, we note that the velocity of 2-MeV neutrons is approximately 2×10^7 m/s, while the average velocity of thermal neutrons (0.0253 eV) is 2.2×10^3 m/s. If we adopt a geometric average velocity of 2×10^5 m/s, and an average mean free path for scattering of 4 cm, *the average time between scattering events will be*

$$T_s = \frac{0.04 \text{ m}}{2 \times 10^5 \text{ m/s}} = 2 \times 10^{-7} \text{ s} \qquad (63\ell)$$

Allowing an average of five scattering events before fission capture, we obtain

$$T_f = 1 \times 10^{-6} \text{ s} \qquad (63\text{m})$$

Owing to the random directions of the inelastic scattering (see Fig. 63G), the average diffusion distance or *straight-line* distance between fission events is from 5 to 8 cm.

The critical mass for a nuclear explosive device should lie

somewhere between the size of a marble (2-cm diameter) and the size of a basketball (24-cm diameter). Visualize, therefore, two spheres of pure U-235 or Pu-239, one large and one small, as shown in Fig. 63H. It is clear that if the average straight-line distance between fission events is 6 cm (see Fig. 63G) few neutrons will be captured in the small sphere, while many will be captured in a mass the size of a basketball.

Whether or not any mass will sustain a chain reaction at all is determined by what is called the *reproduction factor.* The reproduction factor k is given by the ratio

$$k = \frac{\text{rate of neutron production}}{\text{rate of neutron disappearance}} \tag{63n}$$

If the rate of neutron production equals the rate at which neutrons disappear, the mass is said to be *critical,* and $k = 1$.

Curves showing the growth in an assembly where k is slightly greater, and slightly smaller, than unity are given in Fig. 63I. Since

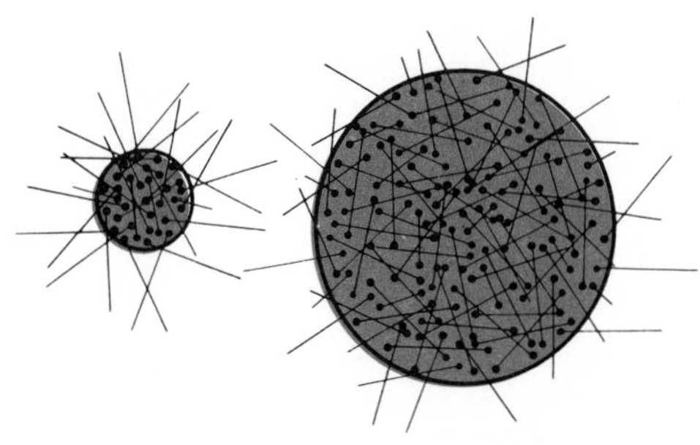

Fig. 63H. Schematic diagram of pure uranium-235, or plutonium-239, showing escape of most of the neutrons for a sub-critical size, and capture of most of the neutrons for greater-than-critical size.

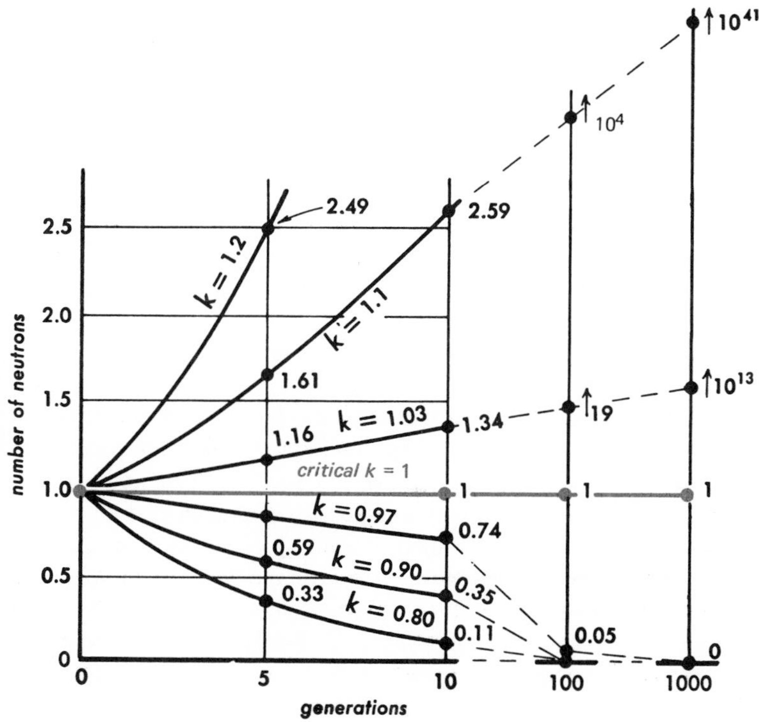

Fig. 63I. Growth curves for neutrons with reproduction factors barely above and below critical, $k = 1$.

one generation of neutrons requires about 1 μs [see Eq.(63m)], the horizontal scale can represent time in microseconds.

In five generations the curve $k = 1.1$ rises to 1.61, since

$$1.1 \times 1.1 \times 1.1 \times 1.1 \times 1.1 = 1.61 \text{ neutrons}$$

In ten generations this same curve rises to $(1.1)^{10}$ or 2.59 neutrons, and in 100 generations to $(1.1)^{100}$ or 1.38×10^5 neutrons. In 1000 generations, or approximately $\frac{1}{1000}$ of a second, the number rises to approximately 2.47×10^{41} neutrons. Since this represents more atoms than would be available in any given assembly, 1000 generations would not materialize.

In pure U-235 or Pu-239 the size of a marble, the reproduction factor is approximately 0.1, while for a sphere the size of a basketball, $k = 2.4$.

The relation between the reproduction factor k and the number of neutrons produced x is given by

$$k^n = x \tag{63o}$$

where n is the number of generations. Taking the logarithm of both sides of Eq.(63o) gives

$$\log k^n = \log x$$

or

$$n \log k = \log x \tag{63p}$$

63.7. Nuclear Reactors

A nuclear reactor, formerly called an atomic pile, is an apparatus in which nuclear fission can be maintained as a self-supporting yet controlled chain reaction. It is a kind of furnace in which uranium is the fuel burned, and many useful products such as heat, neutrons, and radioactive isotopes are produced.

Reactors are of many kinds, sizes, and shapes, the two principal ingredients of them being a quantity of fissionable material, and a moderating substance for slowing down the neutrons to thermal velocities. A reactor is often designated according to the moderator, or coolant, used within it. Because of the immensity of the subject, only the simplest elements of these devices will be described here, and these as illustrations of the basic principles of many others.

A self-sustaining chain reaction cannot be maintained in pure uranium alone, no matter how large the mass. By properly combining or surrounding the metal with a moderator, however, the 2-MeV neutrons produced in the fission of U-235 can be slowed down by elastic scattering to thermal energies of 0.0253 eV. At these relatively low velocities of 2200 m/s, the fission cross section of U-235 has the enormous value of 580 barns (see Table 63B).

Example 3. If the reproduction factor for fission in a mass of pure U-235 is 1.125, how many secondary neutrons will be produced in (a) 10 generations, (b) 100 generations, and (c) 1000 generations?

Solution. The given quantities are $k = 1.125$ and $n = 10, 100,$ and 1000. To use Eq.(63p) we first look up the logarithm of k, and this gives

$$\log k = \log 1.125 = 0.05115$$

Substituting in Eq.(63p) gives

$$\log x = 10 \times 0.05115 \quad = 0.5115$$

$$\log x = 100 \times 0.05115 \quad = 5.1150$$

$$\log x = 1000 \times 0.05115 = 51.1500$$

Looking up the numbers whose logarithms are 0.5115, or 5.1150 or 51.1500, we find

$$\text{(a)} \quad x = 3.2471$$

$$\text{(b)} \quad x = 1.303 \times 10^5$$

$$\text{(c)} \quad x = 1.413 \times 10^{51}$$

The cross sections of a few nuclear fuels at thermal energy are given in Table 63E.

The first self-sustaining chain reaction ever created by man was put into operation at the University of Chicago on December 2, 1942. This device consisted of a huge "pile" of small carbon blocks, carefully laid together to form one solid mass about the size of a normal school room. During construction, lumps of pure uranium metal were inserted at regular intervals throughout the mass.

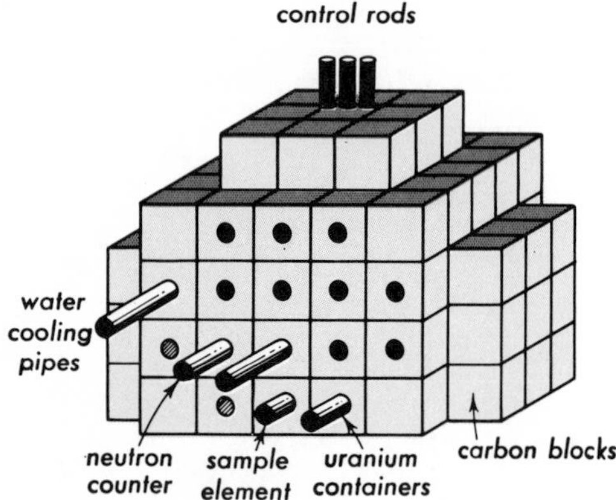

Fig. 63J. Uranium pile of carbon blocks used to produce plutonium-239 and many other radioactive atomic nuclei. (Concrete protective walls are not shown.)

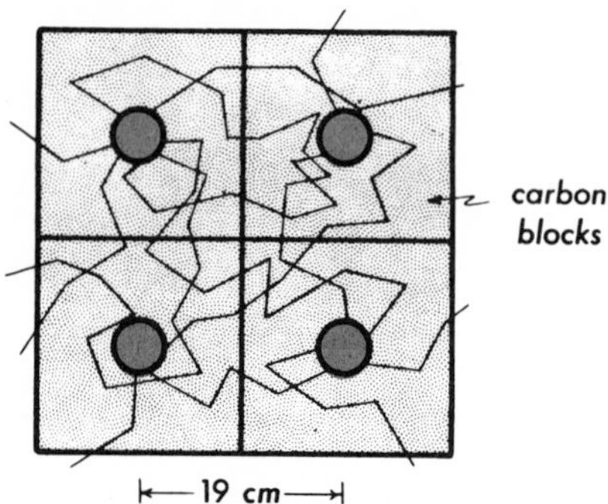

Fig. 63K. Diagram showing moderator action in an atomic reactor. Elastic collisions of neutrons with carbon nuclei slow the neutrons to thermal energies.

A schematic diagram of a pile constructed of large carbon blocks is shown in Fig. 63J. Long cylindrical holes through the blocks provide for the insertion or removal of fuel elements, control rods, detecting devices, samples to be irradiated, etc. The fuel elements consist of pure uranium metal sealed in thin-walled aluminum cylinders.

The distance between uranium fuel elements in the moderator material is of importance in reactor design. The slowing-down distances for three commonly used moderators are as follows:

Ordinary water,	H_2O	5.7 cm
Heavy water,	D_2O	11.0 cm
Carbon blocks,	C	19.0 cm

When, within the uranium metal, a few U-235 nuclei undergo fission, fast neutrons are liberated. Most of these enter the surrounding carbon (the moderator), where they collide elastically with carbon nuclei and slow down. Eventually, many of them enter the uranium metal as thermal neutrons and are captured by U-235 nuclei to cause fission. A diagram showing this process is given in Fig. 63K.

Not all neutrons produced within a reactor result in capture by U-235. Some are lost by escape through the surface, some by radiative capture by U-235 as well as U-238, and some from capture by structural materials and fission products.

The neutron balance in a natural uranium reactor, operating at the critical rate $k = 1$, is shown in Fig. 63L. Of the millions of fast neutrons produced in the reactor in each microsecond, the diagram starts with 1000 fast neutrons at the center, and shows what might reasonably happen to them in regenerating 1000 more fast neutrons. The average number of neutrons produced per fission is 2.5. This factor is directly involved in the bottom four squares where it is used in accounting for reproduction. It should be noted that 60% of the neutrons disappear by other than fission processes.

If the reproduction factor k of the reactor assembly is greater than unity [see Eq.(63n)], the total number of neutrons will rise, and along with it the temperature. To prevent the temperature from rising too high, control rods, which are strong neutron absorbers, are lowered into the central core.

The most widely used control rods, or plates, contain boron or cadmium. Both of these elements have enormous capture cross sections for slow neutrons. When *normal cadmium metal* is subjected to thermal neutrons, the *average cross section* is 2500 barns. Experiments with separated isotopes show that the eight stable isotopes of cadmium have the individual cross sections and abundances shown in Table 63F.

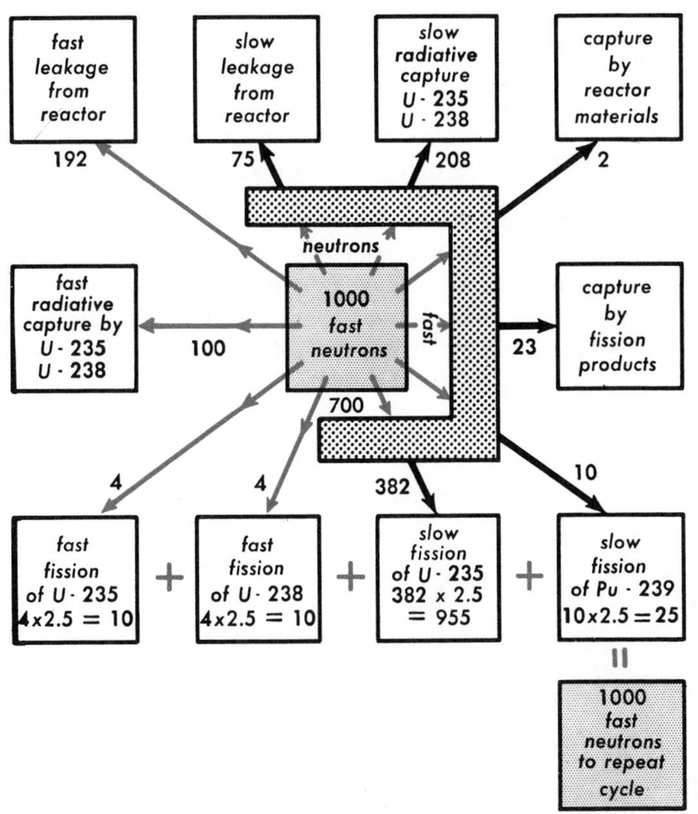

Fig. 63L. A block diagram showing the balance of neutrons in a natural uranium reactor that is just critical. (Calculated numbers by courtesy of Westinghouse Electric Corp.)

TABLE 63F
Thermal neutron capture cross sections for cadmium isotopes

Isotope (A)	*Abundance (%)*	*Cross section (barns)*
106	*1.21*	*0.18*
108	*0.88*	*0.28*
110	12.39	0.20
111	12.75	0.26
112	24.07	0.03
113	12.26	20,000
114	28.86	0.14
116	7.58	1.5

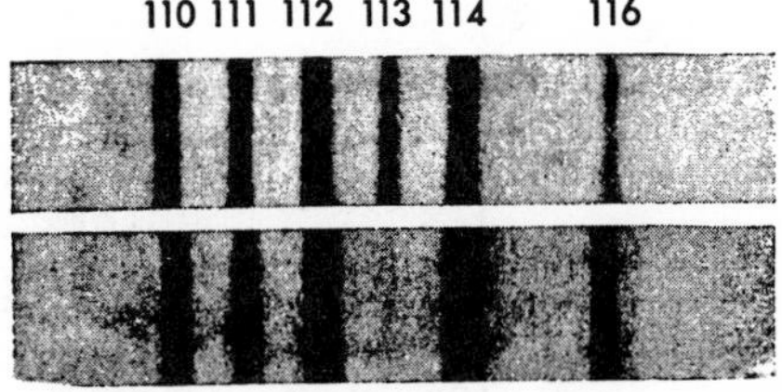

Fig. 63M. Normal cadmium mass spectrogram (above) and isotopes altered by neutron absorption (below). (After Dempster.)

Direct experimental evidence for the large cross section of Cd-113 is shown in Fig. 63M. The upper photograph is a mass-spectrograph record of the six principal stable isotopes of cadmium made with the metal as normally refined. The two rare, but stable isotopes 106 and 108 do not show up in this mass spectrogram. The lower reproduction is a similar record made with cadmium metal after it had been subjected to intense neutron irradiation in a reactor. Note that the isotope 113 is missing and that isotope 114 is enhanced. The capture of a neutron by Cd-113 produces Cd-114.

An excellent demonstration can be made by placing a piece of metallic silver in a thin-walled box made of cadmium metal and subjecting it to a Ra–Be neutron source as shown in Fig. 59D. After some time the silver is removed from the cadmium box and placed near a Geiger or scintillation counter. No counts will be recorded. If the silver metal is subjected to the neutrons without the cadmium shield, it will show considerable β activity, as expected.

63.8. Power Reactors or Nuclear Power Plants

To utilize the natural heat developed in a uranium reactor as a source of great power has long been recognized as a feasible enterprise. The basic principles of one type of "power reactor" are shown in Fig. 63N. A quantity of enriched uranium, in the form of a pure metal or in the form of a solution of soluble salt in water, forms the center of the heat energy source.

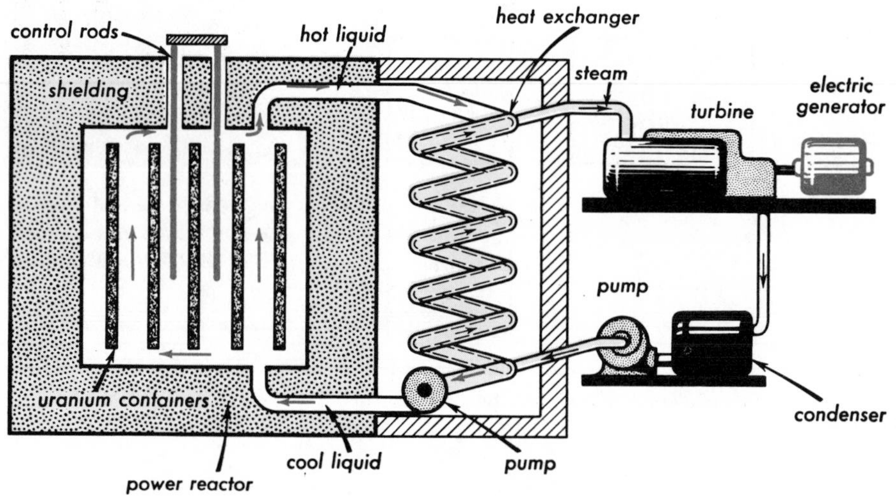

Fig. 63N. Schematic diagram of one type of nuclear power plant.

The energy released by fission produces great quantities of heat, and the rising temperature is regulated to a predetermined value by cadmium rods. To reduce the fission rate, and thereby lower the temperature, the control rods are pushed in a little farther to absorb more neutrons, while to raise the temperature they are pulled out a little farther.

Because of the harmful effects of the intense neutron radiation upon men and equipment, it is not reasonable to vaporize a liquid directly as in a steam boiler; it is better to circulate a fluid through the shielded reactor and heat-exchanger, as shown in the diagram.

The hot liquid flowing through the heat-exchanger vaporizes a more volatile liquid like water; the resulting hot gas or steam under pressure drives a turbine of special design. The turbine in turn drives an electric generator, developing power that can be used to light our cities and factories or to drive ships and submarines through the water and large planes through the air.

One of the problems connected with such power reactors is the effect of the intense neutron radiation on the metal structures. The neutrons change some atoms and permanently displace others from their normal positions in the crystal lattice of the solids, and as a result weaken certain crucial mechanical parts. Intensive studies of the properties of various materials under conditions likely to be encountered in power reactors are continually carried on in our research laboratories.

Another important problem concerns the nature of the coolant; it must be able to withstand high temperatures and must not absorb neutrons and become radioactive to any appreciable extent; yet it must be efficient in the transfer of heat in both the reactor and the heat exchanger. Certain metals with low melting points appear to be most promising in these and other respects.

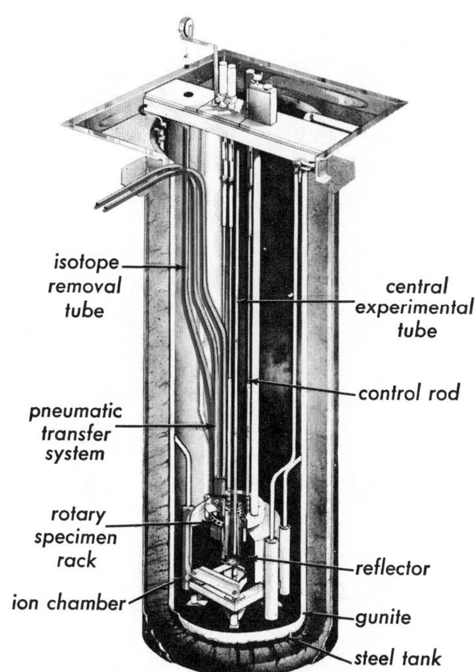

Fig. 63O. Cross-sectional diagram of a "swimming pool" type of reactor, showing fuel elements, carbon moderator, and access channels and equipment at the bottom. (Courtesy of General Atomics.)

63.9. Swimming-Pool Reactor

The swimming-pool type of reactor derives its name from the fact that a large tank of ordinary water is used as a protective shield for the operating personnel. Figure 63O is a cut-away diagram of a typical reactor of this kind, and one that is designed as a multipurpose instrument. The several fuel elements at the bottom of the tank are in the form of small cylindrical rods; each is composed of a solid homogeneous alloy of uranium and zirconium hydride moderator, clad in their aluminum cylinders. The uranium is enriched to 20% of U-235. The three control rods are of boron carbide.

Full physical and visual access to the core is possible at all times from the top, as shown in Fig. 63P. Samples to be irradiated by neutrons can be lowered into the water in the region of the core, and an observer can readily see the blue glow of the water around it, which is caused by the Cerenkov radiation.

A rotary specimen rack ("lazy susan") located just above the large carbon or graphite moderator block provides a water-tight facility for radioactive isotope production. A pneumatic tube running to the bottom of the tank permits a sample element, in a small container called a *rabbit,* to be subjected to neutrons and quickly removed for the measurement of very short half-lives.

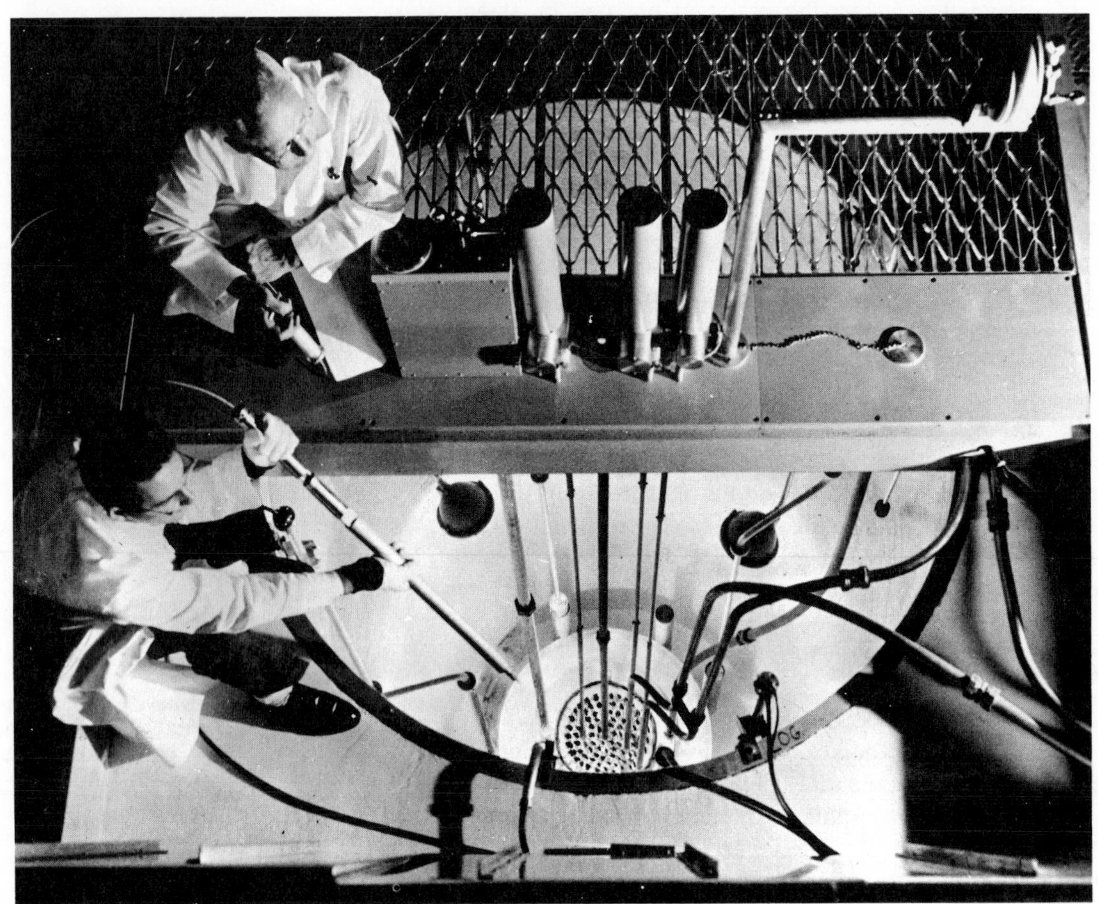

Fig. 63P. Photograph looking down through the water to the principal elements at the bottom of a "swimming pool" type of reactor. (Courtesy, General Atomics.)

63.10. Breeder Reactors

Excess neutrons obtained during the normal operation of a nuclear power plant are used to produce more fissionable material than is consumed. The fissionable isotopes U-233, U-235, Pu-239, and Pu-241 all produce more neutrons than are needed to maintain a reactor running normally. Breeder reactors are designed and operated, therefore, so that excess neutrons are absorbed in either U-238, leading to the production of Pu-239 (see Sec. 62.4), or in Th-232, leading to the production of U-233. The latter involves the reactions

$$
\begin{aligned}
{}_0n^1 + {}_{90}\mathrm{Th}^{232} &\rightarrow {}_{90}\mathrm{Th}^{233} + \gamma \\
{}_{90}\mathrm{Th}^{233} &\rightarrow {}_{91}\mathrm{Pa}^{233} + {}_{-1}e^0 + \nu_e + \gamma \\
{}_{91}\mathrm{Pa}^{233} &\rightarrow {}_{92}\mathrm{U}^{233} \;\; + {}_{-1}e^0 + \nu_e + \gamma
\end{aligned}
$$

Breeder reactors, for example, can extend uranium ore reserves by using from 60 to 90% of the metal. This compared with the 1% realized without the breeder facility is a tremendous saving. Furthermore, there are large ore deposits of thorium in the earth's crust.

63.11. Uncontrolled Fusion

We have seen in Sec. 63.7 how the sun, and other stars, by means of certain nuclear reaction cycles and temperatures of millions of degrees, are able to fuse protons into α particles (hydrogen into helium), with the simultaneous emission of great quantities of energy. While all of the ingredients needed in these reactions are plentiful on the earth's surface, and can be purified and assembled in the research laboratory, the temperature of several million degrees required to cause them to fuse cannot be produced by any of the standard laboratory methods.

Here the atomic bomb employing the process of fission has come to our aid and made such temperatures possible. When an atomic bomb, containing U-235 or Pu-239, explodes, the temperature reached at the central core, although it may last only a small fraction of a second, is comparable to that reached at the center of the sun, and is enough to cause fusion.

While superatomic bombs containing hydrogen and other light elements have been highly successful, the exact materials used, their proportions, the physical size and shape of the devices, and the mechanical and electrical systems involved are all classified by governments as secret military information. These same government agencies, however, do conduct, through their civilian directed laboratories, scientific research projects on the peaceful uses of nuclear explosions.

In the interest of knowledge itself, it should be said that through the study of explosive reactions we can learn more of nature's fathomless mysteries. We can look, for example, at some of the lightest of nuclides and select several reactions that look promising from an energy standpoint. Five promising reactions in-

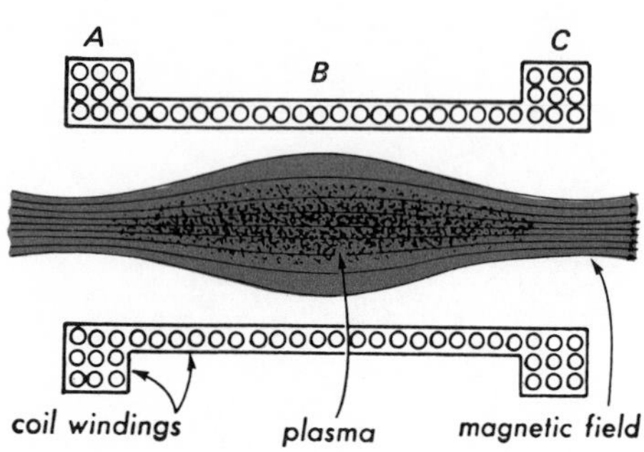

Fig. 63Q. Schematic diagram of a plasma held suspended in a magnetic field: a "magnetic bottle."

volving the hydrogen and lithium isotopes are

$$_1H^2 + {_1H^2} \rightarrow {_2He^3} + {_0n^1} \quad + \quad 4.0 \text{ MeV}$$

$$_1H^2 + {_1H^3} \rightarrow {_2He^4} + {_0n^1} \quad + 17.6 \text{ MeV}$$

$$_1H^2 + {_3Li^6} \rightarrow {_2He^4} + {_2He^4} + 22.1 \text{ MeV}$$

$$_1H^1 + {_3Li^7} \rightarrow {_2He^4} + {_2He^4} + 17.5 \text{ MeV}$$

$$_0n^1 + {_3Li^6} \rightarrow {_2He^4} + {_1H^3} \quad + \quad 4.6 \text{ MeV}$$

Note the particularly large energies released with the fusion of deuterium with tritium, deuterium with lithium-6, and hydrogen with lithium-7.

Lithium is relatively abundant on the earth, and lithium-6 can be separated in reasonable quantities from its more abundant isotope, lithium-7. Tritium, $_1H^3$, on the other hand, is a radioactive isotope of hydrogen not found in nature, because of its relatively short half-life of 12.2 years. It is only produced in quantities, at considerable expense, in atomic reactors.

63.12. Controlled Fusion

The conviction on the part of many physicists that controlled fusion is possible has led, starting a decade ago, to the expenditure of a great deal of scientific manpower.

In principle, one would visualize a jet of fusible material, such as deuterium, being fed from a nozzle into a cavity where, upon fusion, great quantities of energy in the form of heat would be continuously generated and tapped off.

From the very start of all projects working on this problem, it has been realized that, owing to the temperature requirements of millions of degrees, no material walls can be close to the region in which fusion is to be consummated. This has led many to the use of a gaseous discharge called a *plasma,* held suspended in space by the magnetic lines of force of an electromagnet.

A plasma is an electrically neutral stream or mass of ionized atoms, molecules, and electrons and may be produced in various ways. A high-current arc, such as that used in a searchlight, is a good plasma source. Plasma in many devices is confined by what has been termed a *magnetic bottle.* Visualize, as shown in Fig. 63Q, a stream of ionized atoms injected into the central region of a hollow solenoid. Moving with the high speeds of ions in a hot gas, these particles spiral around in the field with the lines of force acting as guides.

As particles spiral into the stronger field at either end, the force components drive them back again toward the center. By increasing and decreasing the currents in the field coils A, B, and C, the field shape can be modified at will and the plasma widened or narrowed. By decreasing the field at the right and progressively increasing the field from left to right, the plasma can be transported lengthwise from one tube to another.

If all fields are increased, the plasma volume is compressed and the temperature rises. A rising temperature means higher ion velocities and greater probability that impacts will produce fusion. If the field is decreased at one end and increased at the other, the plasma may be quickly moved along the cylinder axis, thus constituting a jet. Plasma jet studies by various aircraft and other research laboratories offer promising results for the near future. While much has been learned from the various controlled-fusion study projects, there is still much to be discovered before successful power sources are realized. There are many who now believe that greater research effort should be placed on studies of the basic principles of the plasma itself and that eventual rewards will be well worth the effort.

63.13. A Nuclear Rocket Engine

A nuclear rocket program, as a joint endeavor of the National Aeronautics and Space Administration and the United States Atomic Energy Commission, is providing jet engine research for future space activities.

The nuclear rocket engine achieves its thrust by heating hydrogen to a high temperature and expanding the hot gas through a nozzle. The tremendous heat required to achieve this temperature is supplied by a *nuclear reactor,* a cylindrical shaped unit

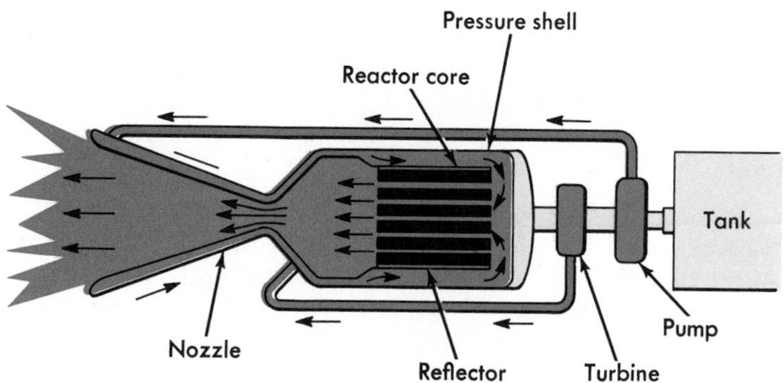

Fig. 63R. A typical nuclear rocket engine, using hydrogen as a propellant. A joint endeavor of NASA and the AEC.

approximately 1 m in diameter and 1 m long (see Fig. 63R). In a typical engine, the flow of hydrogen is from the propellant *tank* shown at the right in the drawing. The hydrogen is stored in liquid form at a temperature of −420°F. From the tank, the hydrogen is pumped through the engine by the *turbine pump.* The flow proceeds to and through the *nozzle* shell, the reactor neutron *reflector,* through the uranium-fueled *reactor core,* where it is heated to approximately 4000°F, and out of the nozzle to produce engine thrust. The engine is about the size of an office desk.

problems

1. Calculate (a) the radius, and (b) the geometrical cross section for the cesium-133 nucleus.

2. Find (a) the radius, and (b) the geometrical cross section for a bismuth-209 nucleus.

3. What is (a) the radius, and (b) the geometrical cross section of a germanium-74 nucleus? [Ans. (a) 5.04×10^{-15} m, (b) 0.797 barns.]

4. What is (a) the radius, and (b) the geometrical cross section of a tantalum-181 nucleus?

5. Find the atomic mass number of a nucleus with a radius of five times the radius of a single nucleon. Note that such a nucleus would have the equivalent of two shells of nucleons around one at the center.

6. Find the number of nucleons in a nucleus with a radius of (a) three, (b) five, and (c) seven times the radius of a single nucleon. Note that such a nucleus would have the equivalent of one, two, and three shells of nucleons around the center. Since their differences would represent the number of nucleons in the first, second, and third shells, (d) find these numbers. [Ans. (a) 27, (b) 125, (c) 353, (d) 26, 98, and 218.]

7. Find the average cross section in barns for thermal neutrons for the eight cadmium isotopes given in Table 63F.

8. Calculate (a) the macroscopic cross section for thermal neutrons in a mass of pure Pu-239. (b) Find the corresponding mean free path. The density of plutonium metal is 17.0×10^3 Kg/m^3.

9.* Find (a) the macroscopic cross section for thermal neutrons in a mass of pure U-233. See Table 63E. (b) Find the mean free path. The density of uranium metal is 18.70×10^3 Kg/m^3.
[Ans. (a) 28.28 cm^{-1}, (b) 0.03535 cm.]

10.* Determine (a) the macroscopic cross section for thermal neutrons in a mass of pure U-235. (b) Determine the mean free path. The density of uranium is 18.7×10^3 Kg/m^3.

11. If the reproduction factor for a mass of pure U-235 is 1.085, how many secondary neutrons will be produced in (a) 10 generations, (b) 100 generations, and (c) 500 generations?

12. If the reproduction factor for pure U-235 is 1.350, how many secondary neutrons will be produced in (a) 5 generations, (b) 10 generations, (c) 50 generations, and (d) 100 generations? [Ans. (a) 4.484, (b) 20.11, (c) 3.286×10^6, (d) 1.080×10^{13}.]

13. The reproduction factor in a mass of pure Pu-239 is 1.180. Find the number of secondary neutrons that will be produced in (a) 5 generations, (b) 10 generations, (c) 50 generations, (d) 100 generations, and (e) 500 generations.

14. The reproduction factor in a mass of pure Pu-239 fuel is 1.135. Find the number of secondary neutrons that will be produced in (a) 5 generations, (b) 10 generations, (c) 50 generations, (d) 100 generations, and (e) 500 generations.

64 Elementary particles

For many decades now physicists have been searching for the ultimate particles of which all matter is composed. From the atom and its electron structure, the search has extended into the nucleus, and from the nucleus to the structure of the nucleons themselves.

The purpose behind the planning and building of bigger and bigger atomic accelerators has been to produce atomic bullets with higher and higher energies. With accelerated particle energies reaching into the GeV and hundreds of GeV ranges, targets have been bombarded and nuclei have been shattered into hosts of new and interesting particles. Over two hundred different elementary atomic particles are known today and undoubtedly more will be discovered as time goes on.

It is certain that only a few of the known particles may be truly elementary and the term is really a misnomer. The questions concerning the origin and nature of these particles present challenging problems to experimentalist and theorist alike. Do these particles exist in some strange form within the nucleus, or are they created from the release of mass and impact energy? If they are created, what is the mechanism involved? How long do they exist, and what becomes of them when they decay?

In this chapter we will take a brief look at the production, observation, classification, and properties of the known particles, and in the following two chapters consider the forces and theories that have been proposed to explain their existence. For want of a better name we will continue to call them "elementary particles."

64.1. The First Four Elementary Particles

With the discovery of the neutron by Chadwick in 1932, the number of elementary particles became four in number: the *electron*, the *proton*, the *neutron*, and the *photon* (see Table 64A).

TABLE 64A
The four basic particles

	Charge	Rest Mass (m_e)	Rest Energy (MeV)	Spin ($h/2\pi$)
electron	−1	1	0.511	½
proton	+1	1836.11	938.256	½
neutron	0	1838.63	939.550	½
photon	0	0	0	1

The first three are the atomic particles of which atoms are built, while the photon is the quantum unit of radiation emitted or absorbed by the electrons in the outer structures of atoms or by the particles within the nucleus. Since they are emitted or absorbed by atoms we should say that they too play an important role in *atomic structure.*

The photon can only exist when traveling with the speed of light, and because of its motion possesses energy $h\nu$. By the mass–energy relation, $E = mc^2$, a photon also has mass $h\nu/c^2$. It possesses mass by virtue of its motion, for at rest it would have no energy and no mass.

The electron, proton, and neutron, on the other hand, have a definite rest mass m_0 and a rest energy m_0c^2. When they are set into motion, their mass increases, and their total energy is given by mc^2.

64.2. Antiparticles

The positron, discovered by Anderson in 1932, is a positively charged electron. We have seen in Sec. 56.11 how electron pairs can be created and how a free positron in coming together with an electron is annihilated with the energy appearing in the form of two γ rays. It is this very property that gives the positron the name *antiparticle*—it destroys itself along with an electron and becomes another form of energy.

We have also seen in Fig. 59O that, when a high-energy photon comes close to the nucleus, a pair of π-mesons may be produced. When a pair of these particles is produced, one positive and one negative, one is the antiparticle of the other. These π-mesons may react with other nuclei or they may decay into muons as shown in Fig. 56R. The muons in turn may decay into electrons and positrons, or they may be captured by some other nucleus.

The discovery of the positron e^+, three pions π^+, π^0, and π^-, the two muons μ^+ and μ^-, along with the two neutrinos ν and $\bar{\nu}$, raised the number of elementary particles by 1947 to twelve (see Table 64B).

TABLE 64B
Elementary particles (1947)

Particle	*Symbol*	*Mass (m_e)*	*Mass Energy (MeV)*	*Spin ($h/2\pi$)*
photon	γ	0	0	1
neutrino	ν	0	0	1/2
neutrino	$\bar{\nu}$	0	0	1/2
electron	e^-	1	0.511	1/2
positron	e^+	1	0.511	1/2
muon	μ^-	206.77	105.659	1/2
muon	μ^+	206.77	105.659	1/2
pion	π^-	273.14	139.578	0
pion	π^0	264.14	134.975	0
pion	π^+	273.14	139.578	0
proton	p^+	1836.10	938.256	1/2
neutron	n^0	1838.63	939.550	1/2

Although the common proton carries a positive charge its symbol is usually written p. A bar over any symbol signifies an antiparticle. For example, $\bar{\nu}$ represents an antineutrino. The positive particles e^+, μ^+, and π^+ are antiparticles, but because they are so common scientists frequently do not bother to put a bar over them.

With the completion of the 18.4-inch cyclotron in 1947, the 6.2-GeV bevatron in 1954, and the large 2-m liquid hydrogen bubble chamber in 1959 at the Lawrence Berkeley Laboratory, Berkeley, as well as the construction of other high energy accelerators in other parts of the world, the number of known particles expanded rapidly between 1947 and 1970.

64.3. Antiprotons

The existence of antiprotons was discovered in 1955 by Chamberlain,* Segrè,† Wiegand, and Ypsilantis at the University of California. The discovery came as the result of long-range plans laid for the purpose of answering the question, "Is there in nature, or can there be created by a strong interaction, a negatively charged particle with the mass of a proton?" One of the principal objectives in building the 6.2-GeV proton accelerator in 1953 was to find an answer to this question. Protons accelerated to a high enough energy should, in colliding with heavier nuclei, impart sufficient energy to create, if such were possible, a pair of protons, one plus, the other minus, p^+ and $\bar{p}^-$.

***Owen Chamberlain (1920–   ) was born in San Francisco, July 10, 1920. He obtained his AB degree at Dartmouth University in 1941, and his Ph.D. degree in physics at the University of Chicago in 1949. He became an instructor of physics at the University of California, Berkeley, in 1948, and professor in 1958. He served in World War II as a physicist at the Los Alamos Laboratory of the University of California, and took an active part in developing the first atomic bomb. He has received a number of honorary awards, is a member of the National Academy of Sciences, and the recipient of the Nobel Prize in physics, jointly with Emilio Segrè, for the discovery of the antiproton. He is a long time friend and colleague of the author of this text.**

†Emilio Gino Segrè (1905–   ) was born in Tivoli, Italy, February 1, 1905. He obtained his Ph.D. in physics under Enrico Fermi at Rome in 1928. After holding several professorships in Italian universities, he came to the United States to join the Radiation Laboratory and the department of physics at the University of California, Berkeley, in 1938. As a United States citizen, he served as a group leader during World War II at the Los Alamos Scientific Laboratory from 1943 to 1946. He has received many honorary awards, and the Nobel Prize in physics, jointly with Owen Chamberlain, in 1959, for the discovery of the antiproton. He is best known for his work in spectroscopy and nuclear physics.

The first antiprotons were discovered as high-energy, negatively charged particles emerging from a copper target in the proton beam of the bevatron and having all of the anticipated properties. By means of a strong magnet the antiprotons were bent away from the protons and into a scintillation counter. Today antiproton events are commonly observed and studied by means of bubble chambers, spark chambers, and other forms of detectors.

With the discovery of the antiproton scientists everywhere came to the conclusion that all regular atomic particles have their antiparticles, and that in the future one could expect that with the discovery of any new particle or antiparticle, its counterpart could automatically be assumed to exist. As yet no violation of this principle has been observed.

This immediately led many scientists to speculate as to the possibility of *antimatter* in space. Hydrogen atoms could be made up of positrons and negatively charged protons, and the spectrum lines from a gas made up of these atoms should be identical in wavelength to those of regular hydrogen. As yet there is no known way of detecting stars made up of antimatter, but it is conjectured that supernovae are evidence of the coming together of two stars, one of matter, the other of antimatter. In a world of antimatter all *regular particles* would readily be annihilated upon the first encounter with their corresponding antiparticles. This means that particles and antiparticles are symmetrical in all of their properties.

To see how many new discoveries are coming out of the field of particle research, we will now study the principal equipment used today in studying high energy atomic collisions.

64.4. The Bevatron

The bevatron, a 6.2-GeV proton accelerator described in Chap. 57, was completed in 1954. Although such huge installations are constructed and maintained at high cost, many different groups of scientists can be stationed around its periphery, and all of them experiment with the beam simultaneously. Furthermore, qualified scientists and graduate students from other laboratories across the country can, by appropriate arrangements, make use of the facilities for their own experiments.

When a beam of high energy particles, such as those produced by any of the GeV accelerators listed at the end of Chap. 57, impinges upon a target of any substance, many kinds of particles and antiparticles emerge from the other side in a forward direction (see Fig. 64A). If this recoiling beam passes through a strong magnetic field, the particles fan out with positives going to one side, negatives to the other, and neutrals straight forward. How this principle is utilized at the bevatron is shown schematically in Fig. 64B.

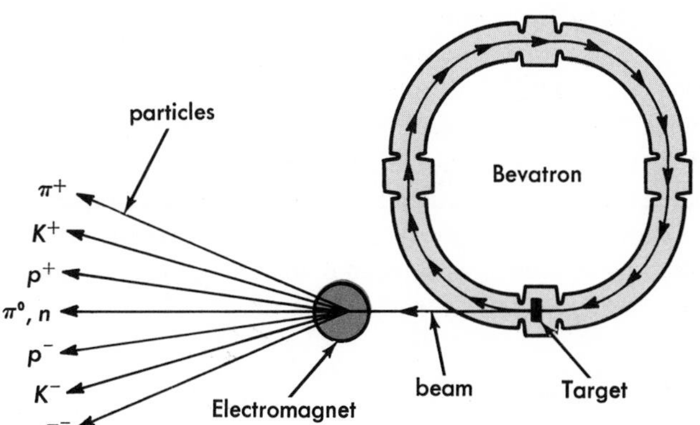

Fig. 64A. Diagram showing how a high energy beam of particles from the target of an accelerator like the bevatron is dispersed along different paths by an electromagnet.

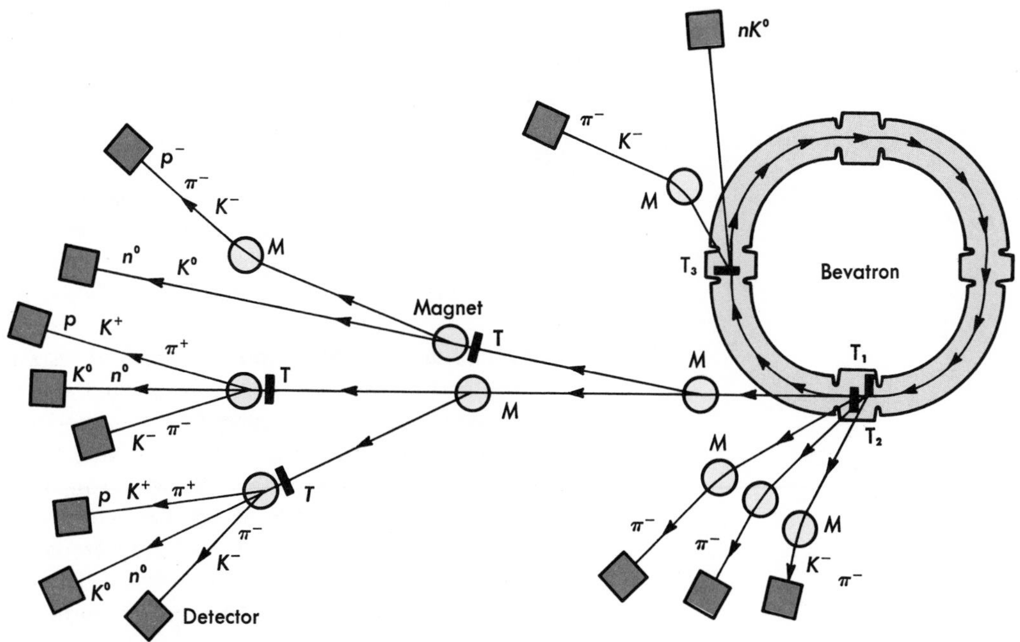

Fig. 64B. Schematic diagram showing the many detectors, electromagnets, particle beams, and targets around the bevatron.

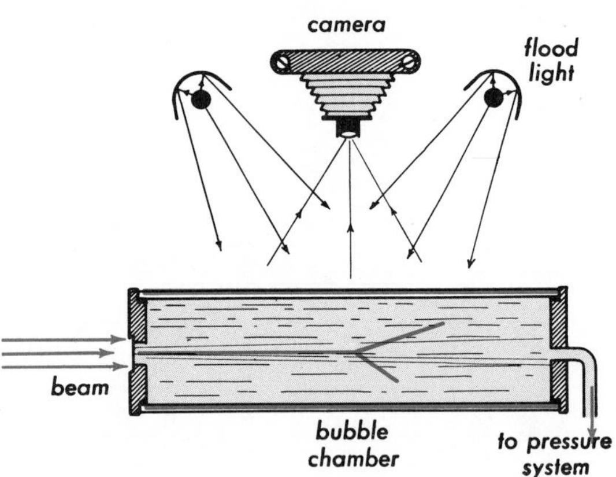

Fig. 64C. Cross-sectional diagram of a bubble chamber showing track illumination, camera, and incident-particle beam.

Appropriately designated targets T_1, T_2 and T_3 are located, within the bevatron proper, to intercept the proton beam as it sweeps around its orbit. Such targets are usually small pieces of metallic copper, platinum, tungsten, or beryllium. Emerging elementary particles, recoiling in the forward direction, pass through magnets M where they are deflected by strong fields to different areas within the huge laboratory.

At different points along any one branch beam, other targets, followed immediately by deflecting magnets, are used to bring particular kinds of particles into appropriate areas. There, different groups of scientists set up their own special detecting equipment, scintillation counters, cloud chambers, bubble chambers, spark chambers, etc. It is in one of these beams that the giant bubble chamber was located for the making of the photographs reproduced at the end of this chapter.

64.5. The Bubble Chamber

The bubble chamber, invented in 1952 by D. H. Glaser, has become one of the most valuable instruments for studying the minute details of high-energy nuclear events. In a cloud chamber, fog drops form on the ions produced by charged atomic particles that have just previously traversed the gas-filled chamber. In the bubble chamber, the ions, formed by charged particles traversing the liquid, form local heat centers in which tiny gas bubbles develop and grow.

The basic principles of the bubble chamber involve the superheating of a liquid and the bubbles that form in the process of boiling. Water, for example, boils at 100°C at standard atmospheric pressure. If the pressure is increased as in a pressure cooker, boiling will not begin until a higher temperature is reached. If the pressure is then suddenly reduced, boiling begins with the sudden formation of tiny bubbles that grow quickly in size.

A simplified diagram of a bubble chamber is shown in Fig. 64C. A box with thick glass walls, filled with a liquid, is connected to a pressure system and then heated to some predetermined temperature. High-energy particles enter the liquid through a thin window. A sudden release of a valve in the pressure system is quickly followed by the flash of floodlights and the snap of a camera shutter. If the chamber is operating properly, and events are correctly timed, sharply defined trails of bubbles formed on the paths of ions made by the traversing particles are photographed (see Figs. 64M through 64Z).

The extensive use of liquid hydrogen in bubble chambers has

been particularly effective in the study of elementary particle events. The difficulties of handling liquid hydrogen at −253°C in large bubble chambers were overcome by L. Alvarez and his colleagues at the University of California, Berkeley, over a period of several years (see Fig. 64D). Liquid hydrogen is particularly useful in that it provides a high concentration of "target protons," the simplest of atomic nuclei, and at the same time greatly shortens the distance between events that would be required in the gas-filled space of a cloud chamber.

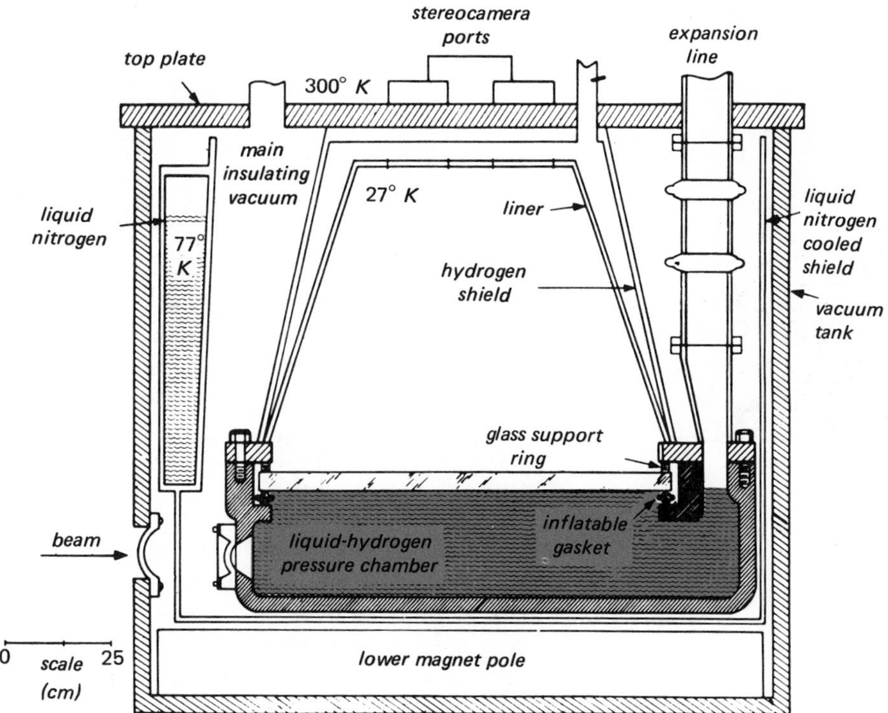

Fig. 64D. Cross-sectional diagram of a 2-m long liquid-hydrogen bubble chamber.

64.6. Spark-Chamber Detectors

One of the more recent instruments developed for use in the study of high-energy nuclear reactions is known as the *spark chamber.* This device is composed of stacks of equally spaced conducting plates as shown in the title page photograph of this book and by the cross-sectional diagram in Fig. 64E.

A typical chamber will have 25 to 100 plates, each about 1 mm thick and 1 m square, and accurately spaced about 6 mm apart. Alternate plates are connected together and the two sets connected to a 10,000 to 15,000 V dc source. The airtight vessel in which the plates are mounted contains pure helium, or a mixture of approximately 90% neon and 10% helium, at a pressure of 1 atmosphere.

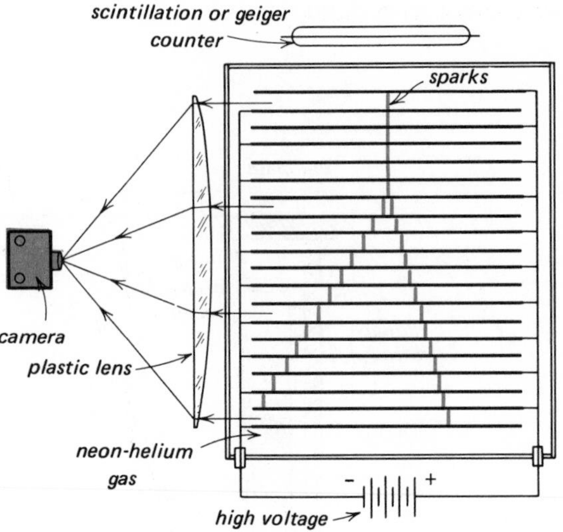

Fig. 64E. Cross-sectional diagram of a spark-chamber detector used for observing high-energy nuclear reactions involving elementary particles.

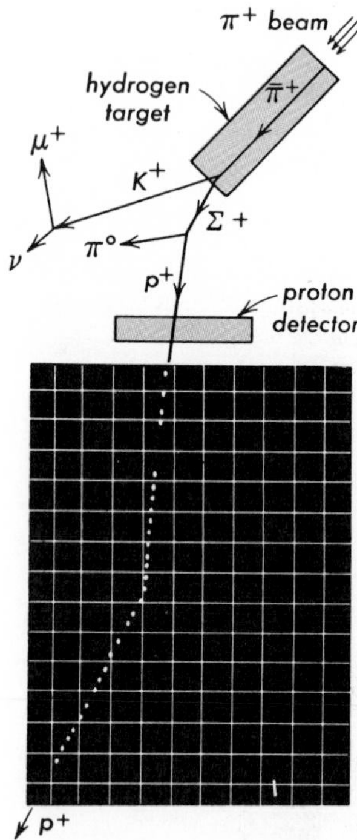

Fig. 64F. Spark chamber photograph of the scattering of a proton by a carbon nucleus. (Courtesy of E. F. Beal, Bruce Cork, D. Keefe, P. G. Murphy, and W. A. Wenzel, and the Lawrence Radiation Laboratory.)

When a high-energy charged particle enters such a chamber, a detector outside the chamber, or inside, triggers the high voltage to the plates, and opens the camera shutter. Traversing the chamber a charged particle produces many ion pairs along its path, and sparks jump between the pairs of oppositely charged plates as indicated. A large lens, cut from clear plastic, makes it possible for a camera to photograph the light from sparks between all plates. A second large lens and camera "looking into" an adjacent side of the box permits the simultaneous taking of two pictures, thereby recording stereoscopic photos of each event.

A photograph of a proton scattered by a carbon nucleus is shown in Fig. 64F. This picture shows only one of several events diagrammed above. A beam of π^+ mesons, produced by the 6.2-GeV proton beam of the bevatron, passed through a target containing hydrogen. Upon collision with another proton, a K^+ meson and a Σ^+ baryon were produced. The K^+ decayed into a μ^+ and a neutrino. The Σ^+ decayed into a proton and a π^0. The proton, detected as it entered the carbon plate spark chamber, was photographed as shown. The horizontal and vertical white lines in the photograph are the image of a grid used for making measurements. The title page insert is a color photograph of many tracks made simultaneously in several spark chambers.

64.7. Photographic Emulsions

When an ionizing particle traverses the sensitive emulsion of a photographic film, the clear silver bromide crystal grains that are penetrated are turned into black silver upon development by regular film-developing processes.

The sensitive emulsion on commercial film is far too thin for this kind of work. Satisfactory emulsions up to 1 mm in thickness, containing about 80% silver bromide, were first developed by C. F. Powell in England. These can be stacked in layers to build up larger volumes, exposed to high-energy nuclear beams, or cosmic rays, and then developed (see Fig. 64G). By studying consecutively numbered films separately, under a suitable measuring microscope, one can observe nuclear collision events and make measurements of the different particles, their directions, ranges, track densities, etc.

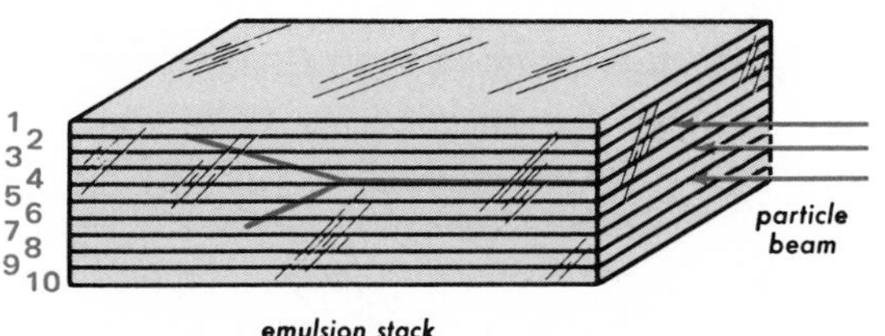

Fig. 64G. Numbered stack of extra-thick photographic emulsions used in photographing high-energy nuclear events.

Track densities vary widely with particle *charge* and *velocity,* as shown in Fig. 64H. The energies required of various particles to travel 1 mm in an average nuclear emulsion are

e	0.7 MeV	p	14.0 MeV
μ	5.5 MeV	d	20.0 MeV
π	6.1 MeV	α	55.0 MeV

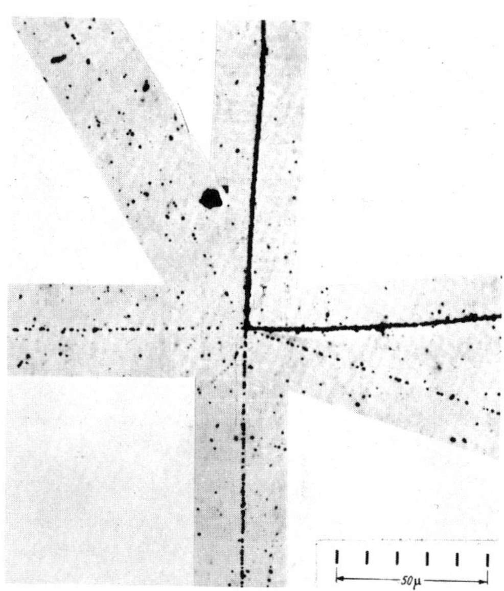

Fig. 64H. Charged particle tracks in a photographic emulsion showing differences in track density. (Courtesy, C. F. Powell, P. H. Fowler, and D. H. Perkins, from *The Study of Elementary Particles,* Pergamon Press Ltd.)

Because emulsion densities are far greater than the gas in a cloud chamber, the track ranges are extremely small. This high-density and short-range feature is particularly useful, therefore, to the study of nuclear events involving very high energy particles.

The procedure used for displaying emulsion tracks is to make enlargements of microscope photographs of neighboring sections, and to piece the photographic prints together as shown in Figs. 64H and 64I. Figure 64I shows a "star" of 22 tracks. A primary cosmic ray, a proton, enters from the top, and collides with a silver or bromine nucleus in the emulsion, causing an explosion. Most of the tracks were made by π mesons, and the others probably by kaons and protons.

While the number of stars of this general nature is small relative to other kinds of nuclear events observed in emulsions, a great many have been observed and studied.

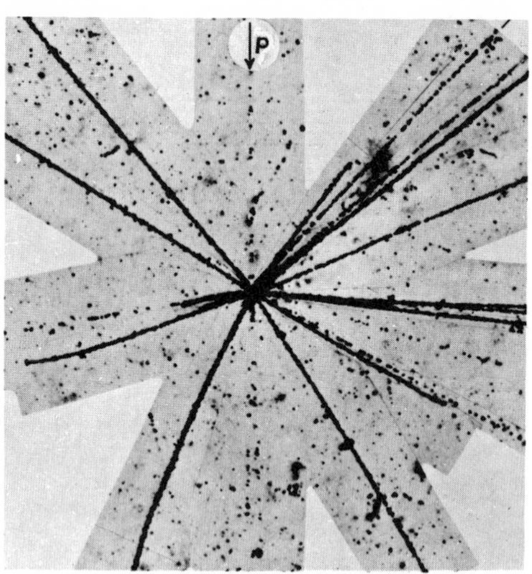

Fig. 64I. Photographic-emulsion star produced by a cosmic-ray proton. (Courtesy of C. F. Powell, P. H. Fowler, and D. H. Perkins, from *The Study of Elementary Particles,* Pergamon Press Ltd.)

64.8. Particle Classification and Decay Modes

All elementary particles known today are classified under one of the three following headings: *leptons, mesons,* and *baryons.* Leptons, the lightest group, are composed of neutrinos, electrons, and muons, and all eight of them have a spin angular momentum of $\frac{1}{2}\,\hbar$. Mesons, the intermediate group, have a spin angular momentum of 0 or 1 $\hbar$. Baryons, the third group, all have masses equal to or greater than protons, and all have half integral spins, $\frac{1}{2}\,\hbar, \frac{3}{2}\,\hbar, \frac{5}{2}\,\hbar$, etc.

$$\textbf{Leptons}\quad \begin{Bmatrix} \nu_e & \nu_\mu & e^- & \mu^- \\ \bar{\nu}_e & \bar{\nu}_\mu & e^+ & \mu^+ \end{Bmatrix}$$

$$\textbf{Mesons}\quad \begin{Bmatrix} \pi^- & \uparrow & K^+ & K^0 & \uparrow & \rho^+ & \uparrow & \uparrow & \uparrow \\ & \pi^0 & & & \eta^0 & & \bar{\rho}^0 & \bar{\omega}^0 & \bar{\phi}^0 \\ \bar{\pi}^+ & \downarrow & \bar{K}^- & \bar{K}^0 & \downarrow & \bar{\rho}^- & \downarrow & \downarrow & \downarrow \end{Bmatrix}$$

$$\textbf{Baryons}\quad \begin{Bmatrix} p^+ & n^0 & \Lambda^0 & \Sigma^+ & \Sigma^0 & \Sigma^- & \Xi^0 & \Xi^- & \Delta^{++} & \Delta^+ & \Delta^0 & \Delta^+ & \Omega^- \\ \bar{p}^- & \bar{n}^0 & \bar{\Lambda}^0 & \bar{\Sigma}^- & \bar{\Sigma}^0 & \bar{\Sigma}^+ & \bar{\Xi}^0 & \bar{\Xi}^+ & \bar{\Delta}^{--} & \bar{\Delta}^- & \bar{\Delta}^0 & \bar{\Delta}^- & \bar{\Omega}^+ \end{Bmatrix}$$

The upper row in each class is composed of *particles,* and directly below each one is its *antiparticle.* The peculiar nature of the neutral mesons π^0, η^0, ρ^0, ω^0, and ϕ^0 is that each one is its own antiparticle. This means that the particle and antiparticle are indistinguishable, and identical.

TABLE 64C
Leptons

Particle	*Symbol*	*Mass Energy (MeV)*	*Mean life*	*Spin ($\hbar$)*
neutrino	ν $\bar{\nu}$	0	stable	1/2
electron	e^- e^+	0.511	stable	1/2
muon	μ^- μ^+	105.66	2.20×10^{-6}s	1/2

Lists of all three classes of particles, along with their *symbols, mass energies, mean lives,* and *spins* are given in Tables 64C, 64D, and 64E. In establishing the existence of any one particle from experimental observations, no event is assumed to be correctly interpreted unless all conservation laws are adhered to. One of these is the law of conservation of energy. Since mass is frequently converted to energy, and energy to mass, it is convenient to express all particle masses in their energy equivalent, MeV.

TABLE 64D
Prominent mesons

Particle	*Symbol*	*Mass Energy (MeV)*	*Mean life*	*Spin ($\hbar$)*
pion	π^+ $\bar{\pi}^-$	139.58	2.60×10^{-8}s	0
pion	π^0	134.97	0.89×10^{-16}s	0
kaon	K^+ $\bar{K}^-$	493.8	1.23×10^{-8}s	0
kaon	$K_S{}^0$ $\bar{K}_S{}^0$	498.0	0.86×10^{-10}s	0
kaon	$K_L{}^0$ $\bar{K}_L{}^0$	498.0	5.38×10^{-10}s	0
eta	η^0	548.8	2.51×10^{-19}s	0
rho	ρ^+ $\bar{\rho}^-$	765	5.3×10^{-24}s	1
rho	ρ^0	765	5.3×10^{-24}s	1
omega	$\bar{\omega}^0$	784	5.2×10^{-23}s	1
phi	$\bar{\phi}^0$	1019	1.7×10^{-23}s	1

TABLE 64E
Prominent baryons

Particle	*Symbol*	*Mass Energy (MeV)*	*Mean life*	*Spin ($\hbar$)*
proton	p^+ $\bar{p}^-$	938.3	stable	1/2
neutron	n^0 $\bar{n}^0$	939.6	932 s	1/2
lambda	Λ^0 $\bar{\Lambda}^0$	1115.6	2.51×10^{-10}s	1/2
sigma	Σ^+ $\bar{\Sigma}^+$	1189.4	0.81×10^{-10}s	1/2
sigma	Σ^0 $\bar{\Sigma}^0$	1192.5	1.00×10^{-14}s	1/2
sigma	Σ^- $\bar{\Sigma}^-$	1197.3	1.64×10^{-10}s	1/2
delta	Δ^{++} $\bar{\Delta}^{--}$	1236	5.48×10^{-24}s	3/2
delta	Δ^+ $\bar{\Delta}^-$	1236	5.48×10^{-24}s	3/2
delta	Δ^0 $\bar{\Delta}^0$	1236	5.48×10^{-24}s	3/2
delta	Δ^- $\bar{\Delta}^+$	1236	5.48×10^{-24}s	3/2
xi	Ξ^0 $\bar{\Xi}^0$	1314.7	3.03×10^{-10}s	1/2
xi	Ξ^- $\bar{\Xi}^+$	1321.2	1.66×10^{-10}s	1/2
omega	Ω^- $\bar{\Omega}^+$	1672.4	1.30×10^{-10}s	3/2

64.9. Leptons

We have already seen in Figs. 56P and 56Q how the charged muons μ^- and μ^+, with mean lives of 2.20×10^{-6} s, decay into electrons with the corresponding charge:

$$\mu^- \rightarrow e^- + \bar{\nu}_e + \nu_\mu \qquad (100\%)$$

$$\mu^+ \rightarrow e^+ + \nu_e + \bar{\nu}_\mu \qquad (100\%)$$

Why each of these decay modes involves two neutrinos and why there are four different kinds will be taken up in the next chapter. For a lepton chart see Fig. 64J. Particles are shown in black and antiparticles in color.

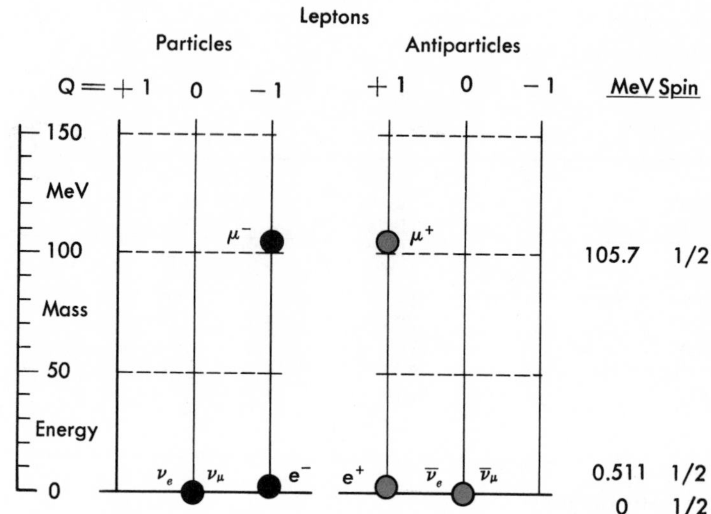

Fig. 64J. Chart of all the known leptons: particles in black and antiparticles in color.

64.10. Pi Mesons

The charged pions belong to the meson class, and the lightest ones have a mass of about 273 electron masses. We have already seen they have no spin angular momentum, and with a mean life of 2.60×10^{-8} s, they decay into muons. For the pion,

$$\pi^- \to \mu^- + \bar{\nu}_\mu \qquad (100\%)$$

and for the antipion

$$\pi^+ \to \mu^+ + \nu_\mu \qquad (100\%)$$

See Fig. 64K.

A pion decay is observed in Fig. 64Y, and antipion decays are observed in Figs. 64M, 64P, 64R, and 64W. The neutral pion, π^0, with an extremely short mean life of 8.9×10^{-17} s, decays 99% of the time into two gamma rays. For an example, see Fig. 64W:

$$\pi^0 \to \gamma + \gamma \qquad (99\%)$$

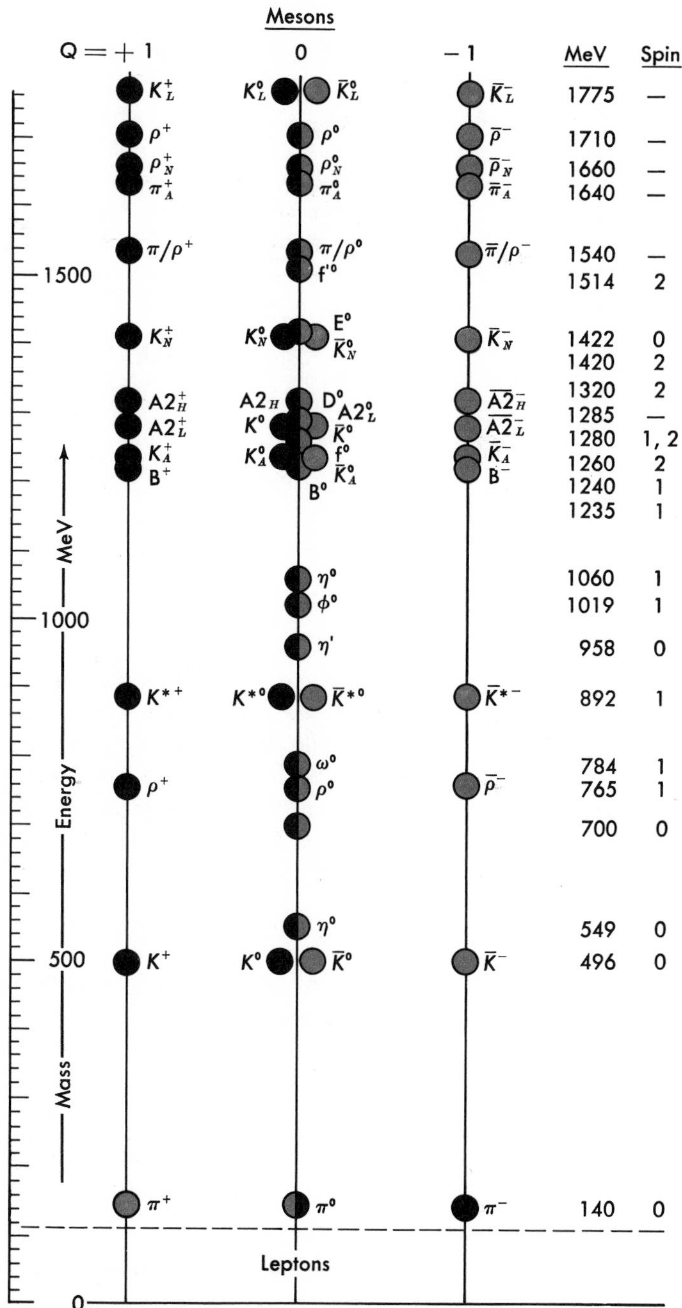

Fig. 64K. Chart of the known mesons. Antiparticles in color are the mirror image of the real particles in black, but with opposite charge.

Occasionally, one of the gamma rays is ejected as an electron pair. Such a *Dalitz pair,* as it is called, appears as oppositely directed spirals, as observed in Figs. 64M, 64S, 64T, and 64X:

$$\pi^0 \rightarrow \gamma + e^- + e^+ \qquad (1\%)$$

64.11. Kaons

The charged kaons, with a mass energy of 493.8 MeV, and mean lives of 1.23 × 10^{-8} s, decay in several ways. The most probable decay modes for the K^+ particles are

$$K^+ \rightarrow \mu^+ + \nu_\mu \qquad (63.6\%)$$

$$K^+ \rightarrow \pi^+ + \pi^0 \qquad (21.0\%)$$

$$K^+ \rightarrow \pi^+ + \pi^- + \pi^+ \qquad (\ 5.6\%)$$

The most probable decay modes for the antikaons are

$$K^- \rightarrow \mu^- + \nu_\mu \qquad (63.6\%)$$

$$K^- \rightarrow \pi^- + \pi^0 \qquad (21.0\%)$$

$$K^- \rightarrow \pi^- + \pi^+ + \pi^- \qquad (\ 5.6\%)$$

The neutral kaons, with a mass energy of 498 MeV, seem to be of two kinds, those with a relatively short mean life of 0.86 × 10^{-10} s, and designated $K_S{}^0$, and those wtih a sixfold longer mean life of 5.28 × 10^{-8} s, and designated $K_L{}^0$ (see Table 64C). The most probable decay modes for the short-lived $K_S{}^0$ are

$$K_S{}^0 \rightarrow \pi^- + \pi^+ \qquad (64.4\%)$$

$$K_S{}^0 \rightarrow \pi^0 + \pi^0 \qquad (31.6\%)$$

Examples of the most probable decay are seen in Figs. 64Q, 64S, 64T, 64U, and 64W.

The most probable decay modes for the long-lived $K_L{}^0$ are

$$K_L{}^0 \rightarrow \pi^+ + e^- + \nu_e \qquad (37.7\%)$$

$$K_L{}^0 \rightarrow \pi^+ + \mu^- + \nu_\mu \qquad (28.1\%)$$

$$K_L{}^0 \rightarrow \pi^0 + \pi^0 + \pi^0 \qquad (21.5\%)$$

Note that the mass energy of 2 π's is 280 MeV, and 3 π's is 420 MeV. Since the kaon mass is approximately 494 MeV, ample mass energy needed for the conversions is observed.

64.12. Other Neutral Mesons

The eta particle, $\eta(549)$, has no spin angular momentum and no charge. It has a very short mean life of 2.51×10^{-19} s, and decays largely in any one of three ways:

$$\eta^0 \rightarrow \gamma + \gamma \qquad (38.2\%)$$

$$\eta^0 \rightarrow \pi^0 + \pi^0 + \pi^0 \qquad (31.4\%)$$

$$\eta^0 \rightarrow \pi^+ + \pi^0 + \pi^- \qquad (23.4\%)$$

Several other neutral mesons whose existence is well established, and shown in Fig. 64K, are $\rho^0(765)$, $\omega^0(784)$, $\phi^0(1019)$, and $\eta^0(1060)$. Their most probable decay modes, abbreviated, are:

$$\rho^0(765) \rightarrow \pi^+ \pi^-$$

$$\omega^0(784) \rightarrow \pi^+ \pi^0 \pi^-, \pi^0 \gamma$$

$$\phi^0(1019) \rightarrow K^+ K^-, K_L{}^0 K_S{}^0, \pi^+ \pi^0 \pi^-$$

$$\eta^0(1060) \rightarrow \pi^+ \pi^-, K^+ \overline{K}^-$$

Note that the mass energy of $2K$'s is approximately 1000 MeV.

64.13. Baryons and Their Properties

All baryons have a mass equal to or greater than one proton. With the exception of the proton itself, all baryons have a finite mean life. As seen in Sec. 59.8, a free neutron has a mean life of 15 min 32 s, and decays into a proton, electron, and a neutrino:

$$n^0 \rightarrow p^+ + e^- + \overline{\nu}_e$$

All the particles listed in Table 64E are baryons. Six of them have mean lives of the order of 1×10^{-10} s, and four of them extremely short mean lives of about 5×10^{-24} s.

A chart of over half of the known baryons is given in Fig. 64L. All baryons up to 1500 MeV are shown. Baryons above 1500 MeV, not shown because of crowding, are: nucleons 1520, 1535, 1670, 1688, 2650, and 3030, deltas 1670, 2420, 2850, and 3230, lambdas 1690, 1815, 1830, and 2350, sigmas 1670, 1765, 2030, 2455, and 2595, and xis 1930, 2250, and 2500 MeV.

A large number of decay events involving the lighter baryons are to be seen in the bubble chamber photographs at the end of

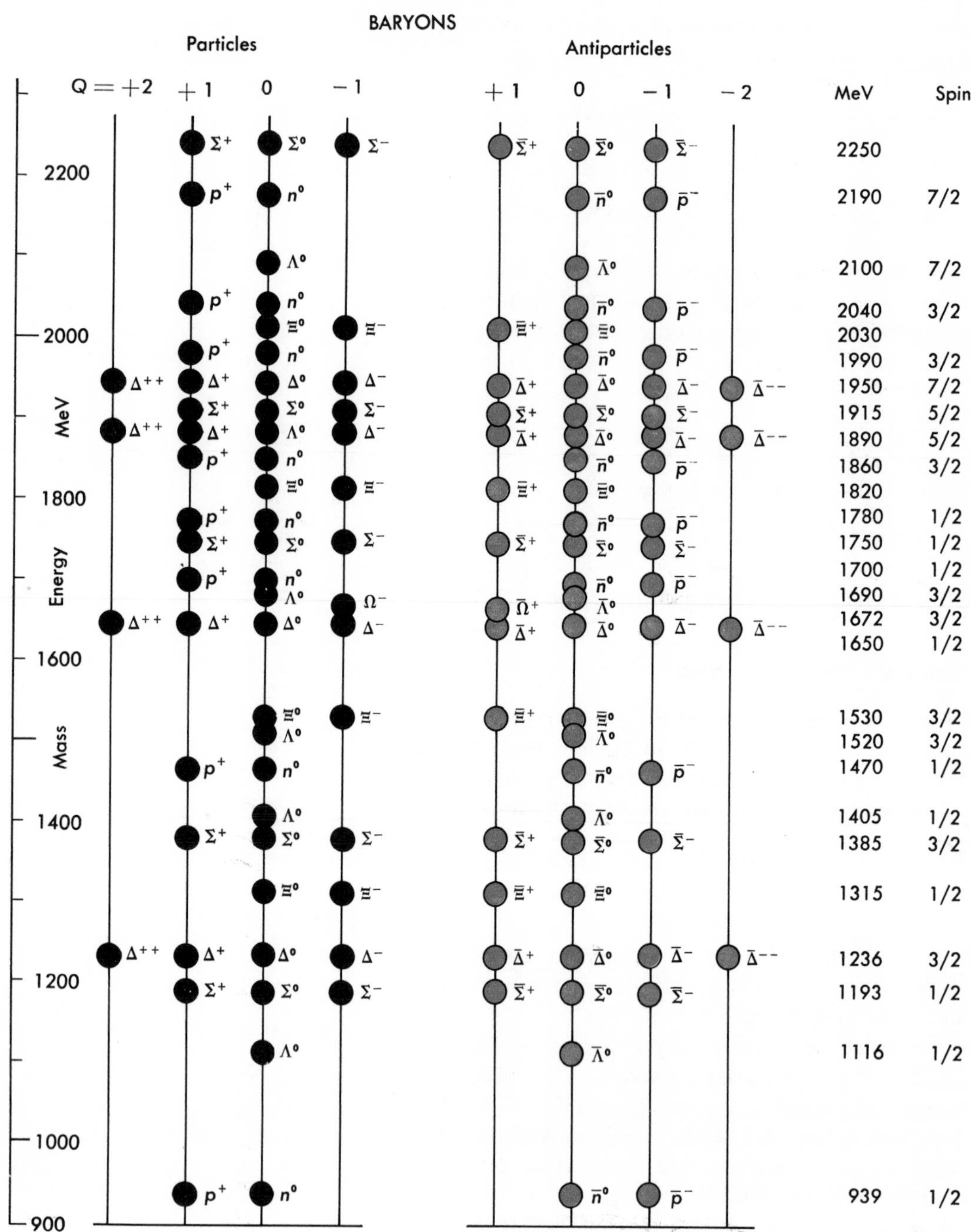

Fig. 64L. Chart of known baryons. Antiparticles in color are the mirror image of the real particles in black, but opposite charge.

this chapter. The following represent but a few of the prominent but typical reactions.

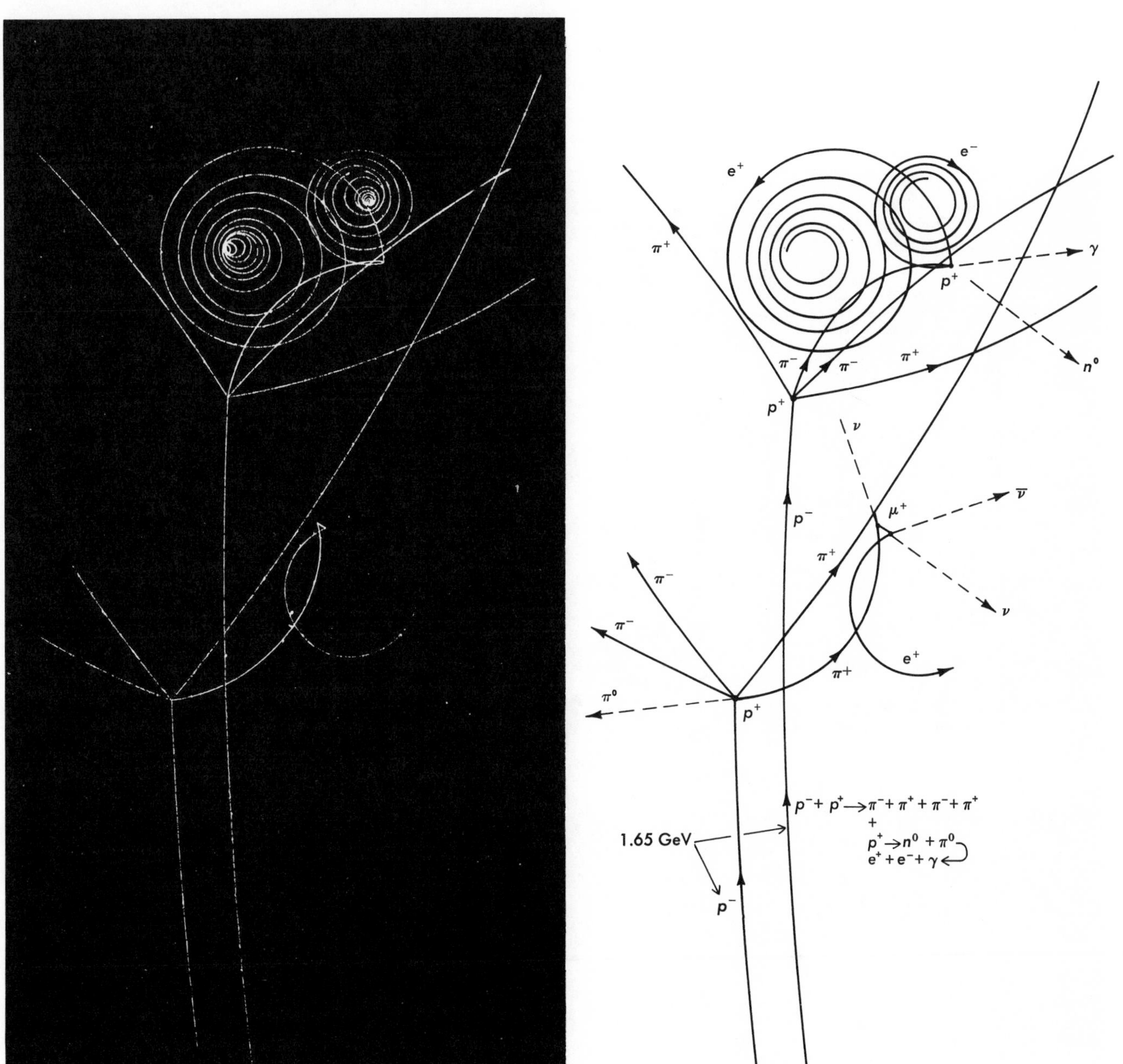

Fig. 64M. Two separate antiproton-proton events. The lower event produces five pions, one of which, π^+, is seen to decay in the usual way, ending with a positron.

heavier than nucleons. Since their mass energy is greater than that of a nucleon plus a pion, it is not surprising that they decay as follows:

$$\Lambda^0 \rightarrow p^+ + \pi^- \qquad (65.3\%)$$

$$\Lambda^0 \rightarrow n^0 + \pi^0 \qquad (34.7\%)$$

Antilambdas decay in quite similar modes:

$$\bar{\Lambda}^0 \rightarrow \bar{p}^- + \bar{\pi}^+ \qquad (65.3\%)$$

$$\bar{\Lambda}^0 \rightarrow \bar{n}^0 + \bar{\pi}^0 \qquad (34.7\%)$$

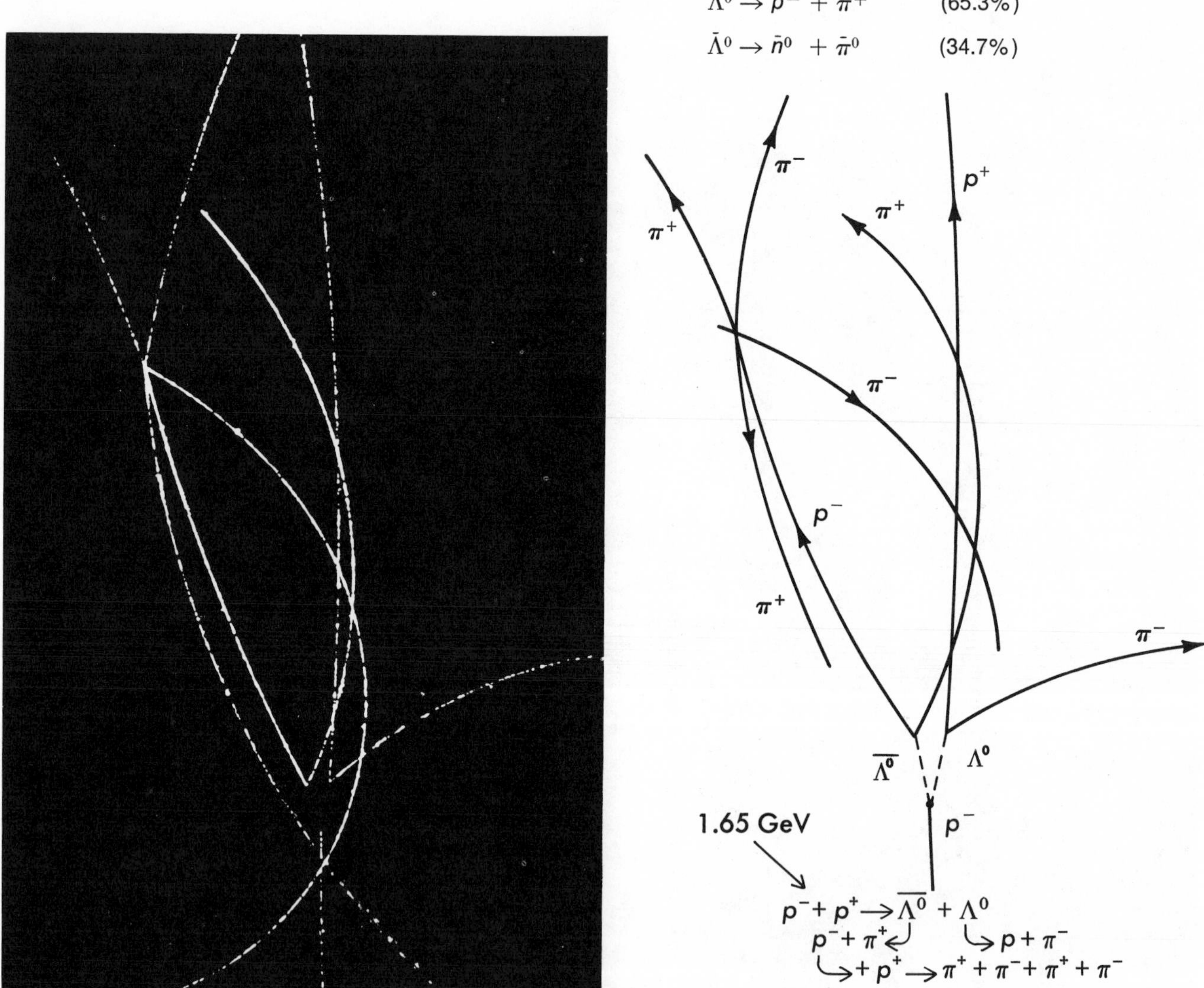

Fig. 64N. High energy antiproton-proton event producing an antilambda-lambda pair. The antilambda decays into a pion and an antiproton. A second antiproton-proton event occurs at the upper left, resulting in two pairs of pions.

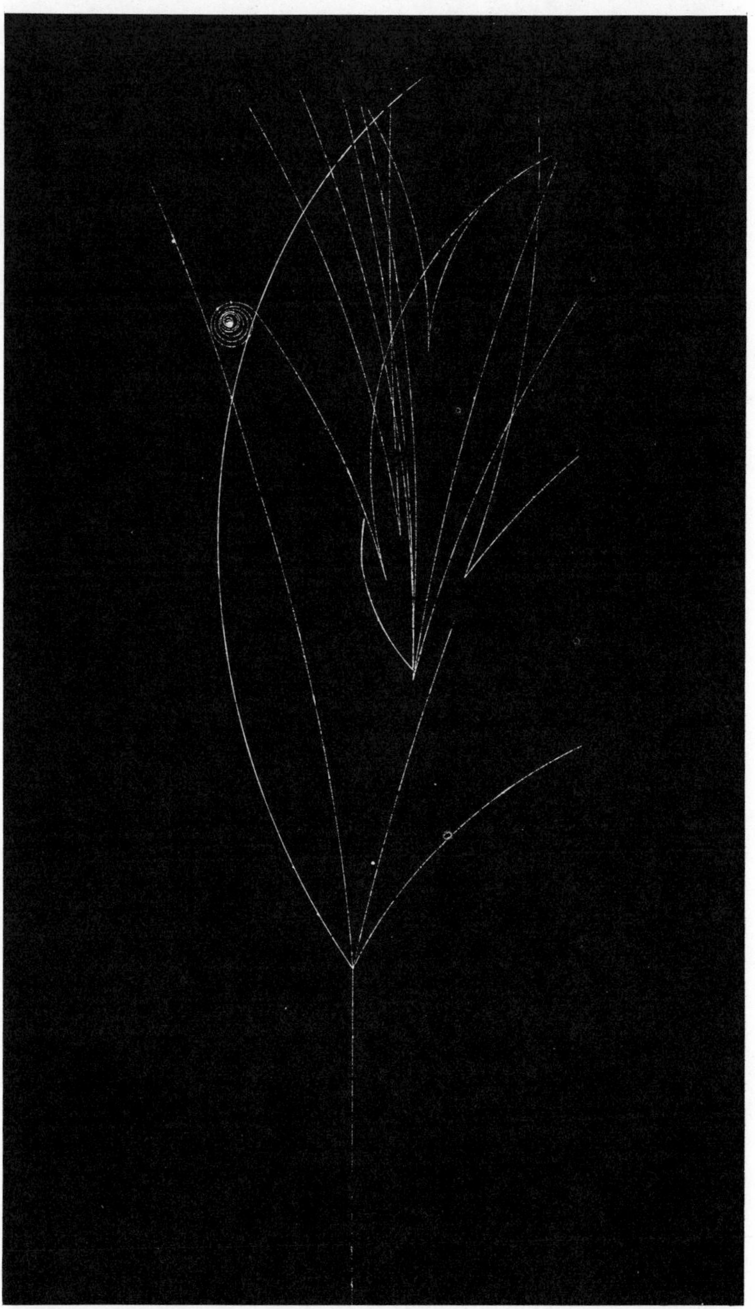

Fig. 64O. A strong interaction of a 28-GeV proton colliding with a stationary proton in a 2-meter bubble chamber. The event is not yet analyzed.

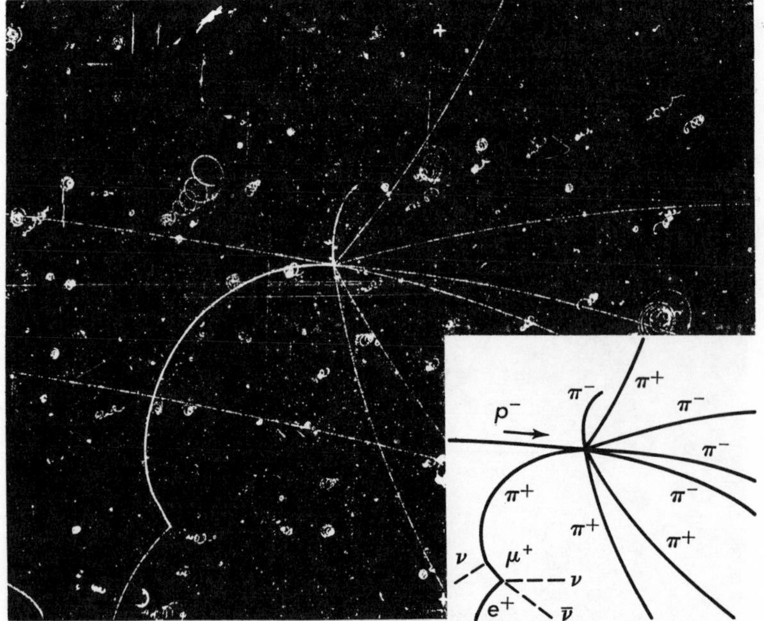

Fig. 64P. Photograph of a strong interaction of a 1.65-GeV antiproton with a stationary proton to produce four pairs of pions. The decay of one of the positive pions is seen at the lower left.

The bubble chamber event reproduced in Fig. 64N involves two antiprotons, and a pair of lambdas. A high energy antiproton from a bevatron target enters from below, and upon collision with a proton in the chamber, they are annihilated to produce a lambda and an antilambda:

$$\bar{p}^- + p^+ \rightarrow \bar{\Lambda}^0 + \Lambda^0$$

Having no charge the two lambdas recoil forward leaving no tracks. In about 2×10^{-10}s, they almost simultaneously decay into

$$\Lambda^0 \rightarrow p^+ + \pi^-$$

$$\bar{\Lambda}^0 \rightarrow \bar{p}^- + \bar{\pi}^+$$

High up at the left the antiproton collides with another proton and, upon annihilation, produces two pairs of pions:

$$\bar{p}^- + p^+ \rightarrow \bar{\pi}^+ + \pi^- + \bar{\pi}^+ + \pi^-$$

All these reactions are combined at the bottom of the legend diagram. Other lambda events are seen in Figs. 64Q, 64S, 64T, 64W, and 64X.

64.15. Sigma Particles

These baryons are of three kinds, Σ^+, Σ^0, Σ^-, and have an average mass energy of approximately 1190 MeV. They have a spin angular momentum of $\frac{1}{2}\hbar$. The charged sigmas decay with a mean life of about 1×10^{-10}s, and the neutral sigmas about 1×10^{-14}s. They all decay by the following modes:

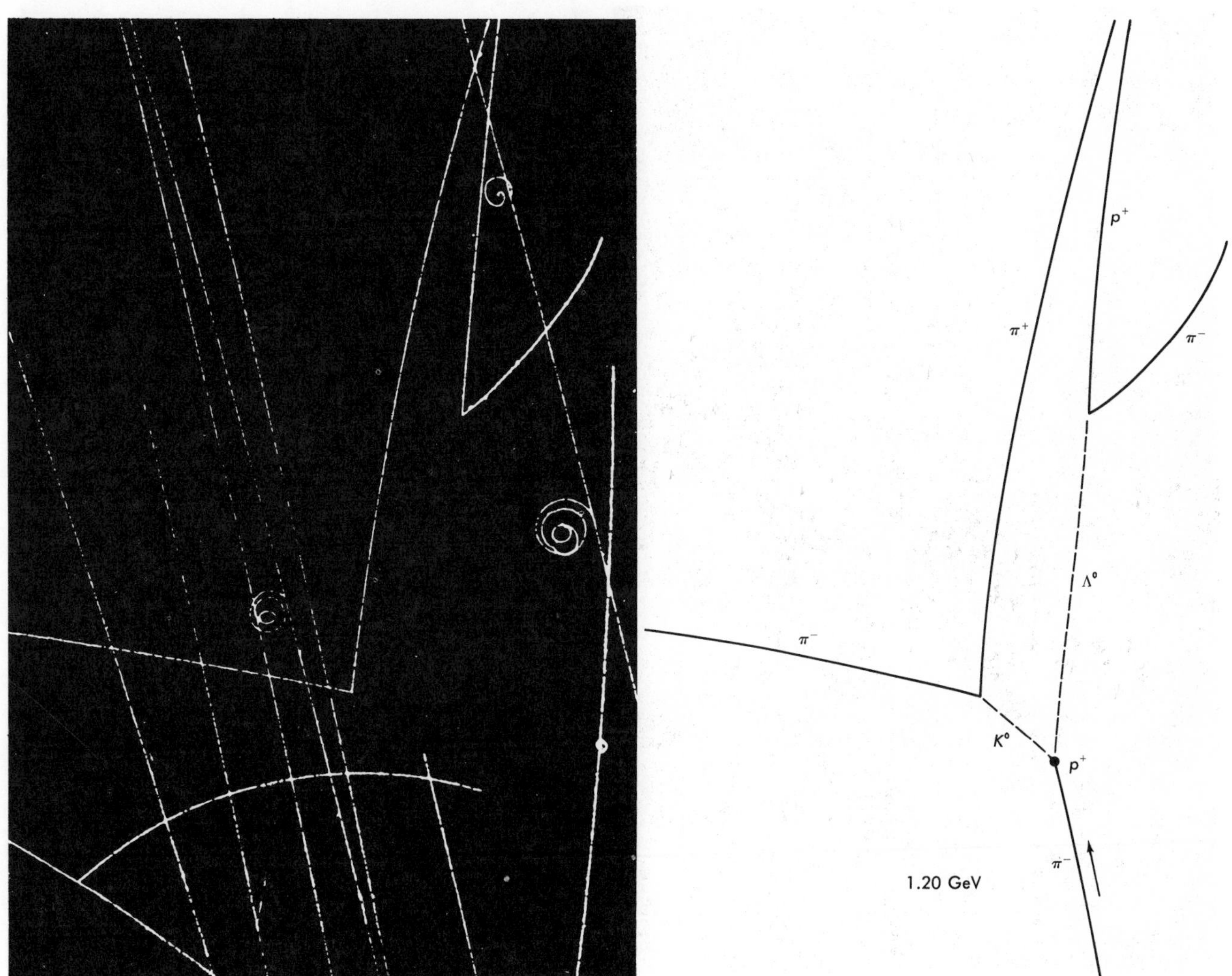

Fig. 64Q. High energy pion-proton event, giving rise to two neutral particles, K^0 and Λ^0. Both particles then decay, one into a proton and a pion, the other into a pair of pions.

$$\Sigma^+ \rightarrow p^+ + \pi^0 \qquad (52.8\%)$$

$$\Sigma^+ \rightarrow n^0 + \pi^+ \qquad (47.2\%)$$

$$\Sigma^0 \rightarrow \Lambda^0 + \gamma \qquad (100\%)$$

$$\Sigma^- \rightarrow n^0 + \pi^0 \qquad (100\%)$$

A Σ^- event may be seen in Fig. 64Z.

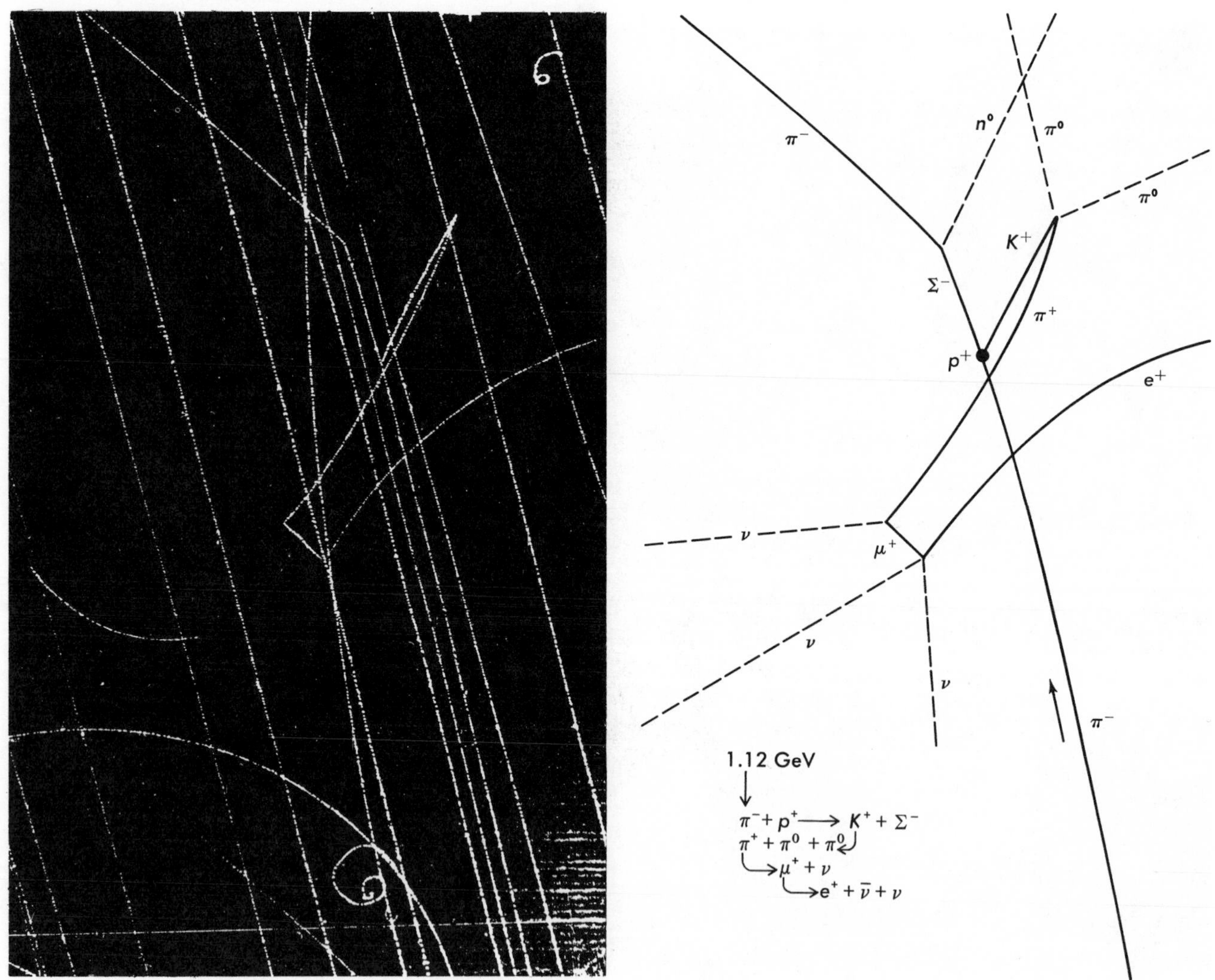

Fig. 64R. High energy pion-proton event, producing a positive kaon and a negative sigma. The kaon decays into three pions, the positive pion decaying into a muon, and the muon into a positron.

64.16. Xi Particles

These baryons have a mass energy about 60 MeV greater than $\Lambda^0 \times \pi$, and have a spin angular momentum of $\frac{1}{2}\hbar$. They decay by the following modes:

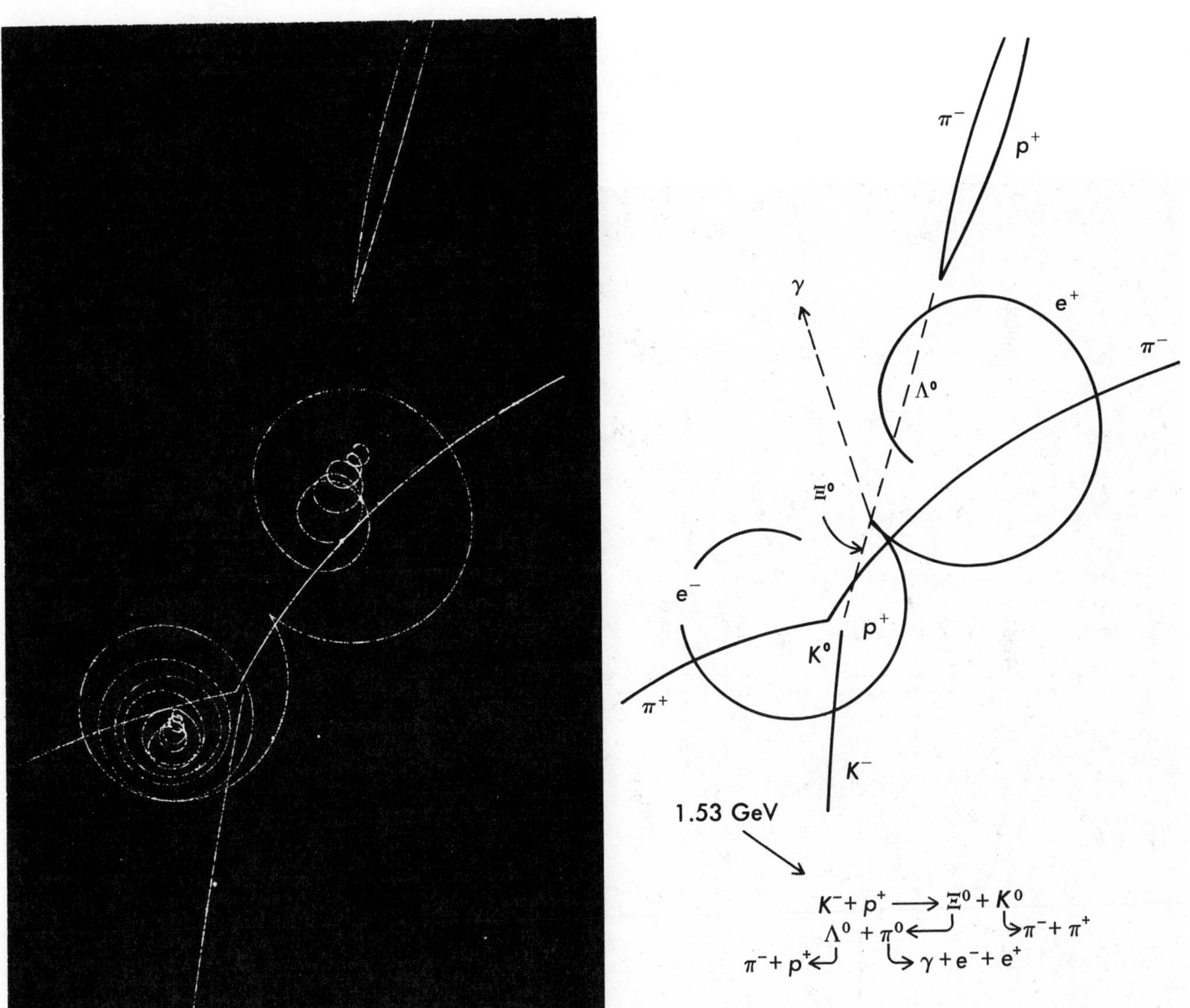

Fig. 64S. A high energy antikaon-proton event, producing a xi baryon, which decays into a lambda and a neutral pion. Both of these particles are seen to decay, one into a proton and a π^-, and the other into a pair of electrons and a gamma ray.

$$\Xi^0 \rightarrow \Lambda^0 + \pi^0 \qquad (100\%)$$

$$\Xi^- \rightarrow \Lambda^0 + \pi^- \qquad (100\%)$$

The antixi particles decay by the corresponding modes:

$$\overline{\Xi}^0 \rightarrow \overline{\Lambda}^0 + \overline{\pi}^0 \qquad (100\%)$$

$$\overline{\Xi}^+ \rightarrow \overline{\Lambda}^0 + \overline{\pi}^+ \qquad (100\%)$$

Photographs of xi events may be seen in Fig. 64X.

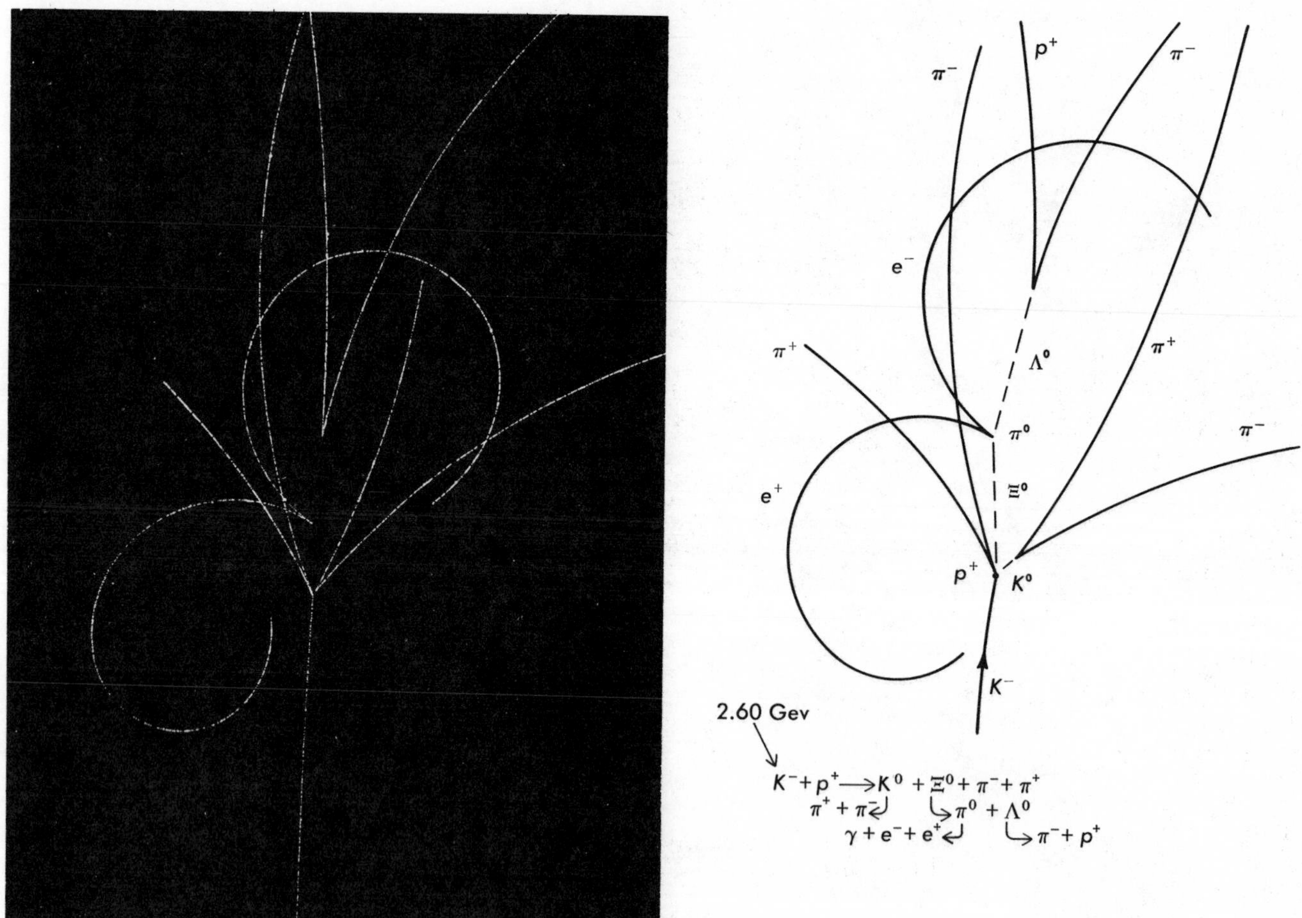

Fig. 64T. High energy antikaon-proton event, producing a neutral xi particle. This baryon decays into a neutral lambda, and finally into a normal proton.

64.17. Delta Particles

These heavy baryons form a number of known quartets, Δ^{++}, Δ^{+}, Δ^{0}, Δ^{-}. As seen in Fig. 64L, the lightest group is designated $\Delta(1236)$. Each of these lightest of the deltas has a spin of $\frac{3}{2}\hbar$, and the extremely short mean life of 5.5×10^{-24}s. Their most probable modes of decay are the following:

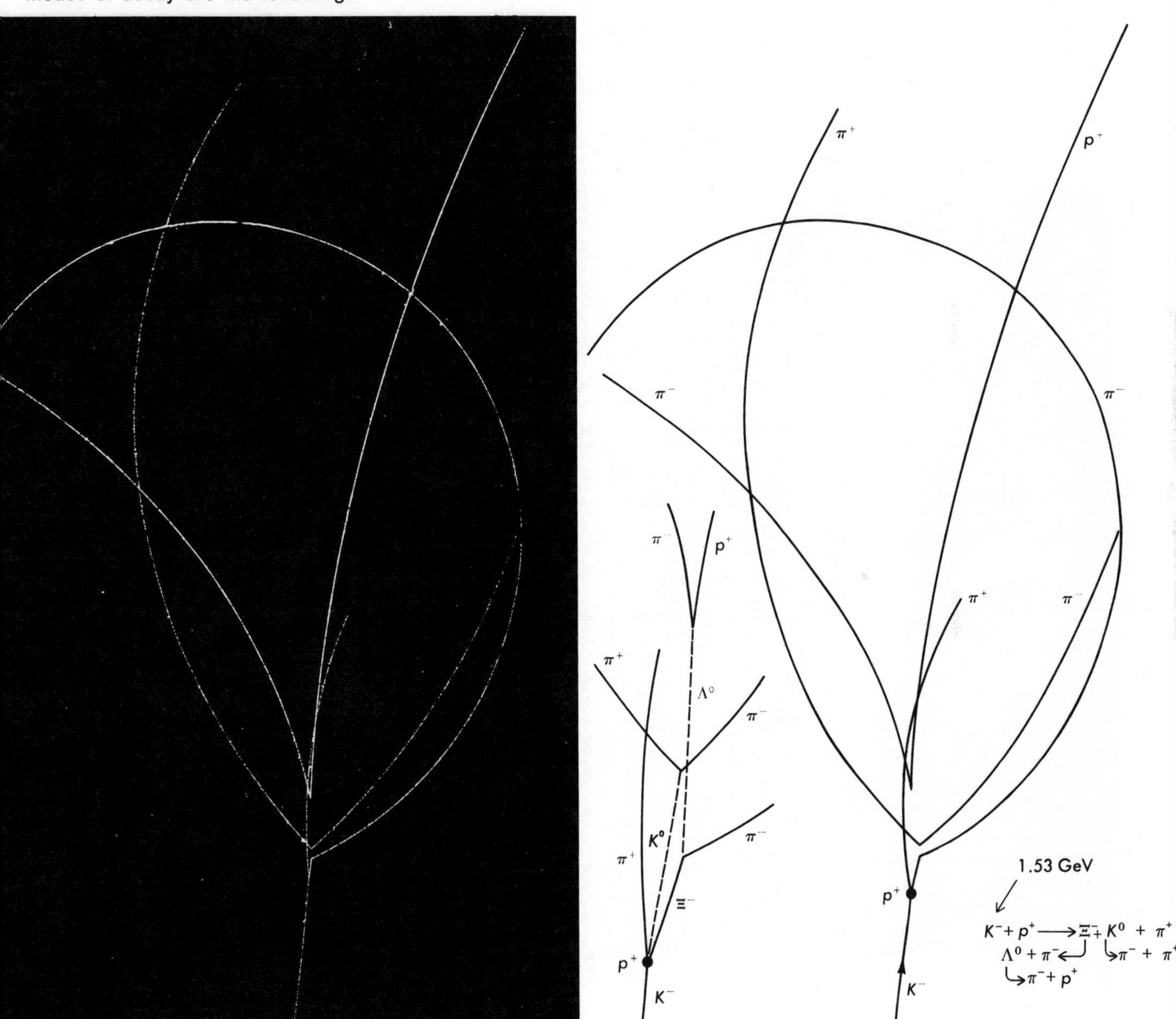

Fig. 64U. A high energy antikaon-proton event, producing xi and lambda baryons. Enlarged legend diagram is exaggerated to show events. Note that one proton and five pions are the result.

$$\Delta^{++} \rightarrow p^{+} + \pi^{+}$$
$$\Delta^{+} \rightarrow p^{+} + \pi^{0}$$
$$\Delta^{0} \rightarrow n^{0} + \pi^{0}$$
$$\Delta^{-} \rightarrow n^{0} + \pi^{-}$$

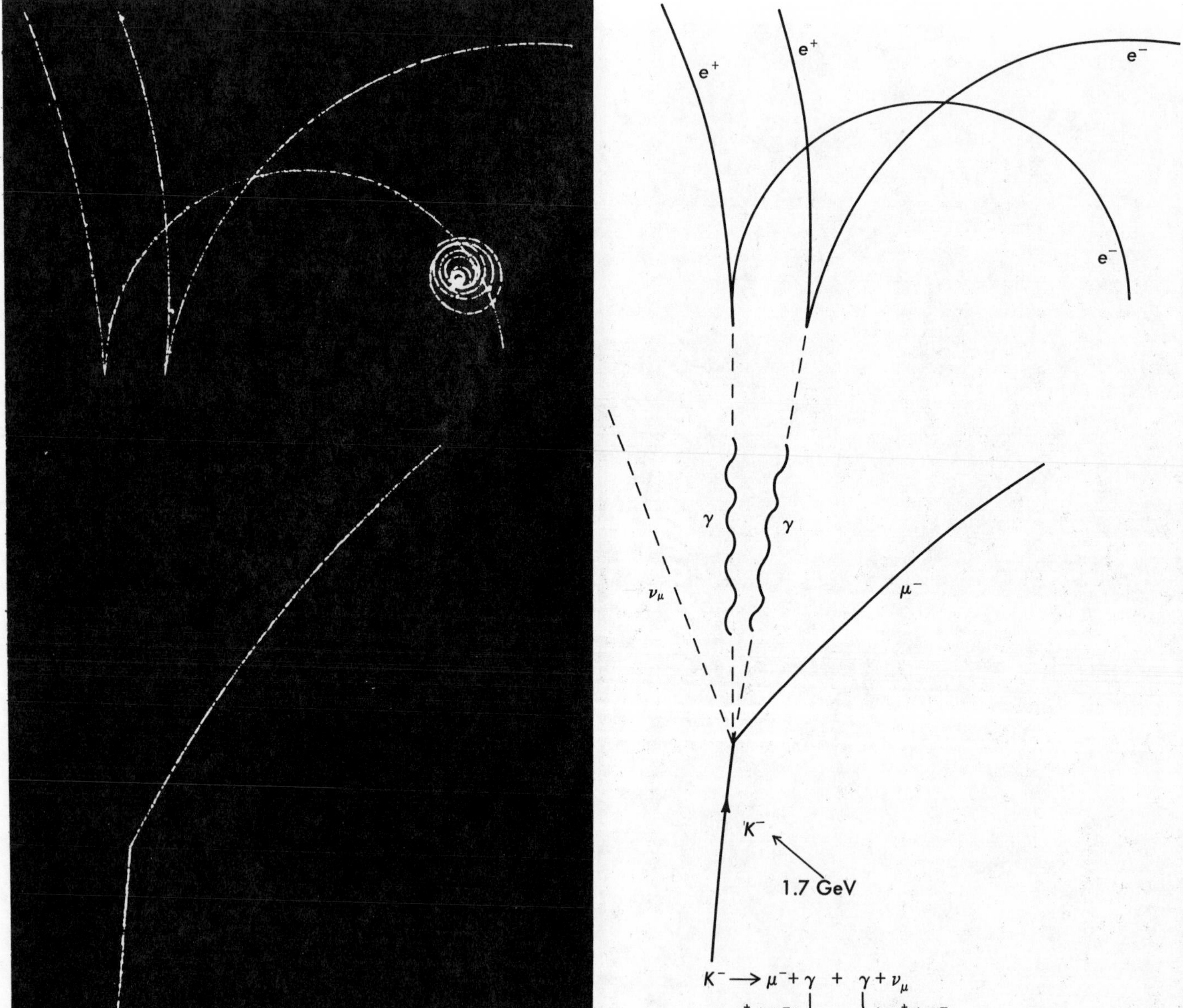

Fig. 64V. An antikaon decays into an antimuon and an antineutrino, and two gamma rays. Each gamma ray produces a pair of electrons.

64.18. Omega Particles

These charged baryons were predicted by theory before they were observed, and form a pair of singlets with a spin of $\frac{3}{2}\hbar$. For such a heavy particle, designated $\Omega(1762)$, it has the relatively long mean life of 1.30×10^{-10}s. The particle is known to decay in

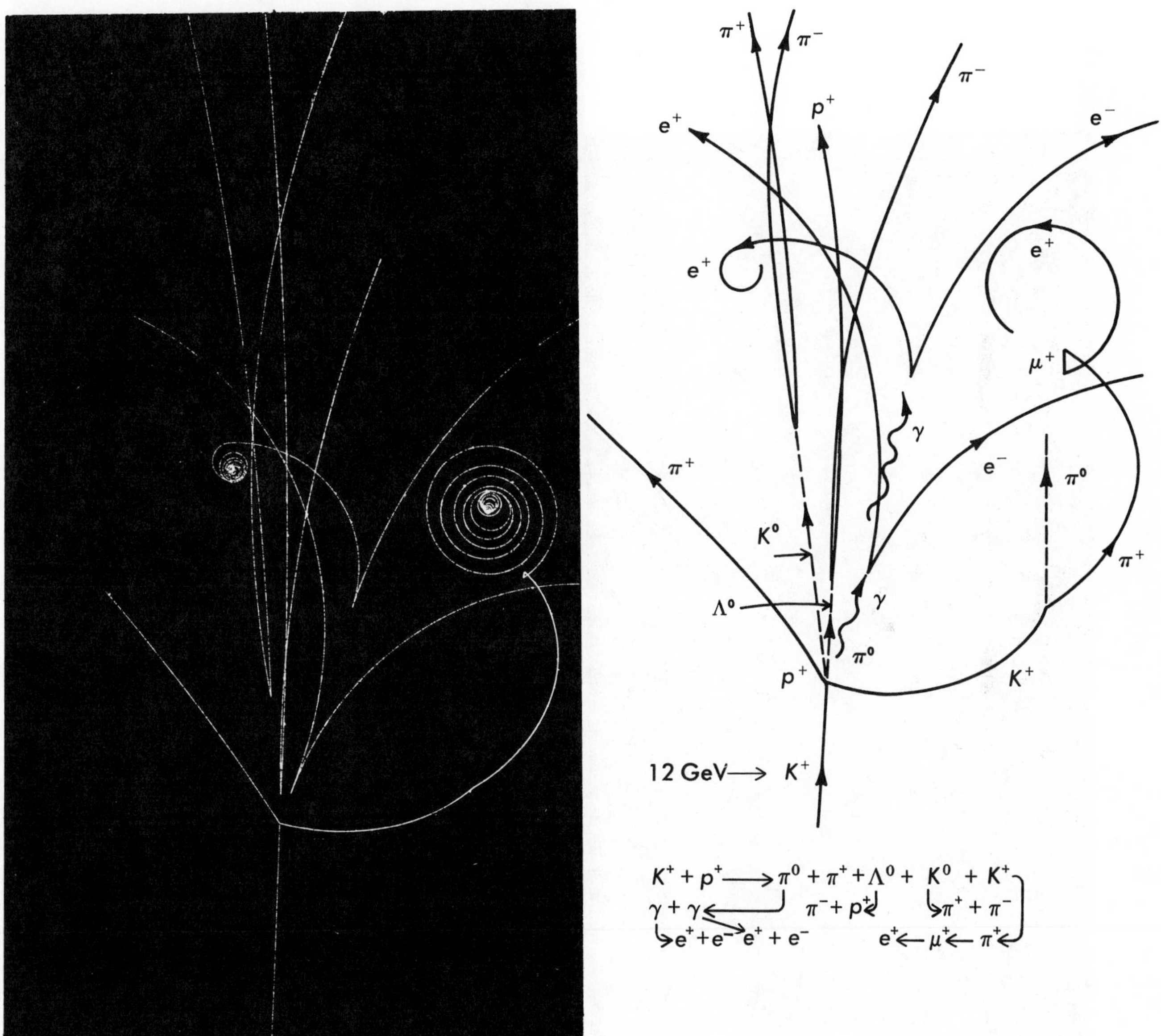

Fig. 64W. High energy kaon-proton event, producing five particles, including a neutral lambda. Three of these particles are seen to decay in the same photo.

at least three ways: $\Xi^0\pi^-$, $\Xi^-\pi^0$ and Λ^0K^-. The writing of the full reaction equations is left as an exercise for the student.

• • •

For an introduction to mass energy level diagrams of elementary particles, see the popular article in *Scientific American*, Feb-

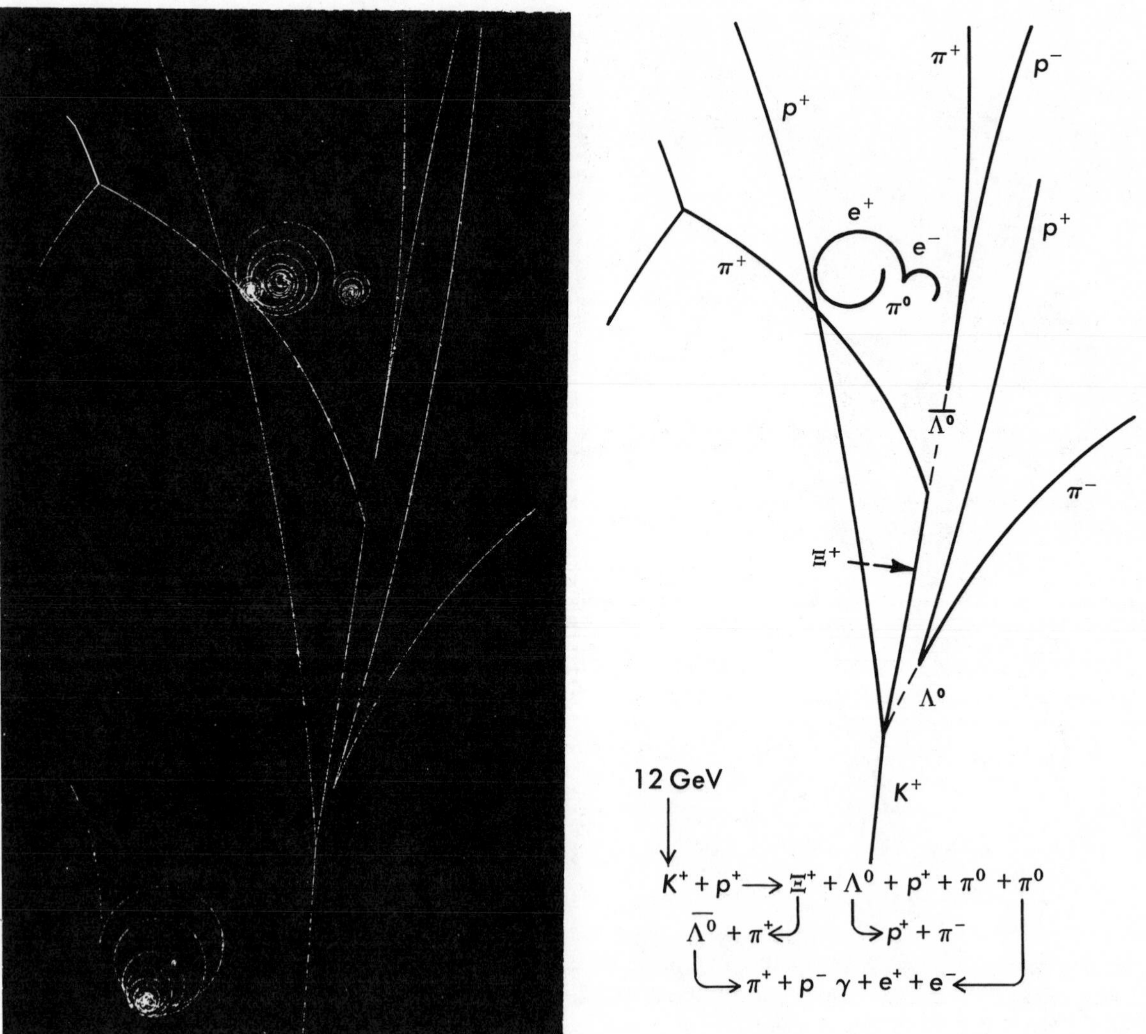

Fig. 64X. A high energy kaon-proton event, producing five particles. Three of these are baryons, two of which are seen to decay. Observe that the antixi particle decays into an antilambda, and then into an antiproton.

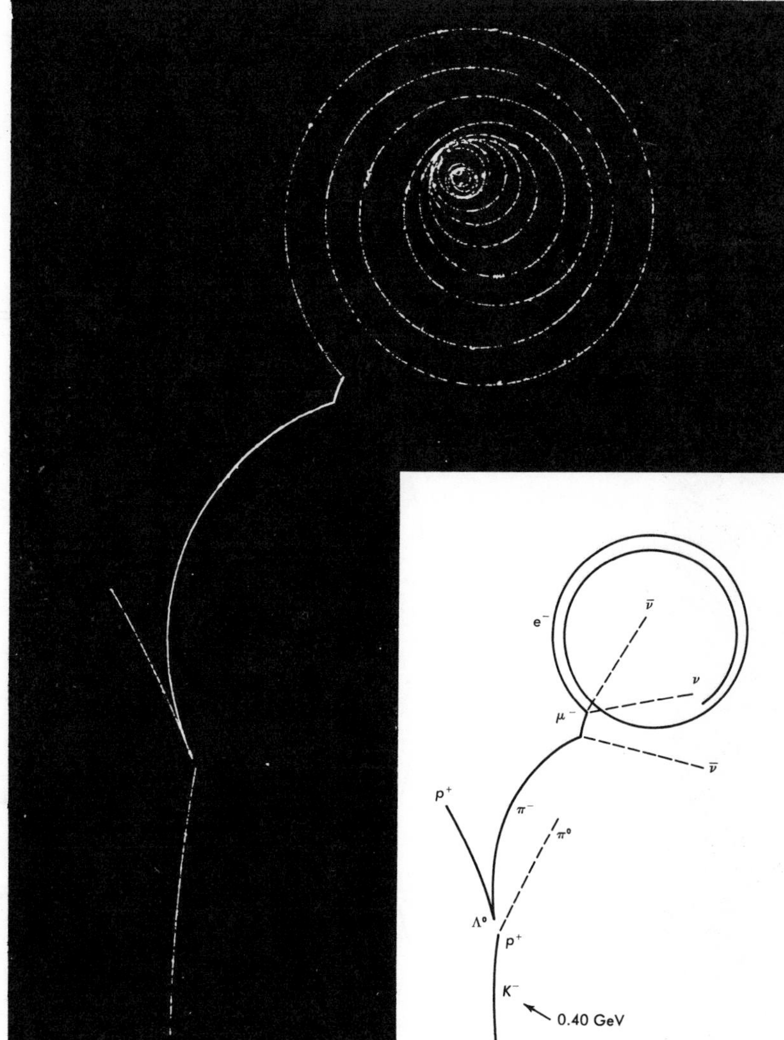

Fig. 64Y. An antikaon-proton event, producing a Λ^0 and a π^0. The Λ^0 decays into a proton and a negative pion, the latter decaying through the normal sequence of $\mu-$ to $e-$ and the necessary neutrinos.

ruary 1964, by G. F. Chew,* M. Gell-Mann,† and A. H. Rosenfeld.‡

All photographs near the end of this chapter were made with the liquid hydrogen bubble chambers at the Lawrence Berkeley Laboratory at the University of California, Berkeley. They are reproduced in this book through the courtesy of L. W. Alvarez, F. S. Crawford, A. H. Rosenfeld, and colleagues. Touch-up to remove all extraneous tracks was done by E. H. Hoedemaker.

*Geoffrey F. Chew (1924–), American physicist, was born in Washington, D.C., June 5, 1924. Dr. Chew obtained his Ph.D. in physics at the University of Chicago in 1948, married, and served during World War II as a theoretical physicist at Los Alamos Scientific Laboratory, New Mexico. He became a professor of physics at the University of California, Berkeley, in 1949. He received the Hughes Prize in 1962 and is best known for his work on strong interactions and their relation to elementary atomic particles. The author has known G. F. Chew as a friend and colleague for many years.

†Murray Gell-Mann (1929–), American physicist, was born in New York City, September 15, 1929. Dr. Gell-Mann obtained his Ph.D. in theoretical physics in 1951 at the Massachusetts Institute of Technology, married in 1955, and has two children. He became professor of physics at the California Institute of Technology in 1953 and was elected to the National Academy of Sciences. He is best known for his work on quantum field theory and elementary atomic particles, for which he received the Nobel Prize in physics in 1969.

‡Arthur H. Rosenfeld (1926–), American physicist, was born in Birmingham, Alabama, June 22, 1926. He obtained his Ph.D. in physics, 1954, at the University of Chicago, married in 1955, and has two children. He joined the Lawrence Berkeley Laboratory at the University of California in 1956 and became professor of physics in

1963. He is an expert on the use of high speed digital computers and is best known for his work on the classification of elementary atomic particles.

Example 1. (a) Write down the reaction for the first event shown in Fig. 64Z. (b) If the incident kaon has a kinetic energy of 1.630 GeV, find the total energy to be divided between the four recoiling particles.

Solution. The reaction is shown at the lower right in the figure, and is written

$$\bar{K}^- + p^+ \rightarrow \Sigma^- + \pi^+ + \pi^- + \pi^+$$

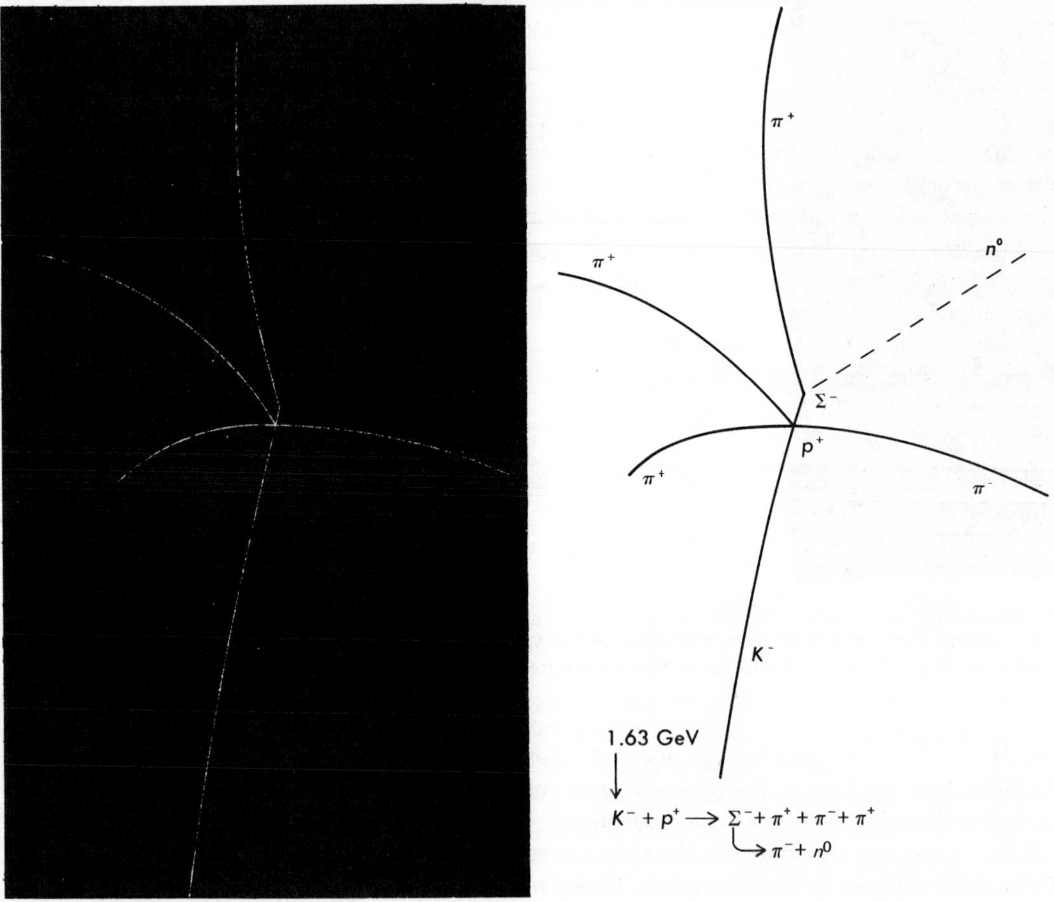

Fig. 64Z. High energy antikaon-proton event, producing a sigma baryon, and three pions. The sigma decays into a negative pion and a common neutron.

The energy of the particles coming together, and the energy of the four recoiling particles, is given for each particle in Table 64D or Table 64E. If we sum them in two different columns, we obtain

$\bar{K}^- = 0.4938$ GeV	$\Sigma^- = 1.1973$ GeV
$p^+ = 0.9383$ GeV	$\pi^+ = 0.1396$ GeV
$E_1 = 1.6300$ GeV	$\pi^- = 0.1396$ GeV
$E = 3.0621$ GeV	$\pi^+ = 0.1396$ GeV
	$E = 1.6161$ GeV

The excess energy is the difference between these two sums, or

$$3.0621 - 1.6161 = +1.446 \text{ GeV}$$

problems

1. Find the minimum energy required to produce a pair of protons, each with a mass of 1836.2 m_e.

2. Calculate the minimum energy required to create a pair of kaons, each with a mass of 966.3 m_e.

3. Find the threshold energy for the creation of a pair of lambda particles, each with a mass of 2183 m_e. [Ans. 2.231 GeV.]

4. Write down the full designations for the neutral mesons given in Sec. 64.12: $\rho^0(765)$, $\omega^0(784)$, $\phi^0(1019)$, and $\eta^0(1060)$.

5. Write down all the reactions shown in Fig. 64P.

6. Write down all the reactions shown in Fig. 64Q. [Ans. $\pi^- + p^+ \rightarrow K^0 + \Lambda^0$, $K^0 \rightarrow \pi^+ + \pi^-$, $\Lambda^0 \rightarrow \pi^- + p^+$.]

7. Write down all the reactions shown in Fig. 64Y.

8. (a) Write down the reaction for the lower event shown in Fig. 64M. If the incident antiproton has a kinetic energy of 1.650 GeV, (b) find the total energy liberated to be divided between the four recoiling particles.

9. (a) Write down the reaction for the first event shown in Fig. 64N. If the incident antiproton has a kinetic energy of 1.650 GeV, (b) find the total energy liberated to be divided between the two recoiling particles. [Ans. (a) $\bar{p}^- + p^+ \rightarrow \bar{\Lambda}^0 + \Lambda^0$, (b) 1.295 GeV.]

10. (a) Find the excess energy imparted to the two neutral particles of the first reaction shown in Fig. 64Q. (b) Write down the reaction.

11. (a) Find the excess energy imparted to the two recoiling charged particles of the first reaction shown in Fig. 64R. (b) Write down the reaction.

12. (a) Write down the reaction for the first event shown in Fig. 64S. If the incident kaon has a kinetic energy equivalent to 1.530 GeV, (b) find the total energy liberated to be divided between the two recoiling neutral particles.

[Ans. (a) $\bar{K}^- + p^+ \rightarrow \Xi^0 + K^0$, (b) 1.149 GeV.]

13. (a) Write down the reaction for the first event shown in Fig. 64T. If the incident negatively charged kaon has a kinetic energy equivalent to 2.60 GeV, (b) find the total energy liberated to be divided between the four recoiling particles.

14. (a) Write down the reaction for the first event shown in Fig. 64W. If the incident kaon has a kinetic energy equivalent to 12.0 GeV, (b) find the total energy liberated to be divided between the five particles recoiling from the event.

15. (a) Write down the reaction for the first event shown in Fig. 64X. If the incident kaon has a kinetic energy equivalent to 12.0 GeV, (b) find the total energy liberated to be divided between the five recoiling particles. [Ans. (a) $K^+ + p^+ \rightarrow \Xi^+ + \Lambda^0 + p^+ + \pi^0 + \pi^0$, (b) 9.79 GeV.]

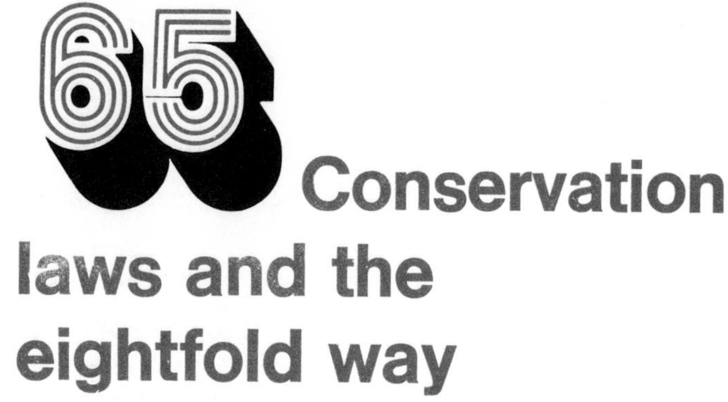

65 Conservation laws and the eightfold way

In the previous chapter we have seen that over two hundred different elementary particles are now known, and that it is certain that others will be discovered in the future. We have also seen that all such particles may be grouped into three distinct classes, *leptons, mesons,* and *baryons.* Overall views of the particles in each of the three classes are given in detailed charts in Figs. 64J, 64K, and 64L.

With so many particles already known, the question arises as to how physicists know when they have found a new particle? The answer is that each particle is identified by a set of seven quantum numbers, represented by the symbols, *m, J, Q, Y, A, I,* and *P.* Each quantum number stands for a particular property of the particle, and together they constitute a kind of "signature" or "fingerprint." It is important, therefore, that we first look, if only briefly, at these quantum numbers to gain some understanding of their roles.

65.1. Mass and Mass Energy

The masses of all atomic particles are commonly given in kilograms (Kg), atomic mass units (amu), electron masses (m_e), or in millions of electron volts (MeV). As elementary particles interact with one another, or decay naturally, some small amount of mass may be converted into energy, or energy may be converted into mass. Since the *electron volt* has become the established unit of particle energy, it is most convenient to express the masses of all particles in eV, KeV, MeV or GeV.

It has been shown that leptons form a closed group of eight particles, the four neutrinos ν_e, ν_μ, $\overline{\nu}_e$, and $\overline{\nu}_\mu$ with a zero rest mass, the two electrons e^- and e^+ with a mass of 0.511 MeV, and two muons μ^- and μ^+ with a rest mass of 105.7 MeV.

The known mesons, over fifty in number, range in mass from the most stable pions at 140 MeV, to higher states of the rhos and kappas at over 1700 MeV.

The baryons begin with the common nucleons n and p, with a mass of $\sim$939 MeV, and extend upward to higher nucleon and delta states at well over 3000 MeV.

65.2. Nuclear Spin J

The concept of nuclear spin J was introduced in Sec. 61.7 to explain the hyperfine structure of spectrum lines, as well as the measured magnetic moments of neutrons and protons. The spin angular momentum of all elementary particles is an important property since angular momentum is conserved in all particle events. For example, the neutrino was first introduced into beta decay in order to retain the laws of *energy, momentum,* and *angular momentum.*

The spins for all three classes of particles are:

$$\text{Leptons,}\quad J = \tfrac{1}{2}\hbar \quad \text{only}$$

$$\text{Mesons,}\quad J = 0\,\hbar,\ 1\,\hbar,\ 2\,\hbar,\ \ldots$$

$$\text{Baryons,}\quad J = \pm\tfrac{1}{2}\hbar,\ \pm\tfrac{3}{2}\hbar,\ \pm\tfrac{5}{2}\hbar,\ \ldots$$

See Tables 64C, 64D, and 64E.

65.3. Charge Q, Average Charge Q, and Hypercharge Y

The electrical charge of every elementary particle is either 0, $+e$, $-e$, $+2e$, or $-2e$. Average charge Q is a number defined as the average charge of all the particles in a family multiplet.

For each of the triplets, $\pi^+\ \pi^0\ \pi^-$, $\rho^+\ \rho^0\ \rho^-$, $\Sigma^+\ \Sigma^0\ \Sigma^-$, etc., $\overline{Q} = 0$. For doublets like, n^0p^+, $\Xi^+\ \Xi^0$, $K^-\ K^0$, etc., $\overline{Q} = +\frac{1}{2}$, while for their antiparticles, $\bar{n}^0\ \bar{p}^-$, $\bar{\Xi}^-\ \bar{\Xi}^0$, $\bar{K}^-\ \bar{K}^0$, etc., $\overline{Q} = -\frac{1}{2}$. For the delta multiplets, $\Delta^{++}\ \Delta^+\ \Delta^0\ \Delta^-$, $\overline{Q} = +\frac{3}{2}$, etc.

While $\overline{Q}$ is a useful quantum number, some values are seen to be half integral, and it is convenient to multiply by 2 and give $2\overline{Q}$ the new symbol Y. This is called *hypercharge*:

$$Y = 2\overline{Q} \tag{65a}$$

$$\text{Singlets,}\quad Y = 0,\ +2,\ -2$$

$$\text{Doublets,}\quad Y = +1,\ -1$$

$$\text{Triplets,}\quad Y = 0$$

$$\text{Quartets,}\quad Y = +1,\ -1$$

65.4. Baryon Number A

The quantum number called *baryon number* is nothing more than what has always been called the *atomic number*; it defines the number of nucleons in the nucleus. For hydrogen $A = 1$, for helium $A = 4$, and for the most abundant of the uranium isotopes $A = 238$, etc.

Particles with an A value of more than one are defined as nuclei; particles with an A value of 1 are called baryons. Since leptons and mesons contain no nucleons, all have $A = 0$. All baryons have baryon number $A = +1$, and antibaryons have $A = -1$.

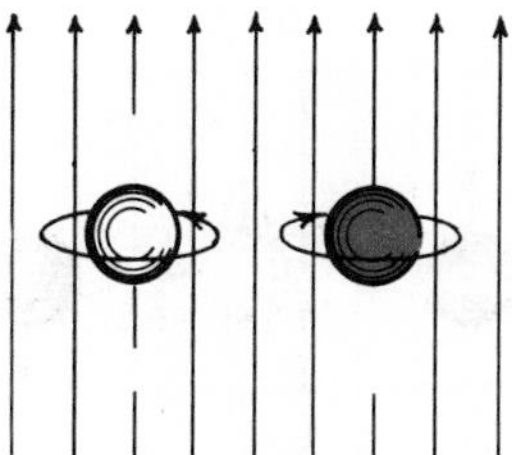

Fig. 65A. Schematic diagram of isotopic spin, a kind of charge quantization for elementary doublets like the neutron and proton.

65.5. Multiplicity, and Isotopic Spin I

The *quantum number I,* called *isotopic spin,* gives the number of particles in a multiplet. The multiplicity is given by

$$M = 2I + 1 \tag{65b}$$

For Δ particles for example, $I = \frac{3}{2}$ and the multiplicity $M = 2 \times \frac{3}{2} + 1 = 4$.

In writing down nuclear reactions as equations, the *law of conservation of electrical charge* is always imposed as part of the balancing process. Since elementary particles carry a charge of +1, 0, or −1, Heisenberg was the first to apply quantum numbers to charge and refer to the concept as *isotopic spin.*

While both words in this term are misnomers, they arose from the idea that pairs of particles like nucleons, and triplets like the π mesons, may be thought of as isotopes and that their charges, differing from each other by unity, suggest space quantization like electron spin and orbit in a magnetic field (see Fig. 45Q).

Within the nucleus, short-range forces between neutrons and protons are exactly alike, but the ever-present Coulomb forces between protons remove this symmetry and we are able to differentiate between the two different kinds of nucleons. In an effort to formulate a theory of these differences, particle charge has been likened to a vector, here called isotopic spin, and differences in charge have been compared with the space quantization of a spin vector in a field (see Fig. 65A).

By this theory a nucleon may be thought of as a particle with an isotopic spin of $I = \frac{1}{2}$ and a *spin average* or center of $\overline{Q} = +\frac{1}{2}$. If the particle spin lines up with the spin average, we have a pro-

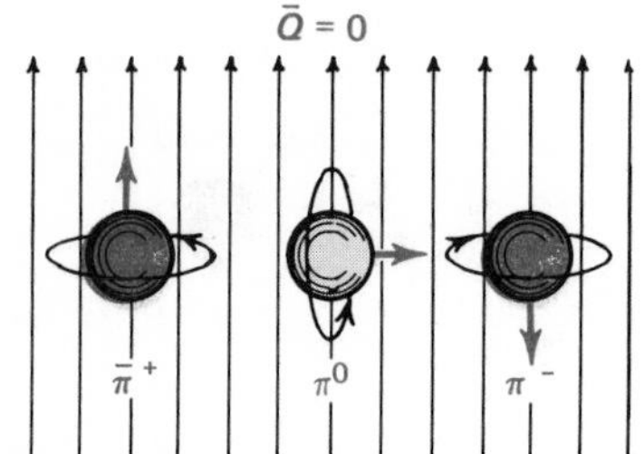

Fig. 65B. Schematic diagram of isotopic spin, a kind of charge quantization for elementary triplets like π mesons.

ton with a total spin $+1$ for $Q = +1$; if it lines up in the opposite direction we have a neutron with a total spin 0 for $Q = 0$.

The isotopic spin of antinucleons is $I = -\frac{1}{2}$, and with a spin average or center of $\bar{Q} = -\frac{1}{2}$, this gives $Q = 0$ for the antineutron and $\bar{Q} = -1$ for the antiproton:

$$\vec{Q} = \vec{I} + \vec{\bar{Q}} \tag{65c}$$

The pions form a triplet, with charges $+1$, 0, -1. This particle is therefore assigned an isotopic spin of $I = 1$. Applying the concept of space quantization to this vector magnitude, we obtain three possible orientations as shown in Fig 65B. These three positions, centered at charge $\bar{Q} = 0$, give $Q = +1$, 0, and -1, corresponding to π^+, π^0, and π^-.

It would seem that this theory of comparing electrical charge with spin orientation in a field has some basic foundation and that additional experimental data will lead to a more general theory of the basic concept we call electric charge.

65.6. Parity P

Parity is concerned with an inherent property having to do with nature's treatment of "right-handed" and "left-handed" phenomena. The subject will be treated in more detail in the last chapter, but suffice it to say that when particles like neutrinos are emitted in the decay of radioactive nuclei, they show a preferential spin direction. When a neutrino spins in the direction of a right-handed screw as it advances, it is said to have helicity of $+1$; spinning in the direction of a left-handed screw its helicity is -1.

Since parity P is related to spin J, the two quantum numbers are usually combined and written as J^P. For example, the assignment $J = \frac{1}{2}$ and $P = +1$ is frequently written $\frac{1}{2}+$. The plus or minus sign is sufficient since parity can only be $+1$ or -1.

65.7. Quantum Number Assignments

The quantum numbers Y, A, and I, assigned all particles belonging to the meson and baryon classes, are given in Tables 65A and 65B. Similar tables constructed for all the corresponding antiparticles are found to have the same numbers, but with all $+$ and $-$ signs reversed. While Y and Q are related by Eq.(65a), both are given in the tables for easy reference purposes. It is important to observe that the more than 200 mesons and baryons fall into but nine families.

TABLE 65A
Meson quantum numbers

Family	*Symbols*	$\bar{Q}$	*Y*	*A*	*I*
Singlets	ω, ϕ, f, f'	0	0	0	0
Doublets	K	+½	+1	0	+½
Triplets	$\{A1, B, A2_L$ $A2_H, \rho, \pi$	0	0	0	+1

TABLE 65B
Baryon quantum numbers

Family	*Baryon*	*Symbol*	$\bar{Q}$	*Y*	*A*	*I*
Singlets	Lambda	Λ	0	0	+1	0
Singlets	Omega	Ω	−1	−2	+1	0
Doublets	Nucleon	N	+½	+1	+1	+1/2
Doublets	Xi	Ξ	−½	−1	+1	+1/2
Triplets	Sigma	Σ	0	0	+1	+1
Quartets	Delta	Δ	+½	+1	+1	+3/2

Because the description of any one particle requires so many quantum numbers, an abbreviated system for general use has been adopted. Since all particles of a multiplet family have the same *Y*, *A*, and *I*, the symbols *N*, Λ, Σ, etc., signify the values of these three quantum numbers. For each particle within a multiplet, the charge *Q* is written in the usual way as a superscript. Finally, in parentheses, the mass *m* is written to the nearest whole number, followed by the parity *P* as a superscript to the spin *J*. Thus, calling any set *Y A I* by the letter *X*, the full designation is written

$$X^Q(m, J^P)$$

which for a proton would be

$$N^+(938, \tfrac{1}{2}^+)$$

Within any family of multiplets the particles have different *m*, *J*, and *P*. Because of page space, only two examples of these three quantum number assignments are given here.

Within each multiplet the particles have different *Q*. For example, we have Σ^+, Σ^-, Σ^+.

TABLE 65C
***K* mesons**

	m	*J*	*P*
K	494	0	−1
K^*	892	+1	−1
K_A	1240	+1	+1
K_N	1420	+2	+1

TABLE 65D
Sigma baryons

	m	*J*	*P*
Σ	1189	+1/2	+1
Σ	1385	+3/2	+1
Σ	1670	+3/2	−1
Σ	1750	+1/2	−1
Σ	1765	+5/2	−1
Σ	1915	+5/2	+1
Σ	2030	+7/2	+1

65.8. Conservation Laws

Throughout the many chapters of this book we have encountered practically all of the fundamental laws of nature, conservation laws, Newton's laws, Kepler's laws, Kirchhoff's laws, gas laws, Ohm's law, Wien's law, and many others. These laws are not to be looked upon as laws of nature so much as they are as a means of describing the way nature behaves.

Nature it seems has chosen only one law and the job of the scientist is to find it. Perhaps someday we will.

Thus far in the history of science man has come up with a number of laws he considers basic. Of these fundamental laws, those classified by the word *conservation* should be listed at the top. Some quantities in nature seem to be conserved in some kinds of processes and not in others, while other quantities seem to be conserved in all situations and under all circumstances.

The following is a list of the seven laws found to hold in all particle interactions.

Law 1. *The total energy, including mass, remains constant.*
Law 2. *The total linear momentum remains constant.*
Law 3. *The total angular momentum remains constant.*
Law 4. *The total charge remains constant.*
Law 5. *The total electron family number remains constant.*
Law 6. *The total muon family number remains constant.*
Law 7. *The total baryon number remains constant.*

Everything that can happen without violating these laws does happen. The first four laws have been employed in establishing all the reactions given in the preceding chapters. The last three laws will now be explained and we will see how they apply to elementary particle interactions.

The electron family is composed of four elementary particles, the electron e^-, the electron neutrino ν_e, the positron e^+, and the positron neutrino $\bar{\nu}_e$. The first two are particles and each has the electron family number +1, while the second two are antiparticles and each has the electron family number −1. All other particles have electron family number 0.

The muon family is composed of four elementary particles, the negative muon μ^-, the muon neutrino ν_μ, the antimuon μ^+, and the antimuon neutrino $\bar{\nu}_\mu$. The first two are particles and each has the muon family number +1, while the second two are antiparticles and each has the muon family number −1. All other particles have muon family number 0.

Example 1. Apply the conservation laws of charge, muon number, and electron number to the natural decay of a negative pion.
Solution. For this reaction, see Eq.(56g):

$$\pi^- \rightarrow \mu^- + \bar{\nu}_\mu$$

Charge No.	$-1 = -1 + 0$
Muon No.	$0 = +1 - 1$
Electron No.	$0 = 0 + 0$

The π^- and μ^- are both particles with numbers as shown. With these as fixed numbers, the muon family law shows that the neutrino must be an antiparticle. Since none of the particles in this decay are members of the electron family, all electron numbers are zero.

Example 2. Apply the charge, muon, and electron number conservation laws to the positive muon decay.
Solution. For this reaction, see Eq.(56k):

$$\bar{\mu}^+ \rightarrow e^+ + \bar{\nu}_\mu + \nu_e$$

Charge No.	$+1 = +1 + 0 + 0$
Muon No.	$-1 = 0 - 1 + 0$
Electron No.	$0 = -1 + 0 + 1$

The balancing of charge is straight-forward and self-explanatory. Since the positive muon is an antiparticle it has a muon family number -1. To balance this, one of the neutrinos must be a muon antineutrino with muon number -1. Since the positron is an antiparticle, its electron number of -1 must be balanced by an electron neutrino with an electron number $+1$.

We have seen in the preceding chapter that all particles having a mass equal to or greater than the proton are called *baryons*. Furthermore the baryon number is none other than what we have previously called the *atomic mass number A*. For most of the elementary particles known today A has the value $+1$ or -1.

In applying the baryon law to interactions we count all baryons as having baryon number $+1$, and their corresponding antibaryons as having baryon number -1 (see Sec. 65.7).

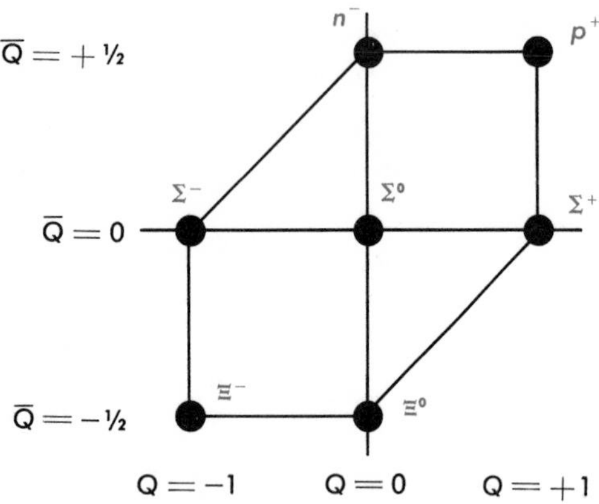

Fig. 65C. Graph of the seven baryons known in January 1961.

Example 3. Apply the charge, electron, muon, and baryon conservation laws to the decay of the neutron.

Solution. By Eq.(59ℓ) the decay of the neutron gives rise to a proton, an electron, and an antineutrino:

	$n^0 \rightarrow p^+ + e^- + \nu_e$
Charge No.	$0 = +1 - 1 \ + 0$
Electron No.	$0 = \ 0 + 1 \ - 1$
Muon No.	$0 = \ 0 + 0 \ + 0$
Baryon No.	$1 = \ 1 + 0 \ + 0$

Note that both the neutron and proton have baryon number +1, but appear on opposite sides of the equation. The electron number law shows that the neutrino must belong to the electron, and it must be an antineutrino to balance the equation.

65.9. *Hexagonal Arrays*

Historically we will start with the eight baryons known in January 1961, and see emperically how the "eightfold way" was developed around the hexagonal arrays of elementary particles. The baryons are n^0, p^+, Σ^+, Σ^0, Σ^-, Ξ^-, and Ξ^0.

In Fig. 65C each baryon is plotted as a black dot, with the charge Q along the horizontal, and the average charge $\overline{Q}$ along the vertical. If other pairs of quantum numbers or combinations of numbers are graphed, nothing very suggestive arises out of the plot, until we try hypercharge Y, and $Q - \overline{Q}$. When these are plotted, as shown in Fig. 65D, the six-sided figure straightens into a regular hexagon.

If we try the same "game" of plotting the seven mesons also known in January 1961, π^+, π^0, π^-, K^+, K^-, $\overline{K}^-$ and $\overline{K}^+$, we obtain a similar hexagon as shown in Fig. 65E. Later in 1961 an eighth neutral meson η^0 was discovered. This particle was then shown by Rosenfeld and colleagues to have the appropriate quantum numbers to go with π^0 at the center of the hexagon. Still later another neutral particle η' was discovered, and it belongs by itself to the right as shown.

By 1964 another set of mesons that form a hexagon was discovered. Shown on the meson chart in Fig. 64K, they are K^{*+}, K^{+0}, $\overline{K^{*0}}$, $\overline{K^*}^-$ (892, 1−), ρ^-, ρ^0, ρ^+ (765, 1−), ω^0 (784, 1−), and ϕ^0 (1019, 1−). The plotting of this hexagon is left as an exercise

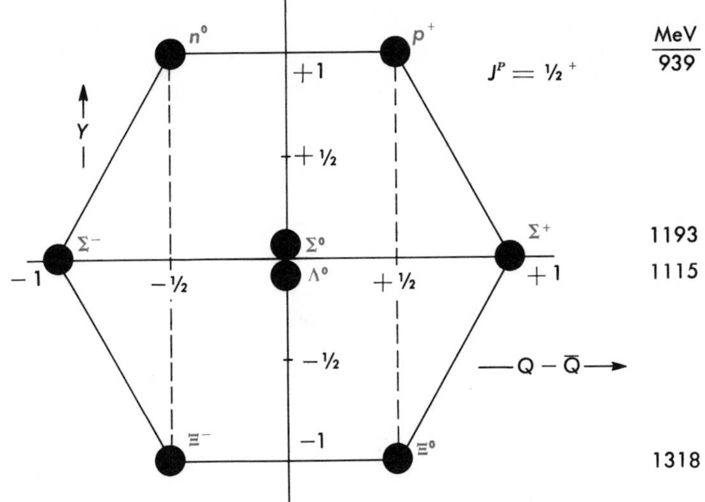

Fig. 65D. Hexagon graph for the eight baryons $J^P = \frac{1}{2}+$.

for the student. Note that ω^0 belongs to the right of the hexagon as in Fig. 65E (see Prob. 8).

When in 1961 the first baryon hexagon was made, the delta quartet multiplet Δ^{++}, Δ^+, Δ^0, Δ^- at (1236, 2+) was well established. Soon another triplet multiplet, Σ^+, Σ^0, Σ^- (1385, 2+), was discovered, and it was realized these were the beginnings of the

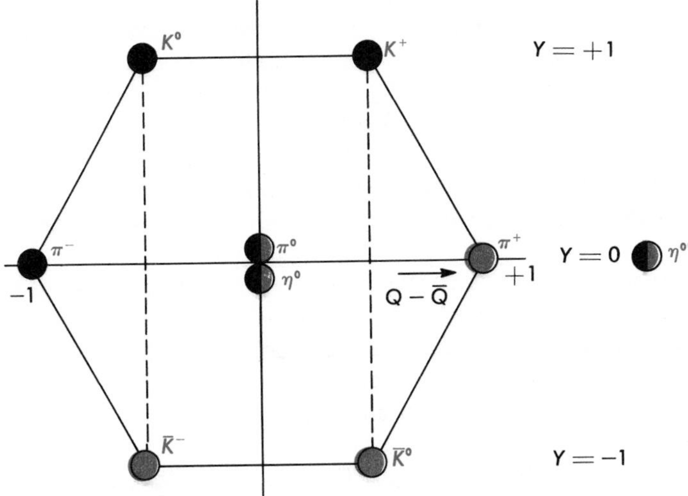

Fig. 65E. Hexagon graph for the eight-plus-one mesons, $J^P = 0^-$.

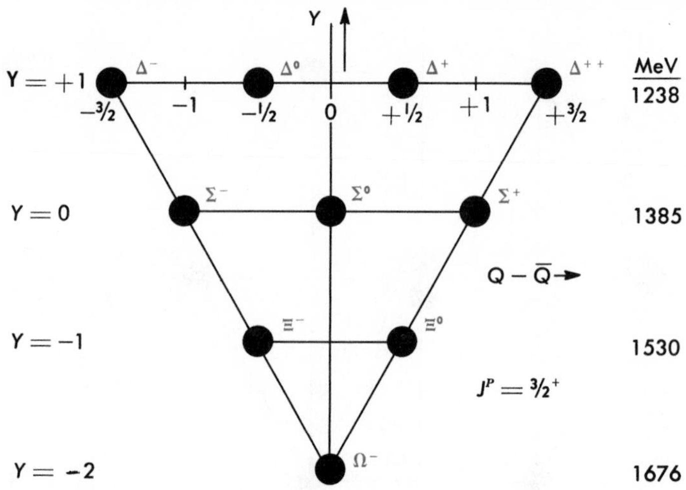

Fig. 65F. Triangle graph for the ten baryons, $J^P = \frac{3}{2}+$.

triangle shown in Fig. 65F. Later after the theory of the "eightfold way" was developed, the remaining doublet Ξ^-, Ξ^0 (1530, 2+) and the singlet Ω^- (1676, 2+) were discovered. It is interesting to observe that the vertical scale in Fig. 65F could have been the particle masses.

65.10. Quarks and the Eightfold Way

The theory of quarks and the "eightfold way" is concerned with the formation of elementary particles, and was first formulated in 1961 by M. Gell-Mann, at the California Institute of Technology, and independently by Y. Ne'eman, at Imperial College, London. Their treatment was mathematical, and postulated the existence of "primitive particles" called "quarks." When appropriate quarks are combined they yield, among other particle information, the sets of particles shown in Figs. 65D, 65E, and 65F.

We begin with three quarks, n_1, p_1, and λ_1, shown as black dots at the corner of a triangle in Fig. 65G. The colored dots at the corners of the second triangle represent hypothetical antiquarks, $\bar{n}_1$, $\bar{p}_1$, and $\bar{\lambda}_1$. As in the hexagon graphs, the vertical axis shows the quarks' hypercharges Y, and the horizontal scale their values of $Q - \bar{Q}$.

The dotted lines, inclined at 30° with the vertical, show that n_1 and λ_1 each have a charge of $-\frac{1}{3}\ e$, while p_1 has a charge of $+\frac{2}{3}e$. The antiquarks $\bar{n}_1$ and $\bar{\lambda}_1$ have charges of $+\frac{1}{3}e$, while $\bar{p}_1$

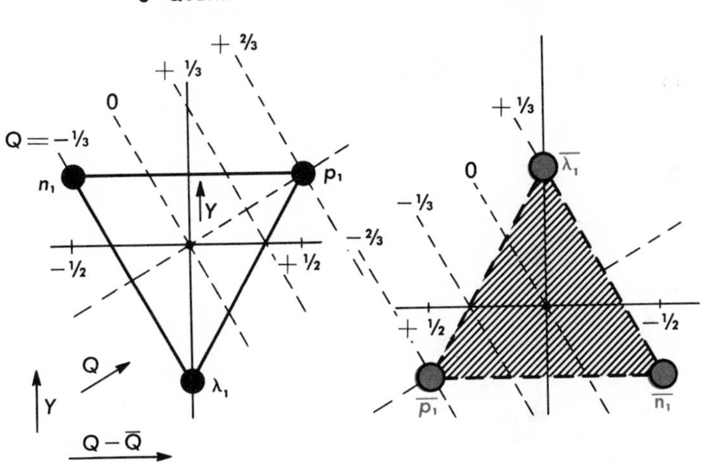

Fig. 65G. Graph of three quarks and three antiquarks, showing their fractional charges and hypercharges.

has a charge of $-\frac{2}{3}e$. Since these are hypothetical sub-electronic charges, it is proposed that quarks have a baryon number $A = +\frac{1}{3}$, and antiquarks a baryon number $A = -\frac{1}{3}$. Observe that in the hexagons and decuplet triangle, Figs. 65D, 65E, and 65F, lines of equal charge are inclined at 30° from the vertical:

	q	Q	A	J
Quarks	n_1	$-\frac{1}{3}$	$+\frac{1}{3}$	$+\frac{1}{2}$
	p_1	$+\frac{2}{3}$	$+\frac{1}{3}$	$+\frac{1}{2}$
	λ_1	$-\frac{1}{3}$	$+\frac{1}{3}$	$+\frac{1}{2}$
Antiquarks	$\bar{n}_1$	$+\frac{1}{3}$	$-\frac{1}{3}$	$-\frac{1}{3}$
	$\bar{p}_1$	$-\frac{2}{3}$	$-\frac{1}{3}$	$-\frac{1}{3}$
	$\bar{\lambda}_1$	$+\frac{1}{3}$	$-\frac{1}{3}$	$-\frac{1}{3}$

Assuming that quarks q and antiquarks $\bar{q}$ are the primary building blocks in nature, we combine them in pairs in Fig. 65H.* Suppose we first combine quark p_1 with antiquarks $\bar{n}_1$, $\bar{p}_1$, and $\bar{\lambda}_1$. To do this we add the Y's and $Q - \bar{Q}$'s by displaying the antiquark triangle centered on p_1, and obtain the particles labeled 1, 2, and 3, at the right. When we take quark n' and add the same three antiquarks by centering the triangle on n_1, we obtain particles 4,

* This graphical addition of quarks is attributed to A. H. Rosenfeld.

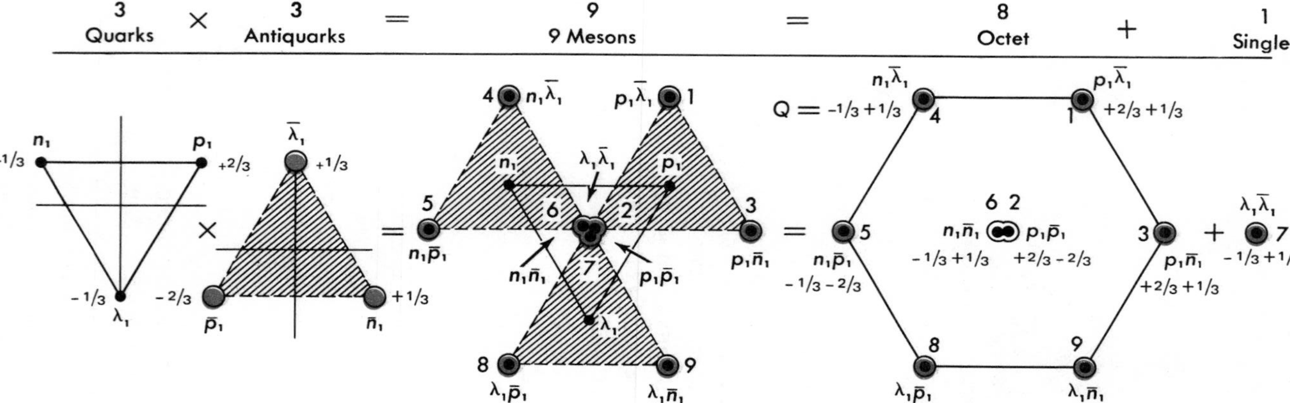

Fig. 65H. Construction diagrams for combining 3 quarks with 3 antiquarks to form the eight-plus-one meson hexagon.

5, and 6. Following the same procedure for $\overline{\lambda}_1$, we obtain the particles 7, 8, and 9.

The result is nine particles, two with a net charge of -1 each, two with a net charge of $+1$ each, and five with no charge. Since each particle consists of one quark and one antiquark, their baryon cores $A = +\frac{1}{3}$ and $A = -\frac{1}{3}$ annihilate to leave mesons with $A = 0$.

Let us now see how we can explain groups of baryons in the same way. While each meson is a combination of one quark and one antiquark, each baryon is formed out of *three* quarks. Since each quark can be n, p, or λ, there are $3 \times 3 \times 3 = 27$ possible combinations.

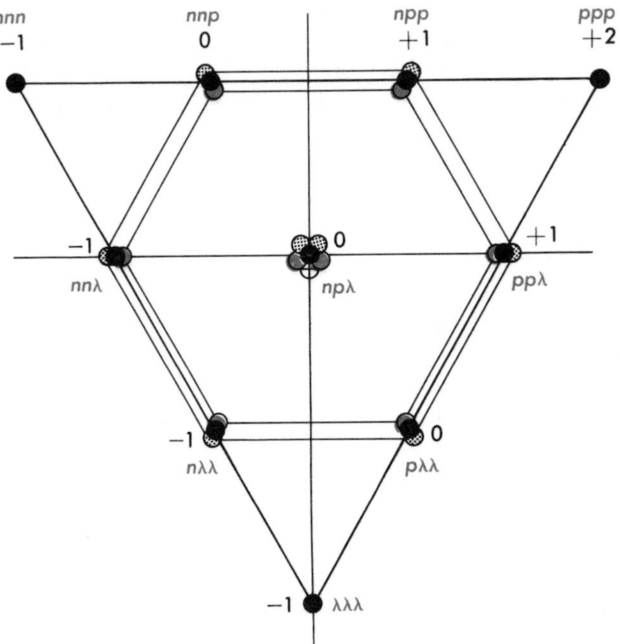

Fig. 65I. Super-multiplet graph of 27 baryons resulting from the addition of three sets of three quarks.

Using group theory mathematics, or addition diagrams similar to Fig. 65H, one can show that the physical interpretation of these 27 combinations will be one singlet, two octets which form the hexagons, and a group of ten which form a triangle decuplet (see Fig. 65I):

$$\text{Meson} = q_1 + \overline{q}_1$$

$$\text{Baryon} = q_1 + q_2 + q_3$$

To obtain whole number spins greater than 0 or 1 for mesons, and half-integral spins greater than $\frac{1}{2}$ and $\frac{3}{2}$ for baryons, add orbital angular momentum to the quark combinations.

The term "eightfold way" was borrowed from the Buddhist and Taoist philosophy, and introduced by Gell-Mann. In addition to the grouping of 10, 8, 8, and 1, etc., the mathematical theory gives relations between masses, and the decay modes of all members of multiplets.

Since unknown particles predicted by theory were looked for experimentally and found, the eightfold way can be considered one of the great achievements of modern science, and one which earned Gell-Mann the Nobel Prize for 1969. Although quarks have been looked for experimentally, they have so far escaped detection. Perhaps with the completion of new higher energy accelerators they will be found. It is also probable that some of the 27 quark combinations shown in Fig. 65I may not be formed, and therefore never observed.

65.11. Hadronic Atoms

These are simply atoms of ordinary matter in which at least one of the orbital electrons has been replaced by a hadron. A hadron (Greek for "strong one") is any elementary particle that interacts strongly with any other elementary particle. The particles that can form such atoms are the negatively charged particles shown in Table 65E.

TABLE 65E
Hadrons

Particle	*Symbol*	*Mean life*	*Mass (m_e)*
Muon	μ^-	2.20×10^{-6}s	206.77
Pion	π^-	2.60×10^{-8}s	273.4
Kaon	K^-	1.23×10^{-8}s	966.34
Antiproton	p^-	stable	1836.1
Sigma	Σ^-	1.64×10^{-10}s	2343.1
Xi	Ξ^-	1.66×10^{-10}s	2585.6
Omega	Ω^-	1.30×10^{-10}s	3272.8

Because of the Coulomb attractive forces between unlike charges, negatively charged particles have a far greater probability of being captured by atomic nuclei than have their positively charged counterparts (see Fig. 64P). There is a relatively high probability that as negatively charged particles pass through matter they may be captured in any one of a number of outside orbits of the atom to form a kind of Bohr atom.

Since hadrons are much heavier than electrons, their orbits lie closer to the nucleus than electron orbits. Except for the special case of the muonic atom, hadronic atoms will remain as atoms for about 10^{-12} s. This is the time it takes the hadron to cascade down the atomic energy levels, and get close enough to the nucleus and be absorbed. This time is so short that few hadrons have time to decay. Muonic atoms, however, have such a small probability of being captured by the nucleus that most of them decay before being captured.

All equations derived for hydrogen in Chap. 44 can be applied to such hadronic atoms. The radius of the circular orbits, for example, is given by

$$r = \frac{h^2}{4\pi^2 m\, e^2 k}\,\frac{n^2}{Z} = r_1\,\frac{n^2}{Z}$$

where m is the mass of the electron, Z is the atomic number, and r_1 is the radius of the first Bohr orbit of hydrogen:

$$r_1 = 5.2918 \times 10^{-11}\ \text{m} \tag{65d}$$

If we now express the mass of the hadron by the product $M \times m$, Eq.(61ℓ) can be written

$$r = r_1\,\frac{n^2}{MZ} \tag{65e}$$

The radius of the allowed orbits $n = 1, 2, 3, 4, \ldots\,.$, for the π^- or μ^- around a proton, for example, will be

$$r_1\,\frac{n^2}{273.14} \qquad \text{and} \qquad r_1\,\frac{n^2}{206.77}$$

respectively. In an atom like ${}_{35}Br^{79}$, the innermost orbit $n = 1$ for a π^- would be

$$r = 5.2918 \times 10^{-11}\,\frac{1^2}{273.14 \times 36} = 5.538 \times 10^{-15}\ \text{m}$$

and the pion would be just skimming over the surface of the nucleus (see Fig. 61S).

The energy levels in hydrogen are given by the Bohr formula:

$$E_n = -R\,\frac{Z^2}{n^2}$$

where

$$R = 2.1799 \times 10^{-18} \text{ J}$$

and is the energy of the ground state, $Z = 1$ and $n = 1$ (see Fig. 44H).

For the π^- and μ^- atoms this equation is just

$$E_n = -R \frac{MZ^2}{n^2} \tag{65f}$$

Transitions between orbits will give rise to the radiation of photons, whose energy is given by the Bohr equation

$$E_2 - E_1 = h\nu \tag{65g}$$

Example 4. A π^- pion is captured by a stable krypton atom, $_{36}Kr^{84}$. Find (a) the radius of the 1*st* and 2*nd* Bohr orbits, (b) the energy levels for $n = 1$ and $n = 2$, (c) the energy radiated from the transition n_2 to n_1, (d) the frequency of the radiation, and (e) its wavelength in angstroms.

Solution. The given quantities are $Z = 36$, $M = 273.14$, $n = 1$ and 2, $r_1 = 5.2918 \times 10^{-11}$ m, and $h = 6.6262 \times 10^{-34}$ Js. By direct substitution in Eq.(65e) we find for the $n = 1$ orbit

$$r = r_1 \frac{n^2}{MZ} = 5.2918 \times 10^{-11} \frac{1^2}{273.14 \times 36}$$

$$r = 5.3816 \times 10^{-15} \text{ m}$$

and for the second orbit, $n = 2$,

$$r = 5.2918 \times 10^{-11} \frac{2^2}{273.14 \times 36}$$

$$r = 21.5266 \times 10^{-15} \text{ m}$$

By direct substitution in Eq.(65f), we find for the energy in the $n = 1$ state

$$E_1 = -R \frac{MZ^2}{n^2} = -2.1799 \times 10^{-18} \frac{273.14 \times 36^2}{1^2}$$

$$E_1 = -7.7166 \times 10^{-13} \text{ J}$$

and for the second state, $n = 2$,

$$E_2 = 2.1788 \times 10^{-18} \frac{273.14 \times 36^2}{2^2}$$

$$E_2 = 1.9292 \times 10^{-13} \text{ J}$$

The difference between these two energy states gives for the radiated energy

$$E = h\nu = 5.7874 \times 10^{-13} \text{ J}$$

and solving for the frequency, we find

$$\nu = \frac{E}{h} = \frac{5.7874 \times 10^{-13} \text{ J}}{6.6262 \times 10^{-34} \text{ Js}}$$

$$\nu = 8.7341 \times 10^{20} \text{ Hz}$$

which corresponds to the wavelength

$$\lambda = \frac{c}{\nu} = \frac{2.9979 \times 10^8}{8.7341 \times 10^{20}} = 3.4324 \times 10^{-13} \text{ m}$$

$$\lambda = 0.0034324 \text{ Å}$$

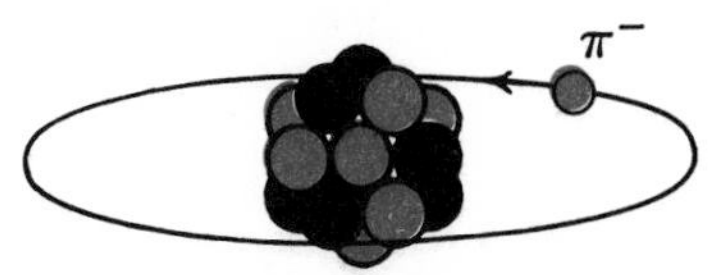

Fig. 65J. Schematic orbital diagram of a π mesonic atom—phosphorus, $_{15}P^{31}$—in the $n = 1$ circular orbit.

The radiation of π^- hadronic atoms is comparable to X rays and γ rays, and was first discovered in 1952 by Cemak, McGuire, Platt, and Schulte. These were produced by a beam of π^- particles from the University of Rochester cyclotron traversing the beryllium, carbon, and oxygen targets.

Similar observations were made by Rainwater and Fitch in 1953 for μ^- particles from another cyclotron. Confirmation of the origin of the radiations is attributed to the agreement between measured wavelengths and those calculated from the above Bohr formulas.

65.12. The Structure of the Neutron and Proton

The high energy electron beam, 20 GeV, from the Stanford Linear Accelerator (SLAC) has been used to study the elastic and inelastic scattering of electrons from neutrons and protons. (See Sec. 57.10 for a description of the accelerator). The work represents the combined efforts of many people, and the results thus far have been published by Henry W. Kendall and Wolfgang K. H. Panofsky.*

* *Scientific American*, June 1971.

The scattering target used for studying the structure of protons was liquid hydrogen, while the target for studying the structure of neutrons was liquid deuterium. To a good approximation the scattering by deuterium nuclei is simply the sum of the scattering from neutrons and protons.

The manner in which ultrahigh energy electrons are scattered indicates that neutrons and protons have a complex internal structure of pointlike entities. Although the nature of these pointlike particles is not known, it has been suggested by R. Feynman they be called *partons.* Feynman and others have been developing a theoretical model of the nucleon that may explain the inelastic scattering that has already been observed. A fairly detailed picture of the nucleon's properties can be constructed mathematically by assuming that the hypothetical partons have the properties formally assigned to the equally hypothetical quarks. The eventual outcome of these and future experimental observations, and their correct theoretical interpretation, will one day form a new chapter for this text.

problems

1. The following quantum numbers are assigned to an atomic particle: $m = 1915$ MeV, $J = \frac{5}{2}$, $Q = -1$, $Y = 0$, $A = -1$, $I = -1$, and $P = +1$. Write down the abbreviated designation for this particle.

2. The following quantum numbers are assigned to an elementary atomic particle: $m = 1890$ MeV, $J = \frac{5}{2}$, $Q = +1$, $Y = -1$, $A = -1$, $I = -\frac{3}{2}$, and $P = +1$. Write down the abbreviated designation for this particle.

3. An elementary atomic particle is designated Σ^+ (1670, $\frac{3}{2}-$). Write down the numerical values of all seven quantum numbers for this particle. [Ans. $m = 1670$ MeV, $J = \frac{3}{2}$, $Q = +1$, $Y = +1$, $A = +1$, $I = +1$, and $P = -1$.]

4. An elementary atomic particle is designated Δ^{++} (1650, $\frac{1}{2}-$). Write down the numerical values of all seven quantum numbers for this particle.

5. Construct a table similar to Table 65B for the six families of antibaryons.

6. Construct a table similar to Table 65A for the three families of antimesons.

7. Apply the conservation laws 3, 4, and 7 to the reaction, $\pi^- + p^+ \rightarrow K^0 + \Lambda^0$.

8. Construct a hexagon for the mesons listed in paragraph four of Section 65.9.

9. Apply conservation laws 3, 4, and 7 to the interaction shown in Fig. 64T: $K^- + p^+ \rightarrow K^0 + \Xi^0 + \pi^- + \pi^+$.

10. Apply conservation laws 3, 4, and 7 to the interaction shown in Fig. 64W: $K^+ + p^+ \rightarrow \pi^0 + \pi^+ + \Lambda^0 + K^0 + K^+$.

11. Apply conservation laws 3, 4, and 7 to the interaction shown in Fig. 64X: $K^+ + p^+ \rightarrow \Xi^+ + \Lambda^0 + p + \pi^0 + \pi^0$.

12. (a) Write down the reaction in which the Λ^0 particle is produced in Fig. 64Y. (b) Apply conservation laws 3, 4, and 7 to this reaction.

$$\left[\begin{array}{llll} \text{ans.} & \text{(a)} & K^- + p^+ & \rightarrow \pi^0 + \Lambda^0 \\ & & J = \;\; 0 + \tfrac{1}{2} & = 0 \;+ \tfrac{1}{2} \\ & \text{(b)} & Q = -1 + 1 & = 0 \;+ 0 \\ & & A = \;\; 0 + 1 & = 0 \;+ 1 \end{array}\right]$$

13. (a) Write down the reaction in which a Σ^- particle is produced in Fig. 64R. (b) Apply the conservation laws 3, 4, and 7 to this reaction.

14. (a) Write down the reaction for the production of a K^0 in Fig. 64Q. (b) Apply the conservation laws 3, 4, and 7 to this reaction.

15. Write down the reaction for the production of a Ξ^0 particle in Fig. 64S. (b) Apply the conservation laws 3, 4, and 7 for this reaction.

$$\left[\begin{array}{llllll} \text{ans. (a)} & & K^- + p^+ & \rightarrow \Xi^0 & + K^0 \\ & J = & 0 + \frac{1}{2} & = +\frac{1}{2} & 0 \\ \text{(b)} & Q = & -1 + 1 & = \ \ 0 & 0 \\ & A = & 0 + 1 & = +1 & 0 \end{array}\right]$$

16. (a) Write down the reaction of the decay of a positive pion. (b) Apply the conservation laws 3, 4, 5, 6, and 7 to this reaction.

17. Make a diagram similar to Fig. 65B for the antisigma triplet, $\bar{\Sigma}^+$, $\bar{\Sigma}^0$, and $\bar{\Sigma}^-$.

18. Make a diagram similar to Fig. 65B for the delta family of particles.

19. Find the radius of the 1*st* Bohr orbit for a μ^- muon circling a potassium nucleus.

20. Find the radius of the 2*nd* Bohr orbit for a μ^- muon circling a chlorine nucleus.

21. A μ^- muon is captured by a calcium nucleus in the 2*nd* Bohr circular orbit. Calculate (a) the energy radiated when the muon jumps from $n = 2$ to $n = 1$, (b) the frequency of the photon, and (c) its wavelength in angstroms. [Ans. (a) 1.3537×10^{-13} J, (b) 2.0430×10^{20} Hz, (c) 0.01467 Å.]

22. A phosphorus nucleus captures a μ^- muon in the 2*nd* Bohr circular orbit. Find (a) the energy of the photon radiated when the muon jumps from $n = 2$ to $n = 1$. Calculate (b) its frequency, and (c) its wavelength in angstroms.

23. A π^- meson is captured by a sodium nucleus. Find the energy of the emitted photons when the pion jumps (a) from orbit $n = 3$ to $n = 2$, and (b) from orbit $n = 2$ to $n = 1$. (c) Find the wavelengths of these photons in angstroms.

24. A beam of negative pions is incident on a magnesium metal target. Some of these pions are captured in quantized energy states. Find (a) the energies of the four lowest states, $n = 1$, 2, 3, and 4, and the wavelengths emitted by jumps of the pion from (b) $n = 4$ to $n = 1$, (c) $n = 3$ to $n = 1$, and (d) $n = 2$ to $n = 1$. Make an energy level diagram and show these transitions. [Ans. (a) 8.5696×10^{-14} J, 2.1424×10^{-14} J, 0.9522×10^{-14} J, 0.5356×10^{-14} J, (b) 0.02473 Å, (c) 0.02608 Å, (d) 0.03091 Å.]

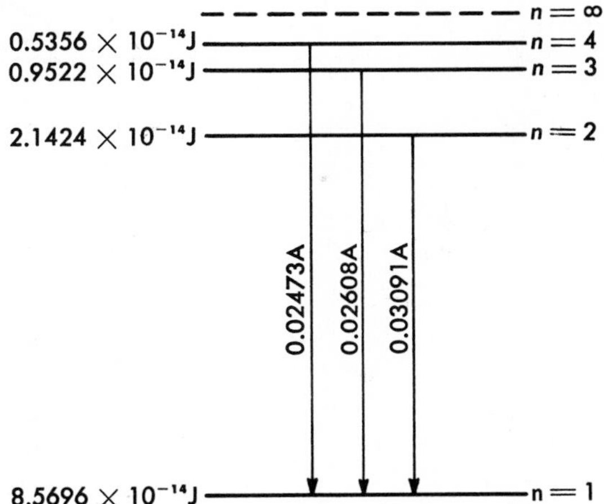

Prob. 24. Energy level diagram and transitions for the pionic orbits around a magnesium nucleus.

66 Field theory and world lines

In the previous chapters the concepts of electric, magnetic, and gravitational fields were introduced as devices to provide a better understanding of gravitation, electricity, and magnetism. Around different kinds of bodies, physicists frequently draw lines of force to represent field directions and field intensities (see Chaps. 12, 23, and 24).

Since the time Faraday and Maxwell conceived of the idea of fields, over one hundred years ago, it has been assumed the lines we draw are a fiction, and are to be used only as a means to a better understanding of nature's laws. Today it is suspected they may be real and of great physical significance.

66.1. Field Theory of Atomic Particles

It was Einstein, through his theory of relativity, who first postulated that all fields around a body or particle should be considered as something real.

The emission of a photon by one excited atom and its subsequent absorption by another are clear indications that electromagnetic fields may be suddenly created or destroyed in chunks. Electrons with their electric and magnetic fields move in the field of a nucleus to which they are attached. Suddenly a chunk of electromagnetic field, a photon, is emitted. Later this chunk of field is absorbed by another similar system of fields, another atom.

Although the dual nature of particles and waves, as described in Chap. 51, is difficult to comprehend, each elementary chunk of energy, whatever its form, may be regarded as a localized region containing some kind of field. All events in the world may then be described as the interactions between various kinds of these localized fields.

The creation of a positron in pair production, for example, may be thought of as the creation of a chunk of positive field. As the positron moves, this field travels through space as a wave, and at some time later collides with the localized field of an electron, and both fields vanish.

At the spot where these charged particle fields disappeared, there are created two electromagnetic fields (photons) propagated through space with the speed of light *c*.

The idea that elementary particle events involve different kinds of fields, acting on one another at a distance, is becoming more and more an acceptable theory. Thus far, however, no one has been able to bring together all of the various kinds of fields into one successful *unified field theory.*

For this reason it is customary to describe all events in the universe, from the strong short-range forces between certain elementary atomic particles to the long-range gravitational forces between astronomical bodies, as arising from the interactions between four different kinds of fields. Listed in the order of decreasing strength, or intensity these are:

Strong fields
Electromagentic fields
Weak fields
Gravitational fields

Around all charged baryons all four of these fields may be assumed to exist. A schematic diagram, based on classical theory and representing a proton, is shown in Fig. 66A.

Although the intensity of all fields decreases to zero only at infinity, their lines are shown terminating at different distances from the center. While the intensity of each field increases with decreasing distance from the center, the so-called *strong field* is by far the strongest at distances less than about 1 fermi, or 1×10^{-15} m.

At distances a little gerater than 1F the strong field drops off rapidly and the Coulomb field, associated with the particle's charge, predominates (see Fig. 61G). While little is known about the properties and extent of the weak field, gravitational fields are known to extend great distances into the space surrounding astronomical bodies.

While electromagnetic fields do not exist for neutral baryons, like Λ^0, Σ^0, Δ^0, etc., all four fields do exist around the charged baryons, Σ^+, Σ^-, Ξ^+, Δ^+, Δ^-, etc. (see Table 66A).

When a low-energy proton collides with another proton at rest, the Coulomb fields interact at some distance and the two particles recoil before their strong fields get close enough together to produce an observable effect. This is *elastic,* or *Rutherford, scattering.*

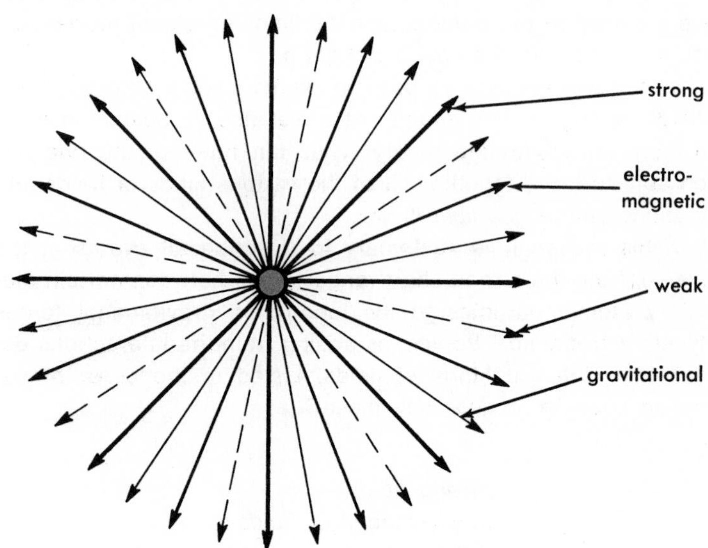

Fig. 66A. Schematic diagram of the various kinds of elementary particle fields around a charged baryon.

TABLE 66A
Relative magnitudes of elementary particle fields

	~100 *Strong*	1 *Elec. Mag.*	$\sim 10^{-11}$ *Weak*	$\sim 10^{-40}$ *Grav.*
p^+, p^-	×	×	×	×
π^+, π^-	×	×	×	×
K^+, K^-	×	×	×	×
π^0, K^0	×	—	×	×
μ^+, μ^-	—	×	×	×
γ	—	×	×	—
ν	—	—	×	—
ω^0, η^0, ϕ^0	—	—	×	×

When a high-energy proton makes a head-on collision with another proton, however, the particles override the Coulomb forces and the strong fields interact at close range. Whatever transformations are brought about as the result of this collision the event is referred to as a *strong interaction.*

In spite of our limited imaginations in describing particle fields, the successes of the mathematics of quantum theory in explaining observations in the atomic world forces us to accept a new picture of elementary particles.

When quantum theory is applied to the strong field around a baryon, like the proton, the classical picture of radial field lines is replaced by a field of mesons as shown in Fig. 66B(a).

Charged and uncharged virtual pions and other mesons are assumed to be shooting out and in, i.e., from and to the central core. These are to be thought of as *virtual mesons* which reveal their *real* properties when, as the result of a collision, one or more of them escape or are captured.

If the proton is moving at high velocity as in diagram (b), virtual mesons may be visualized as leaving the particle at one point in its path, and rejoining it at some other point farther along.

The concept of virtual particles is related to Heisenberg's uncertainty principle, $\Delta E \cdot \Delta t \approx h$ [see Eq.(60e)]. In relativistic quantum theory, mass is equivalent to energy as expressed by Ein-

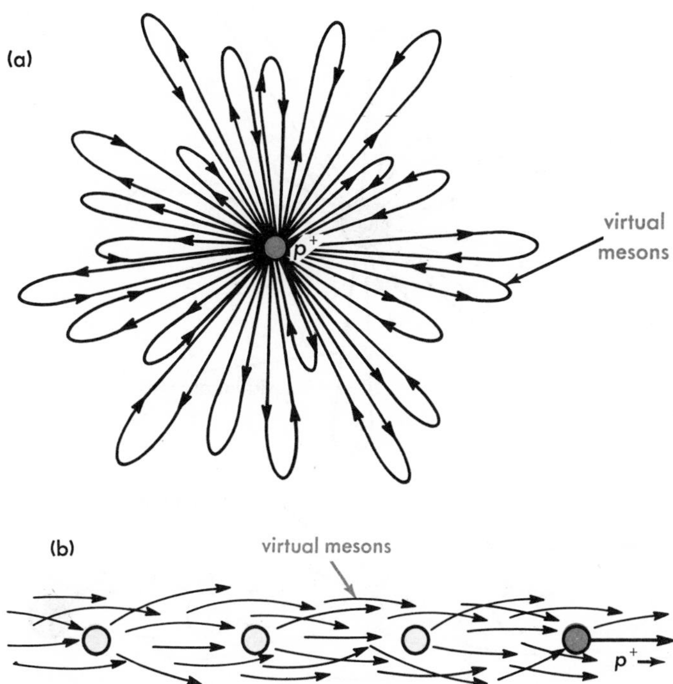

Fig. 66B. Schematic diagrams showing the virtual meson field around a proton: (a) stationary and (b) moving.

stein's relation $E = mc^2$. One can imagine, therefore, that any amount of energy ΔE can be converted into mass m equivalent to the rest mass of some particle provided that $\Delta E \cdot \Delta t$ does not exceed h. In other words, without violating the uncertainty principle one or more particles can appear, exist for a short time, and then disappear (into energy). In a way these particles' existence is hidden by an irreducible uncertainty in our knowledge of the particle system. Virtual particles cannot be observed directly as can real particles.

Most particle models describe the *electromagnetic interaction* between two charged particles as being due to photons. These too can be real or virtual, and subject to the uncertainty principle.

When relativistic quantum theory is applied to the electromagnetic field around an electron or muon, the classical picture of radial field lines is replaced by the emission and absorption of photons as shown in Fig. 66C(a). These electromagnetic waves are to be thought of as virtual photons which reveal their real properties only when, as the result of a high-energy collision, one or more escape or are captured. If the electron is moving with a

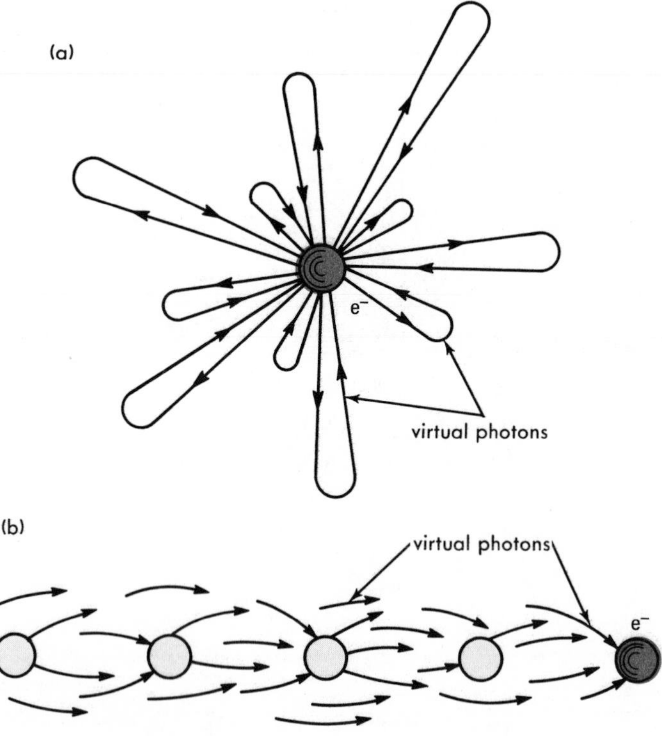

Fig. 66C. Schematic diagram showing the virtual photon field around an electron: (a) stationary and (b) moving in a straight line.

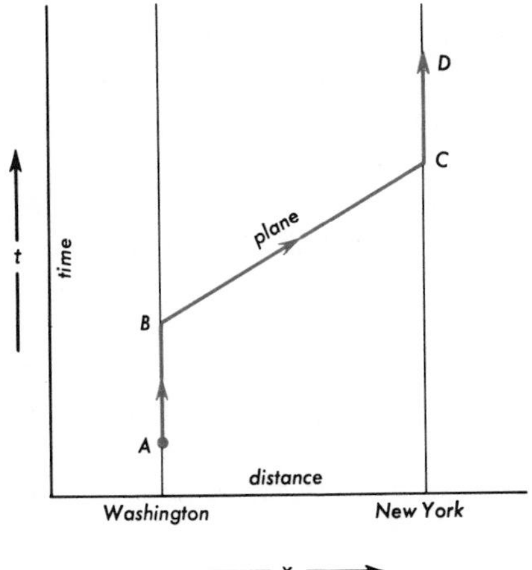

Fig. 66D. World-line graph of a plane flight from Washington to New York.

high velocity as in diagram (b), the photons may be visualized as leaving the particle at one point in its path and rejoining it at some later point farther along.

Very little is known about weak fields and gravitational fields of elementary particles. What is known has been gleaned from events involving particles that exhibit neither strong fields nor electromagnetic fields. These are the neutrinos; they have baryon number zero and no charge.

By analogy it is assumed that the field around each neutrino is to be attributed to the radiation and absorption of virtual atomic particles that have yet to be detected.

In an attempt to explain why the sun is able to exert an inward force on a planet to hold it in its orbit, theoretical physicists have invented a particle called the *graviton.* Around each elementary particle, or large mass of particles, virtual gravitons are pictured being continually emitted and absorbed. Two separated particles are then pictured as exchanging gravitons, and through this exchange realize attractive forces. For large masses of particles these are the forces given by Newton's law of gravitation.

66.3. Feynman, or World Lines

The method of depicting elementary-particle events by means of space–time graphs was introduced by R. Feynman* in 1949. As an introduction to the meaning of these useful graphical pictures, consider the flight of an airplane from one city to another as shown in Fig. 66D. The time t is plotted vertically, and the distance x is plotted horizontally.

***Richard F. Feynman (1918–), American physicist, received his Ph.D. at Princeton University in 1940. He served at the Los Alamos Scientific Laboratory, New Mexico during World War II, and became professor of physics at Cornell University in 1945. In 1951, he became professor of physics at the California Institute of Technology. He won the Einstein Award in 1954. He was elected to the National Academy of Sciences and the Royal Society of London. He is best known for his theoretical work in quantum electrodynamics and his outstanding teaching ability. For his researches in quantum electrodynamics he was awarded the Nobel Prize in physics in 1965.**

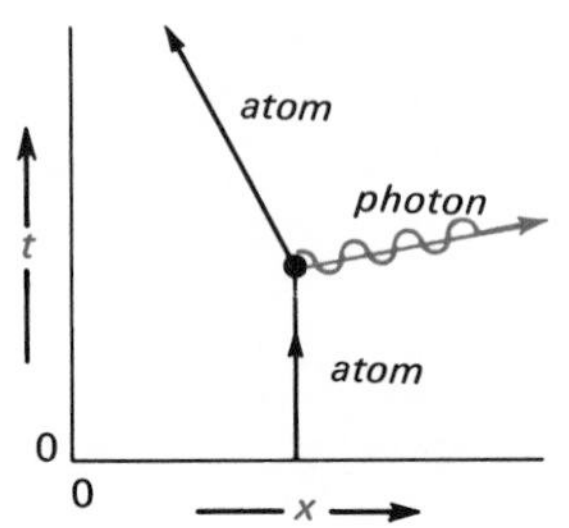

Fig. 66E. World-line graph for the emission of a photon by an atom.

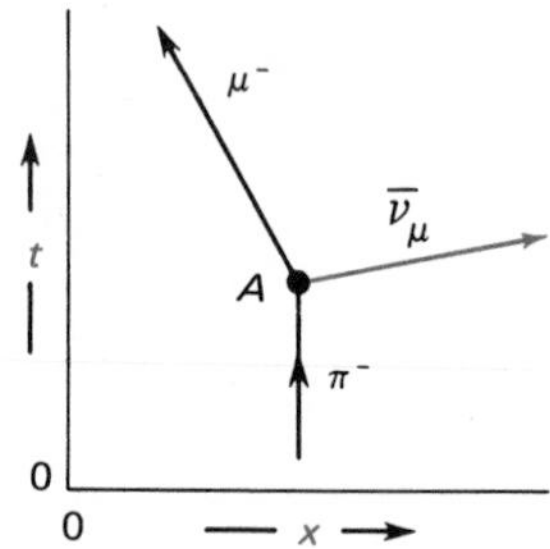

Fig. 66F. World-line graph for the decay of a pion into a muon and a neutrino.

We now represent the plane's history by the solid line ABCD. Parked at the ramp at the Washington Airport, time t is advancing in the direction A to B. The plane takes off, and moving both in time and space, traces out the world line B to C. Landing in New York and coming to rest on the ramp, the plane again moves only in time, and its world line CD is straight upward.

Note there is no such thing as standing still in a space–time graph. A city like Washington moves through time and continually traces out its vertical world line. If one places a ruler horizontally across the bottom of the diagram and then pushes it upward with uniform speed across the diagram, the intersection of the world lines with the ruler edge gives a description of the plane's motion with respect to the two cities.

A narrow horizontal slot in a strip of cardboard is more effective than a ruler. If the strip is moved downward with uniform speed, the dots seen in the slot represent an equally valid motion, namely, that of the plane on its return flight.

Turning now to the world of elementary particles, we may trace the world lines of a simple and well-known event (see Fig. 66E). The diagram represents the emission of a photon by an excited atom.

Initially at rest the atom traces out a vertically straight world line. Upon the emission of a photon with the speed of light, the atom recoils to the left as shown. The slower a particle moves, the more nearly vertical is its world line, while the faster it moves the more nearly horizontal is its world line.

Since no particle can travel from one place to another with infinite speed, no world line can be horizontal. Photons and neutrinos provide the most nearly horizontal world lines since they travel with the speed of light c.

Figure 66F represents the decay of a negative pion:

$$\pi^- \rightarrow \mu^- + \bar{\nu}_\mu$$

The dot at the vertex A indicates the time at which the world line of the pion ends and the world lines of the muon and antineutrino begin.

66.4. Strong Interactions

The strong binding forces known to exist within the nucleus are attributed to the mesons that jump back and forth between the neutrons and protons. When a neutron collides with a proton in free space, the two particles at close approach may exchange one or more mesons and each recoil with a different mass and charge.

Consider the collision event involving two nucleons as shown in Fig. 66G. As the neutron approaches the proton, their strong fields interact at close approach of about 10^{-15} m, a π^- meson is transferred to the proton, and the two particles recoil.

The world-line diagram indicates, however, that this single event probably takes place in two steps. At close approach of about 10^{-15} m at A the neutron emits a π^- meson. A short time later at point B the π^- meson combines with the proton thereby converting it into a neutron. The two reactions may be written

$$n \rightarrow p^+ + \pi^-$$

$$\pi^- + p^+ \rightarrow n$$

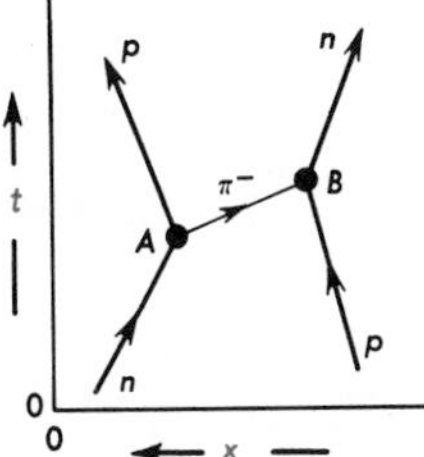

Fig. 66G. World-line diagram of a strong interaction. At the close approach of a neutron and proton, a negative pion makes a transition from neutron to proton.

The approximate time interval for this event to take place may be calculated from Heisenberg's uncertainty principle [see Eq. 60e)]:

$$\Delta E \times \Delta t = h \qquad (66a)$$

The change in energy ΔE is just the total mass of the exchanged π^-:

$$E = mc^2$$

$$E = 273.14 \times 9.110 \times 10^{-31} \times 8.988 \times 10^{16}$$

$$E = 2.2365 \times 10^{-11} \text{ joules}$$

Solving Eq.(66a) for Δt, and substituting, we obtain

$$\Delta t = \frac{h}{\Delta E} = \frac{6.626 \times 10^{-34} \text{ Js}}{2.2365 \times 10^{-11} \text{ J}}$$

$$\Delta t = 2.9627 \times 10^{-22} \text{ s}$$

This extremely short time interval is typical of all strong interactions. Good examples of other strong interactions are to be seen as the primary events in the photographs of Figs. 64M through 64Z. Typical decay interactions are

$$p^- + p^+ \rightarrow \pi^+ + \pi^- + \pi^+ + \pi^-$$

$$\pi^- + p^+ \rightarrow K^0 + \Lambda^0$$

$$K^- + p^+ \rightarrow \Xi^0 + K^0 + \pi^+ + \pi^-$$

$$K^+ + p^+ \rightarrow \Lambda^0 + K^+ + K^0 + \pi^+ + \pi^-$$

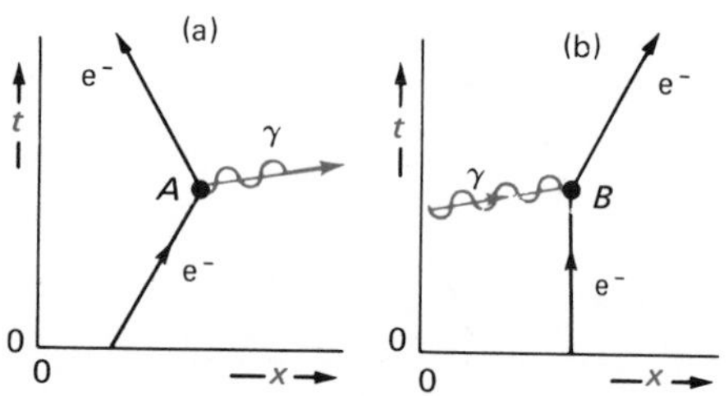

Fig. 66H. World-line diagrams for (a) the electron emission of a photon as in bremsstrahlung, and (b) the absorption of a photon by an electron as in the photoelectric effect.

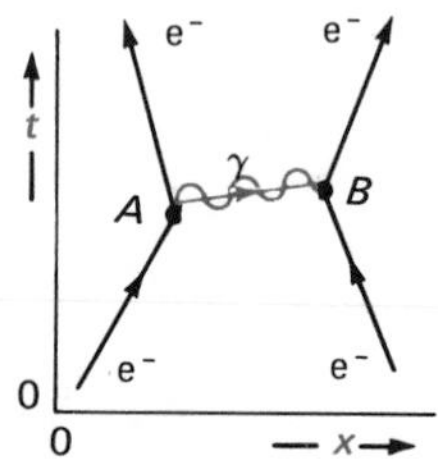

Fig. 66I. World-line diagram of the elastic collision of two electrons.

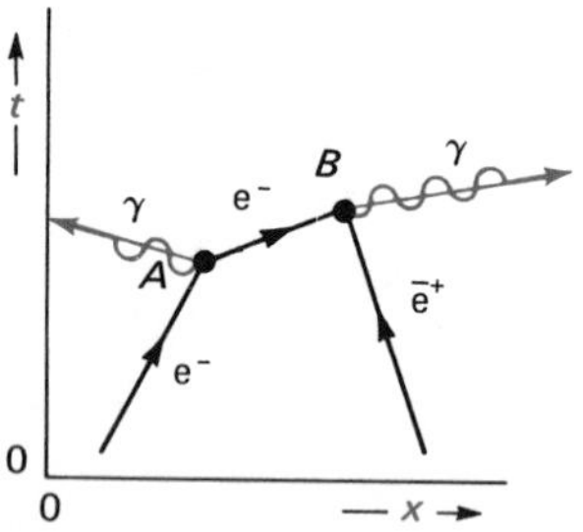

Fig. 66J. World-line diagram of an electron–positron annihilation yielding two photons.

Observe that the K and π mesons, as well as baryons, interact strongly with the protons. This is to be expected since *kaons* frequently decay into *pions,* and the π's are responsible for the strong forces that bind all nuclei together.

66.5. Electromagnetic Interactions

Electromagnetic interactions are confined to events in which the interacting particle fields are electromagnetic in character. Electrons, positrons, and photons fall into this category and none of them possess the strong fields so characteristic of nucleons and baryons. The magnitudes of *electromagnetic forces* are about one one-hundredth those arising from *strong interactions*, but approximately 10^{11} times stronger than those involved in *weak interactions* (see Table 66A).

In the process called bremsstrahlung, an electron passing through the nonhomogeneous field close to a nucleus or an electron is deflected in its path as it emits a photon (see Fig. 50M).

In the photoelectric effect a photon is absorbed by an electron, the latter recoiling from the impact. World-line diagrams for both of these events are shown in Fig. 66H.

By combining these two diagrams we obtain a world-line diagram representing the elastic scattering between two electrons (see Fig. 66I). According to classical theory, when two electrons approach each other they exert equal and opposite forces on one another. These forces give rise to the changes in the energy and momentum of both electrons. If one electron loses energy the other gains an equivalent amount.

According to quantum theory, when the overlapping photon fields of the two electrons are sufficiently great, the one electron loses energy ΔE by emitting a photon at A. A short time Δt later the other electron absorbs the photon, thereby gaining the energy ΔE.

If the relative velocities of the electrons are low, the photon energy ΔE will be small and the wavelength may correspond to visible light. If, however, the relative velocities are close to the speed of light, the photon energy ΔE will be large and the wavelength may correspond to X rays.

A world-line diagram for the annihilation of an electron–positron pair is shown in Fig. 66J. The electron field, at close approach to the positron field, emits a photon at point A. The photon flies away and the recoiling electron later combines with the positron and creates another photon. As a reaction

$$e^- + e^+ = \gamma + \gamma \tag{66b}$$

Typical of the events classified as weak interactions are those involving radioactive beta decay. Consider the well-known decay of a free neutron.

The neutron with its half-life of 15 min 32s decays into a proton, an electron, and an antineutrino (see Fig. 66K).

The neutron initially at rest suddenly explodes into three particles as shown. The reaction is

$$n \rightarrow p^+ + e^- + \bar{\nu}_e \tag{66c}$$

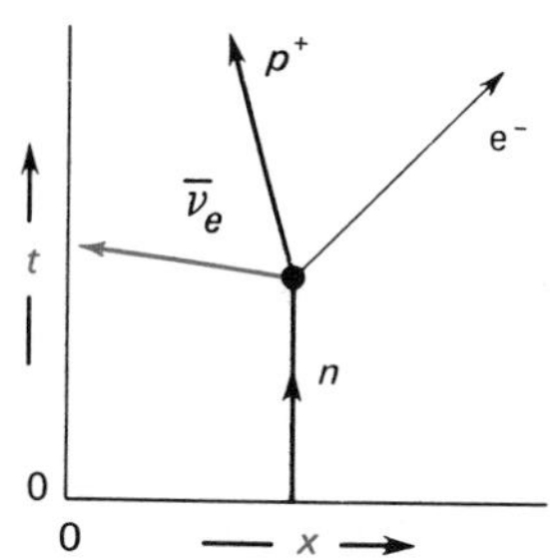

Fig. 66K. World-line graph for the decay of a free neutron into a proton, electron, and an antineutrino.

Note that the world line of the antineutrino has the same slope as a photon.

If the antineutrino later encounters a proton, there is a small probability that it will be captured in what is called the *inverse beta-decay process:*

$$\bar{\nu}_e + p^+ \rightarrow n + e^+ \tag{66d}$$

While the electron appears in the neutron decay process, the laws of charge conservation and electron family conservation require the creation of a positron in the capture process.

The neutron's average life of 15 min 32s means that for the inverse beta-decay process to occur, the field of an antineutrino must be close to that of a proton for that length of time.

Since the antineutrino travels with the speed of light, it will not stay close enough to a proton for capture to occur. In 15 min 32s a neutrino will travel nearly twice the distance from the earth to the sun. It is for this reason that neutrinos have great penetrating power, and that all matter as well as free space is assumed to be packed full of neutrinos.

Although neutrinos are seldom captured by nucleons, their short-range weak field is postulated in order to account for their occasional absorption.

Also typical of the weak interactions are the decay of muons and pions. These events take place in the relatively long times of 10^{-8} to 10^{-6}s. Feynman diagrams for these particles are left as student exercises.

66.7. Gravitational Interactions

The fact that astronomical bodies attract each other over distances of many millions of miles is one of the great mysteries of

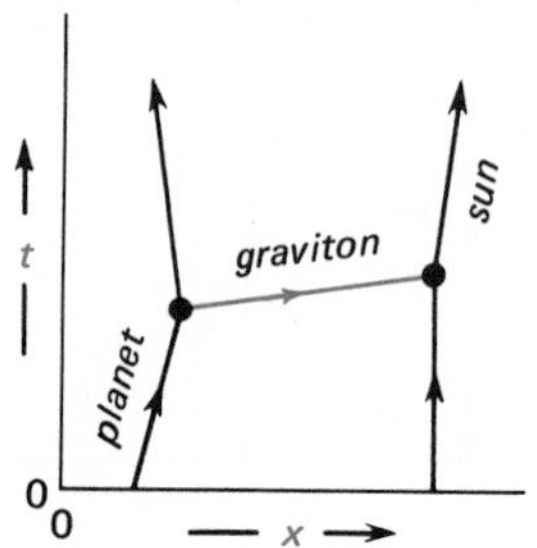

Fig. 66L. World-line diagram for the exchange of a graviton between a planet and the sun.

nature. If one calculates the electrostatic force between a proton and an electron and then compares it with the gravitational force between the same two bodies, he finds the electrostatic force is greater by a factor of 2.3×10^{39}.

In spite of this vast difference in the magnitudes of these force fields, the success of the quantum mechanics in the atomic world suggests the possible existence of new particles called *gravitons* (see end of Sec. 66.2).

By analogy with the photon field around charged bodies, we may visualize the existence of gravitons around each mass (see Fig. 66C).

The world-line diagram in Fig. 66L shows how the emission of a graviton from the sun to a planet gives rise to a force, first on the planet and then on the sun. Billions of gravitons per second, traveling in both directions between the two bodies, are assumed to account for the great total force of attraction.

66.8. Time Reversal Invariance

Suppose an astronaut on his way to a distant galaxy takes motion pictures of our solar system to show the hosts he visits. The hosts at the distant galaxy, being familiar with the laws of mechanics and gravitation, would conclude that what they observed obeyed all natural laws.

But had the film been run backward they would have been equally satisfied since the motion is consistent with the same laws of motion. This is the principle of *time-reversal invariance.* Under a hypothetical reversal of time, all the laws of nature remain unchanged.

Although the time reversal of a complicated event like the explosion of a shell into many fragments may be quite improbable, and for practical purposes next to impossible, the time reversal of events in the world of elementary particles appears to be valid and many of them are observed to happen.

Note how well time reversal works on all world-line diagrams in Figs. 66D, 66E, 66F, 66H, and 66I. When time reversal is applied to Fig. 66K, the coming together of three particles simultaneously is highly improbable, yet is an allowed event and in the center of the sun may readily take place.

An examination of the two diagrams in Fig. 66H suggests the possibility of reversing the time of the photon and obtaining a different but allowed event.

To illustrate how this may be carried out, we start with diagram (a) and reverse the arrowhead of the photon. The diagram is now a twisted version of diagram (b). To bring it into accord with diagram (b) we rotate the new world line of the photon around the vertex until it points forward in time.

When this principle of time reversal is applied to a single charged particle in an observed event the rule is to reverse the charge as well as the particle-antiparticle classification. Such a process is illustrated in Fig. 66M.

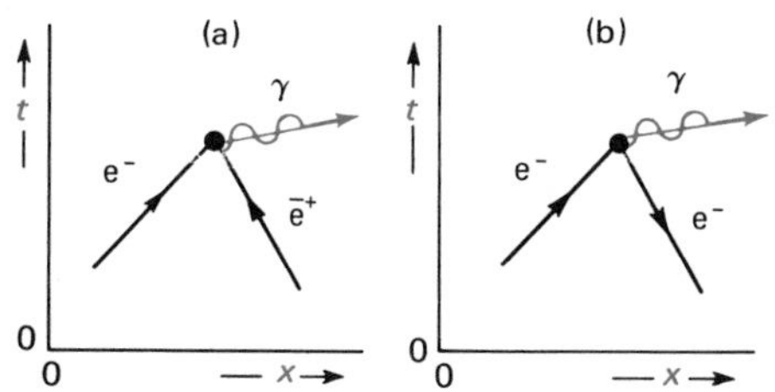

Fig. 66M. World-line diagrams showing the principle of time reversal applied to a single particle. Positron–electron annihilation becomes photon emission as in bremsstrahlung.

Diagram (a) shows the event pictured at vertex B in Fig. 66J. We now reverse the direction of the positron arrowhead, reverse the charge from plus to minus, and the classification from antiparticle to particle.

The result now looks like a twisted version of Fig. 66H(a). To bring it into agreement with observations we swing this newly labeled arrow around the vertex to obtain the same kind of event shown in Fig. 66H(a).

Feynman concluded from this kind of process that the electron–photon vertex is a fundamental principle of nature and that it may be used to represent all known electromagnetic interactions between electrons, positrons, and photons.

Furthermore, the mathematical description of an electron field moving forward in time is identical with the description of a positron field propagating backward in time, and vice-versa.

The principle of time reversal says, therefore, that any particle going forward in time is equivalent to its antiparticle going backward in time. By symmetry, any antiparticle going forward in time is equivalent to its particle going backward in time.

To see how we might apply this principle of *time reversal* to the addition of quarks to form particles, consider the strong interaction event shown in Fig. 64Q:

$$\pi^- + p^+ \rightarrow K^0 + \Lambda^0$$

In the diagram shown in Fig. 66N, each line represents a quark, with q lines running in the particle directions and $\bar{q}$ lines running oppositely. During the interaction the quark content rearranges itself among the particles. Each quark line, retaining its identity, traces out these arrangements or annihilations to form the outgoing particles. During impact, charge and baryon numbers may be annihilated or created in pairs. Note that a p quark from the proton going forward in time changes to an anti $\bar{p}$ quark going backward in time.

66.9. Parity

Parity is a mathematical treatment of what is best described as a mirror symmetry of many natural phenomena. Up until recently it was believed that the mirror image of any physical phenomenon or laboratory experiment is just as true to nature as the direct image itself. This is consistent with the principle called *conservation of parity.*

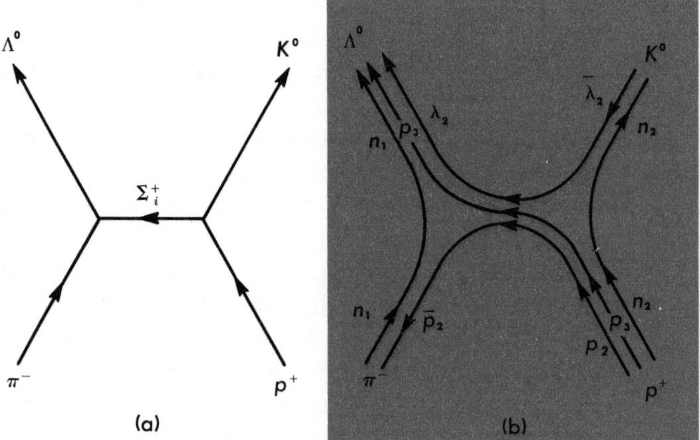

Fig. 66N. (a) Regge diagram for the strong interaction $\pi^- + p \rightarrow K^0 + \Lambda^0$ (see Fig. 64Q). (b) Duality diagram for the rearrangement of quarks during the impact. Time reversal reverses the direction, charge, and baryon numbers of the p_2 and λ_2 quarks.

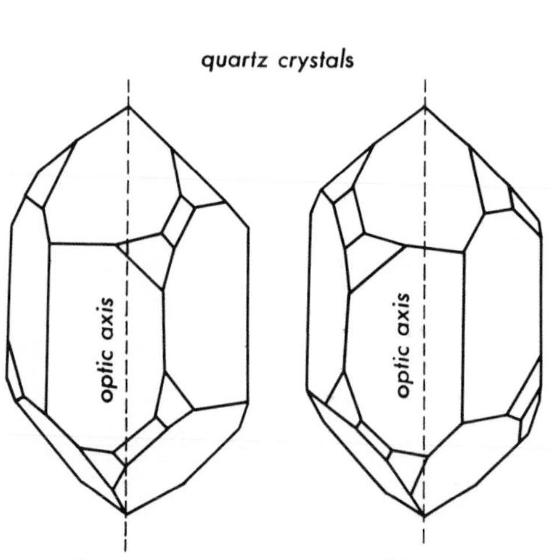

Fig. 66O. Right- and left-handed quartz crystals. Each is a mirror image of the other.

According to the conservation of parity, it was believed that if one observed an experiment by looking in a mirror and was not told he was looking in a mirror, there would be no way in which he would know it. As an example of parity, many crystalline structures show mirror symmetry. With many cubic crystals there is no question, since the image and mirror image have identical structures.

Diagrams of two kinds of quartz crystals found in nature are shown in Fig. 66O. One, called right-handed quartz, has its silicon and oxygen atoms lined up in clockwise spirals around the axis, while the left-handed quartz is a mirror image of the other and has its molecules lined up in a counterclockwise direction. One will rotate plane-polarized light clockwise as it traverses the crystal along the optic axis, while the other will rotate it counterclockwise. The existence of both of these crystals is consistent with the conservation of parity.

The first serious question regarding the conservation of parity arose in the minds of two young theoretical physicists, Yang and Lee, when they pointed out in 1956 that K^+ mesons can decay into two pions (θ mode) or three pions (τ mode) (see Sec. 64.11). An experiment suggested by Yang and Lee to test for parity was carried out by Wu, Ambler, Hayward, Hoppes, and Hudson. This experiment showed that, when radioactive cobalt-60 nuclei were lined up in a solid, with their spin vectors parallel to each other, more β particles were emitted in the parallel direction than in the antiparallel direction.

To realize the significance of this result, consider the common decay of a π^+ meson into a μ^+ and a ν_μ. The π^+ has zero spin, while the μ^+ and ν_μ have spins of $\frac{1}{2}$. To conserve angular momentum, the two particles must fly apart spinning in opposite directions as shown in Fig. 66P. Moving in the direction of the arrows, both are advancing, as would left-handed screws. The mirror image in (b), which is apparently forbidden by nature, shows both particles advancing as right-handed screws. *A spinning particle advancing as a right-handed screw is said to have positive helicity; advancing as a left-handed screw it is said to have negative helicity.*

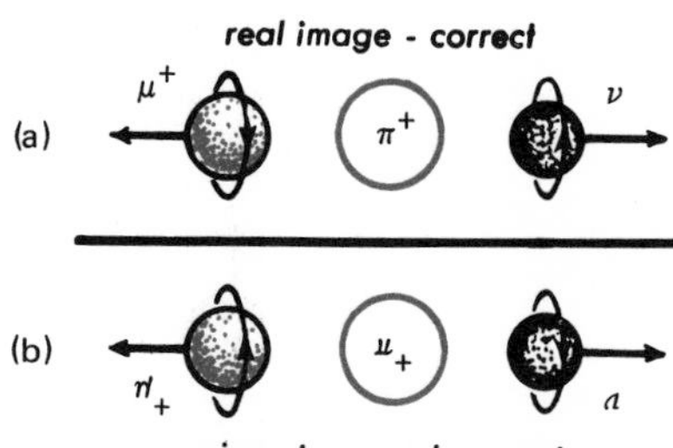

Fig. 66P. Schematic diagram showing the left-handed, or negative, helicity of μ^+ and ν particles in the decay of π^+ mesons.

From the observed spin directions of β particles, it is now known that all *neutrinos have negative helicity* while *antineutrinos have positive helicity*. With this rule and spin conservation, we see from Fig. 66Q that in π^- decay both μ^- and $\bar{\nu}_\mu$ have positive helicity.

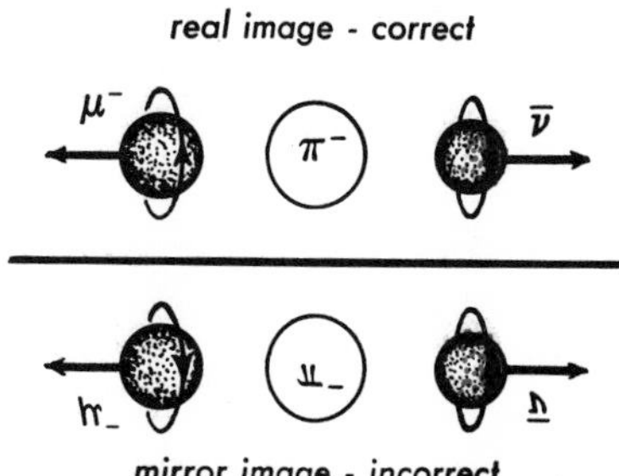

Fig. 66Q. Schematic diagram showing the right-handed, or positive, helicity of of μ^- and $\bar{\nu}$ particles in the decay of π^- mesons.

It should be pointed out that helicity has meaning for neutrinos only, since they move with the speed of light. To an observer moving faster than a muon, for example, the spin direction would appear to be the reverse of that seen by an observer moving slower than the muon.

If all the particles in one or the other of the two mirror images of Figs. 65P and 65Q are changed to their corresponding antiparticles, the resulting interaction becomes the real interaction of the other. Thus there is an over-all symmetry between the two decay reactions.

When a μ^+ decays in the customary way into a positron, a neutrino, and an antineutrino, helicity for the neutrinos as well as the μ^+ is already fixed. What helicity is imparted to the electron and the μ^+ will depend on the relative directions of all recoiling particles. If the neutrinos go off together as shown in Fig. 66R, the positron must recoil with negative helicity. If the antiprotons recoil in opposite directions, the positron, to conserve spin, can have either positive or negative helicity. Drawings for these cases will be left as exercises for the student.

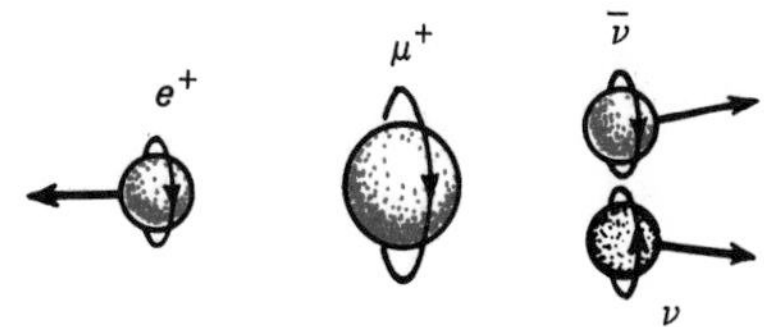

Fig. 66R. Schematic diagram of μ^+ decay showing the helicity of particles where the two neutrinos move off in the same direction.

If a distant world is made of antimatter, there is no known way whereby we on the earth can determine this. Furthermore, though μ^- and μ^+ have positive and negative helicity, respectively, there is no information we could impart to a man on a distant world that would tell him which is which.

We have seen that when high energy particles, like protons from an accelerator, collide with nuclei in a target and produce baryons, or mesons, or both, the event is called a *strong interaction. Conservation of parity* is maintained in all strong interactions.

66.10. Mean Lives of Elementary Particles

The discovery of so many elementary particles in recent years has greatly complicated all previous theories of the atomic nucleus. The fundamental questions arising in the minds of the physicists include not only the different properties of the individual particles but the way they fit into the structure of the atomic nucleus. At the present stage of development, in trying to unravel the many mysteries concerning elementary particles, some important questions stand out.

Are all of the particles shown in Figs. 64K and 64L really elementary, or are they combinations of subatomic particles we have called *quarks?* Do all *quarks* and *antiquarks* have fractional charges and masses? Could it be that some of the stars in the universe, or entire galaxies, are made of antimatter, with hydrogen atoms composed of positrons and antiprotons? Are the antimatter stars going backward in time while the regular stars, like our sun, going forward in time?

Every physicist believes that some day we will know the answers to these and many other questions about the nature of elementary particles. One interesting aspect of the nature of the particles themselves concerns their *mean life* (see Tables 64D and 64E).

The best and most direct means of determining the lifetime of any identified particle is to measure the length of the track it produces in a cloud chamber, bubble chamber, or photographic emulsion, and determine its velocity from conservation laws or the curvature of its path in a magnetic field. The lifetime τ is then given by the distance traveled divided by the velocity.

The lifetime determined in this way is the time the particle existed in the laboratory frame of reference. To find τ_0, the lifetime of the particle in its own moving frame of reference, the special theory of relativity must be used. Starting with the transformation equation, Eq.(48c), we write τ_0 for t' and τ for t^1,

$$\tau_0 = \gamma\left(\tau - \frac{vx}{c^2}\right) \tag{66e}$$

In this equation x represents the distance traveled, and τ the time of travel in the laboratory frame of reference. Placing

$$x = v\tau$$

and

$$\gamma = \frac{1}{\sqrt{1 - \frac{v^2}{c^2}}}$$

we obtain

$$\tau_0 = \tau\sqrt{1 - \frac{v^2}{c^2}} \qquad (66f)$$

This formula has been verified with high accuracy up to velocities of 99.5% the speed of light, and with approximately 10% accuracy at velocities up to 99.95% the speed of light.

Example 1. In the strong interaction event shown in Fig. 64Q, the Λ^0 particle existed long enough to travel 8.15 cm before it decayed into a proton and a negative pion. Traveling this distance with 71.0% the speed of light, find (a) its laboratory lifetime, and (b) its real lifetime.

Solution. The given quantities are $x = 8.15 \times 10^{-2}$ m, and $v = 0.710 \times 2.998 \times 10^8$ m/s $= 2.128 \times 10^8$ m/s. The laboratory lifetime is therefore given by x/v,

$$\tau = \frac{x}{v} = \frac{8.15 \times 10^{-2}}{2.128 \times 10^8}$$

$$\tau = 3.830 \times 10^{-10} \text{ s}$$

In the reference frame of the moving Λ^0 particle, the real lifetime τ_0 is found by direct substitution of known quantities in Eq.(66f):

$$\tau_0 = 3.830 \times 10^{-10} \text{ s}\sqrt{1 - (0.71)^2}$$

$$\tau_0 = 2.696 \times 10^{-10} \text{ s}$$

There is an upper limit, however, to the determination of lifetimes by this direct method. For high-energy particles traveling with 70% the speed of light, an observed track of only 3.0 ×

10^{-3}mm in a photographic emulsion corresponds to a time $\tau = (3.0 \times 10^{-6}\ \text{m})/(2.10 \times 10^{8}\ \text{m/s})$, or 1.40×10^{-14} s. In the reference frame of the moving particle, the real lifetime $\tau_0 = 1.0 \times 10^{-14}$ s.

One of the most interesting questions that has arisen out of modern physics concerns the real existence of the very short-lived elementary particles. Since particles such as p, ω, ϕ, and δ are known to have mean lives of 10^{24} s or less, do we have a right to say they exist long enough to call them particles at all?

One approach to finding an answer to this question is to graphically represent the lifetime of a few commonly recognized natural phenomena or bodies of matter, and to compare the time scales of their existence. The generally accepted lifetime of the earth, from the time of its creation to the present, is 4.5×10^{9} y, or 1.4×10^{17} s. This interval of time is represented by the colored line at the top in Fig. 66S.

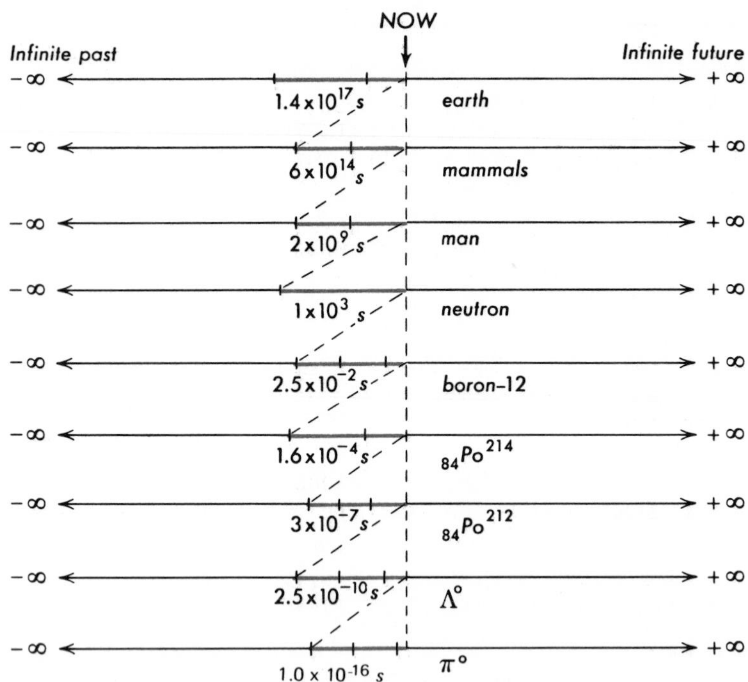

Fig. 66S. Comparison of time-scale graphs for natural bodies from the earth to elementary particles.

Since we admit the earth was created sometime in the past, we must also admit that time existed before this event, and that time must be extended to infinity in the past. While the earth still exists at the present, and will sometime come to an end in the future, time must continue on with succeeding astronomical events and by logical reasoning we find it necessary to extend the time scale to plus infinity. The line is therefore infinitely long in both directions.

Paleontologists agree that mammals have inhabited this earth for approximately two million years, or about 6×10^{14} s. On the earth's time scale this is but a tiny dot, but by a 200-fold expanded scale as in the second line, we can show the finite span of 6×10^{14} s as the colored line. This scale, like the one above it, extends to infinity in the past as well as to infinity in the future.

The average life span of individual man is approximately 70 y, or 2×10^{9} s. On the mammalian scale this is but a dot, but by expanding the scale ten-thousand-fold or more, we obtain the scale shown in the third line of the diagram. It is on this colored line that all the events of our entire life may be represented timewise.

The mean life of a free neutron is approximately 932 s, yet on the time scale of man this is so short an interval that it becomes a mere dot. Since intense beams of neutrons can be produced with atomic accelerators and atomic reactors in the laboratory, and many different kinds of events involving them at great distances from their origin are observed, their existence is just as real as the existence of man.

Let us now carry these time scales down several more steps, through the short-lived radioactive isotopes like boron-12, ${}_{84}Po^{214}$, and ${}_{84}Po^{212}$, until we reach the time scale of a π^0 meson, 2.2×10^{-16} s. Here on a sufficiently expanded time scale the interval looks like all the others. It has a finite length representing creation at the left and radioactive decay on the right. The scale extends infinitely far into the past like all the others, and it extends infinitely far into the future.

If we now step down to the ω^0 particle with a mean life of 5.2×10^{-23} s, the time of its existence had to be determined from reasonably well developed theory. Moving with three-quarters the speed of light, after its creation, this particle exists long enough to travel five to ten nuclear diameters before decaying into three π mesons. It will therefore be left to you the reader to decide whether particles with short lifetimes really exist, and whether or not there is a limit to the shortness of any time scale.

problems

1. Two protons approach each other and are electrically scattered. Construct a world-line diagram for this interaction, and assume that a neutral pion is exchanged.

2. Calculate the interaction time for the elastic scattering of two electrons, where the exchanged photon is visible green light of wavelength 5.40×10^{7} m. See Fig. 66I.

3. If a π^- and a proton come together and create a K^0 and a Λ^0, as shown in Fig. 64Q, show (a) that the conservation laws 3, 4, and 7 in Sec. 65.8 hold. (b) Could the same two colliding particles have produced K^- and Σ^+ particles?

4. Construct a Feynman diagram for the decay of a positively charged pion.

5. Construct a world-line diagram for the decay of a positively charged muon.

6. Construct a world-line diagram for the decay of a K^+ in its most prominent mode. See Sec. 64.11.

7. Construct a Feynman diagram for the decay of a K^- in its third most prominent mode. See Sec. 64.11.

8. Construct a Feynman diagram for the decay of a Λ^0 particle in its most prominent mode. See Sec. 64.14.

9.* Make (a) a Regge diagram, and (b) a duality diagram for the strong interaction shown in Fig. 64S. From the three quarks crossing the middle of the duality diagram, the exchange particle for the Regge diagram can be determined. See Figs. 65F and 65I for appropriate quarks.

10. Using the quark charges shown in Fig. 65G, show that the charge interchange in Fig. 66N gives the proper charge at the four end points. Note that when time reverses, charge reverses as does the particle antiparticle classification.

11.* If the measured distance a Σ^0 particle travels in a bubble chamber is 85.0 cm, between its creation and its decay into a Λ^0 and a γ ray, and the particle speed is 65% the speed of light, find (a) its liftime in the laboratory frame of reference, and (b) its real lifetime.

12.* A Ξ^- particle has a speed of 75% the speed of light and exists long enough to travel 6.25 cm before decaying into a Λ^0 and a π^-. Find its lifetime (a) in the laboratory frame of reference, and (b) its real lifetime. [Ans. (a) 2.780×10^{-10} s, (b) 1.839×10^{-10} s.]

13.* If the measured distance a K^0 particle travels before it decays is 9.25 cm, and the speed of the particle is 62% the speed of light, find (a) the lifetime of the particle in the laboratory frame of reference, and (b) the real lifetime.

14.* If the measured distance a Λ^0 particle travels before it distintegrates is 2.75 cm, and the particle speed is 55% the speed of light, what it its lifetime in (a) the laboratory frame of reference, and (b) in its own frame of reference.

15.* A Σ^+ track in a bubble chamber was measured to be 12.50 cm long, and from the curvature of its track in a magnetic field, its velocity was 75% the speed of light. Find (a) its lifetime in the laboratory, and (b) its real lifetime. [Ans. (a) 5.56×10^{-10} s, (b) 3.678×10^{-10} s.]

Appendix I the English system of units

In science laboratories around the world thousands of experiments of every kind and description are performed daily. From time to time and over a period of many years, science representatives from all the civilized countries of the world have met to adopt standard terminology as well as the most probable values of physical constants.

In all countries, including the United States, the *metric system* has long been the standard for scientific measurements. When the *English system* of units has been employed in civil life, legal standards have been adopted in terms of the adopted metric standards (see Introduction C).

There is a growing movement in the United States today to do away with the cumbersome English system of *inches, feet, yards,* and *miles* as units of *length,* and the *ounce, pound,* and *ton* as units of *weight* and adopt the metric system.

Many students find the most difficult part of the subject of physics to be *mechanics.* This is in large measure due to the practice of teachers and text books to present both the metric system and the English system together, as well as the methods of conversion from one system to the other. Because the *kilogram* is a *unit of mass* in the metric system, and the *pound* is the *unit of force* and *weight* in the English system, the basic principles of mechanics are unduly complicated by equating the two (which is done so often) and then carrying them along together. The relationship between the concepts of weight and mass is important, and to confuse the student with two systems intermixed is unnecessary.

It is for this reason that the author presents the metric system throughout the actual text of this book, and introduces here in the Appendix the conversion factors for transposing from one system to the other. In so doing it is hoped that the subject of physics is made easier for the student.

In referring to the metric system the abbreviation *MKSA* means *meter, kilogram, second,* and *ampere.* The English system, on the other hand, is referred to as the *FPS* system, and stands for *foot, pound, second.*

Since many industries and many branches of engineering in the United States are still using the English system of units, conversion factors and tables are found to be convenient.

Units of Length

In Introduction C it is explained how the legal standard of length in the English system is defined in terms of the standard meter:

$$1 \text{ meter} = 39.370 \text{ inches}$$

This relation is used for calculating all the conversion factors in Table IA.

TABLE IA
Conversion factors for units of length

		Km	*m*	*cm*	*in.*	*ft*	*mi*
1 kilometer	=	1	1000	100,000	39370	3280.83	0.62137
1 meter	=	0.00100	1	100	39.370	3.28083	6.21×10^{-4}
1 centimeter	=	1.0×10^{-5}	0.0100	1	0.39370	0.032808	6.21×10^{-6}
1 inch	=	2.54×10^{-5}	0.02540	2.5400	1	0.08333	1.58×10^{-5}
1 foot	=	3.05×10^{-4}	0.30480	30.480	12	1	1.89×10^{-4}
1 mile	=	1.60935	1609.35	160935	63360	5280	1

When it becomes necessary to change distances from the *MKSA* system to the *FPS* system, or vice versa, the values given in Table IA will be found most useful. To illustrate the use of such a table consider the following example.

Example 1. Find (a) the number of meters in 2.50 miles, and (b) the number of feet in 2.80 kilometers.

Solution. For the answer to (a) we examine the rows and columns of Table IA and find that 1 mile = 1609.35 meters. The answer to (a) is therefore given by the product

$$2.50 \text{ mi} = 2.50 \times 1609.35 = 4023.375 \text{ m}$$

which to four significant figures is 4023 m.

For the answer to (b) we find from the first row in Table IA, 1 kilometer = 3280.83 feet. The answer is therefore given by the product

$$2.80 \text{ mi} = 2.80 \times 3280.83 = 9186.324 \text{ ft}$$

which to four significant figures is 9186 ft.

Speed and Velocity

With the use of Table IA, it is a straight forward calculation to convert distances to speed and velocity, and obtain the following conversion factors.

TABLE IB
Conversion factors for speed and velocity

Velocity		*m/s*	*ft/s*	*Km/h*	*mi/h*	*knots*
1 m/s	=	1	3.281	3.600	2.240	1.940
1 ft/s	=	0.30480	1	1.0973	0.6818	0.5921
1 Km/h	=	0.27778	0.9113	1	0.6214	0.5396
1 mi/h	=	0.44704	1.4667	1.6093	1	0.8684
1 knot	=	0.51480	1.689	1.853	1.152	1

To illustrate the use of this table consider the following example.

Example 2. A car is traveling along a highway with a speed of 60 mi/h. Find its speed in (a) meters per second, and (b) feet per second.

Solution. From Table IB we observe that 1 mi/h = 0.44704 m/s and 1.4667 ft/s. If we multiply both factors by 60, we obtain

$$60 \frac{\text{mi}}{\text{h}} = 60 \times 0.44704 = 26.82 \frac{\text{m}}{\text{s}}$$

$$60 \frac{\text{mi}}{\text{h}} = 60 \times 1.4667 = 88.0 \frac{\text{ft}}{\text{s}}$$

Units of Mass

The unit of mass in the metric system is the *kilogram,* and in the English system it is the *slug.* Because the slug is not familiar to the beginning student, its origin, meaning, and use will be presented here.

In the construction of buildings, bridges, ships, airplanes, washing machines, etc., the engineer measures loads to be carried in pounds. Since the pound is a unit of weight, which is a force, it is necessary in the dynamics of motion to introduce a consistant unit of mass. To see how this comes about we begin with the basic dynamic equation, Newton's second law of motion:

$$F = ma \tag{1}$$

When this equation is applied to the special case of falling bodies, it is usually written in other symbols (see Sec. 4.5):

$$F_g = m\,g \tag{2}$$

In the *MKSA* system F_g is the downward force, or weight, and is measured in *newtons.* The mass m is in *kilograms,* and the acceleration due to gravity is a constant, $g = 9.80$ m/s^2. It can be seen that if the weight F_g is to be measured in pounds, and the acceleration of a freely falling body is a fixed value, a proper selection of a unit of mass is necessary to make Eq. (2) valid.

The acceleration due to gravity varies over the earth's surface. Its value lies between 32.09 ft/s^2 at the equator, and 32.26 ft/s^2 at the North and South Poles. The International Committee on Weights and Measures has adopted as standard, or accepted values, 32.174 ft/s^2 and 9.80665 m/s^2.

For practical purposes it is customary to use the round numbers 32.0 ft/s^2, or 9.80 m/s^2. In the English system we will use

$$g = 32.0 \text{ ft/s}^2 \tag{3}$$

This value differs from the accepted value by less than 1%. We will now apply this value to the freely falling body equation and define the *slug:*

$$m = \frac{F_g}{g} \tag{4}$$

The slug is that force F_g, divided by $g = 32.0$ ft/s^2, that will make $m = 1$. The equation then appears

$$m = \frac{32.0 \text{ lb}}{32.0 \text{ ft/s}^2} = 1 \text{ slug}$$

This means that to find the mass of any object in slugs, divide its weight in pounds by *g,* the acceleration due to gravity.

Example 3. A force of 12 lb is applied to an 80 lb object free to move in the direction of the force. Neglecting friction, what will be its acceleration?

Solution. We first find the mass of the moving object in slugs. Using Eq. (4), we find

$$m = \frac{80 \text{ lb}}{32 \text{ ft/s}^2} = 2.50 \text{ slugs}$$

Upon substituting known values in transposed Eq. (1), we obtain the answer:

$$a = \frac{F}{m} = \frac{12 \text{ lb}}{2.5 \text{ sl}} = 4.80 \text{ ft/s}^2$$

It should be noted that in the *FPS* system, the slug has the fundamental units

$$1 \text{ sl} = 1 \frac{\text{lb s}^2}{\text{ft}} \tag{5}$$

For all problems in dynamics the engineer expresses force in pounds, time in seconds, and mass in slugs.

Using the relations that a 1 lb weight has a mass of 453.6 grams, and that a 32 lb weight has a mass of 1 slug, the following table of conversion factors has been calculated.

TABLE IC
Conversion factors for mass

		g	*Kg*	*MT**	*sl*
1 gram	=	1	1×10^{-3}	1×10^{-6}	6.889×10^{-5}
1 kilogram	=	1×10^{3}	1	1×10^{-3}	6.889×10^{-2}
1 metric ton	=	1×10^{6}	1×10^{3}	1	6.889×10^{1}
1 slug	=	1.451×10^{4}	1.451×10^{1}	1.451×10^{-2}	1

*The metric ton is abbreviated MT.

APPLICATIONS TO SELECTED TOPICS

Gravitation

In applying Newton's law of gravitation to the English system of units, masses should be given in slugs [see Eq. (6a)]:

$$F = -G \frac{m_1 m_2}{d^2} \tag{6}$$

where the universal gravitational constant G has the value

$$G = 3.421 \times 10^{-8} \frac{\text{ft}^3}{\text{sl s}^2} \tag{7}$$

Example 4. Two cars of 4800 lb each are located close together, with their centers of mass only 6 feet apart. What is the gravitational force between them?

Solution. Converting weight in pounds to mass in slugs,

$$m = \frac{4800 \text{ lb}}{32 \text{ ft/s}^2} = 150 \text{ slugs}$$

and substituting directly into Eq. (6) gives

$$F = -3.421 \times 10^{-8} \frac{\text{ft}^3}{\text{sl s}^2} \frac{(150 \text{ sl})^2}{(36 \text{ ft})^2} = 5.94 \times 10^{-7} \text{ lb}$$

Note: This is less than one millionth of 1 lb.

Work and Energy

In calculating work and energy, the engineer uses the work equation, Eq.(9f):

$$W = F \times h \qquad (8)$$

where the force F is in pounds, and the distance h is in feet. The units of *work* are, therefore, ft lb, the product of two fundamental units. Unlike the metric system this product has no other name. (In the metric system newtons $\times$ meters are called joules.)

Example 5. Find the work done in lifting a 650-lb concrete hoist a distance of 120 ft.
Solution. By direct substitution in Eq.(8), we obtain

$$W = 650 \text{ lb} \times 120 \text{ ft} = 78{,}000 \text{ ft lb}$$

As in the metric system potential energy is given by the work equation, Eq.(9f). The engineer, therefore, specifies stored potential energy in ft lb:

$$E_p = F \times h \qquad (9)$$

Example 6. A reservoir, located in the mountains 420 ft above a power house, contains 25,000 tons of water. Calculate the stored potential energy.

Solution. Apply Eq.(9) to these known values, and obtain

$$E_p = 25{,}000 \times 2000 \text{ lb} \times 426 \text{ ft} = 2.130 \times 10^{10} \text{ ft lb}$$

To calculate kinetic energy in the English system, Eq.(9g) is appropriately used:

$$E_k = \tfrac{1}{2} m v^2 \qquad (10)$$

In most practical examples the engineer knows the weight of a moving body in pounds, and its speed in miles per hour. In applying this equation he must, therefore, convert the known weight to mass in slugs, and the speed in mi/h to ft/s.

Example 7. A 4000-lb car has a speed of 60 mi/h along a straight and level highway. What is its kinetic energy?
Solution. The mass in slugs is found by using Eq.(4):

$$m = \frac{4000 \text{ lb}}{32 \text{ ft/s}^2} = 125.0 \text{ sl}$$

The speed is obtained by using Table IB, where in the next to the bottom row we find 1 mi/h = 1.4667 ft/s. The converted speed is, therefore,

$$v = 60 \times 1.4667 = 88.0 \text{ ft/s}$$

Direct substitution in Eq.(10) now gives

$$E_k = \tfrac{1}{2} \times 125 \text{ sl} \times (88 \text{ ft/s})^2 = 4.84 \times 10^5 \text{ ft lb}$$

Power

Power is an important concept in mechanical and electrical engineering. In Chap. 9 power is defined as the time rate of doing work, or the rate at which energy is being expended:

$$\text{Power} = \frac{\text{work}}{\text{time}}$$

$$P = \frac{F \times h}{t} \qquad (11)$$

In the *FPS* system of units, *work* is given in *foot pounds, time* is in *seconds, h* is the distance moved in feet measured in the direction of the force, and *power* is in *foot pounds per second.*

Examples 8. An elevator car weighing 1250 lb rises to a height of 60 ft in 5 s. Find the power developed.
Solution. By direct substitution in Eq.(11), we obtain

$$P = \frac{1250 \text{ lb} \times 60 \text{ ft}}{5 \text{ s}} = 15{,}000 \, \frac{\text{ft lb}}{\text{s}}$$

It is customary for the engineer to express power in units called *horsepower.* Historically this unit is said to be the rate at which a horse can do work. Since this varies between animals, it was James Watt who first defined unit horsepower as equivalent to 550 ft lb/s:

$$1 \text{ hp} = 550 \, \frac{\text{ft lb}}{\text{s}} \tag{12}$$

By comparison with the *MKSA* system of units,

$$550 \, \frac{\text{ft lb}}{\text{s}} = 746 \text{ watts}$$

$$1 \text{ hp} = 746 \text{ W} \tag{13}$$

Example 9. (a) Find the horsepower developed in lifting 4500 lb a distance of 500 ft in 1.0 min. (b) Find the power in watts, or kilowatts.
Solution. First calculate the power developed by using Eq.(11):

$$P = \frac{4500 \text{ lb} \times 500 \text{ ft}}{60 \text{ s}} = 37{,}500 \, \frac{\text{ft lb}}{\text{s}}$$

Dividing by 550 ft lb/s gives

$$\frac{37{,}500 \text{ ft lb/s}}{550 \text{ ft lb/s}} = 68.2 \text{ hp}$$

To convert this answer to watts, we can use Eq.(13), and obtain

$$P = 68.2 \times 746 = 50{,}900 \text{ watts}$$

or

$$P = 50.9 \text{ KW}$$

problems for appendix I

1. Calculate the distance to the moon in feet if the distance is 3.84×10^8m.

2. The radius of the moon is 1.610×10^6 Km. Calculate its diameter in (a) feet, and (b) miles.

3. A train with all its cars is 1520 ft long. Find its length in (a) meters, and (b) kilometers.

4. A tall building is 1260 ft high. Find its height in (a) meters, and (b) in centimeters.

5. In the 1968 Olympics the 200 m hurdles was won by Harry Hillman of the United States. His world record time was 24.6 s. Find his average speed in (a) m/s, (b) ft/s, and (c) mi/h.

6. In the 1968 Olympics the world record in the 100 meter run was set by Jim Hines of the United States in 9.90 s. Calculate his average speed in (a) m/s, (b) ft/s, and (c) mi/h.

7. A jet passenger plane crosses the United States from San Francisco to Washington D.C., a distance of 2800 mi in 4 h 42 min. Find its average cruising speed in (a) mi/h, and (b) m/s.

8. Since the inception of the Olympic Games in 1896 the world records in the following races were set by:

(a) 100 m	Jim Hines	U.S.A.	1968	9.90 s
(b) 200 m	Tommie Smith	U.S.A.	1968	19.80 s
(c) 400 m	Lee Evans	U.S.A.	1968	43.80 s
(d) 800 m	Ralph Doubell	Australia	1968	1 min 44.3 s
(e) 1500 m	Kipchoge Keino	Kenya	1968	3 min 34.9 s
(f) 3000 m	Gaston Roelants	Belgium	1964	8 min 30.8 s
(g) 5000 m	Vladimir Kuts	U.S.S.R.	1956	13 min 39.6 s
(h) 10,000 m	Billy Mills	U.S.A.	1964	28 min 24.4 s

Calculate the average speed of each runner in m/s and in mi/h. Draw a graph of the results by plotting the speed vertically in m/s, and the distance horizontally in meters.

9. The distance from Hawaii to San Francisco is 2200 mi. If a ship cruises at a speed of 18 knots, how long will it take to make the voyage?

10. A propeller-driven plane leaving New York for London cruises at a speed of 385 mi/h. A jet plane leaving the same airport 1 h later cruises at 625 mi/h. (a) How long will it take the second plane to overtake the first plane? (b) How far will they both have traveled?

11. Two planes leave the same airport at the same time to fly to the same distant city. One has a speed of 240 mi/h, and the other a speed of 320 mi/h. How long will it take for the faster plane to get 180 mi ahead of the other?

12. A jet airliner starting from rest at the end of a runway acquires a speed of 160 mi/h in a distance of 5800 ft. Calculate (a) the time in seconds, (b) the acceleration in ft/s^2, and (c) the speed acquired at the end of 15 s.

13. A locomotive starting from rest travels with an acceleration of 1.50 ft/s^2 for 10 s. After traveling at the acquired speed for 8.0 s, the brakes are applied, stopping the locomotive in 7 s. Find (a) the maximum speed acquired, (b) the acceleration during braking, (c) the distance traveled during acceleration, (d) the distance traveled at constant speed, and (e) the distance traveled during braking.

14. A train starting from rest maintains a constant acceleration of 0.25 ft/s^2 How long will it take it to go 2.0 kilometers?

15. The engine of a train 2500 ft long stands at a road crossing. If the train starts up and maintains a constant acceleration of 0.15 ft/s^2, how long must a motorist wait for the end of the train to cross the intersection?

16. A car starts from rest and undergoes a constant acceleration of 6.0 ft/s^2. A motorcycle starts from rest at the same point 2 s later, and maintains an acceleration of 8.0 ft/s^2. (a) Find the time it takes the motorcycle to overtake the car, (b) the distance both have traveled, and (c) the speed of the motorcycle as it passes the car.

17. A plane coming in for a landing travels a distance of 5000 ft along a runway before coming to rest. Assuming constant acceleration and a landing speed of 120 mi/h, find (a) the acceleration, (b) the total time for landing, and (c) the distance traveled during the first 10 s.

18. Arrows are shot vertically upward at 2-s intervals with an initial speed of 160 ft/s. After several arrows have been shot, (a) how long will each arrow be in the air before another passes it, and (b) at what distances above the origin will arrows be passing each other? Check your answers by plotting a graph with distances vertical and time horizontal.

19. A dart shot vertically upward reaches a height of 144 ft during the first second of flight. Find (a) the time to reach the highest point, (b) the maximum height, and (c) the velocity of projection.

20. A 3600-lb car starts from rest and acquires a speed of 30 mi/h in 15 s. Find (a) the mass of the car, (b) the average acceleration in ft/s, and (c) the average accelerating force.

21. A small car of 1200 lb starts from rest and acquires a speed of 45 mi/h in 8 s. Find (a) the mass of the car, (b) the average acceleration in ft/s^2, and (c) the average force in pounds.

22. A Boeing 747 jet passenger plane with a weight of 350 tons has four engines, each with a thrust of 21 tons. If the take-off speed is 170 mi/h, find (a) the mass of the plane, (b) the acceleration in ft/s^2, (c) the time for take-off, and (d) the minimum length of runway.

23. A Lockheed C5-A jet passenger plane has four engines, each with a thrust of 41,000 lb. If it requires a 7500 ft runway to take off at 180 mi/h, find (a) the acceleration, (b) the mass of the plane, (c) the weight of the plane, and (d) the time for take-off.

24. A Douglass Super DC-8 passenger plane with a total take-off weight of 262 tons has four engines. If each engine has a thrust of 9 tons, and the take-off speed is 150 mi/h, find (a) the mass of the plane, (b) the acceleration, (c) the time of take-off, and (d) the minimum length of runway.

25. A Boeing 747 jet passenger plane has a weight of 350 tons, and a cruising speed of 625 mi/h. (a) Find the plane's mass. If the plane is in straight and level flight at 40,000 ft, find (b) the potential energy, and (c) the kinetic energy.

26. A Douglass DC-8 super jet has a weight of 262 tons, and a cruising speed of 600 mi/h when flying at an altitude of 40,000 ft. Find the plane's (a) mass, (b) potential energy, and (c) kinetic energy.

27. A 50-ton rocket takes off from its launching pad and acquires a vertical velocity of 12,000 ft/s at an altitude of 20 mi. Calculate (a) its mass, (b) its potential energy, and (c) its kinetic energy.

28. A 27-ton rocket takes off vertically from its launching pad and acquires a velocity of 1260 mi/h at an altitude of 50,000 ft. Assuming the acceleration due to gravity to be constant at 32 ft/s^2, find (a) its potential energy, and (b) its kinetic energy. Assuming constant acceleration of the rocket, find (c) the acceleration, (d) the total thrust of the rocket motor, (e) the total energy, (f) the time from take-off, and (g) the power developed.

29. A steam-operated catapult 300 ft long launches a 64-ton jet photoreconnaissance plane from the deck of an aircraft carrier. Starting at rest at one end, the plane acquires its take-off speed at 90 mi/h at the other. Find (a) the acceleration, (b) the average force, (c) the work done, (d) the time to accelerate, and (e) the power developed.

30. An elevator car of 1000 lb contains 5 persons whose average weight is 120 lb each. Find the tension in the cable supporting this total load if it is (a) standing still, (b) moving upward with an acceleration of 1 ft/s^2, and (c) starting downward with an acceleration of 1 ft/s^2.

Appendix II elements of trigonometry useful in solving physics problems

Trigonometry of the Right Triangle

Of the mathematics to be encountered in this book, none involves more than the simplest equations in algebra and the three most common functions in trigonometry, *sine, cosine,* and *tangent.* These, however, are quite generally used and a brief review of the trigonometric functions is not out of place here. The principal use of the sin, cos, and tan occurs in problems where the solution requires the solving of a right triangle.

As shown in Fig. 1 the small letters *a, b,* and *c* represent the lengths of the sides of the right triangle and the capital letters *A, B,* and *C* represent their corresponding opposite angles; angle $C = 90°$. By definition

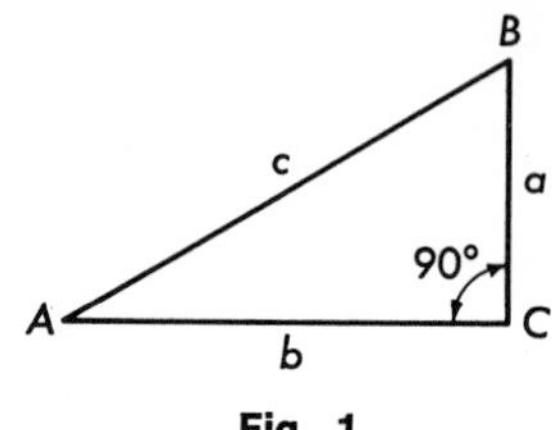

Fig. 1.

$$\sin = \frac{\text{side opposite}}{\text{hypotenuse}}, \qquad \cos = \frac{\text{side adjacent}}{\text{hypotenuse}},$$

$$\tan = \frac{\text{side opposite}}{\text{side adjacent}}$$

It would be well to memorize these definitions and from them and Fig. 1 practice writing down the following equations:

$$(1)\quad \sin A = \frac{a}{c} \qquad (2)\quad \cos A = \frac{b}{c} \qquad (3)\quad \tan A = \frac{a}{b}$$

$$(4)\quad \sin B = \frac{b}{c} \qquad (5)\quad \cos B = \frac{a}{c} \qquad (6)\quad \tan B = \frac{b}{a}$$

Each of these equations is a relation between one angle and two sides of the triangle. By transposing they take on another useful form. Equations (1) and (2), for example, become

$$(7)\quad a = c \sin A \qquad (8)\quad b = c \cos A$$

If two of the sides of any right triangle are known, the other side and the two acute angles can be calculated from the above equations. This is done by making use of trigonometric tables of sin, cos, and tan given in the table on the inside back cover for all angles between 0° and 90°.

Example 1. For a given right triangle, angle $C = 90°$, the side $a = 6$ cm, and side $c = 12$ cm. Find angle A, angle B, and side b.

Solution. Using Eq.(1) and substituting, $\sin A = 6/12 = 0.5$. Looking up 0.500 in the sin column of the table on the inside back cover, the angle 30° is read. Since the sum of the three angles in any triangle is 180°,

$$A + B + C = 180° \tag{9}$$

Subtraction gives angle $B = 60°$. Applying Eq.(8), $b = c \cos A$, we look up the cos of 30° in the tables and find 0.866, which substituted for $\cos A$ gives $b = 12 \times 0.866 = 10.39$ cm.

When two of the sides of a right triangle are known, the other side can also be calculated from the theorem that the square on the hypotenuse equals the sum of the squares of the other two sides:

$$c^2 = a^2 + b^2 \tag{10}$$

When in a right triangle, one of the acute angles is known, only the length of one side need be known to calculate the lengths of the other two sides.

From the definitions of the sin, cos, and tan in Eqs.(1), (2), and (3) it will be noted that the tan is equal to the sin divided by the cos:

$$\tan \theta = \frac{\sin \theta}{\cos \theta} \tag{11}$$

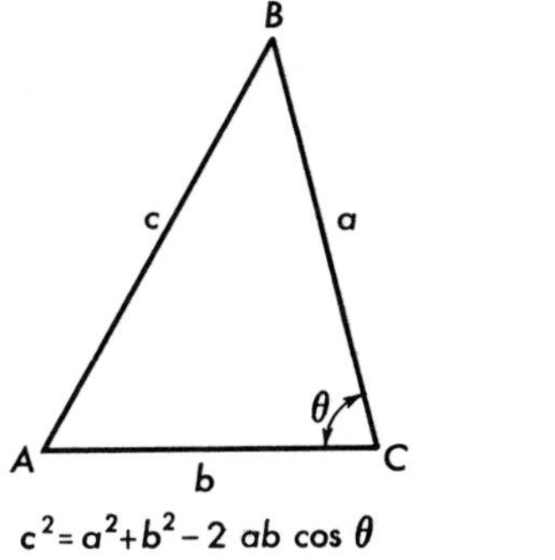

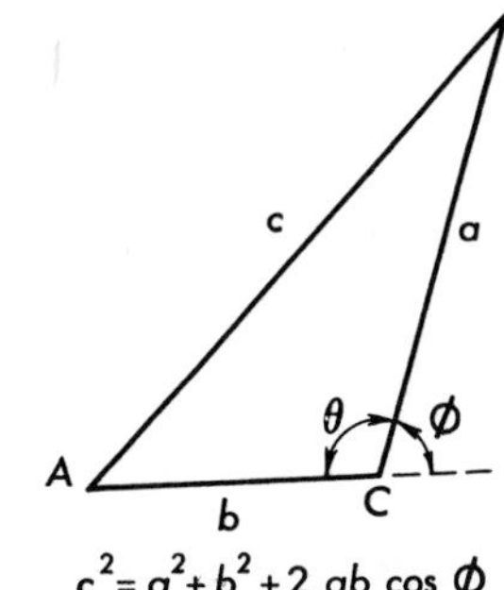

Fig. 2.

Solution of Any Triangle

Many times in the solving of a physics problem it becomes necessary to solve an oblique triangle (see Fig. 2). Where two sides and the included angle of such a triangle are known, the **law of cosines** may be used to calculate the other side:

$$c^2 = a^2 + b^2 - 2ab \cos \theta \tag{12}$$

If the included angle is less than 90° as shown in diagram (a), the values of a and b and $\cos \theta$ are substituted directly into Eq.(12) and the value of the side c calculated. If the angle θ is greater than 90°, as in diagram (b), the supplementary angle ϕ is found and Eq.(13) used:

$$c^2 = a^2 + b^2 + 2ab \cos \phi \tag{13}$$

In reality Eqs.(12) and (13) are one and the same equation since $\phi = 180° - \theta$. In the special case $\theta = 90°$, the cosine term becomes zero, since $\cos 90° = 0$, and both formulas reduce to Eq.(10), as they should.

In words, the *law of cosines* states: *the square of any side of a triangle is equal to the sum of the squares on the other two sides minus twice their product multiplied by the cosine of the included angle.*

When three sides of a triangle are known, the angles can all be determined from Eq.(12). Transposing all but $\cos \theta$ to the same side of the equation,

$$\cos \theta = \frac{a^2 + b^2 - c^2}{2ab} \tag{14}$$

With this as a general formula for angle θ, similar equations for all three angles of any triangle may be written:

$$\cos A = \frac{b^2 + c^2 - a^2}{2bc}, \qquad \cos B = \frac{c^2 + a^2 - b^2}{2ca}, \qquad \cos C = \frac{a^2 + b^2 - c^2}{2ab} \tag{15}$$

A negative value for the cosine calculated from these equations means that the angle is greater than 90°. Its value can be found by looking in the tables for the angle whose sine has the same positive value, and then add 90°. For example, suppose $\cos A$ equals -0.5. Looking up the angle whose sine is $+0.500$ we find 30°. Angle A is therefore $30° + 90°$ or 120°.

If two angles and the included side of an oblique triangle are known, the other two sides are readily calculated from the well-known **law of sines:**

$$\frac{a}{\sin A} = \frac{b}{\sin B} = \frac{c}{\sin C} \tag{16}$$

Any two terms from these equalities give an equation with only one unknown.

The trigonometric functions sin, cos, and tan apply not only to angles between 0° and 90° but to larger angles as well. How they apply is illustrated in Fig. 3, where four circles of unit radius are drawn. Diagram (a) shows a

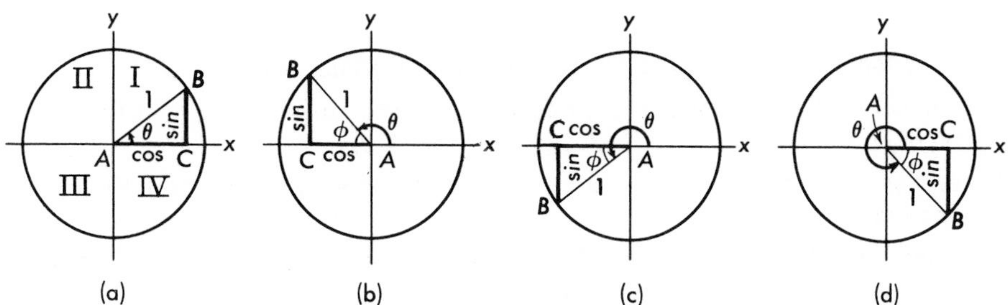

Fig. 3.

right triangle ABC with angle θ in the first quadrant. It follows from the definitions of the sin and cos given by Eqs.(1) and (2) that

$$\sin\theta = BC/AB, \qquad \text{and} \qquad \cos\theta = AC/AB$$

Since $AB = 1$, the $\sin\theta$ becomes just the length of the line BC. From Eq.(11), $\tan\theta = BC/AC$.

All angles between 90° and 180° lie in the second quadrant, and are represented by θ in diagram (b). Similarly, angles between 180° and 270° lie in the third quadrant as illustrated in diagram (c), and angles between 270° and 360° lie in the fourth quadrant as illustrated in diagram (d). In all quadrants the length of the line $BC = \sin\theta$, the length of the line $AC = \cos\theta$, and the ratio $BC/AC = \tan\theta$.

To find the numerical values of the functions for all angles greater than 90°, the angle ϕ is first determined by finding the difference between θ and 180° and/or 360°, as the case may be. The values of $\sin\phi$, $\cos\phi$, and $\tan\phi$ are then read from the table on the inside back cover. In the second quadrant the sin, being in the $+y$ direction, is positive, whereas the cos, being in the $-x$ direction, is negative. In the third quadrant the sine and cosine are both negative, whereas in the fourth quadrant the sine is negative and the cosine positive.

Example 2. Let $\theta = 150°$. Find $\sin\theta$, $\cos\theta$, and $\tan\theta$.

Solution. Subtracting from 180° gives $\phi = 30°$. From the trigonometric table, $\sin 30° = 0.500$, $\cos 30° = 0.866$, and $\tan 30° = 0.577$, giving $\sin 150° = 0.500$, $\cos 150° = -0.866$, and $\tan 150° = -0.577$.

---

problems in trigonometry

1. Find the number of degrees in the following angles: (a) $\sin\theta = 0.342$, (b) $\sin\theta = 0.809$, (c) $\cos\theta = 0.530$, (d) $\cos\theta = 0.454$, (e) $\tan\theta = 0.520$, and (f) $\tan\theta = 1.881$.

2. Find the sin, cos, and tan for the following angles: (a) 32.6°, and (b) 84.3°. [Ans. (a) 0.539, 0.842, 0.639; (b) 0.995, 0.0993, 10.02.]

3. Find the sin, cos, and tan for the following angles: (a) 118°, (b) 205°, and (c) 325°.

4. Find the angle θ for each of the following: (a) $\cos\theta = -0.249$, (b) $\sin\theta = -0.618$, and (c) $\tan\theta = -2.023$. [Ans. (a) 104.4° or 255.6°, (b) 116.3° or 306.3°, (c) 218.2° or 321.8°.]

5. One of the acute angles of a right triangle is 33° and the shortest side is 5 m long. Find the lengths of the other two sides and the remaining angle.

6. One of the acute angles of a right triangle is 48° and the hypotenuse is 6 m long. Find the other angle and the lengths of the other two sides. [Ans. 42°, 4.01 m, 4.46 m.]

7. A right triangle has sides of length: 3 ft, 4 ft, and 5 ft. Make a diagram to scale and measure the angles. Calculate the angles and compare them with those measured.

8. If the hypotenuse of a right triangle is 16 m long and one side is 10 m long, what is the length of the remaining side and the size of the two acute angles? [Ans. 12.5 m, 38.7°, and 51.3°.]

9. From a point on the level ground 180 ft from the base of a flag pole, an observer sights the top at an angle of 48° 24′. How high is the flag pole?

10. A base line 160 m long is measured along the beach; from its ends a rock can be seen some distance off shore. If the angles that the lines of sight from the ends make with the base line are 90° and 72.5°, how far from shore is the rock? [Ans. 508 m.]

11. A base line 20 m long is measured along the bank of a river, and from its ends a tree on the opposite bank is sighted. If the angles that these lines make with the base line are 65.5° and 72.6°, what is the width of the river? Make a diagram to scale.

12. To find the distance to a mountain peak, a base line 2 mi long is measured out on level ground in the valley below. From each end of this line the peak is sighted through a surveyor's telescope, and the lines of sight are found to make angles of 74.5° and 67.2° with the base line. Find the distance to the peak from the ends of the base line. Make a diagram to scale. [Ans. (a) 2.97 mi, (b) 3.11 mi.]

13. A ship in distress is sighted from two lighthouses 10 mi apart. From the first lighthouse the line of sight to the ship is found to make an angle of 125° with the line of sight to the second lighthouse, while from the second the line of sight is found to make 48° with the line of sight to the first lighthouse. How far is the ship from the nearest lighthouse? Make a diagram to scale.

14. When the sun is 35.4° above the horizon, the shadow of a tall tree is found to be 260 ft long, as measured along level ground from the base of the tree. How high is the tree? [Ans. 185 ft.]

15. Two sides of a triangle are 24.8 m and 32.6 m, respectively, and the included angle is 35.5°. Find the length of the other side, and the values of the other two angles.

16. Two sides of a triangle are 5.7 m and 8.4 m, respectively, and the included angle is 115°. Find the length of the other side, and the values of the other two angles. [Ans. 12.0 m, 39.4°, and 35.6°.]

17. From a point on level ground 150 ft from the base of a flag pole, an observer sights the top at an elevation angle of 35°. How high is the flag pole? [Ans. 105 ft.]

18. A base line 400 ft long is measured along the ocean shore, and from the end a rock can be seen offshore. If the angles that the lines of sight make with the base line are 90° and 75°, how far offshore is the rock? [Ans. 1490 ft.]

Appendix III the Nobel Prize winners in physics

1901 Röntgen, Wilhelm Conrad (1845–1923), German. *Discovery of X Rays.*
1902 Lorentz, Hendrik Antoon (1853–1928), Dutch, and
Zeeman, Pieter (1865–1943), Dutch. *Zeeman Effect.*
1903 Becquerel, Henri Antoine (1852–1908), French. *Discovery of Radioactivity.*
Curie, Pierre (1859–1906), French, and
Curie, Marie Sklodowska (1867–1934), Polish chemist in France. *Studies of Radioactivity.*
1904 Lord Rayleigh (John William Strutt) (1842–1919), English. *Studies of Gases.*
1905 Lenard, Philipp (1862–1947), German. *Studies of Cathode Rays.*
1906 Thomson, Sir Joseph John (1856–1940), English. *Discharges through Gases.*
1907 Michelson, Albert A. (1852–1931), American. *Precision Optical Instruments.*
1908 Lippmann, Gabriel (1845–1921), French. *Interference Color Photography.*
1909 Marconi, Guglielmo (1874–1937), Italian, and
Braun, Ferdinand (1850–1918), German. *Development of Wireless.*
1910 Van der Waals, Johannes D. (1837–1923), Dutch. *Gas Laws.*
1911 Wien, Wilhelm (1864–1928), German. *Heat Radiation Laws.*
1912 Dalen, Gustaf (1869–1937), Swedish. *Automatic Lighting of Lighthouses.*
1913 Kamerlingh-Onnes, Heike (1853–1926), Dutch. *Liquid Helium and Low Temperatures.*
1914 Von Laue, Max Theodor Felix (1879–1960), German. *Diffraction of X Rays.*
1915 Bragg, Sir W. H. (1862–1942), English, and his son
Bragg, Sir W. L. (1890–1971), English. *Crystal Structure.*
1917 Barkla, Charles G. (1877–1944), English. *Characteristic X Rays of the Elements.*
1918 Planck, Max (1858–1947), German. *Quantum Theory of Radiation.*
1919 Stark, Johannes (1874–1957), German. *The Stark Effect of Spectrum Lines.*
1920 Guillaume, Charles E. (1861–1938), Spanish. *Study of Nickel-Steel Alloys.*
1921 Einstein, Albert (1879–1955), German. *Theory of Relativity and the Photoelectric Effect.*
1922 Bohr, Niels (1885–1962), Danish. *Theory of Atomic Structure.*
1923 Millikan, Robert A. (1868–1953), American. *Charge on Electron and Photoelectric Effect.*
1924 Siegbahn, Karl M. (1886–   ), Swedish. *X-Ray Spectroscopy.*
1925 Franck, James (1882–1964), German, and
Hertz, Gustav (1887–   ), German. *Electron Impact on Atoms.*

1926 Perrin, Jean B. (1870–1942), French. *Discovery of the Equilibrium of Sedimentation.*
1927 Compton, Arthur H. (1892–1962), American. *Compton Effect.*
Wilson, Charles T. R. (1869–1959), English. *Wilson Cloud Chamber.*
1928 Richardson, Sir Owen Willans (1879–1959), English. *Studies of Thermal Ions.*
1929 De Broglie, Louis V. (1892–), French. *Wave Character of Electrons.*
1930 Raman, Sir Chandrasekhara V. (1888–1970), Indian. *Raman Effect.*
1932 Heisenberg, Werner (1901–), German. *Creation of Quantum Mechanics.*
1933 Schrödinger, Edwin (1887–1961), German, and
Dirac, P. A. M. (1902–), English. *Atomic Theory.*
1935 Chadwick, James (1891–), English. *Discovery of the Neutron.*
1936 Hess, Victor F. (1883–1964), Austrian. *Discovery of Cosmic Rays.*
Anderson, Carl D. (1905–), American. *Discovery of Positron.*
1937 Davisson, Clinton J. (1881–1958), American and
Thompson, George P. (1892–), English. *Electron Diffraction by Crystals.*
1938 Fermi, Enrico (1901–1954), Italian. *Slow-Neutron Reactions.*
1939 Lawrence, Ernest O. (1901–1958), American. *Development of Cyclotron.*
1940, 1941, 1942, not awarded
1943 Stern, O. (1888–1969), German. *Magnetic Moment of Proton.*
1944 Rabi, I. I. (1898–), American. *Magnetic Moments of Nuclei.*
1945 Pauli, W. (1900–1958), Swiss. *Pauli Exclusion Principle.*
1946 Bridgman, P. W. (1882–1961), American. *Physical Effects of High Pressures.*
1947 Appleton, Sir Ed. V. (1892–1965), English. *Exploration of the Ionosphere.*
1948 Blackett, P. M. S. (1897–), English. *Discoveries in Cosmic Radiation.*
1949 Yukawa, H. (1907–), Japanese. *Theoretical Prediction of Mesons.*
1950 Powell, C. F. (1903–1969), English. *Photographic Cosmic-Ray Studies.*
1951 Cockcroft, Sir J. D. (1897–1967), English, and
Walton, E. T. S. (1903–), English. *First Transmutation of Atomic Nuclei.*
1952 Bloch, Felix (1905–), American. *Nuclear Magnetic Moments.*
Purcell, Ed. M. (1912–), American. *Radio Astronomy.*
1953 Zernike, Frits (1888–1966), Dutch. *Phase Contrast Microscope.*
1954 Born, Max (1882–1970), German. *Quantum Mechanics, and Wave Functions.*
Bothe, Walther (1891–1957), German. *Quantum Mechanics, and Wave Functions.*
1955 Kusch, P. (1911–), American, and
Lamb, W. E. (1913–), American. *Microwave Spectroscopy and Atomic Structure.*
1956 Shockley, W. (1910–), American,
Brattain, W. H. (1902–), American, and
Bardeen, J. (1908–), American. *Semiconductors, and Their Application to Transistors.*
1957 Yang, C. N. (1922–), American, and
Lee, T. D. (1926–), American. *Studies of the Concept of Parity in Atomic Physics.*
1958 Cerenkov, P. A. (1904–), Russian,

Tamm, I. E. (1895–1971), Russian, and
Frank, I. M. (1908–), Russian. *Discovery and Study of Cerenkov Radiation.*
1959 Segrè, E. (1905–), American, and
Chamberlain, O. (1920–), American. *Discovery of the Antiproton.*
1960 Glaser, D. A. (1926–), American. *The Bubble Chamber.*
1961 Hofstadter, Robt. (1916–), American, and
Mossbauer, R. L. (1930–), German. *Nuclear Radiation and Absorption.*
1962 Landau, L. D. (1908–1968), Russian. *Mathematical Explanation of Very Low Temperature Phenomena.*
1963 Goeppert-Mayer, Maria (1906–1972), American, and
Jensen, J. Hans D. (1906–), German. *Nuclear Shell Model.*
Wigner, E. (1902–), American. *Theoretical Work on Symmetry and Parity.*
1964 Townes, C. H. (1915–), American,
Basov, N. (1922–), Russian, and
Prokhorov, A. (1916–), Russian. *Development of Lasers and Masers.*
1965 Feynman, R. P. (1918–), American,
Schwinger, J. S. (1918–), American, and
Tomonaga, S. (1906–), Japanese. *Research in Quantum Electrodynamics.*
1966 Kastler, Alfred (1902–), French. *Theoretical Atomic Investigations.*
1967 Bethe, H. A. (1906–), American. *Sources of Solar and Stellar Energy.*
1968 Alvarez, L. W. (1911–), American. *Elementary Atomic Particle Research.*
1969 Gell-Mann, M. (1929–), American. *Nuclear Theory.*
1970 Alfvén, H. (1908–), Swedish. *Study of Plasmas.*
Néel, L. (1905–), French. *Research in Ferrimagnetism and Antiferromagnetism.*
1971 Gabor, D. (1900–), American. *Three Dimensional Lensless Method of Photography (Holography)*

Appendix IV periodic table of the chemical elements

IA	IIA	IIIB	IVB	VB	VIB	VIIB	VIIIB			IB	IIB	IIIA	IVA	VA	VIA	VIIA	
						METALS						NONMETALS					
1 **H** 1.0080																	2 **He** 4.00260
3 **Li** 6.941	4 **Be** 9.01218											5 **B** 10.81	6 **C** 12.011	7 **N** 14.0067	8 **O** 15.9994	9 **F** 18.9984	10 **Ne** 20.179
11 **Na** 22.9898	12 **Mg** 24.305											13 **Al** 26.9815	14 **Si** 28.086	15 **P** 30.9738	16 **S** 32.06	17 **Cl** 35.453	18 **Ar** 39.948
19 **K** 39.102	20 **Ca** 40.08	21 **Sc** 44.9559	22 **Ti** 47.90	23 **V** 50.9414	24 **Cr** 51.996	25 **Mn** 54.9380	26 **Fe** 55.847	27 **Co** 58.9332	28 **Ni** 58.71	29 **Cu** 63.546	30 **Zn** 65.37	31 **Ga** 69.72	32 **Ge** 72.59	33 **As** 74.9216	34 **Se** 78.96	35 **Br** 79.904	36 **Kr** 83.80
37 **Rb** 85.4678	38 **Sr** 87.62	39 **Y** 88.9059	40 **Zr** 91.22	41 **Nb** 92.9064	42 **Mo** 95.94	43 **Tc** 98.9062[a]	44 **Ru** 101.07	45 **Rh** 102.9055	46 **Pd** 106.4	47 **Ag** 107.868	48 **Cd** 112.40	49 **In** 114.82	50 **Sn** 118.69	51 **Sb** 121.75	52 **Te** 127.60	53 **I** 126.9045	54 **Xe** 131.30
55 **Cs** 132.9055	56 **Ba** 137.34	57–71 Lanthanide Elements	72 **Hf** 178.49	73 **Ta** 180.9479	74 **W** 183.85	75 **Re** 186.2	76 **Os** 190.2	77 **Ir** 192.22	78 **Pt** 195.09	79 **Au** 196.9665	80 **Hg** 200.59	81 **Tl** 204.37	82 **Pb** 207.2	83 **Bi** 208.9806	84 **Po** (210)[b]	85 **At** (210)[b]	86 **Rn** (222)[b]
87 **Fr** (223)[b]	88 **Ra** 226.0254[a]	89–103 Actinide Elements	104 **Rf** (258)[b]	105 **Ha** (260)[b]													

Lanthanide Elements (Rare Earth)	57 **La** 138.9055	58 **Ce** 140.12	59 **Pr** 140.9077	60 **Nd** 144.24	61 **Pm** (147)[b]	62 **Sm** 150.4	63 **Eu** 151.96	64 **Gd** 157.25	65 **Tb** 158.9254	66 **Dy** 162.50	67 **Ho** 164.9303	68 **Er** 167.26	69 **Tm** 168.9342	70 **Yb** 173.04	71 **Lu** 174.97
Actinide Elements	89 **Ac** (227)[b]	90 **Th** 232.0381[a]	91 **Pa** 231.0359[a]	92 **U** 238.029	93 **Np** 237.0482[a]	94 **Pu** (242)[b]	95 **Am** (243)[b]	96 **Cm** (247)[b]	97 **Bk** (247)[b]	98 **Cf** (251)[b]	99 **Es** (254)[b]	100 **Fm** (253)[b]	101 **Md** (256)[b]	102 **No** (254)[b]	103 **Lw** (257)[b]

[a] Mass of most commonly available, long-lived isotope. [b] Mass number of most stable or best known isotope.

Appendix V
electron subshells

The table shows the order in which the electron subshells are filled, in the building up of the elements of the periodic table. Atomic weights are given with respect to carbon-12 as 12 even.

n + 1	Sub-Shells	1	2	3	4	5	6	7	8	9	10	11	12	13	14
1	1s	1.0080 H 1	4.003 He 2												
2	2s	6.939 Li 3	9.012 Be 4												
3	2p	10.81 B 5	12.000 C 6	14.007 N 7	15.999 O 8	18.998 F 9	20.183 Ne 10								
	3s	22.990 Na 11	24.312 Mg 12												
4	3p	26.98 Al 13	28.08 Si 14	30.974 P 15	32.064 S 16	35.453 Cl 17	39.948 Ar 18								
	4s	39.102 K 19	40.08 Ca 20												
5	3d	44.96 Sc 21	47.90 Ti 22	50.94 V 23	51.996 Cr 24	54.94 Mn 25	55.85 Fe 26	58.93 Co 27	58.71 Ni 28	63.54 Cu 29	65.37 Zn 30				
	4p	69.72 Ga 31	72.59 Ge 32	74.92 As 33	78.96 Se 34	79.91 Br 35	83.80 Kr 36								
	5s	85.47 Rb 37	87.62 Sr 38												
6	4d	88.90 Y 39	91.22 Zr 40	92.91 Nb 41	95.94 Mo 42	(99) Tc 43	101.1 Ru 44	102.91 Rh 45	106.4 Pd 46	107.870 Ag 47	112.40 Cd 48				
	5p	114.82 In 49	118.69 Sn 50	121.75 Sb 51	127.60 Te 52	126.90 I 53	131.3 Xe 54								
	6s	132.90 Cs 55	137.34 Ba 56												

APPENDIX V (Cont.)

Shell	Subshell														
7	4f	138.91 La 57	140.12 Ce 58	140.91 Pr 59	144.24 Nd 60	(145) Pm 61	150.35 Sm 62	151.96 Eu 63	157.25 Gd 64	158.92 Tb 65	162.50 Dy 66	164.93 Ho 67	167.2 Er 68	168.93 Tm 69	173.04 Yb 70
	5d	174.97 Lu 71	178.5 Hf 72	180.95 Ta 73	183.92 W 74	186.2 Re 75	190.2 Os 76	192.2 Ir 77	195.09 Pt 78	196.97 Au 79	200.59 Hg 80				
	6p	204.37 Tl 81	207.19 Pb 82	208.98 Bi 83	210 Po 84	(210) At 85	222 Rn 86								
	7s	(223) Fr 87	226.05 Ra 88												
8	5f	227 Ac 89	232.04 Th 90	231 Pa 91	238.03 U 92	(237) Np 93	(242) Pu 94	(243) Am 95	(245) Cm 96	(245) Bk 97	(248) Cf 98	(253) Es 99	(254) Fm 100	(256) Md 101	(254) No 102
	6d	Lw 103	(258) Rf 104	(260) Ha 105	106	107	108	109	110	111	112				

Appendix VI
complete list of the stable isotopes of the chemical elements

Atomic weights are based on the atomic mass of C^{12} = 12 even.

At. No.	*Element*	*Symbol*	*Isotopes, Mass No.*	*At. Wt.*
1	hydrogen	H	1, (2)	1.00797[a]
2	helium	He	**4,** (3)	4.0026
3	lithium	Li	6, **7**	6.939
4	beryllium	Be	**9**	9.0122
5	boron	B	10, **11**	10.811[a]
6	carbon	C	**12,** (13)	12.01115[a]
7	nitrogen	N	**14,** (15)	14.0067
8	oxygen	O	**16,** (18), (17)	15.9994[a]
9	fluorine	F	**19**	18.9984
10	neon	Ne	**20,** (21), **22**	20.183
11	sodium	Na	**23**	22.9898
12	magnesium	Mg	**24,** 25, 26	24.312
13	aluminum	Al	**27**	26.9815
14	silicon	Si	**28,** 29, 30	28.086[a]
15	phosphorus	P	**31**	30.9738
16	sulfur	S	**32,** (33), 34, (36)	32.064[a]
17	chlorine	Cl	**35,** 37	35.453[b]
18	argon	Ar	(36), (38), **40**	39.948
19	potassium	K	**39,** (40), 41	39.102
20	calcium	Ca	**40,** (42), (43), 44, (46), 48	40.08
21	scandium	Sc	**45**	44.956
22	titanium	Ti	46, 47, **48,** 49, 50	47.90
23	vanadium	V	(50), **51**	50.942
24	chromium	Cr	50, **52,** 53, 54	51.996[b]
25	manganese	Mn	**55**	54.9380
26	iron	Fe	54, **56,** 57, (58)	55.847[b]
27	cobalt	Co	**59**	58.9332
28	nickel	Ni	**58,** 60, 61, 62, **(64)**	58.71
29	copper	Cu	**63,** 65	63.54

APPENDIX VI (Cont.)

At. No.	*Element*	*Symbol*	*Isotopes, Mass No.*	*At. Wt.*
30	zinc	Zn	**64,** 66, 67, 68, (70)	65.37
31	gallium	Ga	**69,** 71	69.72
32	germanium	Ge	70, 72, 73, **74,** 76	72.59
33	arsenic	As	**75**	74.9216
34	selenium	Se	(74), 76, 77, 78, **80,** 82	78.96
35	bromine	Br	**79, 81**	79.909[b]
36	krypton	Kr	(78), 80, 82, 83, **84,** 86	83.80
37	rubidium	Rb	**85, 87**	85.47
38	strontium	Sr	(84), 86, 87, **88**	87.62
39	yttrium	Y	**89**	88.905
40	zirconium	Zr	**90,** 91, 92, 94, 96	91.22
41	niobium	Nb	**93**	92.906
42	molybdenum	Mo	92, 94, 95, 96, 97, **98,** 100, 102	95.94
43	technetium	Tc	**99**	97.2
44	ruthenium	Ru	96, 98, 99, 100, 101, **102,** 104	101.07
45	rhodium	Rh	**103**	102.905
46	palladium	Pd	(102), 104, 105, **106,** 108, 110	106.4
47	silver	Ag	107, **109**	107.870[b]
48	cadmium	Cd	106, (108), 110, 111, **112,** 113, 114, 116	112.40
49	indium	In	113, **115**	114.82
50	tin	Sn	112, (114), (115), 116, 117, 118, 119, **120,** 122, 124	118.69
51	antimony	Sb	**121, 123**	121.75
52	tellurium	Te	(120), 122, 123, 124, 125, 126, **128,** 130	127.60
53	iodine	I	**127**	126.9044
54	xenon	Xe	(124), (126), 128, **129,** 130, 131, 132, 134, 136	131.30
55	cesium	Cs	**133**	132.905
56	barium	Ba	(130), (132), 134, 135, 136, 137, **138**	137.34
57	lanthanum	La	(138), **139**	138.91
58	cerium	Ce	(136), (138), **140,** 142	140.12
59	praseodymium	Pr	**141**	140.906
60	neodymium	Nd	**142,** 143, **144,** 145, 146, 148, 150	144.24
61	prometeum	Pm		146.0
62	samarium	Sa	144, 147, 148, 149, 150, **152,** 154	150.35
63	europium	Eu	**151, 153**	151.96
64	gadolinium	Gd	(152), 154, 155, **156,** 157, **158,** 160	157.25
65	terbium	Tb	**159**	158.924
66	dysprosium	Dy	(156), (158), 160, 161, 162, 163, **164**	162.50
67	holmium	Ho	**165**	164.930
68	erbium	Er	(162), 164, **166,** 167, 168, 170	167.26
69	thulium	Tm	**169**	168.934
70	ytterbium	Yb	(168), 170, 171, 172, 173, **174,** 176	173.04
71	lutecium	Lu	**175,** 176	174.97
72	hafnium	Hf	(174), 176, 177, 178, 179, **180**	178.49

APPENDIX VI (Cont.)

At. No.	*Element*	*Symbol*	*Isotopes, Mass No.*	*At. Wt.*
73	tantalum	Ta	**181**	180.948
74	tungsten	W	(180), 182, 183, **184, 186**	183.85
75	rhenium	Re	185, **187**	186.2
76	osmium	Os	184, 186, (187), 188, 189, 190, 192	190.2
77	iridium	Ir	191, **193**	192.2
78	platinum	Pt	(190), (192), 194, **195,** 196, 198	195.09
79	gold	Au	**197**	196.967
80	mercury	Hg	(196), 198, 199, 200, 201, **202,** 204	200.59
81	thallium	Tl	203, **205**	204.37
82	lead	Pb	204, 206, 207, **208**	207.19
83	bismuth	Bi	**209**	208.98

[a] Atomic weights so designated are known to be variable because of natural variations in isotopic composition. The observed ranges are: Hydrogen ±0.00001; Boron ±0.003; Carbon ±0.00005; Oxygen ±0.0001; Silicon ±0.001; Sulfur ±0.003.

[b] Atomic weights so designated are believed to have the following experimental uncertainties: Chlorine ±0.001; Chromium ±0.001; Iron ±0.003; Bromine ±0.002; Silver ±0.003.

Parentheses indicate less than 1% relative abundance, bold face indicates the most abundant isotope.

Although some of them are found in nature, elements 84 and up are unstable. For their isotopes see Appendix X.

Appendix VII relative masses of one stable isotope for each of the elements

Based on $C^{12} = 12$.

Symbol	*Mass*	*Symbol*	*Mass*
${}_{1}H^{1}$	1.007 8252	${}_{51}Sb^{121}$	120.903 750
${}_{2}He^{4}$	4.002 6036	${}_{52}Te^{128}$	127.904 710
${}_{3}Li^{7}$	7.016 005	${}_{53}I^{127}$	126.904 352
${}_{4}Be^{9}$	9.012 186	${}_{54}Xe^{129}$	128.904 784
${}_{5}B^{11}$	11.009 3051	${}_{55}Cs^{133}$	132.905 090
${}_{6}C^{12}$	12 even	${}_{56}Ba^{138}$	137.905 010
${}_{7}N^{14}$	14.003 0744	${}_{57}La^{139}$	138.906 060
${}_{8}O^{16}$	15.995 9149	${}_{58}Ce^{140}$	139.905 280
${}_{9}F^{19}$	18.998 4046	${}_{59}Pr^{141}$	140.907 390
${}_{10}Ne^{20}$	19.992 4404	${}_{60}Nd^{142}$	141.907 478
${}_{11}Na^{23}$	22.989 773	${}_{61}Pm^{143}$	143.910 800
${}_{12}Mg^{24}$	23.985 045	${}_{62}Sm^{144}$	143.911 650
${}_{13}Al^{27}$	26.981 535	${}_{63}Eu^{153}$	152.920 720
${}_{14}Si^{28}$	27.976 927	${}_{64}Gd^{156}$	155.922 240
${}_{15}P^{31}$	30.973 763	${}_{65}Tb^{159}$	158.924 300
${}_{16}S^{32}$	31.972 074	${}_{66}Dy^{164}$	163.928 100
${}_{17}Cl^{35}$	34.968 855	${}_{67}Ho^{165}$	164.929 600
${}_{18}Ar^{40}$	39.962 384	${}_{68}Er^{166}$	165.931 900
${}_{19}K^{39}$	38.963 714	${}_{69}Tm^{169}$	165.932 700
${}_{20}Ca^{40}$	39.962 589	${}_{70}Yb^{177}$	176.943 940
${}_{21}Sc^{45}$	44.955 916	${}_{71}Lu^{177}$	176.942 450
${}_{22}Ti^{48}$	47.947 948	${}_{72}Hf^{180}$	179.945 120
${}_{23}V^{51}$	50.943 978	${}_{73}Ta^{181}$	180.646 180
${}_{24}Cr^{52}$	51.940 514	${}_{74}W^{184}$	183.949 150
${}_{25}Mn^{55}$	54.941 293	${}_{75}Re^{187}$	186.954 980
${}_{26}Fe^{56}$	55.934 932	${}_{76}Os^{189}$	188.957 220
${}_{27}Co^{59}$	58.933 189	${}_{77}Ir^{193}$	192.962 340
${}_{28}Ni^{58}$	57.935 342	${}_{78}Pt^{195}$	194.964 460
${}_{29}Cu^{63}$	62.929 594	${}_{79}Au^{197}$	196.966 552
${}_{30}Zn^{64}$	63.929 145	${}_{80}Hg^{202}$	201.970 630

Symbol	*Mass*	*Symbol*	*Mass*
$_{31}Ga^{69}$	68.925 682	$_{81}Tl^{205}$	204.974 462
$_{32}Ge^{74}$	73.921 150	$_{82}Pb^{206}$	205.974 460
$_{33}As^{75}$	74.921 580	$_{83}Bi^{209}$	208.980 417
$_{34}Se^{80}$	79.916 512	$_{84}Po^{214}$	213.995 192
$_{35}Br^{81}$	80.916 344	$_{85}At^{217}$	217.002 405
$_{36}Kr^{84}$	83.911 504	$_{86}Rn^{222}$	222.015 365
$_{37}Rb^{85}$	84.911 710	$_{87}Fr^{221}$	221.014 176
$_{38}Sr^{88}$	87.905 610	$_{88}Ra^{226}$	226.025 360
$_{39}Y^{89}$	88.905 430	$_{89}Ac^{227}$	227.027 814
$_{40}Zr^{90}$	89.904 320	$_{90}Th^{232}$	232.038 211
$_{41}Nb^{93}$	92.906 020	$_{91}Pa^{234}$	234.043 370
$_{42}Mo^{98}$	97.905 510	$_{92}U^{238}$	238.050 760
$_{43}Tc^{99}$	98.907 300	$_{93}Np^{239}$	239.052 938
$_{44}Ru^{102}$	101.903 720	$_{94}Pu^{240}$	240.053 974
$_{45}Rh^{103}$	102.903 800	$_{95}Am^{241}$	241.056 689
$_{46}Pd^{106}$	105.903 200	$_{96}Cm^{242}$	242.058 800
$_{47}Ag^{107}$	106.904 970	$_{97}Bk^{245}$	245.066 240
$_{48}Cd^{112}$	111.902 840	$_{98}Cf^{246}$	246.068 780
$_{49}In^{115}$	114.904 070	$_{99}Es^{249}$	249.076 220
$_{50}Sn^{120}$	119.902 130	$_{100}Fm^{252}$	252.082 650

These values are taken from Everling, König, Mattauch, and Wapstra, *Nucl. Phys.* **18,** 529 (1960); and König, Mattauch, and Wapstra, *Nucl. Phys.* **31,** 18 (1962).

Space is left between third and fourth decimal place to facilitate reading.

Appendix VIII table of isotopes and their properties*

(s = second; m = minute; h = hour; d = day; y = year)
Based upon carbon-12 as 12 even.

Symbol	*Atomic Mass (amu)*	*Mass Excess MeV*	*Abund. or Activity*	*Half-life*
$_{-1}e^0$	0.000 549	0.511	—	stable
$_1p^1$	1.007 276	6.774	—	stable
$_0n^1$	1.008 665	8.071	β^-	13 m
$_1H^1$	1.007 825	7.288	**99.985**	stable
H^2	2.014 103	13.135	**0.015**	stable
H^3	3.016 049	14.949	β^-	12.2 y
$_2He^3$	3.016 030	14.931	**0.00013**	stable
He^4	4.002 604	2.425	**99.9999**	stable
He^5	5.012 296	11.453	$\alpha + n$	inst.
He^6	6.018 900	17.604	β^-	0.82 s
$_3Li^5$	5.012 541	11.681	$\alpha + p$	inst.
Li^6	6.015 126	14.089	**7.52**	stable
Li^7	7.016 005	14.908	**92.48**	stable
Li^8	8.022 488	20.947	β^-	0.86 s
Li^9	9.027 300	25.400	β^-	0.17 s
$_4Be^6$	6.019 780	18.430	β^+	0.4 s
Be^7	7.016 931	15.770	E.C.	53.6 d
Be^8	8.005 308	4.944	2α	inst.
Be^9	9.012 186	11.350	**100**	stable
Be^{10}	10.013 535	12.607	β^-	2.5×10^6 y
$_5B^8$	8.024 612	22.924	β^+	0.6 s
B^9	9.013 335	12.420	$2\alpha + p$	inst.
B^{10}	10.012 939	12.052	**18.6**	stable
B^{11}	11.009 305	8.667	**81.4**	stable
B^{12}	12.014 353	13.369	β^-	0.022 s

APPENDIX VIII (Cont.)

Symbol	*Atomic Mass (amu)*	*Mass Excess MeV*	*Abund. or Activity*	*Half-life*
${}_{6}C^{10}$	10.016 830	15.670	β^+	19.1 s
C^{11}	11.011 433	10.649	β^+	20.5 m
C^{12}	12.000 000	0	**98.892**	stable
C^{13}	13.003 354	3.124	**1.108**	stable
C^{14}	14.003 242	3.020	β^-	5.6×10^3 y
C^{15}	15.010 600	9.873	β^-	2.3 s
${}_{7}N^{12}$	12.018 709	17.426	β^+	0.012 s
N^{13}	13.005 739	5.345	β^+	10.1 m
N^{14}	14.003 074	2.864	**99.635**	stable
N^{15}	15.000 108	0.101	**0.365**	stable
N^{16}	16.006 089	5.672	β^-	7.36 s
N^{17}	17.008 449	7.869	β^-	4.14 s
${}_{8}O^{14}$	14.008 597	8.008	β^+	74 s
O^{15}	15.003 072	2.861	β^+	2.0 m
O^{16}	15.994 915	−4.736	**99.76**	stable
O^{17}	16.999 133	−0.807	**0.04**	stable
O^{18}	17.999 160	−0.782	**0.20**	stable
O^{19}	19.003 577	3.332	β^-	29.4 s
O^{20}	20.004 071	3.792	*n*	13.6 s
${}_{9}F^{17}$	17.002 098	1.954	β^+	66 s
F^{18}	18.000 950	0.884	β^+	1.87 h
F^{19}	18.998 405	−1.486	**100**	stable
F^{20}	19.999 986	−0.013	β^-	11.2 s
F^{21}	20.999 972	−0.026	β^-	5 s
${}_{10}Ne^{18}$	18.005 715	5.323	β^+	1.6 s
Ne^{19}	19.001 892	1.762	β^+	19 s
Ne^{20}	19.992 440	−7.041	**90.92**	stable
Ne^{21}	20.993 849	−5.729	**0.26**	stable
Ne^{22}	21.991 385	−8.025	**8.82**	stable
Ne^{23}	22.994 475	−5.146	β^-	40.2 s
Ne^{24}	23.993 597	−5.964	β^-	3.4 m
${}_{11}Na^{20}$	20.008 890	8.280	β^+	0.3 s
Na^{21}	20.997 638	−2.200	β^+	23 s
Na^{22}	21.994 435	−5.183	β^+, E.C.	2.6 y
Na^{23}	22.989 773	−9.526	**100**	stable
Na^{24}	23.990 967	−8.414	β^-	15.0 h
Na^{25}	24.989 920	−9.390	β^-	60 s
${}_{12}Mg^{23}$	22.994 135	−5.463	β^+, E.C.	11 s
Mg^{24}	23.985 045	−13.930	**78.60**	stable
Mg^{25}	24.985 840	−13.189	**10.11**	stable

APPENDIX VIII (Cont.)

Symbol	Atomic Mass (amu)	Mass Excess MeV	Abund. or Activity	Half-life
Mg^{26}	25.982 591	−16.215	**11.29**	stable
Mg^{27}	26.998 346	−14.581	β^-	9.45 m
Mg^{28}	27.983 880	−15.015	β^-	21.4 h
$_{13}Al^{24}$	24.000 090	0.090	β^+	2.1 s
Al^{25}	24.990 414	−8.928	β^+	7.6 s
Al^{26}	25.986 900	−12.201	β^+, E.C.	10^5 y
Al^{27}	26.981 535	−17.199	**100**	stable
Al^{28}	27.981 908	−16.851	β^-	2.3 m
Al^{29}	28.980 442	−18.217	β^-	6.6 m
$_{14}Si^{27}$	26.986 701	−12.387	β^+, E.C.	4.9 s
Si^{28}	27.976 927	−21.491	**92.27**	stable
Si^{29}	28.976 491	−21.897	**4.68**	stable
Si^{30}	29.973 761	−24.440	**3.05**	stable
Si^{31}	30.975 349	−22.961	β^-	2.6 h
Si^{32}	31.974 020	−24.200	β^-	7×10^2 y
$_{15}P^{28}$	27.991 740	−7.690	β^+	0.28 s
P^{29}	28.981 816	−16.937	β^+	4.4 s
P^{30}	29.978 320	−20.193	β^+	2.5 m
P^{31}	30.973 763	−24.438	**100**	stable
P^{32}	31.973 908	−24.303	β^-	14.3 d
P^{33}	32.971 728	−26.334	β^-	24.4 d
P^{34}	33.973 340	−24.830	β^-	12.4 s
$_{16}S^{31}$	30.979 599	−19.002	β^+	2.6 s
S^{32}	31.972 074	−26.012	**95.054**	stable
S^{33}	32.971 461	−26.583	**0.740**	stable
S^{34}	33.967 865	−29.932	**4.190**	stable
S^{35}	34.969 034	−28.843	β^-	87.1 d
S^{36}	35.967 091	−30.653	**0.016**	stable
S^{37}	36.971 040	−26.980	β^-	5.0 m
S^{38}	37.971 220	−26.800	β^-	6 m
$_{17}Cl^{32}$	31.986 030	−13.010	β^+	0.31 s
Cl^{33}	32.977 446	−21.008	β^+	2.4 s
Cl^{34}	33.973 764	−24.437	β^+	32.4 m
Cl^{35}	34.968 855	−29.010	**75.4**	stable
Cl^{36}	35.968 312	−25.516	β^-, E.C.	3.2 y
Cl^{37}	36.965 898	−31.766	**24.6**	stable
Cl^{38}	37.968 002	−29.804	β^-	37.5 m
Cl^{39}	38.968 003	−29.803	β^-	55.5 m
Cl^{40}	39.970 400	−27.500	β^-	1.4 m
$_{18}Ar^{35}$	34.975 275	−23.030	β^+	1.83 s
Ar^{36}	35.963 548	−30.227	**0.337**	stable

APPENDIX VIII (Cont.)

Symbol	*Atomic Mass (amu)*	*Mass Excess MeV*	*Abund. or Activity*	*Half-life*
Ar^{37}	36.966 772	−30.950	E.C.	34.1 d
Ar^{38}	37.962 725	−34.720	**0.063**	stable
Ar^{39}	38.964 321	−33.233	β^-	2.6×10^{2} y
Ar^{40}	39.962 384	−35.037	**99.600**	stable
Ar^{41}	40.964 508	−33.058	β^-	1.83 h
Ar^{42}	41.963 043	−34.423	β^-	3.5 y
$_{19}K^{38}$	37.969 090	−28.791	β^+	7.7 m
K^{39}	38.963 714	−33.798	**93.08**	stable
K^{40}	39.964 008	−33.524	**0.0119**	10^{9} y
K^{41}	40.961 835	−35.548	**6.91**	stable
K^{42}	41.962 417	−35.006	β^-	12.5 h
K^{43}	42.960 731	−36.577	β^-	22.4 h
K^{44}	43.962 040	−35.360	β^-	22.0 m
$_{20}Ca^{39}$	38.970 706	−27.286	β^+	1.0 s
Ca^{40}	39.962 589	−34.846	**96.97**	stable
Ca^{41}	40.962 279	−35.135	E.C.	2×10^{5} y
Ca^{42}	41.958 628	−38.536	**0.64**	stable
Ca^{43}	42.958 780	−38.394	**0.145**	stable
Ca^{44}	43.955 490	−41.458	**2.06**	stable
Ca^{45}	44.956 189	−40.807	β^-	164 d
Ca^{46}	45.953 689	−43.136	**0.0033**	stable
Ca^{47}	46.954 512	−42.370	β^-	4.9 d
Ca^{48}	47.952 363	−44.371	**0.185**	10^{16} y
Ca^{49}	48.955 662	−41.298	β^-	8.8 m

*For atomic masses in *amu* and mass excess energies in *MeV*, for isotopes in the remainder of the periodic table, see *Nucl. Phys.*, March-April, pp. 28–42, 1962, by L. A. König, J. H. E. Mattauch, and A. H. Wapstra. Also J. H. E. Mattauch, W. Thiele, and A. H. Wapstra, *Nucl. Phys.*, Vol. 67, pp. 1–120, May, 1965.

Appendix IX
common logarithms

(To obtain the Napierian logarithm of a number multiply these logarithms by 2.30258509.)

N	0	1	2	3	4	5	6	7	8	9
0	....	0000	3010	4771	6021	6990	7782	8451	9031	9542
1	0000	0414	0792	1139	1461	1761	2041	2304	2553	2788
2	3010	3222	3424	3617	3802	3979	4150	4314	4472	4624
3	4771	4914	5051	5315	5315	5441	5563	5682	5798	5911
4	6021	6128	6232	6335	6435	6532	6628	6721	6812	6902
5	6990	7076	7160	7243	7324	7404	7482	7559	7634	7709
6	7782	7853	7924	7993	8062	8129	8195	8261	8325	8388
7	8451	8513	7573	8633	8692	8751	8808	8865	8921	8976
8	9031	9085	9138	9191	9243	9294	9345	9395	9445	9494
9	9542	9590	9638	9685	9731	9777	9823	9868	9912	9956
10	0000	0043	0086	0128	0170	0212	0253	0294	0334	0374
11	0414	0453	0492	0531	0569	0607	0645	0682	0719	0755
12	0792	0828	0864	0899	0934	0969	1004	1038	1072	1106
13	1139	1173	1206	1239	1271	1303	1335	1367	1399	1430
14	1461	1492	1523	1553	1584	1614	1644	1673	1703	1732
15	1761	1790	1818	1847	1875	1903	1931	1959	1987	2014
16	2041	2068	2095	2122	2148	2175	2201	2227	2253	2279
17	2304	2330	2355	2380	2380	2430	2455	2480	2504	2529
18	2553	2577	2601	2625	2648	2672	2695	2718	2742	2765
19	2788	2810	2833	2856	2878	2900	2923	2945	2967	2989
20	3010	3032	3054	3075	3096	3118	3139	3160	3181	3201
21	3222	3243	3263	3284	3304	3324	3345	3365	3385	3404
22	3424	3444	3464	3483	3502	3522	3541	3560	3579	3598
23	3617	3636	3655	3674	3692	3711	3729	3747	3766	3784
24	3802	3820	3838	3856	3874	3892	3909	3927	3945	3962
25	3979	3997	4014	4031	4048	4065	4082	4099	4116	4133
26	4150	4166	4183	4200	4216	4232	4249	4265	4281	4298
27	4314	4330	4346	4362	4378	4393	4409	4425	4440	4456
28	4472	4487	4502	4518	4533	4548	4564	4579	4594	4609
29	4624	4639	4654	4669	4683	4698	4713	4728	4742	4757

APPENDIX IX (Cont.)

N	0	1	2	3	4	5	6	7	8	9
30	4771	4786	4800	4814	4829	4843	4857	4871	4886	4900
31	4914	4928	4942	4955	4969	4983	4997	5011	5024	5038
32	5051	5065	5079	5092	5105	5119	5132	5145	5159	5172
33	5185	5198	5211	5224	5237	5250	5263	5276	5289	5302
34	5315	5328	5340	5353	5366	5378	5391	5403	5416	5428
35	5441	5453	5465	5478	5490	5502	5514	5527	5539	5551
36	5563	5575	5587	5599	5611	5623	5635	5647	5658	5670
37	5682	5694	5705	5717	5729	5740	5752	5763	5775	5786
38	5798	5809	5821	5832	5843	5855	5866	5877	5888	5899
39	5911	5922	5933	5944	5955	5966	5977	5988	5999	6010
40	6021	6031	6042	6053	6064	6075	6085	6096	6107	6117
41	6128	6138	6149	6160	6170	6180	6191	6201	6212	6222
42	6232	6243	6253	6263	6274	6284	6294	6304	6314	6325
43	6335	6345	6355	6365	6375	6385	6395	6405	6415	6425
44	6435	6444	6454	6464	6474	6484	6493	6503	6513	6522
45	6532	6542	6551	6561	6571	6580	6590	6599	6609	6618
46	6628	6637	6646	6656	6665	6675	6684	6693	6702	6712
47	6721	6730	6739	6749	6758	6767	6776	6785	6794	6803
48	6812	6821	6830	6839	6848	6857	6866	6875	6884	6893
49	6902	6911	6920	6928	6937	6946	6955	6964	6972	6981
50	6990	6998	7007	7016	7024	7033	7042	7050	7059	7067
51	7076	7084	7093	7101	7110	7118	7126	7135	7143	7152
52	7160	7168	7177	7185	7193	7202	7210	7218	7226	7235
53	7243	7251	7259	7267	7275	7284	7292	7300	7308	7316
54	7324	7332	7340	7348	7356	7364	7372	7380	7388	7396
55	7404	7412	7419	7427	7435	7443	7451	7459	7466	7474
56	7482	7490	7497	7505	7513	7520	7528	7536	7543	7551
57	7559	7566	7574	7582	7589	7597	7604	7612	7619	7627
58	7634	7642	7649	7657	7664	7672	7679	7686	7694	7701
59	7709	7716	7723	7731	7738	7745	7752	7760	7767	7774
60	7782	7789	7796	7803	7810	7818	7825	7832	7839	7846
61	7853	7860	7868	7875	7882	7889	7896	7903	7910	7917
62	7924	7931	7938	7945	7952	7959	7966	7973	7980	7987
63	7993	8000	8007	8014	8021	8028	8035	8041	8048	8055
64	8062	8069	8075	8082	8089	8096	8102	8109	8116	8122
65	8129	8136	8142	8149	8156	8162	8169	8176	8182	8189
66	8195	8202	8209	8215	8222	8228	8235	8241	8248	8254
67	8261	8267	8274	8280	8287	8293	8299	8306	8312	8319
68	8325	8331	8338	8344	8351	8357	8363	8370	8376	8382
69	8388	8395	8401	8407	8414	8420	8426	8432	8439	8445

APPENDIX IX. Common Logarithms (Cont.)

N	0	1	2	3	4	5	6	7	8	9
70	8451	8457	8463	8470	8476	8482	8488	8494	8500	8506
71	8513	8519	8525	8531	8537	8543	8549	8555	8561	8567
72	8573	8579	8585	8591	8597	8603	8609	8615	8621	8627
73	8633	8639	8645	8651	8657	8663	8669	8675	8681	8686
74	8692	8698	8704	8710	8716	8722	8727	8733	8739	8745
75	8751	8756	8762	8768	8774	8779	8785	8791	8797	8802
76	8808	8814	8820	8825	8831	8837	8842	8848	8854	8859
77	8865	8871	8876	8882	8887	8893	8899	8904	8910	8915
78	8921	8927	8932	8938	8943	8949	8954	8960	9865	8971
79	8976	8982	8987	8993	8998	9004	9909	9015	9020	9025
80	9031	9036	9042	9047	9053	9058	9063	9069	9074	9079
81	9085	9090	9096	9101	9106	9112	9117	9122	9128	9133
82	9138	9143	9149	9154	9159	9165	9170	9175	9180	9186
83	9191	9196	9201	9206	9212	9217	9222	9227	9232	9238
84	9243	9248	9253	9258	9263	9269	9274	9279	9284	9289
85	9294	9299	9304	9309	9315	9320	9325	9330	9335	9340
86	9345	9350	9355	9360	9365	9370	9375	9380	9385	9390
87	8395	9400	9405	9410	9415	9420	9425	9430	9435	9440
88	9445	9450	9455	9460	9465	9469	9474	9479	9484	9489
89	9494	9499	9504	9509	9513	9518	9523	9528	9533	9538
90	9542	9547	9552	9557	9562	9566	9571	9576	9581	9586
91	9590	9595	9600	9605	9609	9614	9619	9624	9628	9633
92	9638	9643	9647	9652	9657	9661	9666	9671	9675	9680
93	9685	9689	9694	9699	9703	9708	9713	9717	9722	9727
94	9731	9736	9741	9745	9750	9754	9759	9763	9768	9773
95	9777	9782	9786	9791	9795	9800	9805	9809	9814	9818
96	9823	9827	9832	9836	9841	9845	9850	9854	9859	9863
97	9868	9872	9877	9881	9886	9890	9894	9899	9903	9908
98	9912	9917	9921	9926	9930	9934	9939	9943	9948	9952
99	9956	9961	9965	9969	9974	9978	9983	9987	9991	9996
100	0000	0004	0009	0013	0017	0022	0026	0030	0035	0039
N	0	1	2	3	4	5	6	7	8	9

Appendix X
the radioactive nuclides of the heavy elements showing decay schemes

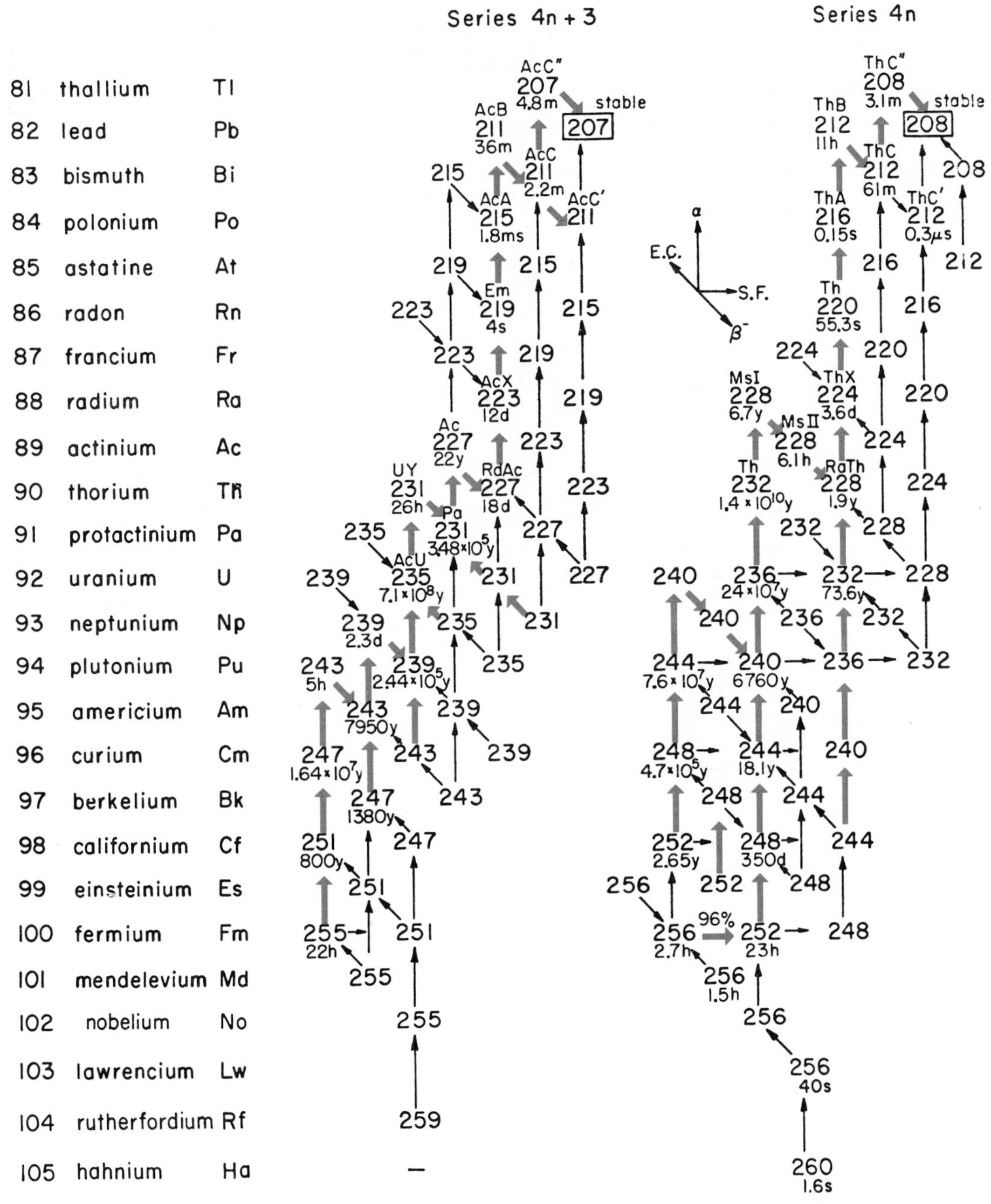

APPENDIX X. (Cont.)

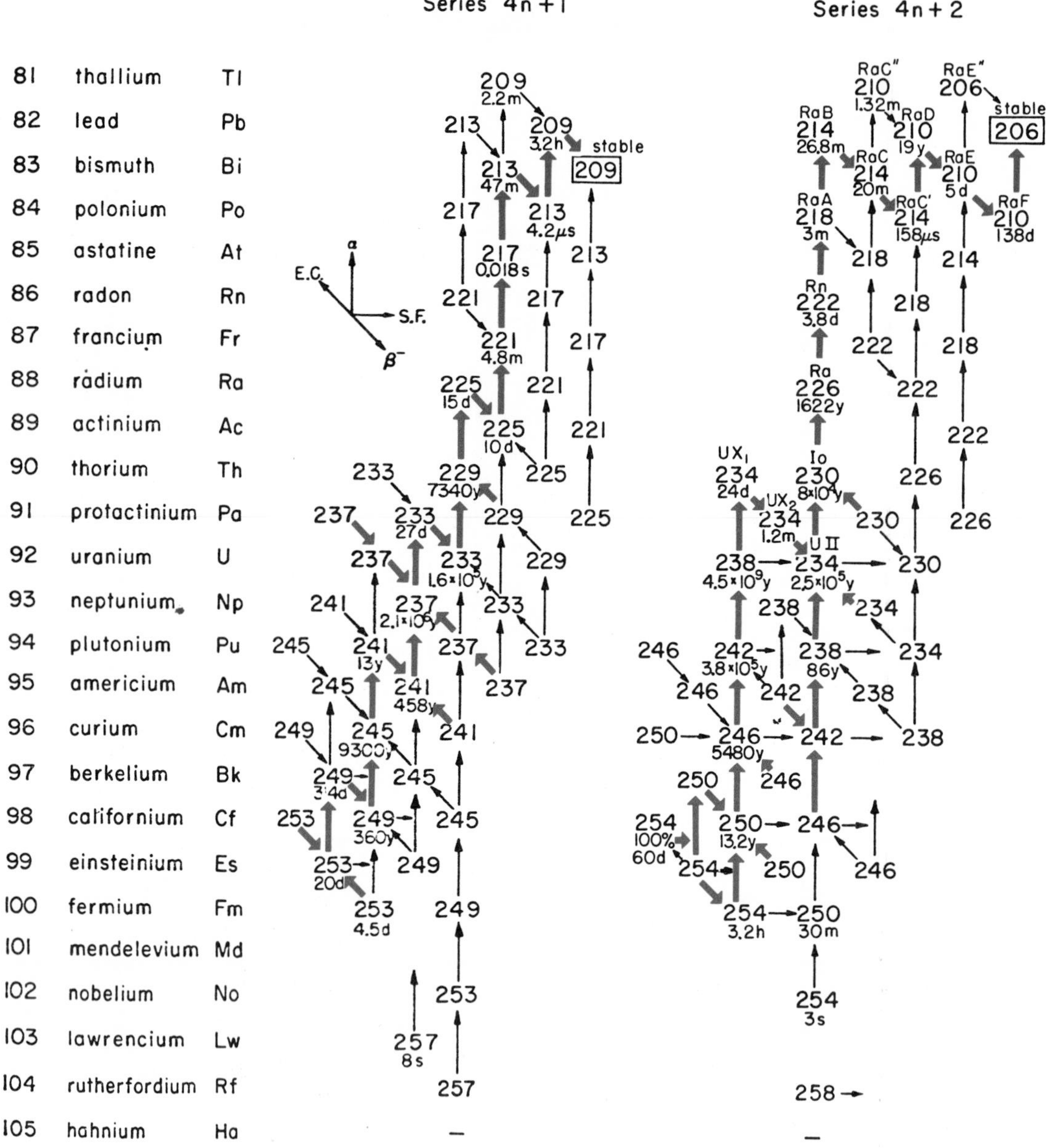
Series 4n+1
Series 4n+2
81 thallium Tl
82 lead Pb
83 bismuth Bi
84 polonium Po
85 astatine At
86 radon Rn
87 francium Fr
88 radium Ra
89 actinium Ac
90 thorium Th
91 protactinium Pa
92 uranium U
93 neptunium Np
94 plutonium Pu
95 americium Am
96 curium Cm
97 berkelium Bk
98 californium Cf
99 einsteinium Es
100 fermium Fm
101 mendelevium Md
102 nobelium No
103 lawrencium Lw
104 rutherfordium Rf
105 hahnium Ha
α
E.C.
S.F.
β⁻
stable
209
206
RaC″
RaE″
RaB
RaD
RaC
RaE
RaA
RaC′
RaF
Rn
Ra
Io
UX₁
UX₂
U II

Appendix XI abbreviations used in this text

A	ampere(s)
A-turn	ampere turn(s)
Å	angstrom unit(s)
A	atomic mass number
amu	atomic mass unit(s)
Z	atomic number
b	barn
BeV	billion electron volts
GeV	or giga electron volts
Btu	British thermal unit
cal	calorie
cm	centimeter
C	coulomb
db	decibel
F	farad
ft	foot
G	gauss
g	gram
H	henry
Hz	hertz
hp	horsepower
h	hour
in.	inch
J	joule
Kcal	kilocalorie
Kc/s	kilocycles/second
Km	kilometers
Kg	kilogram
KHz	kilohertz
KV	kilovolt
KW	kilowatt
Mc/s	megacycles/second
MHz	megahertz
MV	megavolt
MW	megawatt
m	meter
μA	microampere
μCi	microcurie
μF	microfarad
μH	microhenry
$\mu\mu$F	micromicrofarad
μ	micron
μW	microwatt
mi	mile
mm	millimeter
MeV	million electron volts
ms	millisecond
mV	millivolt
mW	milliwatt
min	minute
ns	nanosecond
N	newton
Ω	ohm
rad	radian
rps	revolutions per second
s	second
sl	slug
T	tesla
KeV	thousand electron volts
V	volt
W	watt
Wb	weber
y	year

Index

APPENDIX XII. THE PHYSICAL CONSTANTS

Quantity	Symbol	Value	Error parts per million
Speed of light	c	2.9979250×10^{8} m/s	0.33
Speed of light squared	c^2	8.9875543×10^{16} m²/s²	0.66
Electronic charge	e	$1.6021917 \times 10^{-19}$ C	4.4
Electronic mass	m	$9.1095585 \times 10^{-31}$ Kg	6.0
Proton mass	M_p	$1.6726141 \times 10^{-27}$ Kg	6.6
Neutron mass	M_n	$1.6749201 \times 10^{-27}$ Kg	6.6
Planck's constant	h	$6.6261965 \times 10^{-34}$ Js	7.6
Unit angular momentum	h	$1.0545915 \times 10^{-34}$ Js	7.6
Electronic ratio	e/m_e	1.7588028×10^{11} C/Kg	3.1
Bohr radius	r_1	$5.2917716 \times 10^{-11}$ m	1.5
Bohr magneton	μ_B	$9.2740966 \times 10^{-24}$ Am²	7.0
Nuclear magneton	μ_N	$5.0509515 \times 10^{-27}$ Am²	10.0
Proton/electron mass ratio	M_p/m_e	1836.1091	6.2
Atomic mass unit	amu	$1.6605311 \times 10^{-27}$ Kg	6.6
Energy of 1 amu	E	931.48113 MeV	7.2
Energy of electron mass	V_e	0.5110041 MeV	4.6
Mass energy of electron	m_0c^2	$8.1872652 \times 10^{-14}$ J	6.5
Avogadro's number	N	6.0221694×10^{26}/Kg mol	6.6
Gravitational constant	G	6.673231×10^{-11} m³/Kg s²	460
Compton wavelength	h/m_0c	$2.4263096 \times 10^{-12}$ m	3.1
Gas constant	R	8.3143435 J/mole/°K	42
Stefan-Boltzmann constant	k	5.669620 J/s m² K⁴	170

From *Reviews of Modern Physics,* Vol. 41, 1969.

THE GREEK ALPHABET

Α	α	*Alpha*	Η	η	*Eta*	Ν	ν	*Nu*	Τ	τ	*Tau*
Β	β	*Beta*	Θ	θ	*Theta*	Ξ	ξ	*Xi*	Υ	υ	*Upsilon*
Γ	γ	*Gamma*	Ι	ι	*Iota*	Ο	o	*Omicron*	Φ	ϕ	*Phi*
Δ	δ	*Delta*	Κ	κ	*Kappa*	Π	π	*Pi*	Χ	χ	*Chi*
Ε	ϵ	*Epsilon*	Λ	λ	*Lambda*	Ρ	ρ	*Rho*	Ψ	ψ	*Psi*
Ζ	ζ	*Zeta*	Μ	μ	*Mu*	Σ	σ	*Sigma*	Ω	ω	*Omega*